Index of Applications

FINITE MATHEMATICS AND APPLIED CALCULUS

MAT 210/211

Brief Calculus and Mathematics for Business Analysis

Stefan Waner I Steven Costenoble

 CENGAGE

Australia • Brazil • Mexico • Singapore • United Kingdom • United States

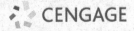

MAT 210/211: Brief Calculus and
Mathematics for Business Analysis

Finite Mathematics and Applied Calculus, Seventh Edition
Stefan Waner | Steven R. Costenoble

© 2018, 2014 Cengage Learning

For product information and technology assistance, contact us at
Cengage Learning Customer & Sales Support, 1-800-354-9706.

For permission to use material from this text or product, submit all
requests online at **www.cengage.com/permissions.**
Further permissions questions can be emailed to
permissionrequest@cengage.com.

This book contains select works from existing Cengage learning resources and
was produced by Cengage learning Custom Solutions for collegiate use. As such,
those adopting and/or contributing to this work are responsible for editorial
content accuracy, continuity and completeness.

Compilation © 2017 Cengage Learning

ISBN: 978-1-337-70540-0

Cengage Learning
20 Channel Street
Boston, MA 02210
USA

Cengage Learning is a leading provider of customized learning solutions
with employees residing in nearly 40 different countries and sales in more
than 125 countries around the world. Find your local representative at:
www.cengage.com.

Cengage Learning products are represented in Canada by
Nelson Education, Ltd.

For your course and learning solutions, visit **www.cengage.com.**

Purchase any of our products at your local college store or at our
preferred online store **www.cengagebrain.com.**

Visit our custom book building website at **www.compose.cengage.com.**

Brief Contents

Contents

Additional Sections

Extreme Values

Preface

Finite Mathematics and Applied Calculus, Seventh Edition, is intended for a one- or two-term course for students majoring in business, the social sciences, or the liberal arts. Like the earlier editions, the seventh edition of *Finite Mathematics and Applied Calculus* is designed to address the challenge of generating enthusiasm and mathematical sophistication in an audience that is often underprepared and lacks motivation for traditional mathematics courses. We meet this challenge by focusing on real-life applications that students can relate to, many on topics of current interest; by presenting mathematical concepts intuitively and thoroughly; and by employing a writing style that is informal, engaging, and occasionally even humorous.

The seventh edition goes farther than earlier editions in implementing support for a wide range of instructional paradigms. On the one hand, the abundant pedagogical content available both in print and online, including comprehensive teaching videos and online tutorials, now allows us to be able to offer complete customizable courses for approaches ranging from on-campus and hybrid classes to distance learning classes. In addition, our careful integration of optional support for multiple forms of technology throughout the text makes it adaptable in classes with no technology, classes in which a single form of technology is used exclusively, and classes that incorporate several technologies.

We fully support three forms of technology in this text: TI-83/84 Plus graphing calculators, spreadsheets, and powerful online utilities we have created for the book. In particular, our comprehensive support for spreadsheet technology, both in the text and online, is highly relevant for students who are studying business and economics, in which skill with spreadsheets may be vital to their future careers.

New To This Edition

Content

- **Chapter 0:** We have added an entire new section on logarithms in the Precalculus Review, up through solving for unknowns in the exponent. Students can refer to this section for review when studying techniques involving the use of logarithms in the mathematics of finance (Chapter 3).

- **Chapter 1:** In our revision of this important introductory chapter, we have down-played the algebra sophistication somewhat so as not to present artificial barriers to the mastery of the important new concepts we discuss.

- **Chapter 2:** The chapter on nonlinear functions and models has been moved earlier in the book. It is now Chapter 2 rather than Chapter 9. Although this material is not required for the finite mathematics chapters, it fits logically with Chapter 1, which discusses functions in general and linear models, and many instructors prefer to cover this material earlier rather than later.

- **Chapter 3:** The Mathematics of Finance chapter has been significantly revised: In the sections on simple and compound interest, we state and use both the year-based formulas and the compounding period-based versions. In the compound interest section, we now emphasize the latter formulation, as this helps with the segue to annuities, in which the period-based approach is the standard formulation. T-bills and zero coupon bonds are a bit esoteric, so the material on T-bills and further discussion of bonds has been moved to the end of the section to a subsection marked as "Optional." The section on annuities has been substantially reorganized: First, we have standardized the definition of "annuities" and now use more transparent and standard terminology to distinguish accumulation and annuitization (or payout). More important, we have added discussion, examples, and exercises on life insurance and mortgage refinancing, including a formula for calculating principal outstanding. The exercise sets have been radically reorganized and expanded, with numerous real-data based applications that follow the new organization of the section text.

- **Chapter 10:** Rather than following other books that avoid discussing the important distinction between discontinuities and domain singularities (for instance, the fact that $1/x$ is continuous on its domain but singular at zero), we discuss this distinction carefully, providing lots of practice and figures.

Current Topics in the Applications

- We have added and updated numerous real data exercises and examples based on topics that are either of intense current interest or of general interest to our students, including many on social networks, and the 2009–2016 economic recovery, and on the 2014 Ebola epidemic, while retaining those of important historical interest, such as the 2008 economic crisis, the SARS outbreak of 2003, the 2010 stock market "flash crash," and many others.

Exercises

- We have added many new conceptual Communication and Reasoning exercises, including many dealing with common student errors and misconceptions.

Online Visualization and Practice Examples

- We have created a variety of web-based interactive apps available both on **www.wanermath.com** and in the new MindTap course that accompanies this edition. Instructors can use these to demonstrate important concepts such as the graphical solution of linear programming problems, the slopes of secant and tangent lines, and marginal and average cost.

- Many key examples in the text are mirrored by web-based randomizable practice examples, which allow students to test their mastery of the textbook examples and provide instructors with material for interactive presentation and class discussion.

Our Approach to Pedagogy

Real-World Orientation   The diversity, breadth, and abundance of examples and exercises included in this edition continue to distinguish our book from others. A large number of these examples and exercises are based on real, referenced data from business, economics, the life sciences, and the social sciences. Our updated examples and exercises in the seventh edition are even more attuned to themes that students can identify with and relate to, from the technology used in their phones and tablets to the social networks in which they participate and many of the corporations they will instantly recognize as important in their lives. Notable events, such as the 1990s dot-com boom, the 2005–2006 real estate bubble, the resulting 2008 economic crisis and stock market panic, and many more, are addressed in examples and exercises throughout the book.

Adapting real data for pedagogical use can be tricky; available data can be numerically complex, intimidating for students, or incomplete. We have modified and streamlined many of the real-world applications, rendering them as tractable as any "made-up" application. At the same time, we have been careful to strike a pedagogically sound balance between applications based on real data and more traditional "generic" applications. Thus, the density and selection of real data-based applications have been tailored to the pedagogical goals and appropriate difficulty level for each section.

Readability   We would like students to read this book. We would like students to *enjoy* reading this book. Therefore, we have written the book in a conversational, student-oriented style and have made frequent use of question-and-answer dialogues to encourage the development of the student's mathematical curiosity and intuition. We hope that this text will give the student insight into how a mathematician develops and thinks about mathematical ideas and their applications to real life.

Pedagogical Aids   We have included our favorite unique and creative approaches to solving the kinds of problems that normally cause difficulties for students and headaches for instructors. To name just a few, we discuss a rewording technique in Chapters 4 and 6 to show how to translate phrases such as "there are (at least/at most) three times as many X as Y" directly into equations or inequalities, "decision algorithms" in Chapter 7 that make calculations of real-life scenarios involving permutations and combinations almost mechanical, verbal forms of the differentiation rules in Chapter 11 to avoid the tendency students often have to juggle multiple formulas they might not really understand, "calculation thought experiments" to help the student decide which rules of differentiation to apply and the order in which to apply them, and a powerful tabular method for integration by parts in Chapter 14 that transforms what is often an agonizingly complicated topic for students into almost a triviality.

Rigor   Mathematical rigor need not be antithetical to the kind of applied focus and conceptual approach that are hallmarks of this book. We have worked hard to ensure that we are always mathematically honest without being unnecessarily formal. Sometimes we do this through the question-and-answer dialogues and sometimes through the "Before we go on . . ." discussions that follow examples, but always in a manner designed to provoke the interest of the student.

Five Elements of Mathematical Pedagogy to Address Different Learning Styles   The "Rule of Four" is a common theme in many texts. Implementing this approach, we discuss many of the central concepts **numerically**, **graphically**, and **algebraically** and clearly delineate these distinctions. The fourth element, **verbal communication** of mathematical concepts, is emphasized through our discussions on translating English sentences into mathematical statements and in our extensive Communication and Reasoning exercises at the end of each section. A fifth element, **interactivity**, is implemented through expanded use of question-and-answer dialogues but is seen most dramatically in the eBook in the MindTap course that accompanies this edition and at **www.wanermath.com** through our new practice and learning modules. These are small interactive apps that help a student visualize new concepts or practice examples similar to those in the text. In addition, the wanermath .com website offers interactive tutorials in the form of games, interactive chapter summaries and chapter review exercises, and online utilities that automate a variety of tasks, from graphing to regression and matrix algebra.

Understand

Examples

Examples are a cornerstone of our approach. Many of the scenarios that we use in application examples and exercises are revisited several times throughout the book. In this way, students will find themselves analyzing the same application from a variety of different perspectives, such as graphing, the use of derivatives, and elasticity. Reusing scenarios and important functions provides unifying threads and shows students the complex texture of real-life problems. Complete solutions are provided with every example.

EXAMPLE 1   **Estimating a Limit Numerically**

Use a table to estimate the following limits:

a. $\lim_{x \to 2} \dfrac{x^3 - 8}{x - 2}$ **b.** $\lim_{x \to 0} \dfrac{e^{2x} - 1}{x}$

Solution

a. We cannot simply substitute $x = 2$, because the function $f(x) = \dfrac{x^3 - 8}{x - 2}$ is not defined at $x = 2$. (Why?)* Instead, we use a table of values as we did above, with x approaching 2 from both sides:

x approaching 2 from the left→   ← *x* approaching 2 from the right

x	1.9	1.99	1.999	1.9999	2	2.0001	2.001	2.01	2.1
$f(x) = \dfrac{x^3 - 8}{x - 2}$	11.41	11.9401	11.9940	11.9994		12.0006	12.0060	12.0601	12.61

Quick Examples

Most definition boxes include quick, straightforward examples that a student can use to solidify each new concept.

Quick Example

4. $\dfrac{x^2 - 1}{x - 1} = x + 1$ for all x except $x = 1$.   Write $\dfrac{x^2 - 1}{x - 1}$ as $\dfrac{(x + 1)(x - 1)}{x - 1}$, and cancel the $(x - 1)$.

Therefore,

$$\lim_{x \to 1} \dfrac{x^2 - 1}{x - 1} = \lim_{x \to 1}(x + 1) = 1 + 1 = 2.$$

Question-and-Answer Dialogues

We frequently use informal question-and-answer dialogues that anticipate the kinds of questions that may occur to the student and also guide the student through the development of new concepts.

Q: *How do we find $\lim_{x \to a} f(x)$ when $x = a$ is a singular point of the function f and we cannot simplify the given function to make a a point of the domain?*

A: In such a case it might be necessary to analyze the function by some other method, such as numerically or graphically. However, if we do not obtain the indeterminate form 0/0 upon substitution, we can often say what the limit is, as the following example shows.

Before We Go On . . .

Most examples are followed by supplementary discussions, which may include a check on the answer, a discussion of the feasibility and significance of a solution, or an in-depth look at what the solution means.

➡ **Before we go on . . .** In Example 1, we could look at the future value as a function of time:

$$FV = 2,500(1 + 0.011t) = 2,500 + 27.5t.$$

Thus, the future value is growing linearly at a rate of $27.50 per year ∎

Lecture Videos

Developed with Principal Lecturer, Jay Abramson, at Arizona State University, these video clips are flexible in their use as lecture starters in class or as an independent resource for students to review concepts on their own. Blending an introduction to concepts with specific examples, the videos let students quickly see the big picture of key concepts they are learning in class. Selected clips involve students and simulate a classroom-type interaction that creates a sense of the familiar and demystifies key concepts they are learning in their course. Frequently asked questions appear periodically throughout the video segments to further enhance learning. All videos are closed captioned and available in the new MindTap and Enhanced WebAssign courses that accompany the text. The topics for the lecture videos were carefully selected to accompany the subject areas that are most frequently taught and target the concepts that students struggle with most.

Online Visualization and Practice Examples

We have created a variety of web-based interactive apps that are available both on the wanermath.com website and in the new MindTap course accompanying this edition. Instructors can use these to demonstrate important concepts such as the graphical solution of linear programming problems, the slopes of secant and tangent lines, and marginal and average cost.

Many key examples in the text are mirrored by web-based randomizable practice examples that allow students to test their mastery of the textbook examples and provide instructors with material for interactive presentation and class discussion.

Visualize the derivative graphically

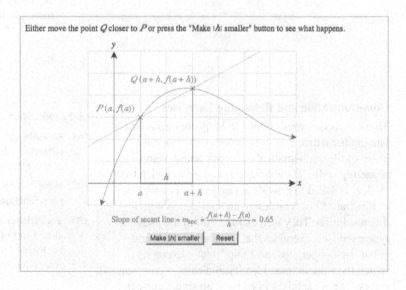

Practice and Apply

Exercises

Our comprehensive collection of exercises provides a wealth of material that can be used to challenge students at almost every level of preparation and includes everything from straightforward drill exercises to interesting and challenging applications. The exercise sets have been carefully curated and ordered to move from straightforward basic exercises and exercises that are similar to examples in the text to more interesting and advanced ones, marked as "more advanced" for easy reference. There are also several much more difficult exercises, designated as "challenging." We have also included, in virtually every section of every chapter, exercises that are ideal for the use of technology.

Application Exercises

Exercises also include interesting applications based on real data to reinforce the applicability of math to real-life situations.

Communication and Reasoning Exercises

These exercises are designed to help students articulate mathematical concepts, broaden the student's grasp of the mathematical concepts, and develop modeling skills. They include exercises in which the student is asked to provide his or her own examples to illustrate a point or design an application with a given solution. They also include "fill in the blank" type exercises, exercises that invite discussion and debate, and—perhaps most important—exercises in which the student must identify and correct common errors. These exercises often have no single correct answer.

3.1   EXERCISES

▼ more advanced   ◆ challenging
Ⓣ indicates exercises that should be solved using technology

In Exercises 1–10, compute the simple interest for the specified length of time and the future value at the end of that time. Round all answers to the nearest cent. [HINT: See Quick Examples 1–5.]

1. $2,000 is invested for 1 year at 6% per year.

2. $1,000 is invested for 10 years at 4% per year.

3. $4,000 is invested for 8 months at 0.5% per month.

Applications

89. *Processor Speeds* The processor speeds, in megahertz (MHz), of Intel processors during the period 1996–2010 can be approximated by the following function of time t in years since the start of 1990:[17]

$$v(t) = \begin{cases} 400t - 2,200 & \text{if } 6 \leq t < 15 \\ 3,800 & \text{if } 15 \leq t \leq 20. \end{cases}$$

a. Compute $\lim_{t \to 15^-} v(t)$ and $\lim_{t \to 15^+} v(t)$, and interpret each answer. [HINT: See Example 3.]

b. Is the function v continuous at $t = 15$? According to the model, was there any abrupt change in processor speeds during the period 1996–2010?

Communication and Reasoning Exercises

101. Describe the algebraic method of evaluating limits as discussed in this section, and give at least one disadvantage of this method.

102. What is a closed-form function? What can we say about such functions?

103. Your friends Rita and Richard are arguing. Rita claims that closed-form functions cannot have points of discontinuity, but Richard retorts, "Ever heard of $f(x) = 1/x$?" On whose side (if any) of the argument should you be? Explain.

Review

At the end of every chapter is a comprehensive list of the key concepts that were covered in each section.

Review exercises provide a great way to consolidate and check understanding and prepare for exams.

Case Studies

Each chapter ends with a section entitled "Case Study," an extended application that uses and illustrates the central ideas of the chapter, focusing on the development of mathematical models appropriate to the topics. These applications are ideal for assignment as projects.

CHAPTER 3   REVIEW

KEY CONCEPTS

www.WanerMath.com
Go to the Website to find a comprehensive and interactive Web-based summary of Chapter 3.

3.2 Compound Interest
Future value for compound interest:
$FV = PV(1 + i)^n$ [p. 213]
Present value for compound interest:

Payments to accumulate a future value:
$PMT = FV \dfrac{i}{(1 + i)^n - 1}$ [p. 227]
Annuitization: present value:

REVIEW EXERCISES

In Exercises 1–6, find the future value of the investment.

1. $6,000 for 5 years at 4.75% simple annual interest

2. $10,000 for 2.5 years at 5.25% simple annual interest

15. The monthly withdrawals possible over 5 years from an account earning 4.75% compounded monthly and starting with $6,000

CASE STUDY   **Reducing Sulfur Emissions**

The Environmental Protection Agency (EPA) wishes to formulate a policy that will encourage utilities to reduce sulfur emissions. Its goal is to reduce annual emissions of sulfur dioxide by a total of 10 million tons from the current level of 25 million tons by imposing a fixed charge for every ton of sulfur released into the environment per year. As a consultant to the EPA, you must determine the amount to be charged per ton of sulfur emissions.

You would like first to know the cost to the utility industry of reducing sulfur emissions. In other words, you would like to have a cost function of the form

$C(q) = $ Cost of removing q tons of sulfur dioxide.

Norbert Schaefer/CORBIS/Getty Images

Focus on Technology

Marginal Technology Notes

We give brief marginal technology notes to outline the use of graphing calculator, spreadsheet, and website technology in appropriate examples. When necessary, the reader is referred to more detailed discussion in the end-of-chapter Technology Guides.

End-of-Chapter Technology Guides

We continue to include detailed TI-83/84 Plus and Spreadsheet Guides at the end of each chapter. These Guides are referenced liberally in marginal technology notes at appropriate points in the chapter, so instructors and students can easily use this material or not, as they prefer.

Using Technology

TI-83/84 Plus
2ND CATALOG
DiagnosticOn
Then STAT CALC option #4:
LinReg(ax+b) [More details in the Technology Guide.]

Spreadsheet
Add a trendline and select the option to "Display R-squared value on chart."
[More details and other alternatives in the Technology Guide.]

Website
www.WanerMath.com
The following two utilities will show regression lines and also r^2 (link to either from Math Tools for Chapter 1):

Simple Regression Utility

Function Evaluator and Grapher

TI-83/84 Plus   Technology Guide

Section 3.2

Example 1 (page 215) In December [...] Bank was paying 1.10% annual interes[t] accounts with balances of $2,500 and up. [...] is compounded quarterly, find the futu[re] $2,500 deposit after 6 years. What is the[...] paid over the time of the investment?

Solution
We could calculate the future value using [...]

(such as the future value of your deposit, which the bank will give back to you) will be a positive number.

Spreadsheet   Technology Guide

Section 3.2

Example 1 (page 215) In December 2015, Radius Bank was paying 1.10% annual interest on savings accounts with balances of $2,500 and up. If the interest is compounded quarterly, find the future value of a

=FV(i, n, PMT, PV)

$i = $ Interest per period   We use B2/B7 for the interest.

$n = $ Number of periods   We use B3*B7 for the number of

Instructor Resources

MindTap: Through personalized paths of dynamic assignments and applications, MindTap is a digital learning solution and representation of your course that turns cookie cutter into cutting edge, apathy into engagement, and memorizers into higher-level thinkers.

The Right Content: With MindTap's carefully curated material, you get the precise content and groundbreaking tools you need for every course you teach. This course includes a dynamic Pre-Course Assessment that tests students on their prerequisite skills, an eBook, algorithmic assignments, and new lecture videos.

Personalization: Customize every element of your course—from rearranging the learning path to inserting videos and activities.

Improved Workflow: Save time when planning lessons with all of the trusted, most current content you need in one place in MindTap.

Tracking Students' Progress in Real Time: Promote positive outcomes by tracking students in real time and tailoring your course as needed based on the analytics.

Learn more at **www.cengage.com/mindtap**.

WebAssign: Exclusively from Cengage Learning, Enhanced WebAssign combines the exceptional mathematics content that you know and love with the most powerful online homework solution, WebAssign. Enhanced WebAssign engages students with immediate feedback, rich tutorial content, and eBooks, helping students to develop a deeper conceptual understanding of their subject matter. Quick Prep and Just In Time exercises provide opportunities for students to review prerequisite skills and content, both at the start of the course and at the beginning of each section. Flexible assignment options give instructors the ability to release assignments conditionally on the basis of students' prerequisite assignment scores. Visit us at **www.cengage.com/ewa** to learn more.

Cognero: Cengage Learning Testing Powered by Cognero is a flexible, online system that allows you to author, edit, and manage test bank content; create multiple test versions in an instant; and deliver tests from your LMS, your classroom, or wherever you choose.

Instructor Companion Site: This collection of book-specific lecture and class tools is available online at **www.cengage.com/login**. Access and download PowerPoint presentations, complete solutions manual, and more.

Student Resources

Student Solutions Manual (ISBN: 978-1-337-27597-2): Go beyond the answers—see what it takes to get there and improve your grade! This manual provides worked-out, step-by-step solutions to the odd-numbered problems in the text. You'll have the information you need to truly understand how the problems are solved.

MindTap: MindTap (assigned by the instructor) is a digital representation of your course that provides you with the tools you need to better manage your limited time, stay organized, and be successful. You can complete assignments whenever and wherever you are ready to learn, with course material specially customized for you by your instructor and streamlined in one proven, easy-to-use interface. With an array of study tools, you'll get a true understanding of course concepts, achieve better grades, and lay the groundwork for your future courses. Learn more at **www.cengage.com/mindtap**.

WebAssign: Enhanced WebAssign (assigned by the instructor) provides you with instant feedback on homework assignments. This online homework system is easy to use and includes helpful links to textbook sections, video examples, and problem-specific tutorials.

CengageBrain: Visit **www.cengagebrain.com** to access additional course materials and companion resources. At the cengagebrain.com home page, search for the ISBN of your title (from the back cover of your book) using the search box at the top of the page. This will take you to the product page where free companion resources can be found.

The Author Website

The authors' website, accessible through **www.wanermath.com**, has been evolving for close to two decades with growing recognition. Students, raised in an environment in which computers suffuse both work and play, can use their web browsers to engage with the material in an active way. The following features of the authors' website are fully integrated with the text and can be used as a personalized study resource:

- **Interactive Tutorials**   Highly interactive tutorials are included on major topics, with guided exercises that parallel the text and a great deal of help and feedback to assist the student.

- **Game Versions of Tutorials**   More challenging tutorials with randomized questions that work as games (complete with "health" scores, "health vials," and an assessment of one's performance at the end of the game) are offered alongside the traditional tutorials. These game tutorials, which mirror the traditional "more gentle" tutorials, randomize all the questions and do not give the student the answers but instead offer hints in exchange for "health points," so that just staying alive (not running out of health) can be quite challenging.

- **Learning and Practice Modules**   These interactive demos illustrate important concepts and randomizable "practice examples" that mirror many examples and quick examples in the text.

- **Detailed Chapter Summaries**   Comprehensive summaries with randomizable interactive elements review all the basic definitions and problem-solving techniques discussed in each chapter. These are a terrific pre-test study tool for students.

- **Downloadable Excel Tutorials**   Detailed Excel tutorials are available for almost every section of the book. These interactive tutorials expand on the examples given in the text.

- **Online Utilities**   Our collection of easy-to-use online utilities, referenced in the marginal notes of the textbook, allow students to solve many of the technology-based application exercises directly on the web. The utilities include a function grapher and evaluator that also graphs derivatives and does curve-fitting, regression tools, a time value of money calculator for annuities, a matrix algebra tool that also manipulates matrices with multinomial entries, a linear programming grapher that automatically solves two-dimensional linear programming problems graphically, a powerful simplex method tool, an interactive Riemann sum grapher with a numerical integrator, and a multifunctional line entry calculator on the main page. These utilities require nothing more than a standard web browser.

- **Chapter True-False Quizzes**   Randomized quizzes that provide feedback for many incorrect answers based on the key concepts in each chapter assist the student in further mastery of the material.

- **Supplemental Topics**   We include complete interactive text and exercise sets for a selection of topics that are not ordinarily included in printed texts but are often requested by instructors.

- **Spanish**   A parallel Spanish version of almost the entire website is now deployed, allowing the user to switch languages on specific pages with a single mouse-click. In particular, all of the chapter summaries and most of the tutorials, game tutorials, and utilities are available in Spanish.

Acknowledgments

This project would not have been possible without the contributions and suggestions of numerous colleagues, students, and friends. We are particularly grateful to our colleagues at Hofstra and elsewhere who used and gave us useful feedback on previous editions and suggestions for this one, and to everyone at Cengage for their encouragement and guidance throughout the project. Specifically, we would like to thank Rita Lombard and Morgan Mendoza for their unflagging enthusiasm, Scott Barnett of Henry Ford Community College for his meticulous check of the mathematical accuracy, and Martha Emry and Teresa Trego for whipping the book into shape. Additionally, we would like to thank the creative force of Jay Abramson of Arizona State University for developing the new lecture videos that accompany our text, and Scott Barnett of Henry Ford Community College, Joe Rody of Arizona State University, Nada Al-Hanna of University of Texas at El Paso, and Kaat Higham of Bergen Community College for their thoughtful reviews and input into the scripts.

We would also like to thank Dario Menasce at CERN who helped us understand the fascinating new cover art, and the numerous reviewers and proofreaders who provided many helpful suggestions that have shaped the development of this book over time:

Christopher Brown, *California Lutheran University*

Melinda Camarillo, *El Paso Community College*

Nathan Carlson, *California Lutheran University*

Scott Fallstrom, *University of Oregon*

Irene Jai, *Raritan Valley Community College*

Latrice Laughlin, *University of Alaska Fairbanks*

Gabriel Mendoza, *El Paso Community College*

Charles Mundy-Castle, *Central New Mexico Community College*

Patrick Mutungi, *University of South Carolina*

Michael Price, *University of Oregon*

Christopher Quarles, *Everett Community College*

Leela Rakesh, *Central Michigan University*

Tom Rosenwinkel, *Concordia University Texas*

Bradley Stewart, *State University of New York at Oswego*

Larry Taylor, *North Dakota State University*

Daniel Wang, *Central Michigan University*

Stefan Waner
Steven R. Costenoble

FINITE MATHEMATICS
AND APPLIED CALCULUS

4

SYSTEMS OF LINEAR EQUATIONS AND MATRICES

CASE STUDY

Hybrid Cars—Optimizing the Degree of Hybridization

You are involved in new model development at a major automobile company. The company is planning to introduce two new plug-in hybrid electric vehicles: the subcompact "Green Town Hopper" and the midsize "Electra Supreme," and your department must decide on the degree of hybridization (DOH) for each of these models that will result in the largest reduction in gasoline consumption. The data you have available show the gasoline savings for only three values of the DOH.

How do you estimate the optimal value?

Fedor Selivanov/Alamy Stock Photo

www.WanerMath.com

At the Website, in addition to the resources listed in the Preface, you will find:

- A Web page that pivots and does row operations
- An Excel worksheet that pivots and does row operations

Introduction

In Chapter 1 we studied single functions and equations. In this chapter we seek solutions to **systems** of two or more equations. For example, suppose we need to *find two numbers whose sum is* 3 *and whose difference is* 1. In other words, we need to find two numbers x and y such that $x + y = 3$ and $x - y = 1$. The only solution turns out to be $x = 2$ and $y = 1$, a solution you might easily guess. But how do we know that this is the only solution, and how do we find solutions systematically? When we restrict ourselves to systems of *linear* equations, there is a very elegant method for determining the number of solutions and finding them all. Moreover, as we will see, many real-world applications give rise to just such systems of linear equations.

We begin in Section 4.1 with systems of two linear equations in two unknowns and some of their applications. In Section 4.2 we study a powerful matrix method, called *row reduction*, for solving systems of linear equations in any number of unknowns. In Section 4.3 we look at more applications.

Computers have been used for many years to solve the large systems of equations that arise in the real world. You probably already have access to devices that will do the row operations that are used in row reduction. Many graphing calculators can do them, as can spreadsheets and various special-purpose applications, including utilities available at the Website. Using such a device or program makes the calculations quicker and helps to avoid arithmetic mistakes. Then there are programs (and calculators) into which you simply feed the system of equations and out pop the solutions. We can think of what we do in this chapter as looking inside the "black box" of such a program. More important, we talk about how, starting from a real-world problem, to get the system of equations to solve in the first place. No computer will do this conversion for us yet.

4.1 Systems of Two Equations in Two Unknowns

Linear Equations and Solutions

Suppose you have $3 in your pocket to spend on snacks and a drink. If x represents the amount you'll spend on snacks and y represents the amount you'll spend on a drink, you can say that $x + y = 3$. On the other hand, if for some reason you want to spend $1 more on snacks than on your drink, you can also say that $x - y = 1$. These are simple examples of **linear equations in two unknowns**.

Linear Equations in Two Unknowns

A **linear equation in two unknowns** is an equation that can be written in the form

$$ax + by = c$$

with a, b, and c being real numbers. The number a is called the **coefficient of x**, and b is called the **coefficient of y**. A **solution** of an equation consists of a pair of numbers: a value for x and a value for y that satisfy the equation.

Quick Example

1. In the linear equation $3x - 2y = 12$, the coefficients are $a = 3$ and $b = -2$. The pair $(x, y) = (4, 0)$ is a solution, because
   $$3(4) - 2(0) = 12.$$

In fact, $(x, y) = (4, 0)$ is not the only solution to the linear equation $3x - 2y = 12$ in Quick Example 1. Linear equations have *infinitely many* solutions, as we now illustrate.

EXAMPLE 1   Solutions of a Linear Equation

Determine all solutions of $3x - 2y = 12$.

Solution If we rewrite the equation $3x - 2y = 12$ by solving for y, we get

$$y = \frac{3}{2}x - 6,$$

which expresses y as a linear function of x, as in Section 1.3. For every value of x that we choose, we can now get the corresponding value of y, giving a solution (x, y), as shown in the following table:

x	-2	0	2	4	6
$y = \dfrac{3}{2}x - 6$	-9	-6	-3	0	3

From the table we find the **particular solutions** $(-2, -9)$, $(0, -6)$, $(2, -3)$, $(4, 0)$, and $(6, 3)$. These are just five of the infinitely many solutions that are possible. Each of these solutions has the form $(x, y) = \left(x, \frac{3}{2}x - 6\right)$ for some arbitrary choice of x, so we call

$$(x, y) = \left(x, \frac{3}{2}x - 6\right); \quad x \text{ arbitrary} \qquad \text{General solution paramaterized by } x$$

the **general solution**, as it incorporates all possible particular solutions: To get a particular solution from the general solution, just choose a value for x. When we write the general solution this way, we say that x is a **parameter**, and we have a solution **parameterized by** x.

Referring to Section 1.3, we see that these solutions are in fact the points on a straight line: the *graph* of $y = \frac{3}{2}x - 6$ (Figure 1). Geometrically, we have a "whole line of solutions," one for each point on the line.

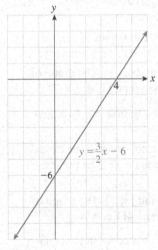

Figure 1

➡ **Before we go on . . .** We could have solved the equation for x instead:

$$x = \frac{2}{3}y + 4$$

and obtained another form of the general solution, parameterized by y:

$$\left(\frac{2}{3}y + 4, y\right); \quad y \text{ arbitrary.} \qquad \text{General solution parameterized by } y \quad \blacksquare$$

The following summarizes what we have just said.

Particular and General Solutions of a Linear Equation in Two Unknowns

A **particular solution** of the linear equation $ax + by = c$ is a specific pair of numbers (x, y) that satisfy the equation. If a and b are not both zero, the linear equation $ax + by = c$ has infinitely many such solutions; these solutions lie on a straight line, the **graph of the equation**.

The **general solution parameterized by x** of the linear equation $ax + by = c$ has the form $(x, f(x))$, where we solve the given equation for y as a function of x, $y = f(x)$ if possible.* Substituting any number for x then results in a particular solution.

Similarly, the **general solution parameterized by y** has the form $(g(y), y)$, where we solve the given equation for $x = g(y)$ if possible.† Substituting any number for y then results in a particular solution.

* That is, if $b \neq 0$, so that y appears in the equation. Otherwise, the general solution cannot be parameterized by x.

† That is, if $a \neq 0$, so that x appears in the equation. Otherwise, the general solution cannot be parameterized by y.

Quick Examples

2. $2x + y = 4$ has the two particular solutions $(0, 4)$ and $(1, 2)$, among infinitely many others. The graph of $2x + y = 4$ consists of all its solutions and is the line $y = -2x + 4$ with slope -2 and y-intercept 4.

   General solution parameterized by x: Solve for y to obtain $y = -2x + 4$, giving the general solution $(x, -2x + 4)$; x arbitrary.

   General solution parameterized by y: Solve for x to obtain $x = -\frac{1}{2}y + 2$, giving the general solution $\left(-\frac{1}{2}y + 2, y\right)$; y arbitrary.

3. $2y = 6$ has the two particular solutions $(0, 3)$ and $(1, 3)$. The graph of $2y = 6$ consists of all its solutions and is the horizontal line $y = 3$.

   General solution parameterized by x: Solve for y to obtain $y = 3$, giving the general solution $(x, 3)$; x arbitrary.

   General solution parameterized by y: As x does not occur in the equation, we cannot solve for x, so the general solution cannot be parameterized by y.

4. $3x = 5$ has the two particular solutions $\left(\frac{5}{3}, 0\right)$ and $\left(\frac{5}{3}, 1\right)$. The graph of $3x = 5$ consists of all its solutions and is the vertical line $x = \frac{5}{3}$.

   General solution parameterized by x: As y does not occur in the equation, we cannot solve for y, so the general solution cannot be parameterized by x.

   General solution parameterized by y: Solve for x to obtain $x = \frac{5}{3}$, giving the general solution $\left(\frac{5}{3}, y\right)$; y arbitrary.

Solutions to Systems of Linear Equations

In this section we are mainly concerned with pairs (x, y) that are solutions of two linear equations at the same time. For example, $(2, 1)$ is a solution of both of the equations $x + y = 3$ and $x - y = 1$, because substituting $x = 2$ and $y = 1$ into these equations gives $2 + 1 = 3$ (true) and $2 - 1 = 1$ (also true), respectively. So in the simple example at the beginning of this section you could spend $2 on snacks and $1 on a drink.

In the examples that follow, we see how to graphically and algebraically solve a system of two linear equations in two unknowns. Then we consider systems of more than two linear equations in two unknowns, and finally, we return to some more interesting applications.

EXAMPLE 2   **Solving a System Graphically and Algebraically**

Find all solutions (x, y) of the following system of two equations:

$$x + y = 3$$
$$x - y = 1.$$

Solution

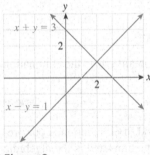

Figure 2

✻ We can add these equations because when we add equal amounts to both sides of an equation, the results are equal. That is, if $A = B$ and $C = D$, then $A + C = B + D$.

Method 1: Graphical We already know that the solutions of a single linear equation are the points on its graph, which is a straight line. For a point to represent a solution of two linear equations, it must lie simultaneously on both of the corresponding lines. In other words, it must be a point where the two lines cross, or intersect. A look at Figure 2 should convince us that the lines cross only at the point $(2, 1)$, so this is the only possible solution.

Method 2: Algebraic: Solving by Elimination This will be our preferred approach. (See the "Before we go on" discussion at the end of this example.) To solve the system algebraically by elimination, we try to combine the equations in such a way as to eliminate one variable. In this case, notice that if we add the left-hand sides of the equations, the terms with y are eliminated. So we add the first equation to the second (that is, add the left-hand sides and add the right-hand sides✻):

$$
\begin{aligned}
x + y &= 3 \\
\underline{x - y} &= \underline{1} \\
2x + 0 &= 4 \\
2x &= 4 \\
x &= 2.
\end{aligned}
$$

Now that we know that x has to be 2, we can substitute back into either equation to find y. Choosing the first equation (it doesn't matter which we choose), we have

$$2 + y = 3$$
$$y = 3 - 2 = 1.$$

We have found that the only possible solution is $x = 2$ and $y = 1$, or

$$(x, y) = (2, 1).$$

Method 3: Algebraic: Solving by Intersection Solution by intersection is based on the idea of the geometric approach: that the solution is the point of intersection of the graphs of two linear functions. To find this intersection point algebraically, we reason that the two functions must have the same value at the point of intersection, so we solve both equations for y,* set the resulting linear functions of x equal to each other, and solve for x:

$$y = -x + 3 \qquad \text{Solve } x + y = 3 \text{ for } y.$$
$$y = x - 1 \qquad \text{Solve } x - y = 1 \text{ for } y.$$
$$-x + 3 = x - 1 \qquad \text{Equate the resulting linear functions of } x.$$
$$-2x = -4$$
$$x = 2 \qquad \text{Solve for } x.$$

> *If y does not occur in an equation, it means that we can use that equation to obtain the value of x directly and then substitute this value in the other equation to obtain y.

We can then substitute this value into either equation (or either linear function we found) to obtain y as in Method 2 and find the solution: $(x, y) = (2, 1)$.

Method 4: Algebraic: Solving by Substitution In the substitution method we solve one of the equations for one of the unknowns and then substitute the resulting expression in the other to solve for the other unknown:

$$y = -x + 3 \qquad \text{Solve } x + y = 3 \text{ for } y.$$
$$x - (-x + 3) = 1 \qquad \text{Substitute the resulting expression in the other equation, } x - y = 1.$$
$$2x - 3 = 1 \quad \Rightarrow \quad 2x = 4$$
$$x = 2. \qquad \text{Solve for } x.$$

We can then substitute this value into either equation to obtain y as in the elimination method to obtain the solution: $(x, y) = (2, 1)$.

➡ **Before we go on...** As we said above, the method of elimination is our preferred algebraic method of solving systems of linear equations and is the algebraic method we will use in most of the examples that follow.

Q: *The intersection and substitution methods seem simpler and more direct. So why is the elimination method the "preferred" method?*

A: Two reasons: First, the elimination method extends more easily to systems with more equations and unknowns than the other two methods. It is the basis for the matrix method of solving systems—a method we will discuss in Section 4.2. So we shall use it exclusively for the rest of this section. Second, the system we considered in Example 2 is a simple one, so very little algebraic manipulation was required in the other methods. In general, the elimination method will, as we see below, allow us to completely avoid fractions and decimals even in systems presented with fractions and decimals, whereas the other methods may require manipulation of complicated expressions involving fractions and/or decimals. ∎

The next example illustrates the drawbacks of the graphical method.

Using Technology

See the Technology Guides at the end of the chapter for details on the graphical solution of Example 1 using a TI-83/84 Plus or a spreadsheet. Here is an outline:

TI-83/84 Plus
Y_1=-X+3 Y_2=X-1
Graph: WINDOW ; Xmin = −4,
Xmax = 4; ZOOM 0
Trace to estimate the point of intersection.
[More details in the Technology Guide.]

Spreadsheet
Headings x, $y1$, and $y2$ in A1–C1;
x-values −4, 4 in A2, A3
=-A2+3 and =A2-1 in B1 and C1;
copy down to B2–C2.
Graph the data in columns A–C with a line-segment scatter plot.
To see a closer view, change the values in A2–A3.
[More details in the Technology Guide.]

Website
www.WanerMath.com
→ Online Utilities
→ Function Evaluator and Grapher
Enter -x+3 for y_1 and x-1 for y_2.
Set Xmin = −4, Xmax = 4 and press "Plot Graphs".
Click on the graph, and use the trace arrows below to estimate the point of intersection.

EXAMPLE 3   **Solving a System: Algebraically versus Graphically**

Solve the following system:

$$\frac{x}{5} + \frac{y}{3} = 0$$

$$0.2x + 0.7y = 0.1.$$

Solution Fractions and decimals can significantly complicate any method used to solve the system, so our approach here—and throughout this chapter—will be to *get rid of fractions and decimals before doing anything:*[*] To get rid of the fractions in the first equation, we can multiply both sides of the equation by a common multiple of the denominators such as 15; and to get rid of the decimals in the second equation, we can multiply both sides by 10:

$$\
(15)\left(\frac{x}{5} + \frac{y}{3}\right) = (15)(0)$$

$$(10)(0.2x + 0.7y) = (10)(0.1),$$

giving

$$3x + 5y = 0$$

$$2x + 7y = 1,$$

which looks a whole lot better! To solve, we try the graphical approach first.

Method 1: Graphical First, solve for y, obtaining $y = -\frac{3}{5}x$ and $y = -\frac{2}{7}x + \frac{1}{7}$. Graphing these equations, we get Figure 3. The lines appear to intersect slightly above and to the left of the origin. Redrawing with a finer scale (or zooming in using graphing technology), we can get the graph in Figure 4.

If we look carefully at Figure 4, we see that the graphs intersect near $(-0.45, 0.27)$. Is the point of intersection *exactly* $(-0.45, 0.27)$? (Substitute these values into the equations to find out.) In fact, it is extremely onerous to find the exact solution of this system graphically, but we now have a ballpark answer that we can use to help check the following algebraic solution.

Method 2: Algebraic: Solving by Elimination We first see that adding the equations is not going to eliminate either x or y. Notice, however, that if we multiply (both sides of) the first equation by 2 and the second by -3, the coefficients of x will become 6 and -6. *Then* if we add them, x will be eliminated. So we proceed as follows:

$$2(3x + 5y) = 2(0)$$

$$-3(2x + 7y) = -3(1)$$

gives

$$6x + 10y = 0$$

$$-6x - 21y = -3.$$

Adding these equations, we get

$$-11y = -3,$$

[*] If fractions and decimals are not necessary at each step of a calculation, why insist on carrying them through the entire calculation like dead weight, complicating all the calculations for no good reason?

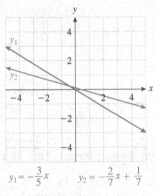

$$y_1 = -\frac{3}{5}x \qquad y_2 = -\frac{2}{7}x + \frac{1}{7}$$

Figure 3

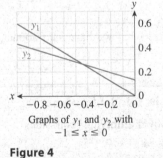

Graphs of y_1 and y_2 with $-1 \le x \le 0$

Figure 4

so

$$y = \frac{3}{11} = 0.\overline{27}.$$

Substituting $y = \frac{3}{11}$ in the first equation gives

$$3x + 5\left(\frac{3}{11}\right) = 0$$

$$3x = -\frac{15}{11}$$

$$x = -\frac{5}{11} = -0.\overline{45}.$$

The solution is $(x, y) = \left(-\frac{5}{11}, \frac{3}{11}\right) = (-0.\overline{45}, 0.\overline{27})$.

Notice that the algebraic method gives us the exact solution that we could not find with the graphical method. Still, we can check that the graph and our algebraic solution agree to the accuracy with which we can read the graph. To be absolutely sure that our answer is correct, we should check it:

$$3\left(-\frac{5}{11}\right) + 5\left(\frac{3}{11}\right) = -\frac{15}{11} + \frac{15}{11} = 0 \quad ✔$$

$$2\left(-\frac{5}{11}\right) + 7\left(\frac{3}{11}\right) = -\frac{10}{11} + \frac{21}{11} = 1. \quad ✔$$

Get in the habit of checking your answers.

➡ **Before we go on . . .**

Q: *In solving the system in Example 3, we multiplied (both sides of) the equations by numbers. How does that affect their graphs?*

A: Multiplying both sides of an equation by a nonzero number has no effect on its solutions, so the graph (which represents the set of all solutions) is unchanged.

Before doing some more examples, we summarize what we have said about solving systems of equations.

Solving a System of Two Linear Equations in Two Unknowns

Before starting, get rid of all decimals and fractions by multiplying (both sides of) each equation by a suitable nonzero number.

Graphical Method of Solution

Graph both equations on the same graph. (For example, solve each for y to find the slope and y-intercept.) A point of intersection gives the solution to the system. To find the point, you may need to adjust the range of x-values you use. To find the point accurately, you may need to use a smaller range (or zoom in if using technology).

Algebraic Methods of Solution

Solving by Elimination (Preferred): To eliminate x, multiply (both sides of) each equation by a nonzero number so that the coefficients of x are the same in absolute value but opposite in sign. Add the two equations to eliminate x; this gives an equation in y that we can solve to find its value. Substitute this value of y into one of the original equations to find the value of x (or we could first eliminate y to find x).

Solving by Intersection: Solve both equations for y, and equate the resulting functions of x to solve for x. Substitute this value of x into one of the original equations to find the value of y.

Solving by Substitution: Solve one equation for y, and then substitute the resulting expression in the other to solve for x. Substitute this value of x into one of the original equations to find the value of y.

Sometimes, something appears to go wrong with these methods. The following examples show what can happen.

EXAMPLE 4 | **Inconsistent System**

Solve the system

$$x - 3y = 5$$
$$-2x + 6y = 8.$$

Solution To eliminate x, we multiply the first equation by 2 and then add:

$$2x - 6y = 10$$
$$-2x + 6y = 8.$$

Adding gives

$$0 = 18.$$

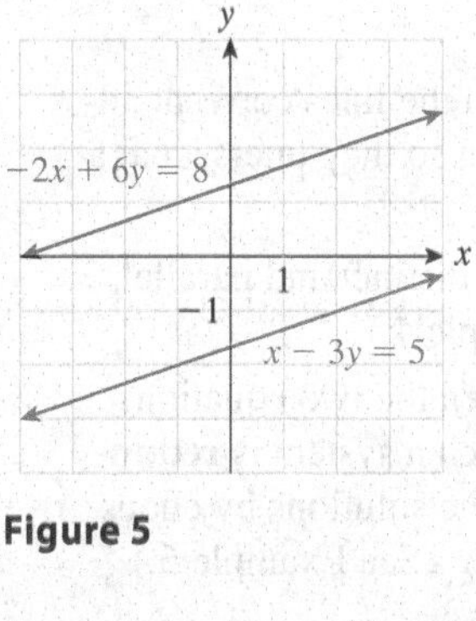

But this is absurd! This calculation shows that if we had two numbers x and y that satisfied both equations, it would be true that $0 = 18$. As 0 is *not* equal to 18, there can be no such numbers x and y. In other words, *the system has no solutions* and is called an **inconsistent system**.

In slope-intercept form, these lines are $y = \frac{1}{3}x - \frac{5}{3}$ and $y = \frac{1}{3}x + \frac{4}{3}$. Notice that they have the same slope but different y-intercepts. This means that they are parallel but different lines. Plotting them confirms this fact (Figure 5). Because they are parallel, they do not intersect. A solution must be a point of intersection, so we again conclude that there is no solution.

Figure 5

EXAMPLE 5 | **Redundant System**

Solve the system

$$x + y = 2$$
$$2x + 2y = 4.$$

Solution Multiplying the first equation by -2 gives

$$-2x - 2y = -4$$
$$2x + 2y = 4.$$

Adding gives the not-very-enlightening result

$$0 = 0.$$

Now what has happened? Looking back at the original system, we note that the second equation is really the first equation in disguise. (It is the first equation multiplied by 2.) Put another way, if we solve both equations for y, we find that, in slope-intercept form, both equations become the same:

$$y = -x + 2,$$

so the two lines represented by the two equations are actually the same line (Figure 6). As these "two" lines intersect at every point, there is a solution for each point on the common line. In other words, we have infinitely many solutions, as in Example 1.

Algebraically, the second equation gives us the same information as the first, so we say that this is a **redundant** or **dependent system**. Put another way, we really have only one equation in two unknowns, so we refer to Example 1 to find the general solution by solving for y (which we did already above):

$$y = -x + 2.$$

Thus, the general solution is

$$(x, -x + 2); \quad x \text{ arbitrary.} \qquad \text{General solution parameterized by } x$$

As in Example 1, different choices of the parameter x lead to different particular solutions. For instance, choosing $x = 3$ gives the particular solution $(x, y) = (3, -1)$. Alternatively, we could solve for x to parameterize the general solution by y:

$$(-y + 2, y); \quad y \text{ arbitrary.} \qquad \text{General solution parameterized by } y$$

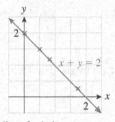

The line of solutions ($y = -x + 2$) and some particular solutions

Figure 6

We summarize the three possible outcomes we have encountered.

> **Possible Outcomes for a System of Two Linear Equations in Two Unknowns**
>
> 1. **A single (or *unique*) solution:** This happens when the lines corresponding to the two equations are distinct and not parallel so they intersect at a single point. (See Example 2.)
> 2. **No solution:** This happens when the two lines are distinct and parallel. We say that the system is **inconsistent**. (See Example 4.)
> 3. **An infinite number of solutions:** This occurs when the two equations represent the same straight line, and we say that such a system is **redundant** or **dependent**. In this case we can represent the solutions by choosing one variable arbitrarily and solving for the other. (See Example 5.)
>
> In cases 1 and 3 we say that the system of equations is **consistent** because it has at least one solution.

You should think about straight lines and convince yourself that these are the only three possibilities.

Applications

EXAMPLE 6   **Resource Allocation**

Acme Baby Foods mixes two strengths of apple juice. One quart of Beginner's juice is made from 30 fluid ounces of water and 2 fluid ounces of apple juice concentrate. One quart of Advanced juice is made from 20 fluid ounces of water and 12 fluid ounces of concentrate. Every day Acme has available 30,000 fluid ounces of water and 3,600 fluid ounces of concentrate. If the company wants to use all the water and concentrate, how many quarts of each type of juice should it mix?

Solution In all applications we follow the same general strategy:

1. *Identify and label the unknowns.* What are we asked to find? To answer this question, it is common to respond by saying, "The unknowns are Beginner's juice and Advanced juice." Quite frankly, this is a baffling statement. Just what is unknown about juice? We need to be more precise:

   *The unknowns are (1) the **number of quarts** of Beginner's juice and (2) the **number of quarts** of Advanced juice made each day.*

   So we label the unknowns as follows: Let

   x = number of quarts of Beginner's juice made each day

   y = number of quarts of Advanced juice made each day.

2. *Use the information given to set up equations in the unknowns.* This step is trickier, and the strategy varies from problem to problem. Here, the amount of juice the company can make is constrained by the fact that it has limited amounts of water and concentrate. This example shows a kind of application we will often see, and it is helpful in these problems to use a table to record the amounts of the resources used.

Using Technology

Website
www.WanerMath.com
At the Website, select the Online Utilities tab, and choose the Pivot and Gauss-Jordan tool. To check Example 6, enter the coefficients of x and y and the right-hand sides of the two equations as shown (no commas in numbers!):

x1	x2	x3
30	20	30000
2	12	3600

Then press "Reduce Completely". The values of x and y will appear in the last column:

x1	x2	x3
1	0	900
0	1	150

(In the next section we will see how this works.)

	Beginner's (x)	Advanced (y)	Available
Water (fluid ounces)	30	20	30,000
Concentrate (fluid ounces)	2	12	3,600

We can now set up an equation for each of the items listed in the left column of the table.

Water: We read across the first row. If Acme mixes x quarts of Beginner's juice, each quart using 30 fluid ounces of water, and y quarts of Advanced juice, each using 20 fluid ounces of water, it will use a total of $30x + 20y$ fluid ounces of water. But we are told that the total has to be 30,000 fluid ounces. Thus, $30x + 20y = 30,000$. This is our first equation.

Concentrate: We read across the second row. If Acme mixes x quarts of Beginner's juice, each using 2 fluid ounces of concentrate, and y quarts of Advanced juice, each using 12 fluid ounces of concentrate, it will use a total of $2x + 12y$ fluid ounces of concentrate. But we are told that the total has to be 3,600 fluid ounces. Thus, $2x + 12y = 3,600$.

Now we have two equations:

$$30x + 20y = 30,000$$
$$2x + 12y = 3,600.$$

To make the numbers easier to work with, let's divide (both sides of) the first equation by 10 and divide the second by 2:

$$3x + 2y = 3,000$$
$$x + 6y = 1,800.$$

We can now eliminate x by multiplying the second equation by -3 and adding:

$$
\begin{aligned}
3x + 2y &= 3,000 \\
-3x - 18y &= -5,400 \\
\hline
-16y &= -2,400.
\end{aligned}
$$

So $y = 2,400/16 = 150$. Substituting this into the equation $x + 6y = 1,800$ gives $x + 900 = 1,800$, so $x = 900$. The solution is $(x, y) = (900, 150)$. In other words, the company should mix 900 quarts of Beginner's juice and 150 quarts of Advanced juice.

SuperStock

EXAMPLE 7 Blending

A medieval alchemist's love potion calls for a number of eyes of newt and toes of frog, the total being 20, but with twice as many newt eyes as frog toes. How many of each are required?

Solution As in Example 6, the first step is to identify and label the unknowns. Let

$$x = \text{number of newt eyes}$$
$$y = \text{number of frog toes.}$$

As for the second step—setting up the equations—a table is less appropriate here than in Example 6. Instead, we translate each phrase of the problem into an equation. The phrase "the total being 20" tells us that the total number of eyes and toes is 20. Thus,

$$x + y = 20.$$

The end of the first sentence gives us more information, but the phrase "twice as many newt eyes as frog toes" is a little tricky: Does it mean that $2x = y$ or that $x = 2y$? We can decide which by rewording the statement using the phrases "the *number of* newt eyes," which is x, and "the *number of* frog toes," which is y. Rephrased, the statement reads:

 The **number of** newt eyes is twice the **number of** frog toes.

(Notice how the word "twice" is forced into a different place.) With this rephrasing, we can translate directly into algebra:

$$x = 2y.$$

In standard form $(ax + by = c)$, this equation reads

$$x - 2y = 0.$$

Thus, we have the two equations:

$$x + y = 20$$
$$x - 2y = 0.$$

To eliminate x, we multiply the second equation by -1 and then add:

$$x + \quad y = 20$$
$$-x + 2y = 0.$$

We'll leave it to you to finish solving the system and find that $x = 13\frac{1}{3}$ and $y = 6\frac{2}{3}$.

So the recipe calls for exactly $13\frac{1}{3}$ eyes of newt and $6\frac{2}{3}$ toes of frog. The alchemist needs a very sharp scalpel and a very accurate balance (not to mention a very strong stomach).

We saw in Chapter 1 that the *equilibrium price* of an item (the price at which supply equals demand) and the *break-even point* (the number of items that must be sold to break even) can both be described as the intersection points of two graphs. If the graphs are straight lines, what we need to do to find the intersection is solve a system of two linear equations in two unknowns, as illustrated in the following problem.

EXAMPLE 8   Equilibrium Price

The demand for refrigerators in West Podunk is given by

$$q = -\frac{p}{10} + 100,$$

where q is the number of refrigerators that the citizens will buy each year if the refrigerators are priced at p dollars each. The supply of refrigerators is

$$q = \frac{p}{20} + 25,$$

where now q is the number of refrigerators the manufacturers will be willing to ship into town each year if the refrigerators are priced at p dollars each. Find the equilibrium price and the number of refrigerators that will be sold at that price.

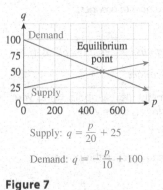

Supply: $q = \dfrac{p}{20} + 25$

Demand: $q = -\dfrac{p}{10} + 100$

Figure 7

Solution Figure 7 shows the demand and supply curves. The equilibrium price occurs at the point where these two lines cross, which is where demand equals supply. The graph suggests that the equilibrium price is $500, and zooming in confirms this.

To solve this system algebraically, the intersection method in Example 2 suggests itself, as both equations are already solved for q, so we just equate them:

$$-\frac{p}{10} + 100 = \frac{p}{20} + 25,$$

and solve for p:

$$-2p + 2{,}000 = p + 500 \qquad \text{Multiply by 20 to clear fractions.}$$
$$-3p = -1{,}500$$
$$p = 500.$$

Substituting this value into the demand equation gives us the corresponding value of q:

$$q = -\frac{500}{10} + 100 = 50.$$

Thus, the equilibrium price is $500, and 50 refrigerators will be sold at this price.

➡ **Before we go on ...** We could also have solved the system of equations in Example 8 by writing both equations in standard form with the unknowns on the left:

$$\frac{p}{10} + q = 100$$

$$-\frac{p}{20} + q = 25.$$

We could then have used elimination as in Example 3 (clearing fractions in the first step). ∎

FAQs

Setting Up the Equations

Q : *Looking through the example applications, I notice that in some, we can tabulate the information given and read off the equations (as in Example 6), whereas in others (such as Example 7), we have to reword each sentence to turn it into an equation. How do I know what approach to use?*

A : There is no hard-and-fast rule, and indeed some applications might call for a bit of each approach. However, it is generally not hard to see when it would be useful to tabulate values: Lists of the numbers of ingredients or components generally lend themselves to tabulation, whereas phrases such as "twice as many of these as those" generally require direct translation into equations (after rewording if necessary).

Q : *Help! Every time I write down the equation form of something like "there are twice as many apples as oranges" I get it backwards! What is going on?*

A : The most common reason for this kind of error is trying to write down an equation before rewording the information as we did in Example 7:

1. First, state what each unknown represents (using the phrase "the number of ..."), as in

   "Let x be the number of apples, and let y be the number of oranges."

   (Don't just say "x = apples, y = oranges.")

2. Then reword all the given information *using the phrase "the number of,"* as in

   "The number of apples is twice the number of oranges."

3. Finally, translate the reworded information directly into symbols, using your statements of what the unknowns represent, as in "x is twice y," or

   $$x = 2y.$$

In the exercise set, you will find a group of exercises to practice this process.

4.1 EXERCISES

▼ more advanced   ◆ challenging
🔲 indicates exercises that should be solved using technology

In Exercises 1–6, find three different particular solutions of the given equation and also its general solution in two forms (if

possible): parameterized by x and parameterized by y.
[HINT: See Example 1 and Quick Examples 2–4.]

1. $2x - y = 1$ **2.** $x + 3y = 3$

3. $3x + 4y = 2$ **4.** $4x - 3y = 6$

5. $4x = -5$ **6.** $-3y = 2$

In Exercises 7–20, find all solutions of the given system of equations, and check your answer graphically.
[HINT: See Examples 2–5.]

7. $x - y = 0$
$x + y = 4$

8. $x - y = 0$
$x + y = -6$

9. $x + y = 4$
$x - y = 2$

10. $2x + y = 2$
$-2x + y = 2$

11. $3x - 2y = 6$
$2x - 3y = -6$

12. $2x + 3y = 5$
$3x + 2y = 5$

[HINT: In Exercises 13–16, first eliminate all fractions and decimals; see Example 3.]

13. $0.5x + 0.1y = 0.7$
$0.2x - 0.2y = 0.6$

14. $-0.3x + 0.5y = 0.1$
$0.1x - 0.1y = 0.4$

15. $\dfrac{x}{3} - \dfrac{y}{2} = 1$
$\dfrac{x}{4} + y = -2$

16. $-\dfrac{2x}{3} + \dfrac{y}{2} = -\dfrac{1}{6}$
$\dfrac{x}{4} - y = -\dfrac{3}{4}$

17. $2x + 3y = 1$
$-x - \dfrac{3y}{2} = -\dfrac{1}{2}$

18. $2x - 3y = 1$
$6x - 9y = 3$

19. $2x + 3y = 2$
$-x - \dfrac{3y}{2} = -\dfrac{1}{2}$

20. $2x - 3y = 2$
$6x - 9y = 3$

In Exercises 21–30, use technology to obtain approximate solutions graphically. All solutions should be accurate to one decimal place. (Zoom in for improved accuracy.)

21. $2x + 8y = 10$
$x + y = 5$

22. $2x - y = 3$
$x + 3y = 5$

23. $3.1x - 4.5y = 6$
$4.5x + 1.1y = 0$

24. $0.2x + 4.5y = 1$
$1.5x + 1.1y = 2$

25. $10.2x + 14y = 213$
$4.5x + 1.1y = 448$

26. $100x + 4.5y = 540$
$1.05x + 1.1y = 0$

27. ▼ Find the intersection of the line through $(0, 1)$ and $(4.2, 2)$ and the line through $(2.1, 3)$ and $(5.2, 0)$.

28. ▼ Find the intersection of the line through $(2.1, 3)$ and $(4, 2)$ and the line through $(3.2, 2)$ and $(5.1, 3)$.

29. ▼ Find the intersection of the line through $(0, 0)$ and $(5.5, 3)$ and the line through $(5, 0)$ and $(0, 6)$.

30. ▼ Find the intersection of the line through $(4.3, 0)$ and $(0, 5)$ and the line through $(2.1, 2.2)$ and $(5.2, 1)$.

In Exercises 31–38, translate the given statement into one or more linear equations in the form $ax + by = c$ using the indicated variable names. Do not try to solve the resulting equation(s). [HINT: See Example 7 and the end of section FAQ.]

31. There are twice as many soccer fans (x) as football fans (y).

32. The number of hockey players (x) is 90% of the number of lacrosse players (y).

33. The number of new clients (x) is 110% of the number of old clients (y).

34. There are half as many bondholders (x) as stockholders (y).

35. There are three times as many gas giants (x) as rocky planets (y) among a total of 12 gas giants and rocky planets in System X12.

36. Among the total of 25 planets in System L5, four times as many support some form of life (x) as do not (y).

37. Of your portfolio consisting of ordinary shares (x) and preferred shares (y), 20% of the total are preferred shares, and there are 15 more ordinary shares than preferred shares.

38. Of your customer base, consisting of paid-up customers (x) and customers who still owe money (y), 75% of your customer base is paid up, the result being that there are 14,000 more paid-up customers than customers who owe money.

Applications

39. *Resource Allocation* You manage an ice cream factory that makes two flavors: Creamy Vanilla and Continental Mocha. Into each quart of Creamy Vanilla go 2 eggs and 3 cups of cream. Into each quart of Continental Mocha go 1 egg and 3 cups of cream. You have in stock 500 eggs and 900 cups of cream. How many quarts of each flavor should you make in order to use up all the eggs and cream? [HINT: See Example 6.]

40. *Class Scheduling* *Enormous State University*'s Math Department offers two courses: Finite Math and Applied Calculus. Each section of Finite Math has 60 students, and each section of Applied Calculus has 50 students. The department will offer a total of 110 sections in a semester, and 6,000 students would like to take a math course. How many sections of each course should the department offer in order to fill all sections and accommodate all of the students? [HINT: See Example 6.]

41. *Nutrition* Gerber Products' Gerber Mixed Cereal for Baby contains, in each serving, 60 calories and 11 grams of carbohydrates. Gerber Mango Tropical Fruit Dessert contains, in each serving, 80 calories and 21 grams of carbohydrates.[1] If you want to provide your child with 200 calories and 43 grams of carbohydrates, how many servings of each should you use?

---

[1] Source: Nutrition information supplied with the products.

42. Nutrition Anthony Altino is mixing food for his young daughter and would like the meal to supply 1 gram of protein and 5 milligrams of iron. He is mixing together cereal, with 0.5 grams of protein and 1 milligram of iron per ounce, and fruit, with 0.2 grams of protein and 2 milligrams of iron per ounce. What mixture will provide the desired nutrition?

43. Nutrition One serving of Campbell Soup Company's Campbell's Pork & Beans contains 5 grams of protein and 21 grams of carbohydrates.[2] A typical slice of white bread provides 2 grams of protein and 11 grams of carbohydrates per slice. The U.S. RDA (Recommended Daily Allowance) is 60 grams of protein each day.[3]

a. I am planning a meal of beans on toast and wish to have it supply one-half of the RDA for protein and 139 grams of carbohydrates. How should I prepare my meal? (Fractions of servings are permitted.)

b. Is it possible to have my meal supply the same amount of protein as in part (a) but only 100 grams of carbohydrates?

44. Nutrition One serving of Campbell Soup Company's Campbell's Pork & Beans contains 5 grams of protein and 21 grams of carbohydrates.[4] A typical slice of "lite" rye bread contains 4 grams of protein and 12 grams of carbohydrates.

a. I am planning a meal of beans on toast and wish to have it supply one-third of the U.S. RDA for protein (see Exercise 43) and 80 grams of carbohydrates. How should I prepare my meal? (Fractions of servings are permitted.)

b. Is it possible to have my meal supply the same amount of protein as in part (a) but only 60 grams of carbohydrates?

Protein Supplements Exercises 45–48 are based on the following data on three popular protein supplements. (Figures shown correspond to a single serving.)[5]

	Protein (g)	Carbohydrates (g)	Sodium (mg)	Cost ($)
Designer Whey (Next)	18	2	80	0.50
Muscle Milk (Cytosport)	32	16	240	1.60
Pure Whey Protein Stack (Champion)	24	3	100	0.60

45. You are thinking of combining Designer Whey and Muscle Milk to obtain a 7-day supply that provides exactly 280 grams of protein and 56 grams of carbohydrates. How many servings of each supplement should you combine in order to meet your requirements? What will it cost?

46. You are thinking of combining Muscle Milk and Pure Whey Protein Stack to obtain a supply that provides exactly 640 grams of protein and 3,200 milligrams of sodium. How many servings of each supplement should you combine in order to meet your requirements? What will it cost?

47. ▼ You have a mixture of Designer Whey and Pure Whey Protein Stack that costs a total of $14 and supplies exactly 540 grams of protein. How many grams of carbohydrates does it supply?

48. ▼ You have a mixture of Designer Whey and Muscle Milk that costs a total of $14 and supplies exactly 104 grams of carbohydrates. How many grams of protein does it supply?

49. Investments: Tech Stocks In December 2014, Twitter (TWTR) stock decreased from $40 to $36 per share, and Microsoft (MSFT) stock decreased from $48 to $45 per share.[6] If you invested a total of $22,400 in these stocks at the beginning of the month and sold them for $20,700 at the end of the month, how many shares of each stock did you buy?

50. Investments: Energy Stocks In the 3-month period November 1, 2014, through January 31, 2015, Hess Corp. (HES) stock decreased from $80 to $64 per share, and Exxon Mobil (XOM) stock decreased from $96 to $80 per share.[7] If you invested a total of $21,600 in these stocks at the beginning of November and sold them for $17,600 3 months later, how many shares of each stock did you buy?

51. ▼ **Investments: Financial Stocks** During the first quarter of 2015, Toronto Dominion Bank (TD) stock cost $45 per share and was expected to yield 4% per year in dividends, while CNA Financial Corp. (CNA) stock cost $40 per share and was expected to yield 2.5% per year in dividends.[8] If you invested a total of $25,000 in these stocks and expected to earn $760 in dividends in a year, how many shares of each stock did you purchase?

52. ▼ **Investments: High Dividend Stocks** During the first quarter of 2015, Plains All American Pipeline L.P. (PAA) stock cost $50 per share and was expected to yield 5% per year in dividends, while Total SA (TOT) stock cost $50 per share and was expected to yield 6% per year in dividends.[9] If you invested a total of $45,000 in these stocks and expected to earn $2,400 in dividends in a year, how many shares of each stock did you purchase?

---

[2] According to the label information on a 16-ounce can.

[3] Recommended Daily Allowance for a person weighing 75 kilograms (165 pounds)

[4] According to the label information on a 16-ounce can.

[5] Source: Nutritional information supplied by the manufacturers (www.netrition.com). Cost per serving is approximate and varies.

[6] Approximate stock prices at or close to the dates cited. Source: http://finance.google.com.

[7] Ibid.

[8] Stock prices and yields are approximate. Source: http://finance.google.com.

[9] Ibid.

53. Voting An appropriations bill passed the U.S. House of Representatives with 49 more members voting in favor than against. If all 435 members of the House voted either for or against the bill, how many voted in favor and how many voted against?

54. Voting The U.S. Senate has 100 members. For a bill to pass with a supermajority, at least twice as many senators must vote in favor of the bill as vote against it. If each of the 100 senators votes either in favor of or against a bill, how many must vote in favor for it to pass with a supermajority?

55. Intramural Sports The best sports dorm on campus, Lombardi House, has won a total of 12 games this semester. Some of these games were soccer games, and the others were football games. According to the rules of the university, each win in a soccer game earns the winning house 2 points, whereas each win in a football game earns the house 4 points. If the total number of points Lombardi House earned was 38, how many of each type of game did it win?

56. Law Five years ago, *Enormous State University*'s campus publication, *The Campus Inquirer*, ran a total of 10 exposés dealing with alleged recruiting violations by the football team and with theft by the student treasurer of the film society. Each exposé dealing with recruiting violations resulted in a $4 million libel suit, and the treasurer of the film society sued the paper for $3 million as a result of each exposé about his alleged theft. Unfortunately for *The Campus Inquirer*, all the lawsuits were successful, and the paper wound up being ordered to pay $37 million in damages. (It closed down shortly thereafter.) How many of each type of exposé did the paper run?

57. Purchasing *(from the GMAT)* Elena purchased Brand X pens for $4.00 apiece and Brand Y pens for $2.80 apiece. If Elena purchased a total of 12 of these pens for $42.00, how many Brand X pens did she purchase?

58. Purchasing *(based on a question from the GMAT)* Earl is ordering supplies. Yellow paper costs $5.00 per ream, while white paper costs $6.50 per ream. He would like to order 100 reams total and has a budget of $560. How many reams of each color should he order?

59. Equilibrium Price The demand and supply functions for pet chias are $q = -60p + 150$ and $q = 80p - 60$, respectively, where p is the price in dollars. At what price should the chias be marked so that there is neither a surplus nor a shortage of chias? [HINT: See Example 8.]

60. Equilibrium Price The demand and supply functions for your college newspaper are $q = -10,000p + 2,000$ and $q = 4,000p + 600$, respectively, where p is the price in dollars. At what price should the newspapers be sold so that there is neither a surplus nor a shortage of papers? [HINT: See Example 8.]

61. Supply and Demand *(from the GRE Economics Test)* The demand curve for widgets is given by $D = 85 - 5P$, and the supply curve is given by $S = 25 + 5P$, where P is the price of widgets. When the widget market is in equilibrium, what is the quantity of widgets bought and sold?

62. Supply and Demand *(from the GRE Economics Test)* In the market for soybeans the demand and supply functions are $Q_D = 100 - 10P$ and $Q_S = 20 + 5P$, where Q_D is quantity demanded, Q_S is quantity supplied, and P is price in dollars. If the government sets a price floor of $7, what will be the resulting surplus or shortage?

63. Equilibrium Price In June 2001 the retail price of a 25-kilogram bag of cornmeal was $8 in Zambia; by December the price had risen to $11. The result was that one retailer reported a drop in sales from 15 bags per day to 3 bags per day.[10] Assume that the retailer is prepared to sell 3 bags per day at $8 and 15 bags per day at $11. Find linear demand and supply equations, and then compute the retailer's equilibrium price.

64. Equilibrium Price At the start of December 2001 the retail price of a 25-kilogram bag of cornmeal was $10 in Zambia; by the end of the month the price had fallen to $6.[11] The result was that one retailer reported an increase in sales from 3 bags per day to 5 bags per day. Assume that the retailer is prepared to sell 18 bags per day at $8 and 12 bags per day at $6. Obtain linear demand and supply equations, and hence compute the retailer's equilibrium price.

65. Pollution Joe Slo, a college sophomore, neglected to wash his dirty laundry for 6 weeks. By the end of that time, his roommate had had enough and tossed Joe's dirty socks and T-shirts into the trash, counting a total of 44 items. (A pair of dirty socks counts as one item.) The roommate noticed that there were three times as many pairs of dirty socks as T-shirts. How many of each item did he throw out?

66. Diet The local sushi bar serves 1-ounce pieces of raw salmon (consisting of 50% protein) and $1\frac{1}{4}$-ounce pieces of raw tuna (40% protein). A customer's total intake of protein amounts to $1\frac{1}{2}$ ounces after consuming a total of three pieces. How many of each type did the customer consume? (Fractions of pieces are permitted.)

67. ▼ Management *(from the GMAT)* A manager has $6,000 budgeted for raises for four full-time and two part-time employees. Each of the full-time employees receives the same raise, which is twice the raise that each of the part-time employees receives. What is the amount of the raise that each full-time employee receives?

68. ▼ Publishing *(from the GMAT)* There were 36,000 hardback copies of a certain novel sold before the paperback version was issued. From the time the first paperback copy was sold until the last copy of the novel was sold, nine times as many paperback copies as hardback copies were

---

[10] The prices quoted are approximate. (Actual prices varied from retailer to retailer.) Source: *New York Times*, December 24, 2001, p. A4.
[11] *Ibid.*

sold. If a total of 441,000 copies of the novel were sold in all, how many paperback copies were sold?

Communication and Reasoning Exercises

69. A system of three equations in two unknowns corresponds to three lines in the plane. Describe how these lines might be positioned if the system has a unique solution.

70. A system of three equations in two unknowns corresponds to three lines in the plane. Describe several ways in which these lines might be positioned if the system has no solutions.

71. Both the supply and demand equations for a certain product have negative slope. Can there be an equilibrium price? Explain.

72. You are solving a system of equations with x representing the number of rocks and y representing the number of pebbles. The solution is $(200, -10)$. What do you conclude?

73. ▼ Referring to Exercise 39, but with different given data, suppose that the solution of the corresponding system of equations was 198.7 quarts of vanilla and 100.89 quarts of mocha. If your factory can produce only whole numbers of quarts, would you recommend rounding the answers to the nearest whole number? Explain.

74. ▼ Referring to Exercise 39, but using different data, suppose that the general solution of the corresponding system of equations was $(200 - y, y)$, where $x =$ number of quarts of vanilla and $y =$ number of quarts of mocha. Your factory can produce only whole numbers of quarts. There are infinitely many combinations of vanilla and mocha that satisfy the constraints—right? Explain.

75. ▼ Select one: Multiplying both sides of a linear equation by a nonzero constant results in a linear equation whose graph is
(A) parallel to   (B) the same as
(C) not always parallel to   (D) not the same as
the graph of the original equation.

76. ▼ Select one: If the addition or subtraction of two linear equations results in the equation $3 = 3$, then the graphs of those equations are
(A) equal.   (B) parallel.
(C) perpendicular.   (D) none of the above.

77. ▼ Select one: If the addition or subtraction of two linear equations results in the equation $0 = 3$, then the graphs of those equations are
(A) equal.   (B) parallel.
(C) perpendicular.   (D) not parallel.

78. ▼ Select one: If adding two linear equations gives $x = 3$ and subtracting them gives $y = 3$, then the graphs of those equations are
(A) equal.   (B) parallel.
(C) perpendicular.   (D) not parallel.

79. ▼ Invent an interesting application that leads to a system of two equations in two unknowns with a unique solution.

80. ▼ Invent an interesting application that leads to a system of two equations in two unknowns with no solution.

81. ◆ How likely do you think it is that a "random" system of two equations in two unknowns has a unique solution? Give some justification for your answer.

82. ◆ How likely do you think it is that a "random" system of three equations in two unknowns has a unique solution? Give some justification for your answer.

4.2   Using Matrices to Solve Systems of Equations

The Augmented Matrix of a System of Linear Equations

In this section we describe a systematic method for solving systems of equations that makes solving large systems of equations in any number of unknowns straightforward. Although this method may seem a little cumbersome at first, it will prove *immensely* useful in this and the next several chapters. First, we introduce some terminology.

Linear Equation

A linear equation in the n variables $x_1, x_2, \ldots, x_n$ has the form

$$a_1 x_1 + \cdots + a_n x_n = b \qquad (a_1, a_2, \ldots, a_n, b \text{ constants}).$$

The numbers $a_1, a_2, \ldots, a_n$ are called the **coefficients**, and the number b is called the **constant term**, or **right-hand side**.

> ### Quick Examples
>
> **1.** $3x - 5y = 0$ Linear equation in x and y
>   Coefficients: 3, −5; constant term: 0
>
> **2.** $x + 2y - z = 6$ Linear equation in x, y, z
>   Coefficients: 1, 2, −1; constant term: 6
>
> **3.** $30x_1 + 18x_2 + x_3 + x_4 = 19$ Linear equation in x_1, x_2, x_3, x_4
>   Coefficients: 30, 18, 1, 1; Constant term: 19

Note When the number of variables is small, we will almost always use $x, y, z, \ldots$ (as in Quick Examples 1 and 2) rather than $x_1, x_2, x_3, \ldots$ as the names of the variables. ∎

Notice that a linear equation in any number of unknowns (for example, $2x - y = 3$) is entirely determined by its coefficients and its constant term. In other words, if we were simply given the row of numbers

$$[2 \quad -1 \quad 3],$$

we could easily reconstruct the original linear equation by multiplying the first number by x, multiplying the second by y, and inserting a plus sign and an equals sign, as follows:

$$2 \cdot x + (-1) \cdot y = 3$$

or $2x - y = 3.$

Similarly, the equation

$$-4x + 2y = 0$$

is represented by the row

$$[-4 \quad 2 \quad 0],$$

and the equation

$$-3y = \frac{1}{4}$$

is represented by the row

$$\left[0 \quad -3 \quad \frac{1}{4} \right].$$

As the last example shows, the first number is always the coefficient of x, and the second is the coefficient of y. If an x or a y is missing, we write a zero for its coefficient. We shall call such a row the **coefficient row** of an equation.

If we have a system of equations, for example, the system

$$2x - y = 3$$
$$-x + 2y = -4,$$

we can put the coefficient rows together like this:

$$\begin{bmatrix} 2 & -1 & 3 \\ -1 & 2 & -4 \end{bmatrix}.$$

We call this the **augmented matrix** of the system of equations. The term "augmented" means that we have included the right-hand sides 3 and -4. We will often drop the word "augmented" and simply refer to the matrix of the system. A **matrix** (plural: **matrices**) is nothing more than a rectangular array of numbers, as above.

Matrix, Augmented Matrix

A **matrix** is a rectangular array of numbers. The **augmented matrix** of a system of linear equations is the matrix whose rows are the coefficient rows of the equations.

Quick Example

4. The augmented matrix of the system

$$x + y = 3$$
$$x - y = 1$$

is $\begin{bmatrix} 1 & 1 & 3 \\ 1 & -1 & 1 \end{bmatrix}.$

We'll be studying matrices in more detail in Chapter 5.

Q: *What good are coefficient rows and matrices?*

A: Think about what we do when we multiply both sides of an equation by a number. For example, consider multiplying both sides of the equation $2x - y = 3$ by -2 to get $-4x + 2y = -6$. All we are really doing is multiplying the coefficients and the right-hand side by -2. This corresponds to *multiplying the row* $[2 \ -1 \ 3]$ *by* -2, that is, multiplying every number in the row by -2. We shall see that any manipulation we want to do with equations can be done instead with rows. This fact leads to a method of solving equations that is systematic and generalizes easily to larger systems.

Here is the same operation in both the language of equations and the language of rows. (We refer to the equation here as *Equation* 1, or simply E_1 for short, and to the row as *Row* 1, or R_1.)

Equation		Row	
E_1: $2x - y = 3$		$[\ 2 \quad -1 \quad 3]$	R_1
Multiply by -2: $(-2)E_1$: $-4x + 2y = -6$		$[-4 \quad 2 \quad -6]$	$(-2)R_1$

Multiplying both sides of an equation by the number a corresponds to multiplying the coefficient row by a.

Now look at what we do when we add two equations.

Equation		Row	
E_1: $2x - y = 3$		$[\ 2 \quad -1 \quad 3]$	R_1
E_2: $-x + 2y = -4$		$[-1 \quad 2 \quad -4]$	R_2
Add: $E_1 + E_2$: $x + y = -1$		$[\ 1 \quad 1 \quad -1]$	$R_1 + R_2$

All we are really doing is *adding the corresponding entries in the rows*, or *adding the rows*. In other words,

Adding two equations corresponds to adding their coefficient rows.

In short, the manipulations of equations that we saw in Section 4.1 can be done more easily with rows in a matrix because we don't have to carry x, y, and other unnecessary notation along with us; x and y can always be inserted at the end if desired.

The manipulations we are talking about are known as **row operations**. In particular, we use three **elementary row operations**.

Elementary Row Operations*

Type 1: Replacing R_i by aR_i (where $a \neq 0$)†
In words: multiplying or dividing a row by a nonzero number.

Type 2: Replacing R_i by $aR_i \pm bR_j$ (where $a \neq 0$)
In words: multiplying a row by a nonzero number and adding or subtracting a multiple of another row.

Type 3: Switching the order of the rows
This corresponds to switching the order in which we write the equations; occasionally, this will be convenient.

For Types 1 and 2 we write the instruction for the row operation *next to the row we wish to replace.* (See the Quick Examples below.)

Quick Examples

5. Type 1: $\begin{bmatrix} 1 & 3 & -4 \\ 0 & 4 & 2 \end{bmatrix} 3R_2 \rightarrow \begin{bmatrix} 1 & 3 & -4 \\ 0 & 12 & 6 \end{bmatrix}$ Replace R_2 by $3R_2$.

6. Type 2: $\begin{bmatrix} 1 & 3 & -4 \\ 0 & 4 & 2 \end{bmatrix} \begin{matrix} 4R_1 - 3R_2 \\ \\ \end{matrix} \rightarrow \begin{bmatrix} 4 & 0 & -22 \\ 0 & 4 & 2 \end{bmatrix}$ Replace R_1 by $4R_1 - 3R_2$.

7. Type 3: $\begin{bmatrix} 1 & 3 & -4 \\ 0 & 4 & 2 \\ 1 & 2 & 3 \end{bmatrix} R_1 \leftrightarrow R_2 \rightarrow \begin{bmatrix} 0 & 4 & 2 \\ 1 & 3 & -4 \\ 1 & 2 & 3 \end{bmatrix}$ Switch R_1 and R_2.

✱ We are using the term "elementary row operations" a little more freely than most books do. Some mathematicians insist that $a = 1$ in an operation of Type 2, but the less restrictive version is very useful.

† Multiplying an equation or row by zero gives us the not very surprising result $0 = 0$. In fact, we lose any information that the equation provided, which usually means that the resulting system has more solutions than the original system.

Using Technology

See the Technology Guides at the end of the chapter to see how to do row operations using a TI-83/84 Plus or a spreadsheet.

Website
www.WanerMath.com
→ Online Utilities
→ Pivot and Gauss-Jordan Tool

Enter the matrix in columns $x1, x2, x3, \dots$. To do a row operation, type the instruction(s) next to the row(s) you are changing as shown, and press "Do Row Ops" once.

One very important fact about the elementary row operations is that they do not change the solutions of the corresponding system of equations. In other words, the new system of equations that we get by applying any one of these operations will have exactly the same solutions as the original system: It is easy to see that numbers that make the original equations true will also make the new equations true, because each of the elementary row operations corresponds to a valid operation on the original equations. That any solution of the new system is a solution of the old system follows from the fact that these row operations are *invertible:* The effects of a row operation can be reversed by applying another row operation, called its **inverse**. Here are some examples of this invertibility. (Try them out in Quick Examples 5–7.)

Operation	Inverse Operation
Replace R_2 by $3R_2$.	Replace R_2 by $\frac{1}{3}R_2$.
Replace R_1 by $4R_1 - 3R_2$.	Replace R_1 by $\frac{1}{4}R_1 + \frac{3}{4}R_2$.
Switch R_1 and R_2.	Switch R_1 and R_2.

Our objective, then, is to use row operations to change the system we are given into one with exactly the same set of solutions in which it is easy to see what the solutions are.

Solving Systems of Equations by Using Row Operations

Now we put row operations to work for us in solving systems of equations. Let's start with a complicated-looking system of equations:

$$-\frac{2x}{3} + \frac{y}{2} = -3$$

$$\frac{x}{4} - y = \frac{11}{4}.$$

We begin by writing the matrix of the system:

$$\begin{bmatrix} -\frac{2}{3} & \frac{1}{2} & -3 \\ \frac{1}{4} & -1 & \frac{11}{4} \end{bmatrix}.$$

Now what do we do with this matrix?

Step 1 *Clear the fractions and/or decimals (if any) using operations of Type 1.* To clear the fractions, we multiply the first row by 6 and the second row by 4. We record the operations by writing the symbolic form of an operation next to the row it will change, as follows:

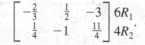

By this we mean that we will replace the first row by $6R_1$ and the second by $4R_2$. Doing these operations gives

$$\begin{bmatrix} -4 & 3 & -18 \\ 1 & -4 & 11 \end{bmatrix}.$$

Step 2 *Designate the first nonzero entry in the first row as the* **pivot.** In this case we designate the entry -4 in the first row as the "pivot" by putting a box around it:

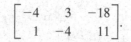

Q : *What is a "pivot"?*

A : A **pivot** is an entry in a matrix that is used to "clear a column." (See Step 3.) In this procedure we will always select the first nonzero entry of a row as our pivot. In Chapter 6, when we study the simplex method, we will select our pivots differently.

Step 3 *Use the pivot to clear its column using operations of Type 2.* By **clearing a column**, we mean changing the matrix so that the pivot is the only nonzero number in its column. The procedure of clearing a column using a designated pivot is also called **pivoting**.

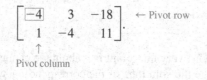

We want to replace R_2 by a row of the form $aR_2 \pm bR_1$ to get a zero in column 1. Moreover—and this will be important when we discuss the simplex method in Chapter 6—*we are going to choose positive values for both a and b.** We need to choose a and b so that we get the desired cancellation. We can do this quite mechanically as follows:

* Thus, the only place a negative sign may appear is between aR_2 and bR_1 as indicated in the formula $aR_2 \pm bR_1$.

a. Write the name of the row you need to change on the left and that of the pivot row on the right:

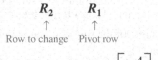

$$
\begin{array}{cc}
R_2 & R_1 \\
\uparrow & \uparrow \\
\text{Row to change} & \text{Pivot row}
\end{array}
$$

b. Focus on the pivot column, $\begin{bmatrix} -4 \\ 1 \end{bmatrix}$. Multiply each row by the *absolute value* of the entry currently in the other. (We are not permitting a or b to be negative.)

$$
\begin{array}{cc}
4R_2 & 1R_1 \\
\uparrow & \uparrow \\
\text{From Row 1} & \text{From Row 2}
\end{array}
$$

The effect is to make the two entries in the pivot column numerically the same. Sometimes, you can accomplish this by using smaller values of a and b.

c. If the entries in the pivot column have opposite signs, insert a plus $(+)$. If they have the same sign, insert a minus $(-)$. Here, we get the instruction

$$4R_2 + 1R_1,$$

or simply $4R_2 + R_1$.

d. Write the operation next to the row you want to change, and then replace that row using the operation:

$$
\begin{bmatrix} \boxed{-4} & 3 & -18 \\ 1 & -4 & 11 \end{bmatrix} \begin{matrix} \\ 4R_2 + 1R_1 \end{matrix} \rightarrow \begin{bmatrix} -4 & 3 & -18 \\ 0 & -13 & 26 \end{bmatrix}.
$$

We have cleared the pivot column and completed Step 3.

Note In general, the row operation you use should always have the following form[†]:

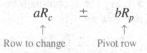

$$
\begin{array}{ccc}
aR_c & \pm & bR_p \\
\uparrow & & \uparrow \\
\text{Row to change} & & \text{Pivot row}
\end{array}
$$

† We are deviating somewhat from the traditional procedure here. It is traditionally recommended first to divide the pivot row by the pivot, turning the pivot into a 1. This allows us to use $a = 1$, but it usually results in fractions. The procedure we use here is easier for hand calculations and, we feel, mathematically more elegant because it illustrates what can be done with matrices whose entries are integers and also eliminates the possible need to work with fractions throughout the calculation. See the end of this section for an example done using the traditional procedure.

with a and b both positive. ∎

The next step is one that can be performed at any time.

Simplification Step (Optional) *If, at any stage of the process, all the numbers in a row are multiples of an integer larger than* **1,** *divide by that integer*—a Type 1 operation.

This is an optional but extremely helpful step: It makes the numbers smaller and easier to work with. In our case, the entries in R_2 are divisible by 13, so we divide that row by 13. (Alternatively, we could divide by -13. Try it.)

$$
\begin{bmatrix} -4 & 3 & -18 \\ 0 & -13 & 26 \end{bmatrix} \begin{matrix} \\ \frac{1}{13}R_2 \end{matrix} \rightarrow \begin{bmatrix} -4 & 3 & -18 \\ 0 & -1 & 2 \end{bmatrix}
$$

Step 4 *Select the first nonzero number in the second row as the pivot, and clear its column.* Here we have combined two steps in one: selecting the new pivot and clearing the column (pivoting). The pivot is shown below, as well as the desired result when the column has been cleared:

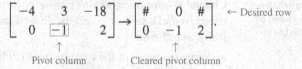

We now wish to get a 0 in place of the 3 in the pivot column. Let's run once again through the mechanical steps to get the row operation that accomplishes this.

a. Write the name of the row you need to change on the left and that of the pivot row on the right:

$$R_1 \qquad\qquad R_2$$
$$\uparrow \qquad\qquad\quad \uparrow$$
Row to change $\qquad$ Pivot row

b. Focus on the pivot column, $\begin{bmatrix} 3 \\ -1 \end{bmatrix}$. Multiply each row by the absolute value of the entry currently in the other:

$$1R_1 \qquad\qquad 3R_2$$
$$\uparrow \qquad\qquad\quad \uparrow$$
From Row 2 $\qquad$ From Row 1

c. If the entries in the pivot column have opposite signs, insert a plus $(+)$. If they have the same sign, insert a minus $(-)$. Here, we get the instruction

$$1R_1 + 3R_2.$$

d. Write the operation next to the row you want to change, and then replace that row using the operation:

$$\begin{bmatrix} -4 & 3 & -18 \\ 0 & \boxed{-1} & 2 \end{bmatrix} \begin{matrix} R_1 + 3R_2 \\ {} \end{matrix} \rightarrow \begin{bmatrix} -4 & 0 & -12 \\ 0 & -1 & 2 \end{bmatrix}.$$

Now we are essentially done, except for one last step.

Final Step *Using operations of Type 1, turn each pivot (the first nonzero entry in each row) into a* **1.** We can accomplish this by dividing the first row by -4 and multiplying the second row by -1:

$$\begin{bmatrix} -4 & 0 & -12 \\ 0 & -1 & 2 \end{bmatrix} \begin{matrix} -\frac{1}{4}R_1 \\ -R_2 \end{matrix} \rightarrow \begin{bmatrix} 1 & 0 & 3 \\ 0 & 1 & -2 \end{bmatrix}.$$

The matrix now has the following nice form:

$$\begin{bmatrix} \boxed{1} & 0 & \# \\ 0 & \boxed{1} & \# \end{bmatrix}.$$

(This is the form we will always obtain with two equations in two unknowns when there is a unique solution.) This form is nice because, when we translate back into equations, we get

$$1x + 0y = 3$$
$$0x + 1y = -2.$$

In other words,

$$x = 3 \quad \text{and} \quad y = -2,$$

so we have found the solution, which we can also write as $(x, y) = (3, -2)$.

∗ Gauss-Jordan reduction is named after Carl Friedrich Gauss (1777–1855) and Wilhelm Jordan (1842–1899). Gauss was one of the great mathematicians, making fundamental contributions to number theory, analysis, probability, and statistics, as well as many fields of science. Gauss also made contributions to a method of solving systems of equations that has become known as Gaussian elimination, even though this method had been described by Isaac Newton in 1707 and, independently, had been known to the Chinese more than 2,000 years ago. (See *Mathematicians of Gaussian Elimination*, Notices of the American Mathematical Society, June/July 2011, for a history of Gaussian elimination.) The method we are showing you here, Gauss-Jordan reduction, is Jordan's variation on Gaussian elimination, first published in 1887.

The procedure we've just demonstrated is called **Gauss-Jordan reduction**[∗] or **row reduction**. It may seem too complicated a way to solve a system of two equations in two unknowns, and it is. However, for systems with more equations and more unknowns, it is very efficient.

In Example 1 below we use row reduction to solve a system of linear equations in *three* unknowns: x, y, and z. Just as for a system in two unknowns, a **solution** of a system in any number of unknowns consists of values for each of the variables that, when substituted, satisfy all of the equations in the system. Again, just as for a system in two unknowns, any system of linear equations in any number of unknowns has either no solution, exactly one solution, or infinitely many solutions. There are no other possibilities.

Solving a system in three unknowns graphically would require the graphing of planes (flat surfaces) in three dimensions. (The graph of a linear equation in three unknowns is a flat surface.) The use of row reduction makes three-dimensional graphing unnecessary.

EXAMPLE 1   **Solving a System by Gauss-Jordan Reduction**

Solve the system

$$x - y + 5z = -6$$
$$3x + 3y - z = 10$$
$$x + 3y + 2z = 5.$$

Solution The augmented matrix for this system is

$$\begin{bmatrix} 1 & -1 & 5 & -6 \\ 3 & 3 & -1 & 10 \\ 1 & 3 & 2 & 5 \end{bmatrix}.$$

Note that the columns correspond to x, y, z, and the right-hand side, respectively. We begin by selecting the pivot in the first row and clearing its column. Remember that clearing the column means that we turn *all* other numbers in the column into zeros. Thus, to clear the column of the first pivot, we need to change two rows, setting up the row operations in exactly the same way as above:

$$\begin{bmatrix} \boxed{1} & -1 & 5 & -6 \\ 3 & 3 & -1 & 10 \\ 1 & 3 & 2 & 5 \end{bmatrix} \begin{matrix} \\ R_2 - 3R_1 \\ R_3 - R_1 \end{matrix} \rightarrow \begin{bmatrix} 1 & -1 & 5 & -6 \\ 0 & 6 & -16 & 28 \\ 0 & 4 & -3 & 11 \end{bmatrix}.$$

Notice that both row operations have the required form

$$aR_c \pm bR_1$$

    ↑   ↑

Row to change Pivot row

with a and b both positive.

Now we use the optional simplification step to simplify R_2:

$$\begin{bmatrix} 1 & -1 & 5 & -6 \\ 0 & 6 & -16 & 28 \\ 0 & 4 & -3 & 11 \end{bmatrix} \tfrac{1}{2}R_2 \rightarrow \begin{bmatrix} 1 & -1 & 5 & -6 \\ 0 & 3 & -8 & 14 \\ 0 & 4 & -3 & 11 \end{bmatrix}.$$

Using Technology

See the Technology Guides at the end of the chapter to see how to use a TI-83/84 Plus or a spreadsheet to solve this system of equations.

W Website

www.WanerMath.com

→ Online Utilities

→ Pivot and Gauss-Jordan Tool

Enter the augmented matrix in columns $x1, x2, x3, \ldots$. At each step, type in the row operations exactly as written above next to the rows to which they apply. For example, for the first step, type: R2 - 3R1 next to Row 2 and R3 - R1 next to Row 3. Press "Do Row Ops" once, and then press "Clear Row Ops" to prepare for the next step. For the last step, type (1/3)R1 next to Row 1 and (1/3)R2 next to Row 2. Press "Do Row Ops" once. The utility also does other things, such as automatic pivoting and complete reduction in one step. Use these features to check your work.

Next, we select the pivot in the second row and clear its column:

$$
\begin{bmatrix}
1 & -1 & 5 & -6 \\
0 & \boxed{3} & -8 & 14 \\
0 & 4 & -3 & 11
\end{bmatrix}
\begin{matrix} 3R_1 + R_2 \\ \\ 3R_3 - 4R_2 \end{matrix}
\rightarrow
\begin{bmatrix}
3 & 0 & 7 & -4 \\
0 & 3 & -8 & 14 \\
0 & 0 & 23 & -23
\end{bmatrix}.
$$

R_1 and R_3 are to be changed.
R_2 is the pivot row.

We simplify R_3:

$$
\begin{bmatrix}
3 & 0 & 7 & -4 \\
0 & 3 & -8 & 14 \\
0 & 0 & 23 & -23
\end{bmatrix}
\begin{matrix} \\ \\ \frac{1}{23}R_3 \end{matrix}
\rightarrow
\begin{bmatrix}
3 & 0 & 7 & -4 \\
0 & 3 & -8 & 14 \\
0 & 0 & 1 & -1
\end{bmatrix}.
$$

Now we select the pivot in the third row and clear its column:

$$
\begin{bmatrix}
3 & 0 & 7 & -4 \\
0 & 3 & -8 & 14 \\
0 & 0 & \boxed{1} & -1
\end{bmatrix}
\begin{matrix} R_1 - 7R_3 \\ R_2 + 8R_3 \\ \end{matrix}
\rightarrow
\begin{bmatrix}
3 & 0 & 0 & 3 \\
0 & 3 & 0 & 6 \\
0 & 0 & 1 & -1
\end{bmatrix}.
$$

R_1 and R_2 are to be changed.
R_3 is the pivot row.

Finally, we turn all the pivots into 1s:

$$
\begin{bmatrix}
3 & 0 & 0 & 3 \\
0 & 3 & 0 & 6 \\
0 & 0 & 1 & -1
\end{bmatrix}
\begin{matrix} \frac{1}{3}R_1 \\ \frac{1}{3}R_2 \\ \end{matrix}
\rightarrow
\begin{bmatrix}
1 & 0 & 0 & 1 \\
0 & 1 & 0 & 2 \\
0 & 0 & 1 & -1
\end{bmatrix}.
$$

The matrix is now reduced to a simple form, so we translate back into equations to obtain the solution:

$$x = 1, \quad y = 2, \quad z = -1, \quad \text{or} \quad (x, y, z) = (1, 2, -1).$$

Notice the form of the very last matrix in the example:

$$
\begin{bmatrix}
1 & 0 & 0 & \# \\
0 & 1 & 0 & \# \\
0 & 0 & 1 & \#
\end{bmatrix}.
$$

The 1s are on the (**main**) **diagonal** of the matrix; the goal in Gauss-Jordan reduction is to reduce our matrix to this form. If we can do so, then we can easily read off the solution, as we saw in Example 1. However, as we will see in several examples in this section, it is not always possible to achieve this ideal state. After Example 6 we will give a form that is always possible to achieve.

EXAMPLE 2 **Solving a System by Gauss-Jordan Reduction**

Solve the system:

$$
\begin{aligned}
2x + y + 3z &= 1 \\
4x + 2y + 4z &= 4 \\
x + 2y + z &= 4.
\end{aligned}
$$

Solution

$$\begin{bmatrix} \boxed{2} & 1 & 3 & 1 \\ 4 & 2 & 4 & 4 \\ 1 & 2 & 1 & 4 \end{bmatrix} \begin{matrix} \\ R_2 - 2R_1 \\ 2R_3 - R_1 \end{matrix} \rightarrow \begin{bmatrix} 2 & 1 & 3 & 1 \\ 0 & 0 & -2 & 2 \\ 0 & 3 & -1 & 7 \end{bmatrix}$$

Now we have a slight problem: The number in the position where we would like to have a pivot—the second column of the second row—is a zero and thus cannot be a pivot. There are two ways out of this problem. One is to move on to the third column and pivot on the -2. Another is to switch the order of the second and third rows so that we can use the 3 as a pivot. We will do the latter:

$$\begin{bmatrix} 2 & 1 & 3 & 1 \\ 0 & 0 & -2 & 2 \\ 0 & 3 & -1 & 7 \end{bmatrix} R_2 \leftrightarrow R_3 \rightarrow \begin{bmatrix} 2 & 1 & 3 & 1 \\ 0 & \boxed{3} & -1 & 7 \\ 0 & 0 & -2 & 2 \end{bmatrix} \begin{matrix} 3R_1 - R_2 \\ \\ \end{matrix}$$

$$\rightarrow \begin{bmatrix} 6 & 0 & 10 & -4 \\ 0 & 3 & -1 & 7 \\ 0 & 0 & -2 & 2 \end{bmatrix} \begin{matrix} \frac{1}{2}R_1 \\ \\ -\frac{1}{2}R_3 \end{matrix} \rightarrow \begin{bmatrix} 3 & 0 & 5 & -2 \\ 0 & 3 & -1 & 7 \\ 0 & 0 & \boxed{1} & -1 \end{bmatrix} \begin{matrix} R_1 - 5R_3 \\ R_2 + R_3 \\ \end{matrix}$$

$$\rightarrow \begin{bmatrix} 3 & 0 & 0 & 3 \\ 0 & 3 & 0 & 6 \\ 0 & 0 & 1 & -1 \end{bmatrix} \begin{matrix} \frac{1}{3}R_1 \\ \frac{1}{3}R_2 \\ \end{matrix} \rightarrow \begin{bmatrix} 1 & 0 & 0 & 1 \\ 0 & 1 & 0 & 2 \\ 0 & 0 & 1 & -1 \end{bmatrix}.$$

Thus, the solution is $(x, y, z) = (1, 2, -1)$, as you can check in the original system.

No Solutions and Infinitely Many Solutions

As in Section 4.1, a system of linear equations with three or more unknowns may have no solution or may have infinitely many solutions, as we see in the next two examples.

EXAMPLE 3 **Inconsistent System**

Solve the system:

$$\begin{aligned} x + y + z &= 1 \\ 2x - y + z &= 0 \\ 4x + y + 3z &= 3. \end{aligned}$$

Solution

$$\begin{bmatrix} \boxed{1} & 1 & 1 & 1 \\ 2 & -1 & 1 & 0 \\ 4 & 1 & 3 & 3 \end{bmatrix} \begin{matrix} \\ R_2 - 2R_1 \\ R_3 - 4R_1 \end{matrix} \rightarrow \begin{bmatrix} 1 & 1 & 1 & 1 \\ 0 & \boxed{-3} & -1 & -2 \\ 0 & -3 & -1 & -1 \end{bmatrix} \begin{matrix} 3R_1 + R \\ \\ R_3 - R_2 \end{matrix}$$

$$\rightarrow \begin{bmatrix} 3 & 0 & 2 & 1 \\ 0 & -3 & -1 & -2 \\ 0 & 0 & 0 & 1 \end{bmatrix}$$

Stop. That last row translates into $0 = 1$, which is nonsense, so, as in Example 4 in Section 4.1, we can say that this system has no solution. We also say, as we did for systems with only two unknowns, that a system with no solution is **inconsistent**. A system with at least one solution is **consistent**.

➡ **Before we go on . . .**

Q : *How, exactly, does the nonsensical equation 0 = 1 tell us that there is no solution of the system in Example 3?*

A : Here is an argument similar to that in Example 4 in Section 4.1: If there *were* three numbers x, y, and z satisfying the original system of equations, then manipulating the equations according to the instructions in the row operations above would lead us to conclude that $0 = 1$. Because 0 is *not* equal to 1, there can be no such numbers x, y, and z.

■

EXAMPLE 4 Infinitely Many Solutions

Solve the system:

$$
\begin{aligned}
x + y + z &= 1 \\
\tfrac{1}{4}x - \tfrac{1}{2}y + \tfrac{3}{4}z &= 0 \\
x + 7y - 3z &= 3.
\end{aligned}
$$

Solution

$$
\begin{bmatrix} 1 & 1 & 1 & 1 \\ \tfrac{1}{4} & -\tfrac{1}{2} & \tfrac{3}{4} & 0 \\ 1 & 7 & -3 & 3 \end{bmatrix}
\begin{matrix} \\ 4R_2 \rightarrow \\ \end{matrix}
\begin{bmatrix} \boxed{1} & 1 & 1 & 1 \\ 1 & -2 & 3 & 0 \\ 1 & 7 & -3 & 3 \end{bmatrix}
\begin{matrix} \\ R_2 - R_1 \\ R_3 - R_1 \end{matrix}
$$

$$
\rightarrow
\begin{bmatrix} 1 & 1 & 1 & 1 \\ 0 & -3 & 2 & -1 \\ 0 & 6 & -4 & 2 \end{bmatrix}
\begin{matrix} 3R_1 + R_2 \\ \\ \tfrac{1}{2}R_3 \end{matrix}
\rightarrow
\begin{bmatrix} 1 & 1 & 1 & 1 \\ 0 & \boxed{-3} & 2 & -1 \\ 0 & 3 & -2 & 1 \end{bmatrix}
\begin{matrix} 3R_1 + R_2 \\ \\ R_3 + R_2 \end{matrix}
$$

$$
\rightarrow
\begin{bmatrix} 3 & 0 & 5 & 2 \\ 0 & -3 & 2 & -1 \\ 0 & 0 & 0 & 0 \end{bmatrix}
$$

There are no nonzero entries in the third row, so there can be no pivot in the third row. We skip to the final step and turn the pivots we did find into 1s:

$$
\begin{bmatrix} 3 & 0 & 5 & 2 \\ 0 & -3 & 2 & -1 \\ 0 & 0 & 0 & 0 \end{bmatrix}
\begin{matrix} \tfrac{1}{3}R_1 \\ -\tfrac{1}{3}R_2 \rightarrow \\ \end{matrix}
\begin{bmatrix} 1 & 0 & \tfrac{5}{3} & \tfrac{2}{3} \\ 0 & 1 & -\tfrac{2}{3} & \tfrac{1}{3} \\ 0 & 0 & 0 & 0 \end{bmatrix}.
$$

Now we translate back into equations and obtain

$$
\begin{aligned}
x \quad + \tfrac{5}{3}z &= \tfrac{2}{3} \\
y - \tfrac{2}{3}z &= \tfrac{1}{3} \\
0 &= 0.
\end{aligned}
$$

But how does this help us find a solution? The last equation doesn't tell us anything useful, so we ignore it. The thing to notice about the other equations is that we can easily solve the first equation for x and the second for y, obtaining

$$
\begin{aligned}
x &= \tfrac{2}{3} - \tfrac{5}{3}z \\
y &= \tfrac{1}{3} + \tfrac{2}{3}z.
\end{aligned}
$$

This is the solution! We can choose z to be any number and get corresponding values for x and y from the formulas above. This gives us infinitely many different solutions. Thus, the general solution (see Example 5 in Section 4.1) is

$$x = \tfrac{2}{3} - \tfrac{5}{3}z$$
$$y = \tfrac{1}{3} + \tfrac{2}{3}z \qquad \text{General solution}$$
$$z \text{ is arbitrary.}$$

We can also write the general solution as

$$\left(\tfrac{2}{3} - \tfrac{5}{3}z, \tfrac{1}{3} + \tfrac{2}{3}z, z\right); \quad z \text{ arbitrary.} \qquad \text{General solution}$$

This general solution has z as the parameter. Specific choices of values for the parameter z give particular solutions. For example, the choice $z = 6$ gives the particular solution

$$x = \tfrac{2}{3} - \tfrac{5}{3}(6) = -\tfrac{28}{3}$$
$$y = \tfrac{1}{3} + \tfrac{2}{3}(6) = \tfrac{13}{3} \qquad \text{Particular solution}$$
$$z = 6,$$

while the choice $z = 0$ gives the particular solution $(x, y, z) = \left(\tfrac{2}{3}, \tfrac{1}{3}, 0\right)$.

Note that, unlike the system given in Example 3, the system given in this example does have solutions and is thus *consistent*.

➡ **Before we go on ...** Why were there infinitely many solutions to Example 4? The reason is that the third equation was really a combination of the first and second equations to begin with, so we effectively had only two equations in three unknowns.* Choosing a specific value for z (say, $z = 6$) has the effect of supplying the "missing" equation. ■

* In fact, you can check that the third equation, E_3, is equal to $3E_1 - 8E_2$. Thus, the third equation could have been left out because it conveys no more information than the first two. The process of row reduction always eliminates such a redundancy by creating a row of zeros.

Q : *How do we know when there are infinitely many solutions?*

A : When there are solutions (we have a consistent system, unlike the one in Example 3), and when the matrix we arrive at by row reduction has fewer pivots than there are unknowns. In Example 4 we had three unknowns but only two pivots.

Q : *How do we know which variables to use as parameters in a parameterized solution?*

A : The variables to use as parameters are those in the columns without pivots. In Example 4 there were pivots in the x and y columns but no pivot in the z column, and it was z that we used as a parameter.

EXAMPLE 5   **Four Unknowns**

Solve the system:

$$x + 3y + 2z - w = 6$$
$$2x + 6y + 6z + 3w = 16$$
$$x + 3y - 2z - 11w = -2$$
$$2x + 6y + 8z + 8w = 20.$$

Solution

$$\begin{bmatrix} \boxed{1} & 3 & 2 & -1 & 6 \\ 2 & 6 & 6 & 3 & 16 \\ 1 & 3 & -2 & -11 & -2 \\ 2 & 6 & 8 & 8 & 20 \end{bmatrix} \begin{matrix} \\ R_2 - 2R_1 \\ R_3 - R_1 \\ R_4 - 2R_1 \end{matrix} \rightarrow \begin{bmatrix} 1 & 3 & 2 & -1 & 6 \\ 0 & 0 & 2 & 5 & 4 \\ 0 & 0 & -4 & -10 & -8 \\ 0 & 0 & 4 & 10 & 8 \end{bmatrix}$$

There is no pivot available in the second column, so we move on to the third column:

$$\begin{bmatrix} 1 & 3 & 2 & -1 & 6 \\ 0 & 0 & \boxed{2} & 5 & 4 \\ 0 & 0 & -4 & -10 & -8 \\ 0 & 0 & 4 & 10 & 8 \end{bmatrix} \begin{matrix} R_1 - R_2 \\ \\ R_3 + 2R_2 \\ R_4 - 2R_2 \end{matrix} \rightarrow \begin{bmatrix} 1 & 3 & 0 & -6 & 2 \\ 0 & 0 & 2 & 5 & 4 \\ 0 & 0 & 0 & 0 & 0 \\ 0 & 0 & 0 & 0 & 0 \end{bmatrix} \begin{matrix} \\ \frac{1}{2}R_2 \\ \\ \end{matrix}$$

$$\rightarrow \begin{bmatrix} 1 & 3 & 0 & -6 & 2 \\ 0 & 0 & 1 & \frac{5}{2} & 2 \\ 0 & 0 & 0 & 0 & 0 \\ 0 & 0 & 0 & 0 & 0 \end{bmatrix}.$$

Translating back into equations, we get

$$x + 3y - 6w = 2$$
$$z + \tfrac{5}{2}w = 2.$$

(We have not written down the equations corresponding to the last two rows, each of which is $0 = 0$.) There are no pivots in the y or w columns, so we use these two variables as parameters. We bring them over to the right-hand sides of the equations above and write the general solution as

$$x = 2 - 3y + 6w$$

y is arbitrary

$$z = 2 - \tfrac{5}{2}w$$

w is arbitrary

or

$$(x, y, z, w) = (2 - 3y + 6w, y, 2 - 5w/2, w); \quad y, w \text{ arbitrary.}$$

➡ **Before we go on...** In Examples 4 and 5 you might have noticed an interesting phenomenon: If at any time in the process, two rows are equal or one is a multiple of the other, then one of those rows (eventually) becomes all zero. ∎

Overdetermined Systems and Underdetermined Systems

Up to this point, we have always been given as many equations as there are unknowns. However, we shall see in Section 4.3 that some applications lead to systems in which the number of equations is not the same as the number of unknowns. Systems with more equations than unknowns are said to be **overdetermined**, while systems with fewer equations than unknowns are said to be **underdetermined**. As the following example illustrates, such systems can be handled in the same way as any other.

EXAMPLE 6   **Number of Equations ≠ Number of Unknowns**

Solve the system:

$$x + y = 1$$
$$13x - 26y = -11$$
$$26x - 13y = 2.$$

Solution We proceed exactly as before and ignore the fact that there is one more equation than there are unknowns:

$$\begin{bmatrix} \boxed{1} & 1 & 1 \\ 13 & -26 & -11 \\ 26 & -13 & 2 \end{bmatrix} \begin{matrix} \\ R_2 - 13R_1 \\ R_3 - 26R_1 \end{matrix} \rightarrow \begin{bmatrix} 1 & 1 & 1 \\ 0 & -39 & -24 \\ 0 & -39 & -24 \end{bmatrix} \begin{matrix} \\ \frac{1}{3}R_2 \\ \frac{1}{3}R_3 \end{matrix}$$

$$\rightarrow \begin{bmatrix} 1 & 1 & 1 \\ 0 & \boxed{-13} & -8 \\ 0 & -13 & -8 \end{bmatrix} \begin{matrix} 13R_1 + R_2 \\ \\ R_3 - R_2 \end{matrix} \rightarrow \begin{bmatrix} 13 & 0 & 5 \\ 0 & -13 & -8 \\ 0 & 0 & 0 \end{bmatrix} \begin{matrix} \frac{1}{13}R_1 \\ -\frac{1}{13}R_2 \\ \\ \end{matrix}$$

$$\rightarrow \begin{bmatrix} 1 & 0 & \frac{5}{13} \\ 0 & 1 & \frac{8}{13} \\ 0 & 0 & 0 \end{bmatrix}.$$

Thus, the solution is $(x, y) = \left(\frac{5}{13}, \frac{8}{13}\right)$.

If, instead of a row of zeros, we had obtained, say, $\begin{bmatrix} 0 & 0 & 6 \end{bmatrix}$ in the last row, we would immediately have concluded that the system was inconsistent.

The fact that we wound up with a row of zeros indicates that one of the equations was actually a combination of the other two; you can check that the third equation can be obtained by multiplying the first equation by 13 and adding the result to the second. Because the third equation therefore tells us nothing that we don't already know from the first two, we call the system of equations **redundant**, or **dependent.** (Compare Example 5 in Section 4.1.)

➡ **Before we go on...** Example 5 above is another example of a redundant system; we could have started with the following smaller system of two equations in four unknowns:

$$x + 3y + 2z - w = 6$$
$$2x + 6y + 6z + 3w = 16$$

and obtained the same general solution as we did with the larger system. Verify this by solving the smaller system. ■

Reduced Row Echelon Form

The preceding examples illustrated that we cannot always reduce a matrix to the form shown before Example 2, with pivots going all the way down the diagonal. What we *can* always do is reduce a matrix to the following form.

Reduced Row Echelon Form

A matrix is said to be in **reduced row echelon form** or to be **row-reduced** if it satisfies the following properties:

P1. The first nonzero entry in each row (called the **leading entry** of that row) is a 1.

P2. The columns of the leading entries are **clear** (i.e., they contain zeros in all positions other than that of the leading entry).

P3. The leading entry in each row is to the right of the leading entry in the row above, and any rows of zeros are at the bottom.

Quick Examples

8. $\begin{bmatrix} 1 & 0 & 0 & 2 \\ 0 & 1 & 0 & 4 \\ 0 & 0 & 1 & -3 \end{bmatrix}$, $\begin{bmatrix} 0 & 1 & -3 \\ 0 & 0 & 0 \end{bmatrix}$, and $\begin{bmatrix} 1 & 3 & 0 & -2 \\ 0 & 0 & 1 & 4 \\ 0 & 0 & 0 & 0 \end{bmatrix}$ are row-reduced.

9. $\begin{bmatrix} 1 & 1 & 0 & 2 \\ 0 & 1 & 0 & 4 \\ 0 & 0 & 1 & -3 \end{bmatrix}$ and $\begin{bmatrix} 0 & 1 & -3 \\ 0 & 0 & 1 \end{bmatrix}$ both violate P2 and so are not row-reduced.

(The column of the leading entry in the second row is not clear in either.)

10. $\begin{bmatrix} 0 & 0 & 1 & 4 \\ 1 & 0 & 0 & -2 \\ 0 & 0 & 0 & 0 \end{bmatrix}$ violates P3 and so is not row-reduced. (The leading entry of Row 2 is not to the right of the leading entry in Row 1.)

You should check in the examples we did that the final matrices were all in reduced row echelon form.

It is an interesting and useful fact, though not easy to prove, that any two people who start with the same matrix and row-reduce it will reach exactly the same row-reduced matrix, even if they use different row operations.

The Traditional Gauss-Jordan Method (Optional)

In the version of the Gauss-Jordan method we have presented, we eliminated fractions and decimals in the first step and then worked with integer matrices, partly to make hand computation easier and partly for mathematical elegance. However, complicated fractions and decimals present no difficulty when we use technology. The following example illustrates the more traditional approach to Gauss-Jordan reduction that is used in many of the computer programs that solve the huge systems of equations that arise in practice.*

* Actually, for reasons of efficiency and accuracy, the methods used in commercial programs are closer to the method presented above. To learn more, consult a text on numerical methods.

EXAMPLE 7 **Solving a System with the Traditional Gauss-Jordan Method**

Solve the following system using the traditional Gauss-Jordan method:

$$2x + y + 3z = 5$$
$$3x + 2y + 4z = 7$$
$$2x + y + 5z = 10.$$

Solution We make two changes in our method. First, there is no need to get rid of decimals (because computers and calculators can handle decimals as easily as they can integers). Second, after selecting a pivot, *divide the pivot row by the pivot value, turning the pivot into a* 1. It is easier to determine the row operations that will clear the pivot column if the pivot is a 1.

If we use technology to solve this system of equations, the sequence of matrices might look like this:

$$
\begin{bmatrix} \boxed{2} & 1 & 3 & 5 \\ 3 & 2 & 4 & 7 \\ 2 & 1 & 5 & 10 \end{bmatrix} \begin{matrix} \frac{1}{2}R_1 \\ \\ \\ \end{matrix} \rightarrow \begin{bmatrix} \boxed{1} & 0.5 & 1.5 & 2.5 \\ 3 & 2 & 4 & 7 \\ 2 & 1 & 5 & 10 \end{bmatrix} \begin{matrix} \\ R_2 - 3R_1 \\ R_3 - 2R_1 \end{matrix}
$$

$$
\rightarrow \begin{bmatrix} 1 & 0.5 & 1.5 & 2.5 \\ 0 & \boxed{0.5} & -0.5 & -0.5 \\ 0 & 0 & 2 & 5 \end{bmatrix} 2R_2 \rightarrow \begin{bmatrix} 1 & 0.5 & 1.5 & 2.5 \\ 0 & \boxed{1} & -1 & -1 \\ 0 & 0 & 2 & 5 \end{bmatrix} \begin{matrix} R_1 - 0.5R_2 \\ \\ \\ \end{matrix}
$$

$$
\rightarrow \begin{bmatrix} 1 & 0 & 2 & 3 \\ 0 & 1 & -1 & -1 \\ 0 & 0 & \boxed{2} & 5 \end{bmatrix} \begin{matrix} \\ \\ \frac{1}{2}R_3 \end{matrix} \rightarrow \begin{bmatrix} 1 & 0 & 2 & 3 \\ 0 & 1 & -1 & -1 \\ 0 & 0 & \boxed{1} & 2.5 \end{bmatrix} \begin{matrix} R_1 - 2R_3 \\ R_2 + R_3 \\ \\ \end{matrix}
$$

$$
\rightarrow \begin{bmatrix} 1 & 0 & 0 & -2 \\ 0 & 1 & 0 & 1.5 \\ 0 & 0 & 1 & 2.5 \end{bmatrix}.
$$

The solution is $(x, y, z) = (-2, 1.5, 2.5)$.

Q: *The solution to Example 7 looked quite easy. Why didn't we use the traditional method from the start like the other textbooks?*

A: It looked easy because we deliberately chose an example that leads to simple decimals. In all but the most contrived examples, the decimals or fractions involved get very complicated very quickly.

FAQs

Getting Unstuck, Going Around in Circles, and Knowing When to Stop

Q: *Help! I have been doing row operations on this matrix for half an hour. I have filled two pages, and I am getting nowhere. What do I do?*

A: Here is a way of keeping track of where you are at any stage of the process and also deciding what to do next.

Starting at the top row of your current matrix:

1. Scan along the row until you get to the leading entry: the first nonzero entry. If there is none—that is, the row is all zero—go to the next row.

2. Having located the leading entry, scan up and down its *column*. If its column is not clear (that is, it contains other nonzero entries), use your leading entry as a pivot to clear its column as in the examples in this section.

3. Now go to the next row, and start again at Step 1.

When you have scanned all the rows and find that all the columns of the leading entries are clear, all that remains to be done is to turn the leading entries into 1s (the "Final Step") and then possibly to reorder the rows so that the leading entries go from left to right as you read down the matrix and zero rows are at the bottom.

Using Technology

W Website
www.WanerMath.com
Follow
→ Everything
→ Chapter 4 Tools
to find the following resources:
- An online Web page that pivots and does row operations automatically
- A TI-83/84 Plus program that pivots and does other row operations
- An Excel worksheet that pivots and does row operations automatically

Q: No good. I have been following these instructions, but every time I try to clear a column, I unclear a column I had already cleared. What is going on?

A: Are you using *leading entries* as pivots? Also, are you *using the pivot* to clear its column? That is, are your row operations all of the following form?

$$aR_c \pm bR_p$$
$$\uparrow \qquad \uparrow$$
Row to change   Pivot row

The instruction next to the row you are changing should involve only that row and the pivot row, even though you might be tempted to use some other row instead.

Q: Must I continue until I get a matrix that has 1s down the leading diagonal and 0s above and below?

A: Not necessarily. You are completely done when your matrix is row-reduced: Each leading entry is a 1, the column of each leading entry is clear, and the leading entries go from left to right. You are done *pivoting* when the column of each leading entry is clear. After that, all that remains is to turn each pivot into a 1 (the "Final Step") and, if necessary, rearrange the rows.

4.2 EXERCISES

▼ more advanced   ◆ challenging
T indicates exercises that should be solved using technology

In Exercises 1–42, use Gauss-Jordan row reduction to solve the given systems of equation. We suggest doing some by hand and others using technology. [**HINT**: See Examples 1–6.]

1. $x + y = 4$
  $x - y = 2$

2. $2x + y = 2$
  $-2x + y = 2$

3. $3x - 2y = 6$
  $2x - 3y = -6$

4. $2x + 3y = 5$
  $3x + 2y = 5$

5. $2x + 3y = 1$
  $-x - \dfrac{3y}{2} = -\dfrac{1}{2}$

6. $2x - 3y = 1$
  $6x - 9y = 3$

7. $2x + 3y = 2$
  $-x - \dfrac{3y}{2} = -\dfrac{1}{2}$

8. $2x - 3y = 2$
  $6x - 9y = 3$

9. $x + y = 1$
  $3x - y = 0$
  $x - 3y = -2$

10. $x + y = 1$
  $3x - 2y = -1$
  $5x - y = \dfrac{1}{5}$

11. $x + y = 0$
  $3x - y = 1$
  $x - y = -1$

12. $x + 2y = 1$
  $3x - 2y = -2$
  $5x - y = \dfrac{1}{5}$

13. $0.5x + 0.1y = 1.7$
  $0.1x - 0.1y = 0.3$
  $x + \quad y = \dfrac{11}{3}$

14. $-0.3x + 0.5y = 0.1$
  $x - \quad y = 4$
  $\dfrac{x}{17} + \dfrac{y}{17} = 1$

15. $-x + 2y - z = 0$
  $-x - y + 2z = 0$
  $2x \qquad - z = 4$

16. $x + 2y \qquad = 4$
  $y - z = 0$
  $x + 3y - 2z = 5$

17. $x + y + 6z = -1$
  $\dfrac{1}{3}x - \dfrac{1}{3}y + \dfrac{2}{3}z = 1$
  $\dfrac{1}{2}x \qquad + z = 0$

18. $x - \dfrac{1}{2}y \qquad = 0$
  $\dfrac{1}{3}x + \dfrac{1}{3}y + \dfrac{1}{3}z = 2$
  $\dfrac{1}{2}x \qquad - \dfrac{1}{2}z = -1$

19. $-\dfrac{1}{2}x + \quad y - \dfrac{1}{2}z = 0$
  $-\dfrac{1}{2}x - \dfrac{1}{2}y + \quad z = 0$
  $x - \dfrac{1}{2}y - \dfrac{1}{2}z = 0$

20. $x - \dfrac{1}{2}y \qquad = 0$
  $\dfrac{1}{2}x \qquad - \dfrac{1}{2}z = -1$
  $3x - \quad y - \quad z = -2$

21. $x + \quad y + 2z = -1$
  $2x + 2y + 2z = 2$
  $\dfrac{3}{5}x + \dfrac{3}{5}y + \dfrac{3}{5}z = \dfrac{2}{5}$

22. $x + y - \quad z = -2$
  $x - y - 7z = 0$
  $\dfrac{2}{7}x \qquad - \dfrac{8}{7}z = 14$

23. $-0.5x + 0.5y + 0.5z = 1.5$
    $4.2x + 2.1y + 2.1z = 0$
    $0.2x \qquad + 0.2z = 0$

24. $0.25x - 0.5y \qquad = 0$
    $0.2x + 0.2y - 0.2z = -0.6$
    $0.5x - 1.5y + \quad z = 0.5$

25. $2x - y + z = 4$ 26. $3x - y - z = 0$
    $3x - y + z = 5$ $x + y + z = 4$

27. $0.75x - 0.75y - \quad z = 4$ 28. $2x - \quad y + \quad z = 4$
    $x - \quad y + 4z = 0$ $-x + 0.5y - 0.5z = 1.5$

29. ▼ $3x + y - z = 12$ 30. ▼ $x + y - 3z = 21$
    (Yes, one equation in three unknowns!)

31. ▼ $x + \quad y + 2z = -1$
    $2x + \quad 2y + 2z = 2$
    $0.75x + 0.75y + \quad z = 0.25$
    $-x \qquad - 2z = 21$

32. ▼ $x + \quad y - \qquad z = -2$
    $x - \quad y - \qquad 7z = 0$
    $0.75x - 0.5y + 0.25z = 14$
    $x + \quad y + \qquad z = 4$

33. ▼ $x + \quad y + 5z \qquad = 1$
    $y + 2z + \quad w = 1$
    $x + 3y + 7z + 2w = 2$
    $x + \quad y + 5z + \quad w = 1$

34. ▼ $x + \quad y \qquad + 4w = 1$
    $2x - 2y - 3z + 3w = -1$
    $4y + 6z + \quad w = 4$
    $2x + 4y + 9z \qquad = 6$

35. ▼ $x + \quad y + 5z \qquad = 1$
    $y + 2z + \quad w = 1$
    $x + \quad y + 5z + \quad w = 1$
    $x + 2y + 7z + 2w = 2$

36. ▼ $x + \quad y \qquad + 4w = 1$
    $2x - 2y - 3z + 2w = -1$
    $4y + 6z + \quad w = 4$
    $3x + 3y + 3z + 7w = 4$

37. ▼ $x - 2y + \quad z - 4w = 1$
    $x + 3y + 7z + 2w = 2$
    $2x + \quad y + 8z - 2w = 3$

38. ▼ $x - 3y - 2z - \quad w = 1$
    $x + 3y + \quad z + 2w = 2$
    $2x \qquad - z + \quad w = 3$

39. ▼ $x + y + z + u + v = 15$
    $y - z + u - v = -2$
    $z + u + v = 12$
    $u - v = -1$
    $v = 5$

40. ▼ $x - y + z - u + v = 1$
    $y + z + u + v = 2$
    $z - u + v = 1$
    $u + v = 1$
    $v = 1$

41. ▼ $x - y + z - u + \quad v = 0$
    $y - z + u - \quad v = -2$
    $x \qquad\qquad - 2v = -2$
    $2x - y + z - u - 3v = -2$
    $4x - y + z - u - 7v = -6$

42. ▼ $x + \quad y + \quad z + \quad u + \quad v = 15$
    $y + \quad z + \quad u + \quad v = 3$
    $x + 2y + 2z + 2u + 2v = 18$
    $x - \quad y - \quad z - \quad u - \quad v = 9$
    $x - 2y - 2z - 2u - 2v = 6$

ⓘ In Exercises 43–46, use technology to solve the systems of equations. Express all solutions as fractions.

43. $x + 2y - \quad z + \quad w = 30$
    $2x \qquad - z + 2w = 30$
    $x + 3y + 3z - 4w = 2$
    $2x - 9y \qquad + \quad w = 4$

44. $4x - 2y + \quad z + \quad w = 20$
    $3y + 3z - 4w = 2$
    $2x + 4y \qquad - \quad w = 4$
    $x + 3y + 3z \qquad = 2$

45. $x + 2y + 3z + 4w + 5t = 6$
    $2x + 3y + 4z + 5w + \quad t = 5$
    $3x + 4y + 5z + \quad w + 2t = 4$
    $4x + 5y + \quad z + 2w + 3t = 3$
    $5x + \quad y + 2z + 3w + 4t = 2$

46 $x - 2y + 3z - 4w \qquad = 0$
    $-2x + 3y - 4z \qquad + \quad t = 0$
    $3x - 4y \qquad + \quad w - 2t = 0$
    $-4x \qquad + z - 2w + 3t = 0$
    $y - 2z + 3w - 4t = 1$

In Exercises 47–50, use technology to solve the system of equations. Express all solutions as decimals, rounded to one decimal place.

47. $1.6x + 2.4y - 3.2z = 4.4$

$5.1x - 6.3y + 0.6z = -3.2$

$4.2x + 3.5y + 4.9z = 10.1$

48. $2.1x + 0.7y - 1.4z = -2.3$

$3.5x - 4.2y - 4.9z = 3.3$

$1.1x + 2.2y - 3.3z = -10.2$

49. $-0.2x + 0.3y + 0.4z - \qquad t = 4.5$

$2.2x + 1.1y - 4.7z + \quad 2t = 8.3$

$9.2y \qquad - 1.3t = 0$

$3.4x \qquad + 0.5z - 3.4t = 0.1$

50. $1.2x - \quad 0.3y + 0.4z - \quad 2t = 4.5$

$1.9x \qquad - 0.5z - 3.4t = 0.2$

$12.1y \qquad - 1.3t = 0$

$3x + \quad 2y - 1.1z \qquad = 9$

Communication and Reasoning Exercises

51. What is meant by a pivot? What does pivoting do?

52. Give instructions to check whether or not a matrix is row-reduced.

53. You are row-reducing a matrix and have chosen a -6 as a pivot in Row 4. Directly above the pivot, in Row 1, is a 15. What row operation can you use to clear the 15?

54. You are row-reducing a matrix and have chosen a -4 as a pivot in Row 2. Directly below the pivot, in Row 4, is a -6. What row operation can you use to clear the -6?

55. In the matrix of a system of linear equations, suppose that two of the rows are equal. What can you say about the row-reduced form of the matrix?

56. In the matrix of a system of linear equations, suppose that one of the rows is a multiple of another. What can you say about the row-reduced form of the matrix?

57. ▼ Your friend Frans tells you that the system of linear equations you are solving cannot have a unique solution because the reduced matrix has a row of zeros. Comment on his claim.

58. ▼ Your other friend Hans tells you that because he is solving a consistent system of five linear equations in six unknowns, he will get infinitely many solutions. Comment on his claim.

59. ▼ If the reduced matrix of a consistent system of linear equations has five rows, three of which are zero, and five columns, how many parameters does the general solution contain?

60. ▼ If the reduced matrix of a consistent system of linear equations has five rows, two of which are zero, and seven columns, how many parameters does the general solution contain?

61. ▼ Suppose a system of equations has a unique solution. What must be true of the number of pivots in the reduced matrix of the system? Why?

62. ▼ Suppose a system has infinitely many solutions. What must be true of the number of pivots in the reduced matrix of the system? Why?

63. ▼ Give an example of a system of three linear equations with the general solution $x = 1$, $y = 1 + z$, z arbitrary. (Check your system by solving it.)

64. ▼ Give an example of a system of three linear equations with the general solution $x = y - 1$, y arbitrary, $z = y$. (Check your system by solving it.)

65. ◆ A system of linear equations is called **homogeneous** if the right-hand side of each equation in the system is 0. If a homogeneous system has a unique solution, what can you say about that solution? Why?

66. ◆ A certain homogeneous system of linear equations in three unknowns (see Exercise 65) has a solution $(1, 2, 0)$. Is this solution unique? Explain.

67. ◆ Can a homogeneous system (see Exercise 65) of linear equations be inconsistent? Explain.

68. ◆ Can a non-homogeneous system (see Exercise 65) of linear equations have the zero solution? Explain.

4.3 Applications of Systems of Linear Equations

In the examples and exercises of this section, we consider scenarios that lead to systems of linear equations in three or more unknowns. Some of these applications will strike you as a little idealized or even contrived in comparison with the kinds of problems you might encounter in the real world.* One reason is that we will not have tools to handle more realistic versions of these applications until we have studied linear programming in Chapter 6.

* See the discussion at the end of the first example below.

In each example that follows, we set up the problem as a linear system and then give the solution. The emphasis in this section is on modeling a scenario by a system of linear equations and then interpreting the solution that results, rather than on obtaining the solution. For practice, you should do the row reduction necessary to get the solution and also explore technologies such as the Pivot and Gauss-Jordan tool at the Website.

EXAMPLE 1   Blending

The *Arctic Juice Company* makes three juice blends: PineOrange, using 2 quarts of pineapple juice and 2 quarts of orange juice per gallon; PineKiwi, using 3 quarts of pineapple juice and 1 quart of kiwi juice per gallon; and OrangeKiwi, using 3 quarts of orange juice and 1 quart of kiwi juice per gallon. Each day the company has 800 quarts of pineapple juice, 650 quarts of orange juice, and 350 quarts of kiwi juice available. How many gallons of each blend should it make each day if it wants to use up all of the supplies?

Solution We take the same steps to understand the problem that we took in Section 4.1. The first step is to identify and label the unknowns. Looking at the question asked in the last sentence, we see that we should label the unknowns like this:

x = number of gallons of PineOrange made each day

y = number of gallons of PineKiwi made each day

z = number of gallons of OrangeKiwi made each day.

Next, we can organize the information we are given in a table:

	PineOrange (x)	PineKiwi (y)	OrangeKiwi (z)	Total Available
Pineapple Juice (quarts)	2	3	0	800
Orange Juice (quarts)	2	0	3	650
Kiwi Juice (quarts)	0	1	1	350

Notice how we have arranged the table: We have placed headings corresponding to the unknowns along the top, rather than down the side, and we have added a heading for the available totals. This gives us a table that is essentially the matrix of the system of linear equations we are looking for. (However, read the caution in the "Before we go on" discussion.)

Now we read across each row of the table. The fact that we want to use exactly the amount of each juice that is available leads to the following three equations:

$$2x + 3y \qquad = 800$$
$$2x \qquad + 3z = 650$$
$$y + \ z = 350.$$

The solution of this system is $(x, y, z) = (100, 200, 150)$, so Arctic Juice should make 100 gallons of PineOrange, 200 gallons of PineKiwi, and 150 gallons of OrangeKiwi each day.

Using Technology

WW Website
www.WanerMath.com
→ Online Utilities
→ Pivot and Gauss-Jordan Tool

Once you have set up the system of equations, you can obtain the solution in a single step using the Pivot and Gauss-Jordan Tool at the Website:

Enter the augmented matrix of the system as shown, and press "Reduce Completely". You can then use the reduced matrix to write down the unique solution or general solution as discussed in Section 4.2.

x1	x2	x3	x4
2	3	0	800
2	0	3	650
0	1	1	350

1	0	0	100
0	1	0	200
0	0	1	150

➡ **Before we go on ...** *Caution:* We do not recommend relying on the coincidence that the table we created to organize the information in Example 1 happened to be the matrix of the system; it is too easy to set up the table "sideways" and get the wrong matrix. You should always write down the system of equations *and be sure you understand each equation.* For example, the equation $2x + 3y = 800$ in Example 1 indicates that the number of quarts of pineapple juice that will be used $(2x + 3y)$ is equal to the amount available (800 quarts). By thinking of the reason for each equation, you can check that you have the correct system. If you have the wrong system of equations to begin with, solving it won't help you.

Q: *Just how realistic is the scenario in Example 1?*

A: This is a very unrealistic scenario, for several reasons:

1. Isn't it odd that we happened to end up with exactly the same number of equations as unknowns? Real scenarios are rarely so considerate. If there had been four equations, there would in all likelihood have been no solution at all. However, we need to understand these idealized problems before we can tackle the real world.
2. Even if a real-world scenario does give the same number of equations as unknowns, there is still no guarantee that there will be a unique solution consisting of positive values. What, for instance, would we have done in this example if x had turned out to be negative?
3. The requirement that we use exactly all the ingredients would be an unreasonable constraint in real life. When we discuss linear programming, we will be able to substitute the more reasonable constraint that you use no more than is available, and we will add the more reasonable objective that you maximize profit.

EXAMPLE 2 Aircraft Purchases: Airbus and Boeing

A new airline has recently purchased a fleet of Airbus A330-300s, Boeing 767-300ERs, and Boeing Dreamliner 787-9s to meet an estimated demand for 5,400 seats. The A330-300s seat 330 passengers and cost \$250 million each, the 767-300ERs seat 270 passengers and cost \$200 million each, while the 787-9s seat 240 passengers and cost \$250 million each.[12] The total cost of the fleet, which had twice as many 787-9s as 767s, was \$4,750 million. How many of each type of aircraft did the company purchase?

Solution We label the unknowns as follows:

x = number of Airbus A330-300s

y = number of Boeing 767-300ERs

z = number of Boeing 787-9s.

We must now set up the equations. We can organize some (but not all) of the given information in a table:

	A330-300	767-300ER	787-9	Total
Capacity	330	270	240	5,400
Cost (\$ million)	250	200	250	4,750

---

[12] The prices are approximate 2015 list prices; actual selling prices are typically around 50% of list prices. Seating capacities depend on configuration and vary considerably from airline to airline. Sources for data: Company websites/Wikipedia.

Reading across, we get the equations expressing the facts that the airline needed to seat 5,400 passengers and that it spent \$4,750 million:

$$330x + 270y + 240z = 5,400$$
$$250x + 200y + 250z = 4,750.$$

There is an additional piece of information we have not yet used: The airline bought twice as many 787s as 767s. As we said in Section 4.1, it is easiest to translate a statement like this into an equation if we first reword it using the phrase "the number of." Thus, we say: "The number of 787s ordered was twice the number of 767s ordered," or

$$z = 2y$$
$$2y - z = 0.$$

We now have a system of three equations in three unknowns:

$$330x + 270y + 240z = 5,400$$
$$250x + 200y + 250z = 4,750$$
$$2y - \quad z = 0.$$

Solving the system, we get the solution $(x, y, z) = (5, 5, 10)$. Thus, the airline ordered five A330-300s, five 767-300ERs, and ten 787-9s.

EXAMPLE 3 **Traffic Flow**

Traffic through downtown Urbanville flows through the one-way system shown in Figure 8. Traffic counting devices installed in the road (shown as boxes) count 200 cars entering town from the west each hour, 150 leaving town on the north each hour, and 50 leaving town on the south each hour.

a. From this information is it possible to determine how many cars drive along Allen, Baker, and Coal streets every hour?

b. What is the maximum possible traffic flow along Baker Street?

c. What is the minimum possible traffic along Allen Street?

d. What is the maximum possible traffic flow along Coal Street?

Solution

a. Our unknowns are

x = number of cars per hour on Allen Street
y = number of cars per hour on Baker Street
z = number of cars per hour on Coal Street.

We now focus on the three intersections shown circled in Figure 9. Assuming that, at each of these intersections, cars do not fall into a pit or materialize out of thin air, then the number of cars entering each intersection has to equal the number exiting.

Intersection of Allen and Baker Streets: We consider *only what is inside the circle around this intersection*, as we see in the magnified view shown in Figure 10. In this zoomed-in view, we see that there are 200 cars entering and $x + y$ cars exiting:

Traffic in = Traffic out
$$200 = x + y.$$

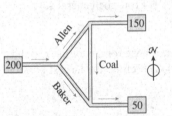

Figure 8

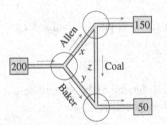

Figure 9

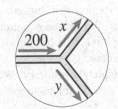

Intersection of Allen and Baker

Figure 10

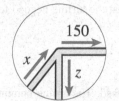

Intersection of Allen and Coal

Figure 11

Intersection of Baker and Coal

Figure 12

Intersection of Allen and Coal Streets (see Figure 11):

> Traffic in = Traffic out
> $$x = z + 150.$$

Intersection of Baker and Coal Streets (see Figure 12):

> Traffic in = Traffic out
> $$y + z = 50.$$

We now have the following system of equations:

$$x + y \qquad = 200$$
$$x \qquad - z = 150$$
$$y + z = 50.$$

If we solve this system using the methods of the preceding section, we find that it has infinitely many solutions. The general solution is

$$x = z + 150$$
$$y = -z + 50$$
$$z \text{ is arbitrary.}$$

Because we do not have a unique solution, it is *not* possible to determine how many cars drive along Allen, Baker, and Coal Streets every hour.

b. The traffic flow along Baker Street is measured by y. From the general solution,

$$y = -z + 50,$$

where z is arbitrary. How arbitrary is z? It makes no sense for any of the variables x, y, or z to be negative in this scenario, so $z \geq 0$. Therefore, the largest possible value y can have is

$$y = -0 + 50 = 50 \text{ cars per hour.}$$

c. The traffic flow along Allen Street is measured by x. From the general solution,

$$x = z + 150,$$

where $z \geq 0$, as we saw in part (b). Therefore, the smallest possible value x can have is

$$x = 0 + 150 = 150 \text{ cars per hour.}$$

d. The traffic flow along Coal Street is measured by z. Referring to the general solution, we see that z shows up in the expressions for both x and y:

$$x = z + 150$$
$$y = -z + 50.$$

In the first of these equations there is nothing preventing z from being as big as we like; the larger we make z, the larger x becomes. However, the second equation places a limit on how large z can be: If $z > 50$, then y is negative, which is impossible. Therefore, the largest value z can take is 50 cars per hour.

From the discussion above, we see that z is not completely arbitrary: We must have $z \geq 0$ and $z \leq 50$. Thus, z has to satisfy $0 \leq z \leq 50$ for us to get a realistic answer.

➡ **Before we go on...** Here are some questions to think about in Example 3: If you wanted to nail down x, y, and z to see where the cars are really going, how would you do it with only one more traffic counter? Would it make sense for z to be fractional? What if you interpreted x, y, and z as *average* numbers of cars per hour over a long period of time?

Traffic flow is only one kind of flow in which we might be interested. Water and electricity flows are others. In each case, to analyze the flow, we use the fact that the amount entering an intersection must equal the amount leaving it. ■

EXAMPLE 4   **Transportation**

A car rental company has four locations in the city: Southwest, Northeast, Southeast, and Northwest. The Northwest location has 20 more cars than it needs, and the Northeast location has 15 more cars than it needs. The Southwest location needs 10 more cars than it has, and the Southeast location needs 25 more cars than it has. It costs $10 (in salary and gas) to have an employee drive a car from Northwest to Southwest. It costs $20 to drive a car from Northwest to Southeast. It costs $5 to drive a car from Northeast to Southwest, and it costs $10 to drive a car from Northeast to Southeast. If the company will spend a total of $475 rearranging its cars, how many cars will it drive from each of Northwest and Northeast to each of Southwest and Southeast?

Solution Figure 13 shows a diagram of this situation. Each arrow represents a route along which the rental company can drive cars. At each location is written the number of extra cars the location has (Northwest and Northeast) or the number it needs (Southwest and Southeast). Along each route is written the cost of driving a car along that route.

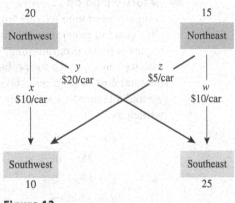

Figure 13

The unknowns are the number of cars the company will drive along each route, so we have the following four unknowns, as indicated in the figure:

x = number of cars driven from Northwest to Southwest

y = number of cars driven from Northwest to Southeast

z = number of cars driven from Northeast to Southwest

w = number of cars driven from Northeast to Southeast

Consider the Northwest location. It has 20 more cars than it needs, so the total number of cars being driven out of Northwest should be 20. This gives us the equation

$$x + y = 20.$$

Similarly, the total number of cars being driven out of Northeast should be 15, so

$$z + w = 15.$$

Considering the number of cars needed at the Southwest and Southeast locations, we get the following two equations as well:

$$x + z = 10$$
$$y + w = 25.$$

There is one more equation that we should write down, the equation that says that the company will spend $475:

$$10x + 20y + 5z + 10w = 475.$$

Thus, we have the following system of five equations in four unknowns:

$$
\begin{aligned}
x + \ y \qquad\qquad\quad &= 20 \\
z + \ \ w &= 15 \\
x \qquad + \ z \qquad\quad &= 10 \\
y \quad + \ \ w &= 25 \\
10x + 20y + 5z + 10w &= 475.
\end{aligned}
$$

Solving this system, we find that $(x, y, z, w) = (5, 15, 5, 10)$. In words, the company will drive 5 cars from Northwest to Southwest, 15 from Northwest to Southeast, 5 from Northeast to Southwest, and 10 from Northeast to Southeast.

➡ **Before we go on ...** A very reasonable question to ask in Example 4 is, Can the company rearrange its cars for less than $475? Even better, what is the least possible cost? In general, a question asking for the optimal cost may require the techniques of linear programming, which we will discuss in Chapter 6. However, in this case we can approach the problem directly. If we remove the equation that says that the total cost is $475 and solve the system consisting of the other four equations, we find that there are infinitely many solutions and that the general solution may be written as

$$x = w - 5$$
$$y = 25 - w$$
$$z = 15 - w$$
$$w \text{ is arbitrary.}$$

This allows us to write the total cost as a function of w:

$$
\begin{aligned}
\text{Cost} &= 10x + 20y + 5z + 10w \\
&= 10(w - 5) + 20(25 - w) + 5(15 - w) + 10w \\
&= 525 - 5w.
\end{aligned}
$$

So the larger we make w, the smaller the total cost will be. The largest we can make w is 15 (why?), and if we do so, we get $(x, y, z, w) = (10, 10, 0, 15)$ and a total cost of $450. ∎

4.3 EXERCISES

▼ more advanced ◆ challenging

Ⓣ indicates exercises that should be solved using technology

Exercises not marked with Ⓣ *result in systems that can be solved by hand using the techniques of Section 4.2, though, of course, you can also use technology like the Pivot and Gauss-Jordan tool to solve them. What is important in all cases is setting up your system correctly and interpreting the solution.*

Applications

1. *Resource Allocation* You manage an ice cream factory that makes three flavors: Creamy Vanilla, Continental Mocha, and Succulent Strawberry. Into each batch of Creamy Vanilla go 2 eggs, 1 cup of milk, and 2 cups of cream. Into each batch of Continental Mocha go 1 egg, 1 cup of milk, and 2 cups of cream, while into each batch of Succulent Strawberry go 1 egg, 2 cups of milk, and 1 cup of cream. You have in stock 350 eggs, 350 cups of milk, and 400 cups of cream. How many batches of each flavor should you make in order to use up all of your ingredients? [HINT: See Example 1.]

2. *Resource Allocation* You own a hamburger franchise and are planning to shut down operations for the day, but you are left with 13 buns, 19 defrosted beef patties, and 15 opened cheese slices. Rather than throwing them out, you decide to use them to make burgers that you will sell at a discount. Plain burgers each require 1 beef patty and 1 bun; double cheeseburgers each require 2 beef patties, 1 bun, and 2 slices of cheese; while regular cheeseburgers each require 1 beef patty, 1 bun, and 1 slice of cheese. How many of each should you make? [HINT: See Example 1.]

3. *Resource Allocation* Urban Community College is planning to offer courses in Finite Math, Applied Calculus, and Computer Methods. Each section of Finite Math has 40 students and earns the college $40,000 in revenue. Each section of Applied Calculus has 40 students and earns the college $60,000, while each section of Computer Methods has 10 students and earns the college $20,000. Assuming that the college wishes to offer a total of six sections, accommodate 210 students, and bring in $260,000 in revenues, how many sections of each course should it offer? [HINT: See Example 2.]

4. *Resource Allocation* The *Enormous State University* History Department offers three courses—Ancient, Medieval, and Modern History—and the chairperson is trying to decide how many sections of each to offer this semester. The department is allowed to offer 45 sections total, there are 5,000 students who would like to take a course, and there are 60 professors to teach them. Sections of Ancient History have 100 students each, sections of Medieval History hold 50 students each, and sections of Modern History have 200 students each. Modern History sections are taught by a team of two professors, while Ancient and Medieval History need only one professor per section. How many sections of each course should the chair schedule in order to offer all the sections that are allowed, accommodate all of the students, and give one teaching assignment to each professor? [HINT: See Example 2.]

5. *Latin Music Sales (Digital)* In 2013, total revenues from digital sales of regional (Mexican/Tejano), pop/rock, and tropical (salsa/merengue/cumbia/bachata) Latin music in the United States amounted to $58 million. Regional music brought in four times as much as tropical music and pop/rock music brought in $10 million more than tropical music.[13] How much revenue was earned from digital sales in each of the three categories?

6. *Latin Music Sales (Digital)* In 2012, total revenues from digital sales of pop/rock, tropical (salsa/merengue/cumbia/bachata), and urban (reggaeton) Latin music in the United States amounted to $24 million. Pop/rock music brought in twice as much as the other two categories combined and $9 million more than tropical music.[14] How much revenue was earned from digital sales in each of the three categories?

7. *Purchasing Aircraft* In Example 2 we saw that Airbus A330-300s seat 330 passengers and cost $250 million each, Boeing 767-300ERs seat 270 passengers and cost $200 million each, while Boeing Dreamliner 787-9s seat 240 passengers and cost $250 million each. You are the purchasing manager of an airline company and have a spending goal of $4,300 million for the purchase of new aircraft to seat a total of 4,980 passengers. Your company has a policy of supporting U.S. industries, and you have been instructed to buy twice as many Boeings as Airbuses. Given the selection of three aircraft, how many of each should you order?

8. *Purchasing Aircraft* Refer to Exercise 7. René DuFleur has just been appointed the new CEO of your airline, and you have received instructions that the company policy is now to purchase as many Airbuses as Boeings. Further, the desired seating capacity has been revised downward to 2,910 passengers, and the cost target has been lowered to $2,400 million. Given the specifications of the three types of aircraft, how many of each should you order?

---

[13] Revenues are approximate. Source: Recording Industry Association of America (http://riaa.com).

[14] *Ibid.*

9. *Supply* A bagel store orders cream cheese from three suppliers: *Cheesy Cream Corp.* (CCC), *Super Smooth & Sons* (SSS), and *Bagel's Best Friend Co.* (BBF). One month, the total order of cheese came to 100 tons. (The store does do a booming trade.) The costs were $80, $50, and $65 per ton from the three suppliers, respectively, with total cost amounting to $5,990. Given that the store ordered the same amount from CCC and BBF, how many tons of cream cheese were ordered from each supplier?

10. *Supply* Refer to Exercise 9. The bagel store's outlay for cream cheese the following month was $2,310, when it purchased a total of 36 tons. Two more tons of cream cheese came from *Bagel's Best Friend Co.* than from *Super Smooth & Sons*. How many tons of cream cheese came from each supplier?

11. *Pest Control* Halmar the Great has boasted to his hordes of followers that many a notorious villain has fallen to his awesome sword: His total of 560 victims consists of evil sorcerers, trolls, and orcs. These he has slain with a total of 620 mighty thrusts of his sword, evil sorcerers and trolls each requiring two thrusts (to the chest) and orcs each requiring one thrust (to the neck). When asked about the number of trolls he has slain, he replies, "I, the mighty Halmar, despise trolls five times as much as I despise evil sorcerers. Accordingly, five times as many trolls as evil sorcerers have fallen to my sword!" How many of each type of villain has he slain?

12. *Manufacturing Perfume* The *Fancy French Perfume Company* recently had its secret formula divulged. It turned out that it was using, as the three ingredients, rose oil, oil of fermented prunes, and alcohol. Moreover, each 22-ounce econo-size bottle contained 4 more ounces of alcohol than oil of fermented prunes, while the amount of alcohol was equal to the combined volume of the other two ingredients. How much of each ingredient did the company use in an econo-size bottle?[15] [**HINT**: The answer is the brand-name of a famous eau de cologne.]

13. *Donations* The *Enormous State University Good Works Society* recently raised funds for three worthwhile causes: the Math Professors' Benevolent Fund (MPBF), the Society of Computer Nerds (SCN), and the NY Jets. Because the society's members are closet jocks, the society donated twice as much to the NY Jets as to the MPBF, and it donated equal amounts to the first two funds. (It is unable to distinguish between mathematicians and nerds.) Further, for every $1 it gave to the MPBF, it decided to keep $1 for itself; for every $1 it gave to the SCN, it kept $2; and for every $1 to the Jets, it also kept $2. The treasurer of the Society, Johnny Treasure, was required to itemize all donations for the Dean of Students but discovered to his consternation that he had lost the receipts! The only information available to him was that the society's bank account had swelled by $4,200. How much did the society donate to each cause?

14. ▼ *Tenure* Professor Walt is up for tenure and wishes to submit a portfolio of written student evaluations as evidence of his good teaching. He begins by grouping all the evaluations into four categories: good reviews, bad reviews (a typical one being "GET RID OF WALT! THE MAN CAN'T TEACH!"), mediocre reviews (such as "I suppose he's OK, given the general quality of teaching at this college"), and reviews left blank. When he tallies up the piles, Walt gets a little worried: There are 280 more bad reviews than good ones and only half as many blank reviews as bad ones. The good reviews and blank reviews together total 170. On an impulse, he decides to even up the piles a little by removing 280 of the bad reviews, and this leaves him with a total of 400 reviews of all types. How many of each category of reviews were there originally?

▌*Airline Costs* Exercises 15 and 16 are based on the following table, which shows the amount spent by four U.S. airlines to fly one available seat 1 mile in the second quarter of 2014.[16] Set up each system and then solve using technology. [**HINT**: See the technology note accompanying Example 1.]

Airline	United Continental	American	JetBlue	Southwest
Cost (¢)	14.9	14.6	11.9	12.4

15. ▼ Suppose that, on a 3,000-mile New York to Los Angeles flight, United Continental, American, and Southwest flew a total of 210 empty seats, costing them a total of $89,760. If United Continental had three times as many empty seats as American, how many empty seats did each of these three airlines carry on its flight?

16. ▼ Suppose that, on a 2,000-mile Miami to Memphis flight, United Continental, JetBlue, and Southwest flew a total of 200 empty seats, costing them a total of $51,100. If JetBlue had twice as many empty seats as Southwest, how many empty seats did each of these three airlines carry on its flight?

Investing: Inverse Mutual Funds *Inverse mutual funds, sometimes referred to as "bear market" or "short" funds, seek to deliver the opposite of the performance of the index or category they track and can thus be used by traders to bet against the stock market. Exercises 17 and 18 are based on the following table, which shows the performance of three such funds as of February 27, 2015:*[17]

---

[16] Costs are rounded to the nearest 0.1¢. Source: Company filings. The cost per available seat-mile (CASM) is a widely used operating statistic in the airline industry.

[17] Based on prices at the close of the stock market on February 27, 2015. YTD losses rounded to the nearest percentage point. Source: www.fidelity.com.

---

[15] Most perfumes consist of 10 to 20% perfume oils dissolved in alcohol. This may or may not be reflected in this company's formula.

	Year-to-Date Loss (%)
SHPIX (Short Smallcap Profund)	4
RYURX (Rydex Inverse S&P 500)	3
RYCWX (Rydex Inverse Dow)	6

17. You invested a total of $9,000 in the three funds at the beginning of 2015, including equal amounts in RYURX and RYCWX. Your year-to-date loss from the first two funds amounted to $260. How much did you invest in each of the three funds?

18. You invested a total of $6,000 in the three funds at the beginning of 2015, including equal amounts in SHPIX and RYURX. Your total year-to-date loss amounted to $260. How much did you invest in each of the three funds?

Investing: Lesser-Known Stocks Exercises 19 and 20 are based on the following information about the stocks of Whitestone REIT, HCC Insurance Holdings, Inc., *and* SanDisk Corporation:[18]

	Price ($)	Dividend Yield (%)
WSR (WSR Whitestone REIT)	16	7
HCC (HCC Insurance Holdings, Inc.)	56	2
SNDK (SanDisk Corporation)	80	2

19. ▼ You invested a total of $8,400 in shares of the three stocks at the given prices and expected to earn $248 in annual dividends. If you purchased a total of 200 shares, how many shares of each stock did you purchase?

20. ▼ You invested a total of $11,200 in shares of the three stocks at the given prices and expected to earn $304 in annual dividends. If you purchased a total of 250 shares, how many shares of each stock did you purchase?

21. ▮ *Internet Audience* At the end of 2003 the four companies with the largest number of home Internet users in the United States were Microsoft, Time Warner, Yahoo, and Google, with a combined audience of 284 million users.[19] Taking x to be the Microsoft audience in millions, y the Time Warner audience in millions, z the Yahoo audience in millions, and u the Google audience in millions, it was observed that

$$z - u = 3(x - y) + 6$$
$$x + y = 50 + z + u$$

and $x - y + z - u = 42.$

How large was the audience of each of the four companies in November 2003?

22. ▮ *Internet Audience* At the end of 2003 the four organizations ranking 5 through 8 in home Internet users in the United States were eBay, the U.S. government, Amazon, and Lycos, with a combined audience of 112 million users.[20] Taking x to be the eBay audience in millions, y the U.S. government audience in millions, z the Amazon audience in millions, and u the Lycos audience in millions, it was observed that

$$y - z = z - u$$
$$x - y = 3(y - u) + 5$$

and $x - y + z - u = 12.$

How large was the audience of each of the four organizations in November 2003?

23. ▼ *Market Share: Homeowners Insurance* Three market leaders in homeowners insurance in Missouri are State Farm, American Family Insurance Group, and Allstate. Based on data from 2007, two relationships between the Missouri homeowners insurance percentage market shares are found to be

$$x = 1 + y + z$$
$$z = 16 - 0.2w,$$

where x, y, z, and w are the percentages of the market held by State Farm, American Family, Allstate, and other companies, respectively.[21] Given that the four groups account for the entire market, obtain a third equation relating x, y, z, and w, and solve the associated system of three linear equations to show how the market shares of State Farm, American Family, and Allstate depend on the share held by other companies. Which of the three companies' market share is most affected by the share held by other companies?

24. ▼ *Market Share: Auto Insurance* Repeat Exercise 23 using the following relationships among the auto insurance percentage market shares:

$$x = -40 + 5y + z$$
$$z = 3 - 2y + w.$$

25. *Inventory Control* Red Bookstore wants to ship books from its warehouses in Brooklyn and Queens to its stores, one on Long Island and one in Manhattan. Its warehouse in Brooklyn has 1,000 books, and its warehouse in Queens has 2,000. Each store orders 1,500 books. It costs $5 to ship each book from Brooklyn to Long Island and $1 to ship each book from Brooklyn to Manhattan. It costs $4 to ship each book from

---

[18] Yields rounded to the nearest percentage point and stock prices at the close of the stock market on February 27, 2015, rounded to the nearest $1. Source: www.finance.yahoo.

[19] Source: Nielsen/NetRatings www.nielsen-netratings.com, January 1, 2004.

[20] *Ibid.*

[21] Source: Missouri Dept. of Insurance (www.insurance.mo.gov).

Queens to Long Island and $2 to ship each book from Queens to Manhattan.

a. If Red has a transportation budget of $9,000 and is willing to spend all of it, how many books should Red ship from each warehouse to each store in order to fill all the orders?

b. Is there a way of doing this for less money? [HINT: See Example 4.]

26. *Inventory Control* The *Tubular Ride Boogie Board Company* has manufacturing plants in Tucson, Arizona, and Toronto, Ontario. You have been given the job of coordinating distribution of the latest model, the Gladiator, to outlets in Honolulu and Venice Beach. The Tucson plant, when operating at full capacity, can manufacture 620 Gladiator boards per week, while the Toronto plant, beset by labor disputes, can produce only 410 boards per week. The outlet in Honolulu orders 500 Gladiator boards per week, while Venice Beach orders 530 boards per week. Transportation costs are as follows:

Tucson to Honolulu: $10 per board; Tucson to Venice Beach: $5 per board.

Toronto to Honolulu: $20 per board; Toronto to Venice Beach: $10 per board.

a. Assuming that you wish to fill all orders and ensure full-capacity production at both plants, is it possible to meet a total transportation budget of $10,200? If so, how many Gladiator boards are shipped from each manufacturing plant to each distribution outlet?

b. Is there a way of doing this for less money? [HINT: See Example 4.]

27. ▼ *Tourism in the 1990s* In the 1990s, significant numbers of tourists traveled from North America and Europe to Australia and South Africa. In 1998 a total of 1,390,000 of these tourists visited Australia, while 1,140,000 of them visited South Africa. Further, 630,000 of them came from North America, and 1,900,000 of them came from Europe.[22] (Assume that no single tourist visited both destinations or traveled from both North America and Europe.)

a. The given information is not sufficient to determine the number of tourists from each region to each destination. Why?

b. If you were given the additional information that a total of 2,530,000 tourists traveled from these two regions to these two destinations, would you now be able to determine the number of tourists from each region to each destination? If so, what are these numbers?

c. If you were given the additional information that the same number of people from Europe visited South Africa as visited Australia, would you now be able to determine the number of tourists from each region to each destination? If so, what are these numbers?

28. ▼ *Tourism in the 1990s* In the 1990s, significant numbers of tourists traveled from North America and Asia to Australia and South Africa. In 1998 a total of 2,230,000 of these tourists visited Australia, while 390,000 of them visited South Africa. Also, 630,000 of these tourists came from North America, and a total of 2,620,000 tourists traveled from these two regions to these two destinations.[23] (Assume that no single tourist visited both destinations or traveled from both North America and Asia.)

a. The given information is not sufficient to determine the number of tourists from each region to each destination. Why?

b. If you were given the additional information that a total of 1,990,000 tourists came from Asia, would you now be able to determine the number of tourists from each region to each destination? If so, what are these numbers?

c. If you were given the additional information that 200,000 tourists visited South Africa from Asia, would you now be able to determine the number of tourists from each region to each destination? If so, what are these numbers?

29. ▼ *Alcohol* The following table shows some data from a 2000 study on substance use among 10th graders in the United States and Europe:[24]

	Used Alcohol	Alcohol-Free	Totals
U.S.	x	y	14,000
Europe	z	w	95,000
Totals	63,550	45,450	

a. The table leads to a linear system of four equations in four unknowns. What is the system? Does it have a unique solution? What does this indicate about the given and the missing data?

b. ▯ Given that the number of U.S. 10th graders who were alcohol-free was 50% more than the number who had used alcohol, find the missing data.

30. ▼ *Tobacco* The following table shows some data from the same study cited in Exercise 29:[25]

	Smoked Cigarettes	Cigarette-Free	Totals
U.S.	x	y	14,000
Europe	z	w	95,000
Totals		70,210	109,000

a. The table leads to a linear system of four equations in four unknowns. What is the system? Does it have a

---

[22] Figures are rounded to the nearest 10,000. Sources: South African Dept. of Environmental Affairs and Tourism; Australia Tourist Commission/*New York Times*, January 15, 2000, p. C1.

[23] *Ibid.*

[24] "Used Alcohol" indicates consumption of alcohol at least once in the past 30 days. Source: Council of Europe/University of Michigan. "Monitoring the Future"/*New York Times*, February 21, 2001, p. A10.

[25] "Smoked Cigarettes" indicates that at least one cigarette was smoked in the past 30 days. Source: *Ibid.*

unique solution? What does this indicate about the missing data?

b. 🖥 Given that 31,510 more European 10th graders smoked cigarettes than U.S. 10th graders, find the missing data.

31. *Traffic Flow* One-way traffic through *Enormous State University* is shown in the figure, where the numbers indicate daily counts of vehicles.

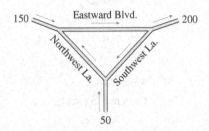

a. Is it possible to determine the daily flow of traffic along each of the three streets from the information given? If your answer is *yes*, what is the traffic flow along each street? If your answer is *no*, what additional information would suffice?

b. Is a flow of 60 vehicles per day along Southwest Lane consistent with the information given?

c. What is the minimum traffic flow possible along Northwest Lane consistent with the information given? [HINT: See Example 3.]

32. *Traffic Flow* The traffic through downtown East Podunk flows through the one-way system shown below.

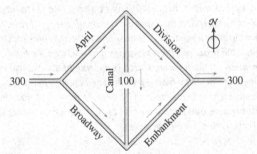

Traffic counters find that 300 vehicles enter town from the west each hour, and 300 leave town toward the east each hour. Also, 100 cars drive down Canal Street each hour.

a. Write down the general solution of the associated system of linear equations. Is it possible to determine the number of vehicles on each street per hour?

b. On which street could you put another traffic counter in order to determine the flow completely?

c. What is the minimum traffic flow along April Street consistent with the information given? [HINT: See Example 3.]

33. *Traffic Flow* The traffic through downtown Johannesburg follows the one-way system shown below, with traffic

movement recorded at incoming and outgoing streets (in cars per minute) as shown.

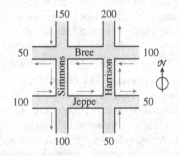

a. Set up and solve a system of equations to solve for the traffic flow along the middle sections of the four streets.

b. Is there sufficient information to calculate the traffic along the middle section of Jeppe Street? If so, what is it? If not, why not?

c. Given that 400 cars per minute flow down the middle section of Bree Street, how many cars per minute flow down the middle section of Simmons?

d. What is the minimum traffic flow along the middle section of Harrison Street?

e. Is there an upper limit to the possible traffic down Simmons Street consistent with the information given? Explain.

34. *Traffic Flow* Officials of the town of Hempstead were planning to make Hempstead Turnpike and the surrounding streets into one-way streets to prepare for the opening of Hofstra USA. In an experiment, they restricted traffic flow along the streets near Hofstra as shown in the diagram. The numbers show traffic flow per minute and the arrows indicate the direction of traffic.

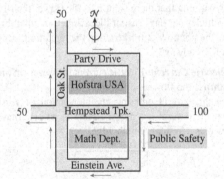

a. Set up and solve the associated traffic flow problem with the following unknowns:

x = Traffic per minute along the middle stretch of Oak St.

y = Traffic per minute along the middle stretch of Hempstead Tpk.

z = Traffic per minute along Einstein Ave.

u = Traffic per minute along Party Drive.

b. If 20 cars per minute drive along Party Drive, what is the traffic like along the middle stretch of Oak Street?

c. If 20 vehicles per minute drive along Einstein Ave. and 90 vehicles per minute drive down the middle stretch of Hempstead Tpk., how many cars per minute drive along the middle stretch of Oak Street?

d. If Einstein Avenue is deserted, what is the minimum traffic along the middle stretch of Hempstead Tpk.?

35. ▼ *Traffic Management* The Outer Village Town Council has decided to convert its (rather quiet) main street, Broadway, to a one-way street but is not sure of the direction of most of the traffic. The accompanying diagram illustrates the downtown area of Outer Village as well as the *net* traffic flow along the intersecting streets (in vehicles per day). (There are no one-way streets. A net traffic flow in a certain direction is defined as the traffic flow in that direction minus the flow in the opposite direction.)

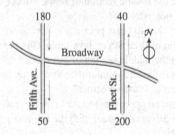

a. Is the given information sufficient to determine the net traffic flow along the three portions of Broadway shown? If your answer is *yes,* give the traffic flow along each stretch. If your answer is *no,* what additional information would suffice? [HINT: For the direction of net traffic flow, choose either east or west. If a corresponding value is negative, it indicates net flow in the opposite direction.]

b. Assuming that there is little traffic (fewer than 160 vehicles per day) east of Fleet Street, in what direction is the net flow of traffic along the remaining stretches of Broadway?

36. ▼ *Electric Current* Electric current measures (in **amperes,** or **amps**) the flow of electrons through wires. Like traffic flow, the current entering an intersection of wires must equal the current leaving it.[26] Here is an electrical circuit known as a **Wheatstone bridge.**

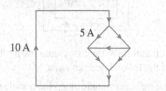

a. If the currents in two of the wires are 10 amps and 5 amps as shown, determine the currents in the unlabeled wires in terms of suitable parameters.

b. In which wire should you measure the current in order to know all of the currents exactly?

37. ▼ *Econometrics (from the GRE Economics Test)* This and the next exercise are based on the following simplified model of the determination of the money stock:

$$M = C + D$$
$$C = 0.2D$$
$$R = 0.1D$$
$$H = R + C,$$

where

$$M = \text{Money stock}$$
$$C = \text{Currency in circulation}$$
$$R = \text{Bank reserves}$$
$$D = \text{Deposits of the public}$$
$$H = \text{High-powered money}$$

If the money stock were $120 billion, what would bank reserves have to be?

38. ▼ *Econometrics (from the GRE Economics Test)* With the model in Exercise 37, if H were equal to $42 billion, what would M equal?

CAT Scans CAT *(computerized axial tomographic) scans are used to map the exact location of interior features of the human body. CAT scan technology is based on the following principles: (1) Different components of the human body (water, gray matter, bone, etc.) absorb X-rays to different extents; and (2) to measure the X-ray absorption by a specific region of, say, the brain, it suffices to pass a number of line-shaped pencil beams of X-rays through the brain at different angles and measure the total absorption for each beam, which is the sum of the absorptions of the regions through which it passes. The accompanying diagram illustrates a simple example. (The number in each region shows its absorption, and the number on each X-ray beam shows the total absorption for that beam.)*[27]

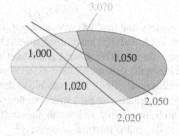

---

[26] This is known as **Kirchhoff's current law,** named after Gustav Robert Kirchhoff (1824–1887). Kirchhoff made important contributions to the fields of geometric optics, electromagnetic radiation, and electrical network theory.

[27] Based on a COMAP video, *Geometry: New Tools for New Technologies,* by J. Malkevitch, Video Applications Library, COMAP, 1992. The absorptions are actually calibrated on a logarithmic scale. In real applications the size of the regions is very small, and very large numbers of beams must be used.

In Exercises 39–44, use the table and the given X-ray absorption diagrams to identify the composition of each of the regions marked by a letter.

Type	Air	Water	Gray matter	Tumor	Blood	Bone
Absorption	0	1,000	1,020	1,030	1,050	2,000

39.

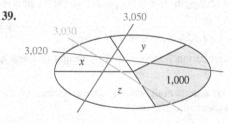

40.

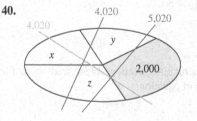

41.

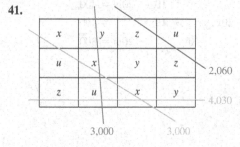

42.

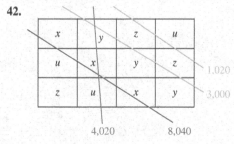

43. ▼ Identify the composition of site *x*.

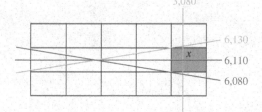

(The horizontal and slanted beams each pass through five regions.)

44. ▼ Identify the composition of site *x*.

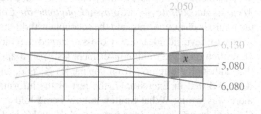

(The horizontal and slanted beams each pass through five regions.)

45. ◆ *Voting* In the 75th Congress (1937–1939) the U.S. House of Representatives had 333 Democrats, 89 Republicans, and 13 members of other parties. Suppose that a bill passed the House with 31 more votes in favor than against, with 10 times as many Democrats voting for the bill as Republicans, and with 36 more non-Democrats voting against the bill than for it. If every member voted either for the bill or against it, how many Democrats, how many Republicans, and how many members of other parties voted in favor of the bill?

46. ◆ *Voting* In the 75th Congress (1937–1939) there were in the Senate 75 Democrats, 17 Republicans, and 4 members of other parties. Suppose that a bill passed the Senate with 16 more votes in favor than against, with three times as many Democrats voting in favor as non-Democrats voting in favor, and with 32 more Democrats voting in favor than Republicans voting in favor. If every member voted either for the bill or against it, how many Democrats, how many Republicans, and how many members of other parties voted in favor of the bill?

47. ◆ *Investments* Things have not been going too well here at *Accurate Accounting, Inc.* since we hired Todd Smiley. He has a tendency to lose important documents, especially around April, when tax returns of our business clients are due. Today Smiley accidentally shredded *Colossal Conglomerate Corp.*'s investment records. We must therefore reconstruct them on the basis of the information he can gather. Todd recalls that the company earned an $8 million return on investments totaling $65 million last year. After a few frantic telephone calls to sources in Colossal, he learned that Colossal had made investments in four companies last year: X, Y, Z, and W. (For reasons of confidentiality we are withholding their names.) Investments in company X earned 15% last year, investments in Y depreciated by 20% last year, investments in Z neither appreciated nor depreciated last year, while investments in W earned 20% last year. Smiley was also told that Colossal invested twice as much in company X as in company Z, and three times as much in company W as in company Z. Does Smiley have sufficient information to piece together Colossal's investment portfolio before its tax return is due next week? If so, what does the investment portfolio look like?

48. ◆ *Investments* Things are going from bad to worse here at *Accurate Accounting, Inc.*! *Colossal Conglomerate Corp.*'s tax return is due tomorrow, and the accountant Todd Smiley seems to have no idea how Colossal earned a return of $8 million on a $65 million investment last year. It appears that, although the returns from companies X, Y, Z, and W were as listed in Exercise 47, the rest of the information there was wrong. What Smiley is now being told is that Colossal invested only in companies X, Y, and Z and that the investment in X amounted to $30 million. His sources in Colossal still maintain that twice as much was invested in company X as in company Z. What should Smiley do?

Communication and Reasoning Exercises

49. Are Exercises 1 and 2 realistic in their expectation of using up all the ingredients? What does your answer have to do with the solution(s) of the associated system of equations?

50. Suppose that you obtained a solution for Exercise 3 or 4 consisting of positive values that were not all whole numbers. What would such a solution signify about the situation in the exercise? Should you round these values to the nearest whole numbers?

In Exercises 51–56, x, y and z represent the weights of the three ingredients X, Y, and Z in a gasoline blend. Say which of the following is represented by a linear equation in x, y, and z, and give a form of the equation when it is.

51. The blend consists of 100 pounds of ingredient X.

52. The blend is free of ingredient X.

53. The blend contains 30% ingredient Y by weight.

54. The weight of ingredient X is the product of the weights of ingredients Y and Z.

55. There is at least 30% ingredient Y by weight.

56. There is twice as much ingredient X by weight as Y and Z combined.

57. Make up an entertaining word problem leading to the following system of equations:

$$10x + 20y + 10z = 100$$
$$5x + 15y \quad\quad = 50$$
$$x + \quad y + \quad z = 10.$$

58. Make up an entertaining word problem leading to the following system of equations:

$$10x + 20y \quad\quad\quad\quad = 300$$
$$10z + 20w = 400$$
$$20x \quad\quad + 10z \quad\quad = 400$$
$$10y \quad\quad + 20w = 300.$$

CHAPTER 4 REVIEW

KEY CONCEPTS

W **www.WanerMath.com**
Go to the Website to find a comprehensive and interactive Web-based summary of Chapter 4.

4.1 Systems of Two Equations in Two Unknowns
Linear equation in two unknowns [p. 258]
Coefficient [p. 258]
Solution of an equation in two unknowns [p. 258]
Particular and general (parameterized) solutions of an equation in two unknowns [p. 260]

Graphical method for solving a system of two linear equations [p. 264]
Algebraic methods for solving a system of two linear equations: elimination, intersection, and substitution [p. 265]
Possible outcomes for a system of two linear equations [p. 266]
Consistent system [p. 266]
Redundant or dependent system [p. 266]

4.2 Using Matrices to Solve Systems of Equations
Linear equation (in any number of unknowns) [p. 274]

Matrix [p. 276]
Augmented matrix of a system of linear equations [p. 276]
Elementary row operations [p. 277]
Pivot [p. 278]
Clearing a column; pivoting [p. 278]
Gauss-Jordan or row reduction [p. 281]
Overdetermined and underdetermined systems [p. 286]
Reduced row echelon form [p. 287]

4.3 Applications of Systems of Linear Equations
Resource allocation [p. 293]
(Traffic) flow [p. 295]
Transportation [p. 297]

REVIEW EXERCISES

In Exercises 1–6, graph the given equations and determine how many solutions the system has, if any.

1. $x + 2y = 4$
$2x - y = 1$

2. $0.2x - 0.1y = 0.3$
$0.2x + 0.2y = 0.4$

3. $\frac{1}{2}x - \frac{3}{4}y = 0$
$6x - 9y = 0$

4. $2x + 3y = 2$
$-x - \frac{3}{2}y = \frac{1}{2}$

5. $x + y = 1$
$2x + y = 0.3$
$3x + 2y = \frac{13}{10}$

6. $3x + 0.5y = 0.1$
$6x + y = 0.2$
$\frac{3x}{10} - 0.05y = 0.01$

In Exercises 7–18, solve the given system of linear equations.

7. $x + 2y = 4$
$2x - y = 1$

8. $0.2x - 0.1y = 0.3$
$0.2x + 0.2y = 0.4$

9. $\frac{1}{2}x - \frac{3}{4}y = 0$
$6x - 9y = 0$

10. $2x + 3y = 2$
$-x - \frac{3}{2}y = \frac{1}{2}$

11. $x + y = 1$
$2x + y = 0.3$
$3x + 2y = \frac{13}{10}$

12. $3x + 0.5y = 0.1$
$6x + y = 0.2$
$\frac{3x}{10} - 0.05y = 0.01$

13. $x + 2y = -3$
$x - z = 0$
$x + 3y - 2z = -2$

14. $x - y + z = 2$
$7x + y - z = 6$
$x - \frac{1}{2}y + \frac{1}{3}z = 1$
$x + y + z = 6$

15. $x - \frac{1}{2}y + z = 0$
$\frac{1}{2}x - \frac{1}{2}z = -1$
$\frac{3}{2}x - \frac{1}{2}y + \frac{1}{2}z = -1$

16. $x + y - 2z = -1$
$-2x - 2y + 4z = 2$
$0.75x + 0.75y - 1.5z = -0.75$

17. $x = \frac{1}{2}y$
$\frac{1}{2}x = -\frac{1}{2}z + 2$
$z = -3x + y$

18. $x - y + z = 1$
$y - z + w = 1$
$x + z - w = 1$
$2x + z = 3$

Exercises 19–22 are based on the following equation relating the Fahrenheit and Celsius (or centigrade) temperature scales:

$$5F - 9C = 160,$$

where F is the Fahrenheit temperature of an object and C is its Celsius temperature.

19. What temperature should an object be if its Fahrenheit and Celsius temperatures are the same?

20. What temperature should an object be if its Celsius temperature is half its Fahrenheit temperature?

21. Is it possible for the Fahrenheit temperature of an object to be 1.8 times its Celsius temperature? Explain.

22. Is it possible for the Fahrenheit temperature of an object to be 30° more than 1.8 times its Celsius temperature? Explain.

In Exercises 23–28, let x, y, z, and w represent the population in millions of four cities A, B, C, and D, respectively. Express the given statement as an equation in x, y, z, and w. If the equation is linear, say so and express it in the standard form $ax + by + cz + dw = k$.

23. The total population of the four cities is 10 million people.

24. City A has three times as many people as cities B and C combined.

25. City D is actually a ghost town; there are no people living in it.

26. The population of City A is the sum of the squares of the populations of the other three cities.

27. City C has 30% more people than City B.

28. City C has 30% fewer people than City B.

Applications: OHaganBooks.com
[Try the game at www.OHaganBooks.com]

Purchasing You are the buyer for OHaganBooks.com and are considering increasing stocks of romance and horror novels at the new OHaganBooks.com warehouse in Texas. You have offers from two publishers: Duffin House *and* Higgins Press. *Duffin offers a package of 5 horror novels and 5 romance novels for $50, and Higgins offers a package of 5 horror and 11 romance novels for $150. Exercises 29–32 give different scenarios for your purchasing options in response to these offers.*

29. How many packages should you purchase from each publisher to get exactly 4,500 horror novels and 6,600 romance novels?

30. You want to spend a total of $50,000 on books and have promised to buy twice as many packages from Duffin as from Higgins. How many packages should you purchase from each publisher?

31. The accountant tells you that the company can actually afford to spend a total of $90,000 on romance and horror books. She also reminds you that you had signed an agreement to spend twice as much money for books from Duffin as from Higgins. How many packages should you purchase from each publisher?

32. Upon revising her records, the accountant now tells you that the company can afford to spend a total of only $60,000 on romance and horror books and that it is company policy to spend the same amount of money at both publishers. How many packages should you purchase from each publisher?

33. *Equilibrium* The demand for *Finite Math the OHagan Way* is given by $q = -1,000p + 140,000$ copies per year, where p is the price per book in dollars. The supply is given by $q = 2,000p + 20,000$ copies per year. Find the price at which supply and demand balance.

34. *Equilibrium* OHaganBooks.com CEO John O'Hagan announces to a stunned audience at the annual board meeting that he is considering expanding into the jumbo jet airline manufacturing business. The demand per year for jumbo jets is given by $q = -2p + 18$, where p is the price per jet in millions of dollars. The supply is given by $q = 3p + 3$. Find the price the envisioned O'Hagan jumbo jet division should charge to balance supply and demand.

35. *Feeding Schedules* Billy-Sean O'Hagan is John O'Hagan's son and a freshman in college. Billy's 36-gallon tropical fish tank contains three types of carnivorous creatures—baby sharks, piranhas, and squids—and he feeds them three types of delicacies: goldfish, angelfish, and butterfly fish. Each baby shark can consume 1 goldfish, 2 angelfish, and 2 butterfly fish per day; each piranha can consume 1 goldfish and 3 butterfly fish per day (the piranhas are rather large as a result of their diet); while each squid can consume 1 goldfish and 1 angelfish per day. After a trip to the local pet store, Billy-Sean was able to feed his creatures to capacity, and he noticed that 21 goldfish, 21 angelfish, and 35 butterfly fish were eaten. How many of each type of creature does he have?

36. *Resource Allocation* Duffin House is planning its annual Song Festival, when it will serve three kinds of delicacies: granola treats, nutty granola treats, and nuttiest granola treats. The following table shows the ingredients required (in ounces) for a single serving of each delicacy, as well as the total amount of each ingredient available:

	Granola	Nutty Granola	Nuttiest Granola	Total Available
Toasted Oats	1	1	5	1,500
Almonds	4	8	8	10,000
Raisins	2	4	8	4,000

The Song Festival planners at Duffin House would like to use up all the ingredients. Is this possible? If so, how many servings of each kind of delicacy can they make?

37. *Website Traffic* OHaganBooks.com has two principal competitors: *JungleBooks.com* and *FarmerBooks.com*. Combined website traffic at the three sites is estimated at 10,000 hits per day. Only 10% of the hits at OHaganBooks .com result in orders, whereas JungleBooks.com and FarmerBooks.com report that 20% of the hits at their sites result in book orders. Together, the three sites process 1,500 book orders per day. FarmerBooks.com appears to be the most successful of the three and gets as many book orders as the other two combined. What is the traffic (in hits per day) at each of the sites?

38. *Sales* As the buyer at OHaganBooks.com, you are planning to increase stocks of books about music, and have been monitoring worldwide sales. Last year, worldwide sales of books about rock, rap, and classical music amounted to $5.8 billion. Books on rock music brought in twice as much revenue as books on rap music and they brought in 900% the revenue of books on classical music. How much revenue was earned in each of the three categories of books?

39. **Investing in Stocks** Billy-Sean O'Hagan is the treasurer at his college fraternity, which recently earned $12,400 in its annual carwash fundraiser. Billy-Sean decided to invest all the proceeds in the purchase of three computer stocks: HAL, POM, and WELL.

	Price per Share ($)	Dividend Yield (%)
HAL	100	0.5
POM	20	1.50
WELL	25	0

If the investment was expected to earn $56 in annual dividends and he purchased a total of 200 shares, how many shares of each stock did he purchase?

40. **Initial Public Offerings (IPOs)** Duffin House, Higgins Press, and Sickle Publications all went public on the same day recently. John O'Hagan had the opportunity to participate in all three initial public offerings (partly because he and Marjory Duffin are good friends). He made a considerable profit when he sold all of the stock 2 days later on the open market. The following table shows the purchase price and percentage yield on the investment in each company:

	Purchase Price per Share ($)	Yield (%)
Duffin House (DHS)	8	20
Higgins Press (HPR)	10	15
Sickle Publications (SPUB)	15	15

He invested $20,000 in a total of 2,000 shares and made a $3,400 profit from the transactions. How many shares in each company did he purchase?

41. **Degree Requirements** During his lunch break, John O'Hagan decides to devote some time to assisting his son Billy-Sean, who is having a terrible time coming up with a college course schedule. One reason for this is the very complicated Bulletin of *Suburban State University*. It reads as follows:

All candidates for the degree of Bachelor of Science at SSU must take a total of 124 credits from the Sciences, Fine Arts, Liberal Arts, and Mathematics,[28] *including an equal number of Science and Fine Arts credits, and*

twice as many Mathematics credits as Science credits and Fine Arts credits combined, but with Liberal Arts credits exceeding Mathematics credits by exactly one-third of the number of Fine Arts credits.

What are all the possible degree programs for Billy-Sean?

42. **Degree Requirements** Having finally decided on his degree program, Billy-Sean learns that the *Suburban State University* Senate (under pressure from the English Department) has revised the Bulletin to include a "Verbal Expression" component in place of the Fine Arts requirement in all programs (including the sciences):

All candidates for the degree of Bachelor of Science at SSU must take a total of 120 credits from the Liberal Arts, Sciences, Verbal Expression, and Mathematics, including an equal number of Science and Liberal Arts credits, and twice as many Verbal Expression credits as Science credits and Liberal Arts credits combined, but with Liberal Arts credits exceeding Mathematics credits by one quarter of the number of Verbal Expression Credits.

What are now the possible degree programs for Billy-Sean?

43. **Network Traffic** All book orders received at the Order Department at OHaganBooks.com are transmitted through a small computer network to the Shipping Department. The following diagram shows the network (which uses two intermediate computers as routers), together with some of the average daily traffic measured in book orders:

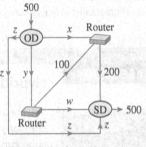

OD = Order department
SD = Shipping department

a. Set up a system of linear equations in which the unknowns give the average traffic along the paths labeled x, y, z, w, and find the general solution.
b. What is the minimum volume of traffic along y?
c. What is the maximum volume of traffic along w?
d. If there is no traffic along z, find the volume of traffic along all the paths.
e. If there is the same volume of traffic along y and z, what is the volume of traffic along w?

44. **Business Retreats** Marjory Duffin is planning a joint business retreat for *Duffin House* and OHaganBooks.com at Laguna Surf City, but she is concerned about traffic conditions. (She feels that too many cars tend to spoil the

---

[28] Strictly speaking, mathematics is not a science; it is the Queen of the Sciences, although we like to think of it as the Mother of all Sciences.

ambiance of a seaside retreat.) She managed to obtain the following map from the Laguna Surf City Engineering Department. (All the streets are one-way as indicated.) The counters show traffic every 5 minutes.

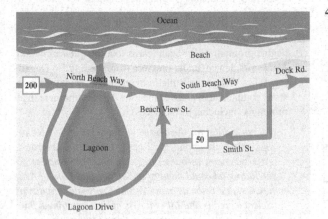

a. Set up and solve the associated system of linear equations. *Be sure to give the general solution.* (Take x = Traffic along North Beach Way, y = Traffic along South Beach Way, z = Traffic along Beach View St., u = Traffic along Lagoon Drive, and v = Traffic along Dock Road.)

b. Assuming that all roads are one-way in the directions shown, what, if any, is the maximum possible traffic along Lagoon Drive?

c. The Laguna Surf City Traffic Department is considering opening up Beach View Street to two-way traffic, but an environmentalist group is concerned that this will result in increased traffic on Lagoon Drive. What, if any, is the maximum possible traffic along Lagoon Drive assuming that Beach View Street is two-way and the traffic counter readings are as shown?

45. **Shipping** On the same day that the sales department at *Duffin House* received an order for 600 packages from the OHaganBooks.com Texas headquarters, it received an additional order for 200 packages from *FantasyBooks.com*, based in California. Duffin House has warehouses in New York and Illinois. The Illinois warehouse is closing down and must clear all 300 packages it has in stock. Shipping costs per package of books are as follows:

New York to Texas: $20   New York to California: $50

Illinois to Texas: $30   Illinois to California: $40

Is it possible to fill both orders and clear the Illinois warehouse at a cost of $22,000? If so, how many packages should be sent from each warehouse to each online bookstore?

46. **Transportation Scheduling** *Duffin House* is about to start a promotional blitz for its new book, *Physics for the Liberal Arts.* The company has 20 salespeople stationed in Chicago and 10 in Denver, and it would like to fly 15 of them to sales fairs at each of Los Angeles and New York. A round-trip plane flight from Chicago to LA costs $200; from Chicago to NY costs $150; from Denver to LA costs $400; and from Denver to NY costs $200. For tax reasons, Duffin House needs to budget exactly $6,500 for the total cost of the plane flights. How many salespeople should the company fly from each of Chicago and Denver to each of LA and NY?

CASE STUDY

Hybrid Cars—Optimizing the Degree of Hybridization

You are involved in new model development at a major automobile company. The company is planning to introduce two new plug-in hybrid electric vehicles: the subcompact "Green Town Hopper" and the midsize "Electra Supreme," and your department must decide on the degree of hybridization (DOH) for each of these models that will result in the largest reduction in gasoline consumption. (The DOH of a vehicle is defined as the ratio of electric motor power to the total power; it typically ranges from 10% to 50%. For example, a model with a 20% DOH has an electric motor that delivers 20% of the total power of the vehicle.)

The tables below show the benefit for each of the two models, measured as the estimated reduction in annual gasoline consumption, as well as an estimate of retail cost increment, for various DOH percentages.[29] (The retail cost increment estimate

---

[29] The figures are approximate and based on data for two actual vehicles as presented in a 2006 paper entitled *Cost-Benefit Analysis of Plug-In Hybrid Electric Vehicle Technology* by A. Simpson. Source: National Renewable Energy Laboratory, U.S. Department of Energy (www.nrel.gov).

is given by the formula $5,000 + 50(DOH - 10)$ for the Green Town Hopper and $7,000 + 50(DOH - 10)$ for the Electra Supreme.)

Green Town Hopper

DOH (%)	10	20	50
Reduction in Annual Consumption (gals)	180	230	200
Retail Cost Increment ($)	5,000	5,500	7,000

Electra Supreme

DOH (%)	10	20	50
Reduction in Annual Consumption (gals)	220	270	260
Retail Cost Increment ($)	7,000	7,500	9,000

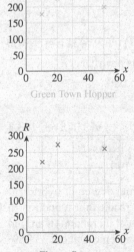

Green Town Hopper

Electra Supreme

Figure 14

Notice that increasing the DOH toward 50% results in a decreased benefit. This is due in part to the need to increase the weight of the batteries while keeping the vehicle performance at a desirable level, thus necessitating a more powerful gasoline engine. The *optimum* DOH is the percentage that gives the largest reduction in gasoline consumption, and this is what you need to determine. Since the optimum DOH may not be 20%, you would like to create a mathematical model to compute the reduction R in gas consumption as a function of the DOH x. Your first inclination is to try linear equations—that is, an equation of the form

$$R = ax + b \quad (a \text{ and } b \text{ constants}),$$

but you quickly discover that the data simply won't fit, no matter what the choice of the constants. The reason for this can be seen graphically by plotting R versus x (Figure 14). In neither case do the three points lie on a straight line. In fact, the data are not even *close* to being linear. Thus, you will need curves to model these data. After giving the matter further thought, you remember something your mathematics instructor once said: The simplest curve passing through any three points not all on the same line is a parabola. Since you are looking for a simple model of the data, you decide to try a parabola. A general parabola has the equation

$$R = ax^2 + bx + c,$$

where a, b, and c are constants. The problem now is: What are a, b, and c? You decide to try substituting the values of R and x for the Green Town Hopper into the general equation, and you get the following:

$$x = 10, R = 180 \quad \text{gives} \quad 180 = 100a + 10b + c$$
$$x = 20, R = 230 \quad \text{gives} \quad 230 = 400a + 20b + c$$
$$x = 50, R = 200 \quad \text{gives} \quad 200 = 2,500a + 50b + c.$$

Now you notice that you have three linear equations in three unknowns! You solve the system:

$$a = -0.15, \quad b = 9.5, \quad c = 100.$$

Thus, your reduction equation for the Green Town Hopper becomes

$$R = -0.15x^2 + 9.5x + 100.$$

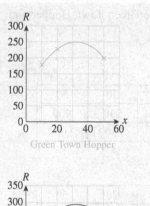

Green Town Hopper

For the Electra Supreme you get

$$x = 10, R = 220: \quad 220 = 100a + 10b + c$$
$$x = 20, R = 270: \quad 270 = 400a + 20b + c$$
$$x = 50, R = 260: \quad 260 = 2{,}500a + 50b + c.$$

$$a = -0.1\overline{3}, \quad b = 9, \quad c = 143.\overline{3},$$

so

$$R = -0.1\overline{3}x^2 + 9x + 143.\overline{3}.$$

Figure 15 shows the parabolas superimposed on the data points. You can now estimate a value for the optimal DOH as the value of x that gives the largest benefit R. Recalling that the x-coordinate of the vertex of the parabola $y = ax^2 + bx + c$ is $x = -\frac{b}{2a}$, you obtain the following estimates:

$$\text{Green Town Hopper:} \quad \text{Optimal DOH} = -\frac{9.5}{2(-0.15)} \approx 31.67\%$$

$$\text{Electra Supreme:} \quad \text{Optimal DOH} = -\frac{9}{2(-0.1\overline{3})} \approx 33.75\%.$$

You can now use the formulas given earlier to estimate the resulting reductions in gasoline consumption and increases in cost:

Green Town Hopper:

Reduction in gasoline consumption $= R \approx -0.15(31.67)^2 + 9.5(31.67) + 100$
$$\approx 250.4 \text{ gallons per year}$$

Retail cost increment $\approx 5{,}000 + 50(31.67 - 10) \approx \$6{,}080.$

Electra Supreme:

Reduction in gasoline consumption $= R = -0.1\overline{3}(33.75)^2 + 9(33.75) + 143.\overline{3}$
$$\approx 295.2 \text{ gallons per year}$$

Retail cost increment $\approx 7{,}000 + 50(33.75 - 10) \approx \$8{,}190.$

You therefore submit the following estimates: The optimal degree of hybridization for the Green Town Hopper is about 31.67% and will result in a reduction in gasoline consumption of 250.4 gallons per year and a retail cost increment of around $6,080. The optimal degree of hybridization for the Electra Supreme is about 33.75% and will result in a reduction in gasoline consumption of 295.2 gallons per year and a retail cost increment of around $8,190.

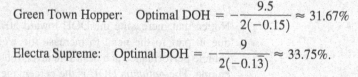

Electra Supreme

Figure 15

EXERCISES

1. Repeat the computations above for the Earth Suburban using the following data:

Earth Suburban

DOH (%)	10	20	50
Reduction in Annual Consumption (gals)	240	330	300
Retail Cost Increment ($)	9,000	9,500	11,000

$$\text{Retail cost increment} = 9{,}000 + 50(DOH - 10)$$

2. ▮ Repeat the analysis for the Green Town Hopper, but this time take x to be the cost increment, in thousands of dollars. (The curve of benefit versus cost is referred to as a *cost-benefit* curve.) What value of DOH corresponds to the optimal cost? What do you notice? Comment on the answer.

3. ▮ Repeat the analysis for the Electra Supreme, but this time use the optimal values, DOH = 33.8, Reduction = 295.2 gallons per year in place of the 20% data. What do you notice?

4. Find the equation of the parabola that passes through the points $(1, 2)$, $(2, 9)$, and $(3, 19)$.

5. Is there a parabola that passes through the points $(1, 2)$, $(2, 9)$, and $(3, 16)$?

6. Is there a parabola that passes though the points $(1, 2)$, $(2, 9)$, $(3, 19)$, and $(-1, 2)$?

7. ▮ You submit your recommendations to your manager, and she tells you, "Thank you very much, but we have additional data for the Green Town Hopper: A 30% DOH results in a saving of 255 gallons per year. Please resubmit your recommendations taking this into account by tomorrow." [**HINT**: You now have four data points on each graph, so try a general cubic instead: $R = ax^3 + bx^2 + cx + d$. Use a graph to estimate the optimal DOH.]

Section 4.1

Example 2 (page 261) Find all solutions (x, y) of the following system of two equations:

$$x + y = 3$$
$$x - y = 1.$$

Solution

You can use a graphing calculator to draw the graphs of the two equations on the same set of axes and to check the solution. First, solve the equations for y, obtaining $y = -x + 3$ and $y = x - 1$. On the TI-83/84 Plus:

1. Set

$$Y_1 = -X + 3$$
$$Y_2 = X - 1$$

2. Decide on the range of x-values you want to use. As in Figure 1, let us choose the range $[-4, 4]$.[30]

3. In the WINDOW menu, set $X\min = -4$ and $X\max = 4$.

4. Press ZOOM, and select ZoomFit to set the y-range.

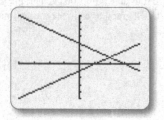

You can now zoom in for a more accurate view by choosing a smaller x-range that includes the point of intersection, such as $[1.5, 2.5]$, and using ZoomFit again. You can also use the trace feature to see the coordinates of points near the point of intersection.

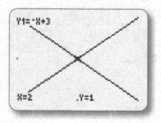

To check that $(2, 1)$ is the correct solution, use the table feature to compare the two values of y corresponding to $x = 2$:

1. Press 2ND TABLE.

2. Set X = 2, and compare the corresponding values of Y_1 and Y_2; they should each be 1.

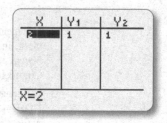

Q: *How accurate is the answer shown using the trace feature?*

A: That depends. We can increase the accuracy up to a point by zooming in on the point of intersection of the two graphs. But there is a limit to this: Most graphing calculators are capable of giving an answer correct to about 13 decimal places. This means, for instance, that, in the eyes of the TI-83/84 Plus, 2.000 000 000 000 1 is exactly the same as 2. (Subtracting them yields 0.) It follows that if you attempt to use a window so narrow that you need approximately 13 significant digits to distinguish the left and right edges, you will run into accuracy problems.

Section 4.2

Row Operations with a TI-83/84 Plus Start by entering the matrix into [A] using MATRIX EDIT. You can then do row operations on [A] using the instructions found in the following table. (*row, *row+, and rowSwap are found in the MATRIX MATH menu.)

---

[30] How did we come up with this interval? Trial and error. You might need to try several intervals before finding one that gives a graph showing the point of intersection clearly.

Row Operation	TI-83/84 Plus Instruction (Matrix name is [A])
$R_i \rightarrow kR_i$	`*row(k,[A],i)→[A]`
Example: $R_2 \rightarrow 3R_2$	`*row(3,[A],2)→[A]`
$R_i \rightarrow R_i + kR_j$	`*row+(k,[A],j,i)→[A]`
Examples: $R_1 \rightarrow R_1 - 3R_2$	`*row+(-3,[A],2,1)→[A]`
$R_1 \rightarrow 4R_1 - 3R_2$	`*row(4,[A],1)→[A]` `*row+(-3,[A],2,1)→[A]`
Swap R_i and R_j	`rowSwap([A],i,j)→[A]`
Example: Swap R_1 and R_2	`rowSwap([A],1,2)→[A]`

Example 1 (page 281)   Solve the system:

$$x - y + 5z = -6$$
$$3x + 3y - z = 10$$
$$x + 3y + 2z = 5.$$

Solution

1. Begin by entering the matrix into [A] using MATRIX EDIT. Only three columns can be seen at a time; you can see the rest of the matrix by scrolling left or right.

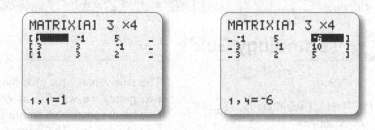

2. Now perform the operations given in Example 1.

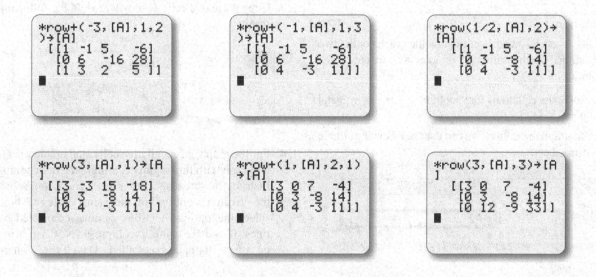

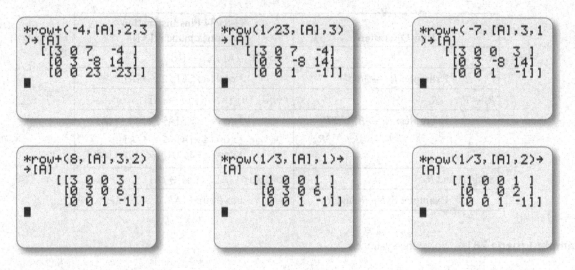

As in Example 1, we can now read the solution from the right-hand column: $x = 1$, $y = 2$, $z = -1$.

Note The TI-83/84 Plus has a function, `rref`, which gives the reduced row echelon form of a matrix in one step. (See the text for the definition of reduced row echelon form.) Internally, it uses a variation of Gauss-Jordan reduction to do this. ∎

Spreadsheet Technology Guide

Section 4.1

Example 2 (page 261) Find all solutions (x, y) of the following system of two equations:

$$x + y = 3$$
$$x - y = 1.$$

Solution

You can use a spreadsheet to draw the graphs of the two equations on the same set of axes and to check the solution.

1. Solve the equations for y, obtaining $y = -x + 3$ and $y = x - 1$.

2. To graph these lines, we can use the following simple worksheet:

	A	B	C
1	x	y1	y2
2	-4	=-A2+3	=A2-1
3	4		

The two values of x give the x-coordinates of the two points we will use as endpoints of the lines. (We have—somewhat arbitrarily—chosen the range $[-4, 4]$ for x.) The formula for the first line, $y = -x + 3$, is in cell B2, and the formula for the second line, $y = x - 1$, is in cell C2.

3. Copy these two cells as shown to yield the following result:

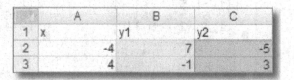

	A	B	C
1	x	y1	y2
2	-4	7	-5
3	4	-1	3

4. For the graph, select all nine cells, and create a scatter graph with line segments joining the data points. Instruct the spreadsheet to insert a chart, and select the "scatter" option. In the same dialogue box, select the option that shows points connected by lines. If you are using Excel, press "Next" to bring up a new dialogue box called "Data Type," where

you should make sure that the "Series in Columns" option is selected, telling the program that the x- and y-coordinates are arranged vertically, down columns. (Other spreadsheet programs have corresponding options you may need to set.) Your graph should appear as shown below.

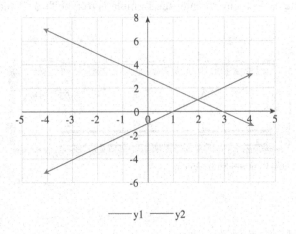

—— y1   —— y2

To zoom in:

1. First decide on a new x-range, say, $[1, 3]$.
2. Change the value in cell A2 to 1 and the value in cell A3 to 3, and the spreadsheet will automatically update the y-values and the graph.[31]

To check that $(2, 1)$ is the correct solution:

1. Enter the value 2 in cell A4 in your spreadsheet.
2. Copy the formulas in cells B3 and C3 down to row 4 to obtain the corresponding values of y.

	A	B	C
1	x	y1	y2
2	-4	7	-5
3	4	-1	3
4	2	1	1

Because the values of y agree, we have verified that $(2, 1)$ is a solution of both equations.

Section 4.2

Row Operations with a Spreadsheet   To a spreadsheet, a block of data with one or more rows or columns is an **array**, and a spreadsheet has built in the capability to handle arrays in much the same way that it handles single cells. Consider the following example:

$$\begin{bmatrix} 1 & 3 & -4 \\ 0 & 4 & 2 \end{bmatrix} 3R_2 \rightarrow \begin{bmatrix} 1 & 3 & -4 \\ 0 & 12 & 6 \end{bmatrix}.$$ Replace R_2 by $3R_2$.

1. Enter the original matrix in a convenient location, say, the cells A1 through C2.
2. To get the first row of the new matrix, which is simply a copy of the first row of the old matrix, decide where you want to place the new matrix, and highlight *the whole row of the new matrix*, say, A4:C4.
3. Enter the formula =A1:C1. (The easiest way to do this is to type "=" and then use the mouse to select cells A1 through C1, that is, the first row of the old matrix.)

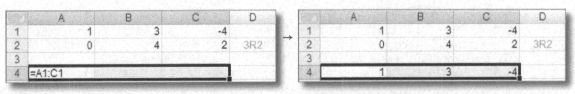

Enter formula for new first row.   Press Control+Shift+Enter.

---

[31] Your spreadsheet will set the y-range of the graph automatically, and the range it chooses may not always be satisfactory. It may sometimes be necessary to "narrow down" the range of one or both axes (in Excel, double-click on the axis in question).

4. Press **Control+Shift+Enter** (instead of "Enter" alone), and the whole row will be copied.[32] Pressing Control+Shift+Enter tells the spreadsheet that your formula is an *array formula,* one that returns an array rather than a single number. Once entered, the spreadsheet will show an array formula enclosed in "curly braces." (Note that you must also use Control+Shift+Enter to delete any array you create: Select the block you wish to delete, and press Delete followed by Control+Shift+Enter.)

5. Similarly, to get the second row, select cells A5 through C5, where the new second row will go, enter the formula =3*A2:C2, and press Control+Shift+Enter. (Again, the easiest way to enter the formula is to type "=3*" and then select cells A2 through C2 using the mouse.)

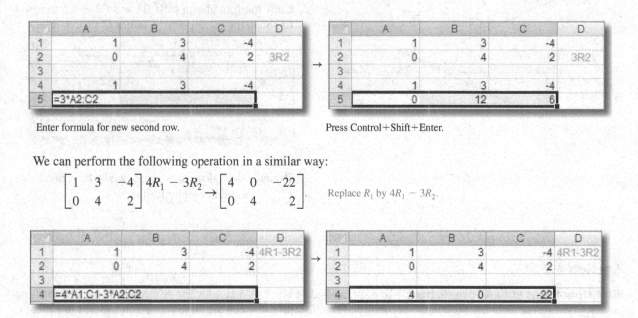

Enter formula for new second row.   Press Control+Shift+Enter.

We can perform the following operation in a similar way:

$$\begin{bmatrix} 1 & 3 & -4 \\ 0 & 4 & 2 \end{bmatrix} \xrightarrow{4R_1 - 3R_2} \begin{bmatrix} 4 & 0 & -22 \\ 0 & 4 & 2 \end{bmatrix}.$$ Replace R_1 by $4R_1 - 3R_2$.

(To easily enter the formula for $4R_1 - 3R_2$, type "=4*", select the first row A1:C1 using the mouse, type "-3*", and then select the second row A2:C2 using the mouse.)

Example 1 (page 281)   Solve the system:

$$x - y + 5z = -6$$
$$3x + 3y - z = 10$$
$$x + 3y + 2z = 5.$$

---

[32] Note that, on a Mac, Command-Enter and Command+Shift+Enter have the same effect as Control+Shift+Enter.

Solution

Here is the complete row reduction as it would appear in a spreadsheet.

	A	B	C	D	E
1	1	-1	5	-6	
2	3	3	-1	10	R2 - 3R1
3	1	3	2	5	R3 - R1
4					
5	=A1:D1				
6	=A2:D2-3*A1:D1				
7	=A3:D3-A1:D1				

	A	B	C	D	E
1	1	-1	5	-6	
2	3	3	-1	10	R2 - 3R1
3	1	3	2	5	R3 - R1
4					
5	1	-1	5	-6	
6	0	6	-16	28	(1/2)R2
7	0	4	-3	11	
8					
9	=A5:D5				
10	=(1/2)*A6:D6				
11	=A7:D7				

	A	B	C	D	E
8					
9	1	-1	5	-6	3R1 + R2
10	0	3	-8	14	
11	0	4	-3	11	3R3 - 4R2
12					
13	=3*A9:D9+A10:D10				
14	=A10*D10				
15	=3*A11:D11-4*A10:D10				

	A	B	C	D	E
12					
13	3	0	7	-4	
14	0	3	-8	14	
15	0	0	23	-23	(1/23)R3
16					
17	=A13:D13				
18	=A14:D14				
19	=(1/23)*A15:D15				

	A	B	C	D	E
16					
17	3	0	7	-4	R1 - 7R3
18	0	3	-8	14	R2 + 8R3
19	0	0	1	-1	
20					
21	=A17:D17-7*A19:D19				
22	=A18:D18+8*A19:D19				
23	=A19:D19				

	A	B	C	D	E
20					
21	3	0	0	3	(1/3)R1
22	0	3	0	6	(1/3)R2
23	0	0	1	-1	
24					
25	=(1/3)*A21:D21				
26	=(1/3)*A22:D22				
27	=A23:D23				

	A	B	C	D
24				
25	1	0	0	1
26	0	1	0	2
27	0	0	1	-1

As in Example 1, we can now read the solution from the right-hand column: $x = 1$, $y = 2$, $z = -1$. What do you notice if you change the entries in cells D1, D2, and D3?

5

MATRIX ALGEBRA AND APPLICATIONS

CASE STUDY

Predicting Market Share

You are the sales director at *Selular*, a cellphone provider, and things are not looking good for your company: *iClone*, a recently launched competitor, is beginning to chip away at Selular's market share. Particularly disturbing are rumors of fierce brand loyalty by iClone customers, with several bloggers suggesting that iClone retains close to 100% of their customers. Worse, you will shortly be presenting a sales report to the board of directors, and the CEO has "suggested" that your report include 2-, 5-, and 10-year projections of Selular's market share given the recent impact on the market by iClone. The CEO also wants a worst-case scenario projecting what would happen if iClone customers were so loyal that none of them ever switch services. You have results from two market surveys, taken one quarter apart, of the major cellphone providers, which show the current market shares and the percentages of subscribers who switched from one service to another during the quarter.

How should you respond?

www.WanerMath.com

At the Website, in addition to the resources listed in the Preface, you will find:

• A matrix algebra utility
• A game theory utility

The following optional extra sections:

• Determinants
• Using Determinants to Solve Systems: Cramer's Rule

Introduction

We used matrices in Chapter 4 simply to organize our work. It is time we examined them as interesting objects in their own right. There is much that we can do with matrices besides row operations: We can add, subtract, multiply, and even, in a sense, "divide" matrices. We use these operations to study game theory and input-output models in this chapter, and Markov chains in a later chapter.

Many calculators, spreadsheets, and other computer programs can do these matrix operations, which is a big help in doing calculations. However, we need to know how these operations are defined to see why they are useful and to understand which to use in any particular application.

5.1 Matrix Addition and Scalar Multiplication

Matrices

Let's start by formally defining what a matrix is and introducing some basic terms.

Matrix, Dimension, and Entries

An **$m \times n$ matrix** A is a rectangular array of real numbers with m rows and n columns. We refer to m and n as the **dimensions** of the matrix. The numbers that appear in the matrix are called its **entries**. We customarily use capital letters $A, B, C, \ldots$ for the names of matrices.

Quick Examples

1. $A = \begin{bmatrix} 2 & 0 & 1 \\ 33 & -22 & 0 \end{bmatrix}$ is a 2×3 matrix because it has two rows and three columns.

2. $B = \begin{bmatrix} 2 & 3 \\ 10 & 44 \\ -1 & 3 \\ 8 & 3 \end{bmatrix}$ is a 4×2 matrix because it has four rows and two columns.*

The entries of A are 2, 0, 1, 33, -22, and 0. The entries of B are the numbers 2, 3, 10, 44, -1, 3, 8, and 3.

---

* Remember that the number of rows is given first and the number of columns second. An easy way to remember this is to think of the acronym "RC" for "Row then Column."

Referring to the Entries of a Matrix

There is a systematic way of referring to particular entries in a matrix. If i and j are numbers, then the entry in the ith row and jth column of the matrix A is called the **ijth entry** of A. We usually write this entry as a_{ij} or A_{ij}. (If the matrix were called B, we would write its ijth entry as b_{ij} or B_{ij}.) Notice that this follows the "RC" convention: The row number is specified first, and the column number is specified second.

> ### Quick Example
>
> **3.** With $A = \begin{bmatrix} 2 & 0 & 1 \\ 33 & -22 & 0 \end{bmatrix}$,
>
> $$a_{13} = 1 \qquad \text{First row, third column}$$
> $$a_{21} = 33. \qquad \text{Second row, first column}$$

According to the labeling convention, the entries of the matrix A above are

$$A = \begin{bmatrix} a_{11} & a_{12} & a_{13} \\ a_{21} & a_{22} & a_{23} \end{bmatrix}.$$

In general, the $m \times n$ matrix A has its entries labeled as follows:

$$A = \begin{bmatrix} a_{11} & a_{12} & a_{13} & \cdots & a_{1n} \\ a_{21} & a_{22} & a_{23} & \cdots & a_{2n} \\ \vdots & \vdots & \vdots & \ddots & \vdots \\ a_{m1} & a_{m2} & a_{m3} & \cdots & a_{mn} \end{bmatrix}.$$

We say that two matrices A and B are **equal** if they have the same dimensions and the corresponding entries are equal. Note that a 3×4 matrix can never equal a 3×5 matrix because they do not have the same dimensions.

EXAMPLE 1 Matrix Equality

Let $A = \begin{bmatrix} 7 & 9 & x \\ 0 & -1 & y + 1 \end{bmatrix}$ and $B = \begin{bmatrix} 7 & 9 & 0 \\ 0 & -1 & 11 \end{bmatrix}$. Find the values of x and y such that $A = B$.

Solution For the two matrices to be equal, we must have corresponding entries equal, so

$$x = 0 \qquad\qquad a_{13} = b_{13}$$
$$y + 1 = 11 \quad \text{or} \quad y = 10. \qquad a_{23} = b_{23}$$

➡ **Before we go on . . .** Note in Example 1 that the matrix equation

$$\begin{bmatrix} 7 & 9 & x \\ 0 & -1 & y + 1 \end{bmatrix} = \begin{bmatrix} 7 & 9 & 0 \\ 0 & -1 & 11 \end{bmatrix}$$

is really six equations in one: $7 = 7$, $9 = 9$, $x = 0$, $0 = 0$, $-1 = -1$, and $y + 1 = 11$. We used only the two that were interesting. ■

Row Matrix, Column Matrix, and Square Matrix

A matrix with a single row is called a **row matrix** or **row vector**. A matrix with a single column is called a **column matrix** or **column vector**. A matrix with the same number of rows as columns is called a **square matrix**.

Quick Examples

4. The 1×5 matrix $C = \begin{bmatrix} 3 & -4 & 0 & 1 & -11 \end{bmatrix}$ is a row matrix.

5. The 4×1 matrix $D = \begin{bmatrix} 2 \\ 10 \\ -1 \\ 8 \end{bmatrix}$ is a column matrix.

6. The 3×3 matrix $E = \begin{bmatrix} 1 & -2 & 0 \\ 0 & 1 & 4 \\ -4 & 32 & 1 \end{bmatrix}$ is a square matrix.

Matrix Addition and Subtraction

The first matrix operations we discuss are matrix addition and subtraction. The rules for these operations are simple.

Matrix Addition and Subtraction

Two matrices can be added (or subtracted) if and only if they have the same dimensions. To add (or subtract) two matrices of the same dimensions, we add (or subtract) the corresponding entries. More formally, if A and B are $m \times n$ matrices, then $A + B$ and $A - B$ are the $m \times n$ matrices whose entries are given by

$$(A + B)_{ij} = A_{ij} + B_{ij} \qquad \text{ijth entry of the sum} = \text{Sum of the ijth entries}$$
$$(A - B)_{ij} = A_{ij} - B_{ij}. \qquad \text{ijth entry of the difference} = \text{Difference of the ijth entries}$$

Visualizing Matrix Addition

$$\begin{bmatrix} 2 & -3 \\ 1 & 0 \end{bmatrix} + \begin{bmatrix} 1 & 1 \\ -2 & 1 \end{bmatrix} = \begin{bmatrix} 3 & -2 \\ -1 & 1 \end{bmatrix}$$

Quick Examples

7. $\begin{bmatrix} 2 & -3 \\ 1 & 0 \\ -1 & 3 \end{bmatrix} + \begin{bmatrix} 9 & -5 \\ 0 & 13 \\ -1 & 3 \end{bmatrix} = \begin{bmatrix} 11 & -8 \\ 1 & 13 \\ -2 & 6 \end{bmatrix}$ Corresponding entries added

8. $\begin{bmatrix} 2 & -3 \\ 1 & 0 \\ -1 & 3 \end{bmatrix} - \begin{bmatrix} 9 & -5 \\ 0 & 13 \\ -1 & 3 \end{bmatrix} = \begin{bmatrix} -7 & 2 \\ 1 & -13 \\ 0 & 0 \end{bmatrix}$ Corresponding entries subtracted

Using Technology

Technology can be used to enter, add, and subtract matrices. Here is an outline (see the Technology Guides at the end of the chapter for additional details on using a TI-83/84 Plus or a spreadsheet):

TI-83/84 Plus

Entering a matrix: MATRIX ; EDIT
Select a name, ENTER ; type in the entries.
Adding two matrices:
Home screen: [A] + [B]
(Use MATRIX ; NAMES to enter them on the Home screen.)
[More details in the Technology Guide.]

Spreadsheet

Entering a matrix: Type entries in a convenient block of cells.
Adding two matrices: Highlight block where you want the answer to appear.
Type "="; highlight first matrix; type "+"; highlight second matrix; press Control+Shift+Enter
[More details in the Technology Guide.]

Website
www.WanerMath.com

→ Online Utilities
→ Matrix Algebra Tool

Enter matrices as shown (use a single letter for the name).

```
Enter your matrices here.
J = [20, 15
10, 12
8, 4]

F = [23, 12,
8, 12
4, 5]
```

To compute their difference, type F-J in the formula box, and press "Compute". (You can enter multiple formulas separated by commas in the formula box. For instance, F+J, F-J will compute both the sum and the difference. *Note:* The utility is case sensitive, so be consistent.)

EXAMPLE 2   **Sales**

The *A-Plus* auto parts store chain has two outlets, one in Vancouver and one in Quebec. Among other things, it sells wiper blades, windshield cleaning fluid, and floor mats. The monthly sales of these items at the two stores for 2 months are given in the following tables:

January Sales

	Vancouver	Quebec
Wiper Blades	20	15
Cleaning Fluid (bottles)	10	12
Floor Mats	8	4

February Sales

	Vancouver	Quebec
Wiper Blades	23	12
Cleaning Fluid (bottles)	8	12
Floor Mats	4	5

Use matrix arithmetic to calculate the change in sales of each product in each store from January to February.

Solution   The tables suggest two matrices:

$$J = \begin{bmatrix} 20 & 15 \\ 10 & 12 \\ 8 & 4 \end{bmatrix} \quad \text{and} \quad F = \begin{bmatrix} 23 & 12 \\ 8 & 12 \\ 4 & 5 \end{bmatrix}.$$

To compute the change in sales of each product for both stores, we want to subtract corresponding entries in these two matrices. In other words, we want to compute the difference of the two matrices:

$$F - J = \begin{bmatrix} 23 & 12 \\ 8 & 12 \\ 4 & 5 \end{bmatrix} - \begin{bmatrix} 20 & 15 \\ 10 & 12 \\ 8 & 4 \end{bmatrix} = \begin{bmatrix} 3 & -3 \\ -2 & 0 \\ -4 & 1 \end{bmatrix}.$$

Thus, the change in sales of each product is the following:

	Vancouver	Quebec
Wiper Blades	3	−3
Cleaning Fluid (bottles)	−2	0
Floor Mats	−4	1

Scalar Multiplication

A matrix A can be added to itself because the expression $A + A$ is the sum of two matrices that have the same dimensions. When we compute $A + A$, we end up doubling every entry in A. So we can think of the expression $2A$ as telling us to *multiply every element in A by 2*.

In general, to multiply a matrix by a number, multiply every entry in the matrix by that number. For example,

$$6 \begin{bmatrix} \frac{5}{2} & -3 \\ 1 & 0 \\ -1 & \frac{5}{6} \end{bmatrix} = \begin{bmatrix} 15 & -18 \\ 6 & 0 \\ -6 & 5 \end{bmatrix}.$$

It is traditional in talking about matrices to call individual numbers **scalars**. For this reason we call the operation of multiplying a matrix by a number **scalar multiplication**.

EXAMPLE 3 **Sales**

The revenue generated by sales in the Vancouver and Quebec branches of the *A-Plus* auto parts store (see Example 2) was as follows:

January Sales in Canadian Dollars		
	Vancouver	**Quebec**
Wiper Blades	140.00	105.00
Cleaning Fluid	30.00	36.00
Floor Mats	96.00	48.00

If the Canadian dollar was worth $0.65 U.S. at the time, compute the revenue in U.S. dollars.

Solution We need to multiply each revenue figure by 0.65. Let A be the matrix of revenue figures in Canadian dollars:

$$A = \begin{bmatrix} 140.00 & 105.00 \\ 30.00 & 36.00 \\ 96.00 & 48.00 \end{bmatrix}.$$

The revenue figures in U.S. dollars are then given by the scalar multiple

$$0.65A = 0.65 \begin{bmatrix} 140.00 & 105.00 \\ 30.00 & 36.00 \\ 96.00 & 48.00 \end{bmatrix} = \begin{bmatrix} 91.00 & 68.25 \\ 19.50 & 23.40 \\ 62.40 & 31.20 \end{bmatrix}.$$

In other words, in U.S. dollars, $91 worth of wiper blades was sold in Vancouver, $68.25 worth of wiper blades was sold in Quebec, and so on.

Formally, scalar multiplication is defined as follows.

Scalar Multiplication

If A is an $m \times n$ matrix and c is a real number, then cA is the $m \times n$ matrix obtained by multiplying all the entries of A by c. (We usually use lowercase letters $c, d, e, \ldots$ to denote scalars.) Thus, the ijth entry of cA is given by

$$(cA)_{ij} = c(A_{ij}).$$

In words, this rule is: To get the ijth entry of cA, multiply the ijth entry of A by c.

Using Technology

Technology can be used to compute scalar multiples:

TI-83/84 Plus
Enter the matrix [A] using MATRIX ; EDIT
Home screen: 0.65 [A]

Spreadsheet
Enter the matrix A in a convenient 3 × 2 block of cells.
Highlight block where you want the answer to appear.
Type =0.65*; highlight matrix A; press Control+Shift+Enter.

Website
www.WanerMath.com
→ Online Utilities
→ Matrix Algebra Tool
Enter the matrix A as shown.

```
Enter your matrices here.
A = [140, 105
30, 36
96, 48]
```

Type 0.65*A in the formula box, and press "Compute".

EXAMPLE 4 **Combining Operations**

Let $A = \begin{bmatrix} 2 & -1 & 0 \\ 3 & 5 & -3 \end{bmatrix}$, $B = \begin{bmatrix} 1 & 3 & -1 \\ 5 & -6 & 0 \end{bmatrix}$, and $C = \begin{bmatrix} x & y & w \\ z & t+1 & 3 \end{bmatrix}$.

Evaluate the following: $4A$, xB, and $A + 3C$.

Solution First, we find $4A$ by multiplying each entry of A by 4:

$$4A = 4\begin{bmatrix} 2 & -1 & 0 \\ 3 & 5 & -3 \end{bmatrix} = \begin{bmatrix} 8 & -4 & 0 \\ 12 & 20 & -12 \end{bmatrix}.$$

Similarly, we find xB by multiplying each entry of B by x:

$$xB = x\begin{bmatrix} 1 & 3 & -1 \\ 5 & -6 & 0 \end{bmatrix} = \begin{bmatrix} x & 3x & -x \\ 5x & -6x & 0 \end{bmatrix}.$$

We get $A + 3C$ in two steps as follows:

$$\begin{aligned} A + 3C &= \begin{bmatrix} 2 & -1 & 0 \\ 3 & 5 & -3 \end{bmatrix} + 3\begin{bmatrix} x & y & w \\ z & t+1 & 3 \end{bmatrix} \\ &= \begin{bmatrix} 2 & -1 & 0 \\ 3 & 5 & -3 \end{bmatrix} + \begin{bmatrix} 3x & 3y & 3w \\ 3z & 3t+3 & 9 \end{bmatrix} \\ &= \begin{bmatrix} 2+3x & -1+3y & 3w \\ 3+3z & 3t+8 & 6 \end{bmatrix}. \end{aligned}$$

Addition and scalar multiplication of matrices have nice properties, reminiscent of the properties of addition and multiplication of real numbers. Before we state them, we need to introduce some more notation.

If A is any matrix, then $-A$ is the matrix $(-1)A$. In other words, $-A$ is A multiplied by the scalar -1. This amounts to changing the signs of all the entries in A. For example,

$$-\begin{bmatrix} 4 & -2 & 0 \\ 6 & 10 & -6 \end{bmatrix} = \begin{bmatrix} -4 & 2 & 0 \\ -6 & -10 & 6 \end{bmatrix}.$$

For any two matrices A and B, $A - B$ is the same as $A + (-B)$. (Why?)

Also, a **zero matrix** is a matrix all of whose entries are zero. Thus, for example, the 2×3 zero matrix is

$$O = \begin{bmatrix} 0 & 0 & 0 \\ 0 & 0 & 0 \end{bmatrix}.$$

Now we state the most important properties of the operations that we have been talking about.

Properties of Matrix Addition and Scalar Multiplication

If A, B, and C are any $m \times n$ matrices and if O is the zero $m \times n$ matrix, then the following hold:

$A + (B + C) = (A + B) + C$ *Associative law*

$A + B = B + A$ *Commutative law*

$$
\begin{aligned}
A + O &= O + A = A & \text{Additive identity law} \\
A + (-A) &= O = (-A) + A & \text{Additive inverse law} \\
c(A + B) &= cA + cB & \text{Distributive law} \\
(c + d)A &= cA + dA & \text{Distributive law} \\
1A &= A & \text{Scalar unit} \\
0A &= O & \text{Scalar zero}
\end{aligned}
$$

These properties would be obvious if we were talking about addition and multiplication of *numbers*, but here we are talking about addition and multiplication of *matrices*. We are using "+" to mean something new: matrix addition. There is no reason why matrix addition has to obey *all* the properties of addition of numbers. It happens that it does obey many of them, which is why it is convenient to call it *addition* in the first place. This means that we can manipulate equations involving matrices in much the same way that we manipulate equations involving numbers. One word of caution: We haven't yet discussed how to multiply matrices, and it probably isn't what you think. It will turn out that multiplication of matrices does *not* obey all the same properties as multiplication of numbers.

Transposition

We mention one more operation on matrices.

Transposition

If A is an $m \times n$ matrix, then its **transpose** is the $n \times m$ matrix obtained by writing its columns as rows, so the *i*th column of the original matrix becomes the *i*th row of the transpose. We denote the transpose of the matrix A by A^T.

Visualizing Transposition

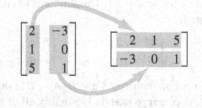

Quick Examples

9. Let $A = \begin{bmatrix} 2 & 0 & 1 & 0 \\ 33 & -22 & 0 & 5 \\ 1 & -1 & 2 & -2 \end{bmatrix}$. Then $A^T = \begin{bmatrix} 2 & 33 & 1 \\ 0 & -22 & -1 \\ 1 & 0 & 2 \\ 0 & 5 & -2 \end{bmatrix}$.

3×4 matrix 4×3 matrix

10. $\begin{bmatrix} -1 & 1 & 2 \end{bmatrix}^T = \begin{bmatrix} -1 \\ 1 \\ 2 \end{bmatrix}$.

1×3 matrix 3×1 matrix

Properties of Transposition

If A and B are $m \times n$ matrices, then the following hold:

$$(A + B)^T = A^T + B^T$$
$$(cA)^T = c(A^T)$$
$$(A^T)^T = A.$$

To see why the laws of transposition are true, let us consider the first one: $(A + B)^T = A^T + B^T$. The left-hand side is the transpose of $A + B$ and so is obtained by first adding A and B and then writing the rows as columns. This is the same as first writing the rows of A and B individually as columns before adding, which gives the right-hand side. Similar arguments can be used to establish the other laws of transposition.

5.1 EXERCISES

▼ more advanced   ◆ challenging
⊤ indicates exercises that should be solved using technology

In Exercises 1–10, find the dimensions of the given matrix, and identify the given entry.

1. $A = \begin{bmatrix} 1 & 5 & 0 & \frac{1}{4} \end{bmatrix}$; a_{13}

2. $B = \begin{bmatrix} 44 & 55 \end{bmatrix}$; b_{12}

3. $C = \begin{bmatrix} \frac{5}{2} \\ 1 \\ -2 \\ 8 \end{bmatrix}$; C_{11}

4. $D = \begin{bmatrix} 15 & -18 \\ 6 & 0 \\ -6 & 5 \\ 48 & 18 \end{bmatrix}$; d_{31}

5. $E = \begin{bmatrix} e_{11} & e_{12} & e_{13} & \cdots & e_{1q} \\ e_{21} & e_{22} & e_{23} & \cdots & e_{2q} \\ \vdots & \vdots & \vdots & \ddots & \vdots \\ e_{p1} & e_{p2} & e_{p3} & \cdots & e_{pq} \end{bmatrix}$; E_{22}

6. $A = \begin{bmatrix} 2 & -1 & 0 \\ 3 & 5 & -3 \end{bmatrix}$; A_{21}

7. $B = \begin{bmatrix} 1 & 3 \\ 5 & -6 \end{bmatrix}$; b_{12}

8. $C = \begin{bmatrix} x & y & w & e \\ z & t+1 & 3 & 0 \end{bmatrix}$; C_{23}

9. $D = \begin{bmatrix} d_1 & d_2 & \cdots & d_n \end{bmatrix}$; D_{1r} (any r with $1 \le r \le n$)

10. $E = \begin{bmatrix} d & d & d & d \end{bmatrix}$; E_{1r} (any r with $1 \le r \le 4$)

11. Solve for $x, y, z,$ and w. [HINT: See Example 1.]
$$\begin{bmatrix} x+y & y+z \\ z+w & w \end{bmatrix} = \begin{bmatrix} 3 & 5 \\ 7 & 4 \end{bmatrix}$$

12. Solve for $x, y, z,$ and w. [HINT: See Example 1.]
$$\begin{bmatrix} x-y & x-z \\ y-w & w \end{bmatrix} = \begin{bmatrix} 0 & 0 \\ 0 & 6 \end{bmatrix}$$

In Exercises 13–20, evaluate the given expression. Take
$$A = \begin{bmatrix} 0 & -1 \\ 1 & 0 \\ -1 & 2 \end{bmatrix}, \quad B = \begin{bmatrix} 0.25 & -1 \\ 0 & 0.5 \\ -1 & 3 \end{bmatrix}, \quad and$$
$$C = \begin{bmatrix} 1 & -1 \\ 1 & 1 \\ -1 & -1 \end{bmatrix}.$$
[HINT: See Example 4 and Quick Examples 7 and 8.]

13. $A + B$

14. $A - C$

15. $A + B - C$

16. $12B$

17. $2A - C$

18. $2A + 0.5C$

19. $2A^T$

20. $A^T + 3C^T$

In Exercises 21–28, evaluate the given expression. Take
$$A = \begin{bmatrix} 1 & -1 & 0 \\ 0 & 2 & -1 \end{bmatrix}, \quad B = \begin{bmatrix} 3 & 0 & -1 \\ 5 & -1 & 1 \end{bmatrix}, \quad and$$
$$C = \begin{bmatrix} x & 1 & w \\ z & r & 4 \end{bmatrix}.$$
[HINT: See Example 4 and Quick Examples 7 and 8.]

21. $A + B$

22. $B - C$

23. $A - B + C$

24. $\frac{1}{2}B$

25. $2A - B$

26. $2A - 4C$

27. $3B^T$

28. $2A^T - C^T$

In Exercises 29–36, use technology to evaluate the given expression. Take

$$A = \begin{bmatrix} 1.5 & -2.35 & 5.6 \\ 44.2 & 0 & 12.2 \end{bmatrix}, \quad B = \begin{bmatrix} 1.4 & 7.8 \\ 5.4 & 0 \\ 5.6 & 6.6 \end{bmatrix}, \quad and$$

$$C = \begin{bmatrix} 10 & 20 & 30 \\ -10 & -20 & -30 \end{bmatrix}.$$

29. $A - C$

30. $C - A$

31. $1.1B$

32. $-0.2B$

33. $A^T + 4.2B$

34. $(A + 2.3C)^T$

35. $(2.1A - 2.3C)^T$

36. $(A - C)^T - B$

Applications

37. Sales The following table shows the number of Mac computers, iPods, and iPhones sold by Apple, in millions of units, in 2012, as well as the year-over-year changes in 2013 and 2014:[1]

	Macs	iPhones	iPads
2012	17.0	135.8	65.7
Change in 2013	0.2	17.6	8.5
Change in 2014	2.4	39.2	-10.8

Use matrix algebra to find the sales of Macs, iPhones, and iPads in 2013 and 2014. [HINT: See Example 2.]

38. Home Prices The following table shows median home prices, in thousands of dollars, in four regions of the United States in May 2013, as well as the year-over-year changes in 2014 and 2015:[2]

	Northeast	Midwest	South	West
May 2013	270	160	183	276
Change in 2014	-13	6	0	18
Change in 2015	12	16	15	30

Use matrix algebra to find the median home price in each region in May 2014 and 2015. [HINT: See Example 2.]

39. Inventory The Left Coast Bookstore chain has two stores, one in San Francisco and one in Los Angeles. It stocks three kinds of book: hardcover, softcover, and plastic (for infants). At the beginning of January the central computer showed the following books in stock:

	Hard	Soft	Plastic
San Francisco	1,000	2,000	5,000
Los Angeles	1,000	5,000	2,000

Suppose its sales in January were as follows: 700 hardcover books, 1,300 softcover books, and 2,000 plastic books sold in San Francisco, and 400 hardcover, 300 softcover, and 500 plastic books sold in Los Angeles. Write these sales figures in the form of a matrix, and then show how matrix algebra can be used to compute the inventory remaining in each store at the end of January.

40. Inventory The Left Coast Bookstore chain discussed in Exercise 39 actually maintained the same sales figures for the first 6 months of the year. Each month, the chain restocked the stores from its warehouse by shipping 600 hardcover, 1,500 softcover, and 1,500 plastic books to San Francisco and 500 hardcover, 500 softcover, and 500 plastic books to Los Angeles.
  a. Use matrix operations to determine the total sales over the 6 months, broken down by store and type of book.
  b. Use matrix operations to determine the inventory in each store at the end of June.

41. Profit Annual revenues and production costs at Luddington's Wellington Boots & Co. are shown in the following spreadsheet.

	A	B	C	D
1	Revenue			
2		2004	2005	2006
3	Full Boots	$10,000	$9,000	$11,000
4	Half Boots	$8,000	$7,200	$8,800
5	Sandals	$4,000	$5,000	$6,000
6				
7	Production Costs			
8		2004	2005	2006
9	Full Boots	$2,000	$1,800	$2,200
10	Half Boots	$2,400	$1,440	$1,760
11	Sandals	$1,200	$1,500	$2,000

Use matrix algebra to compute the profits from each sector each year.

42. Revenue The following spreadsheet gives annual production costs and profits at Gauss-Jordan Sneakers, Inc:

	A	B	C	D
1	Production Costs			
2		2004	2005	2006
3	Gauss Grip	$1,800	$2,200	$2,400
4	Air Gauss	$1,400	$1,700	$1,200
5	Gauss Gel	$1,500	$2,000	$1,300
6				
7	Profit			
8		2004	2005	2006
9	Gauss Grip	$10,000	$14,000	$16,000
10	Air Gauss	$8,000	$12,000	$14,000
11	Gauss Gel	$9,000	$14,000	$12,000

Use matrix algebra to compute the revenues from each sector each year.

43. Population Movement In 2000 the U.S. population, broken down by regions, was 53.6 million in the Northeast, 64.4 million in the Midwest, 100.2 million in the South, and

[1] Source for data: Apple company reports (www.apple.com/investor).
[2] Source for data: National Association of Realtors (www.realtor.org).

63.2 million in the West.[3] In 2010 the population was 55.3 million in the Northeast, 66.9 million in the Midwest, 114.6 million in the South, and 71.9 million in the West. Set up the population figures for each year as a row vector, and then show how to use matrix operations to find the net increase or decrease of population in each region from 2000 to 2010. Assuming the same population growth from 2010 to 2020 as from 2000 to 2010, use matrix operations to predict the population in each region in 2020.

44. *Population Movement* In 1990 the U.S. population, broken down by regions, was 50.8 million in the Northeast, 59.7 million in the Midwest, 85.4 million in the South, and 52.8 million in the West.[4] Between 1990 and 2000 the population in the Northeast grew by 2.8 million, the population in the Midwest grew by 4.7 million, the population in the South grew by 14.8 million, and the population in the West grew by 10.4 million. Set up the population figures for 1990 and the growth figures for the decade as row vectors. Assuming the same population growth from 2000 to 2010 as from 1990 to 2000, use matrix operations to estimate the population in each region in 2010. Compare the predicted 2010 population in the Northeast with the actual population given in Exercise 43.

Foreclosure Crisis *Starting in 2010, on the heels of the 2007–2009 subprime mortgage crisis, the United States saw an epidemic of mortgage foreclosures, often initiated improperly by large financial institutions. Exercises 45–48 are based on the following table, which shows the numbers of foreclosures in three states in April through August of 2011.[5]*

	April	May	June	July	Aug.
California	55,900	51,900	54,100	56,200	59,400
Florida	19,600	19,200	23,800	22,400	23,600
Texas	8,800	9,100	9,300	10,600	10,100

45. Use matrix algebra to determine the total number of foreclosures in each of the given months.

46. Use matrix algebra to determine the total number of foreclosures in each of the given states during the entire period shown.

47. Use matrix algebra to determine in which month the difference between the number of foreclosures in California and in Florida was greatest.

48. Use matrix algebra to determine in which region the difference between the number of foreclosures in April and August was greatest.

[3] Source: U.S. Census Bureau (http://2010.census.gov/2010census/data/apportionment-pop-text.php).

[4] *Ibid.*

[5] Figures are rounded. Source: www.realtytrac.com.

49. ▼ *Inventory* Microbucks Computer Company makes two computers, the Pomegranate II and the Pomegranate Classic, at two different factories. The Pom II requires 2 processor chips, 16 memory chips, and 20 vacuum tubes, while the Pom Classic requires 1 processor chip, 4 memory chips, and 40 vacuum tubes. Microbucks has in stock at the beginning of the year 500 processor chips, 5,000 memory chips, and 10,000 vacuum tubes at the Pom II factory and 200 processor chips, 2,000 memory chips, and 20,000 vacuum tubes at the Pom Classic factory. It manufactures 50 Pom IIs and 50 Pom Classics each month.
  a. Find the company's inventory of parts after 2 months, using matrix operations.
  b. When (if ever) will the company run out of one of the parts?

50. ▼ *Inventory* Microbucks Computer Company, besides having the stock mentioned in Exercise 49, gets shipments of parts every month in the amounts of 100 processor chips, 1,000 memory chips, and 3,000 vacuum tubes at the Pom II factory and 50 processor chips, 1,000 memory chips, and 2,000 vacuum tubes at the Pom Classic factory.
  a. What will the company's inventory of parts be after 6 months?
  b. When (if ever) will the company run out of one of the parts?

51. ▼ *Tourism in the 1990s* The following table gives the number of people (in thousands) who visited Australia and South Africa in 1998:[6]

	To	Australia	South Africa
From	**North America**	440	190
	Europe	950	950
	Asia	1,790	200

It was predicted that in 2008, 20,000 fewer people from North America would visit Australia and 40,000 more would visit South Africa, 50,000 more people from Europe would visit each of Australia and South Africa, and 100,000 more people from Asia would visit South Africa, but there would be no change in the number of people from Asia visiting Australia.
  a. Represent the changes predicted in 2008 in the form of a matrix, and use matrix algebra to predict the number of visitors from the three regions to Australia and South Africa in 2008.
  b. Take A to be the 3×2 matrix whose entries are the 1998 tourism figures, and take B to be the 3×2 matrix whose entries are the 2008 tourism figures. Give a formula (in terms of A and B) that predicts the average of the numbers of visitors from the three regions to Australia and South Africa in 1998 and 2008. Compute its value.

[6] Figures are rounded to the nearest 10,000. Sources: South African Dept. of Environmental Affairs and Tourism; Australia Tourist Commission/*New York Times*, January 15, 2000, p. C1.

52. ▼ *Tourism in the 1990s* Referring to the 1998 tourism figures given in Exercise 51, assume that the following (fictitious) figures represent the corresponding numbers from 1988:

	To	Australia	South Africa
From **North America**		500	100
Europe		900	800
Asia		1,400	50

Take A to be the 3×2 matrix whose entries are the 1998 tourism figures, and take B to be the 3×2 matrix whose entries are the 1988 tourism figures.

a. Compute the matrix $A - B$. What does this matrix represent?

b. Assuming that the changes in tourism over 1988–1998 are repeated in 1998–2008, give a formula (in terms of A and B) that predicts the number of visitors from the three regions to Australia and South Africa in 2008.

Communication and Reasoning Exercises

53. Is it possible for a 2×3 matrix to equal a 3×2 matrix? Explain.

54. If A and B are 2×3 matrices and $A = B$, what can you say about $A - B$? Explain.

55. What does it mean when we say that $(A + B)_{ij} = A_{ij} + B_{ij}$?

56. What does it mean when we say that $(cA)_{ij} = c(A_{ij})$?

57. What would a 5×5 matrix A look like if $A_{ii} = 0$ for every i?

58. What would a matrix A look like if $A_{ij} = 0$ whenever $i \neq j$?

59. ▼ Give a formula for the ijth entry of the transpose of a matrix A.

60. ▼ A matrix is **symmetric** if it is equal to its transpose. Give an example of (a) a nonzero 2×2 symmetric matrix and (b) a nonzero 3×3 symmetric matrix.

61. ▼ A matrix is **skew-symmetric** or **antisymmetric** if it is equal to the negative of its transpose. Give an example of (a) a nonzero 2×2 skew-symmetric matrix and (b) a nonzero 3×3 skew-symmetric matrix.

62. ▼ Referring to Exercises 60 and 61, what can be said about a matrix that is both symmetric and skew-symmetric?

63. ▼ Why is matrix addition associative?

64. ▼ Is matrix subtraction associative? Explain.

65. Describe a scenario (possibly based on one of the preceding examples or exercises) in which you might wish to compute $A + B - C$ for certain matrices A, B, and C.

66. Describe a scenario (possibly based on one of the preceding examples or exercises) in which you might wish to compute $A - 2B$ for certain matrices A and B.

5.2 Matrix Multiplication

Multiplying Matrices

Suppose we download three movies at $10 each and five Chopin albums at $8 each. We calculate our total cost by computing each product's price × quantity and adding:

$$\text{Cost} = 10 \times 3 + 8 \times 5 = \$70.$$

Let us instead put the prices in a row vector,

$$P = \begin{bmatrix} 10 & 8 \end{bmatrix}, \quad \text{The price matrix}$$

and the quantities purchased in a column vector,

$$Q = \begin{bmatrix} 3 \\ 5 \end{bmatrix}. \quad \text{The quantity matrix}$$

Q: *Why do we use a row and a column instead of, say, two rows?*

A: It's rather a long story, but mathematicians found that it works best this way . . .

Because P represents the prices of the items we are purchasing and Q represents the quantities, it would be useful if the product PQ represented the total cost, a *single number* (which we can think of as a 1 × 1 matrix). For this to work, *PQ* should be calculated the same way we calculated the total cost:

$$PQ = \begin{bmatrix} 10 & 8 \end{bmatrix} \begin{bmatrix} 3 \\ 5 \end{bmatrix} = [10 \times 3 + 8 \times 5] = [70].$$

Notice that we obtain the answer by multiplying each entry in *P* (going from left to right) by the corresponding entry in *Q* (going from top to bottom) and then adding the results.

The Product *Row* × *Column*

The **product** *AB* of a row matrix *A* and a column matrix *B* is a 1 × 1 matrix. The length of the row in *A* must match the length of the column in *B* for the product to be defined. To find the product, multiply each entry in *A* (going from left to right) by the corresponding entry in *B* (going from top to bottom), and then add the results.

Visualizing Matrix Multiplication

$$\begin{bmatrix} 2 \\ 10 \\ -1 \end{bmatrix}$$

$$\begin{bmatrix} 2 & 4 & 1 \end{bmatrix}$$

2 × 2	= 4	Product of first entries = 4
4 × 10	= 40	Product of second entries = 40
1 × (−1)	= −1	Product of third entries = −1
	43	Sum of products = 43

Quick Examples

1. $\begin{bmatrix} 2 & 1 \end{bmatrix} \begin{bmatrix} -3 \\ 1 \end{bmatrix} = [2 \times (-3) + 1 \times 1] = [-6 + 1] = [-5]$

2. $\begin{bmatrix} 2 & 4 & 1 \end{bmatrix} \begin{bmatrix} 2 \\ 10 \\ -1 \end{bmatrix} = [2 \times 2 + 4 \times 10 + 1 \times (-1)]$

$$= [4 + 40 + (-1)] = [43]$$

Notes

1. In the discussion so far, *the row is on the left and the column is on the right* (RC again). (Later, we will consider products in which the column matrix is on the left and the row matrix is on the right.)

2. The row size has to match the column size. This means that, if we have a 1 × 3 row on the left, then the column on the right must be 3 × 1 in order for the product to make sense. For example, the product

$$\begin{bmatrix} a & b & c \end{bmatrix} \begin{bmatrix} x \\ y \end{bmatrix}$$

is not defined. ∎

EXAMPLE 1   **Revenue**

The *A-Plus* auto parts store mentioned in examples in Section 5.1 had the following sales in its Vancouver store:

	Vancouver
Wiper Blades	20
Cleaning Fluid (bottles)	10
Floor Mats	8

The store sells wiper blades for $7.00 each, cleaning fluid for $3.00 per bottle, and floor mats for $12.00 each. Use matrix multiplication to find the total revenue generated by sales of these items.

Solution We need to multiply each sales figure by the corresponding price and then add the resulting revenue figures. We represent the sales by a column vector, as suggested by the table:

$$Q = \begin{bmatrix} 20 \\ 10 \\ 8 \end{bmatrix}.$$

We put the selling prices in a row vector:

$$P = [7.00 \quad 3.00 \quad 12.00].$$

We can now compute the total revenue as the product

$$R = PQ = [7.00 \quad 3.00 \quad 12.00] \begin{bmatrix} 20 \\ 10 \\ 8 \end{bmatrix}$$

$$= [140.00 + 30.00 + 96.00] = [266.00].$$

So the sale of these items generated a total revenue of $266.00.

Note We could also have written the quantity sold as a row vector (which would be Q^T) and the prices as a column vector (which would be P^T) and then multiplied them in the opposite order $Q^T P^T$. Try this. ■

EXAMPLE 2   **Relationship with Linear Equations**

a. Represent the matrix equation

$$[2 \quad -4 \quad 1] \begin{bmatrix} x \\ y \\ z \end{bmatrix} = [5]$$

as an ordinary equation.

b. Represent the linear equation $3x + y - z + 2w = 8$ as a matrix equation.

Solution

a. If we perform the multiplication on the left, we get the 1×1 matrix $[2x - 4y + z]$. Thus, the equation may be rewritten as

$$[2x - 4y + z] = [5]. \qquad \text{\small 1×1 matrix on the left = 1×1 matrix on the right}$$

Saying that these two 1×1 matrices are equal means that their entries are equal, so we get the equation

$$2x - 4y + z = 5.$$

b. This is the reverse of part (a):

$$[3 \quad 1 \quad -1 \quad 2] \begin{bmatrix} x \\ y \\ z \\ w \end{bmatrix} = [8].$$

➡ **Before we go on . . .** The row matrix $[3 \quad 1 \quad -1 \quad 2]$ in Example 2 is the row of **coefficients** of the original equation. (See Section 4.1.) ∎

Now we turn to the general case of matrix multiplication.

The Product of Two Matrices: General Case

In general, for matrices A and B we can take the product AB only if the number of columns of A equals the number of rows of B (so that we can multiply the rows of A by the columns of B as above). The product AB is then obtained by taking its ijth entry to be

$$ij\text{th entry of } AB = \text{Row } i \text{ of } A \times \text{Column } j \text{ of } B. \qquad \text{\small As defined above}$$

Quick Examples

(R stands for row; C stands for column.)

3.
$$R_1 \to [2 \quad 0 \quad -1 \quad 3] \begin{bmatrix} \overset{C_1}{\downarrow} & \overset{C_2}{\downarrow} & \overset{C_3}{\downarrow} \\ 1 & 1 & -8 \\ 1 & -6 & 0 \\ 0 & 5 & 2 \\ -3 & 8 & 1 \end{bmatrix} = [R_1 \times C_1 \quad R_1 \times C_2 \quad R_1 \times C_3]$$

$$= [-7 \quad 21 \quad -15]$$

4.
$$\begin{matrix} R_1 \to \\ R_2 \to \end{matrix} \begin{bmatrix} 1 & -1 \\ 0 & 2 \end{bmatrix} \begin{bmatrix} \overset{C_1}{\downarrow} & \overset{C_2}{\downarrow} \\ 3 & 0 \\ 5 & -1 \end{bmatrix} = \begin{bmatrix} R_1 \times C_1 & R_1 \times C_2 \\ R_2 \times C_1 & R_2 \times C_2 \end{bmatrix} = \begin{bmatrix} -2 & 1 \\ 10 & -2 \end{bmatrix}$$

In matrix multiplication we always take

Rows on the left $\times$ Columns on the right.

Look at the dimensions in Quick Examples 3 and 4.

$$
\overset{\text{Match}}{\underset{\downarrow\ \downarrow}{(1 \times 4)(4 \times 3)}} \rightarrow 1 \times 3 \qquad
\overset{\text{Match}}{\underset{\downarrow\ \downarrow}{(2 \times 2)(2 \times 2)}} \rightarrow 2 \times 2
$$

The fact that the number of columns in the left-hand matrix equals the number of rows in the right-hand matrix amounts to saying that the middle two numbers must match as above. If we "cancel" the middle matching numbers, we are left with the dimensions of the product.

Before continuing with examples, we state the rule for matrix multiplication formally.

Multiplication of Matrices: Formal Definition

If A is an $m \times n$ matrix and B is an $n \times k$ matrix, then the product AB is the $m \times k$ matrix whose ijth entry is the product

$$
\overset{\text{Row } i \text{ of } A \ \times \ \text{Column } j \text{ of } B}{\underset{\downarrow \qquad\qquad\qquad \downarrow}{}}
$$

$$
(AB)_{ij} = \begin{bmatrix} a_{i1} & a_{i2} & a_{i3} \dots a_{in} \end{bmatrix} \begin{bmatrix} b_{1j} \\ b_{2j} \\ b_{3j} \\ \vdots \\ b_{nj} \end{bmatrix} = a_{i1}b_{1j} + a_{i2}b_{2j} + a_{i3}b_{3j} + \cdots + a_{in}b_{nj}.
$$

EXAMPLE 3 Matrix Product

Calculate:

a. $\begin{bmatrix} 2 & 0 & -1 & 3 \\ 1 & -1 & 2 & -2 \end{bmatrix} \begin{bmatrix} 1 & 1 & -8 \\ 1 & 0 & 0 \\ 0 & 5 & 2 \\ -2 & 8 & -1 \end{bmatrix}$ **b.** $\begin{bmatrix} -3 \\ 1 \end{bmatrix} \begin{bmatrix} 2 & 1 \end{bmatrix}$

Solution

a. Before we start the calculation, we check that the dimensions of the matrices match up:

$$
\overset{\text{Match}}{\underset{\swarrow \qquad \searrow}{2 \times 4 \qquad 4 \times 3}}
$$

$$
\begin{bmatrix} 2 & 0 & -1 & 3 \\ 1 & -1 & 2 & -2 \end{bmatrix} \begin{bmatrix} 1 & 1 & -8 \\ 1 & 0 & 0 \\ 0 & 5 & 2 \\ -2 & 8 & -1 \end{bmatrix}.
$$

The product of the two matrices is defined, and the product will be a 2×3 matrix (we remove the matching 4s: $(2 \times 4)(4 \times 3) \to 2 \times 3$). To calculate the product, we follow the previous prescription:

$$
\begin{array}{c} \\ R_1 \to \\ R_2 \to \end{array}
\begin{bmatrix} 2 & 0 & -1 & 3 \\ 1 & -1 & 2 & -2 \end{bmatrix}
\begin{matrix} C_1 \ \ C_2 \ \ C_3 \\ \downarrow \ \ \downarrow \ \ \downarrow \\ \begin{bmatrix} 1 & 1 & -8 \\ 1 & 0 & 0 \\ 0 & 5 & 2 \\ -2 & 8 & -1 \end{bmatrix} \end{matrix}
= \begin{bmatrix} R_1 \times C_1 & R_1 \times C_2 & R_1 \times C_3 \\ R_2 \times C_1 & R_2 \times C_2 & R_2 \times C_3 \end{bmatrix}
$$

$$
= \begin{bmatrix} -4 & 21 & -21 \\ 4 & -5 & -2 \end{bmatrix}.
$$

b. The dimensions of the two matrices given are 2×1 and 1×2. Because the 1s match, the product is defined, and the result will be a 2×2 matrix:

$$
\begin{array}{c} R_1 \to \\ R_2 \to \end{array}
\begin{bmatrix} -3 \\ 1 \end{bmatrix}
\begin{matrix} C_1 \ \ C_2 \\ \downarrow \ \ \downarrow \\ [2 \ \ 1] \end{matrix}
= \begin{bmatrix} R_1 \times C_1 & R_1 \times C_2 \\ R_2 \times C_1 & R_2 \times C_2 \end{bmatrix}
= \begin{bmatrix} -6 & -3 \\ 2 & 1 \end{bmatrix}.
$$

Note In part (a) we *cannot* multiply the matrices in the opposite order because the middle dimensions do not match. We say simply that the product in the opposite order is **not defined**. In part (b) we *can* multiply the matrices in the opposite order, but we would get a 1×1 matrix if we did so. Thus, order is important when multiplying matrices. In general, if AB is defined, then BA need not even be defined. If BA is also defined, it may not have the same dimensions as AB. And even if AB and BA have the same dimensions, they may have different entries. (See the next example.) ■

EXAMPLE 4 **AB versus BA**

Let $A = \begin{bmatrix} 1 & -1 \\ 0 & 2 \end{bmatrix}$ and $B = \begin{bmatrix} 3 & 0 \\ 5 & -1 \end{bmatrix}$. Find AB and BA.

Solution Note first that A and B are both 2×2 matrices, so the products AB and BA are both defined and are both 2×2 matrices—unlike the case in Example 3(b). We first calculate AB:

$$
AB = \begin{bmatrix} 1 & -1 \\ 0 & 2 \end{bmatrix}\begin{bmatrix} 3 & 0 \\ 5 & -1 \end{bmatrix} = \begin{bmatrix} -2 & 1 \\ 10 & -2 \end{bmatrix}.
$$

Now let's calculate BA:

$$
BA = \begin{bmatrix} 3 & 0 \\ 5 & -1 \end{bmatrix}\begin{bmatrix} 1 & -1 \\ 0 & 2 \end{bmatrix} = \begin{bmatrix} 3 & -3 \\ 5 & -7 \end{bmatrix}.
$$

Notice that BA has no resemblance to AB! Thus, we have discovered that, even for square matrices:

Matrix multiplication is not commutative.

In other words, $AB \neq BA$ in general, even when AB and BA both exist and have the same dimensions. (There are instances when $AB = BA$ for particular matrices A and B, but this is an exception, not the rule.)

EXAMPLE 5 **Revenue**

January sales at the *A-Plus* auto parts stores in Vancouver and Quebec are given in the following table:

	Vancouver	Quebec
Wiper Blades	20	15
Cleaning Fluid (bottles)	10	12
Floor Mats	8	4

The sale prices for these items are $7.00 each for wiper blades, $3.00 per bottle for cleaning fluid, and $12.00 each for floor mats. The costs to the company were $3.00 each for wiper blades, $1.00 per bottle for cleaning fluid, and $4.00 each for floor mats. Use matrix multiplication to compute the total revenue and total cost of the items listed at each store.

Solution We can do all of the requested calculations at once with a single matrix multiplication. Consider the following two labeled matrices:

$$Q = \begin{array}{c} \\ \mathbf{Wb} \\ \mathbf{Cf} \\ \mathbf{Fm} \end{array} \begin{array}{cc} \mathbf{V} & \mathbf{Q} \\ \begin{bmatrix} 20 & 15 \\ 10 & 12 \\ 8 & 4 \end{bmatrix} \end{array}$$

$$P = \begin{array}{c} \\ \mathbf{Sale\ Prices} \\ \mathbf{Cost\ Prices} \end{array} \begin{array}{ccc} \mathbf{Wb} & \mathbf{Cf} & \mathbf{Fm} \\ \begin{bmatrix} 7.00 & 3.00 & 12.00 \\ 3.00 & 1.00 & 4.00 \end{bmatrix} \end{array}.$$

The first matrix records the quantities sold, while the second records the sales prices and cost prices. To compute the total revenue and costs at both stores, we calculate $T = PQ$:

$$T = PQ = \begin{bmatrix} 7.00 & 3.00 & 12.00 \\ 3.00 & 1.00 & 4.00 \end{bmatrix} \begin{bmatrix} 20 & 15 \\ 10 & 12 \\ 8 & 4 \end{bmatrix}$$

$$= \begin{bmatrix} 266.00 & 189.00 \\ 102.00 & 73.00 \end{bmatrix}.$$

We can label this matrix as follows:

$$R = \begin{array}{c} \\ \mathbf{Sale\ Prices} \\ \mathbf{Cost\ Prices} \end{array} \begin{array}{cc} \mathbf{V} & \mathbf{Q} \\ \begin{bmatrix} 266.00 & 189.00 \\ 102.00 & 73.00 \end{bmatrix} \end{array}.$$

In other words, the sales revenues were $266 for Vancouver and $189 for Quebec, while the total costs were $102 for Vancouver and $73 for Quebec.

➡ **Before we go on...** In Example 5 we were able to calculate PQ because the dimensions matched correctly: $(2 \times 3)(3 \times 2) \rightarrow 2 \times 2$. We could also have multiplied them in the opposite order and gotten a 3×3 matrix. Would the product QP be meaningful? In an application like this, not only do the dimensions have to match, but also the *labels* have to match for the result to be meaningful. The labels on the three columns of P are the parts that were sold, and these are also the labels on the three rows of Q. Therefore, we can "cancel labels" at the same time that we cancel the dimensions in the product. However, the labels on the two columns of Q do not match the labels on the two rows of P, and there is no useful interpretation of the product QP in this situation. ∎

There are very special square matrices of every size: 1×1, 2×2, 3×3, and so on, called the **identity** matrices.

Identity Matrix

The $n \times n$ identity matrix I is the matrix with 1s down the **main diagonal** (the diagonal starting at the top left) and 0s everywhere else. In symbols,

$$I_{ii} = 1, \quad \text{and}$$
$$I_{ij} = 0 \quad \text{if } i \neq j.$$

Quick Examples

5. 1×1 identity matrix $I = \begin{bmatrix} 1 \end{bmatrix}$

6. 2×2 identity matrix $I = \begin{bmatrix} 1 & 0 \\ 0 & 1 \end{bmatrix}$

7. 3×3 identity matrix $I = \begin{bmatrix} 1 & 0 & 0 \\ 0 & 1 & 0 \\ 0 & 0 & 1 \end{bmatrix}$

8. 4×4 identity matrix $I = \begin{bmatrix} 1 & 0 & 0 & 0 \\ 0 & 1 & 0 & 0 \\ 0 & 0 & 1 & 0 \\ 0 & 0 & 0 & 1 \end{bmatrix}$

Note Identity matrices are always square matrices, meaning that they have the same number of rows as columns. There is no such thing, for example, as the "2×4 identity matrix." ∎

The next example shows why I is interesting.

EXAMPLE 6   Identity Matrix

Evaluate the products AI and IA, where $A = \begin{bmatrix} a & b & c \\ d & e & f \\ g & h & i \end{bmatrix}$ and I is the 3×3 identity matrix.

Solution First notice that A is arbitrary; it could be any 3×3 matrix.

$$AI = \begin{bmatrix} a & b & c \\ d & e & f \\ g & h & i \end{bmatrix} \begin{bmatrix} 1 & 0 & 0 \\ 0 & 1 & 0 \\ 0 & 0 & 1 \end{bmatrix} = \begin{bmatrix} a & b & c \\ d & e & f \\ g & h & i \end{bmatrix}$$

Using Technology

Technology can be used to obtain an identity matrix as in Example 6. Here is an outline (see the Technology Guides at the end of the chapter for additional details on using a TI-83/84 Plus or a spreadsheet):

TI-83/84 Plus
3 × 3 identity matrix:
`identity(3)` obtained
from MATRIX ; MATH
[More details in the Technology Guide.]

Spreadsheet
Click on a cell for the top left corner (e.g., B1).
Type `=IF(ROW(B1)-ROW($B$1)=COLUMN(B1)-COLUMN($B$1),1,0)`
Copy across and down.
[More details in the Technology Guide.]

Website
www.WanerMath.com
→ Online Utilities
→ Matrix Algebra Tool
Just use I in the formula box to refer to the identity matrix of any dimension. The program will choose the correct dimension in the context of the formula. For example, if A is a 3 × 3 matrix, then the expression I-A uses the 3 × 3 identity matrix for I.

and

$$IA = \begin{bmatrix} 1 & 0 & 0 \\ 0 & 1 & 0 \\ 0 & 0 & 1 \end{bmatrix} \begin{bmatrix} a & b & c \\ d & e & f \\ g & h & i \end{bmatrix} = \begin{bmatrix} a & b & c \\ d & e & f \\ g & h & i \end{bmatrix}.$$

In both cases the answer is the matrix A we started with. In symbols,

$$AI = A$$

and

$$IA = A$$

no matter which 3 × 3 matrix A you start with. Now this should remind you of a familiar fact from arithmetic:

$$a \cdot 1 = a$$

and

$$1 \cdot a = a.$$

That is why we call the matrix I the 3 × 3 *identity* matrix: because it appears to play the same role for 3 × 3 matrices that the identity 1 does for numbers.

➡ **Before we go on...** Try a similar calculation using 2 × 2 matrices: Let $A = \begin{bmatrix} a & b \\ c & d \end{bmatrix}$, let I be the 2 × 2 identity matrix, and check that $AI = IA = A$. In fact, the equation

$$AI = IA = A$$

works for square matrices of every dimension. It is also interesting to notice that $AI = A$ if I is the 2 × 2 identity matrix and A is any 3 × 2 matrix (try one). In fact, if I is any identity matrix, then $AI = A$ whenever the product is defined, and $IA = A$ whenever this product is defined. ■

We can now add to the list of properties we gave for matrix arithmetic at the end of Section 5.1 by writing down properties of matrix multiplication. In stating these properties, we shall assume that all matrix products we write are defined—that is, that the matrices have correctly matching dimensions. The first eight properties are the ones we've already seen; the rest are new.

Properties of Matrix Addition and Multiplication

If A, B, and C are matrices, if O is a zero matrix, and if I is an identity matrix, then the following hold:

$A + (B + C) = (A + B) + C$	*Additive associative law*
$A + B = B + A$	*Additive commutative law*
$A + O = O + A = A$	*Additive identity law*
$A + (-A) = O = (-A) + A$	*Additive inverse law*
$c(A + B) = cA + cB$	*Distributive law*
$(c + d)A = cA + dA$	*Distributive law*
$1A = A$	*Scalar unit*

$$0A = O \qquad \qquad \textit{Scalar zero}$$
$$A(BC) = (AB)C \qquad \qquad \textit{Multiplicative associative law}$$
$$c(AB) = (cA)B \qquad \qquad \textit{Multiplicative associative law}$$
$$c(dA) = (cd)A \qquad \qquad \textit{Multiplicative associative law}$$
$$AI = IA = A \qquad \qquad \textit{Multiplicative identity law}$$
$$A(B + C) = AB + AC \qquad \qquad \textit{Distributive law}$$
$$(A + B)C = AC + BC \qquad \qquad \textit{Distributive law}$$
$$OA = AO = O \qquad \qquad \textit{Multiplication by zero matrix}$$

Note that we have not included a multiplicative commutative law for matrices, because the equation $AB = BA$ does not hold in general. In other words, matrix multiplication is *not* exactly like multiplication of numbers. (You have to be a little careful because it is easy to apply the commutative law without realizing it.)

We should also say a bit more about transposition. Transposition and multiplication have an interesting relationship. We write down the properties of transposition again, adding one new one.

Properties of Transposition

$$(A + B)^T = A^T + B^T$$
$$(cA)^T = c(A^T)$$
$$(AB)^T = B^T A^T$$

Notice the change in order in the last one. The order is crucial.

Quick Examples

9. $\left(\begin{bmatrix} 1 & -1 \\ 0 & 2 \end{bmatrix} \begin{bmatrix} 3 & 0 \\ 5 & -1 \end{bmatrix} \right)^T = \begin{bmatrix} -2 & 1 \\ 10 & -2 \end{bmatrix}^T = \begin{bmatrix} -2 & 10 \\ 1 & -2 \end{bmatrix}$ $(AB)^T$

10. $\begin{bmatrix} 3 & 0 \\ 5 & -1 \end{bmatrix}^T \begin{bmatrix} 1 & -1 \\ 0 & 2 \end{bmatrix}^T = \begin{bmatrix} 3 & 5 \\ 0 & -1 \end{bmatrix} \begin{bmatrix} 1 & 0 \\ -1 & 2 \end{bmatrix} = \begin{bmatrix} -2 & 10 \\ 1 & -2 \end{bmatrix}$ $B^T A^T$

11. $\begin{bmatrix} 1 & -1 \\ 0 & 2 \end{bmatrix}^T \begin{bmatrix} 3 & 0 \\ 5 & -1 \end{bmatrix}^T = \begin{bmatrix} 1 & 0 \\ -1 & 2 \end{bmatrix} \begin{bmatrix} 3 & 5 \\ 0 & -1 \end{bmatrix} = \begin{bmatrix} 3 & 5 \\ -3 & -7 \end{bmatrix}$ $A^T B^T$

These properties give you a glimpse of the field of mathematics known as **abstract algebra**. Algebraists study operations like these that resemble the operations on numbers but differ in some way, such as the lack of commutativity for multiplication seen here.

We end this section with more on the relationship between linear equations and matrix equations, which is one of the important applications of matrix multiplication.

EXAMPLE 7   Matrix Form of a System of Linear Equations

a. If

$$A = \begin{bmatrix} 1 & -2 & 3 \\ 2 & 0 & -1 \\ -3 & 1 & 1 \end{bmatrix}, \quad X = \begin{bmatrix} x \\ y \\ z \end{bmatrix}, \quad \text{and} \quad B = \begin{bmatrix} 3 \\ -1 \\ 0 \end{bmatrix},$$

rewrite the matrix equation $AX = B$ as a system of linear equations.

b. Express the following system of equations as a matrix equation of the form $AX = B$:

$$2x + y = 3$$
$$4x - y = -1.$$

Solution

a. The matrix equation $AX = B$ is

$$\begin{bmatrix} 1 & -2 & 3 \\ 2 & 0 & -1 \\ -3 & 1 & 1 \end{bmatrix} \begin{bmatrix} x \\ y \\ z \end{bmatrix} = \begin{bmatrix} 3 \\ -1 \\ 0 \end{bmatrix}.$$

As in Example 2(a), we first evaluate the left-hand side and then set it equal to the right-hand side:

$$\begin{bmatrix} 1 & -2 & 3 \\ 2 & 0 & -1 \\ -3 & 1 & 1 \end{bmatrix} \begin{bmatrix} x \\ y \\ z \end{bmatrix} = \begin{bmatrix} x - 2y + 3z \\ 2x - z \\ -3x + y + z \end{bmatrix}$$

$$\begin{bmatrix} x - 2y + 3z \\ 2x - z \\ -3x + y + z \end{bmatrix} = \begin{bmatrix} 3 \\ -1 \\ 0 \end{bmatrix}.$$

Because these two matrices are equal, their corresponding entries must be equal:

$$x - 2y + 3z = 3$$
$$2x \quad\quad - z = -1$$
$$-3x + y + z = 0.$$

In other words, the matrix equation $AX = B$ is equivalent to this system of linear equations. Notice that the coefficients of the left-hand sides of these equations are the entries of the matrix A. We call A the **coefficient matrix** of the system of equations. The entries of X are the unknowns, and the entries of B are the right-hand sides 3, -1, and 0.

b. As we saw in part (a), the coefficient matrix A has entries equal to the coefficients of the left-hand sides of the equations. Thus,

$$A = \begin{bmatrix} 2 & 1 \\ 4 & -1 \end{bmatrix}.$$

X is the column matrix consisting of the unknowns, while B is the column matrix consisting of the right-hand sides of the equations, so

$$X = \begin{bmatrix} x \\ y \end{bmatrix} \quad \text{and} \quad B = \begin{bmatrix} 3 \\ -1 \end{bmatrix}.$$

The system of equations can be rewritten as the matrix equation $AX = B$ with this A, X, and B.

This translation of systems of linear equations into matrix equations is really the first step in the method of solving linear equations discussed in Chapter 4. There, we worked with the **augmented matrix** of the system, which is simply A with B adjoined as an extra column.

Q : *When we write a system of equations as AX = B, couldn't we solve for the unknown X by dividing both sides by A?*

A : If we interpret division as multiplication by the inverse (for example, $2 \div 3 = 2 \times 3^{-1}$), we shall see in Section 5.3 that *certain* systems of the form $AX = B$ can be solved in this way, by multiplying both sides by A^{-1}. We first need to discuss what we mean by A^{-1} and how to calculate it.

5.2 EXERCISES

▼ more advanced   ◆ challenging
T indicates exercises that should be solved using technology

In Exercises 1–28, compute the products. Some of these may be undefined. Exercises marked **T** *should be done by using technology. The others should be done in two ways: by hand and by using technology where possible.* [**HINT:** See Example 3.]

1. $\begin{bmatrix} 1 & 3 & -1 \end{bmatrix} \begin{bmatrix} 9 \\ 1 \\ -1 \end{bmatrix}$ **2.** $\begin{bmatrix} 4 & 0 & -1 \end{bmatrix} \begin{bmatrix} -4 \\ 1 \\ 8 \end{bmatrix}$

3. $\begin{bmatrix} -1 & \frac{1}{2} \end{bmatrix} \begin{bmatrix} -\frac{1}{3} \\ 1 \end{bmatrix}$ **4.** $\begin{bmatrix} -1 & 1 \end{bmatrix} \begin{bmatrix} \frac{3}{4} \\ \frac{1}{4} \end{bmatrix}$

5. $\begin{bmatrix} 0 & -2 & 1 \end{bmatrix} \begin{bmatrix} x \\ y \\ z \end{bmatrix}$ **6.** $\begin{bmatrix} 4 & -1 & 1 \end{bmatrix} \begin{bmatrix} -x \\ x \\ y \end{bmatrix}$

7. $\begin{bmatrix} 1 & 3 & 2 \end{bmatrix} \begin{bmatrix} 1 \\ -1 \end{bmatrix}$ **8.** $\begin{bmatrix} 3 & 2 \end{bmatrix} \begin{bmatrix} 1 & -2 \end{bmatrix}$

9. $\begin{bmatrix} -1 & 1 \end{bmatrix} \begin{bmatrix} -3 & 1 & 4 & 3 \\ 0 & 1 & -2 & 1 \end{bmatrix}$

10. $\begin{bmatrix} 2 & -1 \end{bmatrix} \begin{bmatrix} -3 & 1 & 4 & 3 \\ 4 & 0 & 1 & 3 \end{bmatrix}$

11. $\begin{bmatrix} 1 & -1 & 2 & 3 \end{bmatrix} \begin{bmatrix} -1 & 2 & 0 \\ 2 & -1 & 0 \\ 0 & 5 & 2 \\ -1 & 8 & 1 \end{bmatrix}$

12. $\begin{bmatrix} 0 & 1 & -1 & 2 \end{bmatrix} \begin{bmatrix} 1 & -2 & 1 \\ 0 & 1 & 3 \\ 6 & 0 & 2 \\ -1 & -2 & 11 \end{bmatrix}$

13. $\begin{bmatrix} 1 & 0 & -1 \\ 1 & 1 & 2 \end{bmatrix} \begin{bmatrix} 0 & 1 & -1 \\ 1 & 0 & 1 \\ 4 & 8 & 0 \end{bmatrix}$

14. $\begin{bmatrix} 0 & 1 & -1 \\ 3 & 1 & -1 \end{bmatrix} \begin{bmatrix} 1 & 1 \\ 4 & 2 \\ 0 & 1 \end{bmatrix}$ **15.** $\begin{bmatrix} 1 & 0 \\ 1 & -1 \end{bmatrix} \begin{bmatrix} 0 & 1 \\ 0 & 1 \end{bmatrix}$

16. $\begin{bmatrix} 1 & -1 \\ 1 & -1 \end{bmatrix} \begin{bmatrix} 3 & -3 \\ 5 & -7 \end{bmatrix}$ **17.** $\begin{bmatrix} 0 & 1 \\ 0 & 1 \end{bmatrix} \begin{bmatrix} 1 & 0 \\ 1 & -1 \end{bmatrix}$

18. $\begin{bmatrix} 3 & -3 \\ 5 & -7 \end{bmatrix} \begin{bmatrix} 1 & -1 \\ 1 & -1 \end{bmatrix}$ **19.** $\begin{bmatrix} 1 & -1 \\ 1 & -1 \end{bmatrix} \begin{bmatrix} 2 & 3 \\ 2 & 3 \end{bmatrix}$

20. $\begin{bmatrix} 0 & 1 \\ 1 & 0 \end{bmatrix} \begin{bmatrix} 3 & -3 \\ 2 & -1 \end{bmatrix}$ **21.** $\begin{bmatrix} 1 & -1 \\ -1 & 1 \end{bmatrix} \begin{bmatrix} 2 & 3 \\ 2 & 3 \\ 1 & 1 \end{bmatrix}$

22. $\begin{bmatrix} 0 & 1 & -1 \\ 0 & -1 & 1 \end{bmatrix} \begin{bmatrix} 3 & -3 \\ 2 & -1 \end{bmatrix}$

23. $\begin{bmatrix} 1 & 0 & -1 \\ 2 & -2 & 1 \\ 0 & 0 & 1 \end{bmatrix} \begin{bmatrix} 1 & -1 & 4 \\ 1 & 1 & 0 \\ 0 & 4 & 1 \end{bmatrix}$

24. $\begin{bmatrix} 1 & 2 & 0 \\ 4 & -1 & 1 \\ 1 & 0 & 1 \end{bmatrix} \begin{bmatrix} 1 & 2 & -4 \\ 4 & 1 & 0 \\ 0 & -2 & 1 \end{bmatrix}$

25. $\begin{bmatrix} 1 & 0 & 1 & 0 \\ -1 & 1 & 0 & 1 \\ -2 & 0 & 1 & 4 \\ 0 & -1 & 0 & 1 \end{bmatrix} \begin{bmatrix} 1 \\ -3 \\ 2 \\ 0 \end{bmatrix}$

26. $\begin{bmatrix} 1 & 1 & -7 & 0 \\ -1 & 0 & 2 & 4 \\ -1 & 0 & -2 & 1 \\ 1 & -1 & 1 & 1 \end{bmatrix} \begin{bmatrix} 1 \\ -3 \\ 2 \\ 1 \end{bmatrix}$

27. **T** $\begin{bmatrix} 1.1 & 2.3 & 3.4 & -1.2 \\ 3.4 & 4.4 & 2.3 & 1.1 \\ 2.3 & 0 & -2.2 & 1.1 \\ 1.2 & 1.3 & 1.1 & 1.1 \end{bmatrix} \begin{bmatrix} -2.1 & 0 & -3.3 \\ -3.4 & -4.8 & -4.2 \\ 3.4 & 5.6 & 1 \\ 1 & 2.2 & 9.8 \end{bmatrix}$

28. **T** $\begin{bmatrix} 1.2 & 2.3 & 3.4 & 4.5 \\ 3.3 & 4.4 & 5.5 & 6.6 \\ 2.3 & -4.3 & -2.2 & 1.1 \\ 2.2 & -1.2 & -1 & 1.1 \end{bmatrix} \begin{bmatrix} 9.8 & 1 & -1.1 \\ 8.8 & 2 & -2.2 \\ 7.7 & 3 & -3.3 \\ 6.6 & 4 & -4.4 \end{bmatrix}$

29. Find[7] $A^2 = A \cdot A$, $A^3 = A \cdot A \cdot A$, A^4, and A^{100}, given that

$$A = \begin{bmatrix} 0 & 1 & 1 & 1 \\ 0 & 0 & 1 & 1 \\ 0 & 0 & 0 & 1 \\ 0 & 0 & 0 & 0 \end{bmatrix}.$$

30. Repeat Exercise 29 with $A = \begin{bmatrix} 0 & 2 & 0 & -1 \\ 0 & 0 & 2 & 0 \\ 0 & 0 & 0 & 2 \\ 0 & 0 & 0 & 0 \end{bmatrix}$.

Exercises 31–38 should be done in two ways: by hand and by using technology where possible.

Let

$$A = \begin{bmatrix} 0 & -1 & 0 & 1 \\ 10 & 0 & 1 & 0 \end{bmatrix}, B = \begin{bmatrix} 0 & -1 \\ 1 & 1 \\ -1 & 3 \\ 5 & 0 \end{bmatrix}, C = \begin{bmatrix} 1 & -1 \\ 1 & 1 \\ 1 & 1 \\ 1 & 1 \end{bmatrix}.$$

Evaluate:

31. AB **32.** AC **33.** $A(B - C)$ **34.** $(B - C)A$

Let $A = \begin{bmatrix} 1 & -1 \\ 0 & 2 \\ 0 & -2 \end{bmatrix}, B = \begin{bmatrix} 3 & 0 & -1 \\ 5 & -1 & 1 \end{bmatrix}, C = \begin{bmatrix} x & 1 & w \\ z & r & 4 \end{bmatrix}.$

Evaluate:

35. AB **36.** AC **37.** $A(B + C)$ **38.** $(B + C)A$

In Exercises 39–44, calculate (a) $P^2 = P \cdot P$, (b) $P^4 = P^2 \cdot P^2$, and (c) P^8. (Round all entries to four decimal places.) (d) Without computing it explicitly, find $P^{1,000}$.

39. ▼ $P = \begin{bmatrix} 0.2 & 0.8 \\ 0.2 & 0.8 \end{bmatrix}$ **40.** ▼ $P = \begin{bmatrix} 0.1 & 0.1 \\ 0.9 & 0.9 \end{bmatrix}$

41. ▼ $P = \begin{bmatrix} 0.1 & 0.9 \\ 0 & 1 \end{bmatrix}$ **42.** ▼ $P = \begin{bmatrix} 1 & 0 \\ 0.8 & 0.2 \end{bmatrix}$

43. ▼ $P = \begin{bmatrix} 0.3 & 0.3 & 0.4 \\ 0.3 & 0.3 & 0.4 \\ 0.3 & 0.3 & 0.4 \end{bmatrix}$

What do you notice about the rows of P? Compare with Exercise 39, and state a general result about square matrices that these two exercises seem to suggest.

44. ▼ $P = \begin{bmatrix} -0.3 & -0.3 & -0.3 \\ 0.9 & 0.9 & 0.9 \\ 0.4 & 0.4 & 0.4 \end{bmatrix}$

What do you notice about the columns of P? Compare with Exercise 40, and state a general result about square matrices that these two exercises seem to suggest.

In Exercises 45–48, translate the given matrix equations into systems of linear equations. [HINT: See Example 7.]

45. $\begin{bmatrix} 2 & -1 & 4 \\ -4 & \frac{3}{4} & \frac{1}{3} \\ -3 & 0 & 0 \end{bmatrix} \begin{bmatrix} x \\ y \\ z \end{bmatrix} = \begin{bmatrix} 3 \\ -1 \\ 0 \end{bmatrix}$

46. $\begin{bmatrix} 1 & -1 & 4 \\ -\frac{1}{3} & -3 & \frac{1}{3} \\ 3 & 0 & 1 \end{bmatrix} \begin{bmatrix} x \\ y \\ z \end{bmatrix} = \begin{bmatrix} -3 \\ -1 \\ 2 \end{bmatrix}$

47. $\begin{bmatrix} 1 & -1 & 0 & 1 \\ 1 & 1 & 2 & 4 \end{bmatrix} \begin{bmatrix} x \\ y \\ z \\ w \end{bmatrix} = \begin{bmatrix} -1 \\ 2 \end{bmatrix}$

48. $\begin{bmatrix} 0 & 1 & 6 & 1 \\ 1 & -5 & 0 & 0 \end{bmatrix} \begin{bmatrix} x \\ y \\ z \\ w \end{bmatrix} = \begin{bmatrix} -2 \\ 9 \end{bmatrix}$

In Exercises 49–52, translate the given systems of equations into matrix form. [HINT: See Example 7.]

49. $\begin{aligned} x - y &= 4 \\ 2x - y &= 0 \end{aligned}$ **50.** $\begin{aligned} 2x + y &= 7 \\ -x &= 9 \end{aligned}$

51. $\begin{aligned} x + y - z &= 8 \\ 2x + y + z &= 4 \\ \frac{3x}{4} + \frac{z}{2} &= 1 \end{aligned}$ **52.** $\begin{aligned} x + y + 2z &= -2 \\ 4x + 2y - z &= -8 \\ \frac{x}{2} - \frac{y}{3} &= 4 \end{aligned}$

Applications

53. *Revenue* Your T-shirt operation is doing a booming trade. Last week you sold 50 tie-dyed shirts for $15 each, 40 Suburban State University Crew shirts for $10 each, and 30 Lacrosse T-shirts for $12 each. Use matrix operations to calculate your total revenue for the week. [HINT: See Example 1.]

54. *Revenue* Karen Sandberg, your competitor in *Suburban State U's* T-shirt market, has apparently been undercutting your prices and outperforming you in sales. Last week she sold 100 tie-dyed shirts for $10 each, 50 (low-quality) Crew shirts at $5 apiece, and 70 Lacrosse T-shirts for $8 each. Use matrix operations to calculate her total revenue for the week. [HINT: See Example 1.]

55. *Real Estate* The following table shows the cost of 1,000 square feet of luxury real estate in three cities in March 2014[8] together with the quantity your development company intends to purchase in each city:

---

[7] $A \cdot A \cdot A$ is $A(A \cdot A)$, or the equivalent $(A \cdot A)A$ by the associative law. Similarly, $A \cdot A \cdot A \cdot A = A(A \cdot A \cdot A) = (A \cdot A \cdot A)A = (A \cdot A)(A \cdot A)$; it doesn't matter where we place parentheses.

[8] Data rounded to the nearest 0.05. Source: "10 Most Expensive Markets for Real Estate," March 5, 2014 (www.cnbc.com).

	London	New York	Mumbai
Cost ($ million)	3.70	2.30	0.95
Quantity Purchased (thousands of square feet)	10	20	10

Use matrix multiplication to estimate the total cost of the purchase.

56. Real Estate Repeat Exercise 55 using the following table for Hong Kong, Paris, and Shanghai:[9]

	Hong Kong	Paris	Shanghai
Cost ($ million)	4.50	2.25	2.00
Quantity Purchased (thousands of square feet)	10	30	5

57. Revenue Recall the *Left Coast Bookstore* chain from Section 5.1. In January it sold 700 hardcover books, 1,300 softcover books, and 2,000 plastic books in San Francisco; it sold 400 hardcover, 300 softcover, and 500 plastic books in Los Angeles. Hardcover books sell for $30 each, softcover books sell for $10 each, and plastic books sell for $15 each. Write a column matrix with the price data, and show how matrix multiplication (using the sales and price data matrices) may be used to compute the total revenue at the two stores. [HINT: See Example 5.]

58. Profit Refer back to Exercise 57, and now suppose that each hardcover book costs the stores $10, each softcover book costs $5, and each plastic book costs $10. Use matrix operations to compute the total *profit* at each store in January. [HINT: See Example 5.]

Income *Exercises 59–62 are based on the following spreadsheet, which shows the projected 2020 and 2030 U.S. male and female population in various age groups, as well as per capita incomes:*[10]

	A	B	C	D	E	F
1			2020 Population		2030 population	
2	Age	Mean Income ($1000)	Female (Millions)	Male (Millions)	Female (Millions)	Male (Millions)
3	15 to 24	14	23	24	25	26
4	25 to 44	42	43	43	45	46
5	45 to 64	48	43	41	42	41
6	65 to 84	29	31	20	40	31

59. Use matrix algebra to estimate the total income for females in 2020. (Round the answer to two significant digits.)

60. Use matrix algebra to estimate the total income for males in 2030. (Round the answer to two significant digits.)

61. Give a single matrix formula that expresses the difference in total income between males and females in 2020, and compute its value, rounded to two significant digits.

62. Give a single matrix formula that expresses the total income in 2030, and compute its value, rounded to two significant digits.

63. Consumption of Dairy Products The U.S. per capita consumption of yogurt and ice cream in 1983 and 2013 was as follows:[11]

	1983	2013
Yogurt (pounds)	3.2	14.9
Ice Cream (pounds)	26.3	20.1

Thinking of this table as a (labeled) 2×2 matrix P, compute the matrix product $\begin{bmatrix} -1 & 1 \end{bmatrix} P$. What does this product represent?

64. Consumption of Dairy Products The U.S. per capita consumption of cottage cheese and mozzarella in 1983 and 2013 was as follows:[12]

	1983	2013
Cottage Cheese (pounds)	4.1	2.1
Mozzarella (pounds)	3.7	10.8

Thinking of this table as a (labeled) 2×2 matrix P, compute the matrix product $P \begin{bmatrix} -1 \\ 1 \end{bmatrix}$. What does this product represent?

Foreclosure Crisis *Starting in 2010, on the heels of the 2007–2009 subprime mortgage crisis, the United States saw an epidemic of mortgage foreclosures, often initiated improperly by large financial institutions. Exercises 65–70 are based on the following table, which shows the numbers of foreclosures in three states during three months of 2011:*[13]

	June	July	Aug.
California	54,100	56,200	59,400
Florida	23,800	22,400	23,600
Texas	9,300	10,600	10,100

65. Each month, your law firm handled 10% of all foreclosures in California, 5% of all foreclosures in Florida, and 20% of all foreclosures in Texas. Use matrix multiplication to compute the total number of foreclosures handled by your firm in each of the months shown.

---

[9] See footnote for Exercise 55.

[10] The population figures are Census Bureau estimates, and the income figures are 2007 mean per capita incomes. All figures are approximate. Source: U.S. Census Bureau (www.census.gov).

[11] Figures are approximate. Source: United States Department of Agriculture (www.ers.usda.gov).

[12] *Ibid.*

[13] Figures are rounded. Source: www.realtytrac.com.

66. Your law firm handled 10% of all foreclosures in each state in June, 30% of all foreclosures in July, and 20% of all foreclosures in August 2011. Use matrix multiplication to compute the total number of foreclosures handled by your firm in each of the states shown.

67. Let A be the 3×3 matrix whose entries are the figures in the table, and let $B = \begin{bmatrix} 1 & 1 & 0 \end{bmatrix}$. What does the matrix BA represent?

68. Let A be the 3×3 matrix whose entries are the figures in the table, and let $B = \begin{bmatrix} 1 & 1 & 0 \end{bmatrix}^T$. What does the matrix AB represent?

69. ▼ Write a matrix product whose computation gives the total number by which the combined foreclosures for all three months in California and Texas exceeded the foreclosures in Florida. Calculate the product.

70. ▼ Write a matrix product whose computation gives the total number by which combined foreclosures in August exceeded foreclosures in June. Calculate the product.

71. ▼ *Costs Microbucks Computer Co.* makes two computers, the Pomegranate II and the Pomegranate Classic. The Pom II requires 2 processor chips, 16 memory chips, and 20 vacuum tubes, while the Pom Classic requires 1 processor chip, 4 memory chips, and 40 vacuum tubes. There are two companies that can supply these parts: *Motorel* can supply them at $100 per processor chip, $50 per memory chip, and $10 per vacuum tube, while *Intola* can supply them at $150 per processor chip, $40 per memory chip, and $15 per vacuum tube. Write down all of these data in two matrices: one showing the parts required for each model computer and the other showing the prices for each part from each supplier. Then show how matrix multiplication allows you to compute the total cost for parts for each model when parts are bought from either supplier.

72. ▼ *Profits* Refer back to Exercise 71. It actually costs *Motorel* only $25 to make each processor chip, $10 for each memory chip, and $5 for each vacuum tube. It costs *Intola* $50 per processor chip, $10 per memory chip, and $7 per vacuum tube. Use matrix operations to find the total profit Motorel and Intola would make on each model.

73. ▼ *Tourism in the 1990s* The following table gives the number of people (in thousands) who visited Australia and South Africa in 1998:[14]

	To	Australia	South Africa
From	**North America**	440	190
	Europe	950	950
	Asia	1,790	200

You estimate that 5% of all visitors to Australia and 4% of all visitors to South Africa decide to settle there permanently. Take A to be the 3×2 matrix whose entries are the 1998 tourism figures in the above table, and take

$$B = \begin{bmatrix} 0.05 \\ 0.04 \end{bmatrix} \quad \text{and} \quad C = \begin{bmatrix} 0.05 & 0 \\ 0 & 0.04 \end{bmatrix}.$$

Compute the products AB and AC. What do the entries in these matrices represent?

74. ▼ *Tourism in the 1990s* Referring to the tourism figures in Exercise 73, you estimate that from 1998 to 2018, tourism from North America to each of Australia and South Africa will have increased by 20%, tourism from Europe by 30%, and tourism from Asia by 10%. Take A to be the 3×2 matrix whose entries are the 1998 tourism figures, and take

$$B = \begin{bmatrix} 1.2 & 1.3 & 1.1 \end{bmatrix} \quad \text{and} \quad C = \begin{bmatrix} 1.2 & 0 & 0 \\ 0 & 1.3 & 0 \\ 0 & 0 & 1.1 \end{bmatrix}.$$

Compute the products BA and CA. What do the entries in these matrices represent?

75. ▼ *Population Movement* In 2008 the population of the United States, broken down by regions, was 54.1 million in the Northeast, 65.7 million in the Midwest, 112.9 million in the South, and 70.3 million in the West. The table below shows the population movement during the period 2008–2009. (Thus, 99.23% of the population in the Northeast stayed there, while 0.16% of the population in the Northeast moved to the Midwest, and so on.)[15]

	To	Northeast	Midwest	South	West
From	**Northeast**	0.9923	0.0016	0.0042	0.0019
	Midwest	0.0018	0.9896	0.0047	0.0039
	South	0.0056	0.0059	0.9827	0.0058
	West	0.0024	0.0033	0.0044	0.9899

Set up the 2008 population figures as a row vector. Then use matrix multiplication to estimate the population in each region in 2009. (Round all answers to the nearest 0.1 million.)

76. ▼ *Population Movement* Assume that the percentages given in Exercise 75 also describe the population movements from 2009 to 2010. Use two matrix multiplications to estimate, from the data in Exercise 75, the population in each region in 2010.

---

[14] Figures are rounded to the nearest 10,000. Sources: South African Dept. of Environmental Affairs and Tourism; Australia Tourist Commission/*New York Times*, January 15, 2000, p. C1.

[15] Note that this exercise ignores migration into or out of the country. Source: U.S. Census Bureau, Current Population Survey, 2009 Annual Social and Economic Supplement.

Communication and Reasoning Exercises

77. Give an example of two matrices A and B such that AB is defined but BA is not defined.

78. Give an example of two matrices A and B of different dimensions such that both AB and BA are defined.

79. Compare addition and multiplication of 1×1 matrices to the arithmetic of numbers.

80. In comparing the algebra of 1×1 matrices, as discussed so far, to the algebra of real numbers (see Exercise 79), what important difference do you find?

81. Comment on the following claim: Every matrix equation represents a system of equations.

82. When is it true that both AB and BA are defined, even though neither A nor B is a square matrix?

83. ▼ Find a scenario in which it would be useful to "multiply" two row vectors according to the rule

$$[a \quad b \quad c][d \quad e \quad f] = [ad \quad be \quad cf].$$

84. ▼ Make up an application whose solution reads as follows:

$$\text{"Total revenue} = [10 \quad 100 \quad 30] \begin{bmatrix} 10 & 0 & 3 \\ 1 & 2 & 0 \\ 0 & 1 & 40 \end{bmatrix}."$$

85. ▼ What happens in a spreadsheet if, instead of using the function MMULT, you use "ordinary multiplication" as shown here?

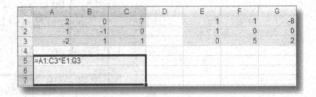

86. ▼ Define the *naïve product* $A \square B$ of two $m \times n$ matrices A and B by

$$(A \square B)_{ij} = A_{ij} B_{ij}.$$

(This is how someone who has never seen matrix multiplication before might think to multiply matrices.) Referring to Example 1 in this section, compute and comment on the meaning of $P \square (Q^T)$.

5.3 Matrix Inversion

Inverse of a Matrix

Now that we've discussed matrix addition, subtraction, and multiplication, you may well be wondering about matrix *division*. In the realm of real numbers, division can be thought of as a form of multiplication: Dividing 3 by 7 is the same as multiplying 3 by 1/7, the inverse of 7. In symbols, $3 \div 7 = 3 \times (1/7)$, or 3×7^{-1}. To imitate division of real numbers in the realm of matrices, we need to discuss the multiplicative **inverse**, A^{-1}, of a matrix A.

Note Because multiplication of real numbers is commutative, we can write, for example, $\frac{3}{7}$ as either 3×7^{-1} or $7^{-1} \times 3$. In the realm of matrices, multiplication is not commutative, so from now on we shall *never* talk about "division" of matrices. (By $\frac{B}{A}$, should we mean $A^{-1}B$ or BA^{-1}?) ∎

Before we try to find the inverse of a matrix, we must first know exactly what we *mean* by the inverse. Recall that the inverse of a number a is the number, often written a^{-1}, with the property that $a^{-1} \cdot a = a \cdot a^{-1} = 1$. For example, the inverse of 76 is the number $76^{-1} = 1/76$, because $(1/76) \cdot 76 = 76 \cdot (1/76) = 1$. This is the number calculated by the x^{-1} button found on many calculators. Not all numbers have an inverse. For example—and this is the only example—the number 0 has no inverse, because you cannot get 1 by multiplying 0 by anything.

The inverse of a matrix is defined similarly. To make life easier, we shall restrict attention to **square** matrices, which are matrices that have the same number of rows as columns.*

* Nonsquare matrices *cannot* have inverses in the sense that we shall be talking about. This is not a trivial fact to prove.

Inverse of a Matrix, Singular Matrix

The **inverse** of an $n \times n$ matrix A is the $n \times n$ matrix A^{-1} that, when multiplied by A on either side, yields the $n \times n$ identity matrix I. Thus,

$$AA^{-1} = A^{-1}A = I.$$

If A has an inverse, it is said to be **invertible**. Otherwise, it is said to be **singular**.

Quick Examples

1. The inverse of the 1×1 matrix $\begin{bmatrix} 3 \end{bmatrix}$ is $\begin{bmatrix} \frac{1}{3} \end{bmatrix}$, because $\begin{bmatrix} 3 \end{bmatrix}\begin{bmatrix} \frac{1}{3} \end{bmatrix} = \begin{bmatrix} 1 \end{bmatrix} = \begin{bmatrix} \frac{1}{3} \end{bmatrix}\begin{bmatrix} 3 \end{bmatrix}$.

2. The inverse of the $n \times n$ identity matrix I is I itself, because $II = I$. Thus, $I^{-1} = I$.

3. The inverse of the 2×2 matrix $A = \begin{bmatrix} 1 & -1 \\ -1 & -1 \end{bmatrix}$ is $A^{-1} = \begin{bmatrix} \frac{1}{2} & -\frac{1}{2} \\ -\frac{1}{2} & -\frac{1}{2} \end{bmatrix}$, because

$$\begin{bmatrix} 1 & -1 \\ -1 & -1 \end{bmatrix}\begin{bmatrix} \frac{1}{2} & -\frac{1}{2} \\ -\frac{1}{2} & -\frac{1}{2} \end{bmatrix} = \begin{bmatrix} 1 & 0 \\ 0 & 1 \end{bmatrix} \qquad AA^{-1} = I$$

and

$$\begin{bmatrix} \frac{1}{2} & -\frac{1}{2} \\ -\frac{1}{2} & -\frac{1}{2} \end{bmatrix}\begin{bmatrix} 1 & -1 \\ -1 & -1 \end{bmatrix} = \begin{bmatrix} 1 & 0 \\ 0 & 1 \end{bmatrix}. \qquad A^{-1}A = I$$

Notes

1. It is possible to show that if A and B are square matrices with $AB = I$, then it must also be true that $BA = I$. In other words, once we have checked that $AB = I$, we know that B is the inverse of A. The second check, that $BA = I$, is unnecessary.

2. If B is the inverse of A, then we can also say that A is the inverse of B (why?). Thus, we sometimes refer to such a pair of matrices as an **inverse pair** of matrices. ■

EXAMPLE 1 Singular Matrix

Can $A = \begin{bmatrix} 1 & 1 \\ 0 & 0 \end{bmatrix}$ have an inverse?

Solution No. To see why not, notice that both entries in the second row of AB will be 0, no matter what B is. So AB cannot equal I, no matter what B is. Hence, A is singular.

➡ **Before we go on . . .** If you think about it, you can write down many similar examples of singular matrices. There is only one number with no multiplicative inverse (0), but there are many matrices that have no inverses. ■

Finding the Inverse of a Square Matrix

Q: In Quick Example 3, it was stated that the inverse of $\begin{bmatrix} 1 & -1 \\ -1 & -1 \end{bmatrix}$ is $\begin{bmatrix} \frac{1}{2} & -\frac{1}{2} \\ -\frac{1}{2} & -\frac{1}{2} \end{bmatrix}$. How was that obtained?

A : We can think of the problem of finding A^{-1} as a problem of finding four unknowns, the four unknown entries of A^{-1}:

$$A^{-1} = \begin{bmatrix} x & y \\ z & w \end{bmatrix}.$$

These unknowns must satisfy the equation $AA^{-1} = I$, or

$$\begin{bmatrix} 1 & -1 \\ -1 & -1 \end{bmatrix} \begin{bmatrix} x & y \\ z & w \end{bmatrix} = \begin{bmatrix} 1 & 0 \\ 0 & 1 \end{bmatrix}.$$

If we were to try to find the first column of A^{-1}, consisting of x and z, we would have to solve

$$\begin{bmatrix} 1 & -1 \\ -1 & -1 \end{bmatrix} \begin{bmatrix} x \\ z \end{bmatrix} = \begin{bmatrix} 1 \\ 0 \end{bmatrix},$$

or

$$x - z = 1$$
$$-x - z = 0.$$

To solve this system by Gauss-Jordan reduction, we would row-reduce the augmented matrix, which is A with the column $\begin{bmatrix} 1 \\ 0 \end{bmatrix}$ adjoined:

$$\begin{bmatrix} 1 & -1 & | & 1 \\ -1 & -1 & | & 0 \end{bmatrix} \rightarrow \begin{bmatrix} 1 & 0 & | & x \\ 0 & 1 & | & z \end{bmatrix}.$$

To find the second column of A^{-1}, we would similarly row-reduce the augmented matrix obtained by tacking on to A the second column of the identity matrix:

$$\begin{bmatrix} 1 & -1 & | & 0 \\ -1 & -1 & | & 1 \end{bmatrix} \rightarrow \begin{bmatrix} 1 & 0 & | & y \\ 0 & 1 & | & w \end{bmatrix}.$$

The row operations used in doing these two reductions would be exactly the same. We could do both reductions simultaneously by "doubly augmenting" A, putting both columns of the identity matrix to the right of A:

$$\begin{bmatrix} 1 & -1 & | & 1 & 0 \\ -1 & -1 & | & 0 & 1 \end{bmatrix} \rightarrow \begin{bmatrix} 1 & 0 & | & x & y \\ 0 & 1 & | & z & w \end{bmatrix}.$$

We carry out this reduction in the following example.

EXAMPLE 2   **Computing the Inverse of a Matrix**

Find the inverse of each matrix.

a. $P = \begin{bmatrix} 1 & -1 \\ -1 & -1 \end{bmatrix}$ **b.** $Q = \begin{bmatrix} 1 & 0 & 1 \\ 2 & -2 & -1 \\ 3 & 0 & 0 \end{bmatrix}$

Solution

a. As described above, we put the matrix P on the left and the identity matrix I on the right to get a 2×4 matrix:

$$\begin{bmatrix} 1 & -1 & | & 1 & 0 \\ -1 & -1 & | & 0 & 1 \end{bmatrix}.$$
$$\quad\;\; P \qquad\qquad I$$

Using Technology

Here is an outline on the use of technology to invert the matrix in Example 2(b) (see the Technology Guides at the end of the chapter for additional details on using a TI-83/84 Plus or a spreadsheet):

TI-83/84 Plus
Enter the matrix [A] using MATRIX ; EDIT
Home screen: [A] x^{-1} ENTER
[More details in the Technology Guide.]

Spreadsheet
Enter the matrix in a convenient block of cells (e.g., A1–C3). Highlight a 3 × 3 block for the answer.
Type =MINVERSE(A1:C3)
Press Control+Shift+Enter.
[More details in the Technology Guide.]

Website
www.WanerMath.com
→ Online Utilities
→ Matrix Algebra Tool
Enter Q as shown:

```
Enter your matrices here.
Q = [1, 0, 1
2, -2,-1
3, 0, 0]
```

Type Q^-1 or Q^(-1) in the formula box, and press "Compute".

We now row-reduce the whole matrix:

$$\left[\begin{array}{cc|cc} 1 & -1 & 1 & 0 \\ -1 & -1 & 0 & 1 \end{array}\right] \begin{array}{c} \\ R_2 + R_1 \end{array} \rightarrow \left[\begin{array}{cc|cc} 1 & -1 & 1 & 0 \\ 0 & -2 & 1 & 1 \end{array}\right] \begin{array}{c} 2R_1 - R_2 \\ \end{array} \rightarrow$$

$$\left[\begin{array}{cc|cc} 2 & 0 & 1 & -1 \\ 0 & -2 & 1 & 1 \end{array}\right] \begin{array}{c} \frac{1}{2}R_1 \\ -\frac{1}{2}R_2 \end{array} \rightarrow \left[\begin{array}{cc|cc} 1 & 0 & \frac{1}{2} & -\frac{1}{2} \\ 0 & 1 & -\frac{1}{2} & -\frac{1}{2} \end{array}\right].$$
$$\qquad\qquad\qquad\qquad\qquad I \qquad\quad P^{-1}$$

We have now solved the systems of linear equations that define the entries of P^{-1}. Thus,

$$P^{-1} = \left[\begin{array}{cc} \frac{1}{2} & -\frac{1}{2} \\ -\frac{1}{2} & -\frac{1}{2} \end{array}\right].$$

b. The procedure to find the inverse of a 3 × 3 matrix (or larger) is just the same as for a 2 × 2 matrix. We place Q on the left and the identity matrix (now 3 × 3) on the right, and reduce:

$$\begin{array}{cc} Q & I \end{array}$$
$$\left[\begin{array}{ccc|ccc} 1 & 0 & 1 & 1 & 0 & 0 \\ 2 & -2 & -1 & 0 & 1 & 0 \\ 3 & 0 & 0 & 0 & 0 & 1 \end{array}\right] \begin{array}{c} \\ R_2 - 2R_1 \\ R_3 - 3R_1 \end{array} \rightarrow \left[\begin{array}{ccc|ccc} 1 & 0 & 1 & 1 & 0 & 0 \\ 0 & -2 & -3 & -2 & 1 & 0 \\ 0 & 0 & -3 & -3 & 0 & 1 \end{array}\right] \begin{array}{c} 3R_1 + R_3 \\ R_2 - R_3 \\ \end{array} \rightarrow$$

$$\left[\begin{array}{ccc|ccc} 3 & 0 & 0 & 0 & 0 & 1 \\ 0 & -2 & 0 & 1 & 1 & -1 \\ 0 & 0 & -3 & -3 & 0 & 1 \end{array}\right] \begin{array}{c} \frac{1}{3}R_1 \\ -\frac{1}{2}R_2 \\ -\frac{1}{3}R_3 \end{array} \rightarrow \left[\begin{array}{ccc|ccc} 1 & 0 & 0 & 0 & 0 & \frac{1}{3} \\ 0 & 1 & 0 & -\frac{1}{2} & -\frac{1}{2} & \frac{1}{2} \\ 0 & 0 & 1 & 1 & 0 & -\frac{1}{3} \end{array}\right].$$
$$\qquad\qquad\qquad\qquad\qquad\qquad\qquad I \qquad\qquad\quad Q^{-1}$$

Thus,

$$Q^{-1} = \left[\begin{array}{ccc} 0 & 0 & \frac{1}{3} \\ -\frac{1}{2} & -\frac{1}{2} & \frac{1}{2} \\ 1 & 0 & -\frac{1}{3} \end{array}\right].$$

We have already checked that P^{-1} is the inverse of P. You should also check that Q^{-1} is the inverse of Q.

The method we used in Example 2 can be summarized as follows.

Inverting an $n \times n$ Matrix

To determine whether or not an $n \times n$ matrix A is invertible, and to find A^{-1} if it does exist, follow this procedure:

1. Write down the $n \times 2n$ matrix $[A\,|\,I]$. (This is A with the $n \times n$ identity matrix set next to it.)

2. Row-reduce $[A\,|\,I]$.

3. If the reduced form is $[I\,|\,B]$ (i.e., has the identity matrix in the left part), then A is invertible and $B = A^{-1}$. If row reduction does not result in I in the left part, then A is singular. (See Example 3.)

Although there is a general formula for the inverse of a matrix, it is not a simple one. In fact, using the formula for anything larger than a 3×3 matrix is so inefficient that the row-reduction procedure is the method of choice even for computer algorithms. However, the general formula is very simple for the special case of 2×2 matrices.

Formula for the Inverse of a 2 × 2 Matrix

The inverse of a 2×2 matrix is

$$\begin{bmatrix} a & b \\ c & d \end{bmatrix}^{-1} = \frac{1}{ad - bc} \begin{bmatrix} d & -b \\ -c & a \end{bmatrix}, \quad \text{provided that } ad - bc \neq 0.$$

If the quantity $ad - bc$ is zero, then the matrix is singular (non-invertible). The quantity $ad - bc$ is called the **determinant** of the matrix $\begin{bmatrix} a & b \\ c & d \end{bmatrix}$.

Quick Examples

4. $\begin{bmatrix} 1 & 2 \\ 3 & 4 \end{bmatrix}^{-1} = \frac{1}{(1)(4) - (2)(3)} \begin{bmatrix} 4 & -2 \\ -3 & 1 \end{bmatrix} = -\frac{1}{2} \begin{bmatrix} 4 & -2 \\ -3 & 1 \end{bmatrix}$

   $= \begin{bmatrix} -2 & 1 \\ \frac{3}{2} & -\frac{1}{2} \end{bmatrix}$

5. $\begin{bmatrix} 1 & -1 \\ 2 & -2 \end{bmatrix}$ has determinant $ad - bc = (1)(-2) - (-1)(2) = 0$ and so is singular.

The formula for the inverse of a 2×2 matrix can be obtained by using the technique of row reduction. (See the Communication and Reasoning Exercises at the end of the section.)

As we mentioned earlier, not every square matrix has an inverse, as we see in the next example.

EXAMPLE 3 **Singular 3 × 3 Matrix**

Find the inverse of the matrix $S = \begin{bmatrix} 1 & 1 & 2 \\ -2 & 0 & 4 \\ 3 & 1 & -2 \end{bmatrix}$ if it exists.

Solution We proceed as before:

$$\begin{array}{cc} S & I \\ \left[\begin{array}{ccc|ccc} 1 & 1 & 2 & 1 & 0 & 0 \\ -2 & 0 & 4 & 0 & 1 & 0 \\ 3 & 1 & -2 & 0 & 0 & 1 \end{array}\right] & \begin{array}{c} \\ R_2 + 2R_1 \to \\ R_3 - 3R_1 \end{array} \end{array} \left[\begin{array}{ccc|ccc} 1 & 1 & 2 & 1 & 0 & 0 \\ 0 & 2 & 8 & 2 & 1 & 0 \\ 0 & -2 & -8 & -3 & 0 & 1 \end{array}\right] \begin{array}{c} 2R_1 - R_2 \\ \\ R_3 + R_2 \end{array}$$

$$\to \left[\begin{array}{ccc|ccc} 2 & 0 & -4 & 0 & -1 & 0 \\ 0 & 2 & 8 & 2 & 1 & 0 \\ 0 & 0 & 0 & -1 & 1 & 1 \end{array}\right].$$

We stopped here, even though the reduction is incomplete, because there is *no hope* of getting the identity on the left-hand side. Completing the row reduction will not change the three zeros in the bottom row. So what is wrong? Nothing. As in Example 1, we have here a singular matrix. Any square matrix that, after row reduction, winds up with a row of zeros is singular. (See Exercise 77.)

➡ **Before we go on ...** In practice, deciding whether a given matrix is invertible or singular is easy: Simply try to find its inverse. If the process works, then the matrix is invertible, and we get its inverse. If the process fails, then the matrix is singular. If you try to invert a singular matrix using a spreadsheet, calculator, or computer program, you should get an error. Sometimes, instead of an error, you will get a spurious answer due to round-off errors in the device. ■

Using the Inverse to Solve a System of n Linear Equations in n Unknowns

Having used systems of equations and row reduction to find matrix inverses, we will now use matrix inverses to solve systems of equations. Recall that, at the end of Section 5.2, we saw that a system of linear equations could be written in the form

$$AX = B,$$

where A is the coefficient matrix, X is the column matrix of unknowns, and B is the column matrix of right-hand sides. Now suppose that there are as many unknowns as equations, so A is a square matrix, and suppose that A is invertible. The object is to solve for the matrix X of unknowns, so we multiply both sides of the equation by the inverse A^{-1} of A, getting

$$A^{-1}AX = A^{-1}B.$$

Notice that we put A^{-1} on the left on both sides of the equation. Order matters when multiplying matrices, so we have to be careful to do the same thing to both sides of the equation. But now $A^{-1}A = I$, so we can rewrite the last equation as

$$IX = A^{-1}B.$$

Also, $IX = X$ (I being the identity matrix), so we really have

$$X = A^{-1}B,$$

and we have solved for X!

Moreover, we have shown that, if A is invertible and $AX = B$, then the *only possible* solution is $X = A^{-1}B$. We should check that $A^{-1}B$ is actually a solution by substituting back into the original equation:

$$AX = A(A^{-1}B) = (AA^{-1})B = IB = B.$$

Thus, $X = A^{-1}B$ is a solution and is the only solution. Therefore, if A is invertible, $AX = B$ has exactly one solution.

On the other hand, if $AX = B$ has no solutions or has infinitely many solutions, we can conclude that A is not invertible (why?). To summarize, we have the following.

Solving the Matrix Equation $AX = B$

If A is an invertible matrix, then the matrix equation $AX = B$ has the unique solution

$$X = A^{-1}B.$$

6. The system of linear equations

$$2x \quad\quad + z = 9$$
$$2x + y - z = 6$$
$$3x + y - z = 9$$

can be written as $AX = B$, where

$$A = \begin{bmatrix} 2 & 0 & 1 \\ 2 & 1 & -1 \\ 3 & 1 & -1 \end{bmatrix}, \quad X = \begin{bmatrix} x \\ y \\ z \end{bmatrix}, \quad \text{and} \quad B = \begin{bmatrix} 9 \\ 6 \\ 9 \end{bmatrix}.$$

The matrix A is invertible with inverse

$$A^{-1} = \begin{bmatrix} 0 & -1 & 1 \\ 1 & 5 & -4 \\ 1 & 2 & -2 \end{bmatrix}. \quad \text{You should check this.}$$

Thus,

$$X = A^{-1}B = \begin{bmatrix} 0 & -1 & 1 \\ 1 & 5 & -4 \\ 1 & 2 & -2 \end{bmatrix} \begin{bmatrix} 9 \\ 6 \\ 9 \end{bmatrix} = \begin{bmatrix} 3 \\ 3 \\ 3 \end{bmatrix},$$

so $(x, y, z) = (3, 3, 3)$ is the (unique) solution to the system.

EXAMPLE 4   **Solving Systems of Equations Using an Inverse**

Solve the following three systems of equations:

a. $2x \quad + z = 1$ **b.** $2x \quad + z = 0$ **c.** $2x \quad + z = 0$
  $2x + y - z = 1$ $2x + y - z = 1$ $2x + y - z = 0$
  $3x + y - z = 1$ $3x + y - z = 2$ $3x + y - z = 0$

Solution We *could* go ahead and row-reduce all three augmented matrices, as we did in Chapter 4, but this would require a lot of work. Notice that the coefficients are the same in all three systems. In other words, we can write the three systems in matrix form as follows:

a. $AX = B$ **b.** $AX = C$ **c.** $AX = D$

where the matrix A is the same in all three cases:

$$A = \begin{bmatrix} 2 & 0 & 1 \\ 2 & 1 & -1 \\ 3 & 1 & -1 \end{bmatrix}.$$

Using Technology

Here is an outline on the use of technology to do the calculations in Example 4 (see the Technology Guides at the end of the chapter for additional details on using a TI-83/84 Plus or a spreadsheet):

TI-83/84 Plus
Enter the four matrices [A], [B], [C], [D] using MATRIX ; EDIT
Home screen: [A]$^{-1}$*[B],
[A]$^{-1}$*[C], [A]$^{-1}$*[D]
[More details in the Technology Guide.]

Spreadsheet
Enter the matrices A and B in convenient blocks of cells (e.g., A1–C3, E1–E3).
Highlight a 3 × 1 block for the answer.
Type =MMULT(MINVERSE(A1:C3), E1:E3)
Press Control+Shift+Enter.
[More details in the Technology Guide.]

Website
www.WanerMath.com
→ Online Utilities
→ Matrix Algebra Tool
Enter A^-1*B, A^-1*C, and A^-1*D to compute these products after entering the matrices A, B, C, and D as shown earlier.

Now the solutions to these systems are

a. $X = A^{-1}B$ **b.** $X = A^{-1}C$ **c.** $X = A^{-1}D$

so the main work is the calculation of the single matrix A^{-1}, which we have already noted (see Quick Example 6) is

$$A^{-1} = \begin{bmatrix} 0 & -1 & 1 \\ 1 & 5 & -4 \\ 1 & 2 & -2 \end{bmatrix}.$$

Thus, the three solutions are as follows:

a. $X = A^{-1}B = \begin{bmatrix} 0 & -1 & 1 \\ 1 & 5 & -4 \\ 1 & 2 & -2 \end{bmatrix}\begin{bmatrix} 1 \\ 1 \\ 1 \end{bmatrix} = \begin{bmatrix} 0 \\ 2 \\ 1 \end{bmatrix}$

b. $X = A^{-1}C = \begin{bmatrix} 0 & -1 & 1 \\ 1 & 5 & -4 \\ 1 & 2 & -2 \end{bmatrix}\begin{bmatrix} 0 \\ 1 \\ 2 \end{bmatrix} = \begin{bmatrix} 1 \\ -3 \\ -2 \end{bmatrix}$

c. $X = A^{-1}D = \begin{bmatrix} 0 & -1 & 1 \\ 1 & 5 & -4 \\ 1 & 2 & -2 \end{bmatrix}\begin{bmatrix} 0 \\ 0 \\ 0 \end{bmatrix} = \begin{bmatrix} 0 \\ 0 \\ 0 \end{bmatrix}$

➡ **Before we go on...** We have been speaking of *the* inverse of a matrix A. Is there only one? It is not hard to prove that a matrix A cannot have more than one inverse. If B and C were both inverses of A, then

$$B = BI \qquad \text{Property of the identity}$$
$$= B(AC) \qquad \text{Because } C \text{ is an inverse of } A$$
$$= (BA)C \qquad \text{Associative law}$$
$$= IC \qquad \text{Because } B \text{ is an inverse of } A$$
$$= C. \qquad \text{Property of the identity}$$

In other words, if B and C were both inverses of A, then B and C would have to be equal. ∎

FAQs

Which Method to Use in Solving a System

Q: *Now we have two methods to solve a system of linear equations AX = B:*
(1) Compute X = A^{-1}B, or (2) row-reduce the augmented matrix. Which is the better method?

A: Each method has its advantages and disadvantages. Method (1), as we have seen, is very efficient when you must solve several systems of equations with the same coefficients, but it works only when the coefficient matrix is *square* (meaning that you have the same number of equations as unknowns) *and invertible* (meaning that there is a unique solution). The row-reduction method will work for all systems. Moreover, for all but the smallest systems the most efficient way to find A^{-1} is to use row reduction. Thus, in practice, the two methods are essentially the same when both apply.

5.3 EXERCISES

▼ more advanced   ◆ challenging
🔳 indicates exercises that should be solved using technology

In Exercises 1–6, determine whether or not the given pairs of matrices are inverse pairs. [HINT: See Quick Examples 1–3.]

1. $A = \begin{bmatrix} 0 & 1 \\ 1 & 0 \end{bmatrix}, B = \begin{bmatrix} 0 & 1 \\ 1 & 0 \end{bmatrix}$

2. $A = \begin{bmatrix} 2 & 0 \\ 0 & 3 \end{bmatrix}, B = \begin{bmatrix} \frac{1}{2} & 0 \\ 0 & \frac{1}{2} \end{bmatrix}$

3. $A = \begin{bmatrix} 2 & 1 & 1 \\ 0 & 1 & 1 \\ 0 & 0 & 1 \end{bmatrix}, B = \begin{bmatrix} \frac{1}{2} & -\frac{1}{2} & 0 \\ 0 & 1 & -1 \\ 0 & 0 & 1 \end{bmatrix}$

4. $A = \begin{bmatrix} 1 & 1 & 1 \\ 0 & 1 & 1 \\ 0 & 0 & 1 \end{bmatrix}, B = \begin{bmatrix} 1 & -1 & 0 \\ 0 & 1 & -1 \\ 0 & 0 & 1 \end{bmatrix}$

5. $A = \begin{bmatrix} a & 0 & 0 \\ 0 & b & 0 \\ 0 & 0 & 0 \end{bmatrix}, B = \begin{bmatrix} a^{-1} & 0 & 0 \\ 0 & b^{-1} & 0 \\ 0 & 0 & 0 \end{bmatrix}$ $(a, b \neq 0)$

6. $A = \begin{bmatrix} a & 0 & 0 \\ 0 & b & 0 \\ 0 & 0 & c \end{bmatrix}, B = \begin{bmatrix} a^{-1} & 0 & 0 \\ 0 & b^{-1} & 0 \\ 0 & 0 & c^{-1} \end{bmatrix}$ $(a, b, c \neq 0)$

In Exercises 7–26, use row reduction to find the inverses of the given matrices if they exist, and check your answers by multiplication. [HINT: See Example 2.]

7. $\begin{bmatrix} 1 & 1 \\ 2 & 1 \end{bmatrix}$ **8.** $\begin{bmatrix} 0 & 1 \\ 1 & 1 \end{bmatrix}$ **9.** $\begin{bmatrix} 0 & 1 \\ 1 & 0 \end{bmatrix}$ **10.** $\begin{bmatrix} 4 & 0 \\ 0 & 2 \end{bmatrix}$

11. $\begin{bmatrix} 2 & 1 \\ 1 & 1 \end{bmatrix}$ **12.** $\begin{bmatrix} 3 & 0 \\ 0 & \frac{1}{2} \end{bmatrix}$ **13.** $\begin{bmatrix} 2 & 1 \\ 4 & 2 \end{bmatrix}$ **14.** $\begin{bmatrix} 1 & 1 \\ 6 & 6 \end{bmatrix}$

15. $\begin{bmatrix} 1 & 1 & 1 \\ 0 & 1 & 1 \\ 0 & 0 & 1 \end{bmatrix}$ **16.** $\begin{bmatrix} 1 & 2 & 3 \\ 0 & 1 & 2 \\ 0 & 0 & 1 \end{bmatrix}$ **17.** $\begin{bmatrix} 1 & 1 & 1 \\ 1 & 0 & 2 \\ 1 & -1 & 1 \end{bmatrix}$

18. $\begin{bmatrix} 1 & 2 & 3 \\ 0 & 2 & 3 \\ 1 & 0 & 1 \end{bmatrix}$ **19.** $\begin{bmatrix} 1 & 1 & 1 \\ 1 & -1 & 0 \\ 1 & 2 & 3 \end{bmatrix}$ **20.** $\begin{bmatrix} 1 & -1 & 3 \\ 0 & 1 & 3 \\ 1 & 1 & 1 \end{bmatrix}$

21. $\begin{bmatrix} 1 & 1 & 1 \\ 1 & 0 & 1 \\ 1 & -1 & 1 \end{bmatrix}$ **22.** $\begin{bmatrix} 1 & 1 & 1 \\ 0 & 1 & 1 \\ 1 & 0 & 0 \end{bmatrix}$

23. $\begin{bmatrix} 1 & 0 & 1 & 0 \\ -1 & 1 & 0 & 1 \\ -1 & 0 & 0 & 1 \\ 0 & -1 & 0 & 1 \end{bmatrix}$ **24.** $\begin{bmatrix} 0 & 1 & 1 & 0 \\ -1 & 1 & 1 & 1 \\ -1 & 1 & 0 & 1 \\ 0 & -1 & 0 & 1 \end{bmatrix}$

25. $\begin{bmatrix} 1 & 2 & 3 & 4 \\ 0 & 1 & 2 & 3 \\ 0 & 0 & 1 & 2 \\ 0 & 0 & 0 & 1 \end{bmatrix}$ **26.** $\begin{bmatrix} 0 & 0 & 0 & 1 \\ 0 & 0 & 1 & 0 \\ 0 & 1 & 0 & 0 \\ 1 & 0 & 0 & 0 \end{bmatrix}$

In Exercises 27–34, compute the determinant of the given matrix. If the determinant is nonzero, use the formula for inverting a 2×2 matrix to calculate the inverse of the given matrix. [HINT: See Quick Examples 4 and 5.]

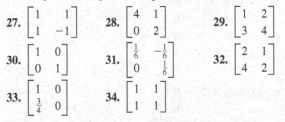

27. $\begin{bmatrix} 1 & 1 \\ 1 & -1 \end{bmatrix}$ **28.** $\begin{bmatrix} 4 & 1 \\ 0 & 2 \end{bmatrix}$ **29.** $\begin{bmatrix} 1 & 2 \\ 3 & 4 \end{bmatrix}$

30. $\begin{bmatrix} 1 & 0 \\ 0 & 1 \end{bmatrix}$ **31.** $\begin{bmatrix} \frac{1}{6} & -\frac{1}{6} \\ 0 & \frac{1}{6} \end{bmatrix}$ **32.** $\begin{bmatrix} 2 & 1 \\ 4 & 2 \end{bmatrix}$

33. $\begin{bmatrix} 1 & 0 \\ \frac{3}{4} & 0 \end{bmatrix}$ **34.** $\begin{bmatrix} 1 & 1 \\ 1 & 1 \end{bmatrix}$

🔳 *In Exercises 35–42, use technology to find the inverse of the given matrix (when it exists). Round all entries in your answer to two decimal places.* [Caution: Because of rounding errors, technology sometimes produces an "inverse" of a singular matrix. These often can be recognized by their huge entries.]

35. $\begin{bmatrix} 1.1 & 1.2 \\ 1.3 & -1 \end{bmatrix}$ **36.** $\begin{bmatrix} 0.1 & -3.2 \\ 0.1 & -1.5 \end{bmatrix}$

37. $\begin{bmatrix} 3.56 & 1.23 \\ -1.01 & 0 \end{bmatrix}$ **38.** $\begin{bmatrix} 9.09 & -5.01 \\ 1.01 & 2.20 \end{bmatrix}$

39. $\begin{bmatrix} 1.1 & 3.1 & 2.4 \\ 1.7 & 2.4 & 2.3 \\ 0.6 & -0.7 & -0.1 \end{bmatrix}$ **40.** $\begin{bmatrix} 2.1 & 2.4 & 3.5 \\ 6.1 & -0.1 & 2.3 \\ -0.3 & -1.2 & 0.1 \end{bmatrix}$

41. $\begin{bmatrix} 0.01 & 0.32 & 0 & 0.04 \\ -0.01 & 0 & 0 & 0.34 \\ 0 & 0.32 & -0.23 & 0.23 \\ 0 & 0.41 & 0 & 0.01 \end{bmatrix}$

42. $\begin{bmatrix} 0.01 & 0.32 & 0 & 0.04 \\ -0.01 & 0 & 0 & 0.34 \\ 0 & 0.32 & -0.23 & 0.23 \\ 0.01 & 0.96 & -0.23 & 0.65 \end{bmatrix}$

In Exercises 43–48, use matrix inversion to solve the given systems of linear equations. (You solved similar systems using row reduction in Chapter 4.) [HINT: See Quick Example 6.]

43. $x + y = 4$
$x - y = 1$

44. $2x + y = 2$
$2x - 3y = 2$

45. $\dfrac{x}{3} + \dfrac{y}{2} = 0$
$\dfrac{x}{2} + y = -1$

46. $\dfrac{2x}{3} - \dfrac{y}{2} = \dfrac{1}{6}$
$\dfrac{x}{2} - \dfrac{y}{2} = -1$

47. $-x + 2y - z = 0$
$-x - y + 2z = 0$
$2x \quad - z = 6$

48. $x + 2y \quad = 4$
$y - z = 0$
$x + 3y - 2z = 5$

In Exercises 49 and 50, use matrix inversion to solve each collection of systems of linear equations. [**HINT:** See Example 4.]

49. a. $-x - 4y + 2z = 4$
$x + 2y - z = 3$
$x + y - z = 8$

b. $-x - 4y + 2z = 0$
$x + 2y - z = 3$
$x + y - z = 2$

c. $-x - 4y + 2z = 0$
$x + 2y - z = 0$
$x + y - z = 0$

50. a. $-x - 4y + 2z = 8$
$x \quad - z = 3$
$x + y - z = 8$

b. $-x - 4y + 2z = 8$
$x \quad - z = 3$
$x + y - z = 2$

c. $-x - 4y + 2z = 0$
$x \quad - z = 0$
$x + y - z = 0$

Applications

Some of the following exercises are similar or identical to exercises and examples in Chapter 4. Use matrix inverses to find the solutions. We suggest that you invert some of the matrices by hand and others using technology.

51. *Nutrition* One serving of Campbell Soup Company's Campbell's Pork & Beans contains 5 grams of protein and 21 grams of carbohydrates.[16] A typical slice of "lite" rye bread contains 4 grams of protein and 12 grams of carbohydrates.

a. I am planning a meal of beans-on-toast, and I want it to supply 20 grams of protein and 80 grams of carbohydrates. How should I prepare my meal?

b. If I require A grams of protein and B grams of carbohydrates, give a formula that tells me how many slices of bread and how many servings of Pork & Beans to use.

52. *Nutrition* According to the nutritional information on a package of General Mills' Honey Nut Cheerios brand cereal, each 1-ounce serving of Cheerios contains 3 grams of protein and 24 grams of carbohydrates.[17] Each half-cup serving of enriched skim milk contains 4 grams of protein and 6 grams of carbohydrates.

a. I am planning a meal of cereal and milk, and I want it to supply 26 grams of protein and 78 grams of carbohydrates. How should I prepare my meal?

b. If I require A grams of protein and B grams of carbohydrates, give a formula that tells me how many servings of milk and Honey Nut Cheerios to use.

53. *Resource Allocation* You manage an ice cream factory that makes three flavors: Creamy Vanilla, Continental Mocha, and Succulent Strawberry. Into each batch of Creamy Vanilla go two eggs, one cup of milk, and two cups of cream. Into each batch of Continental Mocha go one egg, one cup of milk, and two cups of cream. Into each batch of Succulent Strawberry go one egg, two cups of milk, and one cup of cream. Your stocks of eggs, milk, and cream vary from day to day. How many batches of each flavor should you make in order to use up all of your ingredients if you have the following amounts in stock?

a. 350 eggs, 350 cups of milk, and 400 cups of cream

b. 400 eggs, 500 cups of milk, and 400 cups of cream

c. A eggs, B cups of milk, and C cups of cream

54. *Resource Allocation* The *Arctic Juice Company* makes three juice blends: PineOrange, using 2 quarts of pineapple juice and 2 quarts of orange juice per gallon; PineKiwi, using 3 quarts of pineapple juice and 1 quart of kiwi juice per gallon; and OrangeKiwi, using 3 quarts of orange juice and 1 quart of kiwi juice per gallon. The amount of each kind of juice the company has on hand varies from day to day. How many gallons of each blend can it make on a day with the following stocks?

a. 800 quarts of pineapple juice, 650 quarts of orange juice, 350 quarts of kiwi juice.

b. 650 quarts of pineapple juice, 800 quarts of orange juice, 350 quarts of kiwi juice.

c. A quarts of pineapple juice, B quarts of orange juice, C quarts of kiwi juice.

Investing: Inverse ETFs (Exchange Traded Funds) Inverse ETFs, sometimes referred to as "bear market" or "short" funds, are designed to deliver the opposite of the performance of the index or category they track and so can be used by traders to bet against the stock market. Exercises 55–56 are based on the following table, which shows the performance of three such funds as of August 5, 2015:[18]

	Year-to-Date Loss (%)
MYY (ProShares Short Midcap 400)	6
SH (ProShares Short S&P 500)	5
REW (ProShares UltraShort Technology)	7

55. You invested a total of $9,000 in the three funds at the beginning of 2011, including an equal amount in SH and REW. Your year-to-date loss from the first two funds amounted to $400. How much did you invest in each of the three funds?

---

[16] According to the label information on a 16-ounce can.

[17] Actually, it is 23 grams of carbohydrates. We made it 24 grams to simplify the calculation.

[18] Based on prices at noon on August 5, 2015. YTD losses rounded to the nearest percentage point. Source: www.google.com/finance.

56. You invested a total of $6,000 in the three funds at the beginning of 2011, including an equal amount in MYY and SH. Your total year-to-date loss amounted to $360. How much did you invest in each of the three funds?

Investing: Lesser-Known Stocks *Exercises 57–58 are based on the following information about the stocks of* Whitestone REIT, HCC Insurance Holdings, Inc., *and* SanDisk Corporation:[19]

	Price ($)	Dividend Yield (%)
WSR (WSR Whitestone REIT)	16	7
HCC (HCC Insurance Holdings, Inc.)	56	2
SNDK (SanDisk Corporation)	80	2

57. ▼ You invested a total of $8,400 in shares of the three stocks at the given prices and expected to earn $248 in annual dividends. If you purchased a total of 200 shares, how many shares of each stock did you purchase?

58. ▼ You invested a total of $11,200 in shares of the three stocks at the given prices and expected to earn $304 in annual dividends. If you purchased a total of 250 shares, how many shares of each stock did you purchase?

59. ▣ ▼ ***Population Movement*** In 2009 the population of the United States, broken down by regions, was 54.6 million in the Northeast, 66.0 million in the Midwest, 111.8 million in the South, and 70.6 million in the West. The table below shows the population movement during the period 2008–2009. (Thus, 99.23% of the population in the Northeast stayed there, while 0.16% of the population in the Northeast moved to the Midwest, and so on.)[20]

	To	Northeast	Midwest	South	West
From	**Northeast**	0.9923	0.0016	0.0042	0.0019
	Midwest	0.0018	0.9896	0.0047	0.0039
	South	0.0056	0.0059	0.9827	0.0058
	West	0.0024	0.0033	0.0044	0.9899

Set up the 2009 population figures as a row vector. Use matrix inversion and multiplication to estimate the population in each region in 2008. (Round all answers to the nearest 0.1 million.)

60. ▼ ▣ ***Population Movement*** Assume that the percentages given in Exercise 59 also describe the population movements from 2007 to 2008. Use two matrix multiplications to estimate from the data in Exercise 59 the population in each region in 2007.

61. ◆ ▣ ***Rotations*** If a point (x, y) in the plane is rotated counterclockwise about the origin through an angle of 45°, its new coordinates (x', y') are given by

$$\begin{bmatrix} x' \\ y' \end{bmatrix} = R \begin{bmatrix} x \\ y \end{bmatrix}$$

where R is the 2 × 2 matrix $\begin{bmatrix} a & -a \\ a & a \end{bmatrix}$ and $a = \sqrt{1/2} \approx 0.7071$.

a. If the point $(2, 3)$ is rotated counterclockwise through an angle of 45°, what are its (approximate) new coordinates?

b. Multiplication by what matrix would result in a counterclockwise rotation of 90°? 135°? (Express the matrices in terms of R.) [HINT: Think of a rotation through 90° as two successive rotations through 45°.]

c. Multiplication by what matrix would result in a *clockwise* rotation of 45°?

62. ◆ ▣ ***Rotations*** If a point (x, y) in the plane is rotated counterclockwise about the origin through an angle of 60°, its new coordinates (x', y') are given by

$$\begin{bmatrix} x' \\ y' \end{bmatrix} = S \begin{bmatrix} x \\ y \end{bmatrix}$$

where S is the 2 × 2 matrix $\begin{bmatrix} a & -b \\ b & a \end{bmatrix}$ and $a = 1/2$ and $b = \sqrt{3/4} \approx 0.8660$.

a. If the point $(2, 3)$ is rotated counterclockwise through an angle of 60°, what are its (approximate) new coordinates?

b. Referring to Exercise 61, multiplication by what matrix would result in a counterclockwise rotation of 105°? (Express the matrices in terms of S and the matrix R from Exercise 61.) [HINT: Think of a rotation through 105° as a rotation through 60° followed by a rotation through 45°.]

c. Multiplication by what matrix would result in a *clockwise* rotation of 60°?

▣ ***Encryption*** *Matrices are commonly used to encrypt data. Here is a simple form such an encryption can take. First, we represent each letter in the alphabet by a number, so let us take* <space> = 0, A = 1, B = 2 *and so on. Thus, for example,* "ABORT MISSION" *becomes*

$$[1 \quad 2 \quad 15 \quad 18 \quad 20 \quad 0 \quad 13 \quad 9 \quad 19 \quad 19 \quad 9 \quad 15 \quad 14].$$

To encrypt this coded phrase, we use an invertible matrix of any size with integer entries. For instance, let us take A to be the 2 × 2 matrix $\begin{bmatrix} 1 & 2 \\ 3 & 4 \end{bmatrix}$. *We can first arrange the coded sequence of numbers in the form of a matrix with two rows*

---

[19] Yields rounded to the nearest percentage point and stock prices at the close of the stock market on February 27, 2015, rounded to the nearest $1. Source: www.finance.yahoo.

[20] Note that this exercise ignores migration into or out of the country. Source: U.S. Census Bureau, Current Population Survey, 2009 Annual Social and Economic Supplement.

(using zero in the last place if we have an odd number of characters) and then multiply on the left by A:

$$\text{Encrypted matrix} = \begin{bmatrix} 1 & 2 \\ 3 & 4 \end{bmatrix} \begin{bmatrix} 1 & 15 & 20 & 13 & 19 & 9 & 14 \\ 2 & 18 & 0 & 9 & 19 & 15 & 0 \end{bmatrix}$$

$$= \begin{bmatrix} 5 & 51 & 20 & 31 & 57 & 39 & 14 \\ 11 & 117 & 60 & 75 & 133 & 87 & 42 \end{bmatrix},$$

which we can also write as

$$[5 \ 11 \ 51 \ 117 \ 20 \ 60 \ 31 \ 75 \ 57 \ 133 \ 39 \ 87 \ 14 \ 42].$$

To decipher the encoded message, multiply the encrypted matrix by A^{-1}. Exercises 63–66 use the above matrix A for encoding and decoding.

63. ▼ Use the matrix A to encode the phrase "GO TO PLAN B".

64. ▼ Use the matrix A to encode the phrase "ABANDON SHIP".

65. ▼ Decode the following message, which was encrypted using the matrix A.

$$[33 \ 69 \ 54 \ 126 \ 11 \ 27 \ 20 \ 60 \ 29 \ 59 \ 65 \ 149 \ 41 \ 87]$$

66. ▼ Decode the following message, which was encrypted using the matrix A.

$$[59 \ 141 \ 43 \ 101 \ 7 \ 21 \ 29 \ 59 \ 65 \ 149 \ 41 \ 87]$$

Communication and Reasoning Exercises

67. Multiple choice: If A and B are square matrices with $AB = I$ and $BA = I$, then
(A) B is the inverse of A.
(B) A and B must be equal.
(C) A and B must both be singular.
(D) At least one of A and B is singular.

68. Multiple choice: If A is a square matrix with $A^3 = I$ then
(A) A must be the identity matrix.
(B) A is invertible.
(C) A is singular.
(D) A is both invertible and singular.

69. What can you say about the inverse of a 2×2 matrix of the form $\begin{bmatrix} a & b \\ a & b \end{bmatrix}$?

70. If you think of numbers as 1×1 matrices, which numbers are invertible 1×1 matrices?

71. ▼ Use matrix multiplication to check that the inverse of a general 2×2 matrix is given by

$$\begin{bmatrix} a & b \\ c & d \end{bmatrix}^{-1} = \frac{1}{ad - bc} \begin{bmatrix} d & -b \\ -c & a \end{bmatrix}$$

(provided that $ad - bc \neq 0$).

72. ◆ Derive the formula in Exercise 71 using row reduction. (Assume that $ad - bc \neq 0$.)

73. ▼ A **diagonal** matrix D has the following form:

$$D = \begin{bmatrix} d_1 & 0 & 0 & \cdots & 0 \\ 0 & d_2 & 0 & \cdots & 0 \\ 0 & 0 & d_3 & \cdots & 0 \\ \vdots & \vdots & \vdots & \ddots & \vdots \\ 0 & 0 & 0 & \cdots & d_n \end{bmatrix}.$$

When is D singular? Why?

74. ▼ If a square matrix A row-reduces to the identity matrix, must it be invertible? If so, say why. If not, give an example of such a (singular) matrix.

75. ▼ If A and B are invertible, check that $B^{-1}A^{-1}$ is the inverse of AB.

76. ▼ Solve the matrix equation $A(B + CX) = D$ for X. (You may assume that A and C are invertible square matrices.)

77. ◆ In Example 3 we said that, if a square matrix A row-reduces to a matrix with a row of zeros, then it is singular. Why?

78. ◆ Your friend has two square matrices A and B, neither of them the zero matrix, with the property that AB is the zero matrix. You immediately tell him that neither A nor B can possibly be invertible. How can you be so sure?

5.4 Game Theory

Two-Person Zero-Sum Games

It frequently happens that you are faced with making a decision or choosing a best strategy from several possible choices. For instance, you might need to decide whether to invest in stocks or bonds, whether to cut prices of the product you sell, or what offensive play to use in a football game. In these examples the result depends on something you cannot control: In the first case your success depends on the future behavior of the economy. In the second case it depends in part on whether your competitors also cut prices. In the third case it depends on the defensive strategy chosen by the opposing team.

In all three cases you are, in a sense, "playing a game" in which your "opponent" is the economy, your competitors, or the opposing team, respectively. The degree of success resulting from your decision can be measured numerically in each case—your investment profit, increased revenue, or yardage gained on the football field—and we call this your *payoff*. **Game theory** is the mathematical study of situations like these, which, because they involve two "players," are called **two-person games**. The simplest types of two-person games are **zero-sum** games: Each player's gain (or payoff) resulting from a decision is equal to the opponent's loss.*

Game theory is very new in comparison with most of the mathematics you learn. It was invented in the 1920s by the noted mathematicians Emile Borel (1871–1956) and John von Neumann (1903–1957). Game theory's connection with linear programming was discovered even more recently, in 1947, by von Neumann, and further advances were made by the mathematician John Nash (1928–2015),[†] for which he received the 1994 Nobel Prize for Economics.

* An example of a *non-zero-sum game* would be one in which the government taxed the earnings of the winner. In that case the winner's gain would be less than the loser's loss.

† Nash's turbulent life is the subject of the biography *A Beautiful Mind* by Sylvia Nasar (Simon & Schuster, 1998). The 2001 Academy Award–winning movie of the same title is a somewhat fictionalized account.

The Payoff Matrix and Expected Payoff

In two-person zero-sum games we represent the various options and payoffs in a matrix, and we can then calculate the best strategy using matrix algebra and other techniques, as we now illustrate with a simple type of game.

We have probably all played the game "Rock, Paper, Scissors" at some time in our lives. It goes as follows: There are two players—let us call them A and B—and at each turn, each player produces, by a gesture of the hand, either paper, a pair of scissors, or a rock. Rock beats scissors (since a rock can crush scissors) but is beaten by paper (since a rock can be covered by paper), while scissors beat paper (since scissors can cut paper). The round is a draw if both A and B show the same item. We could turn this into a betting game if, at each turn, we require the loser to pay the winner 1¢. For instance, if A shows a rock and B shows paper, then A pays B 1¢.

Rock, Paper, Scissors is an example of a two-person zero-sum game because each player's loss is equal to the other player's gain. We can represent this game by a matrix, called the **payoff matrix**:

$$
\mathbf{A} \begin{array}{c} r \\ p \\ s \end{array} \overset{\overset{\displaystyle \mathbf{B}}{\begin{array}{ccc} r & p & s \end{array}}}{\begin{bmatrix} 0 & -1 & 1 \\ 1 & 0 & -1 \\ -1 & 1 & 0 \end{bmatrix}} \quad \text{or just} \quad P = \begin{bmatrix} 0 & -1 & 1 \\ 1 & 0 & -1 \\ -1 & 1 & 0 \end{bmatrix}
$$

if we choose to omit the labels. In the payoff matrix, Player A's options, or **moves**, are listed on the left, while Player B's options are listed on top. We think of A as playing the rows and B as playing the columns. The entries of the matrix are the **payoffs**. Positive payoffs indicate a win for the row player, while negative payoffs indicate a loss for the row player. Thus, for example, the *p*, *s* entry is the payoff if A plays *p* (paper) and B plays *s* (scissors). In this event, B wins, and the -1 payoff there indicates that A loses 1¢. (If that payoff were -2 instead, it would have meant that A loses 2¢.)

Two-Person Zero-Sum Game, Strategies

A **two-person zero-sum game** is one in which one player's loss equals the other's gain. We assume that the outcome is determined by each player's choice from among a fixed, finite set of moves. If Player A has m moves to choose from and Player B has n, we can represent the game using the **payoff matrix**, the $m \times n$ matrix showing Player A's payoff resulting from each possible pair of choices of moves.

In each round of the game, the way a player chooses a move is called a **strategy**. A player using a **pure strategy** makes the same move each round of the game. For example, if a player in the above game chooses to play scissors at each turn, then that player is using the pure strategy s. A player using a **mixed strategy** chooses each move a certain percentage of the time in a random fashion; for instance, Player A might choose to play p 50% of the time and each of s and r 25% of the time.

Our ultimate goal is to be able to determine which strategy is best for each player to use. To do that, we need to know how to evaluate strategies. The fundamental calculation we need is that of the **expected payoff** resulting from the strategies used by the two players. Let's look at a simple example.

EXAMPLE 1 **Expected Payoff**

Consider the following game:

$$
\begin{array}{c}
\\
\text{A}
\end{array}
\begin{array}{c}
\quad \text{B} \\
\begin{array}{cc} a & b \end{array} \\
\begin{array}{c} p \\ q \end{array}
\left[\begin{array}{cc} 3 & -1 \\ -2 & 3 \end{array}\right].
\end{array}
$$

The row player (Player A) decides to pick moves at random, choosing to play p 75% of the time and q 25% of the time. The column player (Player B) also picks moves at random, choosing a 20% of the time and b 80% of the time. On average, how much does A expect to win or lose?

Solution Suppose they play the game 100 times. Each time they play, there are four possible outcomes:

Case 1: A plays p, B plays a.
Because A plays p only 75% of the time and B plays a only 20% of the time, we expect this case to occur $0.75 \times 0.20 = 0.15$, or 15% of the time, or 15 times out of 100. Each time this happens, A gains 3 points, so we get a contribution of $15 \times 3 = 45$ points to A's total winnings.

Case 2: A plays p, B plays b.
Because A plays p only 75% of the time and B plays b only 80% of the time, we expect this case to occur $0.75 \times 0.80 = 0.60$, or 60 times out of 100. Each time this happens, A loses 1 point, so we get a contribution of $60 \times -1 = -60$ to A's total winnings.

Case 3: A plays q, B plays a.
This case occurs $0.25 \times 0.20 = 0.05$, or 5 out of 100 times, with a loss of 2 points to A each time, giving a contribution of $5 \times -2 = -10$ to A's total winnings.

Case 4: A plays q, B plays b.
This case occurs $0.25 \times 0.80 = 0.20$, or 20 out of 100 times, with a gain of 3 points to A each time, giving a contribution of $20 \times 3 = 60$ to A's total winnings.

Summing to get A's total winnings and then dividing by the number of times the game is played, we get the average value of

$$(45 - 60 - 10 + 60)/100 = 0.35$$

so A can expect to win an average of 0.35 points per play of the game. We call 0.35 the **expected payoff** of the game resulting from these particular strategies for A and B.

This calculation was somewhat tedious, and it would only get worse if A and B had many moves to choose from. There is a far more convenient way of doing exactly the same calculation, using matrix multiplication: We start by representing the player's strategies as matrices. For reasons to become clear in a moment, we record A's strategy as a row matrix:

$$R = [0.75 \quad 0.25].$$

We record B's strategy as a column matrix:

$$C = \begin{bmatrix} 0.20 \\ 0.80 \end{bmatrix}.$$

(We will sometimes write column vectors using transpose notation, writing, for example, $[0.20 \quad 0.80]^T$ for the column above, to save space.) Now: *The expected payoff is the matrix product RPC, where P is the payoff matrix!*

$$\text{Expected payoff} = RPC = [0.75 \quad 0.25] \begin{bmatrix} 3 & -1 \\ -2 & 3 \end{bmatrix} \begin{bmatrix} 0.20 \\ 0.80 \end{bmatrix}$$

$$= [1.75 \quad 0] \begin{bmatrix} 0.20 \\ 0.80 \end{bmatrix} = [0.35].$$

Why does this work? Write out the arithmetic involved in the matrix product *RPC* to see what we calculated:

$$[0.75 \times 3 + 0.25 \times (-2)] \times 0.20 + [0.75 \times (-1) + 0.25 \times 3] \times 0.80$$

$$= 0.75 \times 3 \times 0.20 + 0.25 \times (-2) \times 0.20 + 0.75 \times (-1) \times 0.80 + 0.25 \times 3 \times 0.80$$

$$= \quad \text{Case 1} \quad + \quad \text{Case 3} \quad + \quad \text{Case 2} \quad + \quad \text{Case 4.}$$

So the matrix product does all at once the various cases we considered above.

Using Technology

The use of technology becomes indispensable when we need to do several calculations or when the matrices involved are big. See the technology note accompanying Example 3 in Section 5.2 for instructions on multiplying matrices using a TI-83/84 Plus, a spreadsheet, and the Matrix Algebra Tool at the Website.

Let's summarize what we just saw.

The Expected Payoff Resulting from Mixed Strategies *R* and *C*

The **expected payoff of a game resulting from given mixed strategies** is the average payoff that occurs if the game is played a large number of times with the row and column players using the given strategies.

To compute the expected payoff resulting from given mixed strategies:

1. Write the row player's mixed strategy as a row matrix *R*.
2. Write the column player's mixed strategy as a column matrix *C*.
3. Calculate the product *RPC*, where *P* is the payoff matrix. This product is a 1×1 matrix whose entry is the expected payoff *e*.

Quick Example

1. Consider a game of "Rock, Paper, Scissors" with a dollar payoff for the winner each round:

$$\begin{array}{c} \\ r \\ p \\ s \end{array} \begin{array}{c} \begin{array}{ccc} r & p & s \end{array} \\ \begin{bmatrix} 0 & -1 & 1 \\ 1 & 0 & -1 \\ -1 & 1 & 0 \end{bmatrix} \end{array}$$

Suppose that the row player plays *rock* half the time and each of the other two strategies a quarter of the time and that the column player always plays *paper*. We write

$$R = \begin{bmatrix} \frac{1}{2} & \frac{1}{4} & \frac{1}{4} \end{bmatrix} \quad \text{and} \quad C = \begin{bmatrix} 0 \\ 1 \\ 0 \end{bmatrix}.$$

So

$$e = RPC = \begin{bmatrix} \frac{1}{2} & \frac{1}{4} & \frac{1}{4} \end{bmatrix} \begin{bmatrix} 0 & -1 & 1 \\ 1 & 0 & -1 \\ -1 & 1 & 0 \end{bmatrix} \begin{bmatrix} 0 \\ 1 \\ 0 \end{bmatrix}$$

$$= \begin{bmatrix} \frac{1}{2} & \frac{1}{4} & \frac{1}{4} \end{bmatrix} \begin{bmatrix} -1 \\ 0 \\ 1 \end{bmatrix} = -\frac{1}{4}.$$

Thus, the row player can expect to lose, on average, \$1 every four plays.

Solving a Game

Now that we know how to evaluate particular strategies, we want to find the *best* strategy. The next example takes us another step toward that goal.

EXAMPLE 2 Television Ratings Wars

Commercial TV station RTV and cultural station CTV are competing for viewers in the Tuesday prime-time 9–10 pm time slot. RTV is trying to decide whether to show a sitcom, a docudrama, a reality show, or a movie, while CTV is thinking about either a nature documentary, a symphony concert, a ballet, or an opera. A television rating company estimates the payoffs for the various alternatives as follows. (Each point indicates a shift of 1,000 viewers from one channel to the other; thus, for instance, -2 indicates a shift of 2,000 viewers from RTV to CTV.)

		CTV			
		Nature Doc.	**Symphony**	**Ballet**	**Opera**
	Sitcom	2	1	−2	2
	Docudrama	−1	1	−1	2
RTV	**Reality Show**	−2	0	0	1
	Movie	3	1	−1	1

a. If RTV notices that CTV is showing nature documentaries half the time and symphonies the other half, what would RTV's best strategy be, and how many viewers would it gain if it followed this strategy?

b. If, on the other hand, CTV notices that RTV is showing docudramas half the time and reality shows the other half, what would CTV's best strategy be, and how many viewers would it gain or lose if it followed this strategy?

Solution

a. We are given the matrix of the game, P, in the table above, and we are given CTV's strategy $C = \begin{bmatrix} 0.50 & 0.50 & 0 & 0 \end{bmatrix}^T$. We are not given RTV's strategy R. To say that RTV is looking for its best strategy is to say that it wants the resulting expected payoff $e = RPC$ to be as high as possible. So we take $R = \begin{bmatrix} x & y & z & t \end{bmatrix}$ and look for values for x, y, z, and t that make RPC as high as possible. First, we calculate e in terms of these unknowns:

$$e = RPC = \begin{bmatrix} x & y & z & t \end{bmatrix} \begin{bmatrix} 2 & 1 & -2 & 2 \\ -1 & 1 & -1 & 2 \\ -2 & 0 & 0 & 1 \\ 3 & 1 & -1 & 1 \end{bmatrix} \begin{bmatrix} 0.50 \\ 0.50 \\ 0 \\ 0 \end{bmatrix}$$

$$= \begin{bmatrix} x & y & z & t \end{bmatrix} \begin{bmatrix} 1.5 \\ 0 \\ -1 \\ 2 \end{bmatrix} = 1.5x - z + 2t.$$

Now, the unknowns x, y, z, and t must be nonnegative and add up to 1 (why?). Also, because t has the largest coefficient, 2, we'll get the best result by making it as large as possible, namely, $t = 1$, leaving $x = y = z = 0$. Thus, RTV's best strategy is $R = \begin{bmatrix} 0 & 0 & 0 & 1 \end{bmatrix}$. In other words, RTV should use the pure strategy of showing a movie every Tuesday evening. If it does so, the expected payoff will be

$$e = 1.5(0) - 0 + 2(1) = 2,$$

so RTV can expect to gain 2,000 viewers.

b. Here, we are given $R = \begin{bmatrix} 0 & 0.50 & 0.50 & 0 \end{bmatrix}$ and are not given CTV's strategy C, so this time we take $C = \begin{bmatrix} x & y & z & t \end{bmatrix}^T$ and calculate the resulting expected payoff e:

$$e = RPC = \begin{bmatrix} 0 & 0.50 & 0.50 & 0 \end{bmatrix} \begin{bmatrix} 2 & 1 & -2 & 2 \\ -1 & 1 & -1 & 2 \\ -2 & 0 & 0 & 1 \\ 3 & 1 & -1 & 1 \end{bmatrix} \begin{bmatrix} x \\ y \\ z \\ t \end{bmatrix}$$

$$= \begin{bmatrix} -1.5 & 0.5 & -0.5 & 1.5 \end{bmatrix} \begin{bmatrix} x \\ y \\ z \\ t \end{bmatrix} = -1.5x + 0.5y - 0.5z + 1.5t.$$

Now, CTV wants e to be as *low* as possible (why?). Because x has the largest negative coefficient, CTV would like it to be as large as possible: $x = 1$, so the rest of the unknowns must be zero. Thus, CTV's best strategy is $C = \begin{bmatrix} 1 & 0 & 0 & 0 \end{bmatrix}^T$; that is, show a nature documentary every night. If it does so, the expected payoff will be

$$e = -1.5(1) + 0.5(0) - 0.5(0) + 1.5(0) = -1.5.$$

So CTV can expect to gain 1,500 viewers.

Example 2 illustrates the fact that, no matter what mixed strategy one player selects, the other player can choose an appropriate *pure* counterstrategy to maximize its gain. How does this affect what decisions you should make as one of the players? If you were on the board of directors of RTV, you might reason as follows: Since for every mixed strategy you try, CTV can find a best counterstrategy (as in part (b)), it is in your company's best interest to select a mixed strategy that *minimizes* the effect of CTV's best counterstrategy. This is called the **minimax criterion**.

Minimax Criterion

A player using the **minimax criterion** chooses a strategy that, among all possible strategies, minimizes the effect of the other player's best counterstrategy. That is, an optimal (best) strategy according to the minimax criterion is one that minimizes the maximum damage the opponent can cause.

This criterion assumes that your opponent is determined to win. More precisely, it assumes the following.

Fundamental Principle of Game Theory

Each player tries to use its best possible strategy and assumes that the other player is doing the same.

This principle is not always followed by every player. For example, one of the players may be Nature and may choose its move at random, with no particular purpose in mind. In such a case, criteria other than the minimax criterion may be more appropriate. For example, there is the "maximax" criterion, which maximizes the maximum possible payoff (also known as the "reckless" strategy), or the criterion that seeks to minimize "regret" (the difference between the payoff you get and the payoff you *would have gotten* if you had known beforehand what was going to happen).[*] But we shall assume here the fundamental principle and try to find optimal strategies under the minimax criterion.

Finding the optimal strategy is called **solving the game**. In general, solving a game can be done by using linear programming, as we shall see in Chapter 6. However, we can solve 2 × 2 games "by hand," as we shall see in the next example. First, we notice that some large games can be reduced to smaller games.

Consider the game in Example 2, which had the following matrix:

$$P = \begin{bmatrix} 2 & 1 & -2 & 2 \\ -1 & 1 & -1 & 2 \\ -2 & 0 & 0 & 1 \\ 3 & 1 & -1 & 1 \end{bmatrix}.$$

Compare the second and third columns through the eyes of the column player, CTV. Every payoff in the third column is, from CTV's point of view, as good as or better than the corresponding entry in the second column. Thus, no matter what RTV does, CTV will do better showing a ballet (third column) than a symphony (second

[*] See *Location in Space: Theoretical Perspectives in Economic Geography*, 3rd Edition, by Peter Dicken and Peter E. Lloyd, HarperCollins Publishers, 1990, p. 276.

column). We say that the third column **dominates** the second column. As far as CTV is concerned, we might as well forget about symphonies entirely, so we remove the second column. Similarly, the third column dominates the fourth, so we can remove the fourth column too. This gives us a smaller game to work with:

$$P = \begin{bmatrix} 2 & -2 \\ -1 & -1 \\ -2 & 0 \\ 3 & -1 \end{bmatrix}.$$

Now compare the first and last rows. Every payoff in the last row is larger than the corresponding payoff in the first row, so the last row is always better for RTV. Again, we say that the last row **dominates** the first row, and we can discard the first row. Similarly, the last row dominates the second row, so we discard the second row as well. This reduces us to the following game:

$$P = \begin{bmatrix} -2 & 0 \\ 3 & -1 \end{bmatrix}.$$

In this matrix, neither row dominates the other, and neither column dominates the other. So this is as far as we can go with this line of argument. We call this **reduction by dominance**.

Reduction by Dominance

One *row* **dominates** another if every entry in the former is greater than or equal to the corresponding entry in the latter. Put another way, one row dominates another if it is always at least as good for the row player.

One *column* dominates another if every entry in the former is less than or equal to the corresponding entry in the latter. Put another way, one column dominates another if it is always at least as good for the column player.

Procedure for Reducing by Dominance:
1. Check whether there is any row in the (remaining) matrix that is dominated by another row. Remove all dominated rows.

2. Check whether there is any column in the (remaining) matrix that is dominated by another column. Remove all dominated columns.

3. Repeat Steps 1 and 2 until there are no dominated rows or columns.*

---

* We can also reverse the order of Steps 1 and 2 as we did for the payoff matrix above: First remove dominated columns, then remove dominated rows, and repeat the two steps until there are no dominated columns or rows.

Let us now go back to the television ratings wars example and see how we can solve a game using the minimax criterion once we are down to a 2×2 payoff matrix.

EXAMPLE 3 **Solving a 2 × 2 Game**

Continuing from Example 2:

a. Find the optimal strategy for RTV.

b. Find the optimal strategy for CTV.

c. Find the expected payoff of the game if RTV and CTV use their optimal strategies.

Solution As in the text, we begin by reducing the game by dominance, which brings us down to the following 2×2 game:

		CTV	
		Nature Doc.	**Ballet**
RTV	**Reality Show**	-2	0
	Movie	3	-1

a. Now let's find RTV's optimal strategy. Because we don't yet know what it is, we write down a general strategy:

$$R = \begin{bmatrix} x & y \end{bmatrix}.$$

Because $x + y = 1$, we can replace y by $1 - x$:

$$R = \begin{bmatrix} x & 1 - x \end{bmatrix}.$$

We know that CTV's best counterstrategy to R will be a pure strategy (see the discussion after Example 2), so let's compute the expected payoff that results from each of CTV's possible pure strategies:

$$e = \begin{bmatrix} x & 1 - x \end{bmatrix} \begin{bmatrix} -2 & 0 \\ 3 & -1 \end{bmatrix} \begin{bmatrix} 1 \\ 0 \end{bmatrix}$$

$$= (-2)x + 3(1 - x) = -5x + 3$$

$$f = \begin{bmatrix} x & 1 - x \end{bmatrix} \begin{bmatrix} -2 & 0 \\ 3 & -1 \end{bmatrix} \begin{bmatrix} 0 \\ 1 \end{bmatrix}$$

$$= 0x - (1 - x) = x - 1.$$

Because both e and f depend on x, we can graph them as in Figure 1.

If, for instance, RTV happened to choose $x = 0.5$, then the expected payoffs resulting from CTV's two pure strategies are $e = -5(1/2) + 3 = 1/2$ and $f = 1/2 - 1 = -1/2$. The worst outcome for RTV is the lower of the two, f, and this will be true wherever the graph of f is below the graph of e. On the other hand, if RTV chose $x = 1$, the graph of e would be lower, and the worst possible expected value would be $e = -5(1) + 3 = -2$. Since RTV can choose x to be any value between 0 and 1, the worst possible outcomes are those shown by the colored portion of the graph in Figure 2.

Because RTV is trying to make the worst possible outcome as large as possible (that is, to minimize damages), it is seeking the point on the colored portion of the graph that is highest. This is the intersection point of the two lines. To calculate its coordinates, it's easiest to equate the two functions of x:

$$-5x + 3 = x - 1,$$
$$-6x = -4,$$

or

$$x = \frac{2}{3}.$$

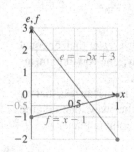

Figure 1

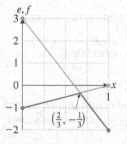

Figure 2

The e (or f) coordinate is then obtained by substituting $x = 2/3$ into the expression for e (or f), giving

$$e = -5\left(\frac{2}{3}\right) + 3$$

$$= -\frac{1}{3}.$$

We conclude that RTV's best strategy is to take $x = 2/3$, giving an expected value of $-1/3$. In other words, RTV's optimal mixed strategy is

$$R = \begin{bmatrix} \frac{2}{3} & \frac{1}{3} \end{bmatrix}.$$

Going back to the original game, RTV should show reality shows 2/3 of the time and movies 1/3 of the time. It should not bother showing any sitcoms or docudramas. It expects to lose, on average, 333 viewers to CTV, but all of its other options are worse.

b. To find CTV's optimal strategy, we must reverse roles and start by writing its unknown strategy as follows:

$$C = \begin{bmatrix} x \\ 1 - x \end{bmatrix}.$$

We calculate the expected payoffs for the two pure row strategies:

$$e = \begin{bmatrix} 1 & 0 \end{bmatrix} \begin{bmatrix} -2 & 0 \\ 3 & -1 \end{bmatrix} \begin{bmatrix} x \\ 1 - x \end{bmatrix}$$

$$= -2x$$

and

$$f = \begin{bmatrix} 0 & 1 \end{bmatrix} \begin{bmatrix} -2 & 0 \\ 3 & -1 \end{bmatrix} \begin{bmatrix} x \\ 1 - x \end{bmatrix}$$

$$= 3x - (1 - x)$$

$$= 4x - 1.$$

As with the row player, we know that the column player's best strategy will correspond to the intersection of the graphs of e and f (Figure 3). (Why is the upper edge colored, rather than the lower edge?) The graphs intersect when

$$-2x = 4x - 1$$

or

$$x = \frac{1}{6}.$$

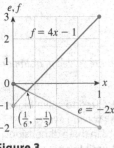

Figure 3

The corresponding value of e (or f) is

$$e = -2\left(\frac{1}{6}\right) = -\frac{1}{3}.$$

Thus, CTV's optimal mixed strategy is $\begin{bmatrix} \frac{1}{6} & \frac{5}{6} \end{bmatrix}^T$, and the expected payoff is $-1/3$. So CTV should show nature documentaries 1/6 of the time and ballets 5/6 of the time. It should not bother to show symphonies or operas. It expects to gain, on average, 333 viewers from RTV.

c. We can now calculate the expected payoff as usual, using the optimal strategies we found in parts (a) and (b):

$$e = RPC$$

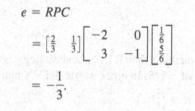

$$= \begin{bmatrix} \frac{2}{3} & \frac{1}{3} \end{bmatrix} \begin{bmatrix} -2 & 0 \\ 3 & -1 \end{bmatrix} \begin{bmatrix} \frac{1}{6} \\ \frac{5}{6} \end{bmatrix}$$

$$= -\frac{1}{3}.$$

➡ **Before we go on ...** In Example 3 it is no accident that the expected payoff resulting from the optimal strategies equals the expected payoff we found in parts (a) and (b). If we call the expected payoff resulting from the optimal strategies the **expected value of the game**, the row player's optimal strategy guarantees an expected payoff no smaller than the expected value, while the column player's optimal strategy guarantees an expected payoff no larger. Together they force the average payoff to be the expected value of the game. ■

Expected Value of a Game

The **expected value of a game** is the expected payoff that results when the row and column players use their optimal (minimax) strategies. By using its optimal strategy, the row player guarantees an expected payoff no lower than the expected value of the game, no matter what the column player does. Similarly, by using its optimal strategy, the column player guarantees an expected payoff no higher than the expected value of the game, no matter what the row player does.

Q : *What about games that don't reduce to 2 × 2 matrices? Are these solved in a similar way?*

A : The method illustrated in Example 3 cannot easily be generalized to solve bigger games (i.e., games that cannot be reduced to 2 × 2 matrices); solving even a 2 × 3 game using this approach would require us to consider graphs in three dimensions. To be able to solve games of arbitrary size, we need to wait until the next chapter (Section 6.5), where we describe a method for solving a game, using the simplex method, that works for all payoff matrices.

Strictly Determined Games

Although we haven't yet discussed how to solve general $m \times n$ games, there are certain kinds of games that can be solved quite simply regardless of size, as illustrated by the following example.

EXAMPLE 4   **Strictly Determined Game**

Solve the following game:

$$
\begin{array}{c}
 & \begin{array}{ccc} p & q & r \end{array} \\
\begin{array}{c} s \\ t \\ u \end{array}
\left[
\begin{array}{ccc}
-4 & -3 & 3 \\
2 & -1 & -2 \\
1 & 0 & 2
\end{array}
\right].
\end{array}
$$

Solution Call the row player A and the column player B. If we look carefully at this matrix, we see that no row dominates another and no column dominates another, so we can't reduce it. Nor do we know how to solve a 3 × 3 game, so it looks as if we're stuck. However, there is a way to understand this particular game. With the minimax criterion in mind, let's begin by considering the worst possible outcomes for the row player for each possible move. We do this by circling the smallest payoff in each row, the **row minima**:

$$
\begin{array}{cc}
\begin{array}{c}
 & \begin{array}{ccc} p & q & r \end{array} \\
\begin{array}{c} s \\ t \\ u \end{array}
\left[
\begin{array}{ccc}
\boxed{-4} & -3 & 3 \\
2 & -1 & \boxed{-2} \\
1 & \boxed{0} & 2
\end{array}
\right]
\end{array}
&
\begin{array}{l}
\text{Row minima} \\[6pt]
-4 \\
-2 \\
0 \leftarrow \text{(largest)}
\end{array}
\end{array}
$$

So, for example, if A plays move s, the worst possible outcome is to lose 4. Player A takes the least risk by using move u, which has the largest row minimum.

We do the same thing for the column player, remembering that smaller payoffs are better for B and larger payoffs are worse. We draw a box around the largest payoff in each column, the **column maxima**:

$$
\begin{array}{c}
 & \begin{array}{ccc} p & q & r \end{array} \\
\begin{array}{c} s \\ t \\ u \end{array}
\left[
\begin{array}{ccc}
-4 & -3 & \boxed{3} \\
\boxed{2} & -1 & -2 \\
1 & \boxed{0} & 2
\end{array}
\right].
\end{array}
$$

Column maxima   2   0   3
                      ↑
                (smallest)

Player B takes the least risk by using move q, which has the smallest column maximum.

Now put the circles and boxes together:

$$
\begin{array}{c}
 & \begin{array}{ccc} p & q & r \end{array} \\
\begin{array}{c} s \\ t \\ u \end{array}
\left[
\begin{array}{ccc}
\boxed{-4} & -3 & \boxed{3} \\
\boxed{2} & -1 & \boxed{-2} \\
1 & \boxed{0} & 2
\end{array}
\right].
\end{array}
$$

Notice that the uq entry is both circled and boxed: It is both a row minimum and a column maximum. We call such an entry a **saddle point**.

Now we claim that the optimal strategy for A is to always play u, while the optimal strategy for B is to always play q. By playing u, A guarantees that the payoff will be 0 or higher, no matter what B does, so the expected value of the game has to be *at least* 0. On the other hand, by playing q, B guarantees that the payoff will be 0 or less, so the expected value of the game has to be *no more than* 0. Combining these facts, we conclude that the expected value of the game must be exactly 0, and A and B have no strategies that could do any better for them than the pure strategies u and q.

➡ **Before we go on . . .** You should consider what happens in an example like the television ratings wars game of Example 3. In that game, the largest row minimum is -1, while the smallest column maximum is 0; there is no saddle point. The row player can force a payoff of at least -1 by playing a pure strategy (always showing movies, for example) but can do better, forcing an expected payoff of $-1/3$, by playing a mixed strategy, as we saw in Example 3. Similarly, the column player can force the payoff to be 0 or less with a pure strategy, but can do better, forcing an expected payoff of $-1/3$, with a mixed strategy. Only when there is a saddle point will pure strategies be optimal. ∎

Strictly Determined Game

A **saddle point** is a payoff v that is simultaneously a row minimum and a column maximum (both boxed and circled in our approach). If a game has a saddle point, the corresponding row and column strategies are the optimal ones, the expected value of the game is the payoff v, and we say that the game is **strictly determined**.

If a game has two or more saddle points, then they all must have the same value, and all of the corresponding strategies are optimal.

FAQs

Solving a Game

Q : *We've seen several ways of trying to solve a game. What should I do and in what order?*

A : Here are the steps you should take when trying to solve a game:

1. Reduce by dominance. This should always be your first step.

2. If you were able to reduce to a 1 × 1 game, you're done. The optimal strategies are the corresponding pure strategies, as they dominate all the others.

3. Look for a saddle point in the reduced game. If it has one, the game is strictly determined, and the corresponding pure strategies are optimal.

4. If your reduced game is 2 × 2 and has no saddle point, use the method of Example 3 to find the optimal mixed strategies.

5. If your reduced game is larger than 2 × 2 and has no saddle point, you have to use linear programming to solve it, but that will have to wait until Chapter 6.

Using Technology

🐺 Website
www.WanerMath.com
To play a two-player zero-sum game against your computer, and also to automatically reduce by dominance and solve arbitrary games up to 5 × 5, follow

→ Online Utilities
→ Game Theory Tool

5.4   EXERCISES

▼ more advanced   ◆ challenging

🅣 indicates exercises that should be solved using technology

In Exercises 1–4, calculate the expected payoff of the game with payoff matrix

$$P = \begin{bmatrix} 2 & 0 & -1 & 2 \\ -1 & 0 & 0 & -2 \\ -2 & 0 & 0 & 1 \\ 3 & 1 & -1 & 1 \end{bmatrix}$$

using the mixed strategies supplied. [**HINT**: See Example 1.]

1. $R = \begin{bmatrix} 0 & 1 & 0 & 0 \end{bmatrix}, C = \begin{bmatrix} 1 & 0 & 0 & 0 \end{bmatrix}^T$

2. $R = \begin{bmatrix} 0 & 0 & 0 & 1 \end{bmatrix}, C = \begin{bmatrix} 0 & 1 & 0 & 0 \end{bmatrix}^T$

3. $R = \begin{bmatrix} 0.5 & 0.5 & 0 & 0 \end{bmatrix}, C = \begin{bmatrix} 0 & 0 & 0.5 & 0.5 \end{bmatrix}^T$

4. $R = \begin{bmatrix} 0 & 0.5 & 0 & 0.5 \end{bmatrix}, C = \begin{bmatrix} 0.5 & 0.5 & 0 & 0 \end{bmatrix}^T$

In Exercises 5–8, either a mixed column or mixed row strategy is given. In each case, use

$$P = \begin{bmatrix} 0 & -1 & 5 \\ 2 & -2 & 4 \\ 0 & 3 & 0 \\ 1 & 0 & -5 \end{bmatrix},$$

and find the optimal pure strategy (or strategies) the other player should use. Express the answer as a row or column matrix. Also determine the resulting expected payoff. [**HINT**: See Example 2.]

5. $C = \begin{bmatrix} 0.25 & 0.75 & 0 \end{bmatrix}^T$

6. $C = \begin{bmatrix} \frac{1}{3} & \frac{1}{3} & \frac{1}{3} \end{bmatrix}^T$

7. $R = \begin{bmatrix} \frac{1}{2} & 0 & \frac{1}{4} & \frac{1}{4} \end{bmatrix}$

8. $R = \begin{bmatrix} 0.8 & 0.2 & 0 & 0 \end{bmatrix}$

In Exercises 9–14, reduce the given payoff matrix by dominance.

9.
$$\begin{array}{c} \\ a \\ b \end{array} \begin{array}{ccc} p & q & r \\ \left[\begin{array}{ccc} 1 & 1 & 10 \\ 2 & 3 & -4 \end{array}\right] \end{array}$$

10.
$$\begin{array}{c} \\ a \\ b \end{array} \begin{array}{ccc} p & q & r \\ \left[\begin{array}{ccc} 2 & 0 & 10 \\ 15 & -4 & -5 \end{array}\right] \end{array}$$

11.
$$\begin{array}{c} \\ 1 \\ 2 \\ 3 \end{array} \begin{array}{ccc} a & b & c \\ \left[\begin{array}{ccc} 2 & -4 & -9 \\ -1 & -2 & -3 \\ 5 & 0 & -1 \end{array}\right] \end{array}$$

12.
$$\begin{array}{c} \\ 1 \\ 2 \\ 3 \end{array} \begin{array}{ccc} a & b & c \\ \left[\begin{array}{ccc} 0 & -1 & -5 \\ -3 & -10 & 10 \\ 2 & 3 & -4 \end{array}\right] \end{array}$$

13.
$$\begin{array}{c} \\ p \\ q \\ r \\ s \end{array} \begin{array}{ccc} a & b & c \\ \left[\begin{array}{ccc} 1 & -1 & -5 \\ 4 & 0 & 2 \\ 3 & -3 & 10 \\ 3 & -5 & -4 \end{array}\right] \end{array}$$

14.
$$\begin{array}{c} \\ p \\ q \\ r \\ s \end{array} \begin{array}{ccc} a & b & c \\ \left[\begin{array}{ccc} 2 & -4 & 9 \\ 1 & 1 & 0 \\ -1 & -2 & -3 \\ 1 & 1 & -1 \end{array}\right] \end{array}$$

In Exercises 15–20, decide whether the game is strictly determined. If it is, give the players' optimal pure strategies and the value of the game. [**HINT**: See Example 4.]

15.
$$\begin{array}{c} \\ a \\ b \end{array} \begin{array}{cc} p & q \\ \left[\begin{array}{cc} 1 & 1 \\ 2 & -4 \end{array}\right] \end{array}$$

16.
$$\begin{array}{c} \\ a \\ b \end{array} \begin{array}{cc} p & q \\ \left[\begin{array}{cc} -1 & 2 \\ 10 & -1 \end{array}\right] \end{array}$$

17.
$$\begin{array}{c} \\ a \\ b \end{array} \begin{array}{ccc} p & q & r \\ \left[\begin{array}{ccc} 2 & 0 & -2 \\ -1 & 3 & 0 \end{array}\right] \end{array}$$

18.
$$\begin{array}{c} \\ a \\ b \end{array} \begin{array}{ccc} p & q & r \\ \left[\begin{array}{ccc} -2 & 1 & -3 \\ -2 & 3 & -2 \end{array}\right] \end{array}$$

19.
$$\begin{array}{c} \\ P \\ Q \\ R \\ S \end{array} \begin{array}{ccc} a & b & c \\ \left[\begin{array}{ccc} 1 & -1 & -5 \\ 4 & -4 & 2 \\ 3 & -3 & -10 \\ 5 & -5 & -4 \end{array}\right] \end{array}$$

20.
$$\begin{array}{c} \\ P \\ Q \\ R \\ S \end{array} \begin{array}{ccc} a & b & c \\ \left[\begin{array}{ccc} -2 & -4 & 9 \\ 1 & 1 & 0 \\ -1 & -2 & -3 \\ 1 & 1 & -1 \end{array}\right] \end{array}$$

In Exercises 21–24, find (a) the optimal mixed row strategy, (b) the optimal mixed column strategy, and (c) the expected value of the game. [**HINT**: See Example 3.]

21. $P = \begin{bmatrix} -1 & 2 \\ 0 & -1 \end{bmatrix}$

22. $P = \begin{bmatrix} -1 & 0 \\ 1 & -1 \end{bmatrix}$

23. $P = \begin{bmatrix} -1 & -2 \\ -2 & 1 \end{bmatrix}$

24. $P = \begin{bmatrix} -2 & -1 \\ -1 & -3 \end{bmatrix}$

Applications

In Exercises 25–32, set up the payoff matrix.

25. **Games to Pass the Time** You and your friend have come up with the following simple game to pass the time: In each round, you simultaneously call "heads" or "tails." If you have both called the same thing, your friend wins 1 point; if your calls differ, you win 1 point.

26. **Games to Pass the Time** Bored with the game in Exercise 25, you decide to use the following variation instead: If you both call "heads," your friend wins 2 points; if you both call "tails," your friend wins 1 point; if your calls differ, then you win 2 points if you called "heads" and 1 point if you called "tails."

27. **War Games** You are deciding whether to invade France, Sweden, or Norway, and your opponent is simultaneously deciding which of these three countries to defend. If you invade a country that your opponent is defending, you will be defeated (payoff: -1), but if you invade a country that your opponent is not defending, you will be successful (payoff: $+1$).

28. **War Games** You must decide whether to attack your opponent by sea or air, and your opponent must simultaneously decide whether to mount an all-out air defense, an all-out

coastal defense (against an attack from the sea), or a combined air and coastal defense. If there is no defense for your mode of attack, you win 100 points. If your attack is met by a shared air and coastal defense, you win 50 points. If your attack is met by an all-out defense, you lose 200 points.

29. ▼ *Marketing* Your fast-food outlet, *Burger Queen*, has obtained a license to open branches in three closely situated South African cities: Brakpan, Nigel, and Springs. Your market surveys show that Brakpan and Nigel each provide a potential market of 2,000 burgers a day, while Springs provides a potential market of 1,000 burgers per day. Your company can finance an outlet in only one of those cities. Your main competitor, *Burger Princess*, has also obtained licenses for these cities and is similarly planning to open only one outlet. If you both happen to locate at the same city, you will share the total business from all three cities equally, but if you locate in different cities, you will each get all the business in the city in which you have located plus half the business in the third city. The payoff is the number of burgers you will sell per day minus the number of burgers your competitor will sell per day.

30. ▼ *Marketing* Repeat Exercise 29, given that the potential sales markets in the three cities are Brakpan: 2,500 per day, Nigel: 1,500 per day, and Springs: 1,200 per day.

31. ▼ *Betting* When you bet on a racehorse with odds of *m–n*, you stand to win *m* dollars for every bet of *n* dollars if your horse wins; for instance, if the horse you bet is running at 5–2 and wins, you will win $5 for every $2 you bet. (Thus, a $2 bet will return $7.) Here are some actual odds from a 1992 race at Belmont Park, New York.[21] The favorite at 5–2 was Pleasant Tap, the second choice was Thunder Rumble at 7–2, while the third choice was Strike the Gold at 4–1. Assume that you are making a $10 bet on one of these horses. The payoffs are your winnings. (If your horse does not win, you lose your entire bet. Of course, it is possible for none of your horses to win.)

32. ▼ *Betting* Referring to Exercise 31, suppose that just before the race, there has been frantic betting on Thunder Rumble with the result that the odds have dropped to 2–5 for that horse. The odds on the other two horses remain unchanged.

33. *Retail Discount Wars* Just one week after your *Abercrom B* men's fashion outlet has opened at a new location near *Burger Prince* in the Mall, your rival, *Abercrom A*, opens up directly across from you. You have been informed that Abercrom A is about to launch either a 30% off everything sale or a 50% off everything sale. You, on the other hand, have decided to either *increase* prices (to make your store seem more exclusive) or do absolutely nothing. You

construct the following payoff matrix, where the payoffs represent the number of customers your outlet can expect to gain from Abercrom A:

$$\begin{array}{cc} & \textbf{Abercrom A} \\ & 30\%\ \text{Off}\quad 50\%\ \text{Off} \\ \textbf{Abercrom B}\ \begin{array}{c} \text{Do Nothing} \\ \text{Increase Prices} \end{array} & \begin{bmatrix} -60 & -40 \\ 30 & -50 \end{bmatrix}. \end{array}$$

There is a 20% chance that Abercrom A will opt for the "30% off" sale and an 80% chance that it will opt for the "50% Off" sale. Your sense from upper management at Abercrom B is that there is a 50% chance you will be given the go-ahead to raise prices. What is the expected resulting effect on your customer base?

34. *More Retail Discount Wars* Your *Abercrom B* men's fashion outlet has a 30% chance of launching an expensive new line of used auto-mechanic dungarees (complete with grease stains) and a 70% chance of staying instead with its traditional torn military-style dungarees. Your rival across from you in the mall, *Abercrom A*, appears to be deciding between a line of torn gym shirts and a more daring line of "empty shirts" (that is, empty shirt boxes). Your corporate spies reveal that there is a 20% chance that Abercrom A will opt for the empty shirt option. The following payoff matrix gives the number of customers your outlet can expect to gain from Abercrom A in each situation:

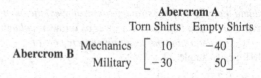

$$\begin{array}{cc} & \textbf{Abercrom A} \\ & \text{Torn Shirts}\quad \text{Empty Shirts} \\ \textbf{Abercrom B}\ \begin{array}{c} \text{Mechanics} \\ \text{Military} \end{array} & \begin{bmatrix} 10 & -40 \\ -30 & 50 \end{bmatrix}. \end{array}$$

What is the expected resulting effect on your customer base?

35. *Factory Location*[22] A manufacturer of electrical machinery is located in a cramped, though low-rent, factory close to the center of a large city. The firm needs to expand, and it could do so in one of three ways: (1) Remain where it is and install new equipment, (2) move to a suburban site near the same city, or (3) relocate in a different part of the country where labor is cheaper. Its decision will be influenced by the fact that one of the following will happen: (I) The government may introduce a program of equipment grants, (II) a new suburban highway may be built, or (III) the government may institute a policy of financial help to companies who move into regions of high unemployment. The value to the company of each combination is given in the following table:

[21] Source: *New York Times*, September 18, 1992, p. B14.

[22] Adapted from an example in *Location in Space: Theoretical Perspectives in Economic Geography* by P. Dicken and P. E. Lloyd (Harper & Row, 1990).

	Government's Options		
	I	**II**	**III**
Manufacturer's Options **1**	200	150	140
2	130	220	130
3	110	110	220

If the manufacturer judges that there is a 20% probability that the government will go with option I, a 50% probability that it will go with option II, and a 30% probability that it will go with option III, what is the manufacturer's best option?

36. *Crop Choice*[23] A farmer has a choice of growing wheat, barley, or rice. Her success will depend on the weather, which could be dry, average, or wet, as measured in the following table:

	Weather		
	Dry	**Average**	**Wet**
Crop Choices **Wheat**	20	20	10
Barley	10	15	20
Rice	10	20	20

If the probability that the weather will be dry is 10%, the probability that it will be average is 60%, and the probability that it will be wet is 30%, what is the farmer's best choice of crop?

37. *Study Techniques* Your mathematics test is tomorrow and will cover the following topics: game theory, linear programming, and matrix algebra. You have decided to do an all-nighter and must determine how to allocate your 8 hours of study time among the three topics. If you were to spend the entire 8 hours on any one of these topics (thus using a pure strategy), you feel confident that you would earn a 90% score on that portion of the test but would not do so well on the other topics. You have come up with the following table, where the entries are your expected scores. (The fact that linear programming and matrix algebra are used in game theory is reflected in these numbers.)

	Test		
Your Strategies	**Game Theory**	**Linear Programming**	**Matrix Algebra**
Game Theory	90	70	70
Linear Programming	40	90	40
Matrix Algebra	60	40	90

You have been told that the test will be weighted as follows: game theory: 25%, linear programming: 50%, and matrix algebra: 25%.

---
[23] See footnote for Exercise 35.

a. If you spend 25% of the night on game theory, 50% on linear programming, and 25% on matrix algebra, what score do you expect to get on the test?
b. Is it possible to improve on this by altering your study schedule? If so, what is the highest score you can expect on the test?
c. If your study schedule is according to part (a) and your teacher decides to forget her promises about how the test will be weighted and instead bases it all on a single topic, which topic would be worst for you, and what score could you expect on the test?

38. *Study Techniques* Your friend Joe has been spending all of his time on fraternity activities and therefore knows absolutely nothing about any of the three topics on tomorrow's math test. (See Exercise 37.) Because you are recognized as an expert on the use of game theory to solve study problems, he has turned to you for advice as to how to spend his all-nighter. As the following table shows, his situation is not so rosy. (Since he knows no linear programming or matrix algebra, the table shows, for instance, that studying game theory all night will not be much use in preparing him for this topic.)

	Test		
Joe's Strategies	**Game Theory**	**Linear Programming**	**Matrix Algebra**
Game Theory	30	0	20
Linear Programming	0	70	0
Matrix Algebra	0	0	70

Assuming that the test will be weighted as described in Exercise 37, what are the answers to parts (a), (b), and (c) as they apply to Joe?

39. ▼ *Staff Cutbacks* Frank Tempest manages a large snowplow service in Manhattan, Kansas, and is alarmed by the recent weather trends; there have been no significant snowfalls in recent years. He is therefore contemplating laying off some of his workers but is unsure about whether to lay off 5, 10, or 15 of his 50 workers. Being very methodical, he estimates his annual net profits based on four possible annual snowfall figures: 0 inches, 20 inches, 40 inches, and 60 inches. (He takes into account the fact that, if he is running a small operation in the face of a large annual snowfall, he will lose business to his competitors because he will be unable to discount on volume.)

	0 Inches	20 Inches	40 Inches	60 Inches
5 Laid Off	−$500,000	−$200,000	$10,000	$200,000
10 Laid Off	−$200,000	$0	$0	$0
15 Laid Off	−$100,000	$10,000	−$200,000	−$300,000

a. During the past 10 years, the region has had 0 inches twice, 20 inches twice, 40 inches three times, and

60 inches three times. Based on this information, how many workers should Tempest lay off, and how much would it cost him?

b. There is a 50% chance that Tempest will lay off 5 workers and a 50% chance that he will lay off 15 workers. What is the worst thing Nature can do to him in terms of snowfall? How much would it cost him?

c. The Gods of Chaos (who control the weather) know that Tempest is planning to use the strategy in part (a) and are determined to hurt Tempest as much as possible. Tempest, being somewhat paranoid, suspects this. What should he do?

40. ▼ *Textbook Writing* You are writing a college-level textbook on finite mathematics and are trying to come up with the best combination of word problems. Over the years, you have accumulated a collection of amusing problems, serious applications, long complicated problems, and generic problems.[24] Before your book is published, it must be scrutinized by several reviewers, who, it seems, are never satisfied with the mix you use. You estimate that there are three kinds of reviewers: the "no-nonsense" types, who prefer applications and generic problems; the "dead serious" types, who feel that a college-level text should contain little or no humor and lots of long complicated problems; and the "laid-back" types, who believe that learning best takes place in a light-hearted atmosphere bordering on anarchy. You have drawn up the following chart, where the payoffs represent the reactions of reviewers on a scale of −10 (ballistic) to +10 (ecstatic):

Reviewers

	No-Nonsense	Dead Serious	Laid-Back
Amusing	−5	−10	10
Serious	5	3	0
Long	−5	5	3
Generic	5	3	−10

You

a. Your first draft of the book contained no generic problems and equal numbers of the other categories. If half the reviewers of your book were "dead serious" and the rest were equally divided between the "no-nonsense" and "laid-back" types, what score would you expect?

b. In your second draft of the book, you tried to balance the content by including some generic problems and eliminating several amusing ones. You wound up with a mix of which one eighth were amusing, one quarter were serious, three eighths were long, and a quarter were generic. What kind of reviewer would be *least* impressed by this mix?

---

[24] Of the following type: "A certain company has three processing plants: A, B, and C, each of which uses three processes: P_1, P_2, and P_3. Process P_1 uses 100 units of chemical C_1, 50 units of C_2, . . ." and so on.

c. What kind of reviewer would be *most* impressed by the mix in your second draft?

41. *Price Wars* Computer Electronics, Inc. (CE) and the Gigantic Computer Store (GCS) are planning to discount the price they charge for the HAL laptop computer, of which they are the only distributors. Because Computer Electronics provides a free warranty service, it can generally afford to charge more. A market survey provides the following data on the gains to CE's market share that will result from different pricing decisions:

		GCS		
		$900	$1,000	$1,200
	$1,000	15%	60%	80%
CE	**$1,200**	15%	60%	60%
	$1,300	10%	20%	40%

a. Use reduction by dominance to determine how much each company should charge. What is the effect on CE's market share?

b. CE, which knows that GCS is planning to use reduction by dominance to determine its pricing policy, wants its own market share to be as large as possible. What effect, if any, would the information about GCS have on CE's best strategy?

42. *More Price Wars* (Refer to Exercise 41.) A new market survey results in the following revised data:

		GCS		
		$900	$1,000	$1,200
	$1,000	20%	60%	60%
CE	**$1,200**	15%	60%	60%
	$1,300	10%	20%	40%

a. Use reduction by dominance to determine how much each company should charge. What is the effect on CE's market share?

b. In general, why do price wars tend to force prices down?

43. *Wrestling Tournaments* City Community College (CCC) plans to host *Midtown Military Academy* (MMA) for a wrestling tournament. Each school has three wrestlers in the 190-pound weight class: CCC has Pablo, Sal, and Edison, while MMA has Carlos, Marcus, and Noto. Pablo can beat Carlos and Marcus, Marcus can beat Edison and Sal, Noto can beat Edison, while the other combinations will result in an even match. Set up a payoff matrix, and use reduction by dominance to decide which wrestler each team should choose as its champion. Does one school have an advantage over the other?

44. *Wrestling Tournaments* (Refer to Exercise 43.) One day before the wrestling tournament discussed in Exercise 43, Pablo sustains a hamstring injury and is replaced by Hans, who (unfortunately for CCC) can be beaten by both Carlos and Marcus. Set up the payoff matrix, and use reduction by dominance to decide which wrestler each team should choose as its champion. Does one school have an advantage over the other?

45. *The Battle of Rabaul-Lae*[25] In the Second World War, during the struggle for New Guinea, intelligence reports revealed that the Japanese were planning to move a troop and supply convoy from the port of Rabaul at the eastern tip of New Britain to Lae, which lies just west of New Britain on New Guinea. The convoy could travel either via a northern route, which was plagued by poor visibility, or by a southern route, where the visibility was clear. General Kenney, who was the commander of the Allied Air Forces in the area, had the choice of concentrating reconnaissance aircraft on one route or the other and bombing the Japanese convoy once it was sighted. Kenney's staff drafted the following outcomes for his choices, where the payoffs are estimated days of bombing time:

		Japanese Commander's Strategies	
		Northern Route	Southern Route
Kenney's Strategies	Northern Route	2	2
	Southern Route	1	3

What would you have recommended to General Kenney? What would you have recommended to the Japanese commander?[26] How much bombing time results if these recommendations are followed?

46. *The Battle of Rabaul-Lae* Referring to Exercise 45, suppose that General Kenney had a third alternative: splitting his reconnaissance aircraft between the two routes, which would result in the following estimates:

		Japanese Commander's Strategies	
		Northern Route	Southern Route
Kenney's Strategies	Northern Route	2	2
	Split Reconnaissance	1.5	2.5
	Southern Route	1	3

What would you have recommended to General Kenney? What would you have recommended to the Japanese com-

mander? How much bombing time results if these recommendations are followed?

47. ▼ *The Prisoner's Dilemma* Slim Lefty and Joe Rap have been arrested for grand theft auto, having been caught red-handed driving away in a stolen 2012 Porsche. Although the police have more than enough evidence to convict them both, a confession would simplify the work of the prosecution. The police decide to interrogate the prisoners separately. Slim and Joe are both told of the following plea-bargaining arrangement: If both confess, they will each receive a 2-year sentence; if neither confesses, they will both receive 5-year sentences; and if only one confesses (and thus squeals on the other), he will receive a suspended sentence, while the other will receive a 10-year sentence. What should Slim do?

48. ▼ *More Prisoners' Dilemmas* Jane Good and Prudence Brown have been arrested for robbery, but the police lack sufficient evidence for a conviction and so decide to interrogate them separately in the hope of extracting a confession. Both Jane and Prudence are told the following: If they both confess, they will each receive a 5-year sentence; if neither confesses, they will be released; if one confesses, she will receive a suspended sentence, while the other will receive a 10-year sentence. What should Jane do?

49. ▼ *Campaign Strategies*[27] Florida and Ohio are "swing states" that have a large bounty of electoral votes and are therefore highly valued by presidential campaign strategists. Suppose that it is now the weekend before Election Day 2012, and each candidate (Romney and Obama) can visit only one more state. Further, to win the election, Romney needs to win both of these states. Currently, Romney has a 40% chance of winning Ohio and a 60% chance of winning Florida. Therefore, he has a $0.40 \times 0.60 = 0.24$, or 24%, chance of winning the election. Assume that each candidate can increase his probability of winning a state by 10% if he but not his opponent visits that state. If both candidates visit the same state, there is no effect.
    a. Set up a payoff matrix with Romney as the row player and Obama as the column player, where the payoff for a specific set of circumstances is the probability (expressed as a percentage) that Romney will win both states.
    b. Where should each candidate visit under the circumstances?

50. ▼ *Campaign Strategies* Repeat Exercise 49, this time assuming that Romney has an 80% chance of winning Ohio and a 90% chance of winning Florida.

51. *Advertising* The *Softex Shampoo Company* is considering how to split its advertising budget between ads on two radio stations: WISH and WASH. Its main competitor, *Splish Shampoo, Inc.*, has found out about this and is considering

---

[25] As discussed in *Games and Decisions* by R. D. Luce and H. Raiffa Section 11.3 (New York: Wiley, 1957). This is based on an article in the *Journal of the Operations Research Society of America* 2 (1954): 365–385.

[26] The correct answers to Exercises 45 and 46 correspond to the actual decisions both commanders made.

[27] Based on *Game Theory for Swingers: What states should the candidates visit before Election Day?* by Jordan Ellenberg. Source: www .slate.com.

countering Softex's ads with its own on the same radio stations. (Proposed jingle: "Softex, Shmoftex; Splash with Splish.") Softex has calculated that, were it to devote its entire advertising budget to ads on WISH, it would increase revenues in the coming month by $100,000 in the event that Splish was running all its ads on the less popular WASH, but Softex would lose $20,000 in revenues if Splish ran its ads on WISH. If, on the other hand, it devoted its entire budget to WASH ads, Softex would neither increase nor decrease revenues in the event that Splish was running all its ads on the more popular WISH and would in fact lose $20,000 in revenues if Splish ran its ads on WASH. What should Softex do, and what effect will this have on revenues?

52. *Labor Negotiations* The management team of the *Abstract Concrete Company* is negotiating a 3-year contract with the labor unions at one of its plants and is trying to decide on its offer for a salary increase. If it offers a 5% increase and the unions accept the offer, Abstract Concrete will gain $20 million in projected profits in the coming year, but if labor rejects the offer, the management team predicts that it will be forced to increase the offer to the union demand of 15%, thus halving the projected profits. If Abstract Concrete offers a 15% increase, the company will earn $10 million in profits over the coming year if the unions accept. If the unions reject, they will probably go out on strike (because management has set 15% as its upper limit), and management has decided that it can then in fact gain $12 million in profits by selling out the defunct plant in retaliation. What intermediate percentage should the company offer, and what profit should it project?

Communication and Reasoning Exercises

53. Why is a saddle point called a "saddle point"?

54. Can the payoff in a saddle point ever be larger than all other payoffs in a game? Explain.

55. ◆ One day, while browsing through an old *Statistical Abstract of the United States,* you come across the following data, which show the number of females employed (in

thousands) in various categories according to their educational attainment:[28]

	Managerial/ Professional	Technical/Sales/ Administrative	Service	Precision Production	Operators/ Fabricators
Less Than 4 Years of High School	260	1,080	2,020	260	1,400
4 Years of High School Only	2,430	9,510	3,600	570	2,130
1 to 3 Years of College	2,690	5,080	1,080	160	350
At Least 4 Years of College	7,210	2,760	380	70	110

Because you have been studying game theory that day, the first thing you do is to search for a saddle point. Having found one, you conclude that, as a female, your best strategy in the job market is to forget about a college career. Find the flaw in this reasoning.

56. ◆ Exercises 37 and 38 seem to suggest that studying a single topic before an exam is better than studying all the topics in that exam. Comment on this discrepancy between the game theory result and common sense.

57. ◆ Explain what is wrong with a decision to play the mixed strategy $[0.5 \quad 0.5]$ by alternating the two strategies: Play the first strategy on the odd-numbered moves and the second strategy on the even-numbered moves. Illustrate your argument by devising a game in which your best strategy is $[0.5 \quad 0.5]$.

58. ◆ Describe a situation in which a mixed strategy and a pure strategy are equally effective.

---

[28] Source: *Statistical Abstract of the United States 1991* (111th Ed.) U.S. Department of Commerce, Economics and Statistics Administration, and Bureau of the Census.

5.5 Input-Output Models

Sectors of the Economy

In this section we look at an application of matrix algebra developed by Wassily Leontief (1906–1999) in the middle of the twentieth century. In 1973 he won the Nobel Prize in Economics for this work. The application involves analyzing national and regional economies by looking at how various parts of the economy interrelate. We'll work out some of the details by looking at a simple scenario.

First, we can think of the economy of a country or a region as being composed of various **sectors**, or groups of one or more industries. Typical sectors are the manufacturing sector, the utilities sector, and the agricultural sector. To introduce the basic concepts, we shall consider two specific sectors: the coal-mining sector (Sector 1) and the electric utilities sector (Sector 2). Each produces a commodity: The coal-mining sector produces coal, and the electric utilities sector produces electricity. We measure these products by their dollar value. By **one unit** of a product, we mean $1 worth of that product.

Here is the scenario:

1. To produce one unit ($1 worth) of coal, assume that the coal-mining sector uses 50¢ worth of coal (to power mining machinery, say) and 10¢ worth of electricity.

2. To produce one unit ($1 worth) of electricity, assume that the electric utilities sector uses 25¢ worth of coal and 25¢ worth of electricity.

These are *internal* usage figures. In addition to this, assume that there is an *external* demand (from the rest of the economy) of 7,000 units ($7,000 worth) of coal and 14,000 units ($14,000 worth) of electricity over a specific time period (1 year, say). Our basic question is: How much should each of the two sectors supply to meet both internal and external demand?

The key to answering this question is to set up equations of the form

Total supply = Total demand.

The unknowns, the values we are seeking, are

x_1 = Total supply (in units) from Sector 1 (coal)

x_2 = Total supply (in units) from Sector 2 (electricity).

Our equations then take the following form:

Total supply from Sector 1 = Total demand for Sector 1 products

$$x_1 = 0.50x_1 \quad + \quad 0.25x_2 \quad + \quad 7,000$$

       ↑   ↑   ↑

Coal required by Sector 1   Coal required by Sector 2   External demand for coal

Total supply from Sector 2 = Total demand for Sector 2 products

$$x_2 = 0.10x_1 \quad + \quad 0.25x_2 \quad + \quad 14,000.$$

       ↑   ↑   ↑

Electricity required by Sector 1   Electricity required by Sector 2   External demand for electricity

This is a system of two linear equations in two unknowns:

$$x_1 = 0.50x_1 + 0.25x_2 + 7,000$$
$$x_2 = 0.10x_1 + 0.25x_2 + 14,000.$$

We can rewrite this system of equations in matrix form as follows:

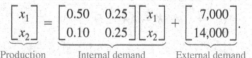

Production   Internal demand   External demand

In symbols,

$$X = AX + D.$$

Here,

$$X = \begin{bmatrix} x_1 \\ x_2 \end{bmatrix}$$

is called the **production vector**. Its entries are the amounts produced by the two sectors. The matrix

$$D = \begin{bmatrix} 7{,}000 \\ 14{,}000 \end{bmatrix}$$

is called the **external demand** vector, and

$$A = \begin{bmatrix} 0.50 & 0.25 \\ 0.10 & 0.25 \end{bmatrix} \quad \text{Organization:} \begin{bmatrix} 1 \to 1 & 1 \to 2 \\ 2 \to 1 & 2 \to 2 \end{bmatrix}$$

is called the **technology matrix**. The entries of the technology matrix have the following meanings:

a_{11} = Units of Sector 1 needed to produce one unit of Sector 1

a_{12} = Units of Sector 1 needed to produce one unit of Sector 2

a_{21} = Units of Sector 2 needed to produce one unit of Sector 1

a_{22} = Units of Sector 2 needed to produce one unit of Sector 2.

Now that we have the matrix equation

$$X = AX + D,$$

we can solve it as follows. First, subtract AX from both sides:

$$X - AX = D.$$

Because $X = IX$, where I is the 2×2 identity matrix, we can rewrite this as

$$IX - AX = D.$$

Now factor out X:

$$(I - A)X = D.$$

If we multiply both sides by the inverse of $(I - A)$, we get the solution

$$X = (I - A)^{-1}D.$$

Input-Output Model

In an input-output model, an economy (or part of one) is divided into n **sectors**. We then record the $n \times n$ **technology matrix** A, whose ijth entry is the number of units from Sector i used in producing one unit from Sector j (in symbols, "$i \to j$"). To meet an **external demand** of D, the economy must produce X, where X is the **production vector**. These are related by the equations

$$X = AX + D$$

or

$$X = (I - A)^{-1}D. \qquad \text{Provided that } (I - A) \text{ is invertible}$$

Quick Example

1. In the scenario above,

$$A = \begin{bmatrix} 0.50 & 0.25 \\ 0.10 & 0.25 \end{bmatrix}, \quad X = \begin{bmatrix} x_1 \\ x_2 \end{bmatrix}, \quad \text{and} \quad D = \begin{bmatrix} 7{,}000 \\ 14{,}000 \end{bmatrix}.$$

The solution is

$$X = (I - A)^{-1}D$$

$$\begin{bmatrix} x_1 \\ x_2 \end{bmatrix} = \left(\begin{bmatrix} 1 & 0 \\ 0 & 1 \end{bmatrix} - \begin{bmatrix} 0.50 & 0.25 \\ 0.10 & 0.25 \end{bmatrix} \right)^{-1} \begin{bmatrix} 7,000 \\ 14,000 \end{bmatrix}$$

$$= \begin{bmatrix} 0.50 & -0.25 \\ -0.10 & 0.75 \end{bmatrix}^{-1} \begin{bmatrix} 7,000 \\ 14,000 \end{bmatrix} \qquad \text{Calculate } I - A.$$

$$= \begin{bmatrix} \frac{15}{7} & \frac{5}{7} \\ \frac{2}{7} & \frac{10}{7} \end{bmatrix} \begin{bmatrix} 7,000 \\ 14,000 \end{bmatrix} \qquad \text{Calculate } (I - A)^{-1}.$$

$$= \begin{bmatrix} 25,000 \\ 22,000 \end{bmatrix}.$$

In other words, to meet the demand, the economy must produce $25,000 worth of coal and $22,000 worth of electricity.

The next example uses actual data from the U.S. economy. (We have rounded the figures to make the computations less complicated.) It is rare to find input-output data already packaged for you as a technology matrix. Instead, the data commonly found in statistical sources come in the form of input-output tables, from which we will have to construct the technology matrix.

EXAMPLE 1   **Petroleum and Natural Gas**

Consider two sectors of the U.S. economy: crude petroleum and natural gas (*crude*) and petroleum refining and related industries (*refining*). According to government figures,[29] in 1998 the crude sector used $27,000 million worth of its own products and $750 million worth of the products of the refining sector to produce $87,000 million worth of goods (crude oil and natural gas). The refining sector in the same year used $59,000 million worth of the products of the crude sector and $15,000 million worth of its own products to produce $140,000 million worth of goods (refined oil and the like). What was the technology matrix for these two sectors? What was left over from each of these sectors for use by other parts of the economy or for export?

Solution First, for convenience, we record the given data in the form of a table, called the **input-output table**. (All figures are in millions of dollars.)

		To	
		Crude	**Refining**
From	**Crude**	27,000	59,000
	Refining	750	15,000
	Total Output	87,000	140,000

---

[29] The data have been rounded to two significant digits. Source: *Survey of Current Business*, December, 2001, U.S. Department of Commerce. The *Survey of Current Business* and the input-output tables themselves are available at the website of the Department of Commerce's Bureau of Economic Analysis (www.bea.gov).

The entries in the top portion are arranged in the same way as those of the technology matrix: The ijth entry represents the number of units of Sector i that went to Sector j. Thus, for instance, the 59,000 million entry in the 1, 2 position represents the number of units of Sector 1, crude, that were used by Sector 2, refining. ("From the side, to the top.")

We now construct the technology matrix. The technology matrix has entries a_{ij} = Units of Sector i used to produce *one* unit of Sector j. Thus,

a_{11} = Units of crude to produce one unit of crude. We are told that 27,000 million units of crude were used to produce 87,000 million units of crude. Thus, to produce *one* unit of crude, $27,000/87,000 \approx 0.31$ units of crude were used, so $a_{11} \approx 0.31$. (We have rounded this value to two significant digits; further digits are not reliable because of rounding of the original data.)

a_{12} = Units of crude to produce one unit of refined:
$a_{12} = 59,000/140,000 \approx 0.42$

a_{21} = Units of refined to produce one unit of crude:
$a_{21} = 750/87,000 \approx 0.0086$

a_{22} = Units of refined to produce one unit of refined:
$a_{22} = 15,000/140,000 \approx 0.11$.

This gives the technology matrix

$$A = \begin{bmatrix} 0.31 & 0.42 \\ 0.0086 & 0.11 \end{bmatrix}. \quad \text{Technology matrix}$$

In short, *we obtained the technology matrix from the input-output table by dividing the Sector 1 column by the Sector 1 total, and the Sector 2 column by the Sector 2 total.*

Now we also know the total output from each sector, so *we have already been given the production vector:*

$$X = \begin{bmatrix} 87,000 \\ 140,000 \end{bmatrix}. \quad \text{Production vector}$$

What we are asked for is the external demand vector D, the amount available for the outside economy. To find D, we use the equation

$$X = AX + D, \quad \text{Relationship of } X, A, \text{ and } D$$

where, this time, we are given A and X and we must solve for D. Solving for D gives

$$D = X - AX$$

$$= \begin{bmatrix} 87,000 \\ 140,000 \end{bmatrix} - \begin{bmatrix} 0.31 & 0.42 \\ 0.0086 & 0.11 \end{bmatrix} \begin{bmatrix} 87,000 \\ 140,000 \end{bmatrix}$$

Why?

$$\approx \begin{bmatrix} 87,000 \\ 140,000 \end{bmatrix} - \begin{bmatrix} 86,000 \\ 16,000 \end{bmatrix} = \begin{bmatrix} 1,000 \\ 124,000 \end{bmatrix}. \quad \text{We rounded to two significant digits.}^*$$

The first number, $1,000 million, is the amount produced by the crude sector that is available to be used by other parts of the economy or to be exported. (In fact, because something has to happen to all that crude petroleum and natural gas, this is the amount that is actually used or exported, where use can include stockpiling.) The second number, $124,000 million, represents the amount produced by the refining sector that is available to be used by other parts of the economy or to be exported.

Note that we could have calculated D more simply from the input-output table. The internal use of units from the crude sector was the sum of the outputs from that sector:

$$27,000 + 59,000 = 86,000.$$

Because 87,000 units were actually produced by the sector, that left a surplus of $87,000 - 86,000 = 1,000$ units for export. We could compute the surplus from the refining sector similarly. (The two calculations actually come out slightly differently because we rounded the intermediate results.) The calculation in Example 2 below cannot be done as trivially, however.

Using Technology

See the Technology Guides at the end of the chapter to see how to compute the technology matrix and the external demand vector in Example 1 using a TI-83/84 Plus or a spreadsheet.

Input-Output Table

National economic data are often given in the form of an **input-output table**. The ijth entry in the top portion of the table is the number of units that go from Sector i to Sector j. The "Total outputs" are the total numbers of units produced by each sector. We obtain the technology matrix from the input-output table by dividing the Sector 1 column by the Sector 1 total, the Sector 2 column by the Sector 2 total, and so on.

> **Quick Example**
>
> 2. Input-output table:

* The production of skateboards required skateboards because skateboard workers tend to commute to work on (what else?) skateboards!

		To	
		Skateboards	**Wood**
From	**Skateboards**	20,000*	0
	Wood	100,000	500,000
	Total Output	200,000	5,000,000

Technology matrix:

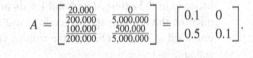

$$A = \begin{bmatrix} \frac{20,000}{200,000} & \frac{0}{5,000,000} \\ \frac{100,000}{200,000} & \frac{500,000}{5,000,000} \end{bmatrix} = \begin{bmatrix} 0.1 & 0 \\ 0.5 & 0.1 \end{bmatrix}.$$

EXAMPLE 2   Rising Demand

Suppose that external demand for refined petroleum rises to $200,000 million, but the demand for crude remains $1,000 million (as in Example 1). How do the production levels of the two sectors considered in Example 1 have to change?

Solution We are being told that now

$$D = \begin{bmatrix} 1,000 \\ 200,000 \end{bmatrix},$$

and we are asked to find X. Remember that we can calculate X from the formula

$$X = (I - A)^{-1}D.$$

Now

$$I - A = \begin{bmatrix} 1 & 0 \\ 0 & 1 \end{bmatrix} - \begin{bmatrix} 0.31 & 0.42 \\ 0.0086 & 0.11 \end{bmatrix} = \begin{bmatrix} 0.69 & -0.42 \\ -0.0086 & 0.89 \end{bmatrix}.$$

We take the inverse using our favorite technique and find that, to four significant digits,[*]

* Because A is accurate to two digits, we should use more than two significant digits in intermediate calculations so as not to lose additional accuracy. We must, of course, round the final answer to two digits.

$$(I - A)^{-1} \approx \begin{bmatrix} 1.458 & 0.6880 \\ 0.01409 & 1.130 \end{bmatrix}.$$

Now we can compute X:

$$X = (I - A)^{-1}D = \begin{bmatrix} 1.458 & 0.6880 \\ 0.01409 & 1.130 \end{bmatrix} \begin{bmatrix} 1,000 \\ 200,000 \end{bmatrix} \approx \begin{bmatrix} 140,000 \\ 230,000 \end{bmatrix}.$$

(As in Example 1, we have rounded all the entries in the answer to two significant digits.) Comparing this vector to the production vector used in Example 1, we see that production in the crude sector has to increase from \$87,000 million to \$140,000 million, while production in the refining sector has to increase from \$140,000 million to \$230,000 million.

⟹ **Before we go on . . .** Using the matrix $(I - A)^{-1}$, we have a slightly different way of solving Example 2. We are asking for the effect on production of a *change* in the final demand of 0 for crude and $200,000 - 124,000 = \$76,000$ million for refined products. If we multiply $(I - A)^{-1}$ by the matrix representing this *change*, we obtain

$$\begin{bmatrix} 1.458 & 0.6880 \\ 0.01409 & 1.130 \end{bmatrix} \begin{bmatrix} 0 \\ 76,000 \end{bmatrix} \approx \begin{bmatrix} 53,000 \\ 90,000 \end{bmatrix}.$$

$(I - A)^{-1} \times$ Change in demand = Change in production

We see the changes required in production: an increase of \$53,000 million in the crude sector and an increase of \$90,000 million in the refining sector.

Notice that the increase in external demand for the products of the refining sector requires the crude sector to increase production as well, even though there is no increase in the *external* demand for its products. The reason is that, to increase production, the refining sector needs to use more crude oil, so the *internal* demand for crude oil goes up. The inverse matrix $(I - A)^{-1}$ takes these **indirect effects** into account in a nice way.

By replacing the \$76,000 by \$1 in the computation we just did, we see that a \$1 increase in external demand for refined products will require an increase in production of \$0.6880 in the crude sector as well as an increase in production of \$1.130 in the refining sector. This is how we interpret the entries in $(I - A)^{-1}$, and this is why it is useful to look at this matrix inverse rather than just solve $(I - A)X = D$ for X using, say, Gauss-Jordan reduction. Looking at $(I - A)^{-1}$, we can also find the effects of an increase of \$1 in external demand for crude: an increase in production of \$1.458 in the crude sector and an increase of \$0.01409 in the refining sector.

Here are some questions to think about: Why are the diagonal entries of $(I - A)^{-1}$ (slightly) larger than 1? Why is the entry in the lower left so small in comparison to the others? ■

Interpreting $(I - A)^{-1}$: Indirect Effects

If A is the technology matrix, then the *ij*th entry of $(I - A)^{-1}$ is the change in the number of units Sector i must produce to meet a one-unit increase in external demand for Sector j products. To meet a rising external demand, the necessary change in production for each sector is given by

$$\text{Change in production} = (I - A)^{-1}D^+,$$

where D^+ is the change in external demand.

Quick Example

3. Take Sector 1 to be skateboards and Sector 2 to be wood, and assume that

$$(I - A)^{-1} = \begin{bmatrix} 1.1 & 0 \\ 0.6 & 1.1 \end{bmatrix}.$$

Then

$a_{11} = 1.1 =$ Number of additional units of skateboards that must be produced to meet a one-unit increase in the demand for skateboards (Why is this number larger than 1?)

$a_{12} = 0 =$ Number of additional units of skateboards that must be produced to meet a one-unit increase in the demand for wood (Why is this number 0?)

$a_{21} = 0.6 =$ Number of additional units of wood that must be produced to meet a one-unit increase in the demand for skateboards

$a_{22} = 1.1 =$ Number of additional units of wood that must be produced to meet a one-unit increase in the demand for wood.

To meet an increase in external demand of 100 skateboards and 400 units of wood, the necessary change in production is

$$(I - A)^{-1}D^+ = \begin{bmatrix} 1.1 & 0 \\ 0.6 & 1.1 \end{bmatrix}\begin{bmatrix} 100 \\ 400 \end{bmatrix} = \begin{bmatrix} 110 \\ 500 \end{bmatrix},$$

so 110 additional skateboards and 500 additional units of wood will need to be produced.

In the preceding examples we used only two sectors of the economy. The data used in Examples 1 and 2 were taken from an input-output table published by the U.S. Department of Commerce, in which the whole U.S. economy was broken down into 85 sectors. This in turn was a simplified version of a model in which the economy was broken into about 500 sectors. Obviously, computers are required to make a realistic input-output analysis possible. Many governments collect and publish input-output data as part of their national planning. The United Nations collects these data and publishes collections of national statistics. These and other useful statistics can be found at the website of the United Nations Statistics Division: http://unstats .un.org/unsd.

EXAMPLE 3   Kenya Economy

Consider four sectors of the economy of Kenya: (1) the traditional economy, (2) agriculture, (3) manufacture of metal products and machinery, and (4) wholesale and retail trade.[30] The input-output table for these four sectors for 1976 looks like this (all numbers are thousands of K£):

		To			
		1	**2**	**3**	**4**
	1	8,600	0	0	0
	2	0	20,000	24	0
From	**3**	1,500	530	15,000	660
	4	810	8,500	5,800	2,900
	Total Output	87,000	530,000	110,000	180,000

Using Technology

Technology can be used to do the computations in Example 3. Here is an outline (see the Technology Guides at the end of the chapter for additional details on using a TI-83/84 Plus or a spreadsheet):

TI-83/84 Plus
Enter the matrices [A] and [D] using MATRIX ; EDIT. (For [A], type the entries as quotients: Column entry/ Column total.) Home screen: (identity(4) - [A])⁻¹[D] [More details in the Technology Guide.]

Spreadsheet
Obtain the technology matrix as in Example 1. Insert the 4 × 4 identity matrix, and then use MINVERSE and MMULT to compute $(I - A)^{-1}D$. [More details in the Technology Guide.]

Website
www.WanerMath.com
→ Online Utilities
→ Matrix Algebra Tool
Enter the matrices A and D. (For A, type the entries as quotients: Column entry/Column total.) Type (I-A)^(-1)*D in the formula box, and press "Compute".

Suppose that external demand for agriculture increased by K£50,000,000 and that external demand for metal products and machinery increased by K£10,000,000. How would production in these four sectors have to change to meet this rising demand?

Solution To find the change in production necessary to meet the rising demand, we need to use the formula

$$\text{Change in production} = (I - A)^{-1}D^{+},$$

where A is the technology matrix and D^{+} is the change in demand:

$$D^{+} = \begin{bmatrix} 0 \\ 50{,}000 \\ 10{,}000 \\ 0 \end{bmatrix}.$$

With entries shown rounded to two significant digits, the matrix A is

$$A = \begin{bmatrix} 0.099 & 0 & 0 & 0 \\ 0 & 0.038 & 0.00022 & 0 \\ 0.017 & 0.001 & 0.14 & 0.0037 \\ 0.0093 & 0.016 & 0.053 & 0.016 \end{bmatrix}.$$

Entries shown are rounded to two significant digits.

The next calculation is best done by using technology:

$$\text{Change in production} = (I - A)^{-1}D^{+} = \begin{bmatrix} 0 \\ 52{,}000 \\ 12{,}000 \\ 1{,}500 \end{bmatrix}.$$

Entries shown are rounded to two significant digits.

---

[30] Figures are rounded. Source: *Input-Output Tables for Kenya 1976*, Central Bureau of Statistics of the Ministry of Economic Planning and Community Affairs, Kenya.

Looking at this result, we see that the changes in external demand will leave the traditional economy unaffected, production in agriculture will rise by K£52 million, production in the manufacture of metal products and machinery will rise by K£12 million, and activity in wholesale and retail trade will rise by K£1.5 million.

➡ **Before we go on...** Can you see why the traditional economy was unaffected in Example 3? Although it takes inputs from other parts of the economy, the traditional economy is not itself an input to any other part. In other words, there is no intermediate demand for the products of the traditional economy coming from any other part of the economy, so an increase in production in any other sector of the economy will require no increase from the traditional economy. On the other hand, the wholesale and retail trade sector does provide input to the agriculture and manufacturing sectors, so increases in those sectors do require an increase in the trade sector.

One more point: If you calculate $(I - A)^{-1}$, you will notice how small the off-diagonal entries are. This tells us that increases in each sector have relatively small effects on the other sectors. We say that these sectors are **loosely coupled**. Regional economies, where many products are destined to be shipped out to the rest of the country, tend to show this phenomenon even more strongly. Notice in Example 2 that those two sectors are **strongly coupled**, because a rise in demand for refined products requires a comparable rise in the production of crude. ∎

5.5 EXERCISES

▼ more advanced   ◆ challenging

Ⓣ indicates exercises that should be solved using technology

1. Let A be the technology matrix $A = \begin{bmatrix} 0.2 & 0.05 \\ 0.8 & 0.01 \end{bmatrix}$, where Sector 1 is paper and Sector 2 is wood. Fill in the missing quantities.
   a. ___ units of wood are needed to produce one unit of paper.
   b. ___ units of paper are used in the production of one unit of paper.
   c. The production of each unit of wood requires the use of ___ units of paper.

2. Let A be the technology matrix $A = \begin{bmatrix} 0.01 & 0.001 \\ 0.2 & 0.004 \end{bmatrix}$, where Sector 1 is processor chips and Sector 2 is silicon. Fill in the missing quantities.
   a. ___ units of silicon are required in the production of one unit of silicon.
   b. ___ units of processor chips are used in the production of one unit of silicon.
   c. The production of each unit of processor chips requires the use of ___ units of silicon.

3. Each unit of television news requires 0.2 units of television news and 0.5 units of radio news. Each unit of radio news requires 0.1 units of television news and no radio news. With Sector 1 as television news and Sector 2 as radio news, set up the technology matrix A.

4. Production of one unit of cologne requires no cologne and 0.5 units of perfume. Into one unit of perfume go 0.1 units of cologne and 0.3 units of perfume. With Sector 1 as cologne and Sector 2 as perfume, set up the technology matrix A.

In Exercises 5–12, you are given a technology matrix A and an external demand vector D. Find the corresponding production vector X. [**HINT:** See Quick Example 1.]

5. $A = \begin{bmatrix} 0.5 & 0.4 \\ 0 & 0.5 \end{bmatrix}, D = \begin{bmatrix} 10,000 \\ 20,000 \end{bmatrix}$

6. $A = \begin{bmatrix} 0.5 & 0.4 \\ 0 & 0.5 \end{bmatrix}, D = \begin{bmatrix} 20,000 \\ 10,000 \end{bmatrix}$

7. $A = \begin{bmatrix} 0.1 & 0.4 \\ 0.2 & 0.5 \end{bmatrix}, D = \begin{bmatrix} 25,000 \\ 15,000 \end{bmatrix}$

8. $A = \begin{bmatrix} 0.1 & 0.2 \\ 0.4 & 0.5 \end{bmatrix}, D = \begin{bmatrix} 24,000 \\ 14,000 \end{bmatrix}$

9. $A = \begin{bmatrix} 0.5 & 0.1 & 0 \\ 0 & 0.5 & 0.1 \\ 0 & 0 & 0.5 \end{bmatrix}, D = \begin{bmatrix} 1,000 \\ 1,000 \\ 2,000 \end{bmatrix}$

10. $A = \begin{bmatrix} 0.5 & 0.1 & 0 \\ 0 & 0.5 & 0.1 \\ 0 & 0 & 0.5 \end{bmatrix}, D = \begin{bmatrix} 3,000 \\ 3,800 \\ 2,000 \end{bmatrix}$

11. $A = \begin{bmatrix} 0.2 & 0.2 & 0 \\ 0.2 & 0.4 & 0.2 \\ 0 & 0.2 & 0.2 \end{bmatrix}, D = \begin{bmatrix} 16,000 \\ 8,000 \\ 8,000 \end{bmatrix}$

12. $A = \begin{bmatrix} 0.2 & 0.2 & 0.2 \\ 0.2 & 0.4 & 0.2 \\ 0.2 & 0.2 & 0.2 \end{bmatrix}, D = \begin{bmatrix} 7,000 \\ 14,000 \\ 7,000 \end{bmatrix}$

13. Given $A = \begin{bmatrix} 0.1 & 0.4 \\ 0.2 & 0.5 \end{bmatrix}$, find the changes in production required to meet an increase in demand of 50 units of Sector 1 products and 30 units of Sector 2 products.

14. Given $A = \begin{bmatrix} 0.5 & 0.4 \\ 0 & 0.5 \end{bmatrix}$, find the changes in production required to meet an increase in demand of 20 units of Sector 1 products and 10 units of Sector 2 products.

15. Let $(I - A)^{-1} = \begin{bmatrix} 1.5 & 0.1 & 0 \\ 0.2 & 1.2 & 0.1 \\ 0.1 & 0.7 & 1.6 \end{bmatrix}$, and assume that the external demand for the products in Sector 1 increases by one unit. By how many units should each sector increase production? What do the columns of the matrix $(I - A)^{-1}$ tell you? [**HINT:** See Quick Example 3.]

16. Let $(I - A)^{-1} = \begin{bmatrix} 1.5 & 0.1 & 0 \\ 0.1 & 1.1 & 0.1 \\ 0 & 0 & 1.3 \end{bmatrix}$, and assume that the external demand for the products in each of the sectors increases by one unit. By how many units should each sector increase production? [**HINT:** See Quick Example 3.]

In Exercises 17 and 18, obtain the technology matrix from the given input-output table. [**HINT:** See Example 1.]

17.

		To		
		A	B	C
	A	1,000	2,000	3,000
From	B	0	4,000	0
	C	0	1,000	3,000
	Total Output	5,000	5,000	6,000

18.

		To		
		A	B	C
	A	0	100	300
From	B	500	400	300
	C	0	0	600
	Total Output	1,000	2,000	3,000

Applications

19. *Campus Food* The two campus cafeterias, the Main Dining Room and Bits & Bytes, typically use each other's food

in doing business on campus. One weekend, the input-output table was as follows:[31]

		To	
		Main DR	**Bits & Bytes**
	Main DR	$10,000	$20,000
From	**Bits & Bytes**	5,000	0
	Total Output	50,000	40,000

Given that the demand for food on campus last weekend was $45,000 from the Main Dining Room and $30,000 from Bits & Bytes, how much did the two cafeterias have to produce to meet the demand last weekend?

20. *Plagiarism* Two student groups at *Enormous State University*, the Choral Society and the Football Club, maintain files of term papers that they write and offer to students for research purposes. Some of these papers they use themselves in generating more papers. To avoid suspicion of plagiarism by faculty members (who seem to have astute memories), each paper is given to students or used by the clubs only once. (No copies are kept.) The number of papers that were used in the production of new papers last year is shown in the following input-output table:

		To	
		Choral Soc.	**Football Club**
	Choral Soc.	20	10
From	**Football Club**	10	30
	Total Output	100	200

Given that 270 Choral Society papers and 810 Football Club papers will be used by students outside of these two clubs next year, how many new papers do the two clubs need to write?

21. **T** *Communication Equipment* Two sectors of the U.S. economy are (1) audio, video, and communication equipment and (2) electronic components and accessories. In 1998 the input-output table involving these two sectors was as follows. (All figures are in millions of dollars):[32]

		To	
		Equipment	**Components**
	Equipment	6,000	500
From	**Components**	24,000	30,000
	Total Output	90,000	140,000

---

[31] For some reason, the Main Dining Room consumes a lot of its own food!

[32] The data have been rounded. Source: *Survey of Current Business*, December 2001, U.S. Department of Commerce.

Determine the production levels necessary in these two sectors to meet an external demand for $80,000 million of communication equipment and $90,000 million of electronic components. Round answers to two significant digits.

22. **Wood and Paper** Two sectors of the U.S. economy are (1) lumber and wood products and (2) paper and allied products. In 1998 the input-output table involving these two sectors was as follows. (All figures are in millions of dollars.)[33]

To

From		Wood	Paper
	Wood	36,000	7,000
	Paper	100	17,000
	Total Output	120,000	120,000

If external demand for lumber and wood products rises by $10,000 million and external demand for paper and allied products rises by $20,000 million, what increase in output of these two sectors is necessary? Round answers to two significant digits.

23. **Australia Economy** Two sectors of the Australian economy are (1) textiles and (2) clothing and footwear. The 1977 input-output table[34] involving these two sectors results in the following value for $(I - A)^{-1}$:

$$(I - A)^{-1} = \begin{bmatrix} 1.228 & 0.182 \\ 0.006 & 1.1676 \end{bmatrix}.$$

Complete the following sentences.

a. _____ additional dollars worth of clothing and footwear must be produced to meet a $1 increase in the demand for textiles.

b. 0.182 additional dollars worth of _____ must be produced to meet a $1 increase in the demand for _____.

24. **Australia Economy** Two sectors of the Australian economy are (1) community services and (2) recreation services. The 1978–79 input-output table[35] involving these two sectors results in the following value for $(I - A)^{-1}$:

$$(I - A)^{-1} = \begin{bmatrix} 1.0066 & 0.00576 \\ 0.00496 & 1.04206 \end{bmatrix}.$$

Complete the following sentences.

a. 0.00496 additional dollars worth of _____ must be produced to meet a $1 increase in the demand for _____.

b. _____ additional dollars worth of community services must be produced to meet a $1 increase in the demand for community services.

Mexico Economy Economists generally divide a country's economy into three broad sectors: primary, secondary, and tertiary. The primary sector is the sector using natural resources to produce raw materials, and includes oil extraction, agriculture, mining, and fishing. The secondary or industrial sector is the sector that uses raw materials to produce manufactured goods, and includes oil refining, textiles, and electronics. The tertiary or services sector provides services, and includes tourism, financial services, and health care. Exercises 25–30 are based on the following technology matrix for Mexico in 2008. (The sectors are in the order primary, secondary, and tertiary, and entries are rounded to two decimal places.)[36]

$$A = \begin{bmatrix} 0.09 & 0.03 & 0.00 \\ 0.14 & 0.23 & 0.08 \\ 0.07 & 0.12 & 0.15 \end{bmatrix}$$

25. In 2008, Mexico produced around 590 billion pesos of raw materials, 11,000 billion pesos of manufactured goods, and 9,600 billion pesos of services.[37] Use these data to construct the input-output table for Mexico in 2008. [HINT: See Example 1.]

26. Suppose, in a particular year, Mexico had produced around 860 billion pesos of raw materials, 23,000 billion pesos of manufactured goods, and 8,500 billion pesos of services. What would the input-output table for the Mexican economy have been? [HINT: See Example 1.]

27. Use the technology matrix and the production data in Exercise 25 to calculate the amounts exported out of the country from each sector of the Mexico economy in 2008. (Round answers to two significant digits.)

28. Use the technology matrix and the production data in Exercise 26 to construct the amounts that would have been exported out of the country from each sector of the Mexico economy. (Round answers to two significant digits.)

29. Determine how the three sectors of the Mexico economy would react to a decrease in demand for tourism (tertiary sector) of 1,000 billion pesos and an increase in the demand for raw materials of 2,000 billion pesos.

30. Determine how the three sectors of the Mexico economy would react to an increase in demand for tourism (tertiary sector) of 1,000 billion pesos and a decrease in the other two sectors of 1,000 billion pesos each.

Exercises 31–34 require the use of technology.

31. **United States Input-Output Table** Four sectors of the U.S. economy are (1) livestock and livestock products, (2) other agricultural products, (3) forestry and fishery products, and (4) agricultural, forestry, and fishery services.

---

[33] See footnote for Exercise 21.

[34] Source: *Australian National Accounts and Input-Output Tables 1978–1979*, Australian Bureau of Statistics.

[35] *Ibid.*

---

[36] Source for data: Instituto Nacional de Estadística y Geografía (www.inegi.org.mx).

[37] *Ibid.*

In 1977 the input-output table involving these four sectors was as follows. (All figures are in millions of dollars.)[38]

To

From		1	2	3	4
	1	11,937	9	109	855
	2	26,649	4,285	0	4,744
	3	0	0	439	61
	4	5,423	10,952	3,002	216
Total Output		97,795	120,594	14,642	47,473

Determine how these four sectors would react to a simultaneous increase in demand of $1,000 million in every sector. (Round answers to four significant digits.)

32. **United States Input-Output Table** Four sectors of the U.S. economy are (1) motor vehicles, (2) truck and bus bodies, trailers, and motor vehicle parts, (3) aircraft and parts, and (4) other transportation equipment. In 1998 the input-output table involving these four sectors was as follows. (All figures in millions of dollars.)[39]

To

From		1	2	3	4
	1	75	1,092	0	1,207
	2	64,858	13,081	7	1,070
	3	0	0	21,782	0
	4	0	0	0	1,375
Total Output		230,676	135,108	129,376	44,133

Determine how these four sectors would react to a simultaneous increase in demand of $1,000 million in every sector. (Round answers to four significant digits.)

33. **Australia Input-Output Table** Four sectors of the Australian economy are (1) agriculture, (2) forestry, fishing, and hunting, (3) meat and milk products, and (4) other food products. In 1978–79 the input-output table involving these four sectors was as follows. (All figures are in millions of Australian dollars.)[40]

To

From		1	2	3	4
	1	678.4	3.7	3,341.5	1,023.5
	2	15.5	6.9	17.1	124.5
	3	47.3	4.3	893.1	145.8
	4	312.5	22.1	83.2	693.5
Total Output		9,401.3	685.8	6,997.3	4,818.3

a. How much additional production by the meat and milk sector is necessary to accommodate a $100 increase in the demand for agriculture?

b. Which sector requires the most of its own product in order to meet a $1 increase in external demand for that product?

34. **Australia Input-Output Table** Four sectors of the Australian economy are (1) petroleum and coal products, (2) nonmetallic mineral products, (3) basic metals and products, and (4) fabricated metal products. In 1978–79 the input-output table involving these four sectors was as follows. (All figures are in millions of Australian dollars.)[41]

To

From		1	2	3	4
	1	174.1	30.5	120.3	14.2
	2	0	190.1	55.8	12.6
	3	2.1	40.2	1,418.7	1,242.0
	4	0.1	7.3	40.4	326.0
Total Output		3,278.0	2,188.8	6,541.7	4,065.8

a. How much additional production by the petroleum and coal products sector is necessary to accommodate a $1,000 increase in the demand for fabricated metal products?

b. Which sector requires the most of the product of some other sector in order to meet a $1 increase in external demand for that product?

Communication and Reasoning Exercises

35. What would it mean if the technology matrix A were the zero matrix?

36. Can an external demand be met by an economy whose technology matrix A is the identity matrix? Explain.

37. ▼ What would it mean if the total output figure for a particular sector of an input-output table were equal to the sum of the figures in the row for that sector?

38. ▼ What would it mean if the total output figure for a particular sector of an input-output table were less than the sum of the figures in the row for that sector?

39. ▼ What does it mean if an entry in the matrix $(I - A)^{-1}$ is zero?

40. ▼ Why do we expect the diagonal entries in the matrix $(I - A)^{-1}$ to be slightly larger than 1?

41. ▼ Why do we expect the off-diagonal entries of $(I - A)^{-1}$ to be less than 1?

42. ▼ Why do we expect all the entries of $(I - A)^{-1}$ to be nonnegative?

---

[38] Source: *Survey of Current Business,* December 2001, U.S. Department of Commerce.

[39] Ibid.

[40] Source: *Australian National Accounts and Input-Output Tables 1978–1979,* Australian Bureau of Statistics.

[41] Ibid.

CHAPTER 5 REVIEW

KEY CONCEPTS

www.WanerMath.com
Go to the Website to find a comprehensive and interactive Web-based summary of Chapter 5.

5.1 Matrix Addition and Scalar Multiplication

$m \times n$ matrix, dimensions, entries [p. 322]

Referring to the entries of a matrix [p. 322]

Matrix equality [p. 323]

Row, column, and square matrices [p. 323]

Addition and subtraction of matrices [p. 324]

Scalar multiplication [p. 326]

Properties of matrix addition and scalar multiplication [p. 327]

The transpose of a matrix [p. 328]

Properties of transposition [p. 329]

5.2 Matrix Multiplication

Multiplying a row by a column [p. 333]

Linear equation as a matrix equation [p. 334]

The product of two matrices: general case [p. 335]

Identity matrix [p. 339]

Properties of matrix addition and multiplication [p. 340]

Properties of transposition and multiplication [p. 341]

A system of linear equations can be written as a single matrix equation [p. 341]

5.3 Matrix Inversion

The inverse of a matrix, singular matrix [p. 348]

Procedure for finding the inverse of a matrix [p. 350]

Formula for the inverse of a 2×2 matrix; determinant of a 2×2 matrix [p. 351]

Using an inverse matrix to solve a system of equations [p. 353]

5.4 Game Theory

Two-person zero-sum game, payoff matrix [p. 359]

A strategy specifies how a player chooses a move [p. 359]

The expected payoff of a game for given mixed strategies R and C [p. 361]

An optimal strategy, according to the minimax criterion, is one that minimizes the maximum damage your opponent can cause you. [p. 364]

The Fundamental Principle of Game Theory [p. 364]

Procedure for reducing by dominance [p. 365]

Procedure for solving a 2×2 game [p. 365]

The expected value of a game is its expected payoff when the players use their optimal strategies [p. 368]

A strictly determined game is one with a saddle point [p. 370]

Steps to follow in solving a game [p. 370]

5.5 Input-Output Models

An input-output model divides an economy into sectors. The technology matrix records the interactions of these sectors and allows us to relate external demand to the production vector. [p. 378]

Procedure for finding a technology matrix from an input-output table [p. 381]

The entries of $(I - A)^{-1}$ [p. 383]

REVIEW EXERCISES

For Exercises 1–10, let

$$A = \begin{bmatrix} 1 & 2 & 3 \\ 4 & 5 & 6 \end{bmatrix}, \quad B = \begin{bmatrix} 1 & -1 \\ 0 & 1 \end{bmatrix},$$

$$C = \begin{bmatrix} -1 & 0 \\ 1 & 1 \\ 0 & 1 \end{bmatrix}, \quad and \quad D = \begin{bmatrix} -3 & -2 & -1 \\ 1 & 2 & 3 \end{bmatrix}.$$

Determine whether each expression is defined. If it is, evaluate it.

1. $A + B$

2. $A - D$

3. $2A^T + C$

4. AB

5. $A^T B$

6. A^2

7. B^2

8. B^3

9. $AC + B$

10. $CD + B$

In Exercises 11–16, find the inverse of the given matrix, or determine that the matrix is singular.

11. $\begin{bmatrix} 1 & -1 \\ 0 & 1 \end{bmatrix}$

12. $\begin{bmatrix} 1 & 2 \\ 0 & 0 \end{bmatrix}$

13. $\begin{bmatrix} 1 & 2 & 3 \\ 0 & 4 & 1 \\ 0 & 0 & 1 \end{bmatrix}$

14. $\begin{bmatrix} 1 & 2 & 3 & 4 \\ 1 & 3 & 4 & 2 \\ 0 & 1 & 2 & 3 \\ 0 & 0 & 1 & 2 \end{bmatrix}$

15. $\begin{bmatrix} 1 & 2 & 3 & 4 \\ 2 & 3 & 3 & 3 \\ 0 & 1 & 2 & 3 \\ 0 & 0 & 1 & 2 \end{bmatrix}$

16. $\begin{bmatrix} 0 & 1 & 0 & 0 \\ 1 & 0 & 0 & 0 \\ 0 & 0 & 0 & 1 \\ 0 & 0 & 1 & 0 \end{bmatrix}$

In Exercises 17–20, write the given system of linear equations as a matrix equation, and solve by inverting the coefficient matrix.

17. $x + 2y = 0$
$\quad 3x + 4y = 2$

18. $x + y + z = 3$
$\quad y + 2z = 4$
$\quad y - z = 1$

19. $x + y + z = 2$
$\quad x + 2y + z = 3$
$\quad x + y + 2z = 1$

20. $x + y \qquad = 0$
$\quad y + z \qquad = 1$
$\qquad z + w = 0$
$\quad x \qquad - w = 3$

In Exercises 21–24, solve the game with the given payoff matrix, and give the expected value of the game.

21. $P = \begin{bmatrix} 2 & 1 & 3 & 2 \\ -1 & 0 & -2 & 1 \\ 2 & 0 & 1 & 3 \end{bmatrix}$

22. $P = \begin{bmatrix} 3 & -3 & -2 \\ -1 & 3 & 0 \\ 2 & 2 & 1 \end{bmatrix}$

23. $P = \begin{bmatrix} -1 & -3 & -2 \\ -1 & 3 & 0 \\ 3 & 3 & -1 \end{bmatrix}$

24. $P = \begin{bmatrix} 1 & 4 & 3 & 3 \\ 0 & -1 & 2 & 3 \\ 2 & 0 & -1 & 2 \end{bmatrix}$

In Exercises 25–28, find the production vector X corresponding to the given technology matrix A and external demand vector D.

25. $A = \begin{bmatrix} 0.3 & 0.1 \\ 0 & 0.3 \end{bmatrix}, D = \begin{bmatrix} 700 \\ 490 \end{bmatrix}$

26. $A = \begin{bmatrix} 0.7 & 0.1 \\ 0.1 & 0.7 \end{bmatrix}, D = \begin{bmatrix} 1,000 \\ 2,000 \end{bmatrix}$

27. $A = \begin{bmatrix} 0.2 & 0.2 & 0.2 \\ 0 & 0.2 & 0.2 \\ 0 & 0 & 0.2 \end{bmatrix}, D = \begin{bmatrix} 32,000 \\ 16,000 \\ 8,000 \end{bmatrix}$

28. $A = \begin{bmatrix} 0.5 & 0.1 & 0 \\ 0.1 & 0.5 & 0.1 \\ 0 & 0.1 & 0.5 \end{bmatrix}, D = \begin{bmatrix} 23,000 \\ 46,000 \\ 23,000 \end{bmatrix}$

Applications: OHaganBooks.com
[Try the game at www.OHaganBooks.com]

It is now July 1, and online sales of romance, science fiction, and horror novels at OHaganBooks.com were disappointingly slow over the past month. Exercises 29–34 are based on the following tables.

Inventory of books in stock on June 1 at the OHaganBooks .com warehouses in Texas and Nevada:

Books in Stock (June 1)

	Romance	Sci Fi	Horror
Texas	2,500	4,000	3,000
Nevada	1,500	3,000	1,000

Online sales during June:

June Sales

	Romance	Sci Fi	Horror
Texas	300	500	100
Nevada	100	600	200

New books purchased each month:

Monthly Purchases

	Romance	Sci Fi	Horror
Texas	400	400	300
Nevada	200	400	300

July Sales (Projected)

	Romance	Sci Fi	Horror
Texas	280	550	100
Nevada	50	500	120

29. *Inventory* Use matrix algebra to compute the inventory at each warehouse at the end of June.

30. *Inventory* Use matrix algebra to compute the change in inventory at each warehouse during June.

31. *Inventory* Assuming that sales continue at the level projected for July for the next few months, write down a matrix equation showing the inventory N at each warehouse x months after July 1. How many months from now will OHaganBooks.com run out of Sci Fi novels at the Nevada warehouse?

32. *Inventory* Assuming that sales continue at the level projected for July for the next few months, write down a matrix equation showing the change in inventory N at each warehouse x months after July 1. How many months from now will OHaganBooks.com have 1,000 more horror novels in stock in Texas than currently?

33. *Revenue* It is now the end of July, and OHaganBooks .com's e-commerce manager bursts into the CEO's office. "I thought you might want to know, John, that our sales figures are exactly what I projected a month ago. Is that good market analysis or what?" OHaganBooks.com has charged an average of $5 for romance novels, $6 for science fiction novels, and $5.50 for horror novels. Use the projected July sales figures from above and matrix arithmetic to compute the total revenue OHaganBooks.com earned at each warehouse in July.

34. *Cost* OHaganBooks.com pays an average of $2 for romance novels, $3.50 for science fiction novels, and $1.50 for horror novels. Use this information together with the monthly purchasing information to compute the monthly purchasing cost.

Acting on a "tip" from Marjory Duffin, John O'Hagan decided that his company should invest a significant sum in shares of Duffin House Publishers *(DHP)* and Duffin Subprime Ventures *(DSV)*. Exercises 35–38 are based on the following table, which shows what information John was able to piece together later, after some of the records had been deleted by an angry student intern.

Date	Number of Shares: DHP	Price per Share: DHP	Number of Shares: DSV	Price per Share: DSV
July 1	?	$20	?	$10
August 1	?	$10	?	$20
September 1	?	$5	?	$40
Total	5,000		7,000	

35. **Investments** Over the 3 months shown, the company invested a total of $50,000 in DHP stock and, on August 15, was paid dividends of 10¢ per share held on that date, for a total of $300. Use matrix inversion to determine how many shares of DHP OHaganBooks.com purchased on each of the three dates shown.

36. **Investments** Over the 3 months shown, the company invested a total of $150,000 in DSV stock and, on July 15, was paid dividends of 20¢ per share held on that date, for a total of $600. Use matrix inversion to determine how many shares of DSV OHaganBooks.com purchased on each of the three dates shown.

37. **Investments** (Refer to Exercise 35.) On October 1 the shares of DHP purchased on July 1 were sold at $3 per share. The remaining shares were sold 1 month later at $1 per share. Use matrix algebra to determine the total loss (taking into account the dividends paid on August 15) incurred as a result of the Duffin stock debacle.

38. **Investments** (Refer to Exercise 36.) On September 15, DSV announced a two-for-one stock split, so each share originally purchased was converted into two shares. On October 1 the company paid an additional special dividend of 10¢ per share. On October 15, OHaganBooks.com sold 3,000 shares at $20 per share. One week later the subprime market crashed, *Duffin Subprime Ventures* declared bankruptcy (after awarding its fund manager a $10 million bonus), and DSV stock became worthless. Use matrix algebra to determine the total loss (taking into account the dividends paid on July 15) incurred as a result of the Duffin stock debacle.

OHaganBooks.com has two main competitors—JungleBooks.com and FarmerBooks.com—and no other competitors of any significance on the horizon. Exercises 39–42 are based on the following table, which shows the movement of customers during July.[42] (Thus, for instance, the first row tells us that

---

[42] By a "customer" of one of the three e-commerce sites, we mean someone who purchases more at that site than at either of the two competitors.

80% of OHaganBooks.com's customers remained loyal, 10% of them went to JungleBooks.com, and the remaining 10% went to FarmerBooks.com.)

	To OHagan	To Jungle	To Farmer
From OHagan	0.8	0.1	0.1
From Jungle	0.4	0.6	0
From Farmer	0.2	0	0.8

At the beginning of July, OHaganBooks.com had an estimated 2,000 customers, while its two competitors had 4,000 each.

39. **Competition** Set up the July 1 customer numbers in a row matrix, and use matrix arithmetic to estimate the number of customers each company has at the end of July.

40. **Competition** Assuming that the July trends continue in August, predict the number of customers each company will have at the end of August.

41. **Competition** Assuming that the July trends continue in August, why is it not possible for a customer of FarmerBooks.com on July 1 to have ended up as a JungleBooks.com customer 2 months later without having ever been an OHaganBooks.com customer?

42. **Competition** Name one or more important factors that the model we have used does not take into account.

Publisher Marjory Duffin reveals that JungleBooks.com *may be launching a promotional scheme in which it will offer either two books for the price of one, or three books for the price of two. (Marjory can't quite seem to remember which and is not certain whether they will go with the scheme at all.) John O'Hagan's marketing advisers Flood and O'Lara seem to have different ideas as to how to respond. Flood suggests that the company counter by offering three books for the price of one, while O'Lara suggests that it offer instead a free copy of the* Finite Mathematics Student Solutions Manual *with every purchase. After a careful analysis, O'Hagan comes up with the following payoff matrix, where the payoffs represent the number of customers, in thousands, he expects to gain from JungleBooks.com:*

	JungleBooks No Promo	JungleBooks 2 for Price of 1	JungleBooks 3 for Price of 2
No Promo	0	−60	−40
O'Hagan 3 for Price of 1	30	20	10
Finite Math	20	0	15

Use the above information in Exercises 43–48.

43. **Competition** After a very expensive dinner at an exclusive restaurant, Marjory suddenly "remembers" that the JungleBooks.com CEO mentioned to her (at a less expensive restaurant) that there is only a 20% chance that JungleBooks.com will launch a "2 for the price of 1" promotion and a 40% chance that it will launch a "3 for the price of 2" promotion. What should OHaganBooks.com do in view of this information, and what will the expected effect be on its customer base?

44. **Competition** JungleBooks.com CEO François Dubois has been told by someone with personal ties to OHaganBooks.com staff that OHaganBooks.com is in fact 80% certain to opt for the "3 for the price of 1" option and will certainly go with one of the two possible promos. What should JungleBooks.com do in view of this information, and what will the expected effect be on its customer base?

45. **Corporate Spies** One of John O'Hagan's trusted marketing advisers has, without knowing it, accidentally sent him a copy of the following e-mail:

> To: René, JungleBooks.com Marketing Department
>
> From: O'Lara
>
> Hey René somehow the CEO here says he has learned that there is a 20% chance that you will opt for the "2 for the price of 1" promotion, and a 40% chance that you will opt for the "3 for the price of 2" promotion. Thought you might want to know. So when do I get my "commission"?—Jim

What will each company do in view of this new information, and what will the expected effect be on its customer base?

46. **More Corporate Spies** The next day, everything changes: OHaganBooks.com's mole at JungleBooks.com, Davíde DuPont, is found unconscious in the coffee room at JungleBooks.com headquarters, clutching in his hand the following correspondence, which he had apparently received moments earlier:

> To: Davíde
> From: John O'Hagan
> Subject: Re: Urgent Information
> Davíde: This information is much appreciated and definitely changes my plans—J
> >
> >To: John O
> >From: Davíde
> >Subject: Urgent Information
> >
> >Thought you might want to know that JungleBooks.com
> >thinks you are 80% likely to opt for 3 for 1 and 20%
> >likely to opt for Finite Math.
> >
> >—D

What will each company do in view of this information, and what will the expected effect be on its customer base?

47. **Things Unravel** John O'Hagan is about to go with the option chosen in Exercise 45 when he hears word about an exposé in the *Publisher Enquirer* on corporate spying in the two companies. Each company now knows that no information about the other's intentions can be trusted. Now what should OHaganBooks.com do, and how many customers should it expect to gain or lose?

48. **Competition** As a result of the *Publisher Enquirer* exposé it is now apparent that, not only can each company make no assumptions about the strategies the other might be using, but the payoff matrix they have been using is wrong. A crack investigative reporter at the *Enquirer* publishes the following revised matrix:

$$P = \begin{bmatrix} 0 & -60 & -40 \\ 30 & 20 & 10 \\ 20 & 0 & 20 \end{bmatrix}.$$

Now what should JungleBooks.com do, and how many customers should it expect to gain or lose?

Some of the books sold by OHaganBooks.com are printed at Bruno Mills, Inc., a combined paper mill and printing company. Exercises 49–52 are based on the following typical monthly input-output table for Bruno Mills's paper and book printing sectors.

		To	
		Paper	**Books**
From	**Paper**	$20,000	$50,000
	Books	2,000	5,000
	Total Output	200,000	100,000

49. **Production** Find the technology matrix for Bruno Mills's paper and book printing sectors.

50. **Production** Compute $(I - A)^{-1}$. What is the significance of the $(1, 2)$ entry?

51. **Production** Approximately $1,700 worth of the books sold each month by OHaganBooks.com are printed at Bruno Mills, and OHaganBooks.com uses approximately $170 worth of Bruno Mills's paper products each month. What is the total value of paper and books that must be produced by Bruno Mills to meet demand from OHaganBooks.com?

52. **Production** Currently, Bruno Mills has a monthly capacity of $500,000 of paper products and $200,000 of books. What level of external demand would cause Bruno Mills to meet the capacity for both products?

Projecting Market Share

You are the sales director at *Selular,* a cellphone provider, and things are not looking good for your company: *iClone,* a recently launched competitor, is beginning to chip away at Selular's market share. Particularly disturbing are rumors of fierce brand loyalty by iClone customers, with several bloggers suggesting that iClone retains close to 100% of their customers. Worse, you will shortly be presenting a sales report to the board of directors, and the CEO has "suggested" that your report include 2-, 5-, and 10-year projections of Selular's market share given the recent impact on the market by iClone. The CEO also wants a worst-case scenario projecting what would happen if iClone customers were so loyal that none of them ever switch services.

The sales department has conducted two market surveys, taken one quarter apart, of the major cellphone providers, which are *iClone, Selular, AB&C,* and some smaller companies lumped together as "Other," and has given you the data shown in Figure 4, which shows the percentages of subscribers who switched from one service to another during the quarter.*

* If you go on to study probability theory in Chapter 8, you will see how this scenario can be interpreted as a Markov system, and you will revisit the analysis below in that context. The percentages in the figure and market shares below reflect actual data for several cellphone services in the United States during a single quarter of 2003. (See the exercises for Section 8.7.)

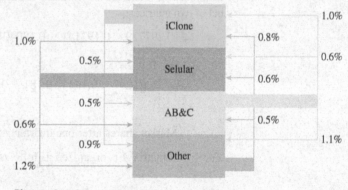

Figure 4

For example, by the end of the quarter, 0.5% of iClone's customers had switched to Selular, 0.5% to AB&C, and 0.9% to Other. The current market shares are as follows: iClone: 29.7%, Selular: 19.3%, AB&C: 18.1%, Other: 32.9%.

"This is simple," you tell yourself. "Since I know the current market shares and percentage movements over one quarter, I can easily calculate the market shares next quarter (assuming that the percentages that switch services remain the same), then repeat the calculation for the following quarter, and so on until I get the long-term prediction I am seeking." So you begin your calculations by computing the market shares next quarter. First you note that, since a total of $0.5 + 0.5 + 0.9 = 1.9\%$ of iClone users switched to other brands, the rest, 98.1%, stayed with iClone. Similarly, 97.2% of Selular users, 97.3% of AB&C, and 98.1% of Other stayed with their respective brands. Then you compute

iClone share after one quarter

$= 98.1\%$ of iClone $+ 1.0\%$ of Selular $+ 1.0\%$ of AB&C $+ 0.8\%$ of Other

$= (0.981)(0.297) + (0.010)(0.193) + (0.010)(0.181) + (0.008)(0.329)$

$= 0.297729$, or 29.7729%.

Similarly,

Selular share:

$$= (0.005)(0.297) + (0.972)(0.193) + (0.006)(0.181) + (0.006)(0.329)$$
$$= 0.192141$$

AB&C share:

$$= (0.005)(0.297) + (0.006)(0.193) + (0.973)(0.181) + (0.005)(0.329)$$
$$= 0.180401$$

Other share:

$$= (0.009)(0.297) + (0.012)(0.193) + (0.011)(0.181) + (0.981)(0.329)$$
$$= 0.329729.$$

So you project the market shares after one quarter to be iClone: 29.7729%, Selular: 19.2141%, AB&C: 18.0401%, Other: 32.9729%. You now begin to realize that repeating this kind of calculation for the large number of quarters required for long-term projections will be tedious. You call in your student intern (who happens to be a mathematics major) to find out whether she can help. After taking one look at the calculations, she makes the observation that all you have really done is compute the product of two matrices:

$$[0.297729 \quad 0.192141 \quad 0.180401 \quad 0.329729]$$

$$= [0.297 \quad 0.193 \quad 0.181 \quad 0.329] \begin{bmatrix} .981 & .005 & .005 & .009 \\ .010 & .972 & .006 & .012 \\ .010 & .006 & .973 & .011 \\ .008 & .006 & .005 & .981 \end{bmatrix}$$

Market shares after one quarter = Market shares at start of quarter $\times A$.

The 4×4 matrix A is organized as follows:

		To			
		iClone	**Selular**	**AB&C**	**Other**
	iClone	.981	.005	.005	.009
From	**Selular**	.010	.972	.006	.012
	AB&C	.010	.006	.973	.011
	Other	.008	.006	.005	.981

Since the market shares one quarter later can be obtained from the shares at the start of the quarter, you realize that you can now obtain the shares *two* quarters later by multiplying the result by A, and at this point, you start using technology (such as the Matrix Algebra Tool at www.WanerMath.com) to continue the calculation:

Market shares after two quarters = Market shares after one quarter $\times A$

$$= [0.297729 \quad 0.192141 \quad 0.180401 \quad 0.329729] \begin{bmatrix} .981 & .005 & .005 & .009 \\ .010 & .972 & .006 & .012 \\ .010 & .006 & .973 & .011 \\ .008 & .006 & .005 & .981 \end{bmatrix}$$

$$\approx [0.298435 \quad 0.191310 \quad 0.179820 \quad 0.330434].$$

Although the use of matrices has simplified your work, multiplying the result by A over and over again to get the market shares for successive months is still tedious. Would it not be possible to get, say, the market share after 10 years (40 quarters) with a single calculation? To explore this, you decide to use symbols for the various market shares:

$$m_0 = \text{Starting market shares} = [0.297 \quad 0.193 \quad 0.181 \quad 0.329]$$
$$m_1 = \text{Market shares after 1 quarter}$$
$$= [0.297729 \quad 0.192141 \quad 0.180401 \quad 0.329729]$$
$$m_2 = \text{Market shares after 2 quarters}$$
$$\vdots$$
$$m_n = \text{Market share after } n \text{ quarters.}$$

You then rewrite the relationships above as

$$m_1 = m_0 A \quad \text{Shares after one quarter} = \text{Shares at start of quarter} \times A$$
$$m_2 = m_1 A \quad \text{Shares after two quarters} = \text{Shares after one quarter} \times A.$$

On an impulse, you substitute the first equation in the second:

$$m_2 = m_1 A = (m_0 A)A = m_0 A^2.$$

Continuing, you get

$$m_3 = m_2 A = (m_0 A^2)A = m_0 A^3$$
$$\vdots$$
$$m_n = m_0 A^n,$$

which is exactly the formula you need! You can now obtain the 2-, 5-, and 10-year projections each in a single step (with the aid of technology):

2-year projection: $m_8 = m_0 A^8$

$$= [0.297 \quad 0.193 \quad 0.181 \quad 0.329] \begin{bmatrix} .981 & .005 & .005 & .009 \\ .010 & .972 & .006 & .012 \\ .010 & .006 & .973 & .011 \\ .008 & .006 & .005 & .981 \end{bmatrix}^8$$

$$\approx [0.302237 \quad 0.186875 \quad 0.176691 \quad 0.334198]$$

5-year projection: $m_{20} = m_0 A^{20} \approx [0.307992 \quad 0.180290 \quad 0.171938 \quad 0.33978]$

10-year projection: $m_{40} = m_0 A^{40} \approx [0.313857 \quad 0.173809 \quad 0.167074 \quad 0.34526].$

In particular, Selular's market shares are projected to decline slightly: 2-year projection: 18.7%, 5-year projection: 18.0%, 10-year projection: 17.4%.

You now move on to the worst-case scenario, which you represent by assuming 100% loyalty by iClone users with the remaining percentages staying the same (Figure 5).

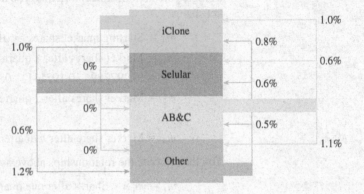

Figure 5

The matrix A corresponding to this diagram is $\begin{bmatrix} 1 & 0 & 0 & 0 \\ .010 & .972 & .006 & .012 \\ .010 & .006 & .973 & .011 \\ .008 & .006 & .005 & .981 \end{bmatrix}$, and

you find

2-year projection: $m_8 = m_0 A^8 \approx [0.346335 \quad 0.175352 \quad 0.165200 \quad 0.313113]$

5-year projection: $m_{20} = m_0 A^{20} \approx [0.413747 \quad 0.152940 \quad 0.144776 \quad 0.288536]$

10-year projection: $m_{40} = m_0 A^{40} \approx [0.510719 \quad 0.123553 \quad 0.117449 \quad 0.248279]$.

Thus, in the worst-case scenario, Selular's market shares are projected to decline more rapidly: 2-year projection: 17.5%, 5-year projection: 15.3%, 10-year projection: 12.4%.

EXERCISES

1. Project Selular's market share 20 and 30 years from now based on the original data shown in Figure 4. (Round all figures to the nearest 0.1%.)

2. Using the original data, what can you say about each company's share in 60 and 80 years (assuming that current trends continue)? (Round all figures to the nearest 0.1%.)

3. Obtain a sequence of projections several hundreds of years into the future using the scenarios in both Figure 4 and Figure 5. What do you notice?

4. Compute a sequence of larger and larger powers of the matrix A for both scenarios with all figures rounded to four decimal places. What do you notice?

5. Suppose the trends noted in the market survey were in place for several quarters *before* the current quarter. Using the scenario in Figure 4, determine what the companies' market shares were one quarter before the present and one year before the present (to the nearest 0.1%). Do the same for the scenario in Figure 5.

6. If A is the matrix from the scenario in Figure 4, compute A^{-1}. In light of the preceding exercise, what do the entries in A^{-1} mean?

Section 5.1

Example 2 (page 325) The *A-Plus* auto parts store chain has two outlets, one in Vancouver and one in Quebec. Among other things, it sells wiper blades, windshield cleaning fluid, and floor mats. The monthly sales of these items at the two stores for 2 months are given in the following tables:

January Sales	Vancouver	Quebec
Wiper Blades	20	15
Cleaning Fluid (bottles)	10	12
Floor Mats	8	4

February Sales	Vancouver	Quebec
Wiper Blades	23	12
Cleaning Fluid (bottles)	8	12
Floor Mats	4	5

Use matrix arithmetic to calculate the change in sales of each product in each store from January to February.

Solution

On the TI-83/84 Plus, matrices are referred to as [A], [B], and so on through [J]. To enter a matrix, press MATRIX to bring up the matrix menu, select EDIT, select a matrix, and press ENTER. Then enter the dimensions of the matrix followed by its entries. When you want to use a matrix, press MATRIX, select the matrix, and press ENTER.

On the TI-83/84 Plus, adding matrices is similar to adding numbers. The sum of the matrices [A] and [B] is [A] + [B]; their difference, of course, is [A] - [B]. As in the text, for this example,

1. Create two matrices, [J] and [F].
2. Compute their difference, [F] - [J] using [F] - [J] → [D].

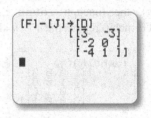

Note that we have stored the difference in the matrix [D] in case we need it for later use.

Section 5.2

Example 3(a) (page 336) Calculate

$$\begin{bmatrix} 2 & 0 & -1 & 3 \\ 1 & -1 & 2 & -2 \end{bmatrix} \begin{bmatrix} 1 & 1 & -8 \\ 1 & 0 & 0 \\ 0 & 5 & 2 \\ -2 & 8 & -1 \end{bmatrix}.$$

Solution

On the TI-83/84 Plus the format for multiplying matrices is the same as for multiplying numbers: [A] [B] or [A] * [B] will give the product. We enter the matrices and then multiply them. (Note that, while editing, you can see only three columns of [A] at a time.)

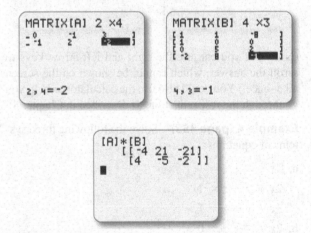

Note that if you try to multiply two matrices whose product is not defined, you will get the error "DIM MISMATCH" (dimension mismatch).

Example 6 (page 339)—Identity Matrix On the TI-83/84 Plus, the function `identity(n)` (in the `MATRIX` MATH menu) returns the $n \times n$ identity matrix.

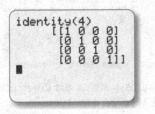

Section 5.3

Example 2(b) (page 349) Find the inverse of

$$Q = \begin{bmatrix} 1 & 0 & 1 \\ 2 & -2 & -1 \\ 3 & 0 & 0 \end{bmatrix}.$$

Solution

On a TI-83/84 Plus, you can invert the square matrix [A] by entering [A] x^{-1} ENTER.

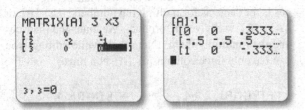

(Note that you can use the right and left arrow keys to scroll the answer, which cannot be shown on the screen all at once.) You could also use the calculator to help you go through the row reduction, as described in Chapter 4.

Example 4 (page 353) Solve the following three systems of equations:

a. $2x \quad + z = 1$
$2x + y - z = 1$
$3x + y - z = 1$

b. $2x \quad + z = 0$
$2x + y - z = 1$
$3x + y - z = 2$

c. $2x \quad + z = 0$
$2x + y - z = 0$
$3x + y - z = 0$

Solution

1. Enter the four matrices A, B, C, and D:

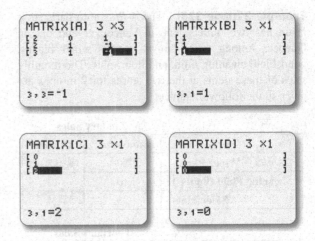

2. Compute the solutions $A^{-1}B$, $A^{-1}C$, and $A^{-1}D$:

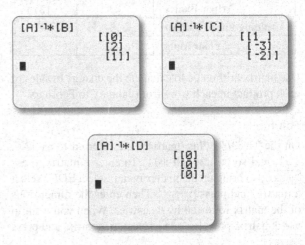

Section 5.5

Example 1 (page 379) Recall that the input-output table in Example 1 looks like this:

		To	
		Crude	**Refining**
From	**Crude**	27,000	59,000
	Refining	750	15,000
	Total Output	87,000	140,000

What was the technology matrix for these two sectors? What was left over from each of these sectors for use by other parts of the economy or for export?

Solution

There are several ways to use these data to create the technology matrix in your TI-83/84 Plus. For small matrices like this the most straightforward is to use the matrix editor, where you can give each entry as the appropriate quotient:

and so on. Once we have the technology matrix [A] and the production vector [B] (remember that we can't use [X] as a matrix name), we can calculate the external demand vector:

Of course, when interpreting these numbers, we must remember to round to two significant digits, because our original data were accurate to only that many digits.

Here is an alternative way to calculate the technology matrix that may be better for examples with more sectors:

1. Begin by entering the columns of the input-output table as lists in the list editor ([STAT] EDIT) (see below left).

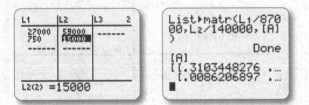

2. We now want to divide each column by the total output of its sector and assemble the results into a matrix. We can do this using the List ▶ matr function (under the [MATRIX] MATH menu) shown on the right above.

Example 3 (page 384) Consider four sectors of the economy of Kenya: (1) the traditional economy, (2) agriculture, (3) manufacture of metal products and machinery, and (4) wholesale and retail trade. The input-output table for these four sectors for 1976 looks like this (all numbers are thousands of K£):

		To			
		1	**2**	**3**	**4**
From	**1**	8,600	0	0	0
	2	0	20,000	24	0
	3	1,500	530	15,000	660
	4	810	8,500	5,800	2,900
	Total Output	87,000	530,000	110,000	180,000

Suppose that external demand for agriculture increased by K£50,000,000 and that external demand for metal products and machinery increased by K£10,000,000. How would production in these four sectors have to change to meet this rising demand?

Solution

1. Enter the technology matrix A as [A] and D^+ as [D] using one of the techniques above:

2. You can then compute the change in production with the formula `(identity(4)-[A])`$^{-1}$`[D]`.

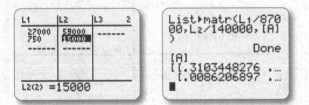

Spreadsheet Technology Guide

Section 5.1

Example 2 (page 325) The *A-Plus* auto parts store chain has two outlets, one in Vancouver and one in Quebec. Among other things, it sells wiper blades, windshield cleaning fluid, and floor mats. The monthly sales of these items at the two stores for 2 months are given in the following tables:

January Sales

	Vancouver	Quebec
Wiper Blades	20	15
Cleaning Fluid (bottles)	10	12
Floor Mats	8	4

February Sales

	Vancouver	Quebec
Wiper Blades	23	12
Cleaning Fluid (bottles)	8	12
Floor Mats	4	5

Use matrix arithmetic to calculate the change in sales of each product in each store from January to February.

Solution

To enter a matrix in a spreadsheet, we put its entries in any convenient block of cells. For example, the matrix A in Quick Example 1 of this section might look like this:

	A	B	C
1	2	0	1
2	33	-22	0

Spreadsheets refer to such blocks of data as **arrays**, which it can handle in much the same way as it handles single cells of data. For instance, in typing a formula, just as clicking on a cell creates a reference to that cell, selecting a whole array of cells will create a reference to that array. An array is referred to using an **array range** consisting of the top left and bottom right cell coordinates, separated by a colon. For example, the array range A1:C2 refers to the 2×3 matrix above, with top left corner A1 and bottom right corner C2.

1. To add or subtract two matrices in a spreadsheet, first input their entries in two separate arrays in the spreadsheet. (We have also added labels as in the previous tables, which you might do if you wanted to save the spreadsheet for later use.)

	A	B	C
1	January Sales		
2		Vancouver	Quebec
3	wiper blades	20	15
4	cleaning fluid (bottles)	10	12
5	floor mats	8	4
6			
7	February Sales		
8		Vancouver	Quebec
9	wiper blades	23	12
10	cleaning fluid (bottles)	8	12
11	floor mats	4	5

2. Select (highlight) a block of the same size (3×2 in this case) where you would like the answer, $F - J$, to appear, enter the formula =B9:C11-B3:C5, and then type Control+Shift+Enter. The easiest way to do this is as follows:

- Highlight cells B15:C17.   *Where you want the answer to appear*
- Type "=".
- Highlight the matrix F.   *Cells B9 through C11*
- Type "-".
- Highlight the matrix J.   *Cells B3 through C5*
- Press Control+Shift+Enter.   *Not just Enter*

	A	B	C
1	January Sales		
2		Vancouver	Quebec
3	wiper blades	20	15
4	cleaning fluid (bottles)	10	12
5	floor mats	8	4
6			
7	February Sales		
8		Vancouver	Quebec
9	wiper blades	23	12
10	cleaning fluid (bottles)	8	12
11	floor mats	4	5
12			
13	Change in Sales		
14		Vancouver	Quebec
15	wiper blades	=B9:C11-B3:C5	
16	cleaning fluid (bottles)		
17	floor mats		

Typing Control+Shift+Enter (instead of Enter) tells the spreadsheet that your formula is an *array formula*, one that returns a matrix rather than a single number.[43] Once entered, the formula bar will show the formula you entered enclosed in "curly braces," indicating that it is an array formula. Note that you must use Control+Shift+Enter to delete any array you create: Select the block you wish to delete and press Delete followed by Control+Shift+Enter.

Section 5.2

Example 3(a) (page 336)   Calculate the product

$$\begin{bmatrix} 2 & 0 & -1 & 3 \\ 1 & -1 & 2 & -2 \end{bmatrix} \begin{bmatrix} 1 & 1 & -8 \\ 1 & 0 & 0 \\ 0 & 5 & 2 \\ -2 & 8 & -1 \end{bmatrix}.$$

Solution

In a spreadsheet the function we use for matrix multiplication is MMULT. (Ordinary multiplication, *, will *not* work.)

1. Enter the two matrices as shown in the spreadsheet, and highlight a block where you want the answer to appear. (Note that it should have the correct dimensions for the product: 2 × 3.)

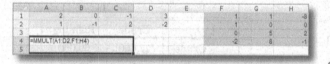

2. Enter the formula =MMULT(A1:D2,F1:H4) (using the mouse to avoid typing the array ranges if you like), and press Control+Shift+Enter. The product will appear in the region you highlighted. If you try to multiply two matrices whose product is not defined, you will get the error "#VALUE!".

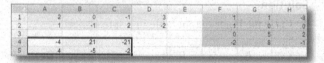

Example 6—Identity Matrix (page 339)   There is no spreadsheet function that returns an identity matrix. If you need a small identity matrix, it's simplest to just enter

the 1s and 0s by hand. If you need a large identity matrix, here is one way to get it quickly.

1. Say we want a 4 × 4 identity matrix in the cells B1:E4. Enter the following formula in cell B1:

   =IF(ROW(B1)-ROW($B$1)
   =COLUMN(B1)-COLUMN($B$1),1,0)

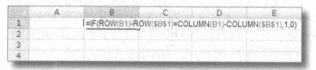

2. Press Enter, then copy cell B1 to cells B1:E4. The formula will return 1s along the diagonal of the matrix and 0s elsewhere, giving you the identity matrix. Why does this formula work?

Section 5.3

Example 2(b) (page 349)   Find the inverse of

$$Q = \begin{bmatrix} 1 & 0 & 1 \\ 2 & -2 & -1 \\ 3 & 0 & 0 \end{bmatrix}.$$

Solution

In a spreadsheet the function MINVERSE computes the inverse of a matrix.

1. Enter Q somewhere convenient, for example, in cells A1:C3.

2. Choose the block where you would like the inverse to appear, highlight the whole block.

3. Enter the formula =MINVERSE(A1:C3) and press Control+Shift+Enter.

The inverse will appear in the region you highlighted. (To convert the answer to fractions, format the cells as fractions.)

---

[43] Note that on a Mac, Command+Enter has the same effect as Control+Shift+Enter.

If a matrix is singular, a spreadsheet will register an error by showing #NUM! in each cell.

	A	B	C	D	E	F	G
1	1	0	1		0	0	0.3333333
2	2	-2	-1		-0.5	-0.5	0.5
3	3	0	0		1	0	-0.3333333

Although the spreadsheet appears to invert the matrix in one step, it is going through the procedure in the text or some variation of it to find the inverse. Of course, you could also use the spreadsheet to help you go through the row reduction, just as in Chapter 4.

Example 4 (page 353)   Solve the following three systems of equations:

a.
$$2x \quad + z = 1$$
$$2x + y - z = 1$$
$$3x + y - z = 1$$

b.
$$2x \quad + z = 0$$
$$2x + y - z = 1$$
$$3x + y - z = 2$$

c.
$$2x \quad + z = 0$$
$$2x + y - z = 0$$
$$3x + y - z = 0$$

Solution

Spreadsheets instantly update calculated results every time the contents of a cell are changed. We can take advantage of this to solve the three systems of equations given above using the same worksheet as follows:

1. Enter the matrices A and B from the matrix equation $AX = B$.

2. Select a 3×1 block of cells for the matrix X.

3. The Excel formula that we can use to calculate X is

$$\text{=MMULT(MINVERSE(A1:C3),E1:E3)} \qquad A^{-1}B$$

	A	B	C	D	E
1	2	0	1		1
2	2	1	-1		1
3	3	1	-1		1
4		A			B
5					
6	=MMULT(MINVERSE(A1:C3),E1:E3)				
7					
8					
9	A⁻¹B				

(As usual, use the mouse to select the ranges for A and B while typing the formula, and don't forget to press Control+Shift+Enter.) Having obtained the solution to part (a), you can now simply modify the entries in column E to see the solutions for parts (b) and (c).

Note Your spreadsheet for part (a) may look like this:

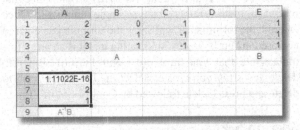

	A	B	C	D	E
1	2	0	1		1
2	2	1	-1		1
3	3	1	-1		1
4		A			B
5					
6	1.11022E-16				
7	2				
8	1				
9	A⁻¹B				

What is that strange number doing in cell A6? "E-16" represents "$\times 10^{-16}$", so the entry is really

$$1.11022 \times 10^{-16} = 0.000\,000\,000\,000\,000\,111022 \approx 0.$$

Mathematically, it is supposed to be *exactly* zero (see the solution to part (a) in the text), but Excel made a small error in computing the inverse of A, resulting in this spurious value. Note, however, that it is accurate (agrees with zero) to 15 decimal places! In practice, when we see numbers arise in matrix calculations that are far smaller than all the other entries, we can often assume that they are supposed to be zero. ∎

Section 5.5

Example 1 (page 379)   Recall that the input-output table in Example 1 looks like this:

		To	
		Crude	**Refining**
From	**Crude**	27,000	59,000
	Refining	750	15,000
	Total Output	87,000	140,000

What was the technology matrix for these two sectors? What was left over from each of these sectors for use by other parts of the economy or for export?

Solution

1. Enter the input-output table in a spreadsheet:

	A	B	C	D
1			To	
2			Crude	Refining
3	From	Crude	27000	59000
4		Refining	750	15000
5		Total Output	87000	140000

2. To obtain the technology matrix, we divide each column by the total output of its sector:

	A	B	C	D
1			To	
2			Crude	Refining
3	From	Crude	27000	59000
4		Refining	750	15000
5		Total Output	87000	140000
6				
7			=C3/C$5	
8				

	A	B	C	D
1			To	
2			Crude	Refining
3	From	Crude	27000	59000
4		Refining	750	15000
5		Total Output	87000	140000
6				
7			0.3103448	0.4214286
8			0.0086207	0.1071429

The formula =C3/C$5 is copied into the shaded 2 × 2 block shown above. (The $ sign in front of the 5 forces the program to always divide by the total in Row 5 even when the formula is copied from Row 7 to Row 8.) The result is the technology matrix shown in the bottom screenshot above.

3. Using the techniques discussed in Section 5.2, we can now compute $D = X - AX$ to find the demand vector.

Example 3 (page 384) Consider four sectors of the economy of Kenya: (1) the traditional economy, (2) agriculture, (3) manufacture of metal products and machinery, and (4) wholesale and retail trade. The input-output table for these four sectors for 1976 looks like this (all numbers are thousands of K£):

		To			
		1	2	3	4
From	1	8,600	0	0	0
	2	0	20,000	24	0
	3	1,500	530	15,000	660
	4	810	8,500	5,800	2,900
	Total Output	87,000	530,000	110,000	180,000

Suppose that external demand for agriculture increased by K£50,000,000 and that external demand for metal products and machinery increased by K£10,000,000.

How would production in these four sectors have to change to meet this rising demand?

Solution

1. Enter the input-output table in the spreadsheet.

2. Compute the technology matrix by dividing each column by the column total.

3. Insert the identity matrix I in preparation for the next step.

4. To see how each sector reacts to rising external demand, you must calculate the inverse matrix $(I - A)^{-1}$, as shown below. (Remember to use Control+Shift+Enter each time.)

5. To compute $(I - A)^{-1}D^+$, enter D^+ as a column, and use the MMULT operation. (See Example 3 in Section 5.2.)

Note Here is one of the beauties of spreadsheet programs: Once you are done with the calculation, you can use the spreadsheet as a template for any 4 × 4 input-output table by just changing the entries of the input-output matrix and/or D^+. The rest of the computation will then be done automatically as the spreadsheet is updated. In other words, you can use it to do your homework! ∎

6

LINEAR PROGRAMMING

CASE STUDY

The Diet Problem

The *Galaxy Nutrition* health-food mega-store chain provides free online nutritional advice and support to its customers. As website technical consultant, you are planning to construct an interactive web page to assist customers in preparing a diet tailored to their nutritional and budgetary requirements. Ideally, the customer would select foods to consider and specify nutritional and/or budgetary constraints, and the tool should return the optimal diet meeting those requirements. You would also like the web page to allow the customer to decide whether, for instance, to find the cheapest possible diet meeting the requirements, the diet with the lowest number of calories, or the diet with the least total carbohydrates.

How do you go about constructing such a web page?

Image Studios/UpperCut Images/Getty Images

 www.WanerMath.com

At the Website, in addition to the resources listed in the Preface, you will find:

- A linear programming grapher
- A pivot and Gauss-Jordan tool
- A simplex method tool

Introduction

In this chapter we begin to look at one of the most important types of problems for business and the sciences: finding the largest or smallest possible value of some quantity (such as profit or cost) under certain constraints (such as limited resources). We call such problems **optimization** problems because we are trying to find the best, or optimum, value. The optimization problems we look at in this chapter involve linear functions only and are known as **linear programming** (LP) problems. One of the main purposes of calculus, which you may study later, is to solve nonlinear optimization problems.

Linear programming problems involving only two unknowns can usually be solved by a graphical method that we discuss in Sections 6.1 and 6.2. When there are three or more unknowns, we must use an algebraic method, as we had to do for systems of linear equations. The method we use is called the **simplex method**. Invented in 1947 by George B. Dantzig* (1914–2005), the simplex method is still the most commonly used technique to solve LP problems in real applications, from finance to the computation of trajectories for guided missiles.

The simplex method can be used for hand calculations when the numbers are fairly small and the unknowns are few. Practical problems often involve large numbers and many unknowns, however. Problems such as routing telephone calls or airplane flights or allocating resources in a manufacturing process can involve tens of thousands of unknowns. Solving such problems by hand is obviously impractical, so computers are regularly used. Although computer programs most often use the simplex method, mathematicians are always seeking faster methods. The first radically different method of solving LP problems was the **ellipsoid algorithm** published in 1979 by the Soviet mathematician Leonid G. Khachiyan[2] (1952–2005). In 1984, Narendra Karmarkar (1957–), a researcher at Bell Labs, created a more efficient method, now known as **Karmarkar's algorithm**. Although these methods (and others since developed) can be shown to be faster than the simplex method in the worst cases, it seems to be true that the simplex method is still the fastest in the applications that arise in practice.

Calculators and spreadsheets are very useful aids in the simplex method. In practice, software packages do most of the work, so you can think of what we teach you here as a peek inside a "black box." What the software cannot do for you is convert a real situation into a mathematical problem, so the most important lessons to get out of this chapter are (1) how to recognize and set up a linear programming problem and (2) how to interpret the results.

* Dantzig is the real-life source of the story of the student who, walking in late to a math class, copies down two problems on the board, thinking they're homework. After much hard work he hands in the solutions, only to discover that he has just solved two famous unsolved problems. This actually happened to Dantzig in graduate school in 1939.[1]

6.1   Graphing Linear Inequalities

Inequalities

By the end of the next section we will be solving linear programming (LP) problems with two unknowns. We use inequalities to describe the *constraints* in such problems, so we start by reviewing some basic notation for inequalities.

---

[1] Sources: D. J. Albers, and C. Reid, "An Interview of George B. Dantzig: The Father of Linear Programming," *College Mathematics Journal,* v. 17 (1986), pp. 293–314. The article is quoted and discussed in the context of the urban legends it inspired at www.snopes.com/college/homework/unsolvable.asp.

[2] Dantzig and Khachiyan died approximately two weeks apart in 2005. The *New York Times* ran their obituaries together on May 23, 2005.

Strict Inequalities	Quick Examples
$a < b$ means that a **is less than** b.	$3 < 99$, $-2 < -1$, $0 < 3$
$a > b$ means that a **is greater than** b.	$4 > 3$, $1.78 > 1.76$, $\dfrac{1}{3} > \dfrac{1}{4}$
Non-Strict Inequalities*	Quick Examples
$a \le b$ means that a **is less than or equal to** b.	$3 \le 99$, $-2 \le -2$, $0 \le 3$
$a \ge b$ means that a **is greater than or equal to** b.	$3 \ge 3$, $1.78 \ge 1.76$, $\dfrac{1}{3} \ge \dfrac{1}{4}$

＊ In this chapter we focus on the non-strict inequalities.

Following are some of the basic rules for manipulating inequalities. Although we illustrate all of them with the inequality $\le$, they apply equally well to inequalities with $\ge$ and to the strict inequalities $<$ and $>$.

Rules for Manipulating Inequalities	Quick Examples
1. The same quantity can be added to or subtracted from both sides of an inequality: If $x \le y$, then $x + a \le y + a$ for any real number a.	$x \le y$ implies $x - 4 \le y - 4$
2. Both sides of an inequality can be multiplied or divided by a positive constant: If $x \le y$ and a is positive, then $ax \le ay$.	$x \le y$ implies $3x \le 3y$
3. Both sides of an inequality can be multiplied or divided by a negative constant if the inequality is *reversed*: If $x \le y$ and a is negative, then $ax \ge ay$.	$x \le y$ implies $-3x \ge -3y$
4. Switching the left and right sides *reverses* the inequality: If $x \le y$, then $y \ge x$; if $y \ge x$, then $x \le y$.	$3x \ge 5y$ implies $5y \le 3x$

Here are the particular kinds of inequalities in which we're interested, again stated in terms of non-strict inequalities.

Linear Inequalities and Solving Inequalities

An **inequality in the unknown x** is the statement that one expression involving x is less than or equal to (or greater than or equal to) another. Similarly, we can have an **inequality in x and y**, which involves expressions that contain x and y; an **inequality in x, y, and z**; and so on. A **linear inequality** in one or more unknowns is an inequality of the form

$$ax \le b \quad \text{or} \quad ax \ge b \quad \text{(a and b real constants)}$$
$$ax + by \le c \quad \text{or} \quad ax + by \ge c \quad \text{(a, b, and c real constants)}$$
$$ax + by + cz \le d \quad \text{(a, b, c, and d real constants)}$$
$$ax + by + cz + dw \le e \quad \text{(a, b, c, d, and e real constants)}$$

and so on.

Quick Examples

1. $2x + 8 \ge 89$ Linear inequality in x

2. $2x^3 \le x^3 + y$ Nonlinear inequality in x and y

3. $3x - 2y \geq 8$ Linear inequality in x and y

4. $x^2 + y^2 \leq 19z$ Nonlinear inequality in x, y, and z

5. $3x - 2y + 4z \leq 0$ Linear inequality in x, y, and z

A **solution** of an inequality in the unknown x is a value for x that makes the inequality true. For example, $2x + 8 \geq 89$ has a solution $x = 50$ because $2(50) + 8 \geq 89$. Of course, it has many other solutions as well. Similarly, a solution of an inequality in x and y is a pair of values (x, y) making the inequality true. For example, $(5, 1)$ is a solution of $3x - 2y \geq 8$ because $3(5) - 2(1) \geq 8$. To **solve** an inequality is to find the set of *all* solutions.

Solving Linear Inequalities in Two Variables

Our first goal is to solve linear inequalities in two variables—that is, inequalities of the form $ax + by \leq c$. As an example, let's solve

$$2x + 3y \leq 6.$$

We already know how to solve the *equation* $2x + 3y = 6$. As we saw in Chapter 1, the solution of this equation may be pictured as the set of all points (x, y) on the straight-line graph of the equation. This straight line has x-intercept 3 (obtained by putting $y = 0$ in the equation) and y-intercept 2 (obtained by putting $x = 0$ in the equation) and is shown in Figure 1.

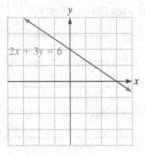

Figure 1

Notice that, if (x, y) is any point on the line, then x and y not only satisfy the *equation* $2x + 3y = 6$, but also satisfy the *inequality* $2x + 3y \leq 6$, because being equal to 6 qualifies as being less than or equal to 6.

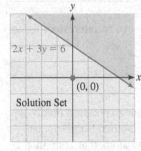

Figure 2

: *Do the points on the line give all possible solutions to the inequality?*

A: No. For example, try the origin, $(0, 0)$. Because $2(0) + 3(0) = 0 \leq 6$, the point $(0, 0)$ is a solution that does not lie on the line. In fact, here is a possibly surprising fact: The solution to any linear inequality in two unknowns is represented by an entire **half plane**: the set of all points on one side of the line (including the line itself). Thus, because $(0, 0)$ is a solution of $2x + 3y \leq 6$ and is not on the line, every point on the same side of the line as $(0, 0)$ is a solution as well. (The colored region below the line in Figure 2 shows which half plane constitutes the solution set.)

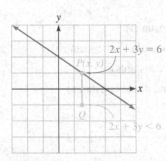

Figure 3

To see why the solution set of $2x + 3y \leq 6$ is the entire half plane shown in Figure 2, start with any point P on the line $2x + 3y = 6$. We already know that P is a solution of $2x + 3y \leq 6$. If we choose any point Q directly below P, the x-coordinate of Q will be the same as that of P, and the y-coordinate will be smaller. So the value of $2x + 3y$ at Q will be smaller than the value at P, which is 6. Thus, $2x + 3y < 6$ at Q, so Q is another solution of the inequality. (See Figure 3.) In other words, *every point beneath the line is a solution of* $2x + 3y \leq 6$. On the other hand, any point above the line is directly above a point on the line, so $2x + 3y > 6$ for such a point. Thus, *no point above the line is a solution of* $2x + 3y \leq 6$.

The same kind of argument can be used to show that the solution set of every inequality of the form $ax + by \leq c$ or $ax + by \geq c$ consists of the half plane above

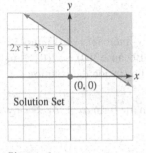

Figure 4

or below the line $ax + by = c$. The "test-point" procedure we describe below gives us an easy method for deciding whether the solution set includes the region above or below the corresponding line.

Now we are going to do something that will appear backward at first (but makes it simpler to sketch sets of solutions of *systems* of linear inequalities). For our standard drawing of the region of solutions of $2x + 3y \leq 6$, we are going to *shade only the part that we do not want and leave the solution region blank*. Think of covering over or "blocking out" the unwanted points, leaving those that we do want in full view (but remember that the points on the boundary line are also points that we want). The result is Figure 4. The reason we do this should become clear in Example 2.

Using Technology

Technology can be used to graph inequalities. Here is an outline (see the Technology Guides at the end of the chapter for additional details on using a TI-83/84 Plus or a spreadsheet):

TI-83/84 Plus
Solve the inequality for *y*, and enter the resulting function of *x*; for example,
$Y_1 = -(2/3)*X+2$
Position the cursor on the icon to the left of Y_1, and press ENTER until you see the kind of shading desired (above or below the line). [More details in the Technology Guide.]

Spreadsheet
Solve the inequality for *y*, and create a scattergraph using two points on the line. Then use the drawing palette to create a polygon to provide the shading. [More details in the Technology Guide.]

W Website
www.WanerMath.com
→ Online Utilities
→ Linear Programming Grapher
Select "Show only the region defined by the following constraints:", enter one or more inequalities (each one on a new line), and press "Solve":

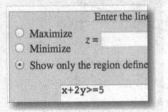

Sketching the Region Represented by a Linear Inequality in Two Variables

1. Sketch the straight line obtained by replacing the given inequality with an equality.

2. Choose a test point that is not on the line; $(0, 0)$ is a good choice if the line does not pass through the origin.

3. If the test point satisfies the inequality, then the set of solutions is the line plus the entire region on the same side of the line as the test point. Otherwise, it is the line plus the region on the other side of the line. In either case, shade (block out) the side that does *not* contain the solutions, leaving the solution set unshaded.

Quick Example

6. Here are the three steps used to graph the inequality $x + 2y \geq 5$:

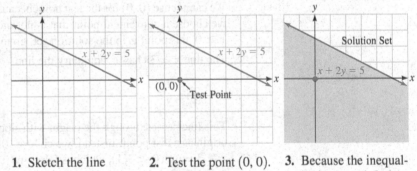

1. Sketch the line $x + 2y = 5$.

2. Test the point $(0, 0)$. $0 + 2(0) \not\geq 5$. The inequality is not satisfied.

3. Because the inequality is not satisfied, shade the region containing the test point.

EXAMPLE 1 **Graphing Single Inequalities**

Sketch the regions determined by each of the following inequalities:

a. $3x - 2y \leq 6$ **b.** $6x \leq 12 + 4y$ **c.** $x \leq -1$ **d.** $y \geq 0$ **e.** $x \geq 3y$

Solution

a. The boundary line $3x - 2y = 6$ has x-intercept 2 and y-intercept -3 (Figure 5). We use $(0, 0)$ as a test point (because it is not on the line). Because $3(0) - 2(0) \leq 6$, the inequality is satisfied by the test point $(0, 0)$, so it lies inside the solution set. The solution set is shown in Figure 5.*

* *Remember here and also in parts (b)–(e) that the solution set also includes the boundary line.

b. The given inequality, $6x \leq 12 + 4y$, can be rewritten in the form $ax + by \leq c$ by subtracting $4y$ from both sides:

$$6x - 4y \leq 12.$$

Dividing both sides by 2 gives the inequality $3x - 2y \leq 6$, which we considered in part (a). Now, *applying the rules for manipulating inequalities does not affect the set of solutions.* Thus, the inequality $6x \leq 12 + 4y$ has the same set of solutions as $3x - 2y \leq 6$. (See Figure 5.)

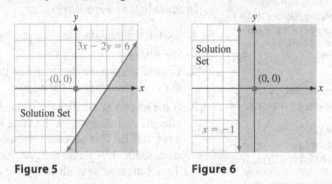

Figure 5   **Figure 6**

c. The region $x \leq -1$ has as boundary the vertical line $x = -1$. The test point $(0, 0)$ is not in the solution set, as shown in Figure 6.

d. The region $y \geq 0$ has as boundary the horizontal line $y = 0$ (that is, the x-axis). We cannot use $(0, 0)$ for the test point because it lies on the boundary line. Instead, we choose a convenient point that is not on the line $y = 0$—say, $(0, 1)$. Because $1 \geq 0$, this point is in the solution set, giving us the region shown in Figure 7.

e. The line $x \geq 3y$ has as boundary the line $x = 3y$ or, solving for y,

$$y = \frac{1}{3}x.$$

This line passes through the origin with slope $1/3$, so again we cannot choose the origin as a test point. Instead, we choose $(0, 1)$. Substituting these coordinates in $x \geq 3y$ gives $0 \geq 3(1)$, which is false, so $(0, 1)$ is not in the solution set, as shown in Figure 8.

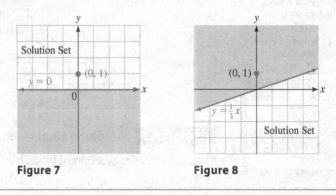

Figure 7   **Figure 8**

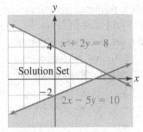

Figure 9

* Although these graphs are quite easy to do by hand, the more lines we have to graph, the more difficult it becomes to get everything in the right place, and this is where graphing technology can become important. This is especially true when, for instance, three or more lines intersect at points that are very close together and hard to distinguish in hand-drawn graphs.

EXAMPLE 2   Graphing Simultaneous Inequalities

Sketch the region of points that satisfy both inequalities:

$$2x - 5y \le 10$$
$$x + 2y \le 8.$$

Solution Each inequality has a solution set that is a half plane. If a point is to satisfy *both* inequalities, it must lie in both sets of solutions. Put another way, if we cover the points that are not solutions to $2x - 5y \le 10$ and then also cover the points that are not solutions to $x + 2y \le 8$, the points that remain uncovered must be the points we want, those that are solutions to both inequalities. The result is shown in Figure 9, where the unshaded region (including its boundary) is the set of solutions.*

As a check, we can look at points in various regions in Figure 9. For example, our graph shows that $(0, 0)$ should satisfy both inequalities, and it does:

$$2(0) - 5(0) = 0 \le 10 \quad ✔$$
$$0 + 2(0) = 0 \le 8. \quad ✔$$

On the other hand, $(0, 5)$ should fail to satisfy one of the inequalities:

$$2(0) - 5(5) = -25 \le 10 \quad ✔$$
$$0 + 2(5) = 10 > 8. \quad ✗$$

One more: $(5, -1)$ should fail one of the inequalities:

$$2(5) - 5(-1) = 15 > 10 \quad ✗$$
$$5 + 2(-1) = 3 \le 8. \quad ✔$$

EXAMPLE 3   Corner Points

Sketch the region of solutions of the following system of inequalities, and list the coordinates of all the corner points.

$$3x - y \le 6$$
$$x + y \ge 6$$
$$y \le 6$$

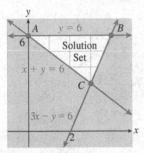

Figure 10

Solution Shading the regions that we do not want leaves us with the triangle shown in Figure 10. We label the corner points A, B, and C as shown.

Each of these corner points lies at the intersection of two of the bounding lines. So to find the coordinates of each corner point, we need to solve the system of equations given by the two lines. To do this systematically, we make the following table:

Point	Lines through Point	Coordinates
A	$y = 6$ $x + y = 6$	$(0, 6)$
B	$y = 6$ $3x - y = 6$	$(4, 6)$
C	$x + y = 6$ $3x - y = 6$	$(3, 3)$

*Technology Note Using the trace feature makes it easy to locate corner points graphically. Remember to zoom in for additional accuracy when appropriate. Of course, you can also use technology to help solve the systems of equations, as we discussed in Chapter 4.

Here, we have solved each system of equations in the middle column to get the point on the right, using the techniques of Chapter 4. You should do this for practice.*

As a partial check that we have drawn the correct region, let us choose any point in its interior—say, $(3, 5)$. We can easily check that $(3, 5)$ satisfies all three given inequalities. It follows that all of the points in the triangular region containing $(3, 5)$ are also solutions.

➡ **Before we go on . . .** What if the constraint $y \le 6$ in Example 3 had instead been, say, $y \le 2$? We would need to adjust Figure 10 by moving the horizontal line at $y = 6$ down to $y = 2$ (below the point C) and then graying out everything above it. What we would find is that everything had been grayed out (see Figure 11)! This means that there would be nothing at all in the solution set. Put another way, the solution set of the system $3x - y \le 6$, $x + y \ge 6$, $y \le 2$ is **empty**.

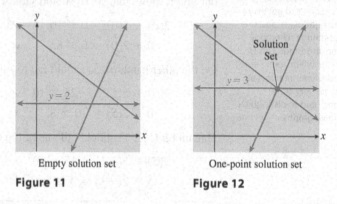

Empty solution set	One-point solution set
Figure 11	**Figure 12**

If, instead, the last constraint had been $y \le 3$, then all three lines would intersect at the single point $(3, 3)$. Even though everything would still be grayed out (see Figure 12), the solution set would consist of that single point $(3, 3)$, because that point is on the boundary of each of the three regions $3x - y \le 6$, $x + y \ge 6$, and $y \le 3$ and hence is in each of their solution sets.

Take another look at the regions of solutions in Examples 2 and 3 (Figures 13 and 14).

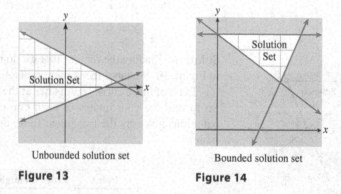

Unbounded solution set	Bounded solution set
Figure 13	**Figure 14**

Notice that the solution set in Figure 13 extends infinitely far to the left, whereas the one in Figure 14 is completely enclosed by a boundary. Sets that are completely enclosed are called **bounded**, and sets that extend infinitely in one or more directions are **unbounded**. For example, all the solution sets in Example 1 are unbounded. ■

EXAMPLE 4   **Resource Allocation**

Socaccio Pistachio, Inc. makes two types of pistachio nuts: Dazzling Red and Organic. Pistachio nuts require food color and salt, and the following table shows the amount of food color and salt required for a 1-kilogram batch of pistachios as well as the total amount of these ingredients available each day:

	Dazzling Red	Organic	Total Available
Food Color (grams)	2	1	20
Salt (grams)	10	20	220

Use a graph to show the possible numbers of batches of each type of pistachio Socaccio can produce each day. This region (the solution set of a system of inequalities) is called the **feasible region**.

Solution As we did in Chapter 4, we start by identifying the unknowns: Let *x* be the number of batches of Dazzling Red manufactured per day, and let *y* be the number of batches of Organic manufactured each day.

Now, because of our experience with systems of linear equations, we are tempted to say: For food color, $2x + y = 20$, and for salt, $10x + 20y = 220$. However, no one is saying that Socaccio has to use all available ingredients; the company might choose to use fewer than the total available amounts if this proves more profitable. Thus, $2x + y$ can be anything *up to a total of* 20. In other words,

$$2x + y \leq 20.$$

Similarly,

$$10x + 20y \leq 220.$$

There are two more restrictions that are not explicitly mentioned: Neither *x* nor *y* can be negative. (The company cannot produce a negative number of batches of nuts.) Therefore, we have the additional restrictions

$$x \geq 0 \quad \text{and} \quad y \geq 0.$$

These two inequalities tell us that the feasible region (solution set) is restricted to the first quadrant, because in the other quadrants, either *x* or *y* or both *x* and *y* are negative. So instead of shading out all other quadrants, we can simply restrict our drawing to the first quadrant.

The (bounded) feasible region shown in Figure 15 is a graphical representation of the limitations the company faces.

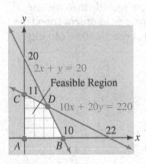

Figure 15

➡ **Before we go on ...** Every point in the feasible region in Example 4 represents a value for *x* and a value for *y* that do not violate any of the company's restrictions. For example, the point (5, 6) lies well inside the region, so the company can produce five batches of Dazzling Red nuts and six batches of Organic without exceeding the limitations on ingredients [that is, $2(5) + 6 = 16 \leq 20$ and $10(5) + 20(6) = 170 \leq 220$]. The corner points *A*, *B*, *C*, and *D* are significant if the company wishes to realize the greatest profit, as we will see in Section 6.2. We can find the corners as in the following table:

Point	Lines through Point	Coordinates
A		$(0, 0)$
B		$(10, 0)$
C		$(0, 11)$
D	$2x + y = 20$ $10x + 20y = 220$	$(6, 8)$

(We have not listed the lines through the first three corners because their coordinates can be read easily from the graph.) Points on the line segment DB represent use of all the food color (because the segment lies on the line $2x + y = 20$), and points on the line segment CD represent use of all the salt (because the segment lies on the line $10x + 20y = 220$). Note that the point D is the only solution that uses all of both ingredients. ■

FAQs

Recognizing Whether to Use a Linear Inequality or a Linear Equation

Q : *How do I know whether to model a situation by a linear inequality such as* $3x + 2y \leq 10$ *or by a linear equation such as* $3x + 2y = 10$?

A : Here are some key phrases to look for: *at most, up to, no more than, at least, or more, exactly.* Suppose, for instance, that nuts cost 3¢, bolts cost 2¢, x is the number of nuts you can buy, and y is the number of bolts you can buy.

- If you have *up to* 10¢ to spend, then $3x + 2y \leq 10$.
- If you must spend *exactly* 10¢, then $3x + 2y = 10$.
- If you plan to spend *at least* 10¢, then $3x + 2y \geq 10$.

The use of inequalities to model a situation is often more realistic than the use of equations; for instance, one cannot always expect to exactly fill all orders, spend the exact amount of one's budget, or keep a plant operating at exactly 100% capacity.

6.1 EXERCISES

▼ more advanced   ◆ challenging

T indicates exercises that should be solved using technology

In Exercises 1–26, sketch the region that corresponds to the given inequalities, say whether the region is bounded or unbounded, and find the coordinates of all corner points (if any). [**HINT**: See Examples 1, 2, and 3.]

1. $2x + y \leq 10$

2. $4x - y \leq 12$

3. $-x - 2y \leq 8$

4. $-x + 2y \geq 4$

5. $3x + 2y \geq 5$

6. $2x - 3y \leq 7$

7. $x \leq 3y$

8. $y \geq 3x$

9. $\dfrac{3x}{4} - \dfrac{y}{4} \leq 1$

10. $\dfrac{x}{3} + \dfrac{2y}{3} \geq 2$

11. $x \geq -5$

12. $y \leq -4$

13. $4x - y \leq 8$
    $x + 2y \leq 2$

14. $2x + y \leq 4$
    $x - 2y \geq 2$

15. $3x + 2y \geq 6$
    $3x - 2y \leq 6$
    $x \qquad \geq 0$

16. $3x + 2y \leq 6$
    $3x - 2y \geq 6$
    $-y \geq 2$

17. $x + y \geq 5$
    $x \qquad \leq 10$
    $y \leq 8$
    $x \geq 0, y \geq 0$

18. $2x + 4y \geq 12$
    $x \qquad \leq 5$
    $y \leq 3$
    $x \geq 0, y \geq 0$

19. $20x + 10y \leq 100$

$10x + 20y \leq 100$

$10x + 10y \leq 60$

$x \geq 0, y \geq 0$

20. $30x + 20y \leq 600$

$10x + 40y \leq 400$

$20x + 30y \leq 450$

$x \geq 0, y \geq 0$

21. $20x + 10y \geq 100$

$10x + 20y \geq 100$

$10x + 10y \geq 80$

$x \geq 0, y \geq 0$

22. $30x + 20y \geq 600$

$10x + 40y \geq 400$

$20x + 30y \geq 600$

$x \geq 0, y \geq 0$

23. $-3x + 2y \leq 5$

$3x - 2y \leq 6$

$x \quad\quad \leq 2y$

$x \geq 0, y \geq 0$

24. $-3x + 2y \leq 5$

$3x - 2y \geq 6$

$y \leq x/2$

$x \geq 0, y \geq 0$

25. $2x - \quad y \geq 0$

$x - 3y \leq 0$

$x \geq 0, y \geq 0$

26. $-x + \quad y \geq 0$

$4x - 3y \geq 0$

$x \geq 0, y \geq 0$

In Exercises 27–32, we suggest that you use technology. Graph the region corresponding to the inequalities, and find the coordinates of all corner points (if any) to two decimal places.

27. $2.1x - 4.3y \geq 9.7$

28. $-4.3x + 4.6y \geq 7.1$

29. $-0.2x + 0.7y \geq 3.3$

$1.1x + 3.4y \geq 0$

30. $0.2x + 0.3y \geq 7.2$

$2.5x - 6.7y \leq 0$

31. $4.1x - 4.3y \leq 4.4$

$7.5x - 4.4y \leq 5.7$

$4.3x + 8.5y \leq 10$

32. $2.3x - 2.4y \leq 2.5$

$4.0x - 5.1y \leq 4.4$

$6.1x + 6.7y \leq 9.6$

Applications

33. *Resource Allocation* You manage an ice cream factory that makes two flavors: Creamy Vanilla and Continental Mocha. Into each quart of Creamy Vanilla go 2 eggs and 3 cups of cream. Into each quart of Continental Mocha go 1 egg and 3 cups of cream. You have in stock 500 eggs and 900 cups of cream. Draw the feasible region showing the number of quarts of vanilla and number of quarts of mocha that can be produced. Find the corner points of the region. [HINT: See Example 4.]

34. *Resource Allocation Podunk Institute of Technology*'s Math Department offers two courses: Finite Math and Applied Calculus. Each section of Finite Math has 60 students, and each section of Applied Calculus has 50. The department is allowed to offer a total of up to 110 sections. Furthermore, no more than 6,000 students want to take a math course. (No student will take more than one math course.) Draw the feasible region that shows the number of sections of each class that can be offered. Find the corner points of the region. [HINT: See Example 4.]

35. *Nutrition Ruff, Inc.* makes dog food out of chicken and grain. Chicken has 10 grams of protein and 5 grams of fat per ounce, and grain has 2 grams of protein and 2 grams of fat per ounce. A bag of dog food must contain at least 200 grams of protein and at least 150 grams of fat. Draw the feasible region that shows the number of ounces of chicken and number of ounces of grain Ruff can mix into each bag of dog food. Find the corner points of the region.

36. *Purchasing Enormous State University*'s Business School is buying computers. The school has two models to choose from: the Pomegranate and the iZac. Each Pomegranate comes with 400 GB of memory and 80 TB of disk space, and each iZac has 300 GB of memory and 100 TB of disk space. For reasons related to its accreditation, the school would like to be able to say that it has a total of at least 48,000 GB of memory and at least 12,800 TB of disk space. Draw the feasible region that shows the number of each kind of computer it can buy. Find the corner points of the region.

37. *Nutrition* Gerber Products' Gerber Mixed Cereal for Baby contains, in each serving, 60 calories and 11 grams of carbohydrates. Gerber Mango Tropical Fruit Dessert contains, in each serving, 80 calories and 21 grams of carbohydrates.[3] You want to provide your child with at least 140 calories and at least 32 grams of carbohydrates. Draw the feasible region that shows the number of servings of cereal and number of servings of dessert that you can give your child. Find the corner points of the region.

38. *Nutrition* Gerber Products' Gerber Mixed Cereal for Baby contains, in each serving, 60 calories, 11 grams of carbohydrates, and no vitamin C. Gerber Apple Banana Juice contains, in each serving, 60 calories, 15 grams of carbohydrates, and 120% of the U.S. Recommended Daily Allowance (RDA) of vitamin C for infants.[4] You want to provide your child with at least 120 calories, at least 26 grams of carbohydrates, and at least 50% of the U.S. RDA of vitamin C for infants. Draw the feasible region that shows the number of servings of cereal and number of servings of juice that you can give your child. Find the corner points of the region.

39. *Municipal Bond Funds* The Pioneer Investment Management Municipal High Income fund (MHI) and the BlackRock Advisors BlackRock Municipal fund (BKK) are tax-exempt municipal bond funds. In 2015 the Pioneer fund was expected to yield 6%, while the BlackRock fund was expected to yield 5%.[5] You would like to invest a total of up to $80,000 and earn at least $4,200 in interest in the coming year (based on the given yields). Draw the feasible region that shows how much money you can invest in each fund. Find the corner points of the region.

---

[3] Source: Nutrition information supplied with the products.

[4] *Ibid.*

[5] Expected yields based on returns as of April 2015. Source: CEF Connect (www.cefconnect.com).

40. *Mutual Funds* In 2015, the Phoenix/Zweig Advisors Zweig Total Return fund (ZTR) was expected to yield 5%, and the Madison Asset Management Madison Strategic Sector Premium fund (MSP) was expected to yield 7%.[6] You would like to invest a total of up to $60,000 and earn at least $3,500 in interest. Draw the feasible region that shows how much money you can invest in each fund (based on the given yields). Find the corner points of the region.

41. ▼ *Investments: Financial Stocks* (Compare Exercise 51 in Section 4.1.) During the first quarter of 2015, Toronto Dominion Bank (TD) stock cost $45 per share and was expected to yield 4% per year in dividends, while CNA Financial Corp. (CNA) stock cost $40 per share and was expected to yield 2.5% per year in dividends.[7] You have up to $25,000 to invest in these stocks and would like to earn at least $760 in dividends over the course of a year. (Assume the dividend to be unchanged for the year.) Draw the feasible region that shows how many shares in each company you can buy. Find the corner points of the region. (Round each coordinate to the nearest whole number.)

42. ▼ *Investments: High-Dividend Stocks* (Compare Exercise 52 in Section 4.1.) During the first quarter of 2015, Plains All American Pipeline L.P. (PAA) stock cost $50 per share and was expected to yield 5% per year in dividends, while Total SA (TOT) stock cost $50 per share and was expected to yield 6% per year in dividends.[8] You have up to $45,000 to invest in these stocks and would like to earn at least $2,400 in dividends over the course of a year. (Assume the dividend to be unchanged for the year.) Draw the feasible region that shows how many shares in each company you can buy. Find the corner points of the region. (Round each coordinate to the nearest whole number.)

43. ▼ *Advertising* You are the marketing director for a company that manufactures bodybuilding supplements, and you are planning to run ads in Sports Illustrated and GQ Magazine. Based on readership data, you estimate that each one-page ad in *Sports Illustrated* will be read by 650,000 people in your target group, while each one-page ad in *GQ* will be read by 150,000.[9] You would like your ads to be read by at least 3 million people in the target group, and, to ensure the broadest possible audience, you would like to place at least three full-page ads in each magazine. Draw the feasible region that shows how many pages you can purchase in each magazine. Find the corner points of the region. (Round each coordinate to the nearest whole number.)

44. ▼ *Advertising* You are the marketing director for a company that manufactures bodybuilding supplements and you are planning to run ads in Sports Illustrated and Muscle and Fitness. Based on readership data, you estimate that each one-page ad in *Sports Illustrated* will be read by 650,000 people in your target group, while each one-page ad in *Muscle and Fitness* will be read by 250,000 people in your target group.[10] You would like your ads to be read by at least 4 million people in the target group, and, to ensure the broadest possible audience, you would like to place at least three full-page ads in each magazine during the year. Draw the feasible region showing how many pages you can purchase in each magazine. Find the corner points of the region. (Round each coordinate to the nearest whole number.)

Communication and Reasoning Exercises

45. Find a system of inequalities whose solution set is unbounded.

46. Find a system of inequalities whose solution set is empty.

47. How would you use linear inequalities to describe the triangle with corner points $(0, 0)$, $(2, 0)$, and $(0, 1)$?

48. Explain the advantage of shading the region of points that do not satisfy the given inequalities. Illustrate with an example.

49. Describe at least one drawback to the method of finding the corner points of a feasible region by drawing its graph, when the feasible region arises from real-life constraints.

50. Draw several bounded regions described by linear inequalities. For each region you draw, find the point that gives the greatest possible value of $x + y$. What do you notice?

In Exercises 51–54, you are mixing x grams of ingredient A and y grams of ingredient B. Choose the equation or inequality that models the given requirement.

51. There should be at least 3 more grams of ingredient A than ingredient B.
(A) $3x - y \leq 0$ (B) $x - 3y \geq 0$
(C) $x - y \geq 3$ (D) $3x - y \geq 0$

52. The mixture should contain at least 25% of ingredient A by weight.
(A) $4x - y \leq 0$ (B) $x - 4y \geq 0$
(C) $x - y \geq 4$ (D) $3x - y \geq 0$

53. ▼ There should be at least 3 parts (by weight) of ingredient A to 2 parts of ingredient B.
(A) $3x - 2y \geq 0$ (B) $2x - 3y \geq 0$
(C) $3x + 2y \geq 0$ (D) $2x + 3y \geq 0$

---

[6] See footnote for Exercise 39.

[7] Stock prices and yields are approximate. Source: http://finance .yahoo.com.

[8] *Ibid.*

[9] The readership data for *Sports Illustrated* is based, in part, on the results of a readership survey taken in March 2000. The readership data for *GQ* is fictitious. Source: Mediamark Research Inc./*New York Times*, May 29, 2000, p. C1.

[10] The readership data for both magazines are based on the results of a readership survey taken in March 2000. Source: Mediamark Research Inc./*New York Times*, May 29, 2000, p. C1.

54. ▼ There should be no more of ingredient A (by weight) than ingredient B.

(A) $x - y = 0$ (B) $x - y \leq 0$
(C) $x - y \geq 0$ (D) $x + y \geq y$

55. ▼ You are setting up a system of inequalities in the unknowns x and y. The inequalities represent constraints faced by *Fly-by-Night Airlines*, where x represents the number of first-class tickets it should issue for a specific flight and y represents the number of business-class tickets it should issue for that flight. You find that the feasible region is empty. How do you interpret this?

56. ▼ In the situation described in Exercise 55, is it possible instead for the feasible region to be unbounded? Explain your answer.

57. ▼ Create an interesting scenario that leads to the following system of inequalities:

$$20x + 40y \leq 1{,}000$$
$$30x + 20y \leq 1{,}200$$
$$x \geq 0, y \geq 0.$$

58. ▼ Create an interesting scenario that leads to the following system of inequalities:

$$20x + 40y \geq 1{,}000$$
$$30x + 20y \geq 1{,}200$$
$$x \geq 0, y \geq 0.$$

6.2 Solving Linear Programming Problems Graphically

Fundamentals

As we saw in Example 4 in Section 6.1, in some scenarios the possibilities are restricted by a system of linear inequalities. In that example it would also be natural to ask which of the various possibilities gives the company the largest profit. This is a kind of problem known as a *linear programming problem* (commonly referred to as an LP problem).

Linear Programming Problems in Two Unknowns

A **linear programming (LP) problem** in two unknowns x and y is one in which we are to find the maximum or minimum value of a linear expression

$$ax + by,$$

called the **objective function**, subject to a number of linear **constraints** of the form

$$cx + dy \leq e \quad \text{or} \quad cx + dy \geq e.$$

The solution set of points (x, y) satisfying all constraints is called the **feasible region** for the problem, the largest or smallest value of the objective function is called the **optimal value**, and a pair of values of x and y that gives the optimal value constitutes an **optimal solution**.

Quick Example

1. Maximize $p = x + y$ Objective function
    subject to $x + 2y \leq 12$
          $2x + y \leq 12$ Constraints
          $x \geq 0, y \geq 0.$

See Example 1 for a method of solving this LP problem (that is, finding an optimal solution and value).

To solve LP problems, we use the following result.

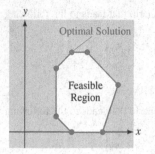

Figure 16

Fundamental Theorem of Linear Programming

(a) Linear programming problems with bounded, nonempty feasible regions always have optimal solutions.

(b) If an LP problem has optimal solutions, then at least one of these solutions occurs at a corner point of the feasible region (Figure 16).

Let's use this to solve an LP problem, and then we'll discuss why it's true.

EXAMPLE 1 **Solving a Linear Programming Problem**

Maximize $p = x + y$
subject to $x + 2y \leq 12$
$2x + y \leq 12$
$x \geq 0, y \geq 0.$

Solution We begin by drawing the feasible region for the problem. We do this using the techniques of Section 6.1, and we get Figure 17. The feasible region is bounded and nonempty, so the first part of the Fundamental Theorem of Linear Programming tells us that the problem has an optimal solution.

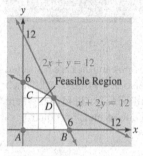

Figure 17

Each **feasible point** (point in the feasible region) gives an x and a y satisfying the constraints. The question now is, which of these points gives the largest value of the objective function $p = x + y$? The second part of the Fundamental Theorem of Linear Programming tells us that the largest value must occur at one (or more) of the corners of the feasible region. In the following table, we list the coordinates of each corner point, and we compute the value of the objective function at each corner:

Corner Point	Lines through Point	Coordinates	$p = x + y$
A		$(0, 0)$	0
B		$(6, 0)$	6
C		$(0, 6)$	6
D	$x + 2y = 12$ $2x + y = 12$	$(4, 4)$	8

Now we simply pick the one that gives the largest value for p, which is D. Therefore, the optimal value of p is 8, and an optimal solution is $(4, 4)$.

Now we owe you an explanation of why one of the corner points should be an optimal solution. The question is, which point in the feasible region gives the largest possible value of $p = x + y$?

Consider first an easier question: Which points result in a *particular value* of p? For example, which points result in $p = 2$? These would be the points on the line $x + y = 2$, which is the line labeled $p = 2$ in Figure 18.

Now suppose we want to know which points make $p = 4$: These would be the points on the line $x + y = 4$, which is the line labeled $p = 4$ in Figure 18. Notice that this line is parallel to but higher than the line $p = 2$. (If p represented profit in an application, we would call these **isoprofit lines**, or **constant-profit lines**.) Imagine moving this line up or down in the picture. As we move the line down, we see smaller values of p, and as we move it up, we see larger values. Several more of these lines are drawn in Figure 18. Look, in particular, at the line labeled $p = 10$. This line does not meet the feasible region, meaning that no feasible point makes p as large as 10. Starting with the line $p = 2$, as we move the line up, increasing p, there will be a last line that meets the feasible region. In the figure, it is clear that this is the line $p = 8$, and this meets the feasible region in only one point, which is the corner point D. Therefore, D gives the greatest value of p of all feasible points.

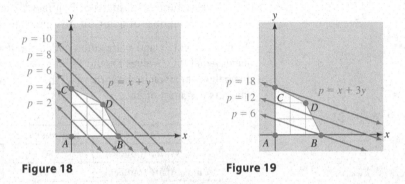

Figure 18   **Figure 19**

If we had been asked to maximize some other objective function, such as $p = x + 3y$, then the optimal solution might be different. Figure 19 shows some of the isoprofit lines for this objective function. This time, the last point that is hit as p increases is C, not D. This tells us that the optimal solution is $(0, 6)$, giving the optimal value $p = 18$.

This discussion should convince you that the optimal value in an LP problem will always occur at one of the corner points. By the way, it is possible for the optimal value to occur at *two* corner points and at all points along an edge connecting them. (Do you see why?) We will see this in Example 3(b).

Here is a summary of the method we have just been using.

Graphical Method for Solving Linear Programming Problems in Two Unknowns (Bounded Feasible Regions)

1. Graph the feasible region, and check that it is bounded.

2. Compute the coordinates of the corner points.

3. Substitute the coordinates of the corner points into the objective function to see which gives the maximum (or minimum) value of the objective function.

4. Any such corner point is an optimal solution.

Note If the feasible region is unbounded, this method will work only if there are optimal solutions; otherwise, it will not work. We will show you a method for deciding this after Example 3. ∎

Applications: Bounded Feasible Regions

EXAMPLE 2   **Resource Allocation**

Acme Baby Foods mixes two strengths of apple juice. One quart of Beginner's juice is made from 30 fluid ounces of water and 2 fluid ounces of apple juice concentrate. One quart of Advanced juice is made from 20 fluid ounces of water and 12 fluid ounces of concentrate. Every day Acme has available 30,000 fluid ounces of water and 3,600 fluid ounces of concentrate. Acme makes a profit of 20¢ on each quart of Beginner's juice and 30¢ on each quart of Advanced juice. How many quarts of each should Acme make each day to get the largest profit? How would this change if Acme made a profit of 40¢ on Beginner's juice and 20¢ on Advanced juice?

Solution The first question we are asked gives unknown quantities as

$$x = \text{number of quarts of Beginner's juice made each day}$$
$$y = \text{number of quarts of Advanced juice made each day.}$$

(In this context, x and y are often called the **decision variables**, because we must decide what their values should be in order to get the largest profit.) We can write down the data given in the form of a table. (The numbers in the first two columns are amounts per quart of juice.)

	Beginner's, x	Advanced, y	Available
Water (ounces)	30	20	30,000
Concentrate (ounces)	2	12	3,600
Profit (¢)	20	30	

Because nothing in the problem says that Acme must use up all the water or concentrate, just that it can use no more than what is available, the first two rows of the table give us two inequalities:

$$30x + 20y \leq 30,000$$
$$2x + 12y \leq 3,600.$$

Dividing the first inequality by 10 and the second by 2 gives

$$3x + 2y \leq 3,000$$
$$x + 6y \leq 1,800.$$

We also have that $x \geq 0$ and $y \geq 0$ because Acme can't make a negative amount of juice. To finish setting up the problem, we are asked to maximize the profit, which is

$$p = 20x + 30y. \quad \text{Expressed in cents}$$

This gives us our LP problem:

$$\text{Maximize} \quad p = 20x + 30y$$
$$\text{subject to} \quad 3x + 2y \leq 3,000$$
$$x + 6y \leq 1,800$$
$$x \geq 0, y \geq 0.$$

The (bounded) feasible region is shown in Figure 20.

The corners and the values of the objective function are listed in the following table:

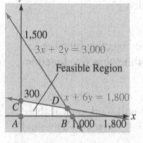

Figure 20

Point	Lines through Point	Coordinates	$p = 20x + 30y$
A		(0, 0)	0
B		(1,000, 0)	20,000
C		(0, 300)	9,000
D	$3x + 2y = 3,000$ $x + 6y = 1,800$	(900, 150)	22,500

We are seeking to maximize the objective function p, so we look for corner points that give the maximum value for p. Because the maximum occurs at the point D, we conclude that the (only) optimal solution occurs at D. Thus, the company should make 900 quarts of Beginner's juice and 150 quarts of Advanced juice, for a largest possible profit of 22,500¢, or $225.

If, instead, the company made a profit of 40¢ on each quart of Beginner's juice and 20¢ on each quart of Advanced juice, then we would have $p = 40x + 20y$. This gives the following table:

Point	Lines through Point	Coordinates	$p = 40x + 20y$
A		(0, 0)	0
B		(1,000, 0)	40,000
C		(0, 300)	6,000
D	$3x + 2y = 3{,}000$ $x + 6y = 1{,}800$	(900, 150)	39,000

We can see that, in this case, Acme should make 1,000 quarts of Beginner's juice and no Advanced juice, for a largest possible profit of 40,000¢, or $400.

➡ **Before we go on ...** Notice that, in the first version of the problem in Example 2, the company used all the water and juice concentrate:

Water: $30(900) + 20(150) = 30{,}000$

Concentrate: $2(900) + 12(150) = 3{,}600.$

In the second version the company used all the water but not all the concentrate:

Water: $30(1{,}000) + 20(0) = 30{,}000$

Concentrate: $2(1{,}000) + 12(0) = 2{,}000 < 3{,}600.$ ∎

EXAMPLE 3   **Investments**

The *Solid Trust Savings & Loan Company* has set aside $25 million for loans to home buyers. Its policy is to allocate at least $10 million annually for luxury condominiums. A government housing development grant that the company receives requires, however, that at least one third of its total loans be allocated to low-income housing.

a. Solid Trust's return on condominiums is 12%, and its return on low-income housing is 10%. How much should the company allocate for each type of housing to maximize its total return?

b. Redo part (a), assuming that the return is 12% on both condominiums and low-income housing.

Solution

a. We first identify the unknowns: Let x be the annual amount (in millions of dollars) allocated to luxury condominiums, and let y be the annual amount allocated to low-income housing.

We now look at the constraints. The first constraint is mentioned in the first sentence: The total the company can invest is $25 million. Thus,

$$x + y \leq 25.$$

(The company is not required to invest all of the $25 million; rather, it can invest *up to* $25 million.) Next, the company has allocated at least $10 million to condos. Rephrasing this in terms of the unknowns, we get

The amount allocated to condos is at least $10 million.

The phrase "is at least" means $\geq$. Thus, we obtain a second constraint:

$$x \geq 10.$$

The third constraint is that at least one third of the total financing must be for low-income housing. Rephrasing this, we say:

The amount allocated to low-income housing is at least one third of the total.

Because the total investment will be $x + y$, we get

$$y \geq \frac{1}{3}(x + y).$$

We put this in the standard form of a linear inequality as follows:

$$3y \geq x + y \qquad \text{Multiply both sides by 3.}$$
$$-x + 2y \geq 0. \qquad \text{Subtract } x + y \text{ from both sides.}$$

There are no further constraints.

Now, what about the return on these investments? According to the data, the annual return is given by

$$p = 0.12x + 0.10y.$$

We want to make this quantity p as large as possible. In other words, we want to

$$\text{Maximize} \quad p = 0.12x + 0.10y$$
$$\text{subject to} \quad x + y \leq 25$$
$$x \geq 10$$
$$-x + 2y \geq 0$$
$$x \geq 0, y \geq 0.$$

(Do you see why the inequalities $x \geq 0$ and $y \geq 0$ are slipped in here?) The feasible region is shown in Figure 21.

We now make a table that gives the (approximate) return on investment at each corner point:

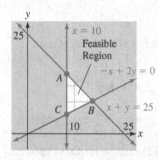

Figure 21

Point	Lines through Point	Coordinates	$p = 0.12x + 0.10y$
A	$x = 10$ $x + y = 25$	$(10, 15)$	2.7
B	$x + y = 25$ $-x + 2y = 0$	$(50/3, 25/3)$	2.833
C	$x = 10$ $-x + 2y = 0$	$(10, 5)$	1.7

From the table we see that the values of x and y that maximize the return are $x = 50/3$ and $y = 25/3$, which give a total return of about $2.833 million. In other words, the most profitable course of action is to invest about $16.667 million in loans for condominiums and $8.333 million in loans for low-income housing, giving a maximum annual return of about $2.833 million.

b. The LP problem is the same as that for part (a) except for the objective function:

$$\text{Maximize} \quad p = 0.12x + 0.12y$$
$$\text{subject to} \quad x + y \le 25$$
$$x \ge 10$$
$$-x + 2y \ge 0$$
$$x \ge 0, y \ge 0.$$

Here are the values of p at the three corners:

Point	Coordinates	$p = 0.12x + 0.12y$
A	$(10, 15)$	3
B	$(50/3, 25/3)$	3
C	$(10, 5)$	1.8

Looking at the table, we see that a curious thing has happened: We get the same maximum annual return at both A and B. Thus, we could choose either option to maximize the annual return. In fact, any point along the line segment AB will yield an annual return of $3 million. For example, the point $(12, 13)$ lies on the line segment AB and also yields an annual revenue of $3 million. This happens because the "isoreturn" lines are parallel to that edge.

➡ **Before we go on ...** What breakdowns of investments would lead to the *lowest* return for parts (a) and (b)? ∎

Unbounded Feasible Regions

The preceding examples all had bounded feasible regions. If the feasible region is unbounded, then, *provided that there are optimal solutions,* the fundamental theorem of linear programming guarantees that the above method will work. The following procedure determines whether or not optimal solutions exist and finds them when they do.

Graphical Method for Solving Linear Programming Problems in Two Unknowns (Unbounded Feasible Regions)

If the feasible region of an LP problem is unbounded, proceed as follows:

1. Draw a rectangle large enough that all the corner points are inside the rectangle (and not on its boundary):

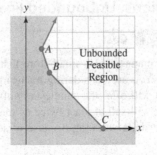

Corner points: A, B, C

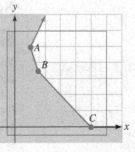

Corner points inside the rectangle

2. Shade the outside of the rectangle so as to define a new bounded feasible region, and locate the new corner points:

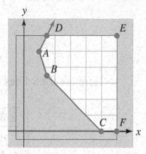

New corner points: D, E, and F

3. Obtain the optimal solutions using this bounded feasible region.

4. If any optimal solutions occur at one of the original corner points (A, B, and C in the figure), then the LP problem has that corner point as an optimal solution. Otherwise, the LP problem has no optimal solutions. When the latter occurs, we say that the **objective function is unbounded**, because it can assume arbitrarily large (positive or negative) values.

Q : *Do I always have to add a bounding rectangle to deal with unbounded regions?*

A : Not always; under some circumstances you can tell right away whether optimal solutions exist when the feasible region is unbounded. *Note that the following apply only when we have the constraints $x \geq 0$ and $y \geq 0$:*

a. If you are minimizing $c = ax + by$ with a and b nonnegative, then optimal solutions always exist.

b. If you are maximizing $p = ax + by$ with a and b both positive, then there is no optimal solution.

c. If you are maximizing $p = ax + by$ with $a \leq 0$ and $b \leq 0$, then optimal solutions always exist.

d. If you are minimizing $c = ax + by$ with a and b both negative, then there is no optimal solution.

Do you see why these statements are true? (Think about what happens in (4) above in each case.)

Applications: Unbounded Feasible Regions

EXAMPLE 4 Cost

You are the manager of a small store that specializes in hats, sunglasses, and other accessories. You are considering a sales promotion of a new line of hats and sunglasses. You will offer the sunglasses only to customers who purchase two or more hats, so you will sell at least twice as many hats as pairs of sunglasses. Moreover, your supplier tells you that, because of seasonal demand, your order of sunglasses cannot exceed 100 pairs. To ensure that the sale items fill out the large display you have set aside, you estimate that you should order at least 210 items in all.

a. Assume that you will lose $3 on every hat and $2 on every pair of sunglasses sold. Given the constraints above, how many hats and pairs of sunglasses should you order to lose the least amount of money in the sales promotion?

b. Suppose instead that you lose $1 on every hat sold but make a profit of $5 on every pair of sunglasses sold. How many hats and pairs of sunglasses should you order to make the largest profit in the sales promotion?

c. Now suppose that you make a profit of $1 on every hat sold but lose $5 on every pair of sunglasses sold. How many hats and pairs of sunglasses should you order to make the largest profit in the sales promotion?

Solution

a. The unknowns are

$$x = \text{number of hats you order}$$
$$y = \text{number of pairs of sunglasses you order.}$$

The objective is to minimize the total loss:

$$c = 3x + 2y.$$

Now for the constraints. The requirement that you will sell at least twice as many hats as sunglasses can be rephrased as

The number of hats is at least twice the number of pairs of sunglasses,

or

$$x \geq 2y,$$

which, in standard form, is

$$x - 2y \geq 0.$$

Next, your order of sunglasses cannot exceed 100 pairs, so

$$y \leq 100.$$

Finally, you would like to sell at least 210 items in all, giving

$$x + y \geq 210.$$

Thus, the LP problem is the following:

$$\text{Minimize} \quad c = 3x + 2y$$
$$\text{subject to} \quad x - 2y \geq 0$$
$$y \leq 100$$
$$x + y \geq 210$$
$$x \geq 0, y \geq 0.$$

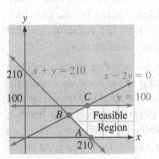

Figure 22

The feasible region is shown in Figure 22. This region is unbounded, so there is no guarantee that there are any optimal solutions. However, the objective is to minimize $c = 3x + 2y$, which has the form $c = ax + by$ with a and b nonnegative, and we do have the constraints $x \geq 0$ and $y \geq 0$. Thus, by part (a) of the Q&A above, this LP problem does have optimal solutions (and there is no need to draw a bounding rectangle). We obtain the solution as usual, by listing the corners of the feasible region along with the corresponding values of the objective function c:

Point	Lines through Point	Coordinates	$c = 3x + 2y$
A		$(210, 0)$	630
B	$x + y = 210$ $x - 2y = 0$	$(140, 70)$	560
C	$x - 2y = 0$ $y = 100$	$(200, 100)$	800

The corner point that gives the minimum value of the objective function c is B. Thus, the combination that gives the smallest loss, $560, is 140 hats and 70 pairs of sunglasses.

b. The LP problem is the following:

$$\text{Maximize} \quad p = -x + 5y$$
$$\text{subject to} \quad x - 2y \geq 0$$
$$y \leq 100$$
$$x + y \geq 210$$
$$x \geq 0, y \geq 0.$$

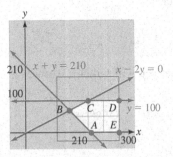

Figure 23

This time, the objective function $p = -x + 5y$ does not have nonnegative coefficients, so we must follow the procedure described above: We enclose the corner points in a rectangle as shown in Figure 23. (There are infinitely many possible rectangles we could have used. We chose one that gives convenient coordinates for the new corners.)

We now list all the corners of this bounded region along with the corresponding values of the objective function c:

Point	Lines through Point	Coordinates	$p = -x + 5y$
A		$(210, 0)$	-210
B	$x + y = 210$ $x - 2y = 0$	$(140, 70)$	210
C	$x - 2y = 0$ $y = 100$	$(200, 100)$	300
D		$(300, 100)$	200
E		$(300, 0)$	-300

The corner point that gives the maximum value of the objective function p is C. Because C is one of the corner points of the original feasible region, we conclude that our LP problem has an optimal solution at C. Thus, the combination that gives the largest profit, $300, is 200 hats and 100 pairs of sunglasses.

c. The objective function is now $p = x - 5y$, which is the negative of the objective function used in part (b). Thus, the table of values of p is the same as in part (b) except that it has opposite signs in the p column. This time we find that the maximum value of p occurs at E. However, E is not a corner point of the original feasible region, so the LP problem has no optimal solution. Referring to Figure 22, we can make the objective p as large as we like by choosing a point far to the right in the unbounded feasible region. Thus, the objective function is unbounded; that is, it is possible to make an arbitrarily large profit.

EXAMPLE 5   **Resource Allocation**

You are composing a very avant-garde ballade for violins and bassoons. In your ballade, each violinist plays a total of two notes, and each bassoonist plays only one note. To make your ballade long enough, you decide that it should contain at least 200 instrumental notes. Furthermore, after playing the requisite two notes, each violinist will sing one soprano note, while each bassoonist will sing three soprano notes.[*] To make the ballade sufficiently interesting, you have decided on a minimum of 300 soprano notes. To give your composition a sense of balance, you wish to have no more than three times as many bassoonists as violinists. Violinists charge \$200 per performance, and bassoonists charge \$400 per performance. How many of each should your ballade call for in order to minimize personnel costs?

Solution First, the unknowns are x = number of violinists and y = number of bassoonists. The constraint on the number of instrumental notes implies that

$$2x + y \geq 200$$

because the total number is to be *at least* 200. Similarly, the constraint on the number of soprano notes is

$$x + 3y \geq 300.$$

The next one is a little tricky. As usual, we reword it in terms of the quantities x and y.

The number of bassoonists should be no more than three times the number of violinists.

Thus, $y \leq 3x$

or $3x - y \geq 0$.

Finally, the total cost per performance will be

$$c = 200x + 400y.$$

We wish to minimize total cost. So our linear programming problem is as follows:

Minimize $c = 200x + 400y$
subject to $2x + \ y \geq 200$
$x + 3y \geq 300$
$3x - \ y \geq 0$
$x \geq 0, y \geq 0.$

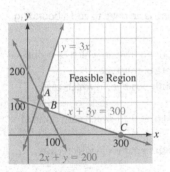

Figure 24

We get the feasible region shown in Figure 24.[†] Although the feasible region is unbounded, we can appeal again to part (a) of the Q&A before Example 4 and conclude that there are optimal solutions without the need to draw a bounding rectangle.

Point	Lines through Point	Coordinates	$c = 200x + 400y$
A	$2x + y = 200$ $3x - y = 0$	(40, 120)	56,000
B	$2x + \ y = 200$ $x + 3y = 300$	(60, 80)	44,000
C		(300, 0)	60,000

From the table we see that the minimum cost occurs at B, so the minimum cost is \$44,000 per performance, employing 60 violinists and 80 bassoonists. (Quite a wasteful ballade, one might say.)

*Whether or not these musicians are capable of singing decent soprano notes will be left to chance. You reason that a few bad notes will add character to the ballade.

† In Figure 24 you can see how graphing technology would help in determining the corner points: Unless you are very confident in the accuracy of your sketch, how do you know that the line $y = 3x$ falls to the left of the point B? If it were to fall to the right, then B would not be a corner point, and the solution would be different. You could (and should) check that B satisfies the inequality $3x - y \geq 0$ so that the line falls to the left of B as shown. However, if you use a graphing calculator or computer, you can be fairly confident of the picture that is produced without doing further calculations.

FAQs

Recognizing a Linear Programming Problem, Setting Up Inequalities, and Dealing with Unbounded Regions

Q : *How do I recognize when an application leads to an LP problem as opposed to a system of linear equations?*

A : Here are some cues that suggest an LP problem:

- Key phrases suggesting inequalities rather than equalities, such as *at most, up to, no more than, at least,* and *or more.*
- A quantity that is being maximized or minimized (this will be the objective). Key phrases are *maximum, minimum, most, least, largest, greatest, smallest, as large as possible,* and *as small as possible.*

Q : *How do I deal with tricky phrases such as "there should be no more than twice as many nuts as bolts" or "at least 50% of the total should be bolts"?*

A : The easiest way to deal with phrases like this is to use the technique we discussed in Chapter 4: Reword the phrases using "the number of . . . ", as in

The number of nuts (x) is no more than twice the number of bolts (y): $x \le 2y$. The number of bolts is at least 50% of the total: $y \ge 0.50(x + y)$.

Q : *When do I not need to add a bounding rectangle to solve an LP problem with an unbounded feasible region?*

A : When you have the constraints $x \ge 0$ and $y \ge 0$, there is no need to add a bounding rectangle if:

- you are minimizing $c = ax + by$ with a and b nonnegative, in which case optimal solutions always exist (Examples 4(a) and 5 are of this type.);
- you are maximizing $p = ax + by$ with a and b both positive, in which case there is no optimal solution;
- you are maximizing $p = ax + by$ with $a \le 0$ and $b \le 0$, in which case optimal solutions always exist; or
- you are minimizing $c = ax + by$ with a and b both negative, in which case there is no optimal solution.

Using Technology

WM Website
www.WanerMath.com
For an online utility that does everything (solves linear programming problems with two unknowns and even draws the feasible region), go to the Website and follow

→ Online Utilities
→ Linear Programming Grapher.

6.2 EXERCISES

▼ more advanced   ◆ challenging
Ⓣ indicates exercises that should be solved using technology

In Exercises 1–24, solve the given LP problem. If no optimal solution exists, indicate whether the feasible region is empty or the objective function is unbounded. [**HINT:** See Example 1.]

1. Maximize $p = x + y$
subject to $x + 2y \le 9$
$2x + y \le 9$
$x \ge 0, y \ge 0.$

2. Maximize $p = x + 2y$
subject to $x + 3y \le 24$
$2x + y \le 18$
$x \ge 0, y \ge 0.$

3. Minimize $c = x + y$
subject to $x + 2y \ge 6$
$2x + y \ge 6$
$x \ge 0, y \ge 0.$

4. Minimize $c = x + 2y$
subject to $x + 3y \ge 30$
$2x + y \ge 30$
$x \ge 0, y \ge 0.$

5. Maximize $p = 3x + y$
subject to $3x - 7y \le 0$
$7x - 3y \ge 0$
$x + y \le 10$
$x \ge 0, y \ge 0.$

6. Maximize $p = x - 2y$
subject to $x + 2y \le 8$
$x - 6y \le 0$
$3x - 2y \ge 0$
$x \ge 0, y \ge 0.$

7. Maximize $p = 3x + 2y$

    subject to $0.2x + 0.1y \leq 1$

                $0.15x + 0.3y \leq 1.5$

                $10x + 10y \leq 60$

                $x \geq 0, y \geq 0.$

8. Maximize $p = x + 2y$

    subject to $30x + 20y \leq 600$

                $0.1x + 0.4y \leq 4$

                $0.2x + 0.3y \leq 4.5$

                $x \geq 0, y \geq 0.$

9. Minimize $c = 0.2x + 0.3y$

    subject to $0.2x + 0.1y \geq 1$

                $0.15x + 0.3y \geq 1.5$

                $10x + 10y \geq 80$

                $x \geq 0, y \geq 0.$

10. Minimize $c = 0.4x + 0.1y$

    subject to $30x + 20y \geq 600$

                $0.1x + 0.4y \geq 4$

                $0.2x + 0.3y \geq 4.5$

                $x \geq 0, y \geq 0.$

11. Maximize and minimize $p = x + 2y$

    subject to $x + y \geq 2$

                $x + y \leq 10$

                $x - y \leq 2$

                $x - y \geq -2.$

12. Maximize and minimize $p = 2x - y$

    subject to $x + y \geq 2$

                $x - y \leq 2$

                $x - y \geq -2$

                $x \leq 10, y \leq 10.$

13. Maximize $p = 2x - y$ **14.** Maximize $p = x - 3y$

    subject to $x + 2y \geq 6$ subject to $2x + y \geq 4$

            $x \quad\quad \leq 8$ $y \leq 5$

            $x \geq 0, y \geq 0.$ $x \geq 0, y \geq 0.$

15. Maximize $p = 2x + 3y$

    subject to $0.1x + 0.2y \geq 1$

                $2x + \quad y \geq 10$

                $x \geq 0, y \geq 0.$

16. Maximize $p = 3x + 2y$

    subject to $0.1x + 0.1y \geq 0.2$

                        $y \leq 10$

                $x \geq 0, y \geq 0.$

17. Minimize $c = x - 3y$

    subject to $3x + \quad y \geq 5$

                $2x - \quad y \geq 0$

                $x - 3y \leq 0$

                $x \geq 0, y \geq 0.$

18. Minimize $c = 3x - y$

    subject to $2x - \quad y \geq 3$

                   $x - \quad y \geq 0$

                 $x - 2y \leq 0$

                $x \geq 0, y \geq 0.$

19. Minimize $c = 2x + 4y$

    subject to $0.1x + 0.1y \geq 1$

                  $x + \quad 2y \geq 14$

                $x \geq 0, y \geq 0.$

20. Maximize $p = 2x + 3y$

    subject to $-x + \quad y \geq 10$

                    $x + 2y \leq 12$

                $x \geq 0, y \geq 0.$

21. Minimize $c = 3x - 3y$

    subject to $\dfrac{x}{4} \leq y$

                    $y \leq \dfrac{2x}{3}$

            $x + \quad y \geq 5$

            $x + 2y \leq 10$

            $x \geq 0, y \geq 0.$

22. Minimize $c = -x + 2y$

    subject to $y \leq \dfrac{2x}{3}$

                 $x \leq 3y$

                 $y \geq 4$

                $x \geq 6$

            $x + y \leq 16.$

23. Maximize $p = x + y$

    subject to $x + 2y \geq 10$

                $2x + 2y \leq 10$

                $2x + \quad y \geq 10$

                $x \geq 0, y \geq 0.$

24. Minimize $c = 3x + y$

    subject to $10x + 20y \geq 100$

                $0.3x + 0.1y \geq 1$

                $x \geq 0, y \geq 0.$

Applications

25. Resource Allocation You manage an ice cream factory that makes two flavors: Creamy Vanilla and Continental Mocha. Into each quart of Creamy Vanilla go 2 eggs and 3 cups of cream. Into each quart of Continental Mocha go 1 egg and 3 cups of cream. You have in stock 500 eggs and 900 cups of cream. You make a profit of $3 on each quart of Creamy Vanilla and $2 on each quart of Continental Mocha. How many quarts of each flavor should you make to earn the largest profit? [HINT: See Example 2.]

26. Resource Allocation *Podunk Institute of Technology*'s Math Department offers two courses: Finite Math and Applied Calculus. Each section of Finite Math has 60 students, and each section of Applied Calculus has 50. The department is allowed to offer a total of up to 110 sections. Furthermore, no more than 6,000 students want to take a math course. (No student will take more than one math course.) Suppose the university makes a profit of $100,000 on each section of Finite Math and $50,000 on each section of Applied Calculus. (The profit is the difference between what the students are charged and what the professors are paid.) How many sections of each course should the department offer to make the largest profit? [HINT: See Example 2.]

27. Nutrition *Ruff, Inc.* makes dog food out of chicken and grain. Chicken has 10 grams of protein and 5 grams of fat per ounce, and grain has 2 grams of protein and 2 grams of fat per ounce. A bag of dog food must contain at least 200 grams of protein and at least 150 grams of fat. If chicken costs 10¢ per ounce and grain costs 1¢ per ounce, how many ounces of each should Ruff use in each bag of dog food to minimize cost? [HINT: See Example 4.]

28. Purchasing *Enormous State University*'s Business School is buying computers. The school has two models from which to choose, the Pomegranate and the iZac. Each Pomegranate comes with 400 GB of memory and 80 TB of disk space; each iZac has 300 GB of memory and 100 TB of disk space. For reasons related to its accreditation the school would like to be able to say that it has a total of at least 48,000 GB of memory and at least 12,800 TB of disk space. If the Pomegranate and the iZac cost $2,000 each, how many of each should the school buy to keep the cost as low as possible? [HINT: See Example 4.]

29. Nutrition Gerber Products' Gerber Mixed Cereal for Baby contains, in each serving, 60 calories and 11 grams of carbohydrates. Gerber Mango Tropical Fruit Dessert contains, in each serving, 80 calories and 21 grams of carbohydrates.[11] If the cereal costs 30¢ per serving and the dessert costs 50¢ per serving, and you want to provide your child with at least 140 calories and at least 32 grams of carbohydrates, how can you do so at the least cost? (Fractions of servings are permitted.)

30. Nutrition Gerber Products' Gerber Mixed Cereal for Baby contains, in each serving, 60 calories, 10 grams of carbohydrates, and no vitamin C. Gerber Apple Banana Juice contains, in each serving, 60 calories, 15 grams of carbohydrates, and 120% of the U.S. Recommended Daily Allowance (RDA) of vitamin C for infants.[12] The cereal costs 10¢ per serving, and the juice costs 30¢ per serving. If you want to provide your child with at least 120 calories, at least 25 grams of carbohydrates, and at least 60% of the U.S. RDA of vitamin C for infants, how can you do so at the least cost? (Fractions of servings are permitted.)

31. Energy Efficiency You are thinking of making your home more energy efficient by replacing some of the light bulbs with compact fluorescent bulbs and insulating part or all of your exterior walls. Each compact fluorescent light bulb costs $4 and saves you an average of $2 per year in energy costs, and each square foot of wall insulation costs $1 and saves you an average of $0.20 per year in energy costs.[13] Your home has 60 light fittings and 1,100 square feet of uninsulated exterior wall. You can spend no more than $1,200 and would like to save as much per year in energy costs as possible. How many compact fluorescent light bulbs and how many square feet of insulation should you purchase? How much will you save in energy costs per year?

32. Energy Efficiency (Compare with Exercise 31.) You are thinking of making your mansion more energy efficient by replacing some of the light bulbs with compact fluorescent bulbs and insulating part or all of your exterior walls. Each compact fluorescent light bulb costs $4 and saves you an average of $2 per year in energy costs, and each square foot of wall insulation costs $1 and saves you an average of $0.20 per year in energy costs.[14] Your mansion has 200 light fittings and 3,000 square feet of uninsulated exterior wall. To impress your friends, you would like to spend as much as possible but save no more than $800 per year in energy costs. (You are proud of your large utility bills.) How many compact fluorescent light bulbs and how many square feet of insulation should you purchase? How much will you save in energy costs per year?

Bodybuilding Supplements *Exercises 33–36 are based on the following data on four bodybuilding supplements. (Figures shown correspond to a single serving.)*[15]

[11] Source: Nutrition information supplied with the products.

[12] *Ibid.*

[13] Source: American Council for an Energy-Efficient Economy/*New York Times*, December 1, 2003, p. C6.

[14] *Ibid.*

[15] Source: Nutritional information supplied by the manufacturers/ www.bodybuilding.com. Cost per serving is approximate and varies considerably. "BCAAs" refers to the branched-chain amino acids leucine, isoleucine, and valine in the optimal 2:1:1 ratio.

	Creatine (grams)	L-Glutamine (grams)	BCAAs (grams)	Cost ($)
Xtend (SciVation)	0	2.5	7	1.00
Gainz (MP Hardcore)	2	3	6	1.10
Strongevity (Bill Phillips)	2.5	1	0	1.20
Muscle Physique (EAS)	2	2	0	1.00

33. Your personal trainer suggests that you supplement with at least 4 grams of creatine, 36 grams of L-glutamine, and 84 grams of BCAAs each week. You are thinking of combining Xtend and Gainz to provide you with the required nutrients. How many servings of each should you combine to obtain a week's supply that meets your trainer's specifications at the least cost?

34. Your friend's personal trainer suggests that she supplement with at least 30 grams of creatine, 42 grams of L-glutamine, and 36 grams of BCAAs each week. Your friend is thinking of combining Gainz and Muscle Physique to provide her with the required nutrients. How many servings of each should she combine to obtain a week's supply that meets her trainer's specifications at the least cost?

35. Your new personal trainer suggests that you supplement with at least 40 grams of creatine and 38 grams of L-glutamine but no more than 90 grams of BCAAs each week. You are thinking of combining Gainz and Strongevity to create a week's supply that meets your new trainer's specifications.
 a. Can you combine the products in such a way that the number of servings of Gainz exceeds that of Strongevity by as much as possible? If so, how many servings of each should you combine? If not, explain why not.
 b. Can you combine the products in such a way that the number of servings of Strongevity exceeds that of Gainz by as much as possible? If so, how many servings of each should you combine? If not, explain why not.

36. Your friend's new personal trainer suggests that she supplement with no more than 20 grams of creatine but at least 20 grams of L-glutamine and 42 grams of BCAAs each week. She is thinking of combining Xtend and Strongevity to create a week's supply that meets her new trainer's specifications.
 a. Can she combine the products in such a way that the number of servings of Xtend exceeds that of Strongevity by as much as possible? If so, how many servings of each should she combine? If not, explain why not.
 b. Can she combine the products in such a way that the number of servings of Strongevity exceeds that of Xtend by as much as possible? If so, how many servings of each should she combine? If not, explain why not.

37. *Resource Allocation* Your salami manufacturing plant can order up to 1,000 pounds of pork and 2,400 pounds of beef per day for use in manufacturing its two specialties: *Count Dracula Salami* and *Frankenstein Sausage*. Production of the Count Dracula variety requires 1 pound of pork and 3 pounds of beef for each salami, while the Frankenstein variety requires 2 pounds of pork and 2 pounds of beef for every sausage. In view of your heavy investment in advertising Count Dracula Salami, you have decided that at least one third of the total production should be Count Dracula. On the other hand, because of the health-conscious consumer climate, your Frankenstein Sausage (sold as having less beef) is earning your company a profit of $3 per sausage, while sales of the Count Dracula variety are down and it is earning your company only $1 per salami. Given these restrictions, how many of each kind of sausage should you produce to maximize profits, and what is the maximum possible profit? [HINT: See Example 3.]

38. *Project Design* The *Megabuck Hospital Corporation* is to build a state-subsidized nursing home serving homeless patients as well as high-income patients. State regulations require that every subsidized nursing home must house a minimum of 1,000 homeless patients and no more than 750 high-income patients in order to qualify for state subsidies. The overall capacity of the nursing home is to be 2,100 patients. The board of directors, under pressure from a neighborhood group, insists that the number of homeless patients should not exceed twice the number of high-income patients. Because of the state subsidy, the nursing home will make an average profit of $10,000 per month for every homeless patient it houses, whereas the profit per high-income patient is estimated at $8,000 per month. How many of each type of patient should the nursing home house to maximize profit? [HINT: See Example 3.]

39. *Television Advertising* On Monday evenings in April 2015, each episode of *The Big Bang Theory* was typically watched by 1.8 million viewers, while each episode of *American Dad* was typically watched by 1.5 million viewers.[16] Your marketing services firm has been hired to promote *Bald No More*'s hair replacement process by buying a total of at least 30 commercial spots during episodes of *The Big Bang Theory* and *American Dad*. You have been quoted a price of $3,000 per spot for *The Big Bang Theory* and $1,000 per spot for *American Dad*. Bald No More's advertising budget for TV commercials is $120,000, and, because of the company president's fondness for physics, it would like no more than 50% of the total number of spots to appear on *American Dad*. How many spots should you purchase on each show to maximize exposure? [HINT: Calculate exposure as Number of ads × Number of viewers.]

---

[16] Ratings are for April 4, 2015. Source: Nielsen Media Research/ www.tvbythenumbers.com.

40. *Television Advertising* On Monday evenings in April 2015, each episode of *WWE Entertainment* was typically watched by 3.8 million viewers, while each episode of *American Dad* was typically watched by 1.5 million viewers.[17] Your marketing services firm has been hired to promote *Gauss Jordan* sneakers by buying at least 40 commercial spots during episodes of *WWE Entertainment* and *American Dad*. You have been quoted a price of $4,000 per spot for *WWE Entertainment* and $1,000 per spot for *American Dad*. Gauss Jordan, Inc.'s advertising budget for TV commercials is $260,000, and it would like at least 75% of the total number of spots to appear on *WWE Entertainment*. How many spots should you purchase on each show to maximize exposure? [HINT: Calculate exposure as Number of ads × Number of viewers.]

Investing Exercises 41 and 42 are based on the following data on four stocks:[18]

	Price ($)	Dividend Yield (%)	52-Week Price Change ($)
OCR (Omnicare)	90	1	28
RCKY (Rocky Brands)	20	2	6
GCO (Genesco)	70	0	−5
ATVI (Activision Blizzard)	25	1	5

41. ▼ You are planning to invest up to $10,000 in OCR and RCKY shares. You want your investment to yield at least $120 in dividends, and, for tax reasons, you want to minimize the 52-week gain in the total value of the shares. How many shares of each company should you purchase? (Fractions of shares are permitted.)

42. ▼ You are planning to invest up to $43,000 in GCO and ATVI shares. For tax reasons you want your investment to yield no more than $10 in dividends. You want to minimize the 52-week gain (or maximize the loss) in the total value of the shares. How many shares of each company should you purchase? (Fractions of shares are permitted.)

43. ▼ *Investments: Financial Stocks* (Compare Exercise 41 in Section 6.1.) During the first quarter of 2015, Toronto Dominion Bank (TD) stock cost $45 per share, was expected to yield 4% per year in dividends, and had a risk index of 3.0 per share, while CNA Financial Corp. (CNA) stock cost $40 per share, was expected to yield 2.5% per year in dividends, and had a risk index of 2.0 per share.[19] You have up to $25,000 to invest in these stocks and would like to earn at least $760 in dividends over the course of a year. (Assume the dividend to be unchanged for the year.) How many shares (to the nearest tenth of a unit) of each stock should you purchase to meet your requirements and minimize the total risk index for your portfolio? What is the minimum total risk index?

44. ▼ *Investments: High-Dividend Stocks* (Compare Exercise 42 in Section 6.1.) During the first quarter of 2015, Plains All American Pipeline L.P. (PAA) stock cost $50 per share, was expected to yield 5% per year in dividends, and had a risk index of 2.0, while Total SA (TOT) stock cost $50 per share, was expected to yield 6% per year in dividends, and had a risk index of 3.0.[20] You have up to $45,000 to invest in these stocks and would like to earn at least $2,400 in dividends over the course of a year. (Assume the dividend to be unchanged for the year.) How many shares of each stock should you purchase to meet your requirements and minimize the total risk index for your portfolio? What is the minimum total risk index?

45. ▼ *Planning* My friends: I, the mighty Brutus, have decided to prepare for retirement by instructing young warriors in the arts of battle and diplomacy. For each hour spent in battle instruction, I have decided to charge 50 ducats. For each hour spent in diplomacy instruction, I shall charge 40 ducats. Because of my advancing years, I can spend no more than 50 hours per week instructing the youths, although the great Jove knows that they are sorely in need of instruction! Because of my fondness for physical pursuits, I have decided to spend no more than one third of the total time in diplomatic instruction. However, the present border crisis with the Gauls is a sore indication of our poor abilities as diplomats. As a result, I have decided to spend at least 10 hours per week instructing in diplomacy. Finally, to complicate things further, there is the matter of Scarlet Brew: I have estimated that each hour of battle instruction will require 10 gallons of Scarlet Brew to quench my students' thirst and that each hour of diplomacy instruction, being less physically demanding, requires half that amount. Because my harvest of red berries has far exceeded my expectations, I estimate that I'll have to use at least 400 gallons per week in order to avoid storing the fine brew at great expense. Given all these restrictions, how many hours per week should I spend in each type of instruction to maximize my income?

46. ▼ *Planning* Repeat Exercise 45 with the following changes: I would like to spend no more than half the total time in diplomatic instruction, and I must use at least 600 gallons of Scarlet Brew.

47. ▼ *Resource Allocation* One day, Gillian the magician summoned the wisest of her women. "Devoted sisters of the Coven," she began, "I have a quandary: As you well know, I possess great expertise in sleep spells and shock spells, but

---

[17] See footnote for Exercise 39.

[18] Approximate price as of May 13, 2015. 52-week price changes are approximate. Source: http://finance.google.com.

[19] Stock prices and yields are approximate, and risk indices are fictitious. Source: http://finance.google.com.

[20] *Ibid.*

unfortunately, these can be a drain on my aural energy resources, and I would like my net expenditure of aural energy to be a minimum yet still meet my commitments in protecting the Sisterhood from the ever-present threat of trolls. Specifically, I have estimated that each sleep spell keeps us safe for an average of 3 hours, while every shock spell protects us for only 1 hour. We certainly require enough protection to last 24 hours of each day and possibly more, just to be safe. At the same time, I have noticed that each of my sleep spells can immobilize two trolls at once, whereas one of my powerful shock spells can immobilize four trolls at once. We are faced, my sisters, with an onslaught of as many as 26 trolls per day! Finally, as you are no doubt aware, the Bylaws of the Coven dictate that for a magician to remain in good standing, she should cast no more shock spells than sleep spells, whereas—and I quote from Bylaw 33c—"The number of sleep spells shall never exceed thrice that of shock spells by more than three." What do I do, oh Wise Ones?" How would they respond if:

a. Each sleep spell uses 50 therms of aural energy and each shock spell uses 20 therms?

b. Each sleep spell uses 40 therms of aural energy whereas each shock spell *boosts* aural energy by 10 therms?

c. Each sleep spell uses 10 therms of aural energy whereas each shock spell boosts aural energy by 40 therms?

[HINT: See Example 4.]

48. ▼ *Risk Management* The Grand Vizier of the Kingdom of Um is being blackmailed by nine individuals and is having a very difficult time keeping them from going public. He has been keeping them at bay with two kinds of payoff: gold from the Royal Treasury and political favors. Through long experience, he has learned that each gold payoff gives him peace for an average of about 1 month and has an exposure risk index of -5, while each political favor earns him about a month and a half of reprieve but has an exposure risk index of $+1$. To maintain his flawless reputation in the Court, he feels that he cannot afford any revelations about his tainted past to come to light within the next year. So it is imperative that he make at least nine payoffs this year, that his blackmailers be kept at bay for 12 months, and that he maintain a total exposure risk index of no more than 3. Furthermore, he would like to keep the number of gold payoffs at no more than 60% of the combined number of payoffs because the outward flow of gold bars might arouse suspicion on the part of the Royal Treasurer. The gold payoffs and political favors tend to affect his travel budget (he frequently travels to the Himalayas for vizier-related reasons). He would like to maintain his flawless reputation in the Court in such a way that the net loss to his travel budget is a minimum. What is he to do, and what is the effect on his travel budget if:

a. Each gold bar removed from the treasury depletes his travel budget by 2 Orbs, and, as a result of administrative costs, each political favor depletes his travel budget by 4 Orbs.

b. Each gold bar removed from the treasury somehow *adds* two Orbs to his travel budget, but each political favor depletes it by one Orb.

c. Each gold bar removed from the treasury depletes his travel budget by 6 Orbs, but, for reasons too complicated to explain, each political favor *adds* an Orb to the budget.

[HINT: See Example 4.]

49. ◆ *Management*[21] You are the service manager for a supplier of closed-circuit television systems. Your company can provide up to 160 hours per week of technical service for your customers, but the demand for technical service far exceeds this amount. As a result, you have been asked to develop a model to allocate service technicians' time between new customers (those still covered by service contracts) and old customers (whose service contracts have expired). To ensure that new customers are satisfied with your company's service, the sales department has instituted a policy that at least 100 hours per week be allocated to servicing new customers. At the same time, your superiors have informed you that the company expects your department to generate at least $1,200 per week in revenues. Technical service time for new customers generates an average of $10 per hour (because much of the service is still under warranty), and that for old customers generates $30 per hour. How many hours per week should you allocate to each type of customer to generate the most revenue?

50. ◆ *Scheduling*[22] The *Scottsville Textile Mill* produces several different fabrics on eight dobby looms that operate 24 hours per day and are scheduled for 30 days in the coming month. The mill will produce only Fabric 1 and Fabric 2 during the coming month. Each dobby loom can turn out 4.63 yards of either fabric per hour. Assume that there is a monthly demand of 16,000 yards of Fabric 1 and 12,000 yards of Fabric 2. Profits are calculated as 33¢ per yard for each fabric produced on the dobby looms.

a. Will it be possible to satisfy total demand?

b. In the event that total demand is not satisfied, the Scottsville Textile Mill will need to purchase the fabrics from another mill to make up the shortfall. Its profits on resold fabrics ordered from another mill amount to 20¢ per yard for Fabric 1 and 16¢ per yard for Fabric 2. How many yards of each fabric should it produce to maximize profits?

---

[21] Loosely based on a similiar problem in *An Introduction to Management Science* (6th Ed.) by D. R. Anderson, D. J. Sweeney, and T. A. Williams (West, 1991).

[22] Adapted from *The Calhoun Textile Mill Case* by J. D. Camm, P. M. Dearing, and S. K. Tadisina as presented for case study in *An Introduction to Management Science* (6th Ed.) by D. R. Anderson, D. J. Sweeney, and T. A. Williams (West, 1991). Our exercise uses a subset of the data given in the cited study.

Communication and Reasoning Exercises

51. If a linear programming problem has a bounded, nonempty feasible region, then optimal solutions
  (A) must exist.   (B) may or may not exist.
  (C) cannot exist.

52. If a linear programming problem has an unbounded, non-empty feasible region, then optimal solutions
  (A) must exist.   (B) may or may not exist.
  (C) cannot exist.

53. What can you say if the optimal value occurs at two adjacent corner points?

54. Describe at least one drawback to using the graphical method to solve a linear programming problem arising from a real-life situation.

55. The feasible region of your LP problem is unbounded, and two of your constraints are $x \geq 0$ and $y \geq 0$. Decide in each case whether a bounding rectangle is necessary to decide whether an optimal solution exists. If it is not necessary, state whether the LP problem does or does not have a solution.
  a. You are minimizing $c = 4x + y$.
  b. You are maximizing $p = 2x$.
  c. You are maximizing $p = 4x - y$.
  d. You are maximizing $p = 2x + y$.

56. The feasible region of your LP problem is unbounded, and two of your constraints are $x \geq 0$ and $y \geq 0$. Decide in each case whether a bounding rectangle is necessary to decide whether an optimal solution exists. If it is not necessary, state whether the LP problem does or does not have a solution.
  a. You are minimizing $c = 4x - y$.
  b. You are minimizing $c = -x - y$.
  c. You are minimizing $c = -5y$.
  d. You are maximizing $p = -2x - y$.

57. Create a linear programming problem in two variables that has no optimal solution.

58. Create a linear programming problem in two variables that has more than one optimal solution.

59. Create an interesting scenario leading to the following linear programming problem:

$$\text{Maximize} \quad p = 10x + 10y$$
$$\text{subject to} \quad 20x + 40y \leq 1,000$$
$$30x + 20y \leq 1,200$$
$$x \geq 0, y \geq 0.$$

60. Create an interesting scenario leading to the following linear programming problem:

$$\text{Minimize} \quad c = 10x + 10y$$
$$\text{subject to} \quad 20x + 40y \geq 1,000$$
$$30x + 20y \geq 1,200$$
$$x \geq 0, y \geq 0.$$

61. ▼ Use an example to show why there may be no optimal solution to a linear programming problem if the feasible region is unbounded.

62. ▼ Use an example to illustrate why, in the event that an optimal solution does occur despite an unbounded feasible region, that solution corresponds to a corner point of the feasible region.

63. ▼ You are setting up an LP problem for Fly-by-Night Airlines with the unknowns x and y, where x represents the number of first-class tickets it should issue for a specific flight and y represents the number of business-class tickets it should issue for that flight, and the problem is to maximize profit. You find that there are two different corner points that maximize the profit. How do you interpret this?

64. ▼ In the situation described in Exercise 63, you find that there are no optimal solutions. How do you interpret this?

65. ◆ Consider the following example of a *nonlinear* programming problem: Maximize $p = xy$ subject to $x \geq 0$, $y \geq 0$, $x + y \leq 2$. Show that p is zero on every corner point but is greater than zero at many non-corner points.

66. ◆ Solve the nonlinear programming problem in Exercise 65.

6.3 The Simplex Method: Solving Standard Maximization Problems

Standard Maximization Problems and Slack Variables

The method discussed in Section 6.2 works quite well for LP problems in two unknowns, but what about three or more unknowns? Because we need an axis for each unknown, we would need to draw graphs in three dimensions (where we have x-, y-, and z-coordinates) to deal with problems in three unknowns, and we would have to draw in hyperspace to answer questions involving four or more unknowns. Given the state of technology as this book is being written, we can't easily do this. So we need another method for solving LP problems that will work for any number of unknowns. One such method, called the **simplex method**, has been the method of choice since it was invented by George Dantzig in 1947. (See the Introduction to this chapter for more about Dantzig.) To illustrate it best, we first use it to solve only so-called standard maximization problems.

General Linear Programming Problem

A **linear programming problem in n unknowns** $x_1, x_2, \ldots, x_n$ is one in which we are to find the maximum or minimum value of a linear **objective function**

$$a_1 x_1 + a_2 x_2 + \cdots + a_n x_n,$$

where $a_1, a_2, \ldots, a_n$ are numbers, subject to a number of linear **constraints** of the form

$$b_1 x_1 + b_2 x_2 + \cdots + b_n x_n \leq c \quad \text{or} \quad b_1 x_1 + b_2 x_2 + \cdots + b_n x_n \geq c,$$

where $b_1, b_2, \ldots, b_n$, and c are numbers.

Standard Maximization Problem

A **standard maximization problem** is an LP problem in which we are required to *maximize* (not minimize) an objective function of the form

$$p = a_1 x_1 + a_2 x_2 + \cdots + a_n x_n$$

subject to the constraints

$$x_1 \geq 0, x_2 \geq 0, \ldots, x_n \geq 0$$

and further constraints of the form

$$b_1 x_1 + b_2 x_2 + \cdots + b_n x_n \leq c$$

with c *nonnegative*. It is important that the relation here be $\leq$, *not* $=$ or $\geq$.

Note As in Chapter 4, we will almost always use $x, y, z, \ldots$ for the unknowns. Subscripted variables $x_1, x_2, \ldots$ are very useful names when you start running out of letters of the alphabet, but we should not find ourselves in that predicament. ∎

Quick Examples

1. Maximize $p = 2x - 3y + 3z$
   subject to
   $$2x \qquad + z \leq 7$$
   $$-x + 3y - 6z \leq 6$$
   $$x \geq 0, y \geq 0, z \geq 0.$$

   This is a standard maximization problem.

2. Maximize $p = 2x_1 + x_2 - x_3 + x_4$
   subject to
   $$x_1 - 2x_2 \qquad + x_4 \leq 0$$
   $$3x_1 \qquad\qquad \leq 1$$
   $$x_2 + x_3 \qquad \leq 2$$
   $$x_1 \geq 0, x_2 \geq 0, x_3 \geq 0, x_4 \geq 0.$$

   This is a standard maximization problem.

3. Maximize $p = 2x - 3y + 3z$
   subject to $\quad 2x \qquad + z \geq 7$
   $\qquad\qquad\quad -x + 3y - 6z \leq 6$
   $\qquad\qquad\quad x \geq 0, y \geq 0, z \geq 0.$ $\qquad$ This is *not* a standard maximization problem.

The inequality $2x + z \geq 7$ cannot be written in the required form. If we reverse the inequality by multiplying both sides by -1, we get $-2x - z \leq -7$, but a negative value on the right side is not allowed.

Consider the following standard maximization problem (which we will actually solve in Example 1 below):

Maximize $\quad p = 3x + 2y + z$
subject to $\quad 2x + 2y + \ z \leq 10$
$\qquad\qquad\quad x + 2y + 3z \leq 15$
$\qquad\qquad\quad x \geq 0, y \geq 0, z \geq 0.$

The constraints are linear inequalities, but the simplex method is a matrix-based method that works by finding nonnegative solutions of a related system of linear *equations* rather than inequalities. Because the solutions that come out of the simplex method will always be nonnegative, we can assume the inequalities $x \geq 0$, $y \geq 0$, and $z \geq 0$ listed at the end and pay them no more attention. This leaves us with the first two inequalities, which we need to convert somehow to linear equations.

Look at the first inequality. It says that the left-hand side, $2x + 2y + z$, must have some positive number (or zero) *added to it* if it is to equal 10. Because we don't yet know what x, y, and z are, we are not yet sure what number to add to the left-hand side. So we invent a new unknown, $s \geq 0$, called a **slack variable**, to "take up the slack," so that

$$2x + 2y + z + s = 10.$$

Turning to the next inequality, $x + 2y + 3z \leq 15$, we now add a slack variable to its left-hand side to get it up to the value of the right-hand side. We might have to add a different number than we did the last time, so we use a new slack variable, $t \geq 0$, and obtain

$$x + 2y + 3z + t = 15. \qquad \text{Use a different slack variable for each constraint.}$$

Now we have a system of three linear equations (including the one that defines the objective function), which we can write in standard form as follows:

$$
\begin{aligned}
2x + 2y + \ z + s \qquad\quad &= 10 \\
x + 2y + 3z \qquad + t \quad &= 15 \\
-3x - 2y - \ z \qquad\qquad + p &= 0.
\end{aligned}
$$

Note three things: First, all the variables are neatly aligned in columns, as they were in Chapter 4. Second, in rewriting the objective function $p = 3x + 2y + z$, we have left the coefficient of p as $+1$ and brought the other variables over to the same side of the equation as p. This will be our standard procedure from now on. *Don't* write $3x + 2y + z - p = 0$ (even though it means the same thing) because the negative coefficients will be important in the simplex method. Third, the above system of equations has fewer equations than unknowns and hence cannot have a unique solution.[*]

[*] That is what we might expect, however. The (possibly infinitely many) solutions that result (with all the variables nonnegative) turn out to correspond to points in the feasible region of the LP problem.

Equation Form of a Standard Maximization Problem

Given a standard maximization problem,

$$\text{Maximize} \quad p = a_1x_1 + a_2x_2 + \cdots + a_nx_n$$
$$\text{subject to} \quad b_1x_1 + b_2x_2 + \cdots + b_nx_n \leq c$$
$$b_1'x_1 + b_2'x_2 + \cdots + b_n'x_n \leq c'$$
$$\vdots$$
$$x_1 \geq 0, x_2 \geq 0, \ldots, x_n \geq 0,$$

its **equation form** is the system of linear equations

$$b_1x_1 + b_2x_2 + \cdots + b_nx_n \; + s_1 \qquad\qquad = c$$
$$b_1'x_1 + b_2'x_2 + \cdots + b_n'x_n \qquad + s_2 \qquad = c'$$
$$\vdots$$
$$-a_1x_1 - a_2x_2 - \cdots - a_nx_n \qquad\qquad + p = 0$$

where $s_1, s_2, \ldots$ are called **slack variables**.

Quick Example

4. The standard LP problem

$$\text{Maximize} \quad p = 2x - 3y + 3z$$
$$\text{subject to} \quad 2x \qquad + z \leq 7$$
$$-x + 3y - 6z \leq 6$$
$$x + y + z \leq 15$$
$$x \geq 0, y \geq 0, z \geq 0$$

has the equation form

$$2x \qquad + z + s \qquad\qquad\qquad = 7$$
$$-x + 3y - 6z \qquad + t \qquad\qquad = 6$$
$$x + y + z \qquad\qquad + u \qquad = 15$$
$$-2x + 3y - 3z \qquad\qquad\qquad + p = 0.$$

The Simplex Method

The idea behind the simplex method is this: In any linear programming problem, there is a feasible region. If there are only two unknowns, we can draw the region; if there are three unknowns, it is a solid region in space; and if there are four or more unknowns, it is an abstract higher-dimensional region. But it is a faceted region with corners (think of a diamond), and it is at one of these corners that we will find the optimal solution. Geometrically, what the simplex method does is to start at the corner where all the unknowns are 0 (possible because we are talking of standard maximization problems) and then walk around the region, from corner to adjacent corner, always increasing the value of the objective function, until the best corner is found. In practice, we will visit only a small number of the corners before finding the right one. Algebraically, as we are about to see, this walking around is accomplished by matrix manipulations of the same sort as those used in the chapter on systems of linear equations.

We describe the method while working through an example.

EXAMPLE 1 **Meet the Simplex Method**

Maximize $p = 3x + 2y + z$

subject to $2x + 2y + z \leq 10$

$\qquad\qquad x + 2y + 3z \leq 15$

$\qquad\qquad x \geq 0, y \geq 0, z \geq 0.$

Solution

Step 1 *Write the LP problem in equation form.* (We already did this above.)

$$2x + 2y + z + s \qquad\qquad = 10$$
$$x + 2y + 3z \qquad + t \qquad = 15$$
$$-3x - 2y - z \qquad\qquad + p = 0$$

Step 2 *Set up the initial tableau.* We represent our system of equations by the following table (which is simply the augmented matrix in disguise), called **the initial tableau**:

x	y	z	s	t	p	
2	2	1	1	0	0	10
1	2	3	0	1	0	15
−3	−2	−1	0	0	1	0

The labels along the top keep track of which columns belong to which variables.

Now notice a peculiar thing. If we rewrite the matrix using the variables s, t, and p first, we get the matrix

$$\begin{matrix} s & t & p & x & y & z & \\ \begin{bmatrix} 1 & 0 & 0 & 2 & 2 & 1 & 10 \\ 0 & 1 & 0 & 1 & 2 & 3 & 15 \\ 0 & 0 & 1 & -3 & -2 & -1 & 0 \end{bmatrix} \end{matrix}, \qquad \text{Matrix with } s, t, \text{ and } p \text{ columns first}$$

which is already in reduced form. We can therefore read off the general solution (see Section 4.2) to our system of equations as

$$s = 10 - 2x - 2y - z$$
$$t = 15 - x - 2y - 3z$$
$$p = 0 + 3x + 2y + z$$
$$x, y, z \text{ arbitrary.}$$

Thus, we get a whole family of solutions, one for each choice of x, y, and z. One possible choice is to set x, y, and z all equal to 0. This gives the particular solution

$$s = 10, \quad t = 15, \quad p = 0, \quad x = 0, \quad y = 0, \quad z = 0. \qquad \text{Set } x = y = z = 0 \text{ above.}$$

This solution is called the **basic solution** associated with the tableau. The variables s and t are called the **active** variables, and x, y, and z are the **inactive** variables. (Other terms used are **basic** and **nonbasic** variables.)[*]

We can obtain the basic solution directly from the tableau as follows:

• The active variables correspond to the cleared columns (columns with only one nonzero entry).

[*] In the language of Chapter 4, $x, y,$ and z are the *parameters* of the general solution. But In the context of the simplex method, they are always chosen to be zero, hence the term *inactive*.

• The values of the active variables are calculated as shown below.

• All other variables are inactive and are set equal to zero.

	Inactive $x = 0$	Inactive $y = 0$	Inactive $z = 0$	Active $s = \frac{10}{1}$	Active $t = \frac{15}{1}$	Active $p = \frac{0}{1}$	
	x	**y**	**z**	**s**	**t**	**p**	
	2	2	1	1	0	0	**10**
	1	2	3	0	1	0	**15**
	−3	−2	−1	0	0	1	**0**

As an additional aid to recognizing which variables are active and which are inactive, we label each row with the name of the corresponding active variable. Thus, the complete initial tableau looks like this:

	x	**y**	**z**	**s**	**t**	**p**	
s	2	2	1	1	0	0	10
t	1	2	3	0	1	0	15
p	−3	−2	−1	0	0	1	0

This basic solution represents our starting position $x = y = z = 0$ in the feasible region in xyz-space.

*See Section 4.2 for a discussion of pivots and pivoting.

We now need to move to another corner point. To do so, we choose a pivot* in one of the first three columns of the tableau and clear its column. Then we will get a different basic solution, which corresponds to another corner point. Thus, to move from corner point to corner point, all we have to do is choose suitable pivots and clear columns in the usual manner.

The next two steps give the procedure for choosing the pivot.

Step 3 *Select the pivot column* (the column that contains the pivot we are seeking).

Selecting the Pivot Column

Choose the negative number with the largest magnitude on the left-hand side of the bottom row (that is, don't consider the last number in the bottom row). Its column is the pivot column. (If there are two or more candidates, choose any one.) If all the numbers on the left-hand side of the bottom row are zero or positive, then we are done, and the basic solution is the optimal solution.

Simple enough. The most negative number in the bottom row is −3, so we choose the x column as the pivot column:

	x	**y**	**z**	**s**	**t**	**p**	
s	2	2	1	1	0	0	10
t	1	2	3	0	1	0	15
p	−3	−2	−1	0	0	1	0

↑
Pivot column

Q : *Why choose the pivot column this way?*

A : The variable labeling the pivot column is going to be increased from 0 to something positive. In the equation $p = 3x + 2y + z$, the fastest way to increase p is to increase x because p would increase by 3 units for every 1-unit increase in x. (If we chose to increase y, then p would increase by only 2 units for every 1-unit increase in y; and if we increased z instead, p would grow even more slowly.) In short, choosing the pivot column this way makes it likely that we'll increase p as much as possible.

Step 4 *Select the pivot in the pivot column.*

Selecting the Pivot

1. The pivot must always be a positive number. (This rules out zeros and negative numbers, such as the -3 in the bottom row.)

2. For each positive entry b in the pivot column, compute the ratio a/b, where a is the number in the rightmost column in that row. We call this a **test ratio**.

3. Of these ratios, choose the smallest one. (If there are two or more candidates, choose any one.) The corresponding number b is the pivot.

In our example the test ratio in the first row is $10/2 = 5$, and the test ratio in the second row is $15/1 = 15$. Here, 5 is the smallest, so the 2 in the upper left is our pivot.

	x	y	z	s	t	p		Test ratios
s	$\boxed{2}$	2	1	1	0	0	10	$10/2 = 5$
t	1	2	3	0	1	0	15	$15/1 = 15$
p	-3	-2	-1	0	0	1	0	

Q : *Why select the pivot this way?*

A : The rule given above guarantees that, after pivoting, all variables will be nonnegative in the basic solution. In other words, it guarantees that we will remain in the feasible region. We will explain further after finishing this example.

Step 5 *Use the pivot to clear the column in the normal manner and then relabel the pivot row with the label from the pivot column.* It is important to follow the exact prescription described in Section 4.2 for formulating the row operations:

$$aR_c \pm bR_p. \qquad a \text{ and } b \text{ both positive}$$

$\uparrow \qquad \uparrow$

Row to change   Pivot row

All entries in the last column should remain nonnegative after pivoting. Furthermore, because the x column (and no longer the s column) will be cleared, x will become an active variable. In other words, the s on the left of the pivot will be replaced by x. We call s the **departing**, or **exiting variable** and x the **entering variable** for this step.

Entering variable
↓

		x	y	z	s	t	p		
Departing variable →	s	2	2	1	1	0	0	10	
	t	1	2	3	0	1	0	15	$2R_2 - R_1$
	p	−3	−2	−1	0	0	1	0	$2R_3 + 3R_1$

This gives

	x	y	z	s	t	p	
x	2	2	1	1	0	0	10
t	0	2	5	−1	2	0	20
p	0	2	1	3	0	2	30

This is the second tableau.

Step 6 *Go to Step 3*. But wait! According to Step 3, we are finished because there are no negative numbers in the bottom row. Thus, we can read off the answer.

Remember, though, that the solution for x, the first active variable, is not just $x = 10$ but is $x = 10/2 = 5$ because the pivot has not been reduced to a 1. Similarly, $t = 20/2 = 10$ and $p = 30/2 = 15$. All the other variables are zero because they are inactive. Thus, the solution is as follows: p has a maximum value of 15, and this occurs when $x = 5$, $y = 0$, and $z = 0$. (The slack variables then have the values $s = 0$ and $t = 10$.)

Q : *Why can we stop when there are no negative numbers in the bottom row? Why does this tableau give an optimal solution?*

A : The bottom row corresponds to the equation $2y + z + 3s + 2p = 30$, or

$$p = 15 - y - \frac{1}{2}z - \frac{3}{2}s.$$

Think of this as part of the general solution to our original system of equations, with $y, z,$ and s as the parameters. Because these variables must be nonnegative, *the largest possible value of p in any feasible solution of the system comes when all three of the parameters are 0.* Thus, the current basic solution must be an optimal solution.[*]

∗ Calculators or spreadsheets could obviously be a big help in the calculations here, just as in Chapter 4. We'll say more about that after the next couple of examples.

We owe some further explanation for Step 4 of the simplex method. After Step 3, we knew that x would be the entering variable, and we needed to choose the departing variable. In the next basic solution, x was to have some positive value, and we wanted this value to be as large as possible (to make p as large as possible) without making any other variables negative. Look again at the equations written in Step 2:

$$s = 10 - 2x - 2y - z$$
$$t = 15 - x - 2y - 3z.$$

We needed to make either s or t into an inactive variable and hence zero. Also, y and z were to remain inactive. If we had made s inactive, then we would have had $0 = 10 - 2x$, so $x = 10/2 = 5$. This would have made $t = 15 - 5 = 10$, which would be fine. On the other hand, if we had made t inactive, then we would have had $0 = 15 - x$, so $x = 15$, and this would have made $s = 10 - 2 \cdot 15 = -20$, which would *not* be fine, because slack variables must be nonnegative. In other words, we had a choice of making $x = 10/2 = 5$ or $x = 15/1 = 15$, but making x larger than 5 would have made another variable negative. We were thus compelled to choose the smaller ratio, 5, and make s the departing variable. Of course, we do not have to think it through this way every time. We just use the rule stated in Step 4. (For a graphical explanation, see Example 3.)

EXAMPLE 2 Simplex Method

Find the maximum value of $p = 12x + 15y + 5z$, subject to the constraints

$$2x + 2y + \ z \le 8$$
$$x + 4y - 3z \le 12$$
$$x \ge 0, y \ge 0, z \ge 0.$$

Solution Following Step 1, we introduce slack variables to write the LP problem in equation form:

$$2x + \ 2y + \ z + s \qquad\qquad = 8$$
$$x + \ 4y - 3z \qquad + t \qquad = 12$$
$$-12x - 15y - 5z \qquad\qquad + p = 0.$$

We now follow with Step 2, setting up the initial tableau:

	x	y	z	s	t	p	
s	2	2	1	1	0	0	8
t	1	4	-3	0	1	0	12
p	-12	-15	-5	0	0	1	0

For Step 3 we select the column over the negative number with the largest magnitude in the bottom row, which is the y column. For Step 4, finding the pivot, we see that the test ratios are 8/2 and 12/4, the smallest being $12/4 = 3$. So we select the pivot in the t row and clear its column:

	x	y	z	s	t	p		
s	2	2	1	1	0	0	8	$2R_1 - R_2$
t	1	$\boxed{4}$	-3	0	1	0	12	
p	-12	-15	-5	0	0	1	0	$4R_3 + 15R_2$

The departing variable is t, and the entering variable is y. This gives the second tableau:

	x	y	z	s	t	p	
s	3	0	5	2	-1	0	4
y	1	4	-3	0	1	0	12
p	-33	0	-65	0	15	4	180

We now go back to Step 3. Because we still have negative numbers in the bottom row, we choose the one with the largest magnitude (which is -65), and thus our pivot column is the z column. Because negative numbers can't be pivots, the only possible choice for the pivot is the 5. (We need not compute the test ratios because there would be only one from which to choose.) We now clear this column, remembering to take care of the departing and entering variables:

	x	y	z	s	t	p		
s	3	0	[5]	2	-1	0	4	
y	1	4	-3	0	1	0	12	$5R_2 + 3R_1$
p	-33	0	-65	0	15	4	180	$R_3 + 13R_1$

This gives

	x	y	z	s	t	p	
z	3	0	5	2	-1	0	4
y	14	20	0	6	2	0	72
p	6	0	0	26	2	4	232

Notice how the value of p keeps climbing: It started at 0 in the first tableau, went up to $180/4 = 45$ in the second, and is currently at $232/4 = 58$. Because there are no more negative numbers in the bottom row, we are done and can write down the solution: p has a maximum value of $232/4 = 58$, and this occurs when

$$x = 0$$

$$y = \frac{72}{20} = \frac{18}{5} \quad \text{and}$$

$$z = \frac{4}{5}.$$

The slack variables are both zero.

As a partial check on our answer, we can substitute these values into the objective function and the constraints:

$$58 = 12(0) + 15(18/5) + 5(4/5) \qquad ✔$$
$$2(0) + 2(18/5) + (4/5) = 8 \le 8 \qquad ✔$$
$$0 + 4(18/5) - 3(4/5) = 12 \le 12. \qquad ✔$$

We say that this is only a partial check because it shows only that our solution is feasible and that we have correctly calculated p. It does not show that we have the optimal solution. This check will *usually* catch any arithmetic mistakes we make, but it is not foolproof.

Applications

In the next example (further exploits of *Acme Baby Foods*—compare Example 2 in Section 6.2) we show how the simplex method relates to the graphical method.

EXAMPLE 3 **Resource Allocation**

Acme Baby Foods makes two puddings, vanilla and chocolate. Each serving of vanilla pudding requires 2 teaspoons of sugar and 25 fluid ounces of water, and each serving of chocolate pudding requires 3 teaspoons of sugar and 15 fluid ounces of water. Acme has available each day 3,600 teaspoons of sugar and 22,500 fluid ounces of water. Acme makes no more than 600 servings of vanilla pudding because that is all that it can sell each day. If Acme makes a profit of 10¢ on each serving of vanilla pudding and 7¢ on each serving of chocolate, how many servings of each should it make to maximize its profit?

Solution We first identify the unknowns. Let

$$x = \text{the number of servings of vanilla pudding}$$
$$y = \text{the number of servings of chocolate pudding.}$$

The objective function is the profit $p = 10x + 7y$, which we need to maximize. For the constraints, we start with the fact that Acme will make no more than 600 servings of vanilla: $x \le 600$. We can put the remaining data in a table as follows:

	Vanilla	Chocolate	Total Available
Sugar (teaspoons)	2	3	3,600
Water (ounces)	25	15	22,500

Because Acme can use no more sugar and water than is available, we get the following two constraints:

$$2x + 3y \le 3,600$$
$$25x + 15y \le 22,500. \qquad \text{Note that all the terms are divisible by 5.}$$

Thus, our linear programming problem is this:

Maximize $p = 10x + 7y$ subject to

$$x \le 600$$
$$2x + 3y \le 3,600$$
$$5x + 3y \le 4,500 \qquad \text{We divided } 25x + 15y \le 22,500 \text{ by 5.}$$
$$x \ge 0, y \ge 0.$$

Next, we introduce the slack variables and set up the initial tableau:

$$x \qquad + s \qquad\qquad = 600$$
$$2x + 3y \qquad + t \qquad = 3,600$$
$$5x + 3y \qquad\qquad + u \quad = 4,500$$
$$-10x - 7y \qquad\qquad\qquad + p = 0.$$

Note that we have had to introduce a third slack variable, u. There need to be as many slack variables as there are constraints (other than those of the $x \ge 0$ variety).

Q: *What do the slack variables say about Acme puddings?*

A: The first slack variable, s, represents the number you must add to the number of servings of vanilla pudding actually made to obtain the maximum of 600 servings. The second slack variable, t, represents the amount of sugar that is left over once the puddings are made, and $(5 \times) u$ represents the amount of water left over.

We now use the simplex method to solve the problem:

	x	y	s	t	u	p		
s	1	0	1	0	0	0	600	
t	2	3	0	1	0	0	3,600	$R_2 - 2R_1$
u	5	3	0	0	1	0	4,500	$R_3 - 5R_1$
p	-10	-7	0	0	0	1	0	$R_4 + 10R_1$

	x	y	s	t	u	p		
x	1	0	1	0	0	0	600	
t	0	3	-2	1	0	0	2,400	$R_2 - R_3$
u	0	3	-5	0	1	0	1,500	
p	0	-7	10	0	0	1	6,000	$3R_4 + 7R_3$

	x	y	s	t	u	p		
x	1	0	1	0	0	0	600	$3R_1 - R_2$
t	0	0	3	1	-1	0	900	
y	0	3	-5	0	1	0	1,500	$3R_3 + 5R_2$
p	0	0	-5	0	7	3	28,500	$3R_4 + 5R_2$

	x	y	s	t	u	p	
x	3	0	0	-1	1	0	900
s	0	0	3	1	-1	0	900
y	0	9	0	5	-2	0	9,000
p	0	0	0	5	16	9	90,000

Using Technology

See the Technology Guides at the end of the chapter for a discussion of using a TI-83/84 Plus to help with the simplex method in Example 3. Or, go to the Website at www.WanerMath.com and follow the path

→ Online Utilities
→ Pivot and Gauss-Jordan Tool

to find a utility that allows you to avoid doing the calculations in each pivot step: Just highlight the entry you wish to use as a pivot, and press "Pivot on Selection".

Thus, the solution is as follows: The maximum value of p is $90,000/9 = 10,000¢ = \$100$, which occurs when $x = 900/3 = 300$, and $y = 9,000/9 = 1,000$. (The slack variables are $s = 900/3 = 300$ and $t = u = 0$.)

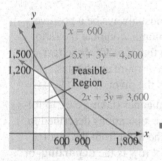

Figure 25

⇒ **Before we go on ...** Because the problem in Example 3 had only two variables, we could have solved it graphically. It is interesting to think about the relationship between the two methods. Figure 25 shows the feasible region. Each tableau in the simplex method corresponds to a corner of the feasible region, given by the corresponding basic solution. In this example the sequence of basic solutions is

$$(x, y) = (0, 0), (600, 0), (600, 500), (300, 1,000).$$

This is the sequence of corners shown in Figure 26. In general, we can think of the simplex method as walking from corner to corner of the feasible region until we locate the optimal solution. In problems with many variables and many constraints, the simplex method usually visits only a small fraction of the total number of corners.

We can also explain again, in a different way, the reason we use the test ratios when choosing the pivot. For example, when choosing the first pivot, we had to choose among the test ratios 600, 1,800, and 900. (Look at the first tableau.) In

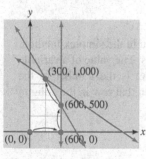

Figure 26

Figure 25, you can see that those are the three x-intercepts of the lines that bound the feasible region. If we had chosen 1,800 or 900, we would have jumped along the x-axis to a point outside of the feasible region, which we do not want to do. In general, the test ratios measure the distance from the current corner to the constraint lines, and we must choose the smallest such distance to avoid crossing any of them into the unfeasible region.

It is also interesting in an application like this to think about the values of the slack variables. We said above that s is the difference between the maximum 600 servings of vanilla that might be made and the number that is actually made. In the optimal solution, $s = 300$, which says that 300 fewer servings of vanilla were made than the maximum possible. Similarly, t was the amount of sugar left over. In the optimal solution, $t = 0$, which tells us that all of the available sugar is used. Finally, $u = 0$, so all of the available water is used as well. ∎

Summary: The Simplex Method for Standard Maximization Problems

To solve a standard maximization problem using the simplex method, we take the following steps:

1. Convert to a system of equations by introducing **slack variables** to turn the constraints into equations and by rewriting the objective function in standard form.

2. Write down the initial **tableau**.

3. Select the pivot column: Choose the negative number with the largest magnitude in the left-hand side of the bottom row. Its column is the pivot column. (If there are two or more candidates, choose any one.) If all the numbers in the left-hand side of the bottom row are zero or positive, then we are finished, and the basic solution maximizes the objective function. (See below for the basic solution.)

4. Select the pivot in the pivot column: The pivot must always be a positive number. For each positive entry b in the pivot column, compute the ratio a/b, where a is the number in the last column in that row. Of these **test ratios**, choose the smallest one. (If there are two or more candidates, choose any one.) The corresponding number b is the pivot.

5. Use the pivot to clear the column in the normal manner (taking care to follow the exact prescription for formulating the row operations described in Chapter 4), and then relabel the pivot row with the label from the pivot column. The variable originally labeling the pivot row is the **departing**, or **exiting**, **variable**, and the variable labeling the column is the **entering variable**.

6. Go to Step 3.

To get the **basic solution** corresponding to any tableau in the simplex method, set to zero all variables that do not appear as row labels. The value of a variable that does appear as a row label (an **active variable**) is the number in the rightmost column in that row divided by the number in that row in the column labeled by the same variable.

Using Technology

Website
www.WanerMath.com
On the
→ Online Utilities
page, you will find utilities that automate the simplex method to varying extents:
- Pivot and Gauss-Jordan Tool (Pivots and does row operations)
- Simplex Method Tool (Solves entire LP problems; shows all tableaux)

FAQs

Troubleshooting the Simplex Method

Q : *What if there is no candidate for the pivot in the pivot column? For example, what do we do with a tableau like the following?*

	x	y	z	s	t	p	
z	0	0	5	2	0	0	4
y	−8	20	0	6	5	0	72
p	−20	0	0	26	15	4	232

A : Here, the pivot column is the x column, but there is no suitable entry for a pivot (because zeros and negative numbers can't be pivots). This happens when the feasible region is unbounded and there is also no optimal solution. In other words, p can be made as large as we like without violating the constraints.

Q : *What should we do if there is a negative number in the rightmost column?*

A : A negative number will not appear above the bottom row in the rightmost column if we follow the procedure correctly. (The bottom right entry is allowed to be negative if the objective takes on negative values as in a negative profit, or loss.) Following are the most likely errors leading to this situation:

- The pivot was chosen incorrectly. (Don't forget to choose the *smallest* test ratio.) When this mistake is made, one or more of the variables will be negative in the corresponding basic solution.
- The row operation instruction was written backward or performed backward (for example, instead of $R_2 - R_1$, it was $R_1 - R_2$). This mistake can be corrected by multiplying the row by -1.
- An arithmetic error occurred. (We all make those annoying errors from time to time.)

Q : *What about zeros in the rightmost column?*

A : Zeros are permissible in the rightmost column. For example, the constraint $x - y \le 0$ will lead to a zero in the rightmost column.[*]

Q : *What happens if we choose a pivot column other than the one with the most negative number in the bottom row?*

A : There is no harm in doing this as long as we choose the pivot in that column using the smallest test ratio. All it might do is slow the whole calculation by adding extra steps.

[*] When there are zeros in the rightmost column there is a potential problem of *cycling*, where a sequence of pivots brings you back to a tableau you already considered, with no change in the objective function. You can usually break out of a cycle by choosing a different pivot. This problem should not arise in the exercises.

One last suggestion: If it is possible to do a simplification step (dividing a row by a positive number) *at any stage*, we should do so. As we saw in Chapter 4, this can help to prevent the numbers from getting out of hand.

6.3 EXERCISES

▼ more advanced   ◆ challenging
⬛ indicates exercises that should be solved using technology

1. Maximize $p = 2x + y$
   subject to
   $$x + 2y \leq 6$$
   $$-x + y \leq 4$$
   $$x + y \leq 4$$
   $$x \geq 0, y \geq 0.$$
   [HINT: See Examples 1 and 2.]

2. Maximize $p = x$
   subject to
   $$x - y \leq 4$$
   $$-x + 3y \leq 4$$
   $$x \geq 0, y \geq 0.$$
   [HINT: See Examples 1 and 2.]

3. Maximize $p = x - y$
   subject to
   $$5x - 5y \leq 20$$
   $$2x - 10y \leq 40$$
   $$x \geq 0, y \geq 0.$$

4. Maximize $p = 2x + 3y$
   subject to
   $$3x + 8y \leq 24$$
   $$6x + 4y \leq 30$$
   $$x \geq 0, y \geq 0.$$

5. Maximize $p = 5x - 4y + 3z$
   subject to
   $$5x + 5z \leq 100$$
   $$5y - 5z \leq 50$$
   $$5x - 5y \leq 50$$
   $$x \geq 0, y \geq 0, z \geq 0.$$

6. Maximize $p = 6x + y + 3z$
   subject to
   $$3x + y \leq 15$$
   $$2x + 2y + 2z \leq 20$$
   $$x \geq 0, y \geq 0, z \geq 0.$$

7. Maximize $p = 7x + 5y + 6z$
   subject to
   $$x + y - z \leq 3$$
   $$x + 2y + z \leq 8$$
   $$x + y \leq 5$$
   $$x \geq 0, y \geq 0, z \geq 0.$$

8. Maximize $p = 3x + 4y + 2z$
   subject to
   $$3x + y + z \leq 5$$
   $$x + 2y + z \leq 5$$
   $$x + y + z \leq 4$$
   $$x \geq 0, y \geq 0, z \geq 0.$$

9. Maximize $z = 3x_1 + 7x_2 + 8x_3$
   subject to
   $$5x_1 - x_2 + x_3 \leq 1{,}500$$
   $$2x_1 + 2x_2 + x_3 \leq 2{,}500$$
   $$4x_1 + 2x_2 + x_3 \leq 2{,}000$$
   $$x_1 \geq 0, x_2 \geq 0, x_3 \geq 0.$$

10. Maximize $z = 3x_1 + 4x_2 + 6x_3$
   subject to
   $$5x_1 - x_2 + x_3 \leq 1{,}500$$
   $$2x_1 + 2x_2 + x_3 \leq 2{,}500$$
   $$4x_1 + 2x_2 + x_3 \leq 2{,}000$$
   $$x_1 \geq 0, x_2 \geq 0, x_3 \geq 0.$$

11. Maximize $p = x + y + z + w$
   subject to
   $$x + y + z \leq 3$$
   $$y + z + w \leq 4$$
   $$x + z + w \leq 5$$
   $$x + y + w \leq 6$$
   $$x \geq 0, y \geq 0, z \geq 0, w \geq 0.$$

12. Maximize $p = x - y + z + w$
   subject to
   $$x + y + z \leq 3$$
   $$y + z + w \leq 3$$
   $$x + z + w \leq 4$$
   $$x + y + w \leq 4$$
   $$x \geq 0, y \geq 0, z \geq 0, w \geq 0.$$

13. ▼ Maximize $p = x + y + z + w + v$
   subject to
   $$x + y \leq 1$$
   $$y + z \leq 2$$
   $$z + w \leq 3$$
   $$w + v \leq 4$$
   $$x \geq 0, y \geq 0, z \geq 0, w \geq 0, v \geq 0.$$

14. ▼ Maximize $p = x + 2y + z + 2w + v$
   subject to
   $$x + y \leq 1$$
   $$y + z \leq 2$$
   $$z + w \leq 3$$
   $$w + v \leq 4$$
   $$x \geq 0, y \geq 0, z \geq 0, w \geq 0, v \geq 0.$$

⬛ *In Exercises 15–20 we suggest the use of technology. Round all answers to two decimal places.*

15. Maximize $p = 2.5x + 4.2y + 2z$
   subject to
   $$0.1x + y - 2.2z \leq 4.5$$
   $$2.1x + y + z \leq 8$$
   $$x + 2.2y \leq 5$$
   $$x \geq 0, y \geq 0, z \geq 0.$$

16. Maximize $p = 2.1x + 4.1y + 2z$

subject to $3.1x + 1.2y + \quad z \le 5.5$

$\qquad x + 2.3y + \quad z \le 5.5$

$\qquad 2.1x + \quad y + 2.3z \le 5.2$

$\qquad x \ge 0, y \ge 0, z \ge 0.$

17. Maximize $p = x + 2y + 3z + w$

subject to $x + 2y + 3z \qquad \le 3$

$\qquad y + \; z + 2.2w \le 4$

$\qquad x + \qquad z + 2.2w \le 5$

$\qquad x + \; y \qquad + 2.2w \le 6$

$\qquad x \ge 0, y \ge 0, z \ge 0, w \ge 0.$

18. Maximize $p = 1.1x - 2.1y + z + w$

subject to $x + 1.3y + z \qquad \le 3$

$\qquad 1.3y + z + w \le 3$

$\qquad x + \qquad z + w \le 4.1$

$\qquad x + 1.3y \qquad + w \le 4.1$

$\qquad x \ge 0, y \ge 0, z \ge 0, w \ge 0.$

19. Maximize $p = x - y + z - w + v$

subject to $x + y \le 1.1$

$\qquad y + z \le 2.2$

$\qquad z + w \le 3.3$

$\qquad w + v \le 4.4$

$\qquad x \ge 0, y \ge 0, z \ge 0, w \ge 0, v \ge 0.$

20. Maximize $p = x - 2y + z - 2w + v$

subject to $x + y \le 1.1$

$\qquad y + z \le 2.2$

$\qquad z + w \le 3.3$

$\qquad w + v \le 4.4$

$\qquad x \ge 0, y \ge 0, z \ge 0, w \ge 0, v \ge 0.$

Applications

21. *Purchasing* You are in charge of purchases at the student-run used-book supply program at your college, and you must decide how many introductory calculus, history, and marketing texts should be purchased from students for resale. Because of budget limitations, you cannot purchase more than 650 of these textbooks each semester. There are also shelf-space limitations: Calculus texts occupy 2 units of shelf space each, history books 1 unit each, and marketing texts 3 units each, and you can spare at most 1,000 units of shelf space for the texts. If the used-book program makes a profit of $10 on each calculus text, $4 on each history text, and $8 on each marketing text, how many of each type of text should you purchase to maximize profit? What is the maximum profit the program can make in a semester? [HINT: See Example 3.]

22. *Sales* The Marketing Club at your college has decided to raise funds by selling three types of T-shirts: one with a single-color "ordinary" design, one with a two-color "fancy" design, and one with a three-color "very fancy" design. The club feels that it can sell up to 300 T-shirts. "Ordinary" T-shirts will cost the club $6 each, "fancy" T-shirts $8 each, and "very fancy" T-shirts $10 each, and the club has a total purchasing budget of $3,000. It will sell "ordinary" T-shirts at a profit of $4 each, "fancy" T-shirts at a profit of $5 each, and "very fancy" T-shirts at a profit of $4 each. How many of each kind of T-shirt should the club order to maximize profit? What is the maximum profit the club can make? [HINT: See Example 3.]

23. *Resource Allocation* Arctic Juice Company makes three juice blends: PineOrange, using 2 portions of pineapple juice and 2 portions of orange juice per gallon; PineKiwi, using 3 portions of pineapple juice and 1 portion of kiwi juice per gallon; and OrangeKiwi, using 3 portions of orange juice and 1 portion of kiwi juice per gallon. Each day the company has 800 portions of pineapple juice, 650 portions of orange juice, and 350 portions of kiwi juice available. Its profit on PineOrange is $1 per gallon, its profit on PineKiwi is $2 per gallon, and its profit on OrangeKiwi is $1 per gallon. How many gallons of each blend should it make each day to maximize profit? What is the largest possible profit the company can make?

24. *Purchasing* Trans Global Tractor Trailers has decided to spend up to $1,500,000 on a fleet of new trucks, and it is considering three models: the Gigahaul, which has a capacity of 6,000 cubic feet and is priced at $60,000; the Mega-haul, with a capacity of 5,000 cubic feet, priced at $50,000; and the Picohaul, with a capacity of 2,000 cubic feet, priced at $40,000. The anticipated annual revenues are $500,000 for each new truck purchased (regardless of size). Trans Global would like a total capacity of up to 130,000 cubic feet and feels that it cannot provide drivers and maintenance for more than 30 trucks. How many of each should it purchase to maximize annual revenue? What is the largest possible revenue it can make?

25. *Resource Allocation* The *Enormous State University* History Department offers three courses—Ancient, Medieval, and Modern History—and the department chairperson is trying to decide how many sections of each to offer this semester. The department may offer up to 45 sections total, up to 5,000 students would like to take a course, and there are 60 professors to teach them. (No student will take more than one history course, and no professor will teach more than one section.) Sections of Ancient History have 100 students each, sections of Medieval History have 50 students each, and sections of Modern History have 200 students each. Modern History sections are taught by a team of two professors, while Ancient History and Medieval History need only one professor per section. Ancient History nets the university $10,000 per section, Medieval nets $20,000 per section, and Modern History nets $30,000 per section. How many sections of each course should the department offer in order to generate the largest profit? What is the largest profit possible? Will there be any unused time slots, any students who did not get into classes, or any professors without anything to teach?

26. *Resource Allocation* You manage an ice cream factory that makes three flavors: Creamy Vanilla, Continental Mocha, and Succulent Strawberry. Into each batch of Creamy Vanilla go 2 eggs, 1 cup of milk, and 2 cups of cream. Into each batch of Continental Mocha go 1 egg, 1 cup of milk, and 2 cups of cream. Into each batch of Succulent Strawberry go 1 egg, 2 cups of milk, and 2 cups of cream. You have in stock 200 eggs, 120 cups of milk, and 200 cups of cream. You make a profit of $3 on each batch of Creamy Vanilla, $2 on each batch of Continental Mocha, and $4 on each batch of Succulent Strawberry.

  a. How many batches of each flavor should you make to maximize your profit?

  b. In your answer to part (a), have you used all the ingredients?

  c. Because of the poor strawberry harvest this year, you cannot make more than 10 batches of Succulent Strawberry. Does this affect your maximum profit?

27. *Agriculture* Your small farm encompasses 100 acres, and you are planning to grow tomatoes, lettuce, and carrots in the coming planting season. Fertilizer costs per acre are $5 for tomatoes, $4 for lettuce, and $2 for carrots. Based on past experience, you estimate that each acre of tomatoes will require an average of 4 hours of labor per week, while tending to lettuce and carrots will each require an average of 2 hours per week. You estimate a profit of $2,000 for each acre of tomatoes, $1,500 for each acre of lettuce, and $500 for each acre of carrots. You can afford to spend no more than $400 on fertilizer, and your farm laborers can supply up to 500 hours per week. How many acres of each crop should you plant to maximize total profits? In this event, will you be using all 100 acres of your farm?

28. *Agriculture* Your farm encompasses 500 acres, and you are planning to grow soybeans, corn, and wheat in the coming planting season. Fertilizer costs per acre are $5 for soybeans, $2 for corn, and $1 for wheat. You estimate that each acre of soybeans will require an average of 5 hours of labor per week, while tending to corn and wheat will each require an average of 2 hours per week. On the basis of past yields and current market prices, you estimate a profit of $3,000 for each acre of soybeans, $2,000 for each acre of corn, and $1,000 for each acre of wheat. You can afford to spend no more than $3,000 on fertilizer, and your farm laborers can supply 3,000 hours per week. How many acres of each crop should you plant to maximize total profits? In this event, will you be using all the available labor?

29. *Resource Allocation* (Compare Exercise 36 in Chapter 4 Review) The *Enormous State University* Choral Society is planning its annual Song Festival, when it will serve three kinds of delicacies: granola treats, nutty granola treats, and nuttiest granola treats. The following table shows some of the ingredients required for a single serving of each delicacy as well as the total amount of each ingredient available:

	Granola	Nutty Granola	Nuttiest Granola	Total Available
Toasted Oats (ounces)	1	1	5	1,500
Almonds (ounces)	4	8	8	10,000
Raisins (ounces)	2	4	8	4,000

The society makes a profit of $6 on each serving of granola, $8 on each serving of nutty granola, and $3 on each serving of nuttiest granola. Assuming that the Choral Society can sell all that it makes, how many servings of each will maximize profits? How much of each ingredient will be left over?

30. *Resource Allocation* Repeat Exercise 29, but this time assume that the Choral Society makes a $3 profit on each of its delicacies.

Gaming *Exercises 31 and 32 are based on the following table, which shows some parameters of various weapons used in role-playing gaming:*[23]

Weapon	Cost (gold pieces)	Damage to Medium Targets	Critical Damage	Weight (pounds)
Axe (Throwing)	8	6	12	2
Javelin	1	6	12	2
Longsword	15	8	32	4
Mace (Light)	5	6	12	4
Spear	2	8	24	6

31. *Orcs* The Orc leader Achlúk has up to 50,000 gold pieces to spend on an arsenal of axes, maces, and spears for his army of orcs for a planned assault on Hobshire, in which he would like to inflict as much damage on medium targets (like humans and hobbits) as possible. To avoid excessive transportation costs, Achlúk needs to limit the total weight of the arsenal to 40,000 pounds or less, and, as his orcs are particularly fond of axes but not particularly skilled at spear-throwing, he would like to include at least as many axes as spears in the arsenal. What should his weapons arsenal look like, and how much damage on medium targets can be inflicted?

32. *Elves* The Elf leader Galandir has up to 30,000 gold pieces to spend on an arsenal of javelins, longswords, and spears

---

[23] Source: Dungeons and Dragons Wiki (www.dandwiki.com). (Critical Damage is a weighted measure of "critical hit damage" as defined there.) See also Paul Tozour's blog at www.gamasutra.com/blogs/PaulTozour/20130707/195718/ for a discussion of similar scenarios in the context of arming a video game battle tank.

for her band of elves for a planned assault on Mordrúk, in which she would like to inflict as much critical damage as possible. For the sake of swiftness the total weight of Galandir's arsenal cannot exceed 3,000 pounds, and, as the elves are particularly skilled at javelin-throwing, she would like to include at least half as many javelins as swords. What should her weapons arsenal look like, and how much critical damage can be inflicted?

33. *Recycling* Safety-Kleen operates the world's largest oil re-refinery in Elgin, Illinois. You have been hired by the company to determine how to allocate its intake of up to 50 million gallons of used oil to its three refinery processes: A, B, and C. You are told that electricity costs for process A amount to $150,000 per million gallons treated, while for processes B and C, the costs are $100,000 and $50,000, respectively, per million gallons treated. Process A can recover 60% of the used oil, process B can recover 55%, and process C can recover only 50%. Assuming a revenue of $4 million per million gallons of recovered oil and an annual electrical budget of $3 million, how much used oil would you allocate to each process to maximize total revenues?[24]

34. *Recycling* Repeat Exercise 33, but this time assume that process C can handle only up to 20 million gallons per year.

Bodybuilding Supplements *Exercises 35 and 36 are based on the following data on four popular bodybuilding supplements. (Figures shown correspond to a single serving.)*[25]

	Creatine (grams)	L-Glutamine (grams)	BCAAs (grams)
Xtend (SciVation)	0	2.5	7
Gainz (MP Hardcore)	2	3	6
Strongevity (Bill Phillips)	2.5	1	0
Muscle Physique (EAS)	2	2	0

35. Your personal trainer suggests that you supplement with as much BCAAs as possible but with no more than 40 grams of creatine and 60 grams of L-glutamine per week. You are thinking of combining Xtend, Gainz, and Strongevity to provide you with the required nutrients. How many servings of each should you combine to obtain a week's supply that meets your trainer's specifications and also includes at least as many servings of Strongevity as Xtend? How much BCAAs will you obtain?

36. Your friend's personal trainer suggests that she supplement with as much L-glutamine as possible but with no more than 60 grams of creatine and 60 grams of BCAAs per week. She is thinking of combining Gainz, Strongevity, and Muscle Physique to provide her with the required nutrients. How many servings of each should she combine to obtain a week's supply that meets her trainer's specifications and also includes no more servings of Gainz than of Muscle Physique? How much L-glutamine will she obtain?

Investing *Exercises 37 and 38 are based on the following data on three stocks:*[26]

	Price ($)	Dividend Yield (%)	52-Week Price Change ($)
DUK (Duke Energy Corp)	80	4	4
DTV (DIRECTV)	100	0	10
OCR (Omnicare, Inc.)	90	1	30

37. ▼ You are planning to invest up to $90,000 in DUK, DTV, and OCR shares. You desire to maximize the 52-week gain but, for tax reasons, want to earn no more than $900 in dividends. Your broker suggests that because DTV stock pays no dividends, you should invest everything in DTV. Is she right?

38. ▼ Repeat Exercise 37 under the assumption that the 52-week change in DTV stock is $30 but its price is unchanged.

39. ⬛ ▼ ***Loan Planning***[27] *Enormous State University's* employee credit union has $5 million available for loans in the coming year. As VP in charge of finances, you must decide how much capital to allocate to each of four different kinds of loans, as shown in the following table:

Type of Loan	Annual Rate of Return (%)
Automobile	8
Furniture	10
Signature	12
Other secured	10

[24] These figures are realistic: Safety-Kleen's actual 1993 capacity was 50 million gallons, its recycled oil sold for approximately $4 per gallon, its recycling process could recover approximately 55% of the used oil, and its electrical bill was $3 million. Source: Oil Recycler Greases Rusty City's Economy, *Chicago Tribune*, May 30, 1993, Section 7, p.1.

[25] Source: Nutritional information supplied by the manufacturers/www.bodybuilding.com. "BCAAs" refers to the branched-chain amino acids leucine, isoleucine, and valine in the optimal 2:1:1 ratio.

[26] Approximate price during May 2014; 52-week price changes and dividend yields are approximate. Source: http://finance.google.com.

[27] Adapted from an exercise in *An Introduction to Management Science* (6th. ed.) by D. R. Anderson, D. J. Sweeney, and T. A. Williams (West, 1991).

State laws and credit union policies impose the following restrictions:

- Signature loans may not exceed 10% of the total investment of funds.
- Furniture loans plus other secured loans may not exceed automobile loans.
- Other secured loans may not exceed 200% of automobile loans.

How much should you allocate to each type of loan to maximize the annual return?

40. ▣ ▼ *Investments* You have $100,000 that you are considering investing in three dividend-yielding bank stocks: Banco Santander Brasil, Bank of Hawaii, and Banco Santander Chile. You have the following data:[28]

Stock	Yield (%)
BSBR (Banco Santander Brasil)	7
BOH (Bank of Hawaii)	5
SAN (Banco Santander Chile)	4

Your broker has made the following suggestions:

- At least 50% of your total investment should be in SAN.
- No more than 10% of your total investment should be in BSBR.

How much should you invest in each stock to maximize your anticipated dividends while following your broker's advice?

41. ▼ *Portfolio Management* If x dollars are invested in a company that controls, say, 30% of the market with five brand names, then $0.30x$ is a measure of market exposure, and $5x$ is a measure of brand-name exposure. Now suppose you are a broker at a large securities firm, and one of your clients would like to invest up to $100,000 in recording industry stocks. You decide to recommend a combination of stocks in four of the world's largest recording companies: Warner Music, Universal Music, Sony, and EMI. (See the table.)[29]

	Warner Music	Universal Music	Sony	EMI
Market Share (%)	12	20	20	15
Number of Labels (brands)	8	20	10	15

You would like your client's brand-name exposure to be as large as possible but his total market exposure to be $15,000 or less. (This would reflect an average of 15%.) Furthermore, you would like at least 20% of the investment to be in Universal because you feel that its control of the DGG and Phillips labels is advantageous for its classical music operations. How much should you advise your client to invest in each company?

42. ▼ *Portfolio Management* Referring to Exercise 41, suppose instead that you wanted your client to maximize his total market exposure but limit his brand-name exposure to 1.5 million or less (representing an average of 15 labels or fewer per company), and still invest at least 20% of the total in Universal. How much should you advise your client to invest in each company?

43. ▣ ▼ *Transportation Scheduling* (This exercise is almost identical to Exercise 26 in Section 4.3 but is more realistic; one cannot always expect to fill all orders exactly and keep all plants operating at 100 percent capacity.) The *Tubular Ride Boogie Board Company* has manufacturing plants in Tucson, Arizona, and Toronto, Ontario. You have been given the job of coordinating distribution of the latest model, the Gladiator, to their outlets in Honolulu and Venice Beach. The Tucson plant, when operating at full capacity, can manufacture 620 Gladiator boards per week, while the Toronto plant, beset by labor disputes, can produce only 410 boards per week. The outlet in Honolulu orders 500 Gladiator boards per week, while the Venice Beach outlet orders 530 boards per week. Transportation costs are as follows: Tucson to Honolulu: $10 per board; Tucson to Venice Beach: $5 per board; Toronto to Honolulu: $20 per board; Toronto to Venice Beach: $10 per board. Your manager has informed you that the company's total transportation budget is $6,550. You realize that it may not be possible to fill all the orders, but you would like the total number of boogie boards shipped to be as large as possible. Given this, how many Gladiator boards should you order shipped from each manufacturing plant to each distribution outlet?

44. ▣ ▼ *Transportation Scheduling* Repeat Exercise 43, but use a transportation budget of $5,050.

45. ▣ ▼ *Transportation Scheduling* Your publishing company is about to start a promotional blitz for its new book, *Advanced Quantum Mechanics for the Liberal Arts*. You have 20 salespeople stationed in Chicago and 10 in Denver. You would like to fly at most 10 salespeople into Los Angeles and at most 15 into New York. A round-trip plane flight from Chicago to Los Angeles costs $195;[30] one from Chicago to New York costs $182; one from Denver to Los

---

[28] Yields are as of September 2011. Source: www.google.com/finance.

[29] The number of labels includes only major labels. Market shares are approximate and represent the period 2000–2002. Sources: various, including www.emigroup.com, http://finance.vivendi.com/discover/financial, and http://business2.com, March 2002.

---

[30] Prices from Travelocity, at www.travelocity.com, for the week of June 3, 2002, as of May 5, 2002.

Angeles costs \$395; and one from Denver to New York costs \$166. You want to spend at most \$4,520 on plane flights. How many salespeople should you fly from each of Chicago and Denver to each of Los Angeles and New York to have the most salespeople on the road?

46. ▣ ▼ *Transportation Scheduling* Repeat Exercise 45, but this time, spend at most \$5,770.

Communication and Reasoning Exercises

47. Can the following linear programming problem be stated as a standard maximization problem? If so, do it; if not, explain why.

$$\text{Maximize} \quad p = 3x - 2y$$
$$\text{subject to} \quad x - y + z \geq 0$$
$$x - y - z \leq 6$$
$$x \geq 0, y \geq 0, z \geq 0.$$

48. Can the following linear programming problem be stated as a standard maximization problem? If so, do it; if not, explain why.

$$\text{Maximize} \quad p = -3x - 2y$$
$$\text{subject to} \quad x - y + z \geq 0$$
$$x - y - z \geq -6$$
$$x \geq 0, y \geq 0, z \geq 0.$$

49. Why is the simplex method useful? (After all, we do have the graphical method for solving LP problems.)

50. Are there any types of linear programming problems that cannot be solved with the methods of this section but that can be solved by using the methods of Section 6.2? Explain.

51. ▼ Your friend Janet is going around telling everyone that if there are only two constraints in a linear programming problem, then, in any optimal basic solution, at most two unknowns (other than the objective) will be nonzero. Is she correct? Explain.

52. ▼ Your other friend Jason is going around telling everyone that if there is only one constraint in a standard linear programming problem, then you will have to pivot at most once to obtain an optimal solution. Is he correct? Explain.

53. ▼ What is a "basic solution"? How might one find a basic solution of a given system of linear equations?

54. ▼ In a typical simplex method tableau, there are more unknowns than equations, and we know from Chapter 4 that this typically implies the existence of infinitely many solutions. How are the following types of solutions interpreted in the simplex method?
a. Solutions in which all the variables are positive.
b. Solutions in which some variables are negative.
c. Solutions in which the inactive variables are zero.

55. ◆ Can the value of the objective function decrease in passing from one tableau to the next? Explain.

56. ◆ Can the value of the objective function remain unchanged in passing from one tableau to the next? Explain.

6.4 The Simplex Method: Solving General Linear Programming Problems

Standard and Nonstandard Linear Programming Problems

We saw in Section 6.3 that a general LP problem may or may not be a standard maximization problem. Recall that, for an LP problem to be standard, it needs to satisfy two requirements:

1. We are *maximizing* (not minimizing) an objective function.

2. The constraints (apart from the requirement that each variable be nonnegative) are all ≤ constraints, with the right-hand sides nonnegative.

General linear programming problems can have constraints such as $2x + 3y \geq 4$, or $2x + 3y = 4$, which violate (2), or we might want to minimize, rather than maximize, the objective function, violating (1). Nonstandard problems like these are almost as easy to deal with as the standard kind, and we use a slight modification of the simplex method to handle them. The best way to illustrate their solution is by means of examples.

First, we discuss nonstandard maximization problems: LP problems that violate (2).

Nonstandard Maximization Problems

EXAMPLE 1   Maximizing with Mixed Constraints

Maximize $p = 4x + 12y + 6z$

subject to $x + y + z \leq 100$

$4x + 10y + 7z \leq 480$

$x + y + z \geq 60$

$x \geq 0, y \geq 0, z \geq 0.$

Solution We begin by turning the first two inequalities into equations as usual because they have the standard form. We get

$$x + y + z + s = 100$$
$$4x + 10y + 7z + t = 480.$$

We are tempted to use a slack variable for the third inequality, $x + y + z \geq 60$, but *adding* something positive to the left-hand side will not make it equal to the right: It will get even bigger. To make it equal to 60, we must *subtract* some nonnegative number. We will call this number u (because we have already used s and t) and refer to u as a **surplus variable** rather than a slack variable. Thus, we write

$$x + y + z - u = 60.$$

Continuing with the setup, we have

$$x + y + z + s = 100$$
$$4x + 10y + 7z + t = 480$$
$$x + y + z - u = 60$$
$$-4x - 12y - 6z + p = 0.$$

This leads to the initial tableau:

	x	y	z	s	t	u	p	
s	1	1	1	1	0	0	0	100
t	4	10	7	0	1	0	0	480
*u	1	1	1	0	0	-1	0	60
p	-4	-12	-6	0	0	0	1	0

We put a star next to the third row because the basic solution corresponding to this tableau is

$$x = y = z = 0, \quad s = 100, \quad t = 480, \quad u = 60/(-1) = -60.$$

Several things are wrong here. First, the values $x = y = z = 0$ do not satisfy the third inequality, $x + y + z \geq 60$. Thus, this basic solution is *not feasible*. Second—and this is really the same problem—the surplus variable u is negative, whereas we said that it should be nonnegative. The star next to the row labeled u alerts us to the fact that the present basic solution is not feasible and that the problem is located in the starred row, where the active variable u is negative.

Whenever an active variable is negative, we star the corresponding row.

In setting up the initial tableau, we star those rows coming from $\geq$ inequalities.

The simplex method as described in Section 6.3 assumed that we began in the feasible region, but now we do not. Our first task is to get ourselves into the feasible region. In practice, we can think of this as getting rid of the stars on the rows. Once we get into the feasible region, we go back to the method of Section 6.3.

There are several ways to get into the feasible region. The method we have chosen is one of the simplest to state and carry out. (We will see why this method works at the end of the example.)

The Simplex Method for General Linear Programming Problems

Star all rows that give a negative value for the associated active variable (except for the objective variable, which is allowed to be negative). If there are starred rows, you will need to begin with Phase I.

Phase I: Getting into the Feasible Region (Getting Rid of the Stars)
In the first starred row, find the largest positive number. Use test ratios as in Section 6.3 to find the pivot in that column (exclude the bottom row), and then pivot on that entry. (If the lowest ratio occurs in both a starred row and an unstarred row, pivot in a starred row rather than the unstarred one.) Check to see which rows should now be starred. Repeat until no starred rows remain, and then go on to Phase II.

Phase II: Use the Simplex Method for Standard Maximization Problems
If there are any negative entries on the left side of the bottom row after Phase I, use the method described in the preceding section. Otherwise, there is nothing to do in Phase II, and you are done.

Because there is a starred row, we need to use Phase I. The largest positive number in the starred row is 1, which occurs three times. Arbitrarily select the first, which is in the first column. In that column the smallest test ratio happens to be given by the 1 in the u row, so this is our first pivot:

Pivot column
↓

	x	y	z	s	t	u	p		
s	1	1	1	1	0	0	0	100	$R_1 - R_3$
t	4	10	7	0	1	0	0	480	$R_2 - 4R_3$
*u	[1]	1	1	0	0	-1	0	60	
p	-4	-12	-6	0	0	0	1	0	$R_4 + 4R_3$

This gives

	x	y	z	s	t	u	p	
s	0	0	0	1	0	1	0	40
t	0	6	3	0	1	4	0	240
x	1	1	1	0	0	-1	0	60
p	0	-8	-2	0	0	-4	1	240

Notice that we removed the star from Row 3. To see why, look at the basic solution given by this tableau:

$$x = 60, \quad y = 0, \quad z = 0, \quad s = 40, \quad t = 240, \quad u = 0.$$

None of the variables is negative anymore, so there are no rows to star. The basic solution is therefore feasible—it satisfies all the constraints.

Now that there are no more stars, we have completed Phase I, so we proceed to Phase II, which is just the method of Section 6.3:

	x	y	z	s	t	u	p		
s	0	0	0	1	0	1	0	40	
t	0	6	3	0	1	4	0	240	
x	1	1	1	0	0	-1	0	60	$6R_3 - R_2$
p	0	-8	-2	0	0	-4	1	240	$3R_4 + 4R_2$

	x	y	z	s	t	u	p	
s	0	0	0	1	0	1	0	40
y	0	6	3	0	1	4	0	240
x	6	0	3	0	-1	-10	0	120
p	0	0	6	0	4	4	3	1,680

And we are finished. Thus, the solution is

$$p = 1{,}680/3 = 560, \quad x = 120/6 = 20, \quad y = 240/6 = 40, \quad z = 0.$$

The slack and surplus variables are

$$s = 40, \quad t = 0, \quad u = 0.$$

➡ **Before we go on . . .** We owe you an explanation of why this method works. When we perform a pivot in Phase I, one of two things will happen. As in Example 1, we may pivot in a starred row. In that case, the negative active variable in that row will become inactive (hence zero), and some other variable will be made active with a positive value because we are pivoting on a positive entry. Thus, at least one star will be eliminated. (We will not introduce any new stars because pivoting on the entry with the smallest test ratio will keep all nonnegative variables nonnegative.[*])

The second possibility is that we may pivot on some row other than a starred row. Choosing the pivot via test ratios again guarantees that no new starred rows are created. A little bit of algebra shows that the value of the negative variable in the first starred row must increase toward zero. (Choosing the *largest* positive entry in the starred row will make it a little more likely that we will increase the value of that variable as much as possible; the rationale for choosing the largest entry is the same as that for choosing the most negative entry in the bottom row during Phase II.) Repeating this procedure as necessary, the value of the variable must eventually become zero or positive, assuming that there are feasible solutions to begin with.

So one way or the other, we can eventually get rid of all of the stars. ∎

Here is an example that begins with two starred rows.

[*] except on rare occasions when the rightmost entry in a previously starred row is zero. We can prevent this from happening by a slight modification in the way that Phase 1 handles rows whose rightmost entry is zero (as implemented in the online Simplex Method Tool at the Website). However, as with cycling, we will not encounter this issue in either the examples or exercises.

> **EXAMPLE 2**   **More Mixed Constraints**

Maximize $p = 2x + y$

subject to $x + y \geq 35$

$x + 2y \leq 60$

$2x + y \geq 60$

$x \leq 25$

$x \geq 0, y \geq 0.$

Solution We introduce slack and surplus variables, and we write down the initial tableau:

$$x + y - s \qquad\qquad\qquad = 35$$
$$x + 2y \quad + t \qquad\qquad\quad = 60$$
$$2x + y \qquad\quad - u \qquad\quad = 60$$
$$x \qquad\qquad\qquad + v \quad = 25$$
$$-2x - y \qquad\qquad\qquad + p = 0.$$

	x	y	s	t	u	v	p	
*s	1	1	−1	0	0	0	0	35
t	1	2	0	1	0	0	0	60
*u	2	1	0	0	−1	0	0	60
v	1	0	0	0	0	1	0	25
p	−2	−1	0	0	0	0	1	0

We locate the largest positive entry in the first starred row (Row 1). There are two to choose from (both 1s); let's choose the one in the x column. The entry with the smallest test ratio in that column is the 1 in the v row, so that is the entry we use as the pivot:

Pivot column
↓

	x	y	s	t	u	v	p		
*s	1	1	−1	0	0	0	0	35	$R_1 - R_4$
t	1	2	0	1	0	0	0	60	$R_2 - R_4$
*u	2	1	0	0	−1	0	0	60	$R_3 - 2R_4$
v	[1]	0	0	0	0	1	0	25	
p	−2	−1	0	0	0	0	1	0	$R_5 + 2R_4$

	x	y	s	t	u	v	p	
*s	0	1	−1	0	0	−1	0	10
t	0	2	0	1	0	−1	0	35
*u	0	1	0	0	−1	−2	0	10
x	1	0	0	0	0	1	0	25
p	0	−1	0	0	0	2	1	50

Notice that both stars are still there because the basic solutions for s and u remain negative (but less so). The only positive entry in the first starred row is the 1 in the y column, and that entry also has the smallest test ratio in its column. (Actually, it is tied with the 1 in the u column, so we could choose either one.)

	x	y	s	t	u	v	p		
*s	0	$\boxed{1}$	-1	0	0	-1	0	10	
t	0	2	0	1	0	-1	0	35	$R_2 - 2R_1$
*u	0	1	0	0	-1	-2	0	10	$R_3 - R_1$
x	1	0	0	0	0	1	0	25	
p	0	-1	0	0	0	2	1	50	$R_5 + R_1$

	x	y	s	t	u	v	p	
y	0	1	-1	0	0	-1	0	10
t	0	0	2	1	0	1	0	15
u	0	0	1	0	-1	-1	0	0
x	1	0	0	0	0	1	0	25
p	0	0	-1	0	0	1	1	60

The basic solution is $x = 25$, $y = 10$, $s = 0$, $t = 15$, $u = 0/(-1) = 0$, and $v = 0$. Because there are no negative variables left (even u has become 0), we are in the feasible region, so we can go on to Phase II, shown next. (Filling in the instructions for the row operations is an exercise.)

	x	y	s	t	u	v	p	
y	0	1	-1	0	0	-1	0	10
t	0	0	2	1	0	1	0	15
u	0	0	$\boxed{1}$	0	-1	-1	0	0
x	1	0	0	0	0	1	0	25
p	0	0	-1	0	0	1	1	60

	x	y	s	t	u	v	p	
y	0	1	0	0	-1	-2	0	10
t	0	0	0	1	$\boxed{2}$	3	0	15
s	0	0	1	0	-1	-1	0	0
x	1	0	0	0	0	1	0	25
p	0	0	0	0	-1	0	1	60

	x	y	s	t	u	v	p	
y	0	2	0	1	0	-1	0	35
u	0	0	0	1	2	3	0	15
s	0	0	2	1	0	1	0	15
x	1	0	0	0	0	1	0	25
p	0	0	0	1	0	3	2	135

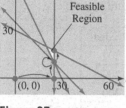

Figure 27

The optimal solution is

$$x = 25, \quad y = 35/2 = 17.5, \quad p = 135/2 = 67.5 \quad (s = 7.5, t = 0, u = 7.5).$$

➡ **Before we go on...** Because Example 2 had only two unknowns, we can picture the sequence of basic solutions on the graph of the feasible region. This is shown in Figure 27.

You can see that there was no way to jump from $(0, 0)$ in the initial tableau directly into the feasible region because the first jump must be along an axis. (Why?) Also notice that the third jump did not move at all. To which step of the simplex method does this correspond? ■

Minimization Problems

Now that we know how to deal with nonstandard constraints, we consider **minimization** problems, problems in which we have to minimize, rather than maximize, the objective function. The idea is to *convert a minimization problem into a maximization problem*, which we can then solve as usual.

Suppose, for instance, that we want to minimize $c = 10x - 30y$ subject to some constraints. The technique is as follows: Define a new variable p by taking p to be the negative of c so that $p = -c$. Then, the larger we make p, the smaller c becomes. For example, if we can make p increase from -10 to -5, then c will decrease from 10 to 5. So if we are looking for the smallest value of c, we might as well look for the largest value of p instead. More concisely,

Minimizing c is the same as maximizing $p = -c$.

Now because $c = 10x - 30y$, we have $p = -10x + 30y$, and the requirement that we "minimize $c = 10x - 30y$" is now replaced by "maximize $p = -10x + 30y$."

Minimization Problems

We convert a minimization problem into a maximization problem by taking the negative of the objective function. All the constraints remain unchanged.

Quick Example

Minimization Problem	$\longrightarrow$	**Maximization Problem**
Minimize $\quad c = 10x - 30y$		Maximize $\quad p = -10x + 30y$
subject to $\quad 2x + y \leq 160$		subject to $\quad 2x + y \leq 160$
$x + 3y \geq 120$		$x + 3y \geq 120$
$x \geq 0, y \geq 0.$		$x \geq 0, y \geq 0.$

EXAMPLE 3   **Purchasing**

You are in charge of ordering furniture for your company's new headquarters. You need to buy at least 200 tables, 500 chairs, and 300 computer desks. *Wall-to-Wall Furniture* (WWF) is offering a package of 20 tables, 25 chairs, and 18 computer desks for $2,000, whereas rival *Acme Furniture* (AF) is offering a package of 10 tables, 50 chairs, and 24 computer desks for $3,000. How many packages should you order from each company to minimize your total cost?

Solution The unknowns here are

x = number of packages ordered from WWF

y = number of packages ordered from AF.

We can put the information about the various kinds of furniture in a table:

	WWF	AF	Needed
Tables	20	10	200
Chairs	25	50	500
Computer Desks	18	24	300
Cost ($)	2,000	3,000	

From this table we get the following LP problem:

$$\begin{aligned}
\text{Minimize} \quad & c = 2{,}000x + 3{,}000y \\
\text{subject to} \quad & 20x + 10y \geq 200 \\
& 25x + 50y \geq 500 \\
& 18x + 24y \geq 300 \\
& x \geq 0,\, y \geq 0.
\end{aligned}$$

Before we start solving this problem, notice that all the inequalities may be simplified. The first is divisible by 10, the second by 25, and the third by 6. (However, this affects the meaning of the surplus variables; see the "Before we go on" discussion below.) Dividing gives the following simpler problem:

$$\begin{aligned}
\text{Minimize} \quad & c = 2{,}000x + 3{,}000y \\
\text{subject to} \quad & 2x + y \geq 20 \\
& x + 2y \geq 20 \\
& 3x + 4y \geq 50 \\
& x \geq 0,\, y \geq 0.
\end{aligned}$$

Following the discussion that preceded this example, we convert to a maximization problem:

$$\begin{aligned}
\text{Maximize} \quad & p = -2{,}000x - 3{,}000y \\
\text{subject to} \quad & 2x + y \geq 20 \\
& x + 2y \geq 20 \\
& 3x + 4y \geq 50 \\
& x \geq 0,\, y \geq 0.
\end{aligned}$$

We introduce surplus variables:

$$\begin{aligned}
2x + y - s &= 20 \\
x + 2y - t &= 20 \\
3x + 4y - u &= 50 \\
2{,}000x + 3{,}000y + p &= 0.
\end{aligned}$$

The initial tableau is then

	x	y	s	t	u	p	
*s	2	1	−1	0	0	0	20
*t	1	2	0	−1	0	0	20
*u	3	4	0	0	−1	0	50
p	2,000	3,000	0	0	0	1	0

The largest entry in the first starred row is the 2 in the upper left, which happens to give the smallest test ratio in its column.

	x	y	s	t	u	p		
*s	[2]	1	−1	0	0	0	20	
*t	1	2	0	−1	0	0	20	$2R_2 - R_1$
*u	3	4	0	0	−1	0	50	$2R_3 - 3R_1$
p	2,000	3,000	0	0	0	1	0	$R_4 - 1{,}000R_1$

	x	y	s	t	u	p		
x	2	1	−1	0	0	0	20	$3R_1 - R_2$
*t	0	[3]	1	−2	0	0	20	
*u	0	5	3	0	−2	0	40	$3R_3 - 5R_2$
p	0	2,000	1,000	0	0	1	−20,000	$3R_4 - 2{,}000R_2$

	x	y	s	t	u	p		
x	6	0	−4	2	0	0	40	$5R_1 - R_3$
y	0	3	1	−2	0	0	20	$5R_2 + R_3$
*u	0	0	4	[10]	−6	0	20	
p	0	0	1,000	4,000	0	3	−100,000	$R_4 - 400R_3$

	x	y	s	t	u	p		
x	30	0	−24	0	6	0	180	$R_1/6$
y	0	15	9	0	−6	0	120	$R_2/3$
t	0	0	4	10	−6	0	20	$R_3/2$
p	0	0	−600	0	2,400	3	−108,000	$R_4/3$

This completes Phase I. We are not yet at the optimal solution, so after performing the simplifications indicated, we proceed with Phase II.

	x	y	s	t	u	p		
x	5	0	−4	0	1	0	30	$R_1 + 2R_3$
y	0	5	3	0	−2	0	40	$2R_2 - 3R_3$
t	0	0	[2]	5	−3	0	10	
p	0	0	−200	0	800	1	−36,000	$R_4 + 100R_3$

	x	y	s	t	u	p	
x	5	0	0	10	−5	0	50
y	0	10	0	−15	5	0	50
s	0	0	2	5	−3	0	10
p	0	0	0	500	500	1	−35,000

The optimal solution is

$$x = 50/5 = 10, \quad y = 50/10 = 5, \quad p = -35{,}000,$$
$$\text{so} \quad c = 35{,}000 \qquad (s = 5, t = 0, u = 0).$$

You should buy 10 packages from Wall-to-Wall Furniture and 5 from Acme Furniture, for a minimum cost of $35,000.

➡ **Before we go on . . .** The surplus variables in Example 3 represent pieces of furniture over and above the minimum requirements. The order you place will give you 50 extra tables ($s = 5$, but s was introduced after we divided the first inequality by 10, so the actual surplus is $10 \times 5 = 50$), the correct number of chairs ($t = 0$), and the correct number of computer desks ($u = 0$). ∎

The preceding LP problem is an example of a **standard minimization problem**—in a sense the opposite of a standard maximization problem: We are *minimizing* an objective function, where all the constraints have the form $Ax + By + Cz + \cdots \geq N$ with N nonnegative. We will discuss standard minimization problems more fully in Section 6.5, as well as another method of solving them.

FAQs

When to Switch to Phase II, Equality Constraints, and Troubleshooting

Q: *How do I know when to switch to Phase II?*

A: After each step, check the basic solution for starred rows. You are not ready to proceed with Phase II until all the stars are gone.

Q: *How do I deal with an equality constraint, such as $2x + 7y - z = 90$?*

A: Although we haven't given examples of equality constraints, they can be treated by the following trick: Replace an equality by two inequalities. For example, replace the equality $2x + 7y - z = 90$ by the two inequalities $2x + 7y - z \leq 90$ and $2x + 7y - z \geq 90$. A little thought will convince you that these two inequalities amount to the same thing as the original equality!

Q: *What happens if it is impossible to choose a pivot using the instructions in Phase I?*

A: In that case, the LP problem has no solution. In fact, the feasible region is empty. If it is impossible to choose a pivot in Phase II, then the feasible region is unbounded, and there is no optimal solution.

6.4 EXERCISES

▼ more advanced   ◆ challenging
🔲 indicates exercises that should be solved using technology

1. Maximize $p = x + y$
   subject to $x + 2y \geq 6$
   $\qquad\qquad -x + y \leq 4$
   $\qquad\qquad 2x + y \leq 8$
   $\qquad x \geq 0, y \geq 0$. [HINT: See Examples 1 and 2.]

2. Maximize $p = 3x + 2y$
   subject to $x + 3y \geq 6$
   $\qquad\qquad -x + y \leq 4$
   $\qquad\qquad 2x + y \leq 8$
   $\qquad x \geq 0, y \geq 0$. [HINT: See Examples 1 and 2.]

3. Maximize $p = 12x + 10y$
subject to
$$x + y \leq 25$$
$$x \geq 10$$
$$-x + 2y \geq 0$$
$$x \geq 0, y \geq 0.$$

4. Maximize $p = x + 2y$
subject to
$$x + y \leq 25$$
$$y \geq 10$$
$$2x - y \geq 0$$
$$x \geq 0, y \geq 0.$$

5. Maximize $p = 2x + 5y + 3z$
subject to
$$x + y + z \leq 150$$
$$x + y + z \geq 100$$
$$x \geq 0, y \geq 0, z \geq 0.$$

6. Maximize $p = 3x + 2y + 2z$
subject to
$$x + y + 2z \leq 38$$
$$2x + y + z \geq 24$$
$$x \geq 0, y \geq 0, z \geq 0.$$

7. Maximize $p = 10x + 20y + 15z$
subject to
$$x + 2y + z \leq 40$$
$$2y - z \geq 10$$
$$2x - y + z \geq 20$$
$$x \geq 0, y \geq 0, z \geq 0.$$

8. Maximize $p = 10x + 10y + 15z$
subject to
$$x - y + z \leq 12$$
$$2x - 2y + z \geq 15$$
$$-y + z \geq 3$$
$$x \geq 0, y \geq 0, z \geq 0.$$

9. Maximize $p = x + y + 3z + w$
subject to
$$x + y + z + w \leq 40$$
$$2x + y - z - w \geq 10$$
$$x + y + z + w \geq 10$$
$$x \geq 0, y \geq 0, z \geq 0, w \geq 0.$$

10. Maximize $p = x + y + 4z + 2w$
subject to
$$x + y + z + w \leq 50$$
$$2x + y - z - w \geq 10$$
$$x + y + z + w \geq 20$$
$$x \geq 0, y \geq 0, z \geq 0, w \geq 0.$$

11. Minimize $c = 6x + 6y$
subject to
$$x + 2y \geq 20$$
$$2x + y \geq 20$$
$$x \geq 0, y \geq 0.$$ [HINT: See Example 3.]

12. Minimize $c = 3x + 2y$
subject to
$$x + 2y \geq 20$$
$$2x + y \geq 10$$
$$x \geq 0, y \geq 0.$$ [HINT: See Example 3.]

13. Minimize $c = 2x + y + 3z$
subject to
$$x + y + z \geq 100$$
$$2x + y \geq 50$$
$$y + z \geq 50$$
$$x \geq 0, y \geq 0, z \geq 0.$$

14. Minimize $c = 2x + 2y + 3z$
subject to
$$x + z \geq 100$$
$$2x + y \geq 50$$
$$y + z \geq 50$$
$$x \geq 0, y \geq 0, z \geq 0.$$

15. Minimize $c = 50x + 50y + 11z$
subject to
$$2x + z \geq 3$$
$$2x + y - z \geq 2$$
$$3x + y - z \leq 3$$
$$x \geq 0, y \geq 0, z \geq 0.$$

16. Minimize $c = 50x + 11y + 50z$
subject to
$$3x + z \geq 8$$
$$3x + y - z \geq 6$$
$$4x + y - z \leq 8$$
$$x \geq 0, y \geq 0, z \geq 0.$$

17. Minimize $c = x + y + z + w$
subject to
$$5x - y + w \geq 1{,}000$$
$$z + w \leq 2{,}000$$
$$x + y \leq 500$$
$$x \geq 0, y \geq 0, z \geq 0, w \geq 0.$$

18. Minimize $c = 5x + y + z + w$
subject to
$$5x - y + w \geq 1{,}000$$
$$z + w \leq 2{,}000$$
$$x + y \leq 500$$
$$x \geq 0, y \geq 0, z \geq 0, w \geq 0.$$

⊤ *In Exercises 19–24, we suggest the use of technology. Round all answers to two decimal places.*

19. Maximize $p = 2x + 3y + 1.1z + 4w$
subject to
$$1.2x + y + z + w \leq 40.5$$
$$2.2x + y - z - w \geq 10$$
$$1.2x + y + z + 1.2w \geq 10.5$$
$$x \geq 0, y \geq 0, z \geq 0, w \geq 0.$$

20. Maximize $p = 2.2x + 2y + 1.1z + 2w$
subject to
$$x + 1.5y + 1.5z + w \leq 50.5$$
$$2x + 1.5y - z - w \geq 10$$
$$x + 1.5y + z + 1.5w \geq 21$$
$$x \geq 0, y \geq 0, z \geq 0, w \geq 0.$$

21. Minimize $c = 2.2x + y + 3.3z$
subject to
$$x + 1.5y + 1.2z \geq 100$$
$$2x + 1.5y \geq 50$$
$$1.5y + 1.1z \geq 50$$
$$x \geq 0, y \geq 0, z \geq 0.$$

22. Minimize $c = 50.3x + 10.5y + 50.3z$

subject to $3.1x \quad + 1.1z \geq 28$

$3.1x + y - 1.1z \geq 23$

$4.2x + y - 1.1z \geq 28$

$x \geq 0, y \geq 0, z \geq 0.$

23. Minimize $c = 1.1x + y + 1.5z - w$

subject to $5.12x - y \quad + w \leq 1,000$

$z + w \geq 2,000$

$1.22x + y \qquad \leq 500$

$x \geq 0, y \geq 0, z \geq 0, w \geq 0.$

24. Minimize $c = 5.45x + y + 1.5z + w$

subject to $5.12x - y \quad + w \geq 1,000$

$z + w \geq 2,000$

$1.12x + y \qquad \leq 500$

$x \geq 0, y \geq 0, z \geq 0, w \geq 0.$

Applications

25. *Agriculture* (Compare Exercise 27 in Section 6.3.) Your small farm encompasses 100 acres, and you are planning to grow tomatoes, lettuce, and carrots in the coming planting season. Fertilizer costs per acre are $5 for tomatoes, $4 for lettuce, and $2 for carrots. Based on past experience, you estimate that each acre of tomatoes will require an average of 4 hours of labor per week, while tending to lettuce and carrots will each require an average of 2 hours per week. You estimate a profit of $2,000 for each acre of tomatoes, $1,500 for each acre of lettuce, and $500 for each acre of carrots. You would like to spend at least $400 on fertilizer (your niece owns the company that manufactures it), and your farm laborers can supply up to 500 hours per week. How many acres of each crop should you plant to maximize total profits? In this event, will you be using all 100 acres of your farm? [HINT: See Example 3.]

26. *Agriculture* (Compare Exercise 28 in Section 6.3.) Your farm encompasses 900 acres, and you are planning to grow soybeans, corn, and wheat in the coming planting season. Fertilizer costs per acre are $5 for soybeans, $2 for corn, and $1 for wheat. You estimate that each acre of soybeans will require an average of 5 hours of labor per week, while tending to corn and wheat will each require an average of 2 hours per week. On the basis of past yields and current market prices, you estimate a profit of $3,000 for each acre of soybeans, $2,000 for each acre of corn, and $1,000 for each acre of wheat. You can afford to spend no more than $3,000 on fertilizer, but your labor union contract stipulates at least 2,000 hours per week of labor. How many acres of each crop should you plant to maximize total profits? In this event, will you be using more than 2,000 hours of labor? [HINT: See Example 3.]

27. *Politics* The political pollster *Canter* is preparing for a national election. It would like to poll at least 1,500 Democrats and 1,500 Republicans. Each mailing to the East Coast gets responses from 100 Democrats and 50 Republicans. Each mailing to the Midwest gets responses from 100 Democrats and 100 Republicans. And each mailing to the West Coast gets responses from 50 Democrats and 100 Republicans. Mailings to the East Coast cost $40 each to produce and mail, mailings to the Midwest cost $60 each, and mailings to the West Coast cost $50 each. How many mailings should Canter send to each area of the country to get the responses it needs at the least possible cost? What will it cost?

28. *Purchasing* *Bingo's Copy Center* needs to buy white paper and yellow paper. Bingo's can buy from three suppliers. *Harvard Paper* sells a package of 20 reams of white and 10 reams of yellow for $60, *Yale Paper* sells a package of 10 reams of white and 10 reams of yellow for $40, and *Dartmouth Paper* sells a package of 10 reams of white and 20 reams of yellow for $50. If Bingo's needs 350 reams of white and 400 reams of yellow, how many packages should it buy from each supplier to minimize the cost? What is the least possible cost?

29. *Resource Allocation* *Succulent Citrus* produces orange juice and orange concentrate. This year the company anticipates a demand of at least 10,000 quarts of orange juice and 1,000 quarts of orange concentrate. Each quart of orange juice requires 10 oranges, and each quart of concentrate requires 50 oranges. The company also anticipates using at least 200,000 oranges for these products. Each quart of orange juice costs the company 50¢ to produce, and each quart of concentrate costs $2.00 to produce. How many quarts of each product should Succulent Citrus produce to meet the demand and minimize total costs?

30. *Resource Allocation* *Fancy Pineapple* produces pineapple juice and canned pineapple rings. This year the company anticipates a demand of at least 10,000 pints of pineapple juice and 1,000 cans of pineapple rings. Each pint of pineapple juice requires 2 pineapples, and each can of pineapple rings requires 1 pineapple. The company anticipates using at least 20,000 pineapples for these products. Each pint of pineapple juice costs the company 20¢ to produce, and each can of pineapple rings costs 50¢ to produce. How many pints of pineapple juice and cans of pineapple rings should Fancy Pineapple produce to meet the demand and minimize total costs?

31. *Latin Music Sales (Digital)* You are about to go live with a Latin music download service called *iYayay* that will compete head-to-head with Apple's iTunes. (Good luck!) You will be selling digital albums of regional (Mexican/Tejano) music for $5 each, pop/rock albums for $4 each, and tropical (salsa/merengue/cumbia/bachata) albums for $6 each. Your servers can handle up to 40,000 downloaded albums per day, and you anticipate on the basis of national sales[31] that sales

[31] In 2013, total U.S. revenues from regional music were about four times those from tropical music. Source: Recording Industry Association of America http://riaa.org.

of regional music will be at least four times those from tropical music. You also anticipate that you will sell at least 10,000 pop/rock albums per day as a result of the very attractive $4 price. On the basis of these assumptions, how many of each type of album should you sell for a maximum daily revenue, and what will your daily revenue be?

32. **Latin Music Sales (Digital)** It seems that your biggest rival, Lupita Pelogrande, has learned about your music store and has decided to launch *iRico*, a competitor Latin music download service that will also offer regional (Mexican/Tejano) music albums for $5 each and pop/rock albums for $4 each. However, instead of tropical music, *iRico* will offer reggaeton albums at only $3 per album. Lupita's servers are more robust than yours and can handle up to 60,000 downloaded albums per day. She anticipates that revenues from regional music can total to up to double those from reggaeton and that *iRico* can sell at least 50,000 albums per day, not even counting reggaeton. On the basis of these assumptions, how many of each type of album should *iRico* sell for a maximum daily revenue, and what will the daily revenue be?

Gaming Exercises 33–36 are based on the following table, which shows some parameters of various weapons used in role-playing gaming:[32]

Weapon	Cost (gold pieces)	Damage to Medium Targets	Critical Damage	Weight (pounds)
Axe (Throwing)	8	6	12	2
Javelin	1	6	12	2
Longsword	15	8	32	4
Mace (Light)	5	6	12	4
Spear	2	8	24	6

33. **Orcs** (Compare Exercise 31 in Section 6.3.) The Orc leader Achlúk has up to 600 gold pieces to spend on an arsenal of axes, maces, and spears for his army of orcs for a planned assault on Hobshire, in which he would like to inflict as much damage on medium targets (such as humans and hobbits) as possible and a total of at least 2,400 units of critical damage. As his orcs are particularly fond of maces but not particularly skilled at spear-throwing, he would like to include at least twice as many maces as spears in the arsenal. What should his weapons arsenal look like, and how much damage on medium targets can be inflicted?

34. **Elves** (Compare Exercise 32 in Section 6.3.) The Elf leader Galandir is assembling an arsenal of up to 6,000 pounds in weight of javelins, longswords, and spears for her band of elves in a planned assault on Mordrúk. She needs to inflict as much critical damage as possible and at least 2,000 units of damage on medium targets. As the elves in her band prefer spears to longswords, she would like to ensure that there are at least as many spears as longswords. What should her weapons arsenal look like, and how much critical damage can be inflicted?

35. **Orcs** Having suffered an embarrassing defeat in Hobshire, Achlúk is rearming his army of orcs with axes, maces, and spears. This time, his budget is tight, and he wants to spend as little as possible but still inflict at least 2,000 units of damage on medium targets and 2,400 units of critical damage while keeping the total weight to no more than 1,000 pounds. What should his weapons arsenal look like, and how much will it cost?

36. **Elves** The Elf leader Galandir is having second thoughts about how to arm her band of elves with javelins, longswords, and spears for the planned assault on Mordrúk. For the sake of swiftness she wants the arsenal to weigh as little as possible but still inflict at least 24,000 units of critical damage and 2,000 units of damage on medium targets at a total cost of no more than 15,000 gold pieces. What should her weapons arsenal look like, and how much will it weigh?

37. **Nutrition** Gerber Products' Gerber Mixed Cereal for Baby contains, in each serving, 60 calories and no vitamin C. Gerber Mango Tropical Fruit Dessert contains, in each serving, 80 calories and 45% of the U.S. Recommended Daily Allowance (RDA) of vitamin C for infants. Gerber Apple Banana Juice contains, in each serving, 60 calories and 120% of the RDA of vitamin C for infants.[33] The cereal costs 10¢ per serving, the dessert costs 53¢ per serving, and the juice costs 27¢ per serving. If you want to provide your child with at least 120 calories and at least 120% of the RDA of vitamin C, how can you do so at the least cost?

38. **Nutrition** Gerber Products' Gerber Mixed Cereal for Baby contains, in each serving, 60 calories, no vitamin C, and 11 grams of carbohydrates. Gerber Mango Tropical Fruit Dessert contains, in each serving, 80 calories, 45% of the RDA of vitamin C for infants, and 21 grams of carbohydrates. Gerber Apple Banana Juice contains, in each serving, 60 calories, 120% of the RDA of vitamin C for infants, and 15 grams of carbohydrates.[34] Assume that the cereal costs 11¢ per serving, the dessert costs 50¢ per serving, and the juice costs 30¢ per serving. If you want to provide your child with at least 180 calories, at least 120% of the RDA of vitamin C, and at least 37 grams of carbohydrates, how can you do so at the least cost?

---

[32] Source: Dungeons and Dragons Wiki (www.dandwiki.com.) (Critical Damage is a weighted measure of "critical hit damage" as defined there.) See also Paul Tozour's blog at www.gamasutra.com/blogs/PaulTozour/20130707/195718/ for a discussion of similar scenarios in the context of arming a video game battle tank.

---

[33] Source: Nutrition information supplied with the products.
[34] *Ibid.*

39. ⬛ *Purchasing* Cheapskate Electronics Store needs to update its inventory of stereos, TVs, and DVD players. There are three suppliers it can buy from: *Nadir* offers a bundle consisting of 5 stereos, 10 TVs, and 15 DVD players for $3,000. *Blunt* offers a bundle consisting of 10 stereos, 10 TVs, and 10 DVD players for $4,000. *Sonny* offers a bundle consisting of 15 stereos, 10 TVs, and 10 DVD players for $5,000. Cheapskate Electronics needs at least 150 stereos, 200 TVs, and 150 DVD players. How can it update its inventory at the least possible cost? What is the least possible cost?

40. ⬛ *Purchasing* Federal Rent-a-Car is putting together a new fleet. It is considering package offers from three car manufacturers. *Fred Motors* is offering 5 small cars, 5 medium cars, and 10 large cars for $500,000. *Admiral Motors* is offering 5 small, 10 medium, and 5 large cars for $400,000. *Chrysalis* is offering 10 small, 5 medium, and 5 large cars for $300,000. Federal would like to buy at least 550 small cars, at least 500 medium cars, and at least 550 large cars. How many packages should it buy from each car maker to keep the total cost as small as possible? What will be the total cost?

⬛ *Bodybuilding Supplements* Exercises 41 and 42 are based on the following data on four bodybuilding supplements. (Figures shown correspond to a single serving.)[35]

	Creatine (grams)	L-Glutamine (grams)	BCAAs (grams)	Approximate Cost ($)
Xtend (SciVation)	0	2.5	7	1.00
Gainz (MP Hardcore)	2	3	6	1.10
Strongevity (Bill Phillips)	2.5	1	0	1.30
Muscle Physique (EAS)	2	2	0	1.00

41. Your personal trainer suggests that you supplement with at least 70 grams of creatine, 50 grams of L-glutamine, and 60 grams of BCAAs per week. You are thinking of combining Xtend, Gainz, and Strongevity to provide you with the required nutrients. How many servings of each should you combine to obtain a week's supply that meets your trainer's specifications at the least cost? How much will the week's supply cost? [HINT: Use the Excel pivot and Gauss-Jordan tool in decimal mode to do the pivoting.]

42. Your friend's personal trainer suggests that she supplement with at least 60 grams of each of creatine, L-glutamine, and

BCAAs per week. She is thinking of combining Gainz, Strongevity, and Muscle Physique to provide her with the required nutrients. How many servings of each should she combine to obtain a week's supply that meets her trainer's specifications at the least cost? How much will the week's supply cost? [HINT: Use the Excel pivot and Gauss-Jordan tool in decimal mode to do the pivoting.]

43. ▼ *Subsidies* The Miami Beach City Council has offered to subsidize hotel development in Miami Beach, and it is hoping for at least two hotels with a total capacity of at least 1,400. Suppose that you are a developer interested in taking advantage of this offer by building a small group of hotels in Miami Beach. You are thinking of three prototypes: a convention-style hotel with 500 rooms costing $100 million, a vacation-style hotel with 200 rooms costing $20 million, and a small motel with 50 rooms costing $4 million. The City Council will approve your plans, provided that you build at least one convention-style hotel and no more than two small motels.
   a. How many of each type of hotel should you build to satisfy the city council's wishes and stipulations while minimizing your total cost?
   b. Now assume that the city council will give developers 20% of the cost of building new hotels in Miami Beach, up to $50 million.[36] Will the city's $50 million subsidy be sufficient to cover 20% of your total costs?

44. ▼ *Subsidies* Refer back to Exercise 43. You are about to begin the financial arrangements for your new hotels when the city council informs you that it has changed its mind and now requires at least two vacation-style hotels and no more than four small motels.
   a. How many of each type of hotel should you build to satisfy the city council's wishes and stipulations while minimizing your total costs?
   b. Will the city's $50 million subsidy limit still be sufficient to cover 20% of your total costs?

45. ▼ *Transportation Scheduling* We return to your exploits coordinating distribution for the *Tubular Ride Boogie Board Company*.[37] You will recall that the company has manufacturing plants in Tucson, Arizona, and Toronto, Ontario, and you have been given the job of coordinating distribution of their latest model, the Gladiator, to their outlets in Honolulu and Venice Beach. The Tucson plant can manufacture up to 620 boards per week, while the Toronto plant, beset by labor disputes, can produce no more than 410 Gladiator boards per week. The outlet in Honolulu orders 500 Gladiator boards per week, while the Venice Beach outlet orders 530 boards per week. Transportation

---

[35] Source: Nutritional information supplied by the manufacturers/ www.bodybuilding.com. Cost per serving is approximate and varies considerably. "BCAAs" refers to the branched-chain amino acids leucine, isoleucine, and valine in the optimal 2:1:1 ratio.

[36] The Miami Beach City Council made such an offer in 1993. (*Chicago Tribune*, June 20, 1993, Section 7, p. 8).

[37] See Exercise 26 in Section 4.3 and Exercise 43 in Section 6.3. This time, we will use the simplex method to solve the version of this problem we first considered in Section 4.3.

costs are as follows: Tucson to Honolulu: $10 per board; Tucson to Venice Beach: $5 per board; Toronto to Honolulu: $20 per board; Toronto to Venice Beach: $10 per board. Your manager has said that you are to be sure to fill all orders and ship the boogie boards at a minimum total transportation cost. How will you do it?

46. ▼ *Transportation Scheduling* In the situation described in Exercise 45, you have just been notified that workers at the Toronto boogie board plant have gone on strike, resulting in a total work stoppage. You are to come up with a revised delivery schedule by tomorrow with the understanding that the Tucson plant can push production to a maximum of 1,000 boards per week. What should you do?

47. ▼ *Finance* Senator Porkbarrel habitually overdraws his three bank accounts: at the *Congressional Integrity Bank, Citizens' Trust,* and *Checks R Us.* There are no penalties because the overdrafts are subsidized by the taxpayer. The Senate Ethics Committee tends to let slide irregular banking activities as long as they are not flagrant. At the moment (because of Congress's preoccupation with a Supreme Court nominee), a total overdraft of up to $10,000 will be overlooked. Porkbarrel's conscience makes him hesitate to overdraw accounts at banks whose names include expressions such as "integrity" and "citizens' trust." The effect is that his overdrafts at the first two banks combined amount to no more than one quarter of the total. On the other hand, the financial officers at Integrity Bank, aware that Senator Porkbarrel is a member of the Senate Banking Committee, "suggest" that he overdraw at least $2,500 from their bank. Find the amount he should overdraw from each bank to avoid investigation by the Ethics Committee and overdraw his account at Integrity by as much as his sense of guilt will allow.

48. ▼ *Scheduling* Because Joe Slim's brother was recently elected to the State Senate, Joe's financial advisement concern, *Inside Information Inc.,* has been doing a booming trade, even though the financial counseling he offers is quite worthless. (None of his seasoned clients pays the slightest attention to his advice.) Slim charges different hourly rates to different categories of individuals: $5,000 per hour for private citizens, $50,000 per hour for corporate executives, and $10,000 per hour for presidents of universities. Because of his taste for leisure, he feels that he can spend no more than 40 hours per week in consultation. On the other hand, Slim feels that it would be best for his intellect were he to devote at least 10 hours of consultation each week to university presidents. However, Slim always feels somewhat uncomfortable dealing with academics, so he would prefer to spend no more than half his consultation time with university presidents. Furthermore, he likes to think of himself as representing the interests of the common citizen, so he wishes to offer at least 2 more hours of his time each week to private citizens than to corporate executives and university presidents combined. Given all these restrictions, how many hours each week should he spend with each type of client to maximize his income?

49. ▼ *Transportation Scheduling* Your publishing company is about to start a promotional blitz for its new book, *Advanced Quantum Mechanics for the Liberal Arts.* You have 20 salespeople stationed in Chicago and 10 in Denver. You would like to fly at least 10 salespeople to Los Angeles and at least 15 to New York. A round-trip plane flight from Chicago to Los Angeles costs $200; from Chicago to New York costs $125; from Denver to Los Angeles costs $225; and from Denver to New York costs $280.[38] How many salespeople should you fly from each of Chicago and Denver to each of Los Angeles and New York to spend the least amount on plane flights?

50. ▼ *Transportation Scheduling* Repeat Exercise 49, but now suppose that you would like at least 15 salespeople in Los Angeles.

51. ▢ ▼ *Hospital Staffing* As the staff director of a new hospital, you are planning to hire cardiologists, rehabilitation specialists, and infectious disease specialists. According to recent data, each cardiology case averages $12,000 in revenue, each physical rehabilitation case averages $19,000, and each infectious disease case averages $14,000.[39] You judge that each specialist you employ will expand the hospital caseload by about 10 patients per week. You already have 3 cardiologists on staff, and the hospital is equipped to admit up to 200 patients per week. According to past experience, each cardiologist and rehabilitation specialist brings in one government research grant per year, while each infectious disease specialist brings in three. Your board of directors would like to see a total of at least 30 grants per year and would like your weekly revenue to be as large as possible. How many of each kind of specialist should you hire?

52. ▢ ▼ *Hospital Staffing* Referring to Exercise 51, you completely misjudged the number of patients each type of specialist would bring to the hospital per week. It turned out that each cardiologist brought in 120 new patients per year, each rehabilitation specialist brought in 90 per year, and each infectious disease specialist brought in 70 per year.[40] It also turned out that your hospital could deal with no more than 1,960 new patients per year. Repeat Exercise 51 in light of this corrected data.

Communication and Reasoning Exercises

53. Explain the need for Phase I in a nonstandard LP problem.

54. Explain the need for Phase II in a nonstandard LP problem.

---

[38] Approximate prices advertised on various websites in September 2011.

[39] These (rounded) figures are based on an Illinois survey of 1.3 million hospital admissions (*Chicago Tribune,* March 29, 1993, Section 4, p. 1). Source: Lutheran General Health System, Argus Associates, Inc.

[40] These (rounded) figures were obtained from the survey referenced in Exercise 51 by dividing the average hospital revenue per physician by the revenue per case.

55. Explain briefly why we would need to use Phase I in solving a linear programming problem with the constraint $x + 2y - z \geq 3$.

56. Which rows do we star, and why?

57. Consider the following linear programming problem:

$$\text{Maximize } p = x + y$$
$$\text{subject to } \quad x - 2y \geq 0$$
$$2x + \ y \leq 10$$
$$x \geq 0, y \geq 0.$$

This problem

(A) must be solved using the techniques of Section 6.4.
(B) must be solved using the techniques of Section 6.3.
(C) can be solved using the techniques of either section.

58. Consider the following linear programming problem:

$$\text{Maximize } p = x + y$$
$$\text{subject to } \quad x - 2y \geq 1$$
$$2x + \ y \leq 10$$
$$x \geq 0, y \geq 0.$$

This problem

(A) must be solved using the techniques of Section 6.4.
(B) must be solved using the techniques of Section 6.3.
(C) can be solved using the techniques of either section.

59. ▼ Find a linear programming problem in three variables that requires one pivot in Phase I.

60. ▼ Find a linear programming problem in three variables that requires two pivots in Phase I.

61. ▼ Find a linear programming problem in two or three variables with no optimal solution, and show what happens when you try to solve it using the simplex method.

62. ▼ Find a linear programming problem in two or three variables with more than one optimal solution, and investigate which solution is found by the simplex method.

6.5   The Simplex Method and Duality

Dual Linear Programming Problems

We mentioned **standard minimization problems** in Section 6.4. These problems have the following form.

Standard Minimization Problem

A **standard minimization problem** is an LP problem in which we are required to *minimize* (not maximize) a linear objective function

$$c = as + bt + cu + \cdots$$

of the variables $s, t, u, \ldots$ (in this section we will always use the letters $s, t, u, \ldots$ for the unknowns in a standard minimization problem) subject to the constraints

$$s \geq 0, \quad t \geq 0, \quad u \geq 0, \ldots$$

and further constraints of the form

$$As + Bt + Cu + \cdots \geq N,$$

where $A, B, C, \ldots$, and N are numbers with N nonnegative.

A **standard linear programming problem** is an LP problem that is either a standard maximization problem or a standard minimization problem. An LP problem satisfies the **nonnegative objective condition** if all the coefficients in the objective function are nonnegative.

> ## Quick Examples
>
> ### Standard Minimization and Maximization Problems
>
> **1.** Minimize $\quad c = 2s + 3t + 3u$
>
>   subject to $\quad 2s \qquad + \quad u \geq 10$
>
> $s + 3t - 6u \geq 5$
>
> $s \geq 0, t \geq 0, u \geq 0.$
>
> This is a standard minimization problem satisfying the nonnegative objective condition.
>
> **2.** Maximize $\quad p = 2x + 3y + 3z$
>
>   subject to $\quad 2x \qquad + \quad z \leq 7$
>
> $x + 3y - 6z \leq 6$
>
> $x \geq 0, y \geq 0, z \geq 0.$
>
> This is a standard maximization problem satisfying the nonnegative objective condition.
>
> **3.** Minimize $\quad c = 2s - 3t + 3u$
>
>   subject to $\quad 2s \qquad + \quad u \geq 10$
>
> $s + 3t - 6u \geq 5$
>
> $s \geq 0, t \geq 0, u \geq 0.$
>
> This is a standard minimization problem that does *not* satisfy the nonnegative objective condition.

We saw a way of solving minimization problems in Section 6.4, but a mathematically elegant relationship between maximization and minimization problems gives us another way of solving minimization problems that satisfy the nonnegative objective condition. This relationship is called **duality**.

To describe duality, we must first represent an LP problem by a matrix. This matrix is *not* the first tableau but something simpler: Pretend you forgot all about slack variables and also forgot to change the signs of the objective function.[*] As an example, consider the following two standard[†] problems:

[*] Forgetting these things is exactly what happens to many students under test conditions!

[†] Although duality does not require the problems to be standard, it does require them to be written in so-called *standard form:* In the case of a maximization problem, all constraints need to be (re)written using ≤, while for a minimization problem, all constraints need to be (re)written using ≥. Note that this means that the right-hand side of a constraint may wind up negative. It is least confusing to stick with standard problems, which is what we will do in this section.

Problem 1

$$\text{Maximize} \quad p = 20x + 20y + 50z$$

$$\text{subject to} \quad 2x + y + 3z \leq 2{,}000$$

$$x + 2y + 4z \leq 3{,}000$$

$$x \geq 0, y \geq 0, z \geq 0.$$

We represent this problem by the matrix

$$\left[\begin{array}{ccc|c} 2 & 1 & 3 & 2{,}000 \\ 1 & 2 & 4 & 3{,}000 \\ \hline 20 & 20 & 50 & 0 \end{array}\right] \begin{array}{l} \text{Constraint 1} \\ \text{Constraint 2} \\ \text{Objective} \end{array}$$

Notice that the coefficients of the objective function go in the bottom row, and we place a zero in the bottom right corner.

Problem 2 (from Example 3 in Section 6.4)

$$\text{Minimize} \quad c = 2{,}000s + 3{,}000t$$

$$\text{subject to} \quad 2s + t \geq 20$$

$$s + 2t \geq 20$$

$$3s + 4t \geq 50$$

$$s \geq 0, t \geq 0.$$

Problem 2 is represented by

$$
\begin{bmatrix}
2 & 1 & 20 \\
1 & 2 & 20 \\
3 & 4 & 50 \\
\hline
2{,}000 & 3{,}000 & 0
\end{bmatrix}
\begin{matrix}
\text{Constraint 1} \\
\text{Constraint 2} \\
\text{Constraint 3} \\
\text{Objective}
\end{matrix}
$$

These two problems are related: The matrix for Problem 1 is the transpose of the matrix for Problem 2. (Recall that the transpose of a matrix is obtained by writing its columns as rows; see Section 5.1.) When we have a pair of LP problems related in this way, we say that the two are *dual* LP problems.

Dual Linear Programming Problems

Two LP problems, one a maximization and one a minimization problem, are **dual** if the matrix that represents one is the transpose of the matrix that represents the other.

Finding the Dual of a Given Problem
Given an LP problem, we find its dual as follows:

1. Represent the problem as a matrix (see above).
2. Take the transpose of the matrix.
3. Write down the dual, which is the LP problem corresponding to the new matrix. If the original problem was a maximization problem, its dual will be a minimization problem, and vice versa.

The original problem is called the **primal problem**, and its dual is referred to as the **dual problem**.

Quick Example

Primal problem

4. Minimize $c = s + 2t$
   subject to $5s + 2t \geq 60$
   $3s + 4t \geq 80$
   $s + t \geq 20$
   $s \geq 0, t \geq 0.$

$\xrightarrow{\text{1}}$

$$
\begin{bmatrix}
5 & 2 & 60 \\
3 & 4 & 80 \\
1 & 1 & 20 \\
1 & 2 & 0
\end{bmatrix}
$$

Dual problem

Maximize $p = 60x + 80y + 20z$
subject to $5x + 3y + z \leq 1$
$2x + 4y + z \leq 2$
$x \geq 0, y \geq 0, z \geq 0.$

$\xrightarrow{\text{2}}$

$$
\begin{bmatrix}
5 & 3 & 1 & 1 \\
2 & 4 & 1 & 2 \\
60 & 80 & 20 & 0
\end{bmatrix}
$$

$\xrightarrow{\text{3}}$

The following theorem justifies what we have been doing, and says that solving the dual problem of an LP problem is equivalent to solving the original problem.

Fundamental Theorem of Duality

(a) If an LP problem has an optimal solution, then so does its dual. Moreover, the primal problem and the dual problem have the same optimal value for their objective functions.

(b) Contained in the final tableau of the simplex method applied to an LP problem is the solution to its dual problem: It is given by the bottom entries in the columns associated with the slack variables, divided by the entry under the objective variable.

* The proof of the theorem is beyond the scope of this book but can be found in a textbook devoted to linear programming, such as *Linear Programming* by Vašek Chvátal (San Francisco: W. H. Freeman and Co., 1983), which has a particularly well-motivated discussion.

The theorem* gives us an alternative way of solving minimization problems that satisfy the nonnegative objective condition. Let's illustrate by solving Problem 2 above.

EXAMPLE 1   Solving by Duality

Minimize $c = 2{,}000s + 3{,}000t$
subject to $2s + t \geq 20$
$s + 2t \geq 20$
$3s + 4t \geq 50$
$s \geq 0, t \geq 0.$

Solution

Step 1 *Find the dual problem.* Write the primal problem in matrix form and take the transpose:

$$\begin{bmatrix} 2 & 1 & 20 \\ 1 & 2 & 20 \\ 3 & 4 & 50 \\ 2{,}000 & 3{,}000 & 0 \end{bmatrix} \rightarrow \begin{bmatrix} 2 & 1 & 3 & 2{,}000 \\ 1 & 2 & 4 & 3{,}000 \\ 20 & 20 & 50 & 0 \end{bmatrix}.$$

The dual problem is

Maximize $p = 20x + 20y + 50z$
subject to $2x + y + 3z \leq 2{,}000$
$x + 2y + 4z \leq 3{,}000$
$x \geq 0, y \geq 0, z \geq 0.$

Step 2 *Use the simplex method to solve the dual problem.* Because we have a standard maximization problem, we do not have to worry about Phase I but go straight to Phase II.

	x	y	z	s	t	p	
s	2	1	[3]	1	0	0	2,000
t	1	2	4	0	1	0	3,000
p	−20	−20	−50	0	0	1	0

	x	y	z	s	t	p	
z	2	1	3	1	0	0	2,000
t	−5	[2]	0	−4	3	0	1,000
p	40	−10	0	50	0	3	100,000

	x	y	z	s	t	p	
z	9	0	6	6	−3	0	3,000
y	−5	2	0	−4	3	0	1,000
p	15	0	0	30	15	3	105,000

Note that the maximum value of the objective function is $p = 105,000/3 = 35,000$. By the theorem this is also the optimal value of c in the primal problem!

Step 3 *Read off the solution to the primal problem by dividing the bottom entries in the columns associated with the slack variables by the entry in the p column.* Here is the final tableau again with the entries in question highlighted:

	x	y	z	s	t	p	
z	9	0	6	6	−3	0	3,000
y	−5	2	0	−4	3	0	1,000
p	15	0	0	30	15	3	105,000

The solution to the primal problem is

$$s = 30/3 = 10, \quad t = 15/3 = 5, \quad c = 105,000/3 = 35,000.$$

(Compare this with the method we used to solve Example 3 in Section 6.4. Which method seems more efficient?)

➡ **Before we go on...** Can you now see the reason for using the variable names $s, t, u, \ldots$ in standard minimization problems? ∎

Q: Is the theorem also useful for solving problems that do not satisfy the nonnegative objective condition?

A: Consider a standard minimization problem that does not satisfy the nonnegative objective condition, such as

Minimize $c = 2s - t$
subject to $2s - 3t \geq 1$
             $5s + 6t \geq 7$
             $s \geq 0, t \geq 0.$

Its dual would be

Maximize $p = x + 7y$
subject to $2x + 5y \leq 2$
             $-3x + 6y \leq -1$
             $x \geq 0, y \geq 0.$

This is not a standard maximization problem because the right-hand side of the second constraint is negative. (Multiplying both sides of the second constraint by −1 to make the right-hand side nonnegative results in a ≥ type inequality.) To solve the dual by the simplex method will require using Phase I as well as Phase II, and we may as well just solve the primal problem that way to begin with. Thus, duality helps us to solve problems only when the primal problem satisfies the nonnegative objective condition.

In general, if a problem does not satisfy the nonnegative objective condition, its dual is not standard.

Shadow Costs

A common kind of economic application is one that leads to a standard minimization problem involving minimizing cost. The minimum cost that is obtained depends on the constraints, which, because it is a standard minimization problem, are all of the form

$$As + Bt + Cu + \cdots \geq N.$$

N is typically the number of units of some required quantity, such as protein, and increasing that requirement will likely raise the minimum cost. In a standard minimization problem it turns out that the minimum cost increases by a fixed amount for each additional unit of N (up to a certain "allowable" maximum), and this fixed amount is called the **shadow cost** of the associated requirement.[*]

In the following example we see how the solution to the dual problem also gives us the shadow costs associated with all the requirements.

*You might recognize the shadow cost as an associated *marginal cost:* the increase in minimum cost per additional unit of the required quantity.

EXAMPLE 2   **Shadow Costs**

You are trying to decide how many vitamin pills to take. SuperV brand vitamin pills each contain 2 milligrams of vitamin X, 1 milligram of vitamin Y, and 1 milligram of vitamin Z. Topper brand vitamin pills each contain 1 milligram of vitamin X, 1 milligram of vitamin Y, and 2 milligrams of vitamin Z. You want to take enough pills daily to get at least 12 milligrams of vitamin X, 10 milligrams of vitamin Y, and 12 milligrams of vitamin Z. However, SuperV pills cost 4¢ each, and Toppers cost 3¢ each, and you would like to minimize the total cost of your daily dosage.

a. How many of each brand of pill should you take?

b. Determine the shadow costs of each vitamin. That is, if you raised the daily requirements of any vitamin, by how much would the cost increase for each additional milligram added to the requirement?

Solution

a. This is a straightforward minimization problem. The unknowns are

s = number of SuperV brand pills
t = number of Topper brand pills.

The linear programming problem is

Minimize $c = 4s + 3t$
subject to $2s + t \geq 12$
$s + t \geq 10$
$s + 2t \geq 12$
$s \geq 0, t \geq 0.$

We solve this problem by using the simplex method on its dual, which is

Maximize $p = 12x + 10y + 12z$
subject to $2x + y + z \leq 4$
$x + y + 2z \leq 3$
$x \geq 0, y \geq 0, z \geq 0.$

After pivoting three times, we arrive at the final tableau:

	x	y	z	s	t	p	
x	6	0	−6	6	−6	0	6
y	0	1	3	−1	2	0	2
p	0	0	6	2	8	1	32

Therefore, the answer to the original problem is that you should take two SuperV vitamin pills and eight Toppers at a cost of 32¢ per day.

b. Now, the key to finding the shadow costs, which determine how changing your daily vitamin requirements would affect your minimum cost, is to look at the solution to the dual problem. From the tableau we see that $x = 1$, $y = 2$, and $z = 0$. To see what x, y, and z might tell us about the original problem, let's look at their units. In the inequality $2x + y + z \le 4$, the coefficient 2 of x has units "milligrams of vitamin X per SuperV pill," and the 4 on the right-hand side has units "cents per SuperV pill." For $2x$ to have the same units as the 4 on the right-hand side, x must have units "cents per milligram of vitamin X." Similarly, y must have units "cents per milligram of vitamin Y," and z must have units "cents per milligram of vitamin Z."

These are exactly the units that the shadow costs we are seeking should have: cost per additional milligram of vitamin. One can show (although we will not do it here) that this is no coincidence: x is in fact the shadow cost of vitamin X. That is, x is the amount that would be added to the minimum cost for each increase[*] of 1 milligram of vitamin X in our daily requirement. For example, if we were to increase our requirement from 12 milligrams to 14 milligrams, an increase of 2 milligrams, the minimum cost would change by $2x = 2$¢, from 32¢ to 34¢. (Try it; you'll end up taking four SuperV pills and six Toppers.)

Similarly, $y = 2$ is the shadow cost of vitamin Y; each increase of 1 milligram in the requirement for vitamin Y would increase the cost by 2¢. The same holds for (small) decreases: Each decrease of 1 milligram in the requirement for vitamin Y would decrease the cost by 2¢ (and similarly for vitamin X).

What about $z = 0$? The shadow cost of vitamin Z is 0¢ per milligram, meaning that you can increase your requirement of vitamin Z without changing your cost. In fact, the solution $s = 2$ and $t = 8$ provides you with 18 milligrams of vitamin Z, so you can increase the required amount of vitamin Z up to 18 milligrams (or decrease it to 0) without changing the solution at all.

We can also interpret the shadow costs as the effective cost to you of each milligram of each vitamin in the optimal solution. You are paying 1¢ per milligram of vitamin X, paying 2¢ per milligram of vitamin Y, and getting the vitamin Z for free. This gives a total cost of $1 \times 12 + 2 \times 10 + 0 \times 12 = 32$¢, as we know. Again, if you change your requirements slightly, these are the amounts you will pay per milligram of each vitamin.

[*] To be scrupulously correct, this works only for changes within a certain range, not necessarily for very large changes.

Application to Game Theory

We return to a topic we discussed in Section 5.4: solving two-person zero-sum games. In that section we described how to solve games that could be reduced to 2×2 games or smaller. It turns out that we can solve larger games using linear programming and duality. We summarize the procedure, work through an example, and then discuss why it works.

Solving a Matrix Game

Step 1 Reduce the payoff matrix by dominance.

Step 2 Add a fixed number k to each of the entries so that they all become nonnegative and no column is all zero.

Step 3 Write 1s to the right of and below the matrix, and then write down the associated standard maximization problem. Solve this primal problem using the simplex method.

Step 4 Find the optimal strategies and the expected value as follows:

Column Strategy

1. Express the solution to the primal problem as a column vector.

2. Normalize by dividing each entry of the solution vector by p (which is also the sum of all the entries).

3. Insert zeros in positions corresponding to the columns deleted during reduction by dominance.

Row Strategy

1. Express the solution to the dual problem as a row vector.

2. Normalize by dividing each entry by p, which will once again be the sum of all the entries.

3. Insert zeros in positions corresponding to the rows deleted during reduction by dominance.

Value of the Game

$$e = \frac{1}{p} - k$$

EXAMPLE 3   **Restaurant Inspector**

You manage two restaurants, *Tender Steaks Inn* (TSI) and *Break for a Steak* (BFS). Even though you run the establishments impeccably, the Department of Health has been sending inspectors to your restaurants on a daily basis and fining you for minor infractions. You've found that you can head off a fine if you're present, but you can cover only one restaurant at a time. The Department of Health, on the other hand, has two inspectors, who sometimes visit the same restaurant and sometimes split up, one to each restaurant. The average fines you have been getting are shown in the following matrix:

		Both at BFS	Both at TSI	One at Each
		Health Inspectors		
You go to	TSI	$8,000	0	$2,000
	BFS	0	$10,000	$4,000

How should you choose which restaurant to visit to minimize your expected fine?

Solution This matrix is not quite the payoff matrix because fines, being penalties, should be negative payoffs. Thus, the payoff matrix is the following:

$$P = \begin{bmatrix} -8{,}000 & 0 & -2{,}000 \\ 0 & -10{,}000 & -4{,}000 \end{bmatrix}.$$

We follow the steps above to solve the game using the simplex method.

Step 1 There are no dominated rows or columns, so this game does not reduce.

Step 2 We add $k = 10{,}000$ to each entry so that none are negative, getting the following new matrix (with no zero column):

$$\begin{bmatrix} 2{,}000 & 10{,}000 & 8{,}000 \\ 10{,}000 & 0 & 6{,}000 \end{bmatrix}.$$

Step 3 We write 1s to the right and below this matrix:

$$\begin{bmatrix} 2{,}000 & 10{,}000 & 8{,}000 & 1 \\ 10{,}000 & 0 & 6{,}000 & 1 \\ 1 & 1 & 1 & 0 \end{bmatrix}.$$

The corresponding standard maximization problem is the following:

Maximize $p = x + y + z$
subject to $2{,}000x + 10{,}000y + 8{,}000z \le 1$
$10{,}000x + 6{,}000z \le 1$
$x \ge 0, y \ge 0, z \ge 0.$

Step 4 We use the simplex method to solve this problem. After pivoting twice, we arrive at the final tableau:

	x	y	z	s	t	p	
y	0	50,000	34,000	5	−1	0	4
x	10,000	0	6,000	0	1	0	1
p	0	0	14,000	5	4	50,000	9

Column Strategy The solution to the primal problem is

$$\begin{bmatrix} x \\ y \\ z \end{bmatrix} = \begin{bmatrix} \frac{1}{10{,}000} \\ \frac{4}{50{,}000} \\ 0 \end{bmatrix}.$$

We divide each entry by $p = 9/50{,}000$, which is also the sum of the entries. This gives the optimal column strategy:

$$C = \begin{bmatrix} \frac{5}{9} \\ \frac{4}{9} \\ 0 \end{bmatrix}.$$

Thus, the inspectors' optimal strategy is to stick together, visiting BFS with probability 5/9 and TSI with probability 4/9.

Row Strategy The solution to the dual problem is

$$\begin{bmatrix} s & t \end{bmatrix} = \begin{bmatrix} \frac{5}{50{,}000} & \frac{4}{50{,}000} \end{bmatrix}.$$

Once again, we divide by $p = 9/50,000$ to find the optimal row strategy:

$$R = \begin{bmatrix} \frac{5}{9} & \frac{4}{9} \end{bmatrix}.$$

Thus, you should visit TSI with probability 5/9 and BFS with probability 4/9.

Value of the Game Your expected average fine is

$$e = \frac{1}{p} - k = \frac{50,000}{9} - 10,000 = -\frac{40,000}{9} \approx -\$4,444.$$

➡ **Before we go on . . .** We owe you an explanation of why the procedure we used in Example 3 works. The main point is to understand how we turn a game into a linear programming problem. It's not hard to see that adding a fixed number k to all the payoffs will change only the payoff, increasing it by k, and will not change the optimal strategies. So let's pick up Example 3 from the point at which we were considering the following game:

$$P = \begin{bmatrix} 2,000 & 10,000 & 8,000 \\ 10,000 & 0 & 6,000 \end{bmatrix}.$$

We are looking for the optimal strategies R and C for the row and column players, respectively; if e is the value of the game, we will have $e = RPC$. Let's concentrate first on the column player's strategy $C = \begin{bmatrix} u & v & w \end{bmatrix}^T$, where u, v, and w are the unknowns we want to find. Because e is the value of the game, if the column player uses the optimal strategy C and the row player uses any old strategy S, the expected value with these strategies has to be e or better for the column player, so $SPC \le e$. Let's write that out for two particular choices of S. First, consider $S = \begin{bmatrix} 1 & 0 \end{bmatrix}$:

$$\begin{bmatrix} 1 & 0 \end{bmatrix} \begin{bmatrix} 2,000 & 10,000 & 8,000 \\ 10,000 & 0 & 6,000 \end{bmatrix} \begin{bmatrix} u \\ v \\ w \end{bmatrix} \le e.$$

Multiplied out, this gives

$$2,000u + 10,000v + 8,000w \le e.$$

Next, do the same thing for $S = \begin{bmatrix} 0 & 1 \end{bmatrix}$:

$$\begin{bmatrix} 0 & 1 \end{bmatrix} \begin{bmatrix} 2,000 & 10,000 & 8,000 \\ 10,000 & 0 & 6,000 \end{bmatrix} \begin{bmatrix} u \\ v \\ w \end{bmatrix} \le e$$

$$10,000u + 6,000w \le e.$$

It turns out that if these two inequalities are true, then $SPC \le e$ for any S at all, which is what the column player wants. These are starting to look like constraints in a linear programming problem, but the variable e appearing on the right is in the way. We get around this by dividing by e, which we know to be positive because all of the payoffs are nonnegative and no column is all zero (so the column player can't force the value of the game to be 0; here is where we need these assumptions). We get the following inequalities:

$$2,000\left(\frac{u}{e}\right) + 10,000\left(\frac{v}{e}\right) + 8,000\left(\frac{w}{e}\right) \le 1$$

$$10,000\left(\frac{u}{e}\right) \qquad\qquad + 6,000\left(\frac{w}{e}\right) \le 1.$$

Now we're getting somewhere. To make these look even more like linear constraints, we replace our unknowns u, v and w with new unknowns, $x = u/e$, $y = v/e$, and $z = w/e$. Our inequalities then become

$$2{,}000x + 10{,}000y + 8{,}000z \leq 1$$
$$10{,}000x \qquad\qquad + 6{,}000z \leq 1.$$

What about an objective function? From the point of view of the column player, the objective is to find a strategy that will minimize the expected value e. To write e in terms of our new variables x, y, and z, we use the fact that our original variables, being the entries in the column strategy, have to add up to 1: $u + v + w = 1$. Dividing by e gives

$$\frac{u}{e} + \frac{v}{e} + \frac{w}{e} = \frac{1}{e}$$

or

$$x + y + z = \frac{1}{e}.$$

Now we notice that, if we *maximize* $p = x + y + z = 1/e$, it will have the effect of minimizing e, which is what we want. So we get the following linear programming problem:

$$\text{Maximize} \quad p = x + y + z$$
$$\text{subject to} \quad 2{,}000x + 10{,}000y + 8{,}000z \leq 1$$
$$10{,}000x \qquad\qquad + 6{,}000z \leq 1$$
$$x \geq 0,\, y \geq 0,\, z \geq 0.$$

Why can we say that x, y, and z should all be nonnegative? Because the unknowns u, v, w, and e must all be nonnegative.

So now, if we solve this linear programming problem to find x, y, z, and p, we can find the column player's optimal strategy by computing $u = xe = x/p$, $v = y/p$, and $w = z/p$. Moreover, the value of the game is $e = 1/p$. (If we added k to all the payoffs, we should now adjust by subtracting k again to find the correct value of the game.)

Turning now to the row player's strategy, if we repeat the above type of argument from the row player's viewpoint, we'll end up with the following linear programming problem to solve:

$$\text{Minimize} \quad c = s + t$$
$$\text{subject to} \quad 2{,}000s + 10{,}000t \geq 1$$
$$10{,}000s \qquad\qquad \geq 1$$
$$8{,}000s + 6{,}000t \geq 1$$
$$s \geq 0,\, t \geq 0.$$

This is, of course, the dual to the problem we solved to find the column player's strategy, so we know that we can read its solution off of the same final tableau. The optimal value of c will be the same as the value of p, so $c = 1/e$ also. The entries in the optimal row strategy will be s/c and t/c. ∎

When to Use Duality

Q: *Given a minimization problem, when should I use duality, and when should I use the two-phase method in Section 6.4?*

A: If the original problem satisfies the nonnegative objective condition (none of the coefficients in the objective function are negative), then you can use duality to convert the problem to a standard maximization one, which can be solved with the one-phase method. If the original problem does not satisfy the nonnegative objective condition, then dualizing results in a nonstandard LP problem, so dualizing may not be worthwhile.

Q: *When is it absolutely necessary to use duality?*

A: Never. Duality gives us an efficient but not necessary alternative for solving standard minimization problems.

6.5 EXERCISES

▼ more advanced   ◆ challenging
T indicates exercises that should be solved using technology

In Exercises 1–8, write down (without solving) the dual LP problem. [**HINT**: See Quick Example 4.]

1. Maximize $p = 2x + y$
   subject to $x + 2y \le 6$
   $-x + y \le 2$
   $x \ge 0, y \ge 0.$

2. Maximize $p = x + 5y$
   subject to $x + y \le 6$
   $-x + 3y \le 4$
   $x \ge 0, y \ge 0.$

3. Minimize $c = 2s + t + 3u$
   subject to $s + t + u \ge 100$
   $2s + t \ge 50$
   $s \ge 0, t \ge 0, u \ge 0.$

4. Minimize $c = 2s + 2t + 3u$
   subject to $s + u \ge 100$
   $2s + t \ge 50$
   $s \ge 0, t \ge 0, u \ge 0.$

5. Maximize $p = x + y + z + w$
   subject to $x + y + z \le 3$
   $y + z + w \le 4$
   $x + z + w \le 5$
   $x + y + w \le 6$
   $x \ge 0, y \ge 0, z \ge 0, w \ge 0.$

6. Maximize $p = x + y + z + w$
   subject to $x + y + z \le 3$
   $y + z + w \le 3$
   $x + z + w \le 4$
   $x + y + w \le 4$
   $x \ge 0, y \ge 0, z \ge 0, w \ge 0.$

7. Minimize $c = s + 3t + u$
   subject to $5s - t + v \ge 1{,}000$
   $u - v \ge 2{,}000$
   $s + t \ge 500$
   $s \ge 0, t \ge 0, u \ge 0, v \ge 0.$

8. Minimize $c = 5s + 2u + v$
   subject to $s - t + 2v \ge 2{,}000$
   $u + v \ge 3{,}000$
   $s + t \ge 500$
   $s \ge 0, t \ge 0, u \ge 0, v \ge 0.$

In Exercises 9–22, solve the given standard minimization problem using duality. (You may already have seen some of these in earlier sections, but now you will be solving them using a different method.) [**HINT**: See Example 1.]

9. Minimize $c = s + t$
   subject to $s + 2t \ge 6$
   $2s + t \ge 6$
   $s \ge 0, t \ge 0.$

10. Minimize $c = s + 2t$

subject to $s + 3t \geq 30$

$2s + t \geq 30$

$s \geq 0, t \geq 0.$

11. Minimize $c = 6s + 6t$

subject to $s + 2t \geq 20$

$2s + t \geq 20$

$s \geq 0, t \geq 0.$

12. Minimize $c = 3s + 2t$

subject to $s + 2t \geq 20$

$2s + t \geq 10$

$s \geq 0, t \geq 0.$

13. Minimize $c = 0.2s + 0.3t$

subject to $2s + t \geq 10$

$s + 2t \geq 10$

$s + t \geq 8$

$s \geq 0, t \geq 0.$

14. Minimize $c = 0.4s + 0.1t$

subject to $3s + 2t \geq 60$

$s + 2t \geq 40$

$2s + 3t \geq 45$

$s \geq 0, t \geq 0.$

15. Minimize $c = 2s + t$

subject to $3s + t \geq 30$

$s + t \geq 20$

$s + 3t \geq 30$

$s \geq 0, t \geq 0.$

16. Minimize $c = s + 2t$

subject to $4s + t \geq 100$

$2s + t \geq 80$

$s + 3t \geq 150$

$s \geq 0, t \geq 0.$

17. Minimize $c = s + 2t + 3u$

subject to $3s + 2t + u \geq 60$

$2s + t + 3u \geq 60$

$s \geq 0, t \geq 0, u \geq 0.$

18. Minimize $c = s + t + 2u$

subject to $s + 2t + 2u \geq 60$

$2s + t + 3u \geq 60$

$s \geq 0, t \geq 0, u \geq 0.$

19. Minimize $c = 2s + t + 3u$

subject to $s + t + u \geq 100$

$2s + t \geq 50$

$t + u \geq 50$

$s \geq 0, t \geq 0, u \geq 0.$

20. Minimize $c = 2s + 2t + 3u$

subject to $s + u \geq 100$

$2s + t \geq 50$

$t + u \geq 50$

$s \geq 0, t \geq 0, u \geq 0.$

21. Minimize $c = s + t + u$

subject to $3s + 2t + u \geq 60$

$2s + t + 3u \geq 60$

$s + 3t + 2u \geq 60$

$s \geq 0, t \geq 0, u \geq 0.$

22. Minimize $c = s + t + 2u$

subject to $s + 2t + 2u \geq 60$

$2s + t + 3u \geq 60$

$s + 3t + 6u \geq 60$

$s \geq 0, t \geq 0, u \geq 0.$

In Exercises 23–28, solve the game with the given payoff matrix. [**HINT**: *See Example 3.*]

23. $P = \begin{bmatrix} -1 & 1 & 2 \\ 2 & -1 & -2 \end{bmatrix}$ **24.** $P = \begin{bmatrix} 1 & -1 & 2 \\ 1 & 2 & 0 \end{bmatrix}$

25. $P = \begin{bmatrix} -1 & 1 & 2 \\ 2 & -1 & -2 \\ 1 & 2 & 0 \end{bmatrix}$ **26.** $P = \begin{bmatrix} 1 & -1 & 2 \\ 1 & 2 & 0 \\ 0 & 1 & 1 \end{bmatrix}$

27. ⊤ $P = \begin{bmatrix} -1 & 1 & 2 & -1 \\ 2 & -1 & -2 & -3 \\ 1 & 2 & 0 & 1 \\ 0 & 2 & 3 & 3 \end{bmatrix}$

28. ⊤ $P = \begin{bmatrix} 1 & -1 & 2 & 0 \\ 1 & 2 & 0 & 1 \\ 0 & 1 & 1 & 0 \\ 2 & 0 & -2 & 2 \end{bmatrix}$

Applications

Many of Exercises 29–40 are similar or identical to ones in preceding exercise sets. Use duality to answer them.

29. *Nutrition* *Meow* makes cat food out of fish and cornmeal. Fish has 8 grams of protein and 4 grams of fat per ounce, and cornmeal has 4 grams of protein and 8 grams of fat. A jumbo can of cat food must contain at least 48 grams of protein and 48 grams of fat. If fish and cornmeal both cost

5¢ per ounce, how many ounces of each should Meow use in each can of cat food to minimize costs? What are the shadow costs of protein and of fat? [**HINT**: See Example 2.]

30. *Nutrition Oz* makes lion food out of giraffe and gazelle meat. Giraffe meat has 18 grams of protein and 36 grams of fat per pound, while gazelle meat has 36 grams of protein and 18 grams of fat per pound. A batch of lion food must contain at least 36,000 grams of protein and 54,000 grams of fat. Giraffe meat costs $2 per pound and gazelle meat costs $4 per pound. How many pounds of each should go into each batch of lion food to minimize costs? What are the shadow costs of protein and fat? [**HINT**: See Example 2.]

31. *Nutrition Ruff* makes dog food out of chicken and grain. Chicken has 10 grams of protein and 5 grams of fat per ounce, and grain has 2 grams of protein and 2 grams of fat per ounce. A bag of dog food must contain at least 200 grams of protein and at least 150 grams of fat. If chicken costs 10¢ per ounce and grain costs 1¢ per ounce, how many ounces of each should Ruff use in each bag of dog food to minimize cost? What are the shadow costs of protein and fat?

32. *Purchasing* The *Enormous State University*'s Business School is buying computers. The school has two models to choose from, the Pomegranate and the iZac. Each Pomegranate comes with 400 GB of memory and 80 TB of disk space, while each iZac has 300 GB of memory and 100 TB of disk space. For reasons related to its accreditation the school would like to be able to say that it has a total of at least 48,000 GB of memory and at least 12,800 TB of disk space. If both the Pomegranate and the iZac cost $2,000 each, how many of each should the school buy to keep the cost as low as possible? What are the shadow costs of memory and disk space?

33. *Nutrition* Gerber Products' Gerber Mixed Cereal for Baby contains, in each serving, 60 calories and no vitamin C. Each serving of Gerber Mango Tropical Fruit Dessert contains 80 calories and 45% of the U.S. Recommended Daily Allowance (RDA) of vitamin C for infants. Each serving of Gerber Apple Banana Juice contains 60 calories and 120% of the U.S. RDA of vitamin C for infants.[41] The cereal costs 10¢ per serving, the dessert costs 53¢ per serving, and the juice costs 27¢ per serving. If you want to provide your child with at least 120 calories and at least 120% of the U.S. RDA of vitamin C, how can you do so at the least cost? What are your shadow costs for calories and vitamin C?

34. *Nutrition* Gerber Products' Gerber Mixed Cereal for Baby contains, in each serving, 60 calories, no vitamin C, and 11 grams of carbohydrates. Each serving of Gerber Mango Tropical Fruit Dessert contains 80 calories, 45% of the U.S. Recommended Daily Allowance (RDA) of vitamin C for infants, and 21 grams of carbohydrates. Each serving of

Gerber Apple Banana Juice contains 60 calories, 120% of the U.S. RDA of vitamin C for infants, and 15 grams of carbohydrates.[42] Assume that the cereal costs 11¢ per serving, the dessert costs 50¢ per serving, and the juice costs 30¢ per serving. If you want to provide your child with at least 180 calories, at least 120% of the U.S. RDA of vitamin C, and at least 37 grams of carbohydrates, how can you do so at the least cost? What are your shadow costs for calories, vitamin C, and carbohydrates?

35. *Politics* The political pollster *Canter* is preparing for a national election. It would like to poll at least 1,500 Democrats and 1,500 Republicans. Each mailing to the East Coast gets responses from 100 Democrats and 50 Republicans. Each mailing to the Midwest gets responses from 100 Democrats and 100 Republicans. Each mailing to the West Coast gets responses from 50 Democrats and 100 Republicans. Mailings to the East Coast cost $40 each to produce and mail, mailings to the Midwest cost $60 each, and mailings to the West Coast cost $50 each. How many mailings should Canter send to each area of the country to get the responses it needs at the least possible cost? What will it cost? What are the shadow costs of a Democratic response and of a Republican response?

36. *Purchasing Bingo's Copy Center* needs to buy white paper and yellow paper. Bingo's can buy from three suppliers. *Harvard Paper* sells a package of 20 reams of white and 10 reams of yellow for $60; *Yale Paper* sells a package of 10 reams of white and 10 reams of yellow for $40, and *Dartmouth Paper* sells a package of 10 reams of white and 20 reams of yellow for $50. If Bingo's needs 350 reams of white and 400 reams of yellow, how many packages should it buy from each supplier to minimize the cost? What is the lowest possible cost? What are the shadow costs of white paper and yellow paper?

37. ▽ *Advertising* You are the marketing director for a company that manufactures bodybuilding supplements, and you are planning to run ads in Sports Illustrated and GQ Magazine. On the basis of readership data, you estimate that each ad in *Sports Illustrated* will be read by 600,000 people in your target group, while each ad in *GQ* will be read by 150,000.[43] You would like your ads to be read by at least 9 million people in the target group, and you plan to place at least 6 ads in *Sports Illustrated* and at least 8 ads in *GQ* during the next year. *Sports Illustrated* quotes you $2,000 per ad, while GQ quotes you $1,000 per ad. How many ads should be placed in each magazine to satisfy your requirements at a minimum cost?

---

[42] *Ibid.*

[43] The readership data for *Sports Illustrated* is roughly based on the results of a readership survey taken in March 2000. The readership data for *GQ* is fictitious. Source: Mediamark Research Inc./*New York Times*, May 29, 2000, p. C1.

[41] Source: Nutrition information supplied with the products.

38. ▼ *Advertising* You are the marketing director for a company that manufactures bodybuilding supplements, and you are planning to run ads in Sports Illustrated and Muscle and Fitness. On the basis of readership data, you estimate that each ad in *Sports Illustrated* will be read by 600,000 people in your target group, while each ad in *Muscle and Fitness* will be read by 300,000 people in your target group.[44] You would like your ads to be read by at least 9 million people in the target group, and you plan to place at least 3 ads in *Sports Illustrated* and at least 4 ads in *Muscle and Fitness* during the next year. *Sports Illustrated* quotes you $3,000 per ad, while *Muscle and Fitness* quotes you $2,000 per ad. How many ads should be placed in each magazine to satisfy your requirements at a minimum cost?

39. ▼ *Resource Allocation* One day, Gillian the Magician summoned the wisest of her women. "Devoted sisters of the Coven," she began, "I have a quandary: As you well know, I possess great expertise in sleep spells and shock spells, but unfortunately, these are proving to be a drain on my aural energy resources; each sleep spell costs me 50 therms of aural energy, while each shock spell requires 20 therms. Clearly, I would like to hold my overall expenditure of aural energy to a minimum and still meet my commitments in protecting the Sisterhood from the ever-present threat of trolls. Specifically, I have estimated that each sleep spell keeps us safe for an average of 1.5 hours, while every shock spell protects us for only one half hour. We certainly require enough protection to last 24 hours of each day and possibly more, just to be safe. At the same time, I have noticed that each of my sleep spells can immobilize 3 trolls at once, while one of my typical shock spells (having a narrower range) can immobilize only 2 trolls at once. We are faced, my sisters, with an onslaught of as many as 52 trolls per day! Finally, as you are no doubt aware, the Bylaws of the Coven dictate that for a magician to remain in good standing, she should cast at least as many shock spells as sleep spells. What do I do, oh Wise Ones?"

40. ▼ *Risk Management* The Grand Vizier of the Kingdom of Um is being blackmailed by numerous individuals and is having a very difficult time keeping his blackmailers from going public. He has been keeping them at bay with two kinds of payoff: gold from the Royal Treasury and political favors. Through bitter experience, he has learned that each gold payoff gives him peace for an average of about 1 month, and each political favor seems to earn him about a month and a half of reprieve. To maintain his flawless reputation in the court, he feels that he cannot afford any revelations about his tainted past to come to light within the next year. Thus, it is imperative that his blackmailers be kept at

bay for at least 12 months. Furthermore, he would like to keep the number of gold payoffs at no more than one quarter of the combined number of payoffs because the outward flow of gold bars might arouse suspicion on the part of the Royal Treasurer. The gold payoffs tend to deplete the Grand Vizier's travel budget. (The treasury has been subsidizing his numerous trips to the Himalayas.) He estimates that each gold bar removed from the treasury will cost him four trips. On the other hand, because the administering of political favors tends to cost him valuable travel time, he suspects that each political favor will cost him about two trips. Now, he would obviously like to keep his blackmailers silenced and lose as few trips as possible. What is he to do? How many trips will he lose in the next year?

41. ▼ *Game Theory: Politics* Incumbent Tax N. Spend and challenger Trick L. Down are running for county executive, and polls show them to be in a dead heat. The election hinges on three cities: Littleville, Metropolis, and Urbantown. The candidates have decided to spend the last weeks before the election campaigning in those three cities; each day each candidate will decide in which city to spend the day. Pollsters have determined the following payoff matrix, where the payoff represents the number of votes gained or lost for each 1-day campaign trip:

		T. N. Spend	
	Littleville	**Metropolis**	**Urbantown**
Littleville	−200	−300	300
Metropolis	−500	500	−100
Urbantown	−500	0	0

(T. L. Down labels the rows.)

What percentage of time should each candidate spend in each city to maximize votes gained? If both candidates use their optimal strategies, what is the expected vote?

42. ▼ *Game Theory: Marketing* Your company's new portable phone/music player/browser/bottle washer, the *Run-Man*, will compete against the established market leader, the *iNod*, in a saturated market. (Thus, for each device you sell, one fewer iNod is sold.) You are planning to launch the RunMan with a traveling road show, concentrating on two cities: New York and Boston. The makers of the iNod will do the same to try to maintain their sales. If, on a given day, you both go to New York, you will lose 1,000 units in sales to the iNod. If you both go to Boston, you will lose 750 units in sales. On the other hand, if you go to New York and your competitor to Boston, you will gain 1,500 units in sales from them. If you go to Boston and they to New York, you will gain 500 units in sales. What percentage of time should you spend in New York and what percentage in Boston, and how do you expect your sales to be affected?

43. ▼ *Game Theory: Morra Games* A three-finger Morra game is a game in which two players simultaneously show

[44] The readership data for both magazines are roughly based on the results of a readership survey taken in March 2000. Source: Mediamark Research Inc./*New York Times*, May 29, 2000, p. C1.

one, two, or three fingers at each round. The outcome depends on a predetermined set of rules. Here is an interesting example: If the numbers of fingers shown by A and B differ by 1, then A loses one point. If they differ by more than 1, the round is a draw. If they show the same number of fingers, A wins an amount equal to the sum of the fingers shown. Determine the optimal strategy for each player and the expected value of the game.

44. ▮ ▼ *Game Theory: Morra Games* Referring to Exercise 43, consider the following rules for a three-finger Morra game: If the sum of the fingers shown is odd, then A wins an amount equal to that sum. If the sum is even, B wins the sum. Determine the optimal strategy for each player and the expected value of the game. [HINT: Use technology to do the pivoting in the associated linear programming problem.]

45. ▮ ◆ *Game Theory: Military Strategy* Colonel Blotto is a well-known game in military strategy.[45] Here is a version of this game: Colonel Blotto has four regiments under his command, while his opponent, Captain Kije, has three. The armies are to try to occupy two locations, and each commander must decide how many regiments to send to each location. The army that sends more regiments to a location captures that location as well as the other army's regiments. If both armies send the same number of regiments to a location, then there is a draw. The payoffs are one point for each location captured and one point for each regiment captured. Find the optimum strategy for each commander and also the value of the game.

46. ▮ ◆ *Game Theory: Military Strategy* Referring to Exercise 45, consider the version of Colonel Blotto with the same payoffs given there except that Captain Kije earns two points for each location captured, while Colonel Blotto continues to earn only one point. Find the optimum strategy for each commander and also the value of the game. Round all figures to two decimal places.

---

[45] See Samuel Karlin, *Mathematical Methods and Theory in Games, Programming and Economics* (Addison-Wesley, 1959).

Communication and Reasoning Exercises

47. A minimization problem has three variables and two constraints (other than those of the form $s \geq 0$, $t \geq 0$, . . .). How many variables and constraints (other than those of the form $x \geq 0$, $y \geq 0$, . . .) does the dual problem have? Why?

48. A minimization problem has more constraints (other than those of the form $s \geq 0$, $t \geq 0$, . . .) than variables. What can you say about the dual problem? Why?

49. Give one possible advantage of using duality to solve a standard minimization problem.

50. To ensure that the dual of a minimization problem will result in a standard maximization problem,
   (A) the primal problem should satisfy the nonnegative objective condition.
   (B) the primal problem should be a standard minimization problem.
   (C) the primal problem should not satisfy the nonnegative objective condition.

51. Give an example of a standard minimization problem whose dual is *not* a standard maximization problem. How would you go about solving your problem?

52. Give an example of a nonstandard minimization problem whose dual is a standard maximization problem.

53. If the primal problem is a standard minimization problem not satisfying the nonnegative objective condition, what can you say about the dual problem? Why?

54. If the primal problem is a nonstandard maximization problem, what can you say about the objective function of the dual problem? Why?

55. ▼ Given a minimization problem, when would you solve it by applying the simplex method to its dual, and when would you apply the simplex method to the minimization problem itself?

56. ▼ Create an interesting application that leads to a standard maximization problem. Solve it using the simplex method, and note the solution to its dual problem. What does the solution to the dual tell you about your application?

KEY CONCEPTS

www.WanerMath.com
Go to the Website to find a comprehensive and interactive Web-based summary of Chapter 6.

6.1 Graphing Linear Inequalities
Inequalities, strict and nonstrict [p. 406]
Linear inequalities [p. 407]
Solution of an inequality [p. 408]
Sketching the region represented by a linear inequality in two variables [p. 409]
Bounded and unbounded regions [p. 412]
Feasible region [p. 413]

6.2 Solving Linear Programming Problems Graphically
Linear programming (LP) problem in two unknowns; objective function; constraints; feasible region; optimal value; optimal solution [p. 417]
Fundamental Theorem of Linear Programming [p. 418]

Graphical method for solving an LP problem [p. 419]
Decision variables [p. 420]
Graphical method for solving an LP problem with an unbounded feasible region [p. 423]

6.3 The Simplex Method: Solving Standard Maximization Problems
General linear programming problem in n unknowns [p. 435]
Standard maximization problem [p. 435]
Slack variable [p. 436]
Equation form of a standard maximization problem [p. 437]
Tableau [p. 438]
Active (or basic) variables; inactive (or nonbasic) variables; basic solution [p. 438]
Rules for selecting the pivot column [p. 439]
Rules for selecting the pivot; test ratios [p. 440]
Departing or exiting variable, entering variable [p. 441]

6.4 The Simplex Method: Solving General Linear Programming Problems
Surplus variable [p. 454]
Phase I and Phase II for solving general LP problems [p. 455]
Using the simplex method to solve a minimization problem [p. 459]

6.5 The Simplex Method and Duality
Standard minimization problem [p. 468]
Standard LP problem [p. 468]
Nonnegative objective condition [p. 468]
Dual LP problems; primal problem; dual problem [p. 470]
Fundamental Theorem of Duality [p. 470]
Shadow costs [p. 473]
Game theory: The LP problem associated with a two-person zero-sum game [p. 474]

REVIEW EXERCISES

In Exercises 1–4, sketch the region corresponding to the given inequalities, say whether it is bounded, and give the coordinates of all corner points.

1. $2x - 3y \leq 12$

2. $x \leq 2y$

3. $x + 2y \leq 20$
$3x + 2y \leq 30$
$x \geq 0, y \geq 0$

4. $3x + 2y \geq 6$
$2x - 3y \leq 6$
$3x - 2y \geq 0$
$x \geq 0, y \geq 0$

In Exercises 5–8, solve the given linear programming problem graphically.

5. Maximize $p = 2x + y$
subject to $3x + y \leq 30$
$x + y \leq 12$
$x + 3y \leq 30$
$x \geq 0, y \geq 0.$

6. Maximize $p = 2x + 3y$
subject to $x + y \geq 10$
$2x + y \geq 12$
$x + y \leq 20$
$x \geq 0, y \geq 0.$

7. Minimize $c = 2x + y$
subject to $3x + y \geq 30$
$x + 2y \geq 20$
$2x - y \geq 0$
$x \geq 0, y \geq 0.$

8. Minimize $c = 3x + y$
subject to $3x + 2y \geq 6$
$2x - 3y \leq 0$
$3x - 2y \geq 0$
$x \geq 0, y \geq 0.$

In Exercises 9–18, solve the given linear programming problem using the simplex method. If no optimal solution exists, indicate whether the feasible region is empty or the objective function is unbounded.

9. Maximize $p = x + y + 2z$
subject to $x + 2y + 2z \leq 60$
$2x + y + 3z \leq 60$
$x \geq 0, y \geq 0, z \geq 0.$

10. Maximize $p = x + y + 2z$
subject to $x + 2y + 2z \leq 60$
$2x + y + 3z \leq 60$
$x + 3y + 6z \leq 60$
$x \geq 0, y \geq 0, z \geq 0.$

11. Maximize $p = x + y + 3z$
subject to $x + y + z \geq 100$
$y + z \leq 80$
$x + z \leq 80$
$x \geq 0, y \geq 0, z \geq 0.$

12. Maximize $p = 2x + y$
   subject to $x + 2y \geq 12$
            $2x + y \leq 12$
            $x + y \leq 5$
            $x \geq 0, y \geq 0.$

13. Minimize $c = x + 2y + 3z$
   subject to $3x + 2y + z \geq 60$
            $2x + y + 3z \geq 60$
            $x \geq 0, y \geq 0, z \geq 0.$

14. Minimize $c = 5x + 4y + 3z$
   subject to $x + y + 4z \geq 30$
            $2x + y + 3z \geq 60$
            $x \geq 0, y \geq 0, z \geq 0.$

15. ⊤ Minimize $c = x - 2y + 4z$
   subject to $3x + 2y - z \geq 10$
            $2x + y + 3z \geq 20$
            $x + 3y - 2z \geq 30$
            $x \geq 0, y \geq 0, z \geq 0.$

16. ⊤ Minimize $c = x + y - z$
   subject to $3x + 2y + z \geq 60$
            $2x + y + 3z \geq 60$
            $x + 3y + 2z \geq 60$
            $x \geq 0, y \geq 0, z \geq 0.$

17. Minimize $c = x + y + z + w$
   subject to $x + y \geq 30$
            $x + z \geq 20$
            $x + y - w \leq 10$
            $y + z - w \leq 10$
            $x \geq 0, y \geq 0, z \geq 0, w \geq 0.$

18. Minimize $c = 4x + y + z + w$
   subject to $x + y \geq 30$
            $y - z \leq 20$
            $z - w \leq 10$
            $x \geq 0, y \geq 0, z \geq 0, w \geq 0.$

In Exercises 19–22, solve the given linear programming problem using duality.

19. Minimize $c = 2x + y$
   subject to $3x + 2y \geq 60$
            $2x + y \geq 60$
            $x + 3y \geq 60$
            $x \geq 0, y \geq 0.$

20. Minimize $c = 2x + y + 2z$
   subject to $3x + 2y + z \geq 100$
            $2x + y + 3z \geq 200$
            $x \geq 0, y \geq 0, z \geq 0.$

21. Minimize $c = 2x + y$
   subject to $3x + 2y \geq 10$
            $2x - y \leq 30$
            $x + 3y \geq 60$
            $x \geq 0, y \geq 0.$

22. Minimize $c = 2x + y + 2z$
   subject to $3x - 2y + z \geq 100$
            $2x + y - 3z \leq 200$
            $x \geq 0, y \geq 0, z \geq 0.$

In Exercises 23–26, solve the game with the given payoff matrix.

23. $P = \begin{bmatrix} -1 & 2 & -1 \\ 1 & -2 & 1 \\ 3 & -1 & 0 \end{bmatrix}$
  24. $P = \begin{bmatrix} -3 & 0 & 1 \\ -4 & 0 & 0 \\ 0 & -1 & -2 \end{bmatrix}$

25. $P = \begin{bmatrix} -3 & -2 & 3 \\ 1 & 0 & 0 \\ -2 & 2 & 1 \end{bmatrix}$
  26. $P = \begin{bmatrix} -4 & -2 & -3 \\ 1 & -3 & -2 \\ -3 & 1 & -4 \end{bmatrix}$

Exercises 27–30 are adapted from the Actuarial Exam on Operations Research.

27. You are given the following linear programming problem:

$$\text{Minimize} \quad c = x + 2y$$
$$\text{subject to} \quad -2x + y \geq 1$$
$$x - 2y \geq 1$$
$$x \geq 0, y \geq 0.$$

Which of the following is true?
(A) The problem has no feasible solutions.
(B) The objective function is unbounded.
(C) The problem has optimal solutions.

28. Repeat Exercise 27 with the following linear programming problem:

$$\text{Maximize} \quad p = x + y$$
$$\text{subject to} \quad -2x + y \leq 1$$
$$x - 2y \leq 2$$
$$x \geq 0, y \geq 0.$$

29. Determine the optimal value of the objective function. You are given the following linear programming problem.

$$\text{Maximize} \quad Z = x_1 + 4x_2 + 2x_3 - 10$$
$$\text{subject to} \quad 4x_1 + x_2 + x_3 \leq 45$$
$$-x_1 + x_2 + 2x_3 \leq 0$$
$$x_1, x_2, x_3 \geq 0.$$

30. Determine the optimal value of the objective function. You are given the following linear programming problem.

$$\text{Minimize} \quad Z = x_1 + 4x_2 + 2x_3 + x_4 + 40$$
$$\text{subject to} \quad 4x_1 + x_2 + x_3 \leq 45$$
$$-x_1 + 2x_2 + x_4 \geq 40$$
$$x_1, x_2, x_3 \geq 0.$$

Applications: OHaganBooks.com
[Try the game at www.OHaganBooks.com]

In Exercises 31–34, you are the buyer for OHaganBooks.com and are considering increasing stocks of romance and horror novels at the new OHaganBooks.com warehouse in Texas. You have offers from several publishers: Duffin House, Higgins Press, McPhearson Imprints, and O'Conell Books. Duffin offers a package of 5 horror novels and 5 romance novels for $50, Higgins offers a package of 5 horror and 10 romance novels for $80, McPhearson offers a package of 10 horror novels and 5 romance novels for $80, and O'Conell offers a package of 10 horror novels and 10 romance novels for $90.

31. How many packages should you purchase from Duffin House and Higgins Press to obtain at least 4,000 horror novels and 6,000 romance novels at minimum cost? What is the minimum cost?

32. How many packages should you purchase from McPhearson Imprints and O'Conell Books to obtain at least 5,000 horror novels and 4,000 romance novels at minimum cost? What is the minimum cost?

33. Refer to the scenario in Exercise 31. As it turns out, John O'Hagan promised Marjory Duffin that OHaganBooks .com would buy at least 20% more packages from Duffin as from Higgins, but you still want to obtain at least 4,000 horror novels and 6,000 romance novels at minimum cost.

a. Referring to your solution of Exercise 31, say which of the following statements are possible *without solving the problem*:
  (A) The cost will stay the same.
  (B) The cost will increase.
  (C) The cost will decrease.
  (D) It will be impossible to meet all the conditions.
  (E) The cost will become unbounded.

b. If you wish to meet all the requirements at minimum cost, how many packages should you purchase from each publisher? What is the minimum cost?

34. Refer to Exercise 32. You are about to place the order meeting the requirements of Exercise 32 when you are told that you can order no more than a total of 500 packages and that at least half of the packages should be from McPhearson. Explain why this is impossible by referring to the feasible region for Exercise 32.

35. *Investments* Marjory Duffin's portfolio manager has suggested two high-yielding stocks: European Emerald Emporium (EEE) and Royal Ruby Retailers (RRR).[46] EEE shares cost $50, yield 4.5% in dividends, and have a risk index of 2.0 per share. RRR shares cost $55, yield 5% in dividends, and have a risk index of 3.0 per share. Marjory has up to $12,100 to invest and would like to earn at least $550 in

dividends. How many shares of each stock should she purchase to meet her requirements and minimize the total risk index for her portfolio? What is the minimum total risk index?

36. *Investments* Marjory Duffin's other portfolio manager has suggested another two high-yielding stocks: Countrynarrow Mortgages (CNM) and Scotland Subprime (SS).[47] CNM shares cost $40, yield 5.5% in dividends, and have a risk index of 1.0 per share. SS shares cost $25, yield 7.5% in dividends, and have a risk index of 1.5 per share. Marjory can invest up to $30,000 in these stocks and would like to earn at least $1,650 in dividends. How many shares of each stock should she purchase to meet her requirements and minimize the total risk index for her portfolio?

37. *Resource Allocation* Billy-Sean O'Hagan has joined the Physics Society at *Suburban State University*, and the group is planning to raise money to support the dying space program by making and selling umbrellas. The society intends to make three models: the Sprinkle, the Storm, and the Hurricane. The amounts of cloth, metal, and wood used in making each model are given in this table:

	Sprinkle	Storm	Hurricane	Total Available
Cloth (square yards)	1	2	2	600
Metal (pounds)	2	1	3	600
Wood (pounds)	1	3	6	600
Profit ($)	1	1	2	

The table also shows the amounts of each material available in a given day and the profits to be made from each model. How many of each model should the society make to maximize its profit?

38. *Profit* *Duffin House*, which is now the largest publisher of books sold at the OHaganBooks.com site, prints three kinds of books: paperback, quality paperback, and hardcover. The amounts of paper, ink, and time on the presses required for each kind of book are given in this table:

	Paperback	Quality Paperback	Hardcover	Total Available
Paper (pounds)	3	2	1	6,000
Ink (gallons)	2	1	3	6,000
Time (minutes)	10	10	10	22,000
Profit ($)	1	2	3	

The table also lists the total amounts of paper, ink, and time available in a given day and the profits made on each kind

[46] RRR and EEE happen to be, respectively, the ticker symbols of RSC Holdings (an equipment rental provider) and Evergreen Energy Inc. (an environmentally friendly energy technology company) and thus have nothing to do with rubies and emeralds.

[47] CNM is actually the ticker symbol of Carnegie Wave, whereas SS is not the ticker symbol of any U.S.-based company we are aware of.

of book. How many of each kind of book should Duffin print to maximize profit?

39. *Purchases* You are just about to place book orders from *Duffin House* and *Higgins Press* (see Exercise 31) when everything changes: Duffin House informs you that, because of a global romance crisis, its packages now each will contain 5 horror novels but only 2 romance novels and still cost $50 per package. Packages from Higgins Press will now contain 10 of each type of novel, but now cost $150 per package. *Ewing Books* enters the fray and offers its own package of 5 horror and 5 romance novels for $100. The sales manager now tells you that at least 50% of the packages must come from Higgins Press, and, as before, you want to obtain at least 4,000 horror novels and 6,000 romance novels at minimum cost. Taking all of this into account, how many packages should you purchase from each publisher? What is the minimum cost?

40. *Purchases* You are about to place book orders from *McPhearson Imprints* and *O'Conell Books* (see Exercise 32) when you get an e-mail from McPhearson Imprints saying sorry, but they have stopped publishing romance novels because of the global romance crisis and can now offer only packages of 10 horror novels for $50. O'Conell is still offering packages of 10 horror novels and 10 romance novels for $90, and now the U.S. Treasury, in an attempt to bolster the floundering romance industry, is offering its own package of 20 romance novels for $120. Furthermore, Congress, in approving this measure, has passed legislation dictating that at least two thirds of the packages in every order must come from the U.S. Treasury. As before, you wish to obtain at least 5,000 horror novels and 4,000 romance novels at minimum cost. Taking all of this into account, how many packages should you purchase from each supplier? What is the minimum cost?

41. *Degree Requirements* During his lunch break, John O'Hagan decides to devote some time to assisting his son Billy-Sean, who continues to have a terrible time planning his college course schedule. The latest *Bulletin of Suburban State University* claims to have added new flexibility to its course requirements, but it remains as complicated as ever. It reads as follows:

> *All candidates for the degree of Bachelor of Arts at SSU must take at least 120 credits from the Sciences, Fine Arts, Liberal Arts, and Mathematics combined, including at least as many Science credits as Fine Arts credits, and at most twice as many Mathematics credits as Science credits, but with Liberal Arts credits exceeding Mathematics credits by no more than one third of the number of Fine Arts credits.*

Science and fine arts credits cost $300 each, and liberal arts and mathematics credits cost $200 each. John would like to have Billy-Sean meet all the requirements at a minimum total cost.

a. Set up (without solving) the associated linear programming problem.

b. ⊤ Use technology to determine how many of each type of credit Billy-Sean should take. What will the total cost be?

42. *Degree Requirements* No sooner had the "new and flexible" course requirement been released than the English Department again pressured the University Senate to include their vaunted "Verbal Expression" component in place of the fine arts requirement in all programs (including the sciences):

> *All candidates for the degree of Bachelor of Science at SSU must take at least 120 credits from the Liberal Arts, Sciences, Verbal Expression, and Mathematics, including at most as many Science credits as Liberal Arts credits, and at least twice as many Verbal Expression credits as Science credits and Liberal Arts credits combined, with Liberal Arts credits exceeding Mathematics credits by at least a quarter of the number of Verbal Expression credits.*

Science credits cost $300 each, while each credit in the remaining subjects now costs $400. John would like to have Billy-Sean meet all the requirements at a minimum total cost.

a. Set up (without solving) the associated linear programming problem.

b. ⊤ Use technology to determine how many of each type of credit Billy-Sean should take. What will the total cost be?

43. *Shipping* On the same day that the sales department at *Duffin House* received an order for 600 packages from the OHaganBooks.com Texas headquarters, it received an additional order for 200 packages from FantasyBooks.com, based in California. Duffin House has warehouses in New York and Illinois. The New York warehouse has 600 packages in stock, but the Illinois warehouse is closing down and has only 300 packages in stock. Shipping costs per package of books are as follows: New York to Texas: $20; New York to California: $50; Illinois to Texas: $30; Illinois to California: $40. What is the lowest total shipping cost for which Duffin House can fill the orders? How many packages should be sent from each warehouse to each online bookstore at a minimum shipping cost?

44. *Transportation Scheduling* *Duffin House* is about to start a promotional blitz for its new book, *Advanced String Theory for the Liberal Arts*. The company has 25 salespeople stationed in Austin and 10 in San Diego, and would like to fly at least 15 to sales fairs in each of Houston and Cleveland. A round-trip plane flight from Austin to Houston costs $200; from Austin to Cleveland costs $150; from San Diego to Houston costs $400; and from San Diego to Cleveland costs $200. How many salespeople should the company fly from each of Austin and San Diego to each of Houston and Cleveland for the lowest total cost in airfare?

45. **Marketing** Marjory Duffin, head of *Duffin House*, reveals to John O'Hagan that FantasyBooks.com is considering several promotional schemes: It may offer two books for the price of one, three books for the price of two, or possibly a free copy of *Brain Surgery for Klutzes* with each order. OHaganBooks.com's marketing advisers Floody and O'Lara seem to have different ideas as to how to respond. Floody suggests offering *three* books for the price of one, while O'Lara suggests instead offering a free copy of the *Finite Mathematics Student Solutions Manual* with every purchase. After a careful analysis, O'Hagan comes up with the following payoff matrix, where the payoffs represent the number of customers, in thousands, O'Hagan expects to gain from FantasyBooks.com:

| | | FantasyBooks | | | |
		No Promo	2 for Price of 1	3 for Price of 2	Brain Surgery
OHagan	No Promo	0	−60	−40	10
	3 for Price of 1	30	20	10	15
	Finite Math	20	0	15	10

Find the optimal strategies for both companies and the expected shift in customers.

46. **Study Techniques** Billy-Sean's friend Pat from college has been spending all of his time in fraternity activities and therefore knows absolutely nothing about any of the three topics on tomorrow's math test. He has turned to Billy-Sean for advice as to how to spend his all-nighter. The table below shows the scores Pat could expect to earn if the entire test were to be in a specific subject. (Because he knows no linear programming or matrix algebra, the table shows, for instance, that studying game theory all night will not be much use in preparing him for this topic.)

| | | Test | | |
		Game Theory	Linear Programming	Matrix Algebra
Pat's Strategies	Study Game Theory	30	0	20
	Study Linear Programming	0	70	0
	Study Matrix Algebra	0	0	70

What percentage of the night should Pat spend on each topic, assuming the principles of game theory, and what score can he expect to get?

CASE STUDY

The Diet Problem

The *Galaxy Nutrition* health-food mega-store chain provides free online nutritional advice and support to its customers. As website technical consultant, you are planning to construct an interactive web page to assist customers in preparing a diet tailored to their nutritional and budgetary requirements. Ideally, the customer would select foods to consider and specify nutritional and/or budgetary constraints, and the tool should return the optimal diet meeting those requirements. You would also like the web page to allow the customer to decide whether, for instance, to find the cheapest possible diet meeting the requirements, the diet with the lowest number of calories, or the diet with the least total carbohydrates.

After doing a little research, you notice that the kind of problem you are trying to solve is quite well known and referred to as the *diet problem*, and that solving the diet problem is a famous example of linear programming. Indeed, there are already some online pages that solve versions of the problem that minimize total cost, so you have adequate information to assist you as you plan the page.*

You decide to start on a relatively small scale with a program that uses a list of 10 foods and minimizes either total caloric intake or total cost and satisfies a small list of requirements. Following is a small part of a table of nutritional information from the demo at the NEOS Wiki (all the values shown are for a single serving) as well as approximate minimum daily requirements:

* See, for instance, the Diet Problem Solver at the NEOS Guide: www.neos-guide.org/content/diet-problem-solver.

	Price per Serving	Calories	Total Fat (grams)	Carbs (grams)	Dietary Fiber (grams)	Protein (grams)	Vit C (IU)
Tofu	$0.31	88.2	5.5	2.2	1.4	9.4	0.1
Roast Chicken	$0.84	277.4	10.8	0	0	42.2	0
Spaghetti with Sauce	$0.78	358.2	12.3	58.3	11.6	8.2	27.9
Tomato	$0.27	25.8	0.4	5.7	1.4	1.0	23.5
Oranges	$0.15	61.6	0.2	15.4	3.1	1.2	69.7
Wheat Bread	$0.05	65.0	1.0	12.4	1.3	2.2	0
Cheddar Cheese	$0.25	112.7	9.3	0.4	0	7.0	0
Oatmeal	$0.82	145.1	2.3	25.3	4.0	6.1	0
Peanut Butter	$0.07	188.5	16.0	6.9	2.1	7.7	0
White Tuna in Water	$0.69	115.6	2.1	0	0	22.7	0
Minimum Requirements		2,200	20	80	25	60	90

Source: www.neos-guide.org/content/diet-problem-solver.

Now you get to work. As always, you start by identifying the unknowns. Since the output of the web page will consist of a recommended diet, the unknowns should logically be the number of servings of each item of food selected by the user. In your first trial run, you decide to include all the 10 food items listed, so you take

x_1 = Number of servings of tofu

x_2 = Number of servings of roast chicken

$\vdots$

x_{10} = Number of servings of white tuna in water.

You now set up a linear programming problem for two sample scenarios.

Scenario 1 (Minimum Cost): Satisfy all minimum nutritional requirements at a minimum cost. Here the linear programming problem is

Minimize

$$c = 0.31x_1 + 0.84x_2 + 0.78x_3 + 0.27x_4 + 0.15x_5 + 0.05x_6 + 0.25x_7$$
$$+ 0.82x_8 + 0.07x_9 + 0.69x_{10}$$

subject to

$$88.2x_1 + 277.4x_2 + 358.2x_3 + 25.8x_4 + 61.6x_5 + 65x_6 + 112.7x_7$$
$$+ 145.1x_8 + 188.5x_9 + 115.6x_{10} \geq 2{,}200$$

$$5.5x_1 + 10.8x_2 + 12.3x_3 + 0.4x_4 + 0.2x_5 + 1x_6 + 9.3x_7 + 2.3x_8$$
$$+ 16x_9 + 2.1x_{10} \geq 20$$

$$2.2x_1 + 58.3x_3 + 5.7x_4 + 15.4x_5 + 12.4x_6 + 0.4x_7 + 25.3x_8 + 6.9x_9 \geq 80$$

$$1.4x_1 + 11.6x_3 + 1.4x_4 + 3.1x_5 + 1.3x_6 + 4x_8 + 2.1x_9 \geq 25$$

$$9.4x_1 + 42.2x_2 + 8.2x_3 + 1x_4 + 1.2x_5 + 2.2x_6 + 7x_7 + 6.1x_8 + 7.7x_9$$
$$+ 22.7x_{10} \geq 60$$

$$0.1x_1 + 27.9x_3 + 23.5x_4 + 69.7x_5 \geq 90.$$

This is clearly the kind of linear programming problem no one in their right mind would like to do by hand (solving it requires 16 tableaus!), so you decide to use the online simplex method tool at the Website (Website → Online Utilities → Simplex Method Tool).

Here is a picture of the input, entered almost exactly as written above. You need to enter each constraint on a new line, and

$$\text{Minimize } c = 0.31x1 + \ldots \text{ Subject to}$$

must be typed on a single line.

```
Type your linear programming problem below. (Press "Example" to see how to set it up.)
Minimize   c =
0.31x1+0.84x2+0.78x3+0.27x4+0.15x5+0.05x6+0.25x7+0.82x8+0.07x9+0.69x10 Subject to
88.2x1+277.4x2+358.2x3+25.8x4+61.6x5+65x6+112.7x7+145.1x8+188.5x9+115.6x10 >= 2200
5.5x1+10.8x2+12.3x3+0.4x4+0.2x5+1x6+9.3x7+2.3x8+16x9+2.1x10 >= 20
2.2x1+58.3x3+5.7x4+15.4x5+12.4x6+0.4x7+25.3x8+6.9x9 >= 80
1.4x1+11.6x3+1.4x4+3.1x5+1.3x6+4x8+2.1x9 >= 25
9.4x1+42.2x2+8.2x3+1x4+1.2x5+2.2x6+7x7+6.1x8+7.7x9+22.7x10 >= 60
0.1x1+0x2+27.9x3+23.5x4+69.7x5 >= 90
```

Clicking "Solve" results in the following solution:

$$c = 0.981126; \quad x_1 = 0, \quad x_2 = 0, \quad x_3 = 0, \quad x_4 = 0, \quad x_5 = 1.29125,$$
$$x_6 = 0, \quad x_7 = 0, \quad x_8 = 0, \quad x_9 = 11.2491, \quad x_{10} = 0.$$

This means that you can satisfy all the daily requirements for less than $1 on a diet of 1.3 servings of oranges and 11.2 servings of peanut butter. Although you enjoy peanut butter, 11.2 servings seems a little over the top, so you modify the LP problem by adding a new constraint (which also suggests to you that some kind of flexibility needs to be built into the site to allow users to set limits on the number of servings of any one item):

$$x_9 \leq 3.$$

This new constraint results in the following solution:

$$c = 1.59981; \quad x_1 = 0, \quad x_2 = 0, \quad x_3 = 0, \quad x_4 = 0, \quad x_5 = 1.29125,$$
$$x_6 = 23.9224, \quad x_7 = 0, \quad x_8 = 0, \quad x_9 = 3, \quad x_{10} = 0.$$

Because wheat bread is cheap and, in large enough quantities, supplies ample protein, the program has now substituted 23.9 servings of wheat bread for the missing peanut butter for a total cost of $1.60.

Unfettered, you now add

$$x_6 \leq 4$$

and obtain the following spaghetti, bread, and peanut butter diet for $3.40 per day:

$$c = 3.40305; \quad x_1 = 0, \quad x_2 = 0, \quad x_3 = 3.83724, \quad x_4 = 0, \quad x_5 = 0,$$
$$x_6 = 4, \quad x_7 = 0, \quad x_8 = 0, \quad x_9 = 3, \quad x_{10} = 0.$$

Scenario 2 (Minimum Calories): Minimize total calories and satisfy all minimum nutritional requirements (except for caloric intake).

Here, the linear programming problem is

Minimize

$$c = 88.2x_1 + 277.4x_2 + 358.2x_3 + 25.8x_4 + 61.6x_5 + 65x_6 + 112.7x_7$$
$$+ 145.1x_8 + 188.5x_9 + 115.6x_{10}$$

subject to

$$5.5x_1 + 10.8x_2 + 12.3x_3 + 0.4x_4 + 0.2x_5 + 1x_6 + 9.3x_7 + 2.3x_8 + 16x_9$$
$$+ 2.1x_{10} \geq 20$$
$$2.2x_1 + 58.3x_3 + 5.7x_4 + 15.4x_5 + 12.4x_6 + 0.4x_7 + 25.3x_8 + 6.9x_9 \geq 80$$
$$1.4x_1 + 11.6x_3 + 1.4x_4 + 3.1x_5 + 1.3x_6 + 4x_8 + 2.1x_9 \geq 25$$
$$9.4x_1 + 42.2x_2 + 8.2x_3 + 1x_4 + 1.2x_5 + 2.2x_6 + 7x_7 + 6.1x_8 + 7.7x_9$$
$$+ 22.7x_{10} \geq 60$$
$$0.1x_1 + 27.9x_3 + 23.5x_4 + 69.7x_5 \geq 90.$$

You obtain the following 716-calorie tofu, tomato, and tuna diet:

$$x_1 = 2.07232, \quad x_2 = 0, \quad x_3 = 0, \quad x_4 = 15.7848, \quad x_5 = 0, \quad x_6 = 0,$$
$$x_7 = 0, \quad x_8 = 0, \quad x_9 = 0, \quad x_{10} = 1.08966.$$

As 16 servings of tomatoes seems a little over the top, you add the new constraint $x_4 \leq 3$ and obtain a 783-calorie tofu, tomato, orange, and tuna diet:

$$x_1 = 2.81682, \quad x_2 = 0, \quad x_3 = 0, \quad x_4 = 3, \quad x_5 = 5.43756, \quad x_6 = 0,$$
$$x_7 = 0, \quad x_8 = 0, \quad x_9 = 0, \quad x_{10} = 1.05713.$$

What the trial runs have shown you is that your website will need to allow the user to set reasonable upper bounds for the number of servings of each kind of food considered. You now get to work writing the algorithm, which appears here:

Website → Online Utilities → Diet Problem Solver

EXERCISES

1. Briefly explain why roast chicken, which supplies protein more cheaply than either tofu or tuna, does not appear in the optimal solution in either scenario.

2. Consider the optimal solution obtained in Scenario 1 when peanut butter and bread were restricted. Experiment on the Simplex Method Tool by increasing the protein requirement 10 grams at a time until chicken appears in the optimal diet. At what level of protein does the addition of chicken first become necessary?

3. What constraints would you add for a person who wants to eat at most two servings of chicken a day and is allergic to tomatoes and peanut butter? What is the resulting diet for Scenario 2?

4. What is the linear programming problem for someone who wants as much protein as possible at a cost of no more than $6 per day with no more than 50 grams of carbohydrates per day, assuming that they want to satisfy the minimum requirements for all the remaining nutrients? What is the resulting diet?

5. Is it possible to obtain a diet with no bread or peanut butter in Scenario 1 costing less than $4 per day?

Section 6.1

Some calculators, including the TI-83/84 Plus, will shade one side of a graph, but you need to tell the calculator which side to shade. For instance, to obtain the solution set of $2x + 3y \leq 6$ shown in Figure 4:

1. Solve the corresponding equation $2x + 3y = 6$ for y, and use the input shown below:

```
Plot1 Plot2 Plot3
▼Y₁◼-(2/3)*X+2
\Y₂=
\Y₃=
\Y₄=
\Y₅=
\Y₆=
\Y₇=
```

2. The icon to the left of "Y_1" tells the calculator to shade above the line. You can cycle through the various shading options by positioning the cursor to the left of Y_1 and pressing [ENTER] until you see the one you want. Here's what the graph will look like:

Section 6.3

Example 3 (page 444) The *Acme Baby Foods* example in the text leads to the following linear programming problem:

$$\text{Maximize} \quad p = 10x + 7y$$
$$\text{subject to} \quad x \leq 600$$
$$2x + 3y \leq 3{,}600$$
$$5x + 3y \leq 4{,}500$$
$$x \geq 0, y \geq 0.$$

Solve it using technology.

Solution

When we introduce slack variables, we get the following system of equations:

$$
\begin{aligned}
x \qquad\quad + s \qquad\qquad\quad &= 600 \\
2x + 3y \qquad + t \qquad\quad &= 3{,}600 \\
5x + 3y \qquad\qquad + u \quad &= 4{,}500 \\
-10x - 7y \qquad\qquad\quad + p &= 0.
\end{aligned}
$$

We use the PIVOT program for the TI-83/84 Plus to help with the simplex method. This program is available at the Website by following

Everything → Math Tools for Chapter 6.

Because the calculator handles decimals as easily as integers, there is no need to avoid them, except perhaps to save limited screen space. If we don't need to avoid decimals, we can use the traditional Gauss-Jordan method (see the discussion at the end of Section 4.2): After selecting your pivot and before clearing the pivot column, *divide the pivot row by the value of the pivot, thereby turning the pivot into a 1.*

The main drawback to using the TI-83/84 Plus is that we can't label the rows and columns. We can mentally label them as we go, but we can do without labels entirely if we wish. We begin by entering the initial tableau as the matrix [A]. (Another drawback to using the TI-83/84 Plus is that it can't show the whole tableau at once. Here and below, we show tableaux across several screens. Use the TI-83/84 Plus's arrow keys to scroll a matrix left and right so you can see all of it.)

The following is the sequence of tableaux we get while using the simplex method with the help of the PIVOT program:

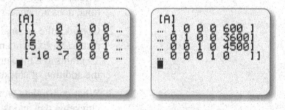

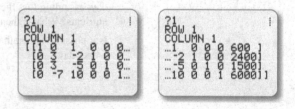

After determining that the next pivot is in the third row and second column, we divide the third row by the pivot, 3, and then pivot:

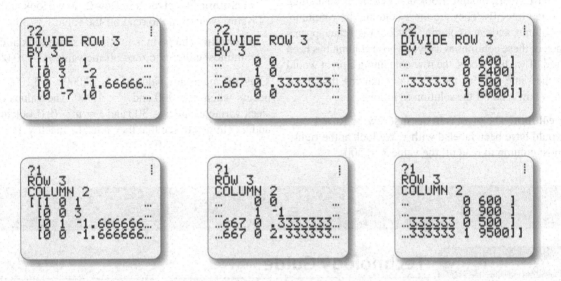

The next pivot is the 3 in the second row, third column. We divide its row by 3 and pivot:

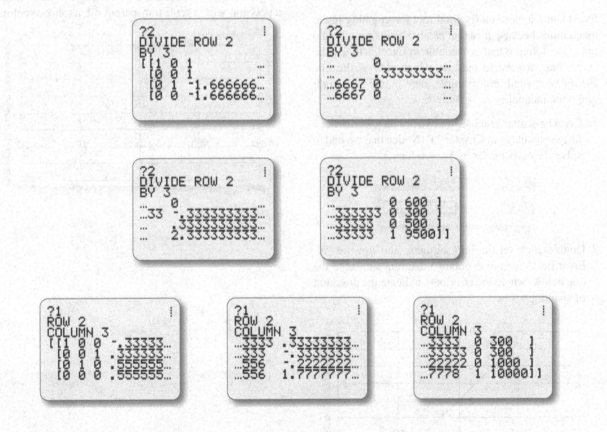

There are no negative numbers in the bottom row, so we're finished. How do we read off the optimal solutions if we don't have labels, though? Look at the columns containing one 1 and three 0s. They are the x column, the y column, the s column, and the p column. Think of the 1 that appears in each of these columns as a pivot whose column has been cleared. If we had labels, the row containing a pivot would have the same label as the column containing that pivot. We can now read off the solution as follows:

x column: The pivot is in the first row, so Row 1 would have been labeled with x. We look at the rightmost column to read off the value $x = 300$.

y column: The pivot is in Row 3, so we look at the rightmost column to read off the value $y = 1,000$.

s column: The pivot is in Row 2, so we look at the rightmost column to read off the value $s = 300$.

p column: The pivot is in Row 3, so we look at the rightmost column to read off the value $p = 10,000$.

Thus, the maximum value of p is $10,000¢ = \$100$, which occurs when $x = 300$ and $y = 1,000$. The values of the slack variables are $s = 300$ and $t = u = 0$. (Look at the t and u columns to see that they must be inactive.)

Spreadsheet Technology Guide

Section 6.1

Excel is not a particularly good tool for graphing linear inequalities because it cannot easily shade one side of a line. One solution that is available in Excel is to use the "error bar" feature to indicate which side of the line *should* be shaded. For example, here is how we might graph the inequality $2x + 3y \leq 6$.

1. Create a scatter graph using two points to construct a line segment (as in Chapter 1). (Notice that we had to solve the equation $2x + 3y = 6$ for y.)

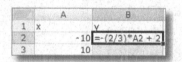

2. Double-click on the line segment, and use the "X-Error Bars" feature to obtain a diagram similar to the one below, where the error bars indicate the direction of shading.

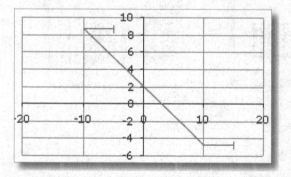

Alternatively, you can use the Drawing Palette to create a polygon with a semi-transparent fill, as shown below.

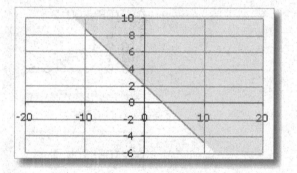

7

SETS AND COUNTING

CASE STUDY

Designing a Puzzle

As Product Design Manager for *Cerebral Toys, Inc.*, you are constantly on the lookout for ideas for intellectually stimulating yet inexpensive toys. Your design team recently came up with an idea for a puzzle consisting of a number of plastic cubes. Each cube will have two faces colored red, two colored white, and two colored blue, and there will be exactly two cubes with each possible configuration of colors. The goal of the puzzle is to seek out the matching pairs, thereby enhancing a child's geometric intuition and three-dimensional manipulation skills.

If the kit is to include every possible configuration of colors, how many cubes will the kit contain?

Image Source/Getty Images

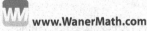

www.WanerMath.com

At the Website, in addition to the resources listed in the Preface, you will find:

- A utility to compute factorials, permutations, and combinations

Introduction

The theory of sets is the foundation for most of mathematics. It also has direct applications—for example, in searching computer databases. We will use set theory extensively in the chapter on probability, so much of this chapter revolves around the idea of a **set of outcomes** of a procedure such as rolling a pair of dice or choosing names from a database. Also important in probability is the theory of **counting** the number of elements in a set, which is called **combinatorics**.

Counting elements is not a trivial proposition; for example, the betting game Lotto (used in many state lotteries) has you pick six numbers from some range—say, 1–55. If your six numbers match the six numbers chosen in the official drawing, you win the top prize. How many Lotto tickets would you need to buy to guarantee that you will win? That is, how many Lotto tickets are possible? By the end of this chapter we will be able to answer these questions.

7.1   Sets and Set Operations

In this section we introduce some of the basic ideas of set theory. Some of the examples and applications we see here are derived from the theory of probability and will recur throughout the rest of this chapter and the next.

Sets

Visualizing a Set

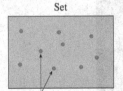

Set

Elements of the set

Sets and Elements

A **set** is a collection of items, referred to as the **elements** of the set.

We usually use a capital letter to name a set and braces to enclose the elements of a set.

$x \in A$ means that x **is an element of** the set A. If x is not an element of A, we write $x \notin A$.

$B = A$ means that A and B have the same elements. The order in which the elements are listed does not matter.

$B \subseteq A$ means that B is a **subset** of A; every element of B is also an element of A.

$B \subset A$ means that B is a **proper subset** of A: $B \subseteq A$, but $B \neq A$.

$\varnothing$ is the **empty set**, the set containing no elements. It is a subset of every set.

A **finite** set has finitely many elements. An **infinite** set does not have finitely many elements.

Quick Examples

$W = \{\text{Amazon, eBay, Apple}\}$
$N = \{1, 2, 3, \ldots\}$

Amazon $\in W$ (W as above)
Microsoft $\notin W$ $2 \in N$

$\{5, -9, 1, 3\} = \{-9, 1, 3, 5\}$
$\{1, 2, 3, 4\} \neq \{1, 2, 3, 6\}$

$\{\text{eBay, Apple}\} \subseteq W$
$\{1, 2, 3, 4\} \subseteq \{1, 2, 3, 4\}$

$\{\text{eBay, Apple}\} \subset W$
$\{1, 2, 3\} \subset \{1, 2, 3, 4\}$
$\{1, 2, 3\} \subset N$ (N as above)

$\varnothing \subseteq W$
$\varnothing \subset W$

$W = \{\text{Amazon, eBay, Apple}\}$
is a finite set.
$N = \{1, 2, 3, \ldots\}$ is an
infinite set.

One type of set we'll use often is the **set of outcomes** of some activity or experiment. For example, if we toss a coin and observe which side faces up, there are two possible outcomes: heads (H) and tails (T). The set of outcomes of tossing a coin once can be written

$$S = \{H, T\}.$$

As another example, suppose we roll a die that has faces numbered 1 through 6, as usual, and observe which number faces up. The set of outcomes *could* be represented as

However, we can much more easily write

$$S = \{1, 2, 3, 4, 5, 6\}.$$

EXAMPLE 1   **Two Dice: Distinguishable versus Indistinguishable**

a. Suppose we have two dice that we can distinguish in some way—say, one is green and one is red. If we roll both dice, what is the set of outcomes?

b. Describe the set of outcomes if the dice are indistinguishable.

Solution

a. A systematic way of laying out the set of outcomes for a distinguishable pair of dice is shown in Figure 1.

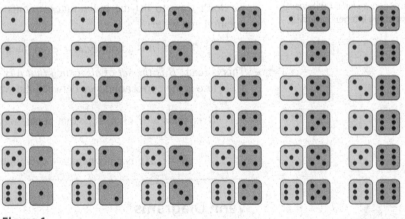

Figure 1

In the first row all the green dice show a 1, in the second row a 2, in the third row a 3, and so on. Similarly, in the first column all the red dice show a 1, in the second column a 2, and so on. The diagonal pairs (top left to bottom right) show all the "doubles." Using the picture as a guide, we can write the set of 36 outcomes as follows:

$$S = \begin{Bmatrix} (1, 1), \ (1, 2), \ (1, 3), \ (1, 4), \ (1, 5), \ (1, 6), \\ (2, 1), \ (2, 2), \ (2, 3), \ (2, 4), \ (2, 5), \ (2, 6), \\ (3, 1), \ (3, 2), \ (3, 3), \ (3, 4), \ (3, 5), \ (3, 6), \\ (4, 1), \ (4, 2), \ (4, 3), \ (4, 4), \ (4, 5), \ (4, 6), \\ (5, 1), \ (5, 2), \ (5, 3), \ (5, 4), \ (5, 5), \ (5, 6), \\ (6, 1), \ (6, 2), \ (6, 3), \ (6, 4), \ (6, 5), \ (6, 6) \end{Bmatrix}.$$ Distinguishable dice

Notice that S is also the set of outcomes when we roll a single die twice, if we take the first number in each pair to be the outcome of the first roll and the second number to be the outcome of the second roll.

b. If the dice are truly indistinguishable, we will have no way of knowing which die is which once they are rolled. Think of placing two identical dice in a closed box and then shaking the box. When we look inside afterward, there is no way to tell which die is which. (If we make a small marking on one of the dice or somehow keep track of it as it bounces around, we are *distinguishing* the dice.) We regard two dice as **indistinguishable** if we make no attempt to distinguish them. Thus, for example, the two different outcomes $(1, 3)$ and $(3, 1)$ from part (a) would represent the same outcome in part (b) (one die shows a 3 and the other a 1). Because the set of outcomes should contain each outcome only once, we can remove $(3, 1)$. Following this approach gives the following smaller set of outcomes:

$$S = \left\{ \begin{array}{l} (1, 1),\ (1, 2),\ (1, 3),\ (1, 4),\ (1, 5),\ (1, 6), \\ \qquad\ (2, 2),\ (2, 3),\ (2, 4),\ (2, 5),\ (2, 6), \\ \qquad\qquad\ (3, 3),\ (3, 4),\ (3, 5),\ (3, 6), \\ \qquad\qquad\qquad\ (4, 4),\ (4, 5),\ (4, 6), \\ \qquad\qquad\qquad\qquad\ (5, 5),\ (5, 6), \\ \qquad\qquad\qquad\qquad\qquad\ (6, 6) \end{array} \right\}. \qquad \text{Indistinguishable dice}$$

EXAMPLE 2   **Set-Builder Notation**

Let $B = \{0, 2, 4, 6, 8\}$. B is the set of all nonnegative✳ even integers less than 10. If we don't want to list the individual elements of B, we can instead use set-builder notation and write

$$B = \{n \,|\, n \text{ is a nonnegative even integer less than } 10\}.$$

This is read "*B is the set of all n such that n is a nonnegative even integer less than 10.*" Here is the correspondence between the words and the symbols:

B is   the set of   all n such that n is a nonnegative even integer less than 10.

$$B = \{n \,|\, n \text{ is a nonnegative even integer less than } 10\}.$$

Venn Diagrams

We can visualize sets and relations between sets using **Venn diagrams**. In a Venn diagram we represent a set as a region, often a disk (Figure 2).

The elements of A are the points inside the region. The following Venn diagrams illustrate the relations we've discussed so far.

Figure 2

Venn Diagrams for Set Relations

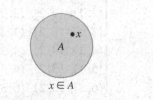

$x \in A$

$x \notin A$

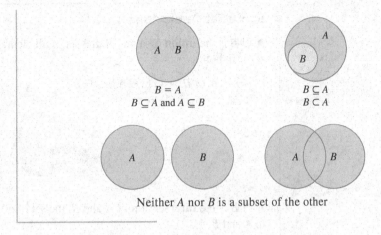

$B = A$
$B \subseteq A$ and $A \subseteq B$

$B \subseteq A$
$B \subset A$

Neither A nor B is a subset of the other

Note Although the diagram for $B \subseteq A$ suggests a proper subset, it is customary to use the same diagram for both subsets and proper subsets. ■

EXAMPLE 3   **Customer Interests**

NobelBooks.com (a fierce competitor of OHaganBooks.com) maintains a database of customers and the types of books they have purchased. In the company's database is the set of customers

$$S = \{\text{Einstein, Bohr, Millikan, Heisenberg, Schrödinger, Dirac}\}.$$

A search of the database for customers who have purchased cookbooks yields the subset

$$A = \{\text{Einstein, Bohr, Heisenberg, Dirac}\}.$$

Another search, this time for customers who have purchased mysteries, yields the subset

$$B = \{\text{Bohr, Heisenberg, Schrödinger}\}.$$

NobelBooks.com wants to promote a new combination mystery/cookbook and wants to target two subsets of customers: those who have purchased either cookbooks or mysteries (or both) and, for additional promotions, those who have purchased both cookbooks and mysteries. Name the customers in each of these subsets.

Solution We can picture the database and the two subsets using the Venn diagram in Figure 3.

The set of customers who have purchased either cookbooks or mysteries (or both) consists of the customers who are in A or B or both: Einstein, Bohr, Heisenberg, Schrödinger, and Dirac. The set of customers who have purchased both cookbooks and mysteries consists of the customers in the overlap of A and B, Bohr and Heisenberg.

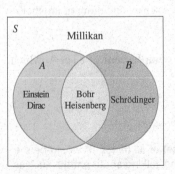

Figure 3

Set Operations

Set operations produce new sets from old ones, just as operations on numbers produce new numbers from old. Following is a list of some important examples.

Some Set Operations

$A \cup B$ is the **union** of A and B, the set of all elements that are either in A or in B (or in both).

$$A \cup B = \{x \mid x \in A \text{ or } x \in B\}$$

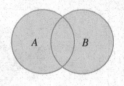

$A \cap B$ is the **intersection** of A and B, the set of all elements that are common to A and B.

$$A \cap B = \{x \mid x \in A \text{ and } x \in B\}$$

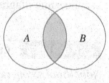

Logical Equivalents
Union: For an element to be in $A \cup B$, it must be in A **or** in B.
Intersection: For an element to be in $A \cap B$, it must be in A **and** in B.

Quick Examples

If $A = \{a, b, c, d\}$ and $B = \{c, d, e, f\}$, then

1. $A \cup B = \{a, b, c, d, e, f\}$
2. $A \cap B = \{c, d\}$.

Note Mathematicians always use "or" in its *inclusive* sense: one thing or another *or both.* ∎

There is one other operation we use, called the **complement** of a set A, which, roughly speaking, is the set of things *not* in A.

Q: *Why only "roughly"? Why not just form the set of things not in A?*

A: This would amount to assuming that there is a set of *all things*. (It would be the complement of the empty set.) Although tempting, talking about entities such as the "set of all things" leads to paradoxes.[*] Instead, we first need to fix a set S of all *objects under consideration*, or the *universe of discourse*, which we generally call the **universal set** for the discussion. For example, when we search the web, we take S to be the set of all web pages. When talking about integers, we take S to be the set of all integers. In other words, our choice of universal set depends on the context. The complement of a set $A \subseteq S$ is then the set of *elements of S* that are not in A.

[*] The most famous such paradox is called Russell's Paradox, after the mathematical logician (and philosopher and pacifist) Bertrand Russell. It goes like this: If there were a set of all things, then there would also be a (smaller) set of all sets. Call it S. Now, because S is the *set of all* sets, it must contain itself as a member. In other words, $S \in S$. Let P be the subset of S consisting of all sets that are *not* members of themselves. Now we pose the following question: Is P a member of itself? If it is, then, because it is the set of all sets that are *not* members of themselves, it is not a member of itself. On the other hand, if it is *not* a member of itself, then it qualifies as an element of P. In other words, it *is* a member of itself! Because neither can be true, something is wrong. What is wrong is the assumption that there is such a thing as the set of all sets or the set of all things.

Complement

If S is the universal set and $A \subseteq S$, then A' is the **complement** of A (in S), the set of all elements of S not in A.

$$A' = \{x \in S \mid x \notin A\}$$ = Green region below

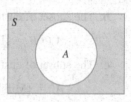

Logical Equivalent

For an element to be in A', it must be in S but **not** in A.

Quick Example

3. If $S = \{a, b, c, d, e, f, g\}$ and $A = \{a, b, c, d\}$, then

$$A' = \{e, f, g\}.$$

In the following example we use set operations to describe the sets we found in Example 3, as well as some others.

EXAMPLE 4   **Customer Interests**

NobelBooks.com maintains a database of customers and the types of books they have purchased. In the company's database is the set of customers

$$S = \{\text{Einstein, Bohr, Millikan, Heisenberg, Schrödinger, Dirac}\}.$$

A search of the database for customers who have purchased cookbooks yields the subset

$$A = \{\text{Einstein, Bohr, Heisenberg, Dirac}\}.$$

Another search, this time for customers who have purchased mysteries, yields the subset

$$B = \{\text{Bohr, Heisenberg, Schrödinger}\}.$$

A third search, for customers who have registered with the site but have not used their first-time customer discount, yields the subset

$$C = \{\text{Millikan}\}.$$

Use set operations to describe the following subsets:

a. The subset of customers who have purchased either cookbooks or mysteries

b. The subset of customers who have purchased both cookbooks and mysteries

c. The subset of customers who have not purchased cookbooks

d. The subset of customers who have purchased cookbooks but have not used their first-time customer discount

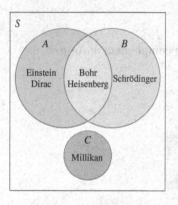

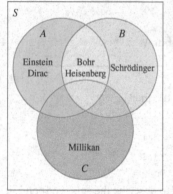

Figure 4

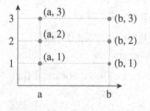

Figure 5

Visualizing $A \times B$

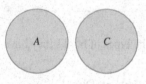

Solution Figure 4 shows two alternative Venn diagram representations of the database. Although the second version shows C overlapping A and B, the placement of the names inside shows that there are no customers in those overlaps.

a. The subset of customers who have bought either cookbooks *or* mysteries is

$$A \cup B = \{\text{Einstein, Bohr, Heisenberg, Schrödinger, Dirac}\}.$$

b. The subset of customers who have bought both cookbooks *and* mysteries is

$$A \cap B = \{\text{Bohr, Heisenberg}\}.$$

c. The subset of customers who have *not* bought cookbooks is

$$A' = \{\text{Millikan, Schrödinger}\}.$$

Note that, for the universal set, we are using the set S of all customers in the database.

d. The subset of customers who have bought cookbooks but have not used their first-time purchase discount is the empty set:

$$A \cap C = \varnothing.$$

When the intersection of two sets is empty, we say that the two sets are **disjoint**. In a Venn diagram, disjoint sets are drawn as regions that don't overlap, as in Figure 5.*

➡ **Before we go on . . .** Computer databases and the web can be searched using so-called Boolean searches. These are search requests using "and," "or," and "not." Using "and" gives the intersection of separate searches, using "or" gives the union, and using "not" gives the complement. In the next section we'll see how web search engines allow such searches. ■

Cartesian Product

There is one more set operation we need to discuss.

Cartesian Product

The **Cartesian product** of two sets, A and B, is the set of all ordered pairs (a, b) with $a \in A$ and $b \in B$.

$$A \times B = \{(a, b) \,|\, a \in A \text{ and } b \in B\}$$

In words, $A \times B$ is the set of all ordered pairs whose first component is in A and whose second component is in B.

Quick Examples

4. If $A = \{a, b\}$ and $B = \{1, 2, 3\}$, then

$$A \times B = \{(a, 1), (a, 2), (a, 3), (b, 1), (b, 2), (b, 3)\}.$$

See the figure in the margin.

5. If $S = \{H, T\}$, then

$$S \times S = \{(H, H), (H, T), (T, H), (T, T)\}.$$

In other words, if S is the set of outcomes of tossing a coin once, then $S \times S$ is the set of outcomes of tossing a coin twice.

6. If $S = \{1, 2, 3, 4, 5, 6\}$, then

$$S \times S = \begin{Bmatrix} (1,1), & (1,2), & (1,3), & (1,4), & (1,5), & (1,6), \\ (2,1), & (2,2), & (2,3), & (2,4), & (2,5), & (2,6), \\ (3,1), & (3,2), & (3,3), & (3,4), & (3,5), & (3,6), \\ (4,1), & (4,2), & (4,3), & (4,4), & (4,5), & (4,6), \\ (5,1), & (5,2), & (5,3), & (5,4), & (5,5), & (5,6), \\ (6,1), & (6,2), & (6,3), & (6,4), & (6,5), & (6,6) \end{Bmatrix}.$$

In other words, if S is the set of outcomes of rolling a die once, then $S \times S$ is the set of outcomes of rolling a die twice (or rolling two distinguishable dice).

7. If $A = \{$red, yellow$\}$ and $B = \{$Mustang, Firebird$\}$, then

$A \times B = \{$(red, Mustang), (red, Firebird), (yellow, Mustang), (yellow, Firebird)$\}$ which we might also write as

$A \times B = \{$red Mustang, red Firebird, yellow Mustang, yellow Firebird$\}$.

EXAMPLE 5   **Representing Cartesian Products**

The manager of an automobile dealership has collected data on the number of pre-owned Acura, Infiniti, Lexus, and Mercedes cars the dealership has from the 2009, 2010, and 2011 model years. In entering this information on a spreadsheet, the manager would like to have each spreadsheet cell represent a particular year and make. Describe this set of cells.

Solution Because each cell represents a year and a make, we can think of the cell as a pair (year, make), as in (2009, Acura). Thus, the set of cells can be thought of as a Cartesian product:

$Y = \{2009, 2010, 2011\}$ Year of car

$M = \{$Acura, Infiniti, Lexus, Mercedes$\}$ Make of car

$$Y \times M = \begin{Bmatrix} (2009, \text{Acura}), & (2009, \text{Infiniti}), & (2009, \text{Lexus}), & (2009, \text{Mercedes}), \\ (2010, \text{Acura}), & (2010, \text{Infiniti}), & (2010, \text{Lexus}), & (2010, \text{Mercedes}), \\ (2011, \text{Acura}), & (2011, \text{Infiniti}), & (2011, \text{Lexus}), & (2011, \text{Mercedes}) \end{Bmatrix}.$$ Cells

Thus, the manager might arrange the spreadsheet as follows:

	A	B	C	D	E
		Acura	**Infiniti**	**Lexus**	**Mercedes**
1					
2	**2009**	(2009 Acura)	(2009 Infiniti)	(2009 Lexus)	(2009 Mercedes)
3	**2010**	(2010 Acura)	(2010 Infiniti)	(2010 Lexus)	(2010 Mercedes)
4	**2011**	(2011 Acura)	(2011 Infiniti)	(2011 Lexus)	(2011 Mercedes)

The highlighting shows the 12 cells to be filled in, representing the numbers of cars of each year and make. For example, in cell B2 should go the number of 2009 Acuras the dealership has.

➡ **Before we go on . . .** The arrangement in the spreadsheet in Example 5 is consistent with the matrix notation in Chapter 5. We could also have used the elements of Y as column labels along the top and the elements of M as row labels down the side. Along those lines, we can also visualize the Cartesian product $Y \times M$ as a set of points in the xy-plane ("Cartesian plane") as shown in Figure 6.

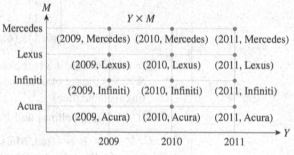

Figure 6

FAQs

The Many Meanings of "And"

Q : Suppose A is the set of actors and B is the set of all baseball players. Then the set of all actors and baseball players is $A \cap B$—right?

A : Wrong. The fact that the word "and" appears in the description of a set does not always mean that the set is an intersection; the word "and" can mean different things in different contexts. $A \cap B$ refers to the set of elements that are in both A and B, hence to actors who are also baseball players. On the other hand, the set of all actors and baseball players is the set of people who are either actors or baseball players (or both), which is $A \cup B$. We can use the word "and" to describe both sets:

$$A \cap B = \{\text{people who are both actors } and \text{ baseball players}\}$$
$$A \cup B = \{\text{people who are actors } or \text{ baseball players}\}$$
$$= \{\text{all actors } and \text{ baseball players}\}.$$

7.1 EXERCISES

▼ more advanced   ◆ challenging

🔲 indicates exercises that should be solved using technology

In Exercises 1–16, list the elements in the given set.

1. The set F consisting of the four seasons

2. The set A consisting of the authors of this book

3. The set I of all positive integers no greater than 6

4. The set N of all negative integers greater than -3

5. $A = \{n \mid n$ is a positive integer and $0 \leq n \leq 3\}$
[HINT: See Example 2.]

6. $A = \{n \mid n$ is a positive integer and $0 < n < 8\}$
[HINT: See Example 2.]

7. $B = \{n \mid n$ is an even positive integer and $0 \leq n \leq 8\}$

8. $B = \{n \mid n$ is an odd positive integer and $0 \leq n \leq 8\}$

9. The set of all outcomes **(a)** of tossing a pair of distinguishable coins and **(b)** of tossing a pair of indistinguishable coins [HINT: See Example 1.]

10. The set of outcomes **(a)** of tossing three distinguishable coins and **(b)** of tossing three indistinguishable coins [HINT: See Example 1.]

11. The set of all outcomes of rolling two distinguishable dice such that the numbers add to 6

12. The set of all outcomes of rolling two distinguishable dice such that the numbers add to 8

13. The set of all outcomes of rolling two indistinguishable dice such that the numbers add to 6

14. The set of all outcomes of rolling two indistinguishable dice such that the numbers add to 8

15. The set of all outcomes of rolling two distinguishable dice such that the numbers add to 13

16. The set of all outcomes of rolling two distinguishable dice such that the numbers add to 1

In Exercises 17–20, draw a Venn diagram that illustrates the relationships among the given sets. [HINT: See Example 3.]

17. S = {eBay, Google, Amazon, OHaganBooks, Hotmail}, A = {Amazon, OHaganBooks}, B = {eBay, Amazon}, C = {Amazon, Hotmail}

18. S = {Apple, Dell, Gateway, Pomegranate, Compaq}, A = {Gateway, Pomegranate, Compaq}, B = {Dell, Gateway, Pomegranate, Compaq}, C = {Apple, Dell, Compaq}

19. S = {eBay, Google, Amazon, OHaganBooks, Hotmail}, A = {Amazon, Hotmail}, B = {eBay, Google, Amazon, Hotmail}, C = {Amazon, Hotmail}

20. S = {Apple, Dell, Gateway, Pomegranate, Compaq}, A = {Apple, Dell, Pomegranate, Compaq}, B = {Pomegranate}, C = {Pomegranate}

Let A = {June, Janet, Jill, Justin, Jeffrey, Jello}, B = {Janet, Jello, Justin}, and C = {Sally, Solly, Molly, Jolly, Jello}. In Exercises 21–34, find the given set. [HINT: See Quick Examples 1 and 2.]

21. $A \cup B$

22. $A \cup C$

23. $A \cup \varnothing$

24. $B \cup \varnothing$

25. $A \cup (B \cup C)$

26. $(A \cup B) \cup C$

27. $C \cap B$

28. $C \cap A$

29. $A \cap \varnothing$

30. $\varnothing \cap B$

31. $(A \cap B) \cap C$

32. $A \cap (B \cap C)$

33. $(A \cap B) \cup C$

34. $A \cup (B \cap C)$

In Exercises 35–42, A = {small, medium, large}, B = {blue, green}, and C = {triangle, square}. [HINT: See Quick Examples 4–7.]

35. List the elements of $A \times C$.

36. List the elements of $B \times C$.

37. List the elements of $A \times B$.

38. The elements of $A \times B \times C$ are the ordered triples (a, b, c) with $a \in A$, $b \in B$, and $c \in C$. List all the elements of $A \times B \times C$.

39. ▦ Represent $B \times C$ as cells in a spreadsheet. [HINT: See Example 5.]

40. ▦ Represent $A \times C$ as cells in a spreadsheet. [HINT: See Example 5.]

41. ▦ Represent $A \times B$ as cells in a spreadsheet.

42. ▦ Represent $A \times A$ as cells in a spreadsheet.

Let A = {H, T} be the set of outcomes when a coin is tossed, and let B = {1, 2, 3, 4, 5, 6} be the set of outcomes when a die is rolled. In Exercises 43–46, write the given set in terms of A and/or B, and list its elements.

43. The set of outcomes when a die is rolled and then a coin tossed

44. The set of outcomes when a coin is tossed twice

45. The set of outcomes when a coin is tossed three times

46. The set of outcomes when a coin is tossed twice and then a die is rolled

Let S be the set of outcomes when two distinguishable dice are rolled, let E be the subset of outcomes in which at least one die shows an even number, and let F be the subset of outcomes in which at least one die shows an odd number. In Exercises 47–52, list the elements in the given subset.

47. E'

48. F'

49. $(E \cup F)'$

50. $(E \cap F)'$

51. $E' \cup F'$

52. $E' \cap F'$

In Exercises 53–60, use Venn diagrams to illustrate the given identity for subsets A, B, and C of S.

53. ▼ $(A \cup B)' = A' \cap B'$ DeMorgan's law

54. ▼ $(A \cap B)' = A' \cup B'$ DeMorgan's law

55. ▼ $(A \cap B) \cap C = A \cap (B \cap C)$ Associative law

56. ▼ $(A \cup B) \cup C = A \cup (B \cup C)$ Associative law

57. ▼ $A \cup (B \cap C) = (A \cup B) \cap (A \cup C)$ Distributive law

58. ▼ $A \cap (B \cup C) = (A \cap B) \cup (A \cap C)$ Distributive law

59. ▼ $S' = \varnothing$

60. ▼ $\varnothing' = S$

Applications

Databases A freelance computer consultant keeps a database of her clients, which contains the names

S = {Acme, Brothers, Crafts, Dion, Effigy, Floyd, Global, Hilbert}.

The following clients owe her money:

A = {Acme, Crafts, Effigy, Global}.

The following clients have done at least $10,000 worth of business with her:

B = {Acme, Brothers, Crafts, Dion}.

The following clients have employed her in the last year:

C = {Acme, Crafts, Dion, Effigy, Global, Hilbert}.

In Exercises 61–68, a subset of clients is described that the consultant could find using her database. Write the subset in terms of A, B, and C, and list the clients in that subset. [HINT: See Example 4.]

61. The clients who owe her money and have done at least $10,000 worth of business with her

62. The clients who owe her money or have done at least $10,000 worth of business with her

63. The clients who have done at least $10,000 worth of business with her or have employed her in the last year

64. The clients who have done at least $10,000 worth of business with her and have employed her in the last year

65. The clients who do not owe her money and have employed her in the last year

66. The clients who do not owe her money or have employed her in the last year

67. ▼ The clients who owe her money, have not done at least $10,000 worth of business with her, and have not employed her in the last year

68. ▼ The clients who either do not owe her money, have done at least $10,000 worth of business with her, or have employed her in the last year

69. ⬛ *Boat Sales* You are given data on revenues from sales of sailboats, motor boats, and yachts for each of the years 2003 through 2006. How would you represent these data in a spreadsheet? The cells in your spreadsheet represent elements of which set?

70. ⬛ *Health-Care Spending* Spending in most categories of health care in the United States increased dramatically in the last 30 years of the 1900s.[1] You are given data showing total spending on prescription drugs, nursing homes, hospital care, and professional services for each of the last three decades of the 1900s. How would you represent these data in a spreadsheet? The cells in your spreadsheet represent elements of which set?

Communication and Reasoning Exercises

71. You sell iPads and *jPads*. Let *I* be the set of all iPads you sold last year, and let *J* be the set of all jPads you sold last year. What set represents the collection of all iPads and jPads you sold combined?

72. You sell two models of music players: the *yoVaina Grandote* and the *yoVaina Minúsculito,* and each comes in three colors: Infraroja, Ultravioleta, and Radiografía. Let *M* be the set of models, and let *C* be the set of colors. What set represents the different choices a customer can make?

73. You are searching online for techno music that is neither European nor Dutch. In set notation, which set of music files are you searching for?
(A) Techno ∩ (European ∩ Dutch)'
(B) Techno ∩ (European ∪ Dutch)'
(C) Techno ∪ (European ∩ Dutch)'
(D) Techno ∪ (European ∪ Dutch)'

74. You would like to see either a World War II movie, or one that is based on a comic book character but does not feature aliens. Which set of movies are you interested in seeing?
(A) WWII ∩ (Comix ∩ Aliens')
(B) WWII ∩ (Comix ∪ Aliens')
(C) WWII ∪ (Comix ∩ Aliens')
(D) WWII ∪ (Comix ∪ Aliens')

75. ▼ Explain, illustrating by means of an example, why $(A \cap B) \cup C \neq A \cap (B \cup C)$.

76. ▼ Explain, making reference to operations on sets, why the statement "He plays soccer or rugby and cricket" is ambiguous.

77. ▼ Explain the meaning of a universal set, and give two different universal sets that could be used in a discussion about sets of positive integers.

78. ▼ Is the set of outcomes when two indistinguishable dice are rolled (Example 1) a Cartesian product of two sets? If so, which two sets? If not, why not?

79. ▼ Design a database scenario that leads to the following statement: To keep the factory operating at maximum capacity, the plant manager should select the suppliers in $A \cap (B \cup C')$.

80. ▼ Design a database scenario that leads to the following statement: To keep her customers happy, the bookstore owner should stock periodicals in $A \cup (B \cap C')$.

81. ▼ Rewrite in set notation: She prefers movies that are not violent, are shorter than 2 hours, and have neither a tragic ending nor an unexpected ending.

82. ▼ Rewrite in set notation: He will cater for any event as long as there are no more than 1,000 people, it lasts for at least 3 hours, and it is within a 50-mile radius of Toronto.

83. ▼ When this book was being written, the copy editor wanted to delete the comma in the following sentence (see Exercise 74): "You would like to see either a World War II movie, or one that is based on a comic book character but does not feature aliens." Explain why this would have resulted in an ambiguity.

84. ▼ When an older version of this book was being written, the copy editor wanted to delete the comma in the following sentence: "You would like to see a World War II movie, based on a comic book character but not featuring aliens." Explain why removing the comma would have had no effect on the meaning of the sentence.

---

[1] Source: Department of Health and Human Services/*New York Times*, January 8, 2002, p. A14.

7.2 Cardinality

In this section we begin to look at a deceptively simple idea: the size of a set, which we call its **cardinality**.

Visualizing Cardinality

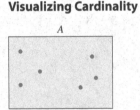

$n(A) = 6$

Cardinality

If A is a finite set, then its **cardinality** is

$$n(A) = \text{number of elements in } A.$$

Quick Examples

1. Let $S = \{a, b, c\}$. Then $n(S) = 3$.
2. Let S be the set of outcomes when two distinguishable dice are rolled. Then $n(S) = 36$ (see Example 1 in Section 7.1).
3. $n(\varnothing) = 0$ because the empty set has no elements.

Counting the elements in a small, simple set is straightforward. To count the elements in a large, complicated set, we try to describe the set as built of simpler sets using the set operations. We then need to know how to calculate the number of elements in, for example, a union, based on the number of elements in the simpler sets whose union we are taking.

The Cardinality of a Union

How can we calculate $n(A \cup B)$ if we know $n(A)$ and $n(B)$? Our first guess might be that $n(A \cup B)$ is $n(A) + n(B)$. But consider a simple example. Let

$$A = \{a, b, c\}$$

and

$$B = \{b, c, d\}.$$

Then $A \cup B = \{a, b, c, d\}$, so $n(A \cup B) = 4$, but $n(A) + n(B) = 3 + 3 = 6$. The calculation $n(A) + n(B)$ gives the wrong answer because the elements b and c are counted twice: once for being in A and again for being in B. To correct for this over-counting, we need to subtract the number of elements that get counted twice, which is the number of elements that A and B have in common, or $n(A \cap B) = 2$ in this case. So we get the right number for $n(A \cup B)$ from the following calculation:

$$n(A) + n(B) - n(A \cap B) = 3 + 3 - 2 = 4.$$

This argument leads to the following general formula.

Cardinality of a Union

If A and B are finite sets, then

$$n(A \cup B) = n(A) + n(B) - n(A \cap B).$$

Visualizing Cardinality of a Union

Disjoint sets

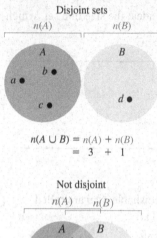

$$n(A \cup B) = n(A) + n(B)$$
$$= 3 + 1$$

Not disjoint

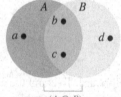

$$n(A \cup B) = n(A) + n(B) - n(A \cap B)$$
$$= 3 + 3 - 2$$

* We confirmed this number by a search for "asteroid threat" OR "William Burrows."

† For example, in September 2015 a search on Google gave the following results: "Romulan mind probe": 6 results, "Abraham Lincoln is born on Earth": 4 results, "Romulan mind probe" OR "Abraham Lincoln is born on Earth": 3,840 results!

In particular, if A and B are disjoint (meaning that $A \cap B = \varnothing$), then

$$n(A \cup B) = n(A) + n(B).$$

(When A and B are disjoint, we say that $A \cup B$ is a **disjoint union**.)

Quick Examples

4. If $A = \{a, b, c, d\}$ and $B = \{b, c, d, e, f\}$, then

$$n(A \cup B) = n(A) + n(B) - n(A \cap B) = 4 + 5 - 3 = 6.$$

In fact, $A \cup B = \{a, b, c, d, e, f\}$.

5. If $A = \{a, b, c\}$ and $B = \{d, e, f\}$, then $A \cap B = \varnothing$, so

$$n(A \cup B) = n(A) + n(B) = 3 + 3 = 6.$$

EXAMPLE 1 Wikipedia Searches

In September 2015 a search on Wikipedia for the phrase "asteroid threat" yielded 9 articles containing that phrase, and a search for "William Burrows" yielded 30 articles. A search for articles containing both phrases yielded 2 articles. How many articles contained either "asteroid threat," "William Burrows," or both?

Solution Let A be the set of sites containing "asteroid threat," and let B be the set of sites containing "William Burrows." We are told that

$$n(A) = 9$$
$$n(B) = 30$$
$$n(A \cap B) = 2. \quad \text{"asteroid threat" AND "William Burrows"}$$

The formula for the cardinality of the union tells us that

$$n(A \cup B) = n(A) + n(B) - n(A \cap B) = 9 + 30 - 2 = 37.^*$$

So 37 articles in the Wikipedia database contained one or both of the phrases "asteroid threat" and "William Burrows."

➡ **Before we go on...** Most search engines use "OR" for union and "AND" for intersection, as does that of Wikipedia. Note that the popular web search engines like Google and Bing do not adhere to the search rule you enter but instead present results that *they think* you want. So although the formula

$$n(A \cup B) = n(A) + n(B) - n(A \cap B)$$

always holds mathematically, you will usually find that, in Google or Bing searches, the numbers don't add up.† ∎

Q : *Is there a similar formula for $n(A \cap B)$?*

A : The formula for the cardinality of a union can also be thought of as a formula for the cardinality of an intersection. We can solve for $n(A \cap B)$ to get

$$n(A \cap B) = n(A) + n(B) - n(A \cup B).$$

In fact, we can think of this formula as an equation relating four quantities. If we know any three of them, we can use the equation to find the fourth. (See Example 2 below.)

 : *Is there a similar formula for n(A′)?*

A : We can get a formula for the cardinality of a complement as follows: If *S* is our universal set and $A \subseteq S$, then *S* is the disjoint union of *A* and its complement. That is,

$$S = A \cup A' \quad \text{and} \quad A \cap A' = \varnothing.$$

Applying the cardinality formula for a disjoint union, we get

$$n(S) = n(A) + n(A').$$

We can then solve for $n(A')$ or for $n(A)$ to get the formulas shown below.

Visualizing Cardinality of a Complement

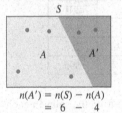

$$n(A') = n(S) - n(A)$$
$$= 6 - 4$$

Cardinality of a Complement

If *S* is a finite universal set and *A* is a subset of *S*, then

$$n(A') = n(S) - n(A)$$

and

$$n(A) = n(S) - n(A').$$

Quick Example

6. If $S = \{a, b, c, d, e, f\}$ and $A = \{a, b, c, d\}$, then

$$n(A') = n(S) - n(A) = 6 - 4 = 2.$$

In fact, $A' = \{e, f\}$.

EXAMPLE 2 **Database Searches**

In September 2015 a search on Amazon.com found 65,000 cookbooks.[2] Of these, 14,000 were on regional cooking, 5,000 were on vegetarian cooking, and 17,000 were on either regional or vegetarian cooking (or both). How many of these books were not on both regional and vegetarian cooking?

Solution Let *S* be the set of all 65,000 books on cooking, let *A* be the set of books on regional cooking, and let *B* be the set of books on vegetarian cooking. We wish to find the size of the complement of the set of books on both regional and vegetarian cooking—that is, $n((A \cap B)')$. Using the formula for the cardinality of a complement, we have

$$n((A \cap B)') = n(S) - n(A \cap B) = 65,000 - n(A \cap B).$$

To find $n(A \cap B)$, we use the formula for the cardinality of a union:

$$n(A \cup B) = n(A) + n(B) - n(A \cap B).$$

---

[2] Precisely, it found that number of books under the subject "Cookbooks, Food & Wine." Regional cooking falls under "Regional & International," and vegetarian cooking falls under "Vegetarian & Vegan." Figures are rounded to the nearest 1,000.

Substituting the values we were given, we find

$$17{,}000 = 14{,}000 + 5{,}000 - n(A \cap B),$$

which we can solve to get

$$n(A \cap B) = 2{,}000.$$

Therefore,

$$n((A \cap B)') = 65{,}000 - n(A \cap B) = 65{,}000 - 2{,}000 = 63{,}000.$$

So 63,000 of the cookbooks were not on both regional and vegetarian cooking.

EXAMPLE 3 Apple Sales

The following table shows sales, in millions of items, of Macs, iPhones, and iPads sold by **Apple** in 2012, 2013, and 2014:[3]

	Macs (A)	iPhones (B)	iPads (C)	Total
2012 (U)	18	125	58	201
2013 (V)	16	150	71	238
2014 (W)	19	169	68	256
Total	53	444	197	695

Let S be the set of all these items sold, and label the sets representing the sales in each row and column as shown (so that, for example, A is the set of all Macs sold during the 3 years). Describe the following sets and compute their cardinality:

a. U' **b.** $A \cap U'$ **c.** $(A \cap U)'$ **d.** $C \cup U$

Solution Before answering parts (a)–(d), first notice that each number in the table is the cardinality of a specific set; for instance, the 18 million Macs sold in 2012 is the cardinality of the set $A \cap U$ of items that were Macs and also sold in 2012, the 125 million iPhones sold in 2012 is the cardinality of $B \cap U$, and so on:

	Macs (A)	iPhones (B)	iPads (C)	Total
2012 (U)	$n(A \cap U)$	$n(B \cap U)$	$n(C \cap U)$	$n(U)$
2013 (V)	$n(A \cap V)$	$n(B \cap V)$	$n(C \cap V)$	$n(V)$
2014 (W)	$n(A \cap W)$	$n(B \cap W)$	$n(C \cap W)$	$n(W)$
Total	$n(A)$	$n(B)$	$n(C)$	$n(S)$

Now let us answer the specific questions: Because all the figures are stated in millions of items, we'll give our calculations and results in millions of items as well.

a. U' is the set of all items not sold in 2012. To compute its cardinality, we could add the totals for all the other years listed in the rightmost column:

$$n(U') = n(V) + n(W) = 238 + 256 = 494 \text{ million items.}$$

---

[3] Figures are rounded. Source: Apple quarterly press releases, www.investor.apple.com.

Alternatively, we can use the formula for the cardinality of a complement (referring again to the totals in the table):

$$n(U') = n(S) - n(U) = 695 - 201 = 494 \text{ million items.}$$

b. $A \cap U'$ is the intersection of the set of all Macs and the set of all items not sold in 2012. In other words, it is the set of all Macs not sold in 2012. Here is the table with the corresponding sets A and U' shaded ($A \cap U'$ is the overlap):

	Macs (A)	iPhones (B)	iPads (C)	Total
2012 (U)	18	125	58	201
2013 (V)	16	150	71	238
2014 (W)	19	169	68	256
Total	53	444	197	695

From the table,

$$n(A \cap U') = 16 + 19 = 35 \text{ million items.}$$

c. $A \cap U$ is the set of all Macs sold in 2012, so $(A \cap U)'$ is the set of all items remaining if we exclude Macs sold in 2012:

	Macs (A)	iPhones (B)	iPads (C)	Total
2012 (U)	18	125	58	201
2013 (V)	16	150	71	238
2014 (W)	19	169	68	256
Total	53	444	197	695

From the formula for the cardinality of a complement,

$$
\begin{aligned}
n((A \cap U)') &= n(S) - n(A \cap U) \\
&= 695 - 18 = 677 \text{ million items.}
\end{aligned}
$$

d. $C \cup U$ is the set of items that either were iPads or sold in 2012:

	Macs (A)	iPhones (B)	iPads (C)	Total
2012 (U)	18	125	58	201
2013 (V)	6	150	71	238
2014 (W)	19	169	68	256
Total	53	444	197	695

To compute it, we can use the formula for the cardinality of a union:

$$
\begin{aligned}
n(C \cup U) &= n(C) + n(U) - n(C \cap U) \\
&= 197 + 201 - 58 = 340 \text{ million items.}
\end{aligned}
$$

To determine the cardinality of a union of three or more sets, for example, $n(A \cup B \cup C)$, we can think of $A \cup B \cup C$ as a union of two sets, $(A \cup B)$ and C, and then analyze each piece using the techniques we already have. Alternatively, there are formulas for the cardinalities of unions of any number of sets, but these formulas get more and more complicated as the number of sets grows. In many applications, such as the following example, we can use Venn diagrams instead.

EXAMPLE 4 Reading Lists

A survey of 300 college students found that 100 had read *War and Peace,* 120 had read *Crime and Punishment,* and 100 had read *The Brothers Karamazov.* It also found that 40 had read only *War and Peace,* 70 had read *War and Peace* but not *The Brothers Karamazov,* and 80 had read *The Brothers Karamazov* but not *Crime and Punishment.* Only 10 had read all three novels. How many had read none of these three novels?

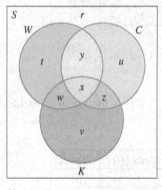

Figure 7

Solution There are four sets mentioned in the problem: the universe S consisting of the 300 students surveyed, the set W of students who had read *War and Peace,* the set C of students who had read *Crime and Punishment,* and the set K of students who had read *The Brothers Karamazov.* Figure 7 shows a Venn diagram representing these sets.

We have put labels in the various regions of the diagram to represent the number of students in each region. For example, x represents the number of students in $W \cap C \cap K$, which is the number of students who have read all three novels. We are told that this number is 10, so

$$x = 10.$$

(You should draw the diagram for yourself and fill in the numbers as we go along.) We are also told that 40 students had read only *War and Peace,* so

$$t = 40.$$

We are given none of the remaining regions directly. However, because 70 had read *War and Peace* but not *The Brothers Karamazov,* we see that t and y must add up to 70. Because we already know that $t = 40$, it follows that $y = 30$. Further, because a total of 100 students had read *War and Peace,* we have

$$x + y + t + w = 100.$$

Substituting the known values of x, y, and t gives

$$10 + 30 + 40 + w = 100,$$

so $w = 20$. Because 80 students had read *The Brothers Karamazov* but not *Crime and Punishment,* we see that $v + w = 80$, so $v = 60$ (because we know that $w = 20$). We can now calculate z using the fact that a total of 100 students had read *The Brothers Karamazov:*

$$60 + 20 + 10 + z = 100,$$

giving $z = 10$. Similarly, we can now get u using the fact that 120 students had read *Crime and Punishment:*

$$10 + 30 + 10 + u = 120,$$

giving $u = 70$. Of the 300 students surveyed, we've now found $x + y + z + w + t + u + v = 240$. This leaves

$$r = 60$$

who had read none of the three novels.

The Cardinality of a Cartesian Product

We've covered all the operations except Cartesian product. To find a formula for $n(A \times B)$, consider the following simple example:

$$A = \{H, T\}$$
$$B = \{1, 2, 3, 4, 5, 6\},$$

so

$$A \times B = \{H1, H2, H3, H4, H5, H6, T1, T2, T3, T4, T5, T6\}.$$

As we saw in Example 5 in Section 7.1, the elements of $A \times B$ can be arranged in a table or spreadsheet with $n(A) = 2$ rows and $n(B) = 6$ elements in each row:

	A	B	C	D	E	F	G
1		1	2	3	4	5	6
2	H	H1	H2	H3	H4	H5	H6
3	T	T1	T2	T3	T4	T5	T6

In a region with two rows and six columns, there are $2 \times 6 = 12$ cells. So

$$n(A \times B) = n(A)n(B)$$

in this case. There is nothing particularly special about this example, however, and that formula holds true in general.

Cardinality of a Cartesian Product

If A and B are finite sets, then

$$n(A \times B) = n(A)n(B).$$

Quick Example

7. If $A = \{a, b, c\}$ and $B = \{x, y, z, w\}$, then

$$n(A \times B) = n(A)n(B) = 3 \times 4 = 12.$$

EXAMPLE 5 **Coin Tosses**

a. If we toss a coin twice and observe the sequence of heads and tails, how many possible outcomes are there?

b. If we toss a coin three times, how many possible outcomes are there?

c. If we toss a coin ten times, how many possible outcomes are there?

Solution

a. Let $A = \{H, T\}$ be the set of possible outcomes when a coin is tossed once. The set of outcomes when a coin is tossed twice is $A \times A$, which has

$$n(A \times A) = n(A)n(A) = 2 \times 2 = 4$$

possible outcomes.

b. When a coin is tossed three times, we can think of the set of outcomes as the product of the set of outcomes for the first two tosses, which is $A \times A$, and the set of outcomes for the third toss, which is just A. The set of outcomes for the three tosses is then $(A \times A) \times A$, which we usually write as $A \times A \times A$ or A^3. The number of outcomes is

$$n((A \times A) \times A) = n(A \times A)n(A) = (2 \times 2) \times 2 = 8.$$

c. Considering the result of part (b), we can easily see that the set of outcomes here is $A^{10} = A \times A \times \cdots \times A$ (10 copies of A), or the set of ordered sequences of ten Hs and Ts. It's also easy to see that

$$n(A^{10}) = [n(A)]^{10} = 2^{10} = 1{,}024.$$

➡ **Before we go on...** We can start to see the power of these formulas for cardinality. In Example 5 we were able to calculate that there are 1,024 possible outcomes when we toss a coin 10 times without writing out all 1,024 possibilities and counting them. ∎

7.2 EXERCISES

▼ more advanced   ◆ challenging
🔲 indicates exercises that should be solved using technology

Let A = {Dirk, Johan, Frans, Sarie}, *B* = {Frans, Sarie, Tina, Klaas, Henrika}, *C* = {Hans, Frans}. *Find the numbers indicated in Exercises 1–6.* [**HINT:** See Quick Examples 1–5.]

1. $n(A) + n(B)$ **2.** $n(A) + n(C)$

3. $n(A \cup B)$ **4.** $n(A \cup C)$

5. $n(A \cup (B \cap C))$ **6.** $n(A \cap (B \cup C))$

7. Verify that $n(A \cup B) = n(A) + n(B) - n(A \cap B)$ with A and B as above.

8. Verify that $n(A \cup C) = n(A) + n(C) - n(A \cap C)$ with A and C as above.

Let A = {H, T}, *B* = {1, 2, 3, 4, 5, 6}, *and C* = {red, green, blue}. *Find the numbers indicated in Exercises 9–14.* [**HINT:** See Example 5.]

9. $n(A \times A)$ **10.** $n(B \times B)$

11. $n(B \times C)$ **12.** $n(A \times C)$

13. $n(A \times B \times B)$ **14.** $n(A \times B \times C)$

15. If $n(A) = 43, n(B) = 20$, and $n(A \cap B) = 3$, find $n(A \cup B)$.

16. If $n(A) = 60, n(B) = 20$, and $n(A \cap B) = 1$, find $n(A \cup B)$.

17. If $n(A \cup B) = 100$ and $n(A) = n(B) = 60$, find $n(A \cap B)$.

18. If $n(A) = 100, n(A \cup B) = 150$, and $n(A \cap B) = 40$, find $n(B)$.

Let S = {Barnsley, Manchester United, Southend, Sheffield United, Liverpool, Maroka Swallows, Witbank Aces, Royal Tigers, Dundee United, Lyon} *be a universal set, A* = {Southend, Liverpool, Maroka Swallows, Royal Tigers}, *and B* = {Barnsley, Manchester United, Southend}. *Find the numbers indicated in Exercises 19–24.* [**HINT:** See Quick Example 6.]

19. $n(A')$ **20.** $n(B')$ **21.** $n((A \cap B)')$

22. $n((A \cup B)')$ **23.** $n(A' \cap B')$ **24.** $n(A' \cup B')$

25. With S, A, and B as above, verify that
$n((A \cap B)') = n(A') + n(B') - n((A \cup B)').$

26. With S, A, and B as above, verify that
$n(A' \cap B') + n(A \cup B) = n(S).$

In Exercises 27–30, use the given information to complete the solution of each partially solved Venn diagram. [**HINT:** See Example 4.]

27.

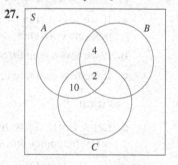

$n(A) = 20, n(B) = 20, n(C) = 28,$
$n(B \cap C) = 8, n(S) = 50$

28.

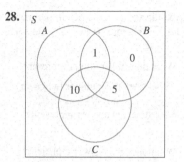

$n(A) = 16, n(B) = 11, n(C) = 30, n(S) = 40$

29. ▼

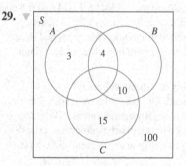

$n(A) = 10, n(B) = 19, n(S) = 140$

30. ▼

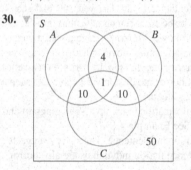

$n(A \cup B) = 30, n(B \cup C) = 30, n(A \cup C) = 35$

Applications

31. Web Searches In November 2011 a search using the web search engine Bing for "asteroid" yielded 25.0 million websites containing that word. A search for "comet" yielded 93.5 million sites. A search for sites containing both words yielded 3.1 million sites.[4] How many websites contained either "asteroid" or "comet" or both? [**HINT**: See Example 1.]

32. Web Searches In November 2011 a search using the web search engine Bing for "tea party" yielded 58.0 million websites containing that phrase. A search for "coffee party" yielded 0.6 million sites. A search for sites containing both phrases yielded 0.1 million sites.[5] How many websites

___

[4] Back in 2011, Bing (but not Google) could still be relied on to adhere to the search rule you entered (see the "Before we go on" discussion following Example 1). Figures are rounded to the nearest 0.1 million.
[5] *Ibid.*

contained either "tea party" or "coffee party" or both? [**HINT**: See Example 1.]

33. Amusement On a particularly boring transatlantic flight, one of the authors amused himself by counting the heads of the people in the seats in front of him. He noticed that all 37 of them either had black hair or had a whole row to themselves (or both). Of this total, 33 had black hair, and 6 were fortunate enough to have a whole row of seats to themselves. How many of the black-haired people had whole rows to themselves?

34. Restaurant Menus While scanning through the dessert menu of your favorite restaurant, you notice that it lists 14 desserts that include yogurt, fruit, or both. Of these, 8 include yogurt, and 9 include fruit. How many of the desserts with yogurt also include fruit?

35. Mobile Gamers Of a total of 132 million mobile gamers (people who use smartphones or tablets or both for gaming) in India in 2014, 123 million used smartphones, and 44 million used tablets.[6] How many used only tablets?

36. Mobile Gamers Of a total of 208 million mobile gamers (people who use smartphones or tablets or both for gaming) in India in 2016, 194 million used smartphones, and 73 million used tablets.[7] How many did not use tablets?

Publishing *Exercises 37–42 are based on the following table, which shows the results of a survey of authors by a fictitious publishing company:*

	New Authors	Established Authors	Total
Successful	5	25	30
Unsuccessful	15	55	70
Total	20	80	100

Consider the following subsets of the set S of all authors represented in the table: C, the set of successful authors; U, the set of unsuccessful authors; N, the set of new authors; and E, the set of established authors. [**HINT**: See Example 3.]

37. Describe the sets $C \cap N$ and $C \cup N$ in words. Use the table to compute $n(C), n(N), n(C \cap N)$, and $n(C \cup N)$. Verify that $n(C \cup N) = n(C) + n(N) - n(C \cap N)$.

38. Describe the sets $N \cap U$ and $N \cup U$ in words. Use the table to compute $n(N), n(U), n(N \cap U)$, and $n(N \cup U)$. Verify that $n(N \cup U) = n(N) + n(U) - n(N \cap U)$.

39. Describe the set $C \cap N'$ in words, and find the number of elements it contains.

40. Describe the set $U \cup E'$ in words, and find the number of elements it contains.

41. ▼ What percentage of established authors are successful? What percentage of successful authors are established?

___

[6] Figures are rounded. Source for data: www.emarketer.com.
[7] Figures are estimates; the last two by www.emarketer.com.

42. ▼ What percentage of new authors are unsuccessful? What percentage of unsuccessful authors are new?

Housing Starts *Exercises 43–48 are based on the following table, which shows the number of new (single-unit) houses started, in thousands, in the different regions of the United States during 2012–2014.[8] Take S to be the set of all housing starts represented in the table, and label the sets representing the housing starts in each row and column as shown (so, for example, N is the set of all housing starts in the Northeast during 2012–2014).*

	Northeast (N)	Midwest (M)	South (T)	West (W)	Total
2012 (A)	50	90	280	110	530
2013 (B)	60	100	330	130	620
2014 (C)	50	110	350	150	660
Total	160	300	960	390	1,810

In each exercise, use symbols to describe the given set, and compute its cardinality.

43. The set of housing starts in the Midwest in 2014

44. The set of housing starts either in the West or in 2012

45. The set of housing starts in 2013 excluding housing starts in the South

46. The set of housing starts in the Northeast after 2012

47. ▼ The set of housing starts in 2013 in the West and Midwest

48. ▼ The set of housing starts in the South and West in years other than 2012

Stocks *Exercises 49–54 are based on the following table, which shows the stock market performance of 40 industries from five sectors of the U.S. economy as of noon on September 11, 2015.[9] (Take S to be the set of all 40 industries represented in the table.)*

	Increased (X)	Decreased (Y)	Unchanged (Z)	Totals
Financials (F)	3	4	1	8
Manufacturing (M)	8	3	3	14
Information Technology (T)	6	1	0	7
Health Care (H)	4	1	1	6
Utilities (U)	3	1	1	5
Totals	24	10	6	40

49. Use symbols to describe the set of non-manufacturing industries that increased. How many elements are in this set?

50. Use symbols to describe the set of industries in the manufacturing sector that did not increase. How many elements are in this set?

51. Compute $n(H' \cup Z)$. What does this number represent?

52. Compute $n(H \cup Z')$. What does this number represent?

53. Calculate $\dfrac{n(T \cap Y)}{n(Y)}$. What does the answer represent?

54. Calculate $\dfrac{n(U \cap X)}{n(U)}$. What does the answer represent?

55. ▼ *Medicine* In a study of Tibetan children,[10] a total of 1,556 children were examined. Of these, 1,024 had rickets. Of the 243 urban children in the study, 93 had rickets.
 a. How many children living in nonurban areas had rickets?
 b. How many children living in nonurban areas did not have rickets?

56. ▼ *Medicine* In a study of Tibetan children,[11] a total of 1,556 children were examined. Of these, 615 had caries (cavities). Of the 1,313 children living in nonurban areas, 504 had caries.
 a. How many children living in urban areas had caries?
 b. How many children living in urban areas did not have caries?

57. *Entertainment* According to a survey of 100 people regarding their movie attendance in the last year, 40 had seen a science fiction movie, 55 had seen an adventure movie, and 35 had seen a horror movie. Moreover, 25 had seen a science fiction movie and an adventure movie, 5 had seen an adventure movie and a horror movie, and 15 had seen a science fiction movie and a horror movie. Only 5 people had seen a movie from all three categories.
 a. Use the given information to set up a Venn diagram and solve it. [HINT: See Example 4.]
 b. Complete the following sentence: The survey suggests that __ % of science fiction movie fans are also horror movie fans.

58. *Athletics* Of the 4,700 students at *Medium Suburban College*, 50 play collegiate soccer, 60 play collegiate lacrosse, and 96 play collegiate football. Only 4 students play both collegiate soccer and lacrosse, 6 play collegiate soccer and football, and 16 play collegiate lacrosse and football. No students play all three sports.
 a. Use the given information to set up a Venn diagram and solve it. [HINT: See Example 4.]
 b. Complete the following sentence: __ % of the college soccer players also play one of the other two sports at the collegiate level.

59. *Entertainment* In a survey of 100 *Enormous State University* students, 21 enjoyed classical music, 22 enjoyed rock music, and 27 enjoyed house music. Five of the students

---

[8] Figures are rounded. Source: www.census.gov.

[9] Unchanged" includes industries that moved by less than 0.1%. Source for data: Fidelity https://eresearch.fidelity.com.

[10] Source: N. S. Harris et al., "Nutritional and Health Status of Tibetan Children Living at High Altitudes," *New England Journal of Medicine*, 344(5), February 1, 2001, pp. 341–347.

[11] *Ibid.*

enjoyed both classical and rock. How many of those who enjoyed rock did not enjoy classical music?

60. *Entertainment* Refer back to Exercise 59. You are also told that 5 students enjoyed all three kinds of music while 53 enjoyed music in none of these categories. How many students enjoyed both classical and rock but disliked house music?

Communication and Reasoning Exercises

61. If A and B are finite sets with $A \subset B$, how are $n(A)$ and $n(B)$ related?

62. If A and B are subsets of the finite set S with $A \subset B$, how are $n(A')$ and $n(B')$ related?

63. Why is the Cartesian product referred to as a "product"? [HINT: Think about cardinality.]

64. Refer back to your answer to Exercise 63. What set operation could you use to represent the *sum* of two disjoint sets A and B? Why?

65. Formulate an interesting application whose answer is $n(A \cap B) = 20$.

66. Formulate an interesting application whose answer is $n(A \times B) = 120$.

67. ▼ When is $n(A \cup B) \neq n(A) + n(B)$?

68. ▼ When is $n(A \times B) = n(A)$?

69. ▼ When is $n(A \cup B) = n(A)$?

70. ▼ When is $n(A \cap B) = n(A)$?

71. ◆ Use a Venn diagram or some other method to obtain a formula for $n(A \cup B \cup C)$ in terms of $n(A)$, $n(B)$, $n(C)$, $n(A \cap B)$, $n(A \cap C)$, $n(B \cap C)$, and $n(A \cap B \cap C)$.

72. ◆ Suppose that A and B are sets with $A \subset B$ and $n(A)$ at least 2. Arrange the following numbers from smallest to largest (if two numbers are equal, say so): $n(A)$, $n(A \times B)$, $n(A \cap B)$, $n(A \cup B)$, $n(B \times A)$, $n(B)$, $n(B \times B)$.

7.3 Decision Algorithms: The Addition and Multiplication Principles

The Addition and Multiplication Principles

Let's start with a really simple example. You walk into an ice cream parlor and find that you can choose between ice cream, of which there are 15 flavors, and frozen yogurt, of which there are 5 flavors. If you want a single scoop of one of these, how many different selections can you make? Clearly, you have $15 + 5 = 20$ different desserts from which to choose. Mathematically, this is an example of the formula for the cardinality of a disjoint union: If we let A be the set of ice creams you can choose from and let B be the set of frozen yogurts, then $A \cap B = \varnothing$ and we want $n(A \cup B)$. But the formula for the cardinality of a disjoint union is $n(A \cup B) = n(A) + n(B)$, which gives $15 + 5 = 20$ in this case.

This example illustrates a very useful general principle.

Addition Principle

When choosing among r disjoint alternatives, suppose that

> alternative 1 has n_1 possible outcomes,
> alternative 2 has n_2 possible outcomes,
> $\vdots$
> alternative r has n_r possible outcomes,

with no two of these outcomes the same. Then there are a total of $n_1 + n_2 + \cdots + n_r$ possible outcomes.

Quick Example

1. At a restaurant you can choose among 8 chicken dishes, 10 beef dishes, 4 seafood dishes, and 12 vegetarian dishes. This gives a total of $8 + 10 + 4 + 12 = 34$ different dishes to choose from.

Here is another simple example. In that ice cream parlor, not only can you choose from 15 flavors of ice cream, but you can also choose from 3 different sizes of cone. How many different ice cream cones can you select from? This time, we want to choose both a flavor and a size, or, in other words, a pair (flavor, size). Therefore, if we let A again be the set of ice cream flavors and now let C be the set of cone sizes, the pair we want to choose is an element of $A \times C$, the Cartesian product. To find the number of choices we have, we use the formula for the cardinality of a Cartesian product: $n(A \times C) = n(A)n(C)$. In this case we get $15 \times 3 = 45$ different ice cream cones we can select.

This example illustrates another general principle.

Multiplication Principle

When making a sequence of choices with r steps, suppose that

step 1 has n_1 possible outcomes

step 2 has n_2 possible outcomes

$\vdots$

step r has n_r possible outcomes

and that each sequence of choices results in a distinct outcome.[*] Then there are a total of $n_1 \times n_2 \times \cdots \times n_r$ possible outcomes.

Quick Example

2. At a restaurant you can choose among 5 appetizers, 34 main dishes, and 10 desserts. This gives a total of $5 \times 34 \times 10 = 1,700$ different meals (each including one appetizer, one main dish, and one dessert) from which you can choose.

---

[*] See Example 3 for a case in which different sequences of choices can lead to the same outcome, with the result that the multiplication principle does not apply.

Things get more interesting when we have to use the addition and multiplication principles in tandem.

EXAMPLE 1 **Desserts**

You walk into an ice cream parlor and find that you can choose between ice cream, of which there are 15 flavors, and frozen yogurt, of which there are 5 flavors. In addition, you can choose among 3 different sizes of cones for your ice cream or 2 different sizes of cups for your yogurt. If you want only a single item, how many different desserts can you choose from?

Solution It helps to think about a definite procedure for deciding which dessert you will choose. Here is one we can use:

Alternative 1: An ice cream cone
   Step 1 Choose a flavor.
   Step 2 Choose a size.

Alternative 2: A cup of frozen yogurt
   Step 1 Choose a flavor.
   Step 2 Choose a size.

That is, we can choose between alternative 1 and alternative 2. If we choose alternative 1, we have a sequence of two choices to make: flavor and size. The same is true of alternative 2. We shall call a procedure in which we make a sequence of decisions a **decision algorithm**.[*] Once we have a decision algorithm, we can use the addition and multiplication principles to count the number of possible outcomes.

*An algorithm is a procedure with definite rules for what to do at every step.

Alternative 1: An ice cream cone
    Step 1 Choose a flavor: 15 choices.
    Step 2 Choose a size: 3 choices.
    There are $15 \times 3 = 45$ possible choices in alternative 1.   Multiplication principle

Alternative 2: A cup of frozen yogurt
    Step 1 Choose a flavor: 5 choices.
    Step 2 Choose a size: 2 choices.
    There are $5 \times 2 = 10$ possible choices in alternative 2.   Multiplication principle

So there are $45 + 10 = 55$ possible choices of desserts.   Addition principle

➡ **Before we go on . . .** Decision algorithms can be illustrated by **decision trees**. To simplify the picture, suppose we had fewer choices in Example 1—say, only two choices of ice cream flavor: vanilla and chocolate, and two choices of yogurt flavor: banana and raspberry. This would give us a total of $2 \times 3 + 2 \times 2 = 10$ possible desserts. We can illustrate the decisions we need to make when choosing what to buy in the diagram in Figure 8, called a *decision tree*.

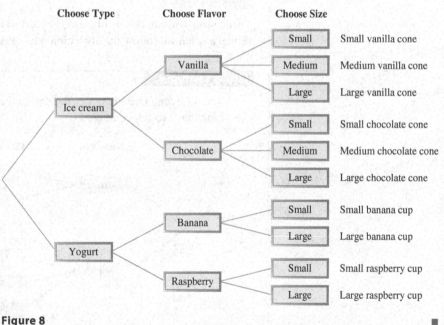

Figure 8

Decision Algorithms and Decision Trees

We referred to the sequence of decisions we made in Example 1 as an example of a *decision algorithm*. Let's look at these gadgets a little more closely.

To count the number of possible gadgets, pretend you are *designing* a gadget, and list the decisions to be made at each stage.

Decision Algorithm

A **decision algorithm** is a procedure in which we make a sequence of decisions. We can use decision algorithms to determine the number of possible items of a specified type (for example, ice cream cones) by pretending that we are *designing* such an item and listing the decisions or choices we should make at each stage of the process.

Quick Example

3. Your local Apple store has iPads in two sizes: the larger Air and the smaller Mini. The Air is available in two colors (blue, green), and the Mini is available in four colors (blue, green, pink, purple). A decision algorithm for "designing" an iPad is as follows:

> *Alternative 1:* Select an Air:
> **Step 1** Choose a color: Two choices.
> (So there are two choices for alternative 1.)

> *Alternative 2:* Select a Mini:
> **Step 1** Choose a color: Four choices.
> (So there are four choices for alternative 2.)

Thus, there are $2 + 4 = 6$ possible choices of iPads.

Decision Tree

A decision algorithm can be illustrated by a **decision tree** in which the choices we make when we follow the algorithm are represented by branches.

Quick Example

4. The following tree illustrates the decision algorithm in Quick Example 3 to select an iPad:

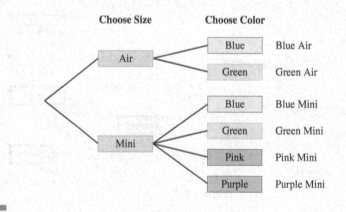

We do not use decision trees much in this chapter because, while they provide a good way of thinking about decision algorithms, they're not really practical for counting large sets. Similar diagrams will be very useful, however, in the chapter on probability.

Caution

For a decision algorithm to give the correct number of possible items, there must be a one-to-one correspondence between sequences of choices and resulting items. So it is necessary that each sequence of choices results in a distinct item. In other words, *changing one or more choices must result in a different item.* (See Example 3.)

EXAMPLE 2   Exams

An exam is broken into two parts, Part A and Part B, both of which you are required to do. In Part A you can choose between answering 10 true-false questions and answering 4 multiple-choice questions, each of which has 5 answers to choose from. In Part B you can choose between answering 8 true-false questions and answering 5 multiple-choice questions, each of which has 4 answers to choose from. How many different collections of answers are possible?

Solution While deciding what answers to write down, we use the following decision algorithm:

Step 1 Do Part A.

> *Alternative 1:* Answer the 10 true-false questions.
>> **Steps 1–10** Choose true or false for each question: 2 choices each.
>> There are $2 \times 2 \times \cdots \times 2 = 2^{10} = 1{,}024$ choices in alternative 1.

> *Alternative 2:* Answer the 4 multiple-choice questions.
>> **Steps 1–4** Choose one answer for each question: 5 choices each.
>> There are $5 \times 5 \times 5 \times 5 = 5^4 = 625$ choices in alternative 2.
> $1{,}024 + 625 = 1{,}649$ choices in step 1

Step 2 Do Part B.

> *Alternative 1:* Answer the 8 true-false questions: 2 choices each.
>> $2^8 = 256$ choices in alternative 1

> *Alternative 2:* Answer the 5 multiple-choice questions, 4 choices each.
>> $4^5 = 1{,}024$ choices in alternative 2
> $256 + 1{,}024 = 1{,}280$ choices in step 2

There are $1{,}649 \times 1{,}280 = 2{,}110{,}720$ different collections of answers possible.

The next example illustrates the need to select your decision algorithm with care.

EXAMPLE 3   Scrabble

You are playing Scrabble and have the following letters to work with: k, e, r, e. Because you are losing the game, you would like to use all your letters to make a single word, but you can't think of any four-letter words that use all these letters. In desperation, you decide to list *all* the four-letter sequences possible to see whether there are any valid words among them. How large is your list?

Solution It may first occur to you to try the following decision algorithm.

Step 1 Select the first letter: 4 choices.
Step 2 Select the second letter: 3 choices.
Step 3 Select the third letter: 2 choices.
Step 4 Select the last letter: 1 choice.

This gives $4 \times 3 \times 2 \times 1 = 24$ choices. However, something is wrong with the algorithm.

> **Q**: *What is wrong with this decision algorithm?*
>
> **A**: We didn't take into account the fact that there are two "e"s;* different decisions in Steps 1–4 can produce the same sequence. Suppose, for example, that we selected the first "e" in step 1, the second "e" in step 2, and then the "k" and the "r." This would produce the sequence "eekr." If we selected the *second* "e" in step 1, the *first* "e" in step 2, and then the "k" and "r," we would obtain the *same* sequence: "eekr." In other words, the decision algorithm produces two copies of the sequence "eekr" in the associated decision tree. (In fact, it produces two copies of each possible sequence of the letters.) In short, different sequences of choices produce the same result, violating the requirement in the note of caution that precedes Example 2:
>
> *For a decision algorithm to be valid, each sequence of choices must produce a different result.*

* Consider the following extreme case: If all four letters were "e," then there would be only a single sequence—"eeee"—and not the 24 predicted by the decision algorithm.

Because our original algorithm is not valid, we need a new one. Here is a strategy that works nicely for this example. Imagine, as before, that we are going to construct a sequence of four letters. This time we are going to imagine that we have a sequence of four empty slots: ☐☐☐☐. Instead of selecting letters to fill the slots from left to right, we are going to select *slots* in which to place each of the letters. Remember that we have to use the letters k, e, r, e. We proceed as follows, leaving the "e"s until last:

Step 1 Select an empty slot for the k: 4 choices. (e.g., ☐☐k☐)
Step 2 Select an empty slot for the r: 3 choices. (e.g., r☐k☐)
Step 3 Place the "e"s in the remaining two slots: 1 choice!

Thus, the multiplication principle yields $4 \times 3 \times 1 = 12$ choices.

➡ **Before we go on . . .** You should try constructing a decision tree for Example 3. You will see that each sequence of four letters is produced exactly once when we use the correct (second) decision algorithm. ■

FAQs

Creating and Testing a Decision Algorithm

> **Q**: *How do I set up a decision algorithm to count how many items there are in a given scenario?*
>
> **A**: Pretend that you are *designing* such an item (for example, pretend that you are designing an ice cream cone), and come up with a systematic procedure for doing so, listing the decisions you should make at each stage.
>
> **Q**: *In my decision algorithm, where do I use alternatives, and where do I use steps?*
>
> **A**: Think of your procedure in terms of "or" and "and": If your procedure includes a list of consecutive instructions "Do this *and* that *and* that *and* that . . .", then use steps for that part of the decision algorithm; if your procedure includes a list of different possibilities ("Do this *or* that *or* that *or* that . . ."), then use alternatives for that part of the decision algorithm.

Q: *Once I have my decision algorithm, how do I check whether it is valid?*

A: Ask yourself the following question: "Is it possible to get the same item (the exact same ice cream cone, say) by making different decisions when applying the algorithm?" If the answer is "yes," then your decision algorithm is invalid. Otherwise, it is valid.

7.3 EXERCISES

▼ more advanced   ◆ challenging
🅣 indicates exercises that should be solved by using technology

1. An experiment requires a choice among three initial setups. The first setup can result in two possible outcomes, the second in three possible outcomes, and the third in five possible outcomes. What is the total number of outcomes possible? [**HINT:** See Quick Example 1.]

2. A surgical procedure requires choosing among four alternative methodologies. The first can result in four possible outcomes, the second can result in three possible outcomes, and the remaining methodologies can each result in two possible outcomes. What is the total number of outcomes possible? [**HINT:** See Quick Example 1.]

3. An experiment requires a sequence of three steps. The first step can result in two possible outcomes, the second in three possible outcomes, and the third in five possible outcomes. What is the total number of outcomes possible? [**HINT:** See Quick Example 2.]

4. A surgical procedure requires four steps. The first can result in four possible outcomes, the second in three possible outcomes, and the remaining two can each result in two possible outcomes. What is the total number of outcomes possible? [**HINT:** See Quick Example 2.]

For the decision algorithms in Exercises 5–12, find how many outcomes are possible. [**HINT:** See Example 1.]

5. Alternative 1:
   Step 1: 1 outcome
   Step 2: 2 outcomes

Alternative 2:
   Step 1: 2 outcomes
   Step 2: 2 outcomes
   Step 3: 1 outcome

6. Alternative 1:
   Step 1: 1 outcome
   Step 2: 2 outcomes
   Step 3: 2 outcomes

Alternative 2:
   Step 1: 2 outcomes
   Step 2: 2 outcomes

7. Step 1:
   Alternative 1: 1 outcome
   Alternative 2: 2 outcomes

Step 2:
   Alternative 1: 2 outcomes
   Alternative 2: 2 outcomes
   Alternative 3: 1 outcome

8. Step 1:
   Alternative 1: 1 outcome
   Alternative 2: 2 outcomes
   Alternative 3: 2 outcomes

Step 2:
   Alternative 1: 2 outcomes
   Alternative 2: 2 outcomes

9. Alternative 1:
   Step 1:
      Alternative 1: 3 outcomes
      Alternative 2: 1 outcome
   Step 2: 2 outcomes

Alternative 2: 5 outcomes

10. Alternative 1: 2 outcomes

Alternative 2:
   Step 1:
      Alternative 1: 4 outcomes
      Alternative 2: 1 outcome
   Step 2: 2 outcomes

11. Step 1:
   Alternative 1:
      Step 1: 3 outcomes
      Step 2: 1 outcome
   Alternative 2: 2 outcomes

Step 2: 5 outcomes

12. Step 1: 2 outcomes

Step 2:
   Alternative 1:
      Step 1: 4 outcomes
      Step 2: 1 outcome
   Alternative 2: 2 outcomes

13. How many different four-letter sequences can be formed from the letters a, a, a, b? [**HINT:** See Example 3.]

14. How many different five-letter sequences can be formed from the letters a, a, a, b, c? [**HINT:** See Example 3.]

Applications

15. *Ice Cream* When Baskin-Robbins was founded in 1945, it made 31 different flavors of ice cream.[12] If you had a choice of having a single flavor of ice cream in a cone, a cup, or a sundae, how many different desserts could you have?

16. *Ice Cream* At the beginning of 2002, Baskin-Robbins claimed to have "nearly 1,000 different ice cream flavors."[13] Assuming that you could choose from 1,000 different flavors, that you could have a single flavor of ice cream in a cone, a cup, or a sundae, and that you could choose from a dozen different toppings, how many different desserts could you have?

17. *Binary Codes* A binary digit, or "bit," is either 0 or 1. A nybble is a four-bit sequence. How many different nybbles are possible?

---

[12] Source: Company website (www.baskinrobbins.com).

[13] *Ibid.*

18. **Ternary Codes** A ternary digit is either 0, 1, or 2. How many sequences of six ternary digits are possible?

19. **Ternary Codes** A ternary digit is either 0, 1, or 2. How many sequences of six ternary digits are possible containing a single 1 and a single 2?

20. **Binary Codes** A binary digit, or "bit," is either 0 or 1. A nybble is a four-bit sequence. How many different nybbles containing a single 1 are possible?

21. **Reward** While selecting candy for students in his class, Professor Murphy must choose between gummy candy and licorice nibs. Gummy candy packets come in three sizes, while packets of licorice nibs come in two. If he chooses gummy candy, he must select gummy bears, gummy worms, or gummy dinos. If he chooses licorice nibs, he must choose between red and black. How many choices does he have? [HINT: See Example 2.]

22. **Productivity** Professor Oger must choose between an extra writing assignment and an extra reading assignment for the upcoming spring break. For the writing assignment there are two essay topics to choose from and three different mandatory lengths (30 pages, 35 pages, or 40 pages). The reading topic would consist of one scholarly biography combined with one volume of essays. There are five biographies and two volumes of essays to choose from. How many choices does she have? [HINT: See Example 2.]

23. **DVD Discs** DVD discs at your local computer store are available in two types (DVD-R and DVD-RW), packaged singly, in spindles of 50, or in spindles of 100. When purchasing singly, you can choose from five colors; when purchasing in spindles of 50 or 100, you have two choices: silver or an assortment of colors. If you are purchasing DVD discs, how many possibilities do you have to choose from?

24. **Radar Detectors** Radar detectors are either powered by their own battery or plug into the cigarette lighter socket. All radar detectors come in two models: no-frills and fancy. In addition, detectors powered by their own batteries detect either radar or laser or both, whereas the plug-in types come in models that detect either radar or laser, but not both. How many different radar detectors can you buy?

25. **Multiple-Choice Tests** Professor Easy's final examination has 10 true-false questions followed by 2 multiple-choice questions. In each of the multiple-choice questions, you must select the correct answer from a list of five. How many answer sheets are possible?

26. **Multiple-Choice Tests** Professor Tough's final examination has 20 true-false questions followed by 3 multiple-choice questions. In each of the multiple-choice questions, you must select the correct answer from a list of six. How many answer sheets are possible?

27. **Tests** A test requires that you answer either Part A or Part B. Part A consists of 8 true-false questions, and Part B consists of 5 multiple-choice questions with one correct answer out of five. How many different completed answer sheets are possible?

28. **Tests** A test requires that you answer first Part A and then either Part B or Part C. Part A consists of 4 true-false questions, Part B consists of 4 multiple-choice questions with one correct answer out of five, and Part C consists of 3 multiple-choice questions with one correct answer out of six. How many different completed answer sheets are possible?

29. **Stock Portfolios** Your broker has suggested that you diversify your investments by splitting your portfolio among mutual funds, municipal bond funds, stocks, and precious metals. She suggests four good mutual funds, three municipal bond funds, eight stocks, and three precious metals (gold, silver, and platinum).
   a. Assuming that your portfolio is to contain one of each type of investment, how many different portfolios are possible?
   b. Assuming that your portfolio is to contain three mutual funds, two municipal bond funds, one stock, and two precious metals, how many different portfolios are possible?

30. **Menus** The local diner offers a meal combination consisting of an appetizer, a soup, a main course, and a dessert. There are five appetizers, two soups, four main courses, and five desserts. Your diet restricts you to choosing between a dessert and an appetizer. (You cannot have both.) Given this restriction, how many three-course meals are possible?

31. **Computer Codes** A computer byte consists of eight bits, each bit being either a 0 or a 1. If characters are represented using a code that uses a byte for each character, how many different characters can be represented?

32. **Computer Codes** Some written languages, such as Chinese and Japanese, use tens of thousands of different characters. If a language uses roughly 50,000 characters, a computer code for this language would have to use how many bytes per character? (See Exercise 31.)

33. **Symmetries of a Five-Pointed Star** A five-pointed star will appear unchanged if it is rotated through any one of the angles 0°, 72°, 144°, 216°, or 288°. It will also appear unchanged if it is flipped about the axis shown in the figure. A *symmetry* of the five-pointed star consists of either a rotation, or a rotation followed by a flip. How many different symmetries are there altogether?

34. *Symmetries of a Six-Pointed Star* A six-pointed star will appear unchanged if it is rotated through any one of the angles 0°, 60°, 120°, 180°, 240°, or 300°. It will also appear unchanged if it is flipped about the axis shown in the figure. A *symmetry* of the six-pointed star consists of either a rotation, or a rotation followed by a flip. How many different symmetries are there altogether?

35. *Variables in Visual Basic* A variable name in the programming language Visual Basic must begin with a letter (uppercase or lowercase) possibly followed by letters, digits (0–9), and various special characters. How many different Visual Basic variable names of length up to three are possible that consist of letters and digits and end in a digit?

36. *Employee IDs* A company assigns to each of its employees an ID code that consists of one, two, or three uppercase letters followed by a digit from 0 through 9. How many employee codes does the company have available?

37. *Tournaments* How many ways are there of filling in the blanks for the following (fictitious) soccer tournament?

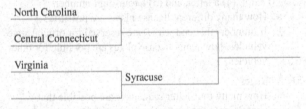

38. *Tournaments* How many ways are there of filling in the blanks for a (fictitious) soccer tournament involving the four teams San Diego State, De Paul, Colgate, and Hofstra?

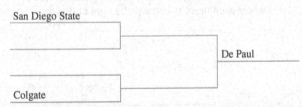

39. ▼ *Telephone Numbers* Suppose a telephone number consists of a sequence of seven digits not starting with 0 or 1.
   a. How many telephone numbers are possible?
   b. How many of them begin with either 463, 460, or 400?
   c. How many telephone numbers are possible if no two adjacent digits are the same? (For example, 235-9350 is permitted, but 223-6789 is not.)

40. ▼ *Social Security Numbers* A Social Security Number is a sequence of nine digits.
   a. How many Social Security Numbers are possible?
   b. How many of them begin with either 023 or 003?
   c. How many Social Security Numbers are possible if no two adjacent digits are the same? (For example, 235-93-2345 is permitted, but 126-67-8189 is not.)

41. ▼ *Credit Card Numbers* The vast majority of Visa and Discover Card credit cards have 16-digit card numbers. The first digit is either 4 (Visa) or 6 (Discover), digits 2 through 6 identify the issuer, digits 7 through 15 identify the customer, and the last digit is a "check digit" determined by the digits that precede it.[14] Your company, *CreditXplosion, Inc.*, issues both Visa and Discover credit cards.
   a. How many different CreditXplosion cards are possible?
   b. How many different CreditXplosion Discover card numbers are possible in which the check digit is wrong?

42. ▼ *Credit Card Numbers* Credit cards issued by American Express have 15-digit card numbers. The first two digits are either 34 or 37, digits 3 and 4 identify the currency, digits 5 through 11 identify the account, digits 12 through 14 identify the card within the account, and the last digit is a "check digit" determined by the digits that precede it.[15]
   a. Your company, *BuyersXplosion, Inc.*, has an account at American Express. How many different cards issued to BuyersXplosion's account are possible based on U.S. dollars and Mexican pesos?
   b. How many different U.S. dollar–denominated American Express cards (issued to anybody's account, not just BuyersXplosion's) are possible with a wrong check digit?

43. ▼ *DNA Chains: Life in Nature* DNA (deoxyribonucleic acid) is the basic building block of reproduction in living things. A DNA chain is a sequence of chemicals called *bases*. There are four possible bases: thymine (T), cytosine (C), adenine (A), and guanine (G).
   a. How many three-element DNA chains are possible?
   b. How many n-element DNA chains are possible?
   c. A human DNA chain has 2.1×10^{10} elements. How many human DNA chains are possible?

44. ▼ *DNA Chains: Synthetic Life* (Refer to Exercise 43.) In 2014, scientists announced the creation of the first reproducing organisms using an expanded DNA alphabet with two new bases ("X" and "Y") in addition to the four found in nature.[16]
   a. How many four-element expanded DNA chains are possible?
   b. How many n-element expanded DNA chains are possible?

[14] Source: wikipedia.org.

[15] *Ibid.*

[16] Source: D. A. Malyshev et al., "A Semi-synthetic Organism with an Expanded Genetic Alphabet," *Nature*, 509, 2014, pp. 385–388 (http://dx.doi.org/10.1038/nature13314).

c. A "super-human" DNA chain would, like that of natural humans, have 2.1×10^{10} elements but using the expanded alphabet. How many super-human DNA chains are possible?

45. ▼ *HTML* Colors in HTML (the language in which many web pages are written) can be represented by six-digit hexadecimal codes: sequences of six integers ranging from 0 to 15 (represented as 0, ..., 9, A, B, ..., F).

a. How many different colors can be represented?

b. Some monitors can display only colors encoded with pairs of repeating digits (such as 44DD88). How many colors can these monitors display?

c. Grayscale shades are represented by sequences *xyxyxy* consisting of a repeated pair of digits. How many grayscale shades are possible?

d. The pure colors are pure red: *xy*0000; pure green: 00*xy*00; and pure blue: 0000*xy*. (*xy = FF* gives the brightest pure color, while *xy* = 00 gives the darkest: black.) How many pure colors are possible?

46. ▼ *Telephone Numbers* In the past, a local telephone number in the United States consisted of a sequence of two letters followed by five digits. Three letters were associated with each number from 2 to 9 (just as in the standard telephone layout shown in the figure) so that each telephone number corresponded to a sequence of seven digits. How many different sequences of seven digits were possible?

47. ▼ *Romeo and Juliet* Here is a list of the main characters in Shakespeare's *Romeo and Juliet*. The first seven characters are male, and the last four are female.

Escalus, *prince of Verona*
Paris, *kinsman to the prince*
Romeo, *of Montague Household*
Mercutio, *friend of Romeo*
Benvolio, *friend of Romeo*
Tybalt, *nephew to Lady Capulet*
Friar Lawrence, *a Franciscan*
Lady Montague, *of Montague Household*
Lady Capulet, *of Capulet Household*
Juliet, *of Capulet Household*
Juliet's Nurse

A total of 10 male and 8 female actors are available to play these roles. How many possible casts are there? (All roles are to be played by actors of the same gender as the character.)

48. ▼ *Swan Lake* The *Enormous State University*'s Accounting Society has decided to produce a version of the ballet *Swan Lake* in which all the female roles (including all of the swans) will be danced by men and vice versa. Here are the main characters:

Prince Siegfried
Prince Siegfried's Mother
Princess Odette, *the White Swan*
The Evil Duke Rotbart
Odile, *the Black Swan*
Cygnet #1, *young swan*
Cygnet #2, *young swan*
Cygnet #3, *young swan*

The ESU Accounting Society has on hand a total of 4 female dancers and 12 male dancers who are to be considered for the main roles. How many possible casts are there?

49. ▼ *License Plates* Many U.S. license plates display a sequence of three letters followed by three digits.

a. How many such license plates are possible?

b. To avoid confusion of letters with digits, some states do not issue standard plates with the last letter an I, O, or Q. How many license plates are still possible?

c. Assuming that the letter combinations VET, MDZ, and DPZ are reserved for disabled veterans, medical practitioners, and disabled persons, respectively, how many license plates are possible for other vehicles, also taking the restriction in part (b) into account?

50. ▼ *License Plates*[17] License plates in Montana have a sequence consisting of (1) a digit from 1 to 9, (2) a letter, (3) a dot, (4) a letter, and (5) a four-digit number.

a. How many different license plates are possible?

b. If numbers that end with 0 are reserved for official state vehicles, how many license plates are possible for other vehicles?

51. ▼ *Mazes*

a. How many four-letter sequences are possible that contain only the letters R and D, with D occurring only once?

b. Use part (a) to calculate the number of possible routes from Start to Finish in the maze shown in the figure, where each move is either to the right or down.

c. Comment on what would happen if we also allowed left and up moves.

---

[17] Source: The License Plates of the World website (http://servo.oit .gatech.edu/~mk5/).

52. ▽ *Mazes*

    a. How many six-letter sequences are possible that contain only the letters R and D, with D occurring only once?

    b. Use part (a) to calculate the number of possible routes from Start to Finish in the maze shown in the figure, where each move is either to the right or down.

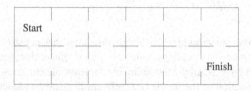

    c. Comment on what would happen if we also allowed left and up moves.

53. ▽ *Car Engines*[18] In a six-cylinder V6 engine, the even-numbered cylinders are on the left, and the odd-numbered cylinders are on the right. A good firing order is a sequence of the numbers 1 through 6 in which right and left sides alternate.

    a. How many possible good firing sequences are there?

    b. How many good firing sequences are there that start with a cylinder on the left?

54. ▽ *Car Engines* Repeat Exercise 53 for an eight-cylinder V8 engine.

55. ▽ *Minimalist Art* You are exhibiting your collection of minimalist paintings. Art critics have raved about your paintings, each of which consists of 10 vertical colored lines set against a white background. You have used the following rule to produce your paintings: Every second line, starting with the first, is to be either blue or gray, while the remaining five lines are to be either all light blue, all red, or all purple. Your collection is complete: Every possible combination that satisfies the rules occurs. How many paintings are you exhibiting?

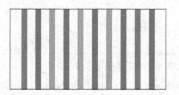

56. ▽ *Combination Locks* Dripping wet after your shower, you have clean forgotten the combination of your lock. It is one of those "standard" combination locks, which uses a three-number combination with each number in the range 0 through 39. All you remember is that the second number is either 27 or 37, while the third number ends in a 5. In desperation you decide to go through all possible combinations

using the information you remember. Assuming that it takes about 10 seconds to try each combination, what is the longest possible time you may have to stand dripping in front of your locker?

57. ▽ *Product Design* Your company has patented an electronic digital padlock that a user can program with his or her own four-digit code. (Each digit can be 0 through 9.) The padlock is designed to open if either the correct code is keyed in or—and this is helpful for forgetful people—if exactly one of the digits is incorrect.

    a. How many incorrect codes will open a programmed padlock?

    b. How many codes will open a programmed padlock?

58. ▽ *Product Design* Your company has patented an electronic digital padlock that has a telephone-style keypad. Each digit from 2 through 9 corresponds to three letters of the alphabet (see the figure for Exercise 46). How many different four-letter sequences correspond to a single four-digit sequence using digits in the range 2 through 9?

59. ▽ *Calendars* The *World Almanac*[19] features a "perpetual calendar," a collection of 14 possible calendars. Why does this suffice to ensure that there is a calendar for every conceivable year?

60. ▽ *Calendars* How many possible calendars are there that have February 12 falling on a Sunday, Monday, or Tuesday?

61. ▽ *Programming in Visual Basic* (Some programming knowledge is assumed for this exercise.) How many iterations will be carried out in the following routine?

```
For i = 1 to 10
    For j = 2 to 20
        For k = 1 to 10
            Print i, j, k
        Next k
    Next j
Next i
```

62. ▽ *Programming in JavaScript* (Some programming knowledge is assumed for this exercise.) How many iterations will be carried out in the following routine?

```
for (i = 1; i <= 2; i++) {
    for (j = 1; j <= 2; j++) {
        for (k = 1; k <= 2; k++) {
            sum += i+j+k;
        }
    }
}
```

63. ◆ *Building Blocks* Use a decision algorithm to show that a rectangular solid with dimensions $m \times n \times r$ can be

---

[18] Adapted from an exercise in *Basic Techniques of Combinatorial Theory* by D. I. A. Cohen (New York: John Wiley, 1978).

[19] Source: *The World Almanac and Book of Facts* 1992 (New York: Pharos Books, 1992).

constructed with $m \cdot n \cdot r$ cubical $1 \times 1 \times 1$ blocks. (See the figure.)

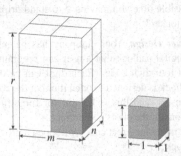

Rectangular Solid Made Up of $1 \times 1 \times 1$ Cubes

64. ◆ *Matrices* (Some knowledge of matrices is assumed for this exercise.) Use a decision algorithm to show that an $m \times n$ matrix must have $m \cdot n$ entries.

65. ◆ *Morse Code* In Morse code, each letter of the alphabet is encoded by a different sequence of dots and dashes. Different letters may have sequences of different lengths. How long should the longest sequence be to allow for every possible letter of the alphabet?

66. ◆ *Numbers* How many odd numbers between 10 and 99 have distinct digits?

Communication and Reasoning Exercises

67. Complete the following sentence: The multiplication principle is based on the cardinality of the _____ of two sets.

68. Complete the following sentence: The addition principle is based on the cardinality of the _____ of two disjoint sets.

69. You are packing for a short trip and want to take 2 of the 10 shirts you have hanging in your closet. Critique the following decision algorithm and calculation of how many different ways you can choose two shirts to pack: Step 1, choose one shirt, 10 choices. Step 2, choose another shirt, 9 choices. Hence, there are 90 possible choices of two shirts.

70. You are designing an advertising logo that consists of a tower of five squares. Three are yellow, one is blue, and one is green. Critique the following decision algorithm and calculation of the number of different five-square sequences: Step 1: Choose the first square, 5 choices. Step 2: Choose the second square, 4 choices. Step 3: Choose the third square: 3 choices. Step 4: Choose the fourth square, 2 choices. Step 5: Choose the last square: 1 choice. Hence, there are 120 possible five-square sequences.

71. ▼ Construct a decision algorithm that gives the correct number of five-square sequences in Exercise 70.

72. ▼ Find an interesting application that requires a decision algorithm with two steps in which each step has two alternatives.

7.4 Permutations and Combinations

Certain classes of counting problems come up frequently, and it is useful to develop formulas to deal with them without having to invoke decision algorithms.

Permutations

EXAMPLE 1 **Casting**

Ms. Birkitt, the English teacher at Brakpan Girls High School, wanted to stage a production of R. B. Sheridan's play *The School for Scandal*. The casting was going well until she was left with five unfilled characters and five seniors who were yet to be assigned roles. The characters were Lady Sneerwell, Lady Teazle, Mrs. Candour, Maria, and Snake; the unassigned seniors were April, May, June, Julia, and Augusta. How many possible assignments are there?

Solution To decide on a specific assignment, we use the following algorithm:

Step 1 Choose a senior to play Lady Sneerwell: 5 choices.

Step 2 Choose one of the remaining seniors to play Lady Teazle: 4 choices.

Step 3 Choose one of the now remaining seniors to play Mrs. Candour: 3 choices.

Step 4 Choose one of the now remaining seniors to play Maria: 2 choices.

Step 5 Choose the remaining senior to play Snake: 1 choice.

Thus, there are $5 \times 4 \times 3 \times 2 \times 1 = 120$ possible assignments of seniors to roles.

What the situation in Example 1 has in common with many others is that we start with a set—here, the set of seniors—and we want to know how many ways we can put the elements of that set in order in a list. In this example, an ordered list of the five seniors, for instance,

1. May
2. Augusta
3. June
4. Julia
5. April

corresponds to a particular casting:

Cast

Lady Sneerwell	May
Lady Teazle	Augusta
Mrs. Candour	June
Maria	Julia
Snake	April

We call an ordered list of items a **permutation** of those items.

If we have n items, how many permutations of those items are possible? We can use a decision algorithm similar to the one we used in Example 1 to select a permutation.

Step 1 Select the first item: n choices.

Step 2 Select the second item: $n - 1$ choices.

Step 3 Select the third item: $n - 2$ choices.

⋮

Step $n - 1$ Select the next-to-last item: 2 choices.

Step n Select the last item: 1 choice.

Thus, there are $n \times (n - 1) \times (n - 2) \times \cdots \times 2 \times 1$ possible permutations. We call this number **n factorial**, which we write as $n!$.

Visualizing Permutations
Permutations of three colors in a flag:

$3! = 3 \times 2 \times 1 = 6$ possible flags

Permutations

A **permutation of n items** is an ordered list of those items. The number of possible permutations of n items is given by **n factorial**, which is

$$n! = n \times (n - 1) \times (n - 2) \times \cdots \times 2 \times 1$$

for n a positive integer, and

$$0! = 1.$$

Quick Examples

1. The number of permutations of five items is
   $5! = 5 \times 4 \times 3 \times 2 \times 1 = 120.$

Using Technology

Technology can be used to compute factorials. For instance, to compute 5!:

TI-83/84 Plus
Home screen: 5 !
(To obtain the ! symbol, press MATH , choose PRB, and select 4 : !.)

Spreadsheet
Use the formula
=FACT(5)

Website
www.WanerMath.com
On the Main Page, enter 5 ! and press "Calculate".

2. The number of ways four CDs can be played in sequence is
$4! = 4 \times 3 \times 2 \times 1 = 24$.

3. The number of ways three cars can be matched with three drivers is
$3! = 6$.

Sometimes, instead of constructing an ordered list of *all* the items of a set, we might want to construct a list of only *some* of the items, as in the next example.

EXAMPLE 2 Corporations[20]

In the second quarter of 2015 the 10 largest publicly traded companies (by market capitalization) were, in order of ranking, Apple, Microsoft, Exxon Mobil, Berkshire Hathaway, Google, Petro China, ICBC, Wells Fargo, Johnson & Johnson, and General Electric. You would like to apply to six of these companies for a job, and you would like to list them in order of job preference. How many such ordered lists are possible?

Solution We want to count ordered lists, but we can't use the permutation formula because we don't want all 10 companies in the list, just 6 of them. So we fall back to a decision algorithm:

Step 1 Choose the first company: 10 choices.

Step 2 Choose the second company: 9 choices.

Step 3 Choose the third one: 8 choices.

Step 4 Choose the fourth one: 7 choices.

Step 5 Choose the fifth one: 6 choices.

Step 6 Choose the sixth one: 5 choices.

Thus, there are $10 \times 9 \times 8 \times 7 \times 6 \times 5 = 151,200$ possible lists of 6. We call this number the **number of permutations of 6 items chosen from 10**, or the **number of permutations of 10 items taken 6 at a time**.

➡ **Before we go on . . .** We wrote the answer as the product $10 \times 9 \times 8 \times 7 \times 6 \times 5$. But it is useful to notice that we can write this number in a more compact way:

$$10 \times 9 \times 8 \times 7 \times 6 \times 5 = \frac{10 \times 9 \times 8 \times 7 \times 6 \times 5 \times 4 \times 3 \times 2 \times 1}{4 \times 3 \times 2 \times 1}$$

$$= \frac{10!}{4!} = \frac{10!}{(10 - 6)!}$$

So we can generalize our definition of permutation to allow for the case in which we use only some of the items, not all. Check that, if $r = n$ below, this is the same definition we gave above.

---

[20] Based on the Financial Times Global 500 rankings. Source: www.wikipedia.org.

Using Technology

Technology can be used to compute permutations. For instance, to compute $P(6, 2)$:

TI-83/84 Plus
Home screen: `6 nPr 2`
(To obtain the `nPr` symbol, press MATH, choose PRB, and select `2:nPr`.)

Spreadsheet
Use the formula
`=PERMUT(6,2)`

Website
www.WanerMath.com
On the Main Page, enter
`perm(6,2)`
and press "Calculate".

Permutations of n items taken r at a time

A **permutation of n items taken r at a time** is an ordered list of r items chosen from a set of n items. The number of permutations of n items taken r at a time is given by

$$P(n, r) = n \times (n - 1) \times (n - 2) \times \cdots \times (n - r + 1).$$

(There are r terms multiplied together.) We can also write

$$P(n, r) = \frac{n!}{(n - r)!}.$$

Quick Example

4. The number of permutations of six items taken two at a time is

$$P(6, 2) = 6 \times 5 = 30,$$

which we could also calculate as

$$P(6, 2) = \frac{6!}{(6 - 2)!} = \frac{6!}{4!} = \frac{720}{24} = 30.$$

Combinations

What if we don't care about the order of the items we're choosing? Consider the following example.

EXAMPLE 3 Corporations

Suppose we simply wanted to pick two of the 10 companies listed in Example 2 to apply to, without regard to order. How many possible choices do we have? What if we wanted to choose six to apply to, without regard to order?

Solution To answer the first question, our first guess might be $P(10, 2) = 10 \times 9 = 90$. However, that is the number of *ordered lists* of two companies. We said that we don't care which is first and which is second. For example, we consider the list

1. Microsoft
2. Johnson & Johnson

to be the same as

1. Johnson & Johnson
2. Microsoft.

Because every set of two companies occurs twice in the 90 lists, once in one order and again in the reverse order, we would count every set of two twice. Thus, there are $90/2 = 45$ possible choices of two companies.

Now, if we wish to pick six companies, again we might start with $P(10, 6) = 151,200$. But now, every set of six companies appears as many times as there are different orders in which they could be listed. Six things can be listed in $6! = 720$ different orders, so the number of ways of choosing six companies is $151,200/720 = 210$.

In Example 3 we were concerned with counting not the number of ordered lists, but the number of *unordered sets* of companies. For ordered lists we used the word *permutation*; for unordered sets we use the word **combination**.

Permutations and Combinations

Visualizing Permutation versus Combination

1.
2. ⬤
3. ⬤

Permutation   Combination

A **permutation** of n items taken r at a time is an *ordered list* of r items chosen from n. A **combination** of n items taken r at a time is an *unordered set* of r items chosen from n.

Note Because lists are usually understood to be ordered, when we refer to a list of items, we will always mean an *ordered* list. Similarly, because sets are understood to be unordered, when we refer to a set of items, we will always mean an *unordered* set. In short:

Lists are ordered. Sets are unordered. ■

Quick Example

5. There are six permutations of the three letters a, b, c taken two at a time:

    1. a, b;   2. b, a;   3. a, c;   4. c, a;   5. b, c;   6. c, b.

    There are six lists containing two of the letters a, b, c.

There are three combinations of the three letters a, b, c taken two at a time:

    1. {a, b};   2. {a, c};   3. {b, c}.

    There are three sets containing two of the letters a, b, c.

How do we count the number of possible combinations of n items taken r at a time? We generalize the calculation done in Example 3. The number of permutations is $P(n, r)$, but each set of r items occurs $r!$ times because this is the number of ways in which those r items can be ordered. So the number of combinations is $P(n, r)/r!$.

Combinations of *n* items taken *r* at a time

The number of **combinations of n items taken r at a time** is given by

$$C(n, r) = \frac{P(n, r)}{r!} = \frac{n \times (n - 1) \times (n - 2) \times \cdots \times (n - r + 1)}{r!}.$$

We can also write

$$C(n, r) = \frac{n!}{r!(n - r)!}.$$

Quick Examples

6. The number of combinations of six items taken two at a time is

$$C(6, 2) = \frac{6 \times 5}{2 \times 1} = 15,$$

which we can also calculate as

$$C(6, 2) = \frac{6!}{2!(6-2)!} = \frac{6!}{2!4!} = \frac{720}{2 \times 24} = 15.$$

7. The number of sets of four marbles chosen from six is

$$C(6, 4) = \frac{6 \times 5 \times 4 \times 3}{4 \times 3 \times 2 \times 1} = 15.$$

Note There are other common notations for $C(n, r)$. Calculators often have $_nC_r$. In mathematics we often write $\binom{n}{r}$, which is also known as a **binomial coefficient**. Because $C(n, r)$ is the number of ways of choosing a set of r items from n, it is often read "n choose r." ∎

EXAMPLE 4 Calculating Combinations

Calculate: **a.** $C(11, 3)$ **b.** $C(11, 8)$

Solution The easiest way to calculate $C(n, r)$ by hand is to use the first formula above:

$$C(n, r) = \frac{P(n, r)}{r!}$$

$$= \frac{n \times (n-1) \times (n-2) \times \cdots \times (n-r+1)}{r \times (r-1) \times (r-2) \times \cdots \times 1}.$$

Both the numerator and the denominator have r factors, so we can begin with n/r and then continue multiplying by decreasing numbers on the top and the bottom until we hit 1 in the denominator. When calculating, it helps to cancel common factors from the numerator and denominator before doing the multiplication in either one.

a. $C(11, 3) = \dfrac{11 \times 10 \times 9}{3 \times 2 \times 1} = \dfrac{11 \times \overset{5}{10} \times \overset{3}{9}}{3 \times 2 \times 1} = 165$

b. $C(11, 8) = \dfrac{11 \times 10 \times 9 \times 8 \times 7 \times 6 \times 5 \times 4}{8 \times 7 \times 6 \times 5 \times 4 \times 3 \times 2 \times 1}$

$$= \dfrac{11 \times \overset{5}{10} \times \overset{3}{9}}{3 \times 2 \times 1} = 165$$

Using Technology

Technology can be used to compute combinations. For instance, to compute C(11, 8):

TI-83/84 Plus
Home screen: `11 nCr 8`
(To obtain the nCr symbol, press `MATH`, choose PRB, and select `3:nCr`.)

Spreadsheet
Use the formula
`=COMBIN(11,8)`

Website
www.WanerMath.com
On the Main Page, enter `comb(11,8)` and press "Calculate".

➡ **Before we go on . . .** It is no coincidence that the answers for parts (a) and (b) of Example 4, and also for Quick Examples 6 and 7, are the same. Consider what each represents. $C(11, 3)$ is the number of ways of choosing 3 items from 11—for example, electing 3 trustees from a slate of 11. Electing those 3 is the same as choosing the 8 who *do not* get elected. Thus, there are exactly as many ways to choose 3 items from 11 as there are ways to choose 8 items from 11. So $C(11, 3) = C(11, 8)$. In general,

$$C(n, r) = C(n, n-r).$$

We can also see this equality by using the formula

$$C(n, r) = \frac{n!}{r!(n - r)!}.$$

If we substitute $n - r$ for r, we get exactly the same formula.

Use the equality $C(n, r) = C(n, n - r)$ to make your calculations easier. Choose the one with the smaller denominator to begin with. ∎

EXAMPLE 5 **Calculating Combinations**

Calculate: **a.** $C(11, 11)$ **b.** $C(11, 0)$

Solution

a. $C(11, 11) = \dfrac{11 \times 10 \times 9 \times 8 \times 7 \times 6 \times 5 \times 4 \times 3 \times 2 \times 1}{11 \times 10 \times 9 \times 8 \times 7 \times 6 \times 5 \times 4 \times 3 \times 2 \times 1} = 1$

b. What do we do with that 0? What does it mean to multiply 0 numbers together? We know from above that $C(11, 0) = C(11, 11)$, so we must have $C(11, 0) = 1$. How does this fit with the formulas? Go back to the calculation of $C(11, 11)$:

$$1 = C(11, 11) = \frac{11!}{11!(11 - 11)!} = \frac{11!}{11! \, 0!}.$$

This equality is true only if we agree that $0! = 1$, which we do. Then

$$C(11, 0) = \frac{11!}{0! \, 11!} = 1.$$

➡ **Before we go on . . .** There is nothing special about 11 in the calculation in Example 5. In general,

$$C(n, n) = C(n, 0) = 1.$$

After all, there is only one way to choose n items out of n: Choose them all. Similarly, there is only one way to choose 0 items out of n: Choose none of them. ∎

Now for a few more complicated examples that illustrate the applications of the counting techniques we've discussed.

EXAMPLE 6 **Lotto**

In the betting game Lotto, used in many state lotteries, you choose six different numbers in the range 1–55 (the upper number varies). The order in which you choose them is irrelevant. If your six numbers match the six numbers chosen in the official drawing, you win the top prize. If Lotto tickets cost $1 for two sets of numbers and you decide to buy tickets that cover every possible combination, thereby guaranteeing that you will win the top prize, how much money will you have to spend?

Solution We first need to know how many sets of numbers are possible. Because order does not matter, we are asking for the number of combinations of 55 numbers taken 6 at a time. This is

$$C(55, 6) = \frac{55 \times 54 \times 53 \times 52 \times 51 \times 50}{6 \times 5 \times 4 \times 3 \times 2 \times 1} = 28{,}989{,}675.$$

Because \$1 buys you two of these, you need to spend $28{,}989{,}675/2 = \$14{,}494{,}838$ (rounding up to the nearest dollar) to be assured of a win!

➡ **Before we go on...** The calculation in Example 6 shows that you should not bother buying all these tickets if the winning prize is less than about \$14.5 million. Even if the prize is higher, you need to account for the fact that many people will play and the prize may end up split among several winners, not to mention the impracticality of filling out millions of betting slips. ■

EXAMPLE 7   Marbles

A bag contains three red marbles, three blue ones, three green ones, and two yellow ones (all distinguishable from one another).

a. How many sets of four marbles are possible?

b. How many sets of four are there such that each one is a different color?

c. How many sets of four are there in which at least two are red?

d. How many sets of four are there in which none are red but at least one is green?

Solution

a. We simply need to find the number of ways of choosing 4 marbles out of 11, which is

$$C(11, 4) = 330 \text{ possible sets of 4 marbles.}$$

b. We use a decision algorithm for choosing such a set of marbles:

Step 1 Choose one red one from the three red ones: $C(3, 1) = 3$ choices.
Step 2 Choose one blue one from the three blue ones: $C(3, 1) = 3$ choices.
Step 3 Choose one green one from the three green ones: $C(3, 1) = 3$ choices.
Step 4 Choose one yellow one from the two yellow ones: $C(2, 1) = 2$ choices.

This gives a total of $3 \times 3 \times 3 \times 2 = 54$ possible sets.

c. We need another decision algorithm. To say that at least two marbles must be red means that either two are red or three are red (with a total of three red ones). In other words, we have two *alternatives*.

Alternative 1: Exactly two red marbles
   Step 1 Choose two red ones: $C(3, 2) = 3$ choices.
   Step 2 Choose two nonred ones. There are eight of these, so we get $C(8, 2) = 28$ possible choices.

Thus, the total number of choices for this alternative is $3 \times 28 = 84$.

Alternative 2: Exactly three red marbles.
   Step 1 Choose the three red ones: $C(3, 3) = 1$ choice.
   Step 2 Choose one nonred one: $C(8, 1) = 8$ choices.

Thus, the total number of choices for this alternative is $1 \times 8 = 8$.

By the addition principle, we get a total of $84 + 8 = 92$ sets.

d. The phrase "at least one green" tells us that we again have some alternatives:

Alternative 1: One green marble
   Step 1 Choose one green marble from the three: $C(3, 1) = 3$ choices.
   Step 2 Choose three nongreen, nonred marbles: $C(5, 3) = 10$ choices.

Thus, the total number of choices for alternative 1 is $3 \times 10 = 30$.

Alternative 2: Two green marbles

    Step 1 Choose two green marbles from the three: $C(3, 2) = 3$ choices.

    Step 2 Choose two nongreen, nonred marbles: $C(5, 2) = 10$ choices.

Thus, the total number of choices for alternative 2 is $3 \times 10 = 30$.

Alternative 3: Three green marbles

    Step 1 Choose three green marbles from the three: $C(3, 3) = 1$ choice.

    Step 2 Choose one nongreen, nonred marble: $C(5, 1) = 5$ choices.

Thus, the total number of choices for alternative 3 is $1 \times 5 = 5$.

The addition principle now tells us that the number of sets of four marbles with none red but at least one green is $30 + 30 + 5 = 65$.

➡ **Before we go on . . .** Here is an easier way to answer Example 7(d). First, the total number of sets having *no* red marbles is $C(8, 4) = 70$. Next, of those, the number containing no green marbles is $C(5, 4) = 5$. This leaves $70 - 5 = 65$ sets that contain no red marbles but have at least one green marble. (We have really used here the formula for the cardinality of the complement of a set.) ∎

The last example concerns poker hands. For those unfamiliar with playing cards, here is a short description. A standard deck consists of 52 playing cards. Each card is in one of 13 denominations: ace (A), 2, 3, 4, 5, 6, 7, 8, 9, 10, jack (J), queen (Q), and king (K), and in one of four suits: hearts (♥), diamonds (♦), clubs (♣), and spades (♠). Thus, for instance, the jack of spades, J♠, refers to the denomination of jack in the suit of spades. The entire deck of cards is thus

A♥	2♥	3♥	4♥	5♥	6♥	7♥	8♥	9♥	10♥	J♥	Q♥	K♥
A♦	2♦	3♦	4♦	5♦	6♦	7♦	8♦	9♦	10♦	J♦	Q♦	K♦
A♣	2♣	3♣	4♣	5♣	6♣	7♣	8♣	9♣	10♣	J♣	Q♣	K♣
A♠	2♠	3♠	4♠	5♠	6♠	7♠	8♠	9♠	10♠	J♠	Q♠	K♠

EXAMPLE 8   **Poker Hands**

In the card game poker, a hand consists of a set of 5 cards from a standard deck of 52. A **full house** is a hand consisting of three cards of one denomination ("three of a kind"—e.g., three 10s) and two of another ("two of a kind"—e.g., two queens). Here is an example of a full house: 10♣, 10♦, 10♠, Q♥, Q♣.

a. How many different poker hands are there?

b. How many different full houses are there that contain three 10s and two queens?

c. How many different full houses are there altogether?

Solution

a. Because the order of the cards doesn't matter, we simply need to know the number of ways of choosing a set of 5 cards out of 52, which is

$$C(52, 5) = 2{,}598{,}960 \text{ hands.}$$

b. Here is a decision algorithm for choosing a full house with three 10s and two queens:

    Step 1 Choose three 10s. Because there are four 10s to choose from, we have $C(4, 3) = 4$ choices.

    Step 2 Choose two queens: $C(4, 2) = 6$ choices.

Thus, there are $4 \times 6 = 24$ possible full houses with three 10s and two queens.

c. Here is a decision algorithm for choosing a full house:

Step 1 Choose a denomination for the three of a kind; 13 choices.

Step 2 Choose three cards of that denomination. Because there are four cards of each denomination (one for each suit), we get $C(4, 3) = 4$ choices.

Step 3 Choose a different denomination for the two of a kind. There are only 12 denominations left, so we have 12 choices.

Step 4 Choose two of that denomination: $C(4, 2) = 6$ choices.

Thus, by the multiplication principle there are a total of $13 \times 4 \times 12 \times 6 = 3,744$ possible full houses.

FAQs

Recognizing When to Use Permutations or Combinations

Q : *How can I tell whether a given application calls for permutations or combinations?*

A : Decide whether the application calls for ordered lists (as in situations in which order is implied) or for unordered sets (as in situations in which order is not relevant). Ordered lists are permutations, whereas unordered sets are combinations.

7.4   EXERCISES

▼ more advanced   ◆ challenging
🔲 indicates exercises that should be solved using technology

In Exercises 1–16, evaluate the number. [**HINT**: See Quick Examples 4–7.]

1. 6!

2. 7!

3. 8!/6!

4. 10!/8!

5. $P(6, 4)$

6. $P(8, 3)$

7. $P(6, 4)/4!$

8. $P(8, 3)/3!$

9. $C(3, 2)$

10. $C(4, 3)$

11. $C(10, 8)$

12. $C(11, 9)$

13. $C(20, 1)$

14. $C(30, 1)$

15. $C(100, 98)$

16. $C(100, 97)$

17. How many ordered lists are there of four items chosen from six?

18. How many ordered sequences are possible that contain three objects chosen from seven?

19. How many unordered sets are possible that contain three objects chosen from seven?

20. How many unordered sets are there of four items chosen from six?

21. How many five-letter sequences are possible that use the letters b, o, g, e, y once each?

22. How many six-letter sequences are possible that use the letters q, u, a, k, e, s once each?

23. How many three-letter sequences are possible that use the letters q, u, a, k, e, s at most once each?

24. How many three-letter sequences are possible that use the letters b, o, g, e, y at most once each?

25. How many three-letter (unordered) sets are possible that use the letters q, u, a, k, e, s at most once each?

26. How many three-letter (unordered) sets are possible that use the letters b, o, g, e, y at most once each?

27. ▼ How many six-letter sequences are possible that use the letters a, u, a, a, u, k? [**HINT**: Use the decision algorithm discussed in Example 3 of Section 7.3.]

28. ▼ How many six-letter sequences are possible that use the letters f, f, a, a, f, f? [**HINT**: See the hint for Exercise 27.]

Marbles For Exercises 29–42, a bag contains three red marbles, two green ones, one lavender one, two yellows, and two orange marbles. [**HINT**: See Example 7.]

29. How many possible sets of four marbles are there?

30. How many possible sets of three marbles are there?

31. How many sets of four marbles include all the red ones?

32. How many sets of three marbles include all the yellow ones?

33. How many sets of four marbles include none of the red ones?

34. How many sets of three marbles include none of the yellow ones?

35. How many sets of four marbles include one of each color other than lavender?

36. How many sets of five marbles include one of each color?

37. How many sets of five marbles include at least two red ones?

38. How many sets of five marbles include at least one yellow one?

39. How many sets of five marbles include at most one of the yellow ones?

40. How many sets of five marbles include at most one of the red ones?

41. ▼ How many sets of five marbles include either the lavender one or exactly one yellow one but not both colors?

42. ▼ How many sets of five marbles include at least one yellow one but no green ones?

Dice If a die is rolled 30 times, there are 6^{30} different sequences possible. Exercises 43–46 ask how many of these sequences satisfy certain conditions. [HINT: Use the decision algorithm discussed in Example 3 of Section 7.3.]

43. ▼ What fraction of these sequences have exactly five 1s?

44. ▼ What fraction of these sequences have exactly five 1s and five 2s?

45. ▼ What fraction of these sequences have exactly 15 even numbers?

46. ▼ What fraction of these sequences have exactly 10 numbers less than or equal to 2?

In Exercises 47–52, calculate how many different sequences can be formed that use the letters of each given word. Leave your answer as a product of terms of the form $C(n, r)$. [HINT: Decide where, for example, all the s's will go rather than what will go in each position.]

47. ▼ mississippi   **48.** ▼ mesopotamia

49. ▼ megalomania   **50.** ▼ schizophrenia

51. ▼ casablanca   **52.** ▼ desmorelda

Applications

53. *Itineraries* Your international diplomacy trip requires stops in Thailand, Singapore, Hong Kong, and Bali. How many possible itineraries are there? [HINT: See Examples 1 and 2.]

54. *Itineraries* Refer back to Exercise 53. How many possible itineraries are there in which the last stop is Thailand?

Poker Hands A poker hand consists of 5 cards from a standard deck of 52. (See the chart preceding Example 8.) In Exercises 55–60, find the number of different poker hands of the specified type. [HINT: See Example 8.]

55. Two pairs (two of one denomination, two of another denomination, and one of a third)

56. Three of a kind (three of one denomination, one of another denomination, and one of a third)

57. Two of a kind (two of one denomination and three of different denominations)

58. Four of a kind (all four of one denomination and one of another)

59. ▼ Straight (five cards of consecutive denominations: A, 2, 3, 4, 5 up through 10, J, Q, K, A, not all of the same suit) (Note that the ace counts either as a 1 or as the denomination above king.)

60. ▼ Flush (five cards all of the same suit but not consecutive denominations)

Dogs of the Dow The "Dogs of the Dow" are the stocks listed on the Dow with the highest dividend yield. Exercises 61 and 62 are based on the following table, which shows the top 10 stocks of the "Dogs of the Dow" list for 2015, based on their performance the preceding year.[21]

Symbol	Company	Price ($)	Yield
T	AT&T	33.59	5.48%
VZ	Verizon	46.78	4.70%
CVX	Chevron	112.18	3.82%
MCD	McDonald's	93.70	3.63%
PFE	Pfizer	31.15	3.60%
GE	General Electric	25.27	3.48%
MRK	Merck	56.79	3.17%
CAT	Caterpillar	91.53	3.06%
XOM	ExxonMobil	92.45	2.99%
KO	Coca-Cola	42.22	2.89%

61. You decide to make a small portfolio consisting of a collection of 5 of the top 10 Dogs of the Dow.
 a. How many portfolios are possible?
 b. How many of these portfolios contain VZ and MCD but neither KO nor XOM?
 c. How many of these portfolios contain at least four stocks with yields above 3.5%?

62. You decide to make a small portfolio consisting of a collection of 6 of the top 10 Dogs of the Dow.
 a. How many portfolios are possible?
 b. How many of these portfolios contain MRK but not PFE?
 c. How many of these portfolios contain at most one stock priced above $60?

---

[21] Source: www.dogsofthedow.com.

Day Trading *Day traders typically buy and sell stocks (or other investment instruments) during the trading day and sell all investments by the end of the day. Exercises 63 and 64 are based on the following table, which shows the closing prices on September 22, 2015, of 12 stocks selected by your broker, Prudence Swift, as well as the change that day.*[22]

Tech Stocks	Close	Change
AAPL (Apple)	$113.40	−1.81
ADBE (Adobe Systems)	$84.66	1.34
EBAY (eBay)	$25.61	−0.31
MSFT (Microsoft)	$3.90	−0.21
S (Sprint)	$4.40	0.02
WIFI (Boingo Wireless)	$8.51	0.56
Non-Tech Stocks		
ANF (Abercrombie & Fitch)	$21.81	−0.02
B (Boeing)	$133.99	−2.03
F (Ford Motor Co.)	$13.91	−0.40
GE (General Electric)	$25.10	0.01
GIS (General Mills)	$57.12	0.33
JNJ (Johnson & Johnson)	$93.26	0.13

63. On the morning of September 22, 2015, Swift advised you to purchase a collection of three tech stocks and two non-tech stocks, all chosen at random from those listed in the table. You were to sell all the stocks at the end of the trading day.
   a. How many possible collections are possible?
   b. You tend to have bad luck with stocks—they usually start going down the moment you buy them. How many of the collections in part (a) consist entirely of stocks that declined in value by the end of the day?
   c. Using the answers to parts (a) and (b), what would you say your chances were of choosing a collection consisting entirely of stocks that declined in value by the end of the day?

64. On the morning of September 22, 2015, Swift advised your friend to purchase a collection of three stocks chosen at random from those listed in the table. Your friend was to sell all the stocks at the end of the trading day.
   a. How many possible collections are possible?
   b. How many of the collections in part (a) included exactly two tech stocks that increased in value by the end of the day?
   c. Using the answers to parts (a) and (b), what would you say the chances were that your friend chose a collection that included exactly two tech stocks that increased in value by the end of the day?

Elimination Tournaments *In an elimination tournament the teams are arranged in opponent pairs for the first round, and the winner of each round goes on to the next round until the champion emerges. The following diagram illustrates a 16-team tournament bracket, in which the 16 participating teams are arranged on the left under Round 1 and the winners of each round are added as the tournament progresses. The top team in each game is considered the "home" team, so the top-to-bottom order matters.*

To seed a tournament means to select which teams to play each other in the first round according to their preliminary ranking. For instance, in professional tennis and NCAA basketball the seeding is set up in the following order based on the preliminary rankings: 1 versus 16, 8 versus 9, 5 versus 12, 4 versus 13, 6 versus 11, 3 versus 14, 7 versus 10, and 2 versus 15.[23] *Exercises 65–68 are based on various types of elimination tournaments. (Leave each answer as a formula.)*

65. a. How many different seedings of a 16-team tournament are possible? (Express the answer as a formula.)
   b. In how many seedings will the top-ranked team play the bottom-ranked team, the second-ranked team play the second-lowest-ranked team, and so on?

66. a. How many different seedings of an 8-team tournament are possible? (Express the answer as a formula.)
   b. In how many seedings will each team play a team with adjacent ranking?

67. ▼ In 2014, after the NCAA basketball 64-team tournament had already been seeded, Quicken Loans, backed by investor Warren Buffett, offered a billion dollar prize for picking all the winners.[24] An *upset* occurs when a team beats a higher-ranked team. How many configurations (filling in of all the winners in all the rounds) were possible in which there were exactly 15 upsets in the first four rounds?

68. ▼ Refer back to Exercise 67. In the 2013 NCAA playoffs there were 10 upsets in the first round, 4 in the second round, and 3 in each of the third and fourth rounds.[25] How many configurations (filling in of all the winners in all the rounds) of this type were possible? (In the last two rounds, rankings are not taken into consideration.)

Popular Movies in 2011 *Exercises 69 and 70 are based on the following list of top DVD rentals (based on revenue) for the weekend ending November 6, 2011:*[26]

Title	Rank
Captain America: The First Avenger	1
Bad Teacher	2
Fast Five	3
Cars 2	4
Trespass	5
Bridesmaids	6
Zookeeper	7
Transformers: Dark of the Moon	8
Scream	9
Thor	10

69. ▼ Rather than studying for math, you and your buddies decide to get together for a marathon movie-watching, popcorn-guzzling event on Saturday night. You decide to watch four movies selected at random from the above list.
   a. How many sets of four movies are possible?
   b. Your best friends, the Lara twins, refuse to see *Bridesmaids* on the grounds that it is "for girlie men" and also insist that at least one of *Captain America* or *Thor* be among the movies selected. How many of the possible groups of four will satisfy the twins?
   c. Comparing the answers in parts (a) and (b), would you say that the Lara twins are more likely than not to be satisfied with your random selection?

70. ▼ Rather than studying for astrophysics, you and your friends decide to get together for a marathon movie-watching, gummy-bear-munching event on Saturday night. You decide to watch three movies selected at random from the above list.
   a. How many sets of three movies are possible?
   b. Your best friends, the Pelogrande twins, refuse to see either *Cars 2* or *Zookeeper* on the grounds that they are "for idiots" and also insist that no more than one of *Bad Teacher* and *Fast Five* should be among the movies selected. How many of the possible groups of three will satisfy the twins?
   c. Comparing the answers in parts (a) and (b), would you say that the Pelogrande twins are more likely than not to be satisfied with your random selection?

71. ▼ ***Traveling Salesperson*** Suppose you are a salesperson who must visit the following 23 cities: Dallas, Tampa, Orlando, Fairbanks, Seattle, Detroit, Chicago, Houston, Arlington, Grand Rapids, Urbana, San Diego, Aspen, Little Rock, Tuscaloosa, Honolulu, New York, Ithaca, Charlottesville, Lynchville, Raleigh, Anchorage, and Los Angeles. Leave all your answers in factorial form.
   a. How many possible itineraries are there that visit each city exactly once?
   b. Repeat part (a) in the event that the first five stops have already been determined.
   c. Repeat part (a) in the event that your itinerary must include the sequence Anchorage, Fairbanks, Seattle, Chicago, and Detroit, in that order.

72. ▼ ***Traveling Salesperson*** Refer back to Exercise 71 (and leave all your answers in factorial form).
   a. How many possible itineraries are there that start and end at Detroit and visit every other city exactly once?
   b. How many possible itineraries are there that start and end at Detroit and visit Chicago twice and every other city once?
   c. Repeat part (a) in the event that your itinerary must include the sequence Anchorage, Fairbanks, Seattle, Chicago, and New York, in that order.

73. ▼ (***From the GMAT***) Ben and Ann are among seven contestants from which four semifinalists are to be selected. Of the different possible selections, how many contain neither Ben nor Ann?
   (A) 5   (B) 6   (C) 7   (D) 14   (E) 21

74. ▼ (***Based on a question from the GMAT***) Ben and Ann are among seven contestants from which four semifinalists are to be selected. Of the different possible selections, how many contain Ben but not Ann?
   (A) 5   (B) 8   (C) 9   (D) 10   (E) 20

---

[24] No one won the prize, and the offer was scrapped the following year as a result of a series of lawsuits and countersuits by Yahoo, SCA Promotions (a sweepstakes company), and Berkshire-Hathaway. Sources: http://abcnews.go.com/Sports/warren-buffet-backs-billion-dollar-march-madness-challenge/story?id=21615743, http://money.cnn.com/2015/03/12/news/buffett-ncaa-bracket-bet/index.html.

[25] Source: *Washington Post*, March 16, 2014 (www.washingtonpost.com).

[26] Source: Home Media Magazine (www.imdb.com/Charts/videolast).

75. ◆ (*From the GMAT exam*) If 10 persons meet at a reunion and each person shakes hands exactly once with each of the others, what is the total number of handshakes?
    (A) $10 \cdot 9 \cdot 8 \cdot 7 \cdot 6 \cdot 5 \cdot 4 \cdot 3 \cdot 2 \cdot 1$ (B) $10 \cdot 10$
    (C) $10 \cdot 9$ (D) 45 (E) 36

76. ◆ (*Based on a question from the GMAT exam*) If 12 businesspeople have a meeting and each pair exchanges business cards, how many business cards, total, get exchanged?
    (A) $12 \cdot 11 \cdot 10 \cdot 9 \cdot 8 \cdot 7 \cdot 6 \cdot 5 \cdot 4 \cdot 3 \cdot 2 \cdot 1$ (B) $12 \cdot 12$
    (C) $12 \cdot 11$ (D) 66 (E) 72

77. ◆ *Product Design* The Honest Lock Company plans to introduce what it refers to as the "true combination lock." The lock will open if the correct set of three numbers from 0 through 39 is entered in any order.
    a. How many different combinations of three different numbers are possible?
    b. If it is allowed that a number appear twice (but not three times), how many more possibilities are created?
    c. If it is allowed that any or all of the numbers may be the same, what is the total number of combinations possible?

78. ◆ *Product Design* Repeat Exercise 77 for a lock based on selecting from the numbers 0 through 19.

79. ◆ *Theory of Linear Programming* (Some familiarity with linear programming is assumed for this exercise.) Suppose you have a linear programming problem with two unknowns and 20 constraints. You decide that graphing the feasible region would take a lot of work, but then you recall that corner points are obtained by solving a system of two equations in two unknowns obtained from two of the constraints. Thus, you decide that it might pay instead to locate all the possible corner points by solving all possible combinations of two equations and then checking whether each solution is a feasible point.
    a. How many systems of two equations in two unknowns will you be required to solve?
    b. Generalize this to n constraints.

80. ◆ *More Theory of Linear Programming* (Some familiarity with linear programming is assumed for this exercise.) Before the advent of the simplex method for solving linear programming problems, the following method was used: Suppose you have a linear programming problem with three unknowns and 20 constraints. You locate corner points as follows: Selecting three of the constraints, you turn them into equations (by replacing the inequalities with equalities), solve the resulting system of three equations in three unknowns, and then check to see whether the solution is feasible.
    a. How many systems of three equations in three unknowns will you be required to solve?
    b. Generalize this to n constraints.

Communication and Reasoning Exercises

81. If you were hard pressed to study for an exam on counting and had only enough time to study one topic, would you choose the formula for the number of permutations or the multiplication principle? Give reasons for your choice.

82. The formula for $C(n, r)$ is written as a ratio of two whole numbers. Can $C(n, r)$ ever be a fraction and not a whole number? Explain (without actually discussing the formula itself).

83. Which of the following represent permutations?
    (A) An arrangement of books on a shelf
    (B) A group of 10 people in a bus
    (C) A committee of 5 senators chosen from 100
    (D) A presidential cabinet of 5 portfolios chosen from 20

84. Which of the following represent combinations?
    (A) A portfolio of five stocks chosen from the S&P Top Ten
    (B) A group of 5 tenors for a choir chosen from 12 singers
    (C) A new company CEO and a new CFO chosen from five candidates
    (D) The *New York Times* Top Ten Bestseller list

85. When you click on "Get Driving Directions" on Mapquest .com, do you get a permutation or a combination of driving instructions? Explain, and give a simple example to illustrate why the answer is important.

86. If you want to know how many possible lists, arranged in alphabetical order, there are of five students selected from your class, you would use the formula for permutations—right? (Explain your answer.)

87. You are tutoring your friend for a test on sets and counting, and she asks the question "How do I know what formula to use for a given problem?" What is a good way to respond?

88. Complete the following: If a counting procedure has five alternatives, each of which has four steps of two choices each, then there are ___ outcomes. On the other hand, if there are five steps, each of which has four alternatives of two choices each, then there are ___ outcomes.

89. ▼ A textbook has the following exercise: "Three students from a class of 50 are selected to take part in a play. How many casts are possible?" Comment on this exercise.

90. ▼ Explain why the coefficient of a $a^2 b^4$ in $(a + b)^6$ is $C(6, 2)$. (This is a consequence of the **binomial theorem**.) [HINT: In the product $(a + b)(a + b) \cdots (a + b)$ (six times), in how many different ways can you pick two a's and four b's to multiply together?]

CHAPTER 7 REVIEW

KEY CONCEPTS

WWW www.WanerMath.com
Go to the Website to find a comprehensive and interactive Web-based summary of Chapter 7.

7.1 Sets and Set Operations
Sets, elements, subsets, proper subsets, empty set, finite and infinite sets [p. 496]

Visualizing sets and relations between sets using Venn diagrams [p. 498]

Union:
$A \cup B = \{x \,|\, x \in A \text{ or } x \in B\}$ [p. 500]

Intersection: $A \cap B =$
$\{x \,|\, x \in A \text{ and } x \in B\}$ [p. 500]

Universal sets, complements [p. 501]

Disjoint sets: $A \cap B = \varnothing$ [p. 502]

Cartesian product: $A \times B =$
$\{(a, b) \,|\, a \in A \text{ and } b \in B\}$ [p. 502]

7.2 Cardinality
Cardinality: $n(A) =$
number of elements in A. [p. 507]

If A and B are finite sets, then
$n(A \cup B) =$
$n(A) + n(B) - n(A \cap B)$. [p. 507]

If A and B are disjoint finite sets, then $n(A \cup B) = n(A) + n(B)$. In this case we say that $A \cup B$ is a **disjoint union**. [p. 508]

If S is a finite universal set and A is a subset of S, then
$n(A') = n(S) - n(A)$ and
$n(A) = n(S) - n(A')$. [p. 509]

If A and B are finite sets, then
$n(A \times B) = n(A)n(B)$. [p. 513]

7.3 Decision Algorithms: The Addition and Multiplication Principles
Addition principle [p. 517]

Multiplication principle [p. 518]

Decision algorithm: a procedure for making a sequence of decisions to choose an element of a set [p. 520]

7.4 Permutations and Combinations
n factorial:
$n! = n \times (n - 1) \times (n - 2) \times \cdots \times 2 \times 1$ [p. 529]

Permutation of n items taken r at a time:

$$P(n, r) = \frac{n!}{(n - r)!}$$ [p. 531]

Combination of n items taken r at a time:

$$C(n, r) = \frac{P(n, r)}{r!} = \frac{n!}{r!(n - r)!}$$
[p. 532]

Using the equality
$C(n, r) = C(n, n - r)$ to simplify calculations of combinations [p. 533]

REVIEW EXERCISES

In Exercises 1–5, list the elements of the given set.

1. The set N of all negative integers greater than or equal to -3

2. The set of all outcomes of tossing a coin five times

3. The set of all outcomes of tossing two distinguishable dice such that the numbers are different

4. The sets $(A \cap B) \cup C$ and $A \cap (B \cup C)$, where $A = \{1, 2, 3, 4, 5\}$, $B = \{3, 4, 5\}$, and $C = \{1, 2, 5, 6, 7\}$

5. The sets $A \cup B'$ and $A \times B'$, where $A = \{a, b\}$, $B = \{b, c\}$, and $S = \{a, b, c, d\}$

In Exercises 6–10, write the indicated set in terms of the given sets.

6. S: the set of all customers; A: the set of all customers who owe money; B: the set of all customers who owe at least $1,000. The set of all customers who owe money but owe less than $1,000

7. A: the set of outcomes when a day in August is selected; B: the set of outcomes when a time of day is selected. The set of outcomes when a day in August and a time of that day are selected

8. S: the set of outcomes when two dice are rolled; E: those outcomes in which at most one die shows an even number,

F: those outcomes in which the sum of the numbers is 7. The set of outcomes in which both dice show an even number or sum to seven

9. S: the set of all integers; E: the set of all even integers; Q: the set of all integers that are perfect squares ($Q = \{0, 1, 4, 9, 16, 25, \ldots\}$). The set of all integers that are not odd perfect squares

10. S: the set of all integers; N: the set of all negative integers; E: the set of all even integers; T: the set of all integers that are multiples of 3 ($T = \{0, 3, -3, 6, -6, 9, -9, \ldots\}$). The set of all even integers that are neither negative nor multiples of three

In Exercises 11–14, give a formula for the cardinality rule or rules needed to answer the question, and then give the solution.

11. You have read 150 of the 400 novels in your home, but your sister Roslyn has read 200, of which only 50 are novels you have read as well. How many have neither of you read?

12. There are 32 students in categories A and B combined; 24 are in A, and 24 are in B. How many are in both A and B?

13. You roll two dice, one red and one green. Losing combinations are doubles (both dice show the same number) and outcomes in which the green die shows an odd number and the red die shows an even number. The other combinations are winning ones. How many winning combinations are there?

14. The Apple iMac used to come in three models, each with five colors to choose from. How many combinations were possible?

Recall that a poker hand consists of 5 cards from a standard deck of 52. In Exercises 15–18, find the number of different poker hands of the specified type. Leave your answer in terms of combinations.

15. Two of a kind with no aces

16. A full house with either two kings and three queens or two queens and three kings

17. Straight flush (five cards of the same suit with consecutive denominations: A, 2, 3, 4, 5 up through 10, J, Q, K, A)

18. Three of a kind with no aces

In Exercises 19–24, consider a bag containing four red marbles, two green ones, one transparent one, three yellow ones, and two orange ones.

19. How many possible sets of five marbles are there in which all of them are red or green?

20. How many possible sets of five marbles are there in which none of them are red or green?

21. How many sets of five marbles include all the red ones?

22. How many sets of five marbles do not include all the red ones?

23. How many sets of five marbles include at least two yellow ones?

24. How many sets of five marbles include at most one of the red ones but no yellow ones?

Applications: OHaganBooks.com
[Try the game at www.OHaganBooks.com]

Inventories OHaganBooks.com currently operates three warehouses: one in Washington, one in California, and the new one in Texas. Exercises 25–30 are based on the following table, which shows the book inventories at each warehouse:

	Sci Fi	Horror	Romance	Other	Total
Washington	10,000	12,000	12,000	30,000	64,000
California	8,000	12,000	6,000	16,000	42,000
Texas	15,000	15,000	20,000	44,000	94,000
Total	33,000	39,000	38,000	90,000	200,000

Take the first letter of each category to represent the corresponding set of books; for instance, S is the set of sci fi books in stock, W is the set of books in the Washington warehouse, and so on. In each exercise, describe the given set in words, and compute its cardinality.

25. $S \cup T$

26. $H \cap C$

27. $C \cup S'$

28. $(R \cap T) \cup H$

29. $R \cap (T \cup H)$

30. $(S \cap W) \cup (H \cap C')$

Customers OHaganBooks.com has two main competitors: JungleBooks.com and FarmerBooks.com. At the beginning of August, OHaganBooks.com had 3,500 customers. Of these, a total of 2,000 customers were shared with JungleBooks.com, and 1,500 were shared with FarmerBooks.com. Furthermore, 1,000 customers were shared with both. JungleBooks.com has a total of 3,600 customers, FarmerBooks.com has 3,400, and they share 1,100 customers between them. Use these data for Exercises 31–36.

31. How many of all these customers are exclusive OHaganBooks.com customers?

32. How many customers of the other two companies are not customers of OHaganBooks.com?

33. Which of the three companies has the largest number of exclusive customers?

34. Which of the three companies has the smallest number of exclusive customers?

35. OHaganBooks.com is interested in merging with one of its two competitors. Which merger would give it the largest combined customer base, and how large would that be?

36. Referring to Exercise 35, which merger would give OHaganBooks.com the largest *exclusive* customer base, and how large would that be?

Online IDs As the customer base at OHaganBooks.com grows, IT manager Ruth Nabarro is thinking of introducing identity codes for all the customers, using capital letters and/or numbers. Help her answer the questions in Exercises 37–40.

37. If she uses three-letter codes, how many different customers can be identified?

38. If she uses codes with three different letters, how many different customers can be identified?

39. It appears that Nabarro has finally settled on codes consisting of two letters followed by two digits. For technical reasons, the letters must be different, and the first digit cannot be a zero. How many different customers can be identified?

40. O'Hagan sends Nabarro the following memo:

> To: Ruth Nabarro, Software Manager
> From: John O'Hagan, CEO
> Subject: Customer Identity Codes
>
> I have read your proposal for the customer ID codes. However, due to our ambitious expansion plans, I would like our system software to allow for at least 500,000 customers. Please adjust your proposal accordingly.

Nabarro is determined to have a sequence of letters followed by some digits, and, for reasons too complicated to explain, there cannot be more than two letters, the letters must be different, the digits must all be different, and the first digit cannot be a zero. What is the form of the shortest code she can use to satisfy the CEO, and how many different customers can be identified?

Degree Requirements *After an exhausting day at the office, John O'Hagan returns home and finds himself having to assist his son Billy-Sean, who continues to have a terrible time planning his first-year college course schedule. The latest* Bulletin of Suburban State University *reads as follows:*

> *All candidates for the degree of Bachelor of Arts at SSU must take, in their first year, at least 10 courses in the Sciences, Fine Arts, Liberal Arts, and Mathematics combined, of which at least 2 must be in each of the Sciences and Fine Arts, and exactly 3 must be in each of the Liberal Arts and Mathematics.*

Help him with the answers to Exercises 41–43.

41. If the bulletin lists exactly five first-year-level science courses and six first-year-level courses in each of the other categories, how many course combinations are possible that meet the minimum requirements?

42. Reading through the course descriptions in the bulletin a second time, John O'Hagan notices that Calculus I (listed as one of the mathematics courses) is a required course for many of the other courses and so decides that it would be best if Billy-Sean included Calculus I. Further, two of the Fine Arts courses cannot both be taken in the first year. How many course combinations are possible that meet the minimum requirements and include Calculus I?

43. To complicate things further, in addition to the requirement in Exercise 42, Physics II has Physics I as a prerequisite. (Both are listed as first-year science courses, but it is not necessary to take both.) How many course combinations are possible that include Calculus I and meet the minimum requirements?

CASE STUDY

Designing a Puzzle

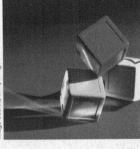

As Product Design Manager for *Cerebral Toys, Inc.*, you are constantly on the lookout for ideas for intellectually stimulating yet inexpensive toys. You recently received the following memo from Felix Frost, the developmental psychologist on your design team.

To: Felicia
From: Felix
Subject: Crazy Cubes

We've hit on an excellent idea for a new educational puzzle (which we are calling "Crazy Cubes" until Marketing comes up with a better name). Basically, Crazy Cubes will consist of a set of plastic cubes. Two faces of each cube will be colored red, two will be colored blue, and two will be colored white, and there will be exactly two cubes with each possible configuration of colors. The goal of the puzzle is to seek out the matching pairs, thereby enhancing a child's geometric intuition and three-dimensional manipulation skills. The kit will include every possible configuration of colors. We are, however, a little stumped on the following question: How many cubes will the kit contain? In other words, how many possible ways can one color the faces of a cube so that two faces are red, two are blue, and two are white?

Looking at the problem, you reason that the following three-step decision algorithm ought to suffice:

Step 1 Choose a pair of faces to color red; $C(6, 2) = 15$ choices.

Step 2 Choose a pair of faces to color blue; $C(4, 2) = 6$ choices.

Step 3 Choose a pair of faces to color white; $C(2, 2) = 1$ choice.

This algorithm appears to give a total of $15 \times 6 \times 1 = 90$ possible cubes. However, before sending your reply to Felix, you realize that something is wrong, because there are different choices that result in the same cube. To describe some

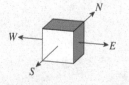

Figure 9

Figure 10

Figure 11

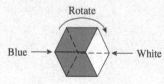

Figure 12

* There is a beautiful way of calculating this and similar numbers, called Pólya enumeration, but it requires a discussion of topics well outside the scope of this book. Take this as a hint that counting techniques can use some of the most sophisticated mathematics.

A tetrahedron

of these choices, imagine a cube oriented so that four of its faces are facing the four compass directions (Figure 9). Consider choice 1, with the top and bottom faces blue, north and south faces white, and east and west faces red; and choice 2, with the top and bottom faces blue, north and south faces red, and east and west faces white. These cubes are actually the same, as you see by rotating the second cube 90 degrees (Figure 10).

You therefore decide that you need a more sophisticated decision algorithm. Here is one that works:

Alternative 1: Faces with the same color opposite each other. Place one of the blue faces down. Then the top face is also blue. The cube must look like the one drawn in Figure 10. Thus, there is only one choice here.

Alternative 2: Red faces opposite each other and the other colors on adjacent pairs of faces. Again there is only one choice, as you can see by putting the red faces on the top and bottom and then rotating.

Alternative 3: White faces opposite each other and the other colors on adjacent pairs of faces; one possibility.

Alternative 4: Blue faces opposite each other and the other colors on adjacent pairs of faces; one possibility.

Alternative 5: Faces with the same color adjacent to each other. Look at the cube so that the edge common to the two red faces is facing you and horizontal (Figure 11). Then the faces on the left and right must be of different colors because they are opposite each other. Assume that the face on the right is white. (If it's blue, then rotate the die with the red edge still facing you to move it there, as in Figure 12.) This leaves two choices for the other white face, on the upper or the lower of the two back faces. This alternative gives two choices.

It follows that there are $1 + 1 + 1 + 1 + 2 = 6$ choices. Because the Crazy Cubes kit will feature two of each cube, the kit will require 12 different cubes.*

EXERCISES

In all of the following exercises, there are three colors to choose from: red, white, and blue.

1. To enlarge the kit, Felix suggests including two each of two-colored cubes (using two of the colors red, white, and blue) with three faces one color and three another. How many additional cubes will be required?

2. If Felix now suggests adding two each of cubes with two faces one color, one face another color, and three faces the third color, how many additional cubes will be required?

3. Felix changes his mind and suggests that the kit use tetrahedral blocks with two colors instead (see the figure). How many of these would be required?

4. Once Felix finds the answer to Exercise 3, he decides to go back to the cube idea, but this time he insists that all possible combinations of up to three colors should be included. (For instance, some cubes will be all one color, others will be two colors.) How many cubes should the kit contain?

8

PROBABILITY

CASE STUDY

The Monty Hall Problem

On the game show *Let's Make a Deal*, you are shown three doors—A, B, and C—and behind one of them is the Big Prize. After you select one of them—say, door A—to make things more interesting, the host (Monty Hall) opens one of the other doors—say, door B—revealing that the Big Prize is not there. He then offers you the opportunity to change your selection to the remaining door, door C. Should you switch or stick with your original guess?

Does it make any difference?

Everett Collection, Inc.

---

www.WanerMath.com

At the Website, in addition to the resources listed in the Preface, you will find:

- A matrix algebra tool
- A Markov system simulation

Introduction

What is the probability of winning the lottery twice? What are the chances that a college athlete whose drug test is positive for steroid use is actually using steroids? You are playing poker and have been dealt two jacks. What is the likelihood that one of the next three cards you are dealt will also be a jack? These are all questions about probability.

Understanding probability is important in many fields, ranging from risk management in business through hypothesis testing in psychology to quantum mechanics in physics. Historically, the theory of probability arose in the sixteenth and seventeenth centuries from attempts by mathematicians such as Gerolamo Cardano, Pierre de Fermat, Blaise Pascal, and Christiaan Huygens to understand games of chance. Andrey Nikolaevich Kolmogorov set forth the foundations of modern probability theory in his 1933 book *Foundations of the Theory of Probability*.

The goal of this chapter is to familiarize you with the basic concepts of modern probability theory and to give you a working knowledge that you can apply in a variety of situations. In the first two sections the emphasis is on translating real-life situations into the language of sample spaces, events, and probability. Once we have mastered the language of probability, we spend the rest of the chapter studying some of its theory and applications. The last section gives an interesting application of both probability and matrix arithmetic.

8.1   Sample Spaces and Events

Sample Spaces

At the beginning of a football game, to ensure fairness, the referee tosses a coin to decide who will get the ball first. When the ref tosses the coin and observes which side faces up, there are two possible results: heads (H) and tails (T). These are the *only* possible results, ignoring the (remote) possibility that the coin lands on its edge. The act of tossing the coin is an example of an **experiment**. The two possible results, H and T, are possible **outcomes** of the experiment, and the set $S = \{H, T\}$ of all possible outcomes is the **sample space** for the experiment.

Experiments, Outcomes, and Sample Spaces

An **experiment** is an occurrence with a result, or **outcome**, that is uncertain before the experiment takes place. The set of all possible outcomes is called the **sample space** for the experiment.

Quick Examples

1. **Experiment:** Flip a coin, and observe the side facing up.
   Outcomes: H, T
   Sample Space: $S = \{H, T\}$

2. **Experiment:** Select a student in your class.
   Outcomes: The students in your class
   Sample Space: The set of students in your class

3. **Experiment:** Select a student in your class, and observe the color of his or her hair.
   Outcomes: red, black, brown, blond, green, . . .
   Sample Space: {red, black, brown, blond, green, . . .}

4. **Experiment:** Cast a die, and observe the number facing up.
   Outcomes: 1, 2, 3, 4, 5, 6
   Sample Space: $S = \{1, 2, 3, 4, 5, 6\}$

5. **Experiment:** Cast two distinguishable dice (see Example 1(a) of Section 7.1), and observe the numbers facing up.
   Outcomes: $(1, 1), (1, 2), \ldots, (6, 6)$ (36 outcomes)

$$\textbf{Sample Space:} \quad S = \begin{Bmatrix} (1, 1), & (1, 2), & (1, 3), & (1, 4), & (1, 5), & (1, 6), \\ (2, 1), & (2, 2), & (2, 3), & (2, 4), & (2, 5), & (2, 6), \\ (3, 1), & (3, 2), & (3, 3), & (3, 4), & (3, 5), & (3, 6), \\ (4, 1), & (4, 2), & (4, 3), & (4, 4), & (4, 5), & (4, 6), \\ (5, 1), & (5, 2), & (5, 3), & (5, 4), & (5, 5), & (5, 6), \\ (6, 1), & (6, 2), & (6, 3), & (6, 4), & (6, 5), & (6, 6) \end{Bmatrix}$$

   $n(S)$ = the number of outcomes in S = 36

6. **Experiment:** Cast two indistinguishable dice (see Example 1(b) of Section 7.1), and observe the numbers facing up.
   Outcomes: $(1, 1), (1, 2), \ldots, (6, 6)$ (21 outcomes)

$$\textbf{Sample Space:} \quad S = \begin{Bmatrix} (1, 1), & (1, 2), & (1, 3), & (1, 4), & (1, 5), & (1, 6), \\ & (2, 2), & (2, 3), & (2, 4), & (2, 5), & (2, 6), \\ & & (3, 3), & (3, 4), & (3, 5), & (3, 6), \\ & & & (4, 4), & (4, 5), & (4, 6), \\ & & & & (5, 5), & (5, 6), \\ & & & & & (6, 6) \end{Bmatrix}$$

   $n(S) = 21$

7. **Experiment:** Cast two dice, and observe the *sum* of the numbers facing up.
   Outcomes: 2, 3, 4, 5, 6, 7, 8, 9, 10, 11, 12
   Sample Space: $S = \{2, 3, 4, 5, 6, 7, 8, 9, 10, 11, 12\}$

8. **Experiment:** Choose 2 cars (without regard to order) at random from a fleet of 10.
   Outcomes: Collections of 2 cars chosen from 10
   Sample Space: The set of all collections of 2 cars chosen from 10

   $n(S) = C(10, 2) = 45$

The following example introduces a sample space that we'll use in several other examples.

> **EXAMPLE 1** **School and Work**

In a survey conducted by the Bureau of Labor Statistics,[1] the high school graduating class of 2010 was divided into those who went on to college and those who did not. Those who went on to college were further divided into those who went to 2-year colleges and those who went to 4-year colleges. All graduates were also asked whether they were working or not. Find the sample space for the experiment "Select a member of the high school graduating class of 2010, and classify his or her subsequent school and work activity."

Solution The tree in Figure 1 shows the various possibilities.

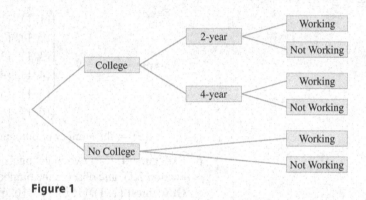

Figure 1

The sample space is

$$S = \{\text{2-year college \& working, 2-year college \& not working,}$$
$$\text{4-year college \& working, 4-year college \& not working,}$$
$$\text{no college \& working, no college \& not working}\}.$$

Events

In Example 1, suppose we are interested in the event that a 2010 high school graduate was working. In mathematical language we are interested in the *subset* of the sample space consisting of all outcomes in which the graduate was working.

Visualizing an Event
In the following figure, the favorable outcomes (events in E) are shown in green.

Sample Space S

> **Events**
>
> Given a sample space S, an **event** E is a subset of S. The outcomes in E are called the **favorable** outcomes. We say that E **occurs** in a particular experiment if the outcome of that experiment is one of the elements of E—that is, if the outcome of the experiment is favorable.

---

[1] "College Enrollment and Work Activity of High School Graduates," U.S. Bureau of Labor Statistics (www.bls.gov/news.release/hsgec.htm)

Quick Examples

9. **Experiment:** Roll a die, and observe the number facing up.

$$S = \{1, 2, 3, 4, 5, 6\}$$

Event: E: The number observed is odd.

$$E = \{1, 3, 5\}$$

10. **Experiment:** Roll two distinguishable dice, and observe the numbers facing up.

$$S = \{(1, 1), (1, 2), \ldots, (6, 6)\}$$

Event: F: The dice show the same number.

$$F = \{(1, 1), (2, 2), (3, 3), (4, 4), (5, 5), (6, 6)\}$$

11. **Experiment:** Roll two distinguishable dice, and observe the numbers facing up.

$$S = \{(1, 1), (1, 2), \ldots, (6, 6)\}$$

Event: G: The sum of the numbers is 1.

$$G = \varnothing \qquad \text{There are no favorable outcomes.}$$

12. **Experiment:** Select a city beginning with "J."
    Event: E: The city is Johannesburg.

$$E = \{\text{Johannesburg}\} \qquad \text{An event can consist of a single outcome.}$$

13. **Experiment:** Roll a die, and observe the number facing up.
    Event: E: The number observed is either even or odd.

$$E = S = \{1, 2, 3, 4, 5, 6\} \qquad \text{An event can consist of all possible outcomes.}$$

14. **Experiment:** Select a student in your class.
    Event: E: The student has red hair.

$$E = \{\text{red-haired students in your class}\}$$

15. **Experiment:** Draw a hand of 2 cards from a deck of 52.
    Event: H: Both cards are diamonds.

    H is the set of all hands of 2 cards chosen from 52 such that both cards are diamonds.

Here are some more examples of events.

EXAMPLE 2 **Dice**

We roll a red die and a green die and observe the numbers facing up. Describe the following events as subsets of the sample space.

a. E: The sum of the numbers showing is 6.

b. F: The sum of the numbers showing is 2.

Solution Here (again) is the sample space for the experiment of throwing two dice:

$$S = \begin{Bmatrix} (1,1),\ (1,2),\ (1,3),\ (1,4),\ (1,5),\ (1,6), \\ (2,1),\ (2,2),\ (2,3),\ (2,4),\ (2,5),\ (2,6), \\ (3,1),\ (3,2),\ (3,3),\ (3,4),\ (3,5),\ (3,6), \\ (4,1),\ (4,2),\ (4,3),\ (4,4),\ (4,5),\ (4,6), \\ (5,1),\ (5,2),\ (5,3),\ (5,4),\ (5,5),\ (5,6), \\ (6,1),\ (6,2),\ (6,3),\ (6,4),\ (6,5),\ (6,6) \end{Bmatrix}.$$

a. In mathematical language, E is the subset of S that consists of all those outcomes in which the sum of the numbers showing is 6. Here is the sample space once again, with the outcomes in question shown in color:

$$S = \begin{Bmatrix} (1,1),\ (1,2),\ (1,3),\ (1,4),\ (1,5),\ (1,6), \\ (2,1),\ (2,2),\ (2,3),\ (2,4),\ (2,5),\ (2,6), \\ (3,1),\ (3,2),\ (3,3),\ (3,4),\ (3,5),\ (3,6), \\ (4,1),\ (4,2),\ (4,3),\ (4,4),\ (4,5),\ (4,6), \\ (5,1),\ (5,2),\ (5,3),\ (5,4),\ (5,5),\ (5,6), \\ (6,1),\ (6,2),\ (6,3),\ (6,4),\ (6,5),\ (6,6) \end{Bmatrix}.$$

Thus, $E = \{(1,5), (2,4), (3,3), (4,2), (5,1)\}$.

b. The only outcome in which the numbers showing add to 2 is $(1,1)$. Thus,

$$F = \{(1,1)\}.$$

EXAMPLE 3   School and Work

Let S be the sample space of Example 1. List the elements in the following events:

a. The event E that a 2010 high school graduate was working.

b. The event F that a 2010 high school graduate was not going to a 2-year college.

Solution

a. We had this sample space:

$S = \{$2-year college & working, two-year college & not working, 4-year college & working, four-year college & not working, no college & working, no college & not working$\}$.

We are asked for the event that a graduate was working. Whenever we encounter a phrase involving "the event that . . . ," we mentally translate this into mathematical language by changing the wording.

Replace the phrase "the event that . . ." by the phrase "the subset of the sample space consisting of all outcomes in which . . . ."

Thus, we are interested in the subset of the sample space consisting of all outcomes in which the graduate was working. This gives

$E = \{$2-year college & working, 4-year college & working, no college & working$\}$.

The outcomes in E are illustrated by the shaded cells in Figure 2.

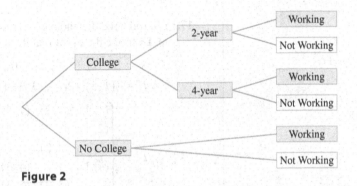

Figure 2

b. We are looking for the event that a graduate was not going to a 2-year college; that is, the subset of the sample space consisting of all outcomes in which the graduate was not going to a 2-year college. Thus,

$$F = \{\text{4-year college \& working, 4-year college \& not working,}$$
$$\text{no college \& working, no college \& not working}\}.$$

The outcomes in F are illustrated by the shaded cells in Figure 3.

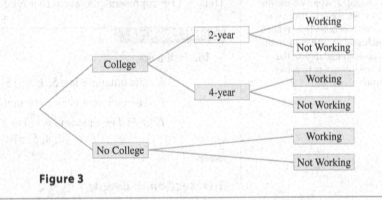

Figure 3

Complement, Union, and Intersection of Events

Events may often be described in terms of other events, using set operations such as complement, union, and intersection.

Complement of an Event

The **complement** of an event E is the set of outcomes not in E. Thus, the complement of E represents the event that E *does not occur*.

Visualizing the Complement

Sample Space S

Quick Examples

16. You take four shots at the goal during a soccer game and record the number of times you score. Describe the event that you score at least twice, and also describe its complement.

   $S = \{0, 1, 2, 3, 4\}$ Set of outcomes
   $E = \{2, 3, 4\}$ Event that you score at least twice
   $E' = \{0, 1\}$ Event that you do not score at least twice

17. You roll a red die and a green die and observe the two numbers facing up. Describe the event that the sum of the numbers is not 6.

$$S = \{(1, 1), (1, 2), \ldots, (6, 6)\}$$
$$F = \{(1, 5), (2, 4), (3, 3), (4, 2), (5, 1)\} \quad \text{Sum of numbers is 6.}$$

$$F' = \begin{Bmatrix} (1, 1), & (1, 2), & (1, 3), & (1, 4), & & (1, 6), \\ (2, 1), & (2, 2), & (2, 3), & & (2, 5), & (2, 6), \\ (3, 1), & (3, 2), & & (3, 4), & (3, 5), & (3, 6), \\ (4, 1), & & (4, 3), & (4, 4), & (4, 5), & (4, 6), \\ & (5, 2), & (5, 3), & (5, 4), & (5, 5), & (5, 6), \\ (6, 1), & (6, 2), & (6, 3), & (6, 4), & (6, 5), & (6, 6) \end{Bmatrix}$$

Sum of numbers is not 6.

Union of Events

The **union** of the events E and F is the set of all outcomes in E or F (or both). Thus, $E \cup F$ represents the event that E occurs *or* F occurs (or both).*

* As in Chapter 7, when we use the word "or," we agree to mean one or the other *or both*. This is called the **inclusive or**, and mathematicians have agreed to take this as the meaning of *or* to avoid confusion.

Quick Example

18. Roll a die.

E: The outcome is a 5; $E = \{5\}$.

F: The outcome is an even number; $F = \{2, 4, 6\}$.

$E \cup F$: The outcome is either a 5 *or* an even number:
$$E \cup F = \{2, 4, 5, 6\}$$

Intersection of Events

The **intersection** of the events E and F is the set of all outcomes common to E and F. Thus, $E \cap F$ represents the event that both E *and* F occur.

Quick Example

19. Roll two dice: one red and one green.

E: The red die is 2.

F: The green die is odd.

$E \cap F$: The red die is 2, and the green die is odd:
$$E \cap F = \{(2, 1), (2, 3), (2, 5)\}.$$

EXAMPLE 4 Weather

Let R be the event that it will rain tomorrow, let P be the event that it will be pleasant, let C be the event that it will be cold, and let H be the event that it will be hot.

a. Express in words: $R \cap P', R \cup (P \cap C)$.

b. Express in symbols: Tomorrow will be either a pleasant day or a cold and rainy day; it will not, however, be hot.

Solution The key here is to remember that intersection corresponds to *and* and union to *or*.

a. $R \cap P'$ is the event that it will rain *and* it will not be pleasant.

$R \cup (P \cap C)$ is the event that either it will rain, or it will be pleasant and cold.

b. If we rephrase the given statement using *and* and *or* we get "Tomorrow will be either a pleasant day or a cold and rainy day, and it will not be hot."

$$[P \cup (C \cap R)] \cap H' \qquad \text{\small Pleasant, or cold and rainy, and not hot.}$$

The nuances of the English language play an important role in this formulation. For instance, the effect of the pause (comma) after "rainy day" suggests placing the preceding clause $P \cup (C \cap R)$ in brackets. In addition, the phrase "cold and rainy" suggests that C and R should be grouped together in their own parentheses.

The next example is essentially Example 3 in Section 7.2, but translated here into the language of events.

EXAMPLE 5 **Apple Sales**

The following table shows sales, in millions of items, of Macs, iPhones, and iPads sold by Apple in 2012, 2013, and 2014.[2]

	Macs (A)	iPhones (B)	iPads (C)	Total
2012 (U)	18	125	58	201
2013 (V)	16	150	71	238
2014 (W)	19	169	68	256
Total	53	444	197	695

Consider the experiment in which a device is selected at random from the 695 million devices represented in the table. Label the events representing the items in each row and column as shown (so that, for example, A is the event that the device selected was a Mac). Describe the following events and compute their cardinality:

a. U' **b.** $A \cap U'$ **c.** $(A \cap U)'$ **d.** $C \cup U$

Solution Before answering parts (a)–(d), first notice that the sample space S is the set of all items represented in the table, so S has a total of 695 million outcomes. Also, each number in the table is the cardinality of a specific event; for instance, the 18 million Macs sold in 2012 is the cardinality of the event $A \cap U$ that the device selected was a Mac and also sold in 2012, the 125 million iPhones sold in 2012 is the cardinality of the event $B \cap U$, and so on:

	Macs (A)	iPhones (B)	iPads (C)	Total
2012 (U)	$n(A \cap U)$	$n(B \cap U)$	$n(C \cap U)$	$n(U)$
2013 (V)	$n(A \cap V)$	$n(B \cap V)$	$n(C \cap V)$	$n(V)$
2014 (W)	$n(A \cap W)$	$n(B \cap W)$	$n(C \cap W)$	$n(W)$
Total	$n(A)$	$n(B)$	$n(C)$	$n(S)$

---

[2] Figures are rounded. Source: Apple quarterly press releases, www.investor.apple.com.

Now let us answer the specific questions: Because all the figures are stated in millions of items, we'll give our calculations and results in millions of items as well.

a. U' is the event that the device was not sold in 2012. Its cardinality is

$$n(U') = n(S) - n(U) = 695 - 201 = 494 \text{ million items.}$$

b. $A \cap U'$ is the event that the device was a Mac not sold in 2012:

	Macs (A)	iPhones (B)	iPads (C)	Total
2012 (U)	18	125	58	201
2013 (V)	16	150	71	238
2014 (W)	19	169	68	256
Total	53	444	197	695

From the table,

$$n(A \cap U') = 16 + 19 = 35 \text{ million items.}$$

c. $A \cap U$ is the event that the device was a Mac sold in 2012, so $(A \cap U)'$ is the event that the device was not a Mac sold in 2012:

	Macs (A)	iPhones (B)	iPads (C)	Total
2012 (U)	18	125	58	201
2013 (V)	16	150	71	238
2014 (W)	19	169	68	256
Total	53	444	197	695

From the formula for the cardinality of the complement of an event, its cardinality is

$$n((A \cap U)') = n(S) - n(A \cap U)$$
$$= 695 - 18 = 677 \text{ million items.}$$

d. $C \cup U$ is the event that the device was either an iPad or sold in 2012:

	Macs (A)	iPhones (B)	iPads (C)	Total
2012 (U)	18	125	58	201
2013 (V)	16	150	71	238
2014 (W)	19	169	68	256
Total	53	444	197	695

From the formula for the cardinality of a union, we have

$$n(C \cup U) = n(C) + n(U) - n(C \cap U)$$
$$= 197 + 201 - 58 = 340 \text{ million items.}$$

The case in which $E \cap F$ is empty is interesting, and we give it a name.

Mutually Exclusive Events

If E and F are events, then E and F are said to be **disjoint** or **mutually exclusive** if $E \cap F$ is empty. (Hence, they have no outcomes in common.)

Interpretation

It is impossible for mutually exclusive events to occur simultaneously.

Quick Examples

In each of the following examples, E and F are mutually exclusive events.

20. Roll a die, and observe the number facing up. E: The outcome is even; F: The outcome is odd.

$$E = \{2, 4, 6\}, F = \{1, 3, 5\}$$

21. Toss a coin three times, and record the sequence of heads and tails. E: All three tosses land the same way up, F: One toss shows heads, and the other two show tails.

$$E = \{HHH, TTT\}, F = \{HTT, THT, TTH\}$$

22. Observe the weather at 10 am tomorrow. E: It is raining; F: There is not a cloud in the sky.

Visualizing Mutually Exclusive Events

Sample Space S

FAQs

Specifying the Sample Space

Q : *How do I determine the sample space in a given application?*

A : Strictly speaking, an experiment should include a description of what kinds of objects are in the sample space, as in:

> *Cast a die, and observe the number facing up.*
> Sample space: the possible numbers facing up, $\{1, 2, 3, 4, 5, 6\}$.

> *Choose a person at random, and record her Social Security number and whether she is blonde.*
> Sample space: pairs (nine-digit number, Y/N).

However, in many of the scenarios discussed in this chapter and the next, an experiment is specified more vaguely, as in "Select a student in your class." In cases like this, the nature of the sample space should be determined from the context. For example, if the discussion is about grade-point averages and gender, the sample space can be taken to consist of pairs (grade-point average, M/F).

8.1 EXERCISES

▼ more advanced   ◆ challenging
🔲 indicates exercises that should be solved using technology

In Exercises 1–18, describe the sample space S of the experiment, and list the elements of the given event. (Assume that the coins are distinguishable and that what is observed are the faces or numbers that face up.) [**HINT**: See Examples 1–3.]

1. Two coins are tossed; the result is at most one tail.

2. Two coins are tossed; the result is one or more heads.

3. Three coins are tossed; the result is at most one head.

4. Three coins are tossed; the result is more tails than heads.

5. Two distinguishable dice are rolled; the numbers add to 5.

6. Two distinguishable dice are rolled; the numbers add to 9.

7. Two indistinguishable dice are rolled; the numbers add to 4.

8. Two indistinguishable dice are rolled; one of the numbers is even and the other is odd.

9. Two indistinguishable dice are rolled; both numbers are prime.[3]

10. Two indistinguishable dice are rolled; neither number is prime.

11. A letter is chosen at random from those in the word *Mozart*; the letter is a vowel.

12. A letter is chosen at random from those in the word *Mozart*; the letter is neither *a* nor *m*.

13. A sequence of two different letters is randomly chosen from those of the word *sore*; the first letter is a vowel.

14. A sequence of two different letters is randomly chosen from those of the word *hear*; the second letter is not a vowel.

15. A sequence of two different digits is randomly chosen from the digits 0–4; the first digit is larger than the second.

16. A sequence of two different digits is randomly chosen from the digits 0–4; the first digit is twice the second.

17. You are considering purchasing either a domestic car, an imported car, a van, an antique car, or an antique truck; you do not buy a car.

18. You are deciding whether to enroll for Psychology 1, Psychology 2, Economics 1, General Economics, or Math for Poets; you decide to avoid economics.

19. A packet of gummy candy contains four strawberry gums, four lime gums, two black currant gums, and two orange gums. April May sticks her hand in and selects four at random. Complete the following sentences:
    a. The sample space is the set of . . . .
    b. April is particularly fond of combinations of two strawberry and two black currant gums. The event that April will get the combination she desires is the set of . . . .

20. A bag contains three red marbles, two blue ones, and four yellow ones. Alexandra Great pulls out three of them at random. Complete the following sentences:
    a. The sample space is the set of . . . .
    b. The event that Alexandra gets one of each color is the set of . . . .

21. ▼ President Barack H. Obama's first cabinet consisted of the Secretaries of Agriculture, Commerce, Defense, Education, Energy, Health and Human Services, Homeland Security, Housing and Urban Development, Interior, Labor, State, Transportation, Treasury, Veterans Affairs, and the Attorney General.[4] Assuming that President Obama had 20 candidates, including Hillary Clinton, to fill these posts

(and wished to assign no one to more than one post), complete the following sentences:
    a. The sample space is the set of . . . .
    b. The event that Hillary Clinton is the Secretary of State is the set of . . . .

22. ▼ A poker hand consists of a set of 5 cards chosen from a standard deck of 52 playing cards. You are dealt a poker hand. Complete the following sentences:
    a. The sample space is the set of . . . .
    b. The event "a full house" is the set of . . . . (Recall that a full house is three cards of one denomination and two of another.)

Suppose two dice (one red, one green) are rolled. Consider the following events. A: the red die shows 1; B: the numbers add to 4; C: at least one of the numbers is 1; and D: the numbers do not add to 11. In Exercises 23–30, express the stated event in symbolic form and say how many elements it contains.
[**HINT:** See Example 5.]

23. The red die shows 1, and the numbers add to 4.

24. The red die shows 1, but the numbers do not add to 11.

25. The numbers do not add to 4.

26. The numbers add to 11.

27. The numbers do not add to 4, but they do add to 11.

28. Either the numbers add to 11 or the red die shows a 1.

29. At least one of the numbers is 1, or the numbers add to 4.

30. Either the numbers add to 4, or they add to 11, or at least one of them is 1.

Let W be the event that you will use the book's Website tonight, let I be the event that your math grade will improve, and let E be the event that you will use the Website every night. In Exercises 31–38, express the given event in symbols.

31. You will use the Website tonight, and your math grade will improve.

32. You will use the Website tonight, or your math grade will not improve.

33. Either you will use the Website every night or your math grade will not improve.

34. Your math grade will not improve even though you use the Website every night.

35. ▼ Either your math grade will improve, or you will use the Website tonight but not every night.

36. ▼ You will use the Website either tonight or every night, and your grade will improve.

37. ▼ (Compare Exercise 35.) Either your math grade will improve or you will use the Website tonight, but you will not use it every night.

38. ▼ (Compare Exercise 36.) Either you will use the Website tonight, or you will use it every night and your grade will improve.

---

[3] A positive integer is **prime** if it is neither 1 nor a product of smaller integers.

[4] Source: The White House website (www.whitehouse.gov).

In Exercises 39–42, Pablo randomly picks three marbles from a bag of eight marbles (four red ones, two green ones, and two yellow ones).

39. How many outcomes are there in the sample space? How many outcomes are there in the event that none of the marbles he picks are red?

40. How many outcomes are there in the sample space? How many outcomes are there in the event that all of the marbles he picks are red?

41. ▼ How many outcomes are there in the event that Pablo picks one marble of each color?

42. ▼ How many outcomes are there in the event that the marbles Pablo picks are not all the same color?

Applications

Housing Prices *Exercises 43–48 are based on the map below, which shows the percentage change in housing prices from June 2014 to June 2015 in each of nine regions (U.S. Census divisions).*[5]

43. You are choosing a region of the country to move to. Describe the event E that the region you choose saw an increase in housing prices of 6% or more.

44. You are choosing a region of the country to move to. Describe the event E that the region you choose saw an increase in housing prices of less than 4%.

45. You are choosing a region of the country to move to. Let E be the event that the region you choose saw an increase in housing prices of 6% or more, and let F be the event that the region you choose is on the east coast. Describe the events $E \cup F$ and $E \cap F$ both in words and by listing the outcomes of each.

46. You are choosing a region of the country to move to. Let E be the event that the region you choose saw an increase in housing prices of less than 4%, and let F be the event that the region you choose is not on the east coast. Describe the events $E \cup F$ and $E \cap F$ both in words and by listing the outcomes of each.

47. ▼ You are choosing a region of the country to move to. Which of the following pairs of events are mutually exclusive?
a. E: You choose a region from among the two with the highest percentage increase in housing prices.
F: You choose a region that is not on the east or west coast.
b. E: You choose a region from among the two with the highest percentage increase in housing prices.
F: You choose a region that is on the east coast.

48. ▼ You are choosing a region of the country to move to. Which of the following pairs of events are mutually exclusive?
a. E: You choose a region from among the three with the least increase in housing prices.
F: You choose a region from among the central divisions.
b. E: You choose a region from among the three with the least increase in housing prices.
F: You choose a region on the east or west coast.

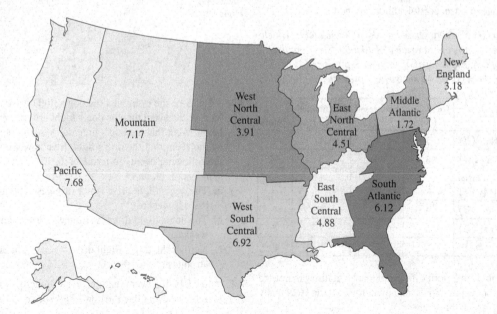

_____
[5] Source: Federal Housing Finance Agency (www.fhfa.gov).

Publishing Exercises 49–56 are based on the accompanying table, which shows the results of a survey of authors by a (fictitious) publishing company. [HINT: See Example 5.]

	New Authors	Established Authors	Total
Successful	5	25	30
Unsuccessful	15	55	70
Total	20	80	100

Consider the following events: S: An author is successful; U: An author is unsuccessful; N: An author is new; and E: An author is established.

49. Describe the events $S \cap N$ and $S \cup N$ in words. Use the table to compute $n(S \cap N)$ and $n(S \cup N)$.

50. Describe the events $N \cap U$ and $N \cup U$ in words. Use the table to compute $n(N \cap U)$ and $n(N \cup U)$.

51. Which of the following pairs of events are mutually exclusive: N and E; N and S; S and E?

52. Which of the following pairs of events are mutually exclusive: U and E; U and S; S and N?

53. Describe the event $S \cap N'$ in words, and find the number of elements it contains.

54. Describe the event $U \cup E'$ in words, and find the number of elements it contains.

55. ▼ What percentage of established authors are successful? What percentage of successful authors are established?

56. ▼ What percentage of new authors are unsuccessful? What percentage of unsuccessful authors are new?

Stocks Exercises 57–62 are based on the following table, which shows the stock market performance of 40 industries from five sectors of the U.S. economy as of noon on September 11, 2015.[6] (Take S to be the set of all 40 industries represented in the table.)

	Increased (X)	Decreased (Y)	Unchanged (Z)	Totals
Financials (F)	3	4	1	8
Manufacturing (M)	8	3	3	14
Information Technology (T)	6	1	0	7
Health Care (H)	4	1	1	6
Utilities (U)	3	1	1	5
Totals	24	10	6	40

57. Use symbols to describe the event that an industry increased in value but was not in the manufacturing sector. How many elements are in this event?

58. Use symbols to describe the event that an industry was in the manufacturing sector and did not increase in value. How many elements are in this event?

59. Describe the event $H' \cup Z$ in words, and compute $n(H' \cup Z)$.

60. Describe the event $H \cup Z'$ in words, and compute $n(H \cup Z')$.

61. Find all pairs of mutually exclusive events among the events F, M, T, X, Y, and Z.

62. Find all pairs of events that are not mutually exclusive among the events M, T, Y and Z.

Animal Psychology Exercises 63–68 concern the following chart, which shows the way in which a dog moves its facial muscles when torn between the drives of fight and flight.[7] The "fight" drive increases from left to right; the "flight" drive increases from top to bottom. (Notice that an increase in the "fight" drive causes the dog's upper lip to lift, while an increase in the "flight" drive draws its ears downward.)

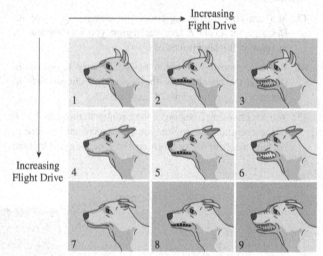

63. ▼ Let E be the event that the dog's flight drive is strongest, let F be the event that the dog's flight drive is weakest, let G be the event that the dog's fight drive is strongest, and let H be the event that the dog's fight drive is weakest. Describe the following events in terms of E, F, G, and H using the symbols ∩, ∪, and '.
   a. The dog's flight drive is not strongest, and its fight drive is weakest.
   b. The dog's flight drive is strongest, or its fight drive is weakest.
   c. Neither the dog's flight drive nor its fight drive is strongest.

64. ▼ Let E be the event that the dog's flight drive is strongest, let F be the event that the dog's flight drive is weakest, let G

---

[6] "Unchanged" includes industries that moved by less than 0.1%. Source for data: Fidelity (https://eresearch.fidelity.com).

[7] Source: *On Aggression* by Konrad Lorenz (Fakenham, Norfolk: University Paperback Edition, Cox & Wyman Limited, 1967).

be the event that the dog's fight drive is strongest, and let H be the event that the dog's fight drive is weakest. Describe the following events in terms of E, F, G, and H using the symbols $\cap$, $\cup$, and $'$.

a. The dog's flight drive is weakest, and its fight drive is not weakest.

b. The dog's flight drive is not strongest, or its fight drive is weakest.

c. Either the dog's flight drive or its fight drive fails to be strongest.

65. ▽ Describe the following events explicitly (as subsets of the sample space):

a. The dog's fight and flight drives are both strongest.

b. The dog's fight drive is strongest, but its flight drive is neither weakest nor strongest.

66. ▽ Describe the following events explicitly (as subsets of the sample space):

a. Neither the dog's fight drive nor its flight drive is strongest.

b. The dog's fight drive is weakest, but its flight drive is neither weakest nor strongest.

67. ▽ Describe the following events in words:

a. $\{1, 4, 7\}$ **b.** $\{1, 9\}$ **c.** $\{3, 6, 7, 8, 9\}$

68. ▽ Describe the following events in words:

a. $\{7, 8, 9\}$ **b.** $\{3, 7\}$ **c.** $\{1, 2, 3, 4, 7\}$

Exercises 69–72 use counting arguments from the preceding chapter.

69. ▽ *Gummy Bears* A bag contains six gummy bears. Noel picks four at random. How many possible outcomes are there? If one of the gummy bears is raspberry, how many of these outcomes include the raspberry gummy bear?

70. ▽ *Chocolates* My couch potato friend enjoys sitting in front of the TV and grabbing handfuls of 5 chocolates at random from his snack jar. Unbeknownst to him, I have replaced one of the 20 chocolates in his jar with a cashew. (He hates cashews with a passion.) How many possible outcomes are there the first time he grabs 5 chocolates? How many of these include the cashew?

71. ▽ *Horse Races* The seven contenders in the fifth horse race at Aqueduct on February 18, 2002, were Pipe Bomb, Expect a Ship, All That Magic, Electoral College, Celera, Cliff Glider, and Inca Halo.[8] You are interested in the first three places (winner, second place, and third place) for the race.

a. Find the cardinality $n(S)$ of the sample space S of all possible finishes of the race. (A finish for the race consists of a first, a second, and a third place winner.)

b. Let E be the event that Electoral College is in second or third place, and let F be the event that Celera is the winner. Express the event $E \cap F$ in words, and find its cardinality.

72. ▽ *Intramurals* The following five teams will be participating in *Urban University*'s hockey intramural tournament: the Independent Wildcats, the Phi Chi Bulldogs, the Gate Crashers, the Slide Rule Nerds, and the City Slickers. Prizes will be awarded for the winner and runner-up.

a. Find the cardinality $n(S)$ of the sample space S of all possible outcomes of the tournament. (An outcome of the tournament consists of a winner and a runner-up.)

b. Let E be the event that the City Slickers are runners-up, and let F be the event that the Independent Wildcats are neither the winners nor runners-up. Express the event $E \cup F$ in words, and find its cardinality.

Communication and Reasoning Exercises

73. Complete the following sentence. An event is a ____.

74. Complete the following sentence. Two events E and F are mutually exclusive if their intersection is ____.

75. If E and F are events, then $(E \cap F)'$ is the event that ____.

76. If E and F are events, then $(E' \cap F')$ is the event that ____.

77. Let E be the event that you meet a tall, dark stranger. Which of the following could reasonably represent the experiment and sample space in question?

(A) You go on vacation and lie in the sun; S is the set of cloudy days.

(B) You go on vacation and spend an evening at the local dance club; S is the set of people you meet.

(C) You go on vacation and spend an evening at the local dance club; S is the set of people you do not meet.

78. Let E be the event that you buy a Porsche. Which of the following could reasonably represent the experiment and sample space in question?

(A) You go to an auto dealership and select a Mustang; S is the set of colors available.

(B) You go to an auto dealership and select a red car; S is the set of cars you decide not to buy.

(C) You go to an auto dealership and select a red car; S is the set of car models available.

79. ▽ True or false? Every set S is the sample space for some experiment. Explain.

80. ▽ True or false? Every sample space S is a finite set. Explain.

81. ▽ Describe an experiment in which a die is cast and the set of outcomes is $\{0, 1\}$.

82. ▽ Describe an experiment in which two coins are flipped and the set of outcomes is $\{0, 1, 2\}$.

83. ▽ Two distinguishable dice are rolled. Could there be two mutually exclusive events that both contain outcomes in which the numbers facing up add to 7?

84. ▽ Describe an experiment in which two dice are rolled, and describe two mutually exclusive events that both contain outcomes in which both dice show a 1.

---

[8] Source: *Newsday*, Feb. 18, 2002, p. A36.

8.2   Relative Frequency

Fundamentals

Suppose you have a coin that you think is not fair and you would like to determine the likelihood that heads will come up when it is tossed. You could estimate this likelihood by tossing the coin a large number of times and counting the number of times heads comes up. Suppose, for instance, that in 100 tosses of the coin, heads comes up 58 times. The fraction of times that heads comes up, $58/100 = .58$, is the **relative frequency**, or **estimated probability** of heads coming up when the coin is tossed. In other words, saying that the relative frequency of heads coming up is .58 is the same as saying that heads came up 58% of the time in your series of experiments.

Now let's think about this example in terms of sample spaces and events. First of all, there is an experiment that has been repeated $N = 100$ times: Toss the coin, and observe the side facing up. The sample space for this experiment is $S = \{H, T\}$. Also, there is an event E in which we are interested: the event that heads comes up, which is $E = \{H\}$. The number of times E has occurred, or the **frequency** of E, is $fr(E) = 58$. The relative frequency of the event E is then

$$P(E) = \frac{fr(E)}{N} \qquad \frac{\text{Frequency of event } E}{\text{Number of repetitions } N}$$

$$= \frac{58}{100} = .58.$$

Notes

1. The relative frequency gives us an *estimate* of the likelihood that heads will come up when that particular coin is tossed. This is why statisticians often use the alternative term *estimated probability* to describe it.

2. The larger the number of times the experiment is performed, the more accurate an estimate we expect this estimated probability to be. ∎

Visualizing Relative Frequency

$P(E) = \dfrac{fr(E)}{N} = \dfrac{4}{10} = .4$

Relative Frequency

When an experiment is performed a number of times, the **relative frequency** or **estimated probability** of an event E is the fraction of times that the event E occurs. If the experiment is performed N times and the event E occurs $fr(E)$ times, then the relative frequency is given by

$$P(E) = \frac{fr(E)}{N}. \qquad \text{Fraction of times } E \text{ occurs}$$

The number $fr(E)$ is called the **frequency** of E. N, the number of times that the experiment is performed, is called the number of **trials** or the **sample size**. If E consists of a single outcome s, then we refer to $P(E)$ as the relative frequency or estimated probability of the outcome s, and we write $P(s)$.

The collection of the estimated probabilities of *all* the outcomes is the **relative frequency distribution** or **estimated probability distribution**.

Quick Examples

1. **Experiment:** Roll a pair of dice, and add the numbers that face up.

   Event: E: The sum is 5.

If the experiment is repeated 100 times and E occurs on 10 of the rolls, then the relative frequency of E is

$$P(E) = \frac{fr(E)}{N} = \frac{10}{100} = .10.$$

2. If 10 rolls of a single die resulted in the outcomes 2, 1, 4, 4, 5, 6, 1, 2, 2, 1, then the associated relative frequency distribution is shown in the following table:

Outcome	1	2	3	4	5	6
Rel. Frequency	.3	.3	0	.2	.1	.1

3. **Experiment:** Note the cloud conditions on a particular day at noon.

   If the experiment is repeated a number of times and the sky is clear 20% of those times, partly cloudy 30% of those times, and overcast the rest of those times, then the relative frequency distribution is as follows:

Outcome	Clear	Partly Cloudy	Overcast
Rel. Frequency	.20	.30	.50

EXAMPLE 1   **Sales of Hybrid Vehicles**

* The official plural form of Prius, according to Toyota.

In a survey of 250 hybrid vehicles sold in the United States, 125 were Toyota Prii,* 30 were Honda Civics, 20 were Toyota Camrys, 15 were Ford Escapes, and the rest were other makes.[9] What is the relative frequency that a hybrid vehicle sold in the United States is not a Toyota Camry?

Solution The experiment consists of choosing a hybrid vehicle sold in the United States and determining its make. The sample space suggested by the information given is

$$S = \{\text{Toyota Prius, Honda Civic, Toyota Camry, Ford Escape, Other}\},$$

and we are interested in the event

$$E = \{\text{Toyota Prius, Honda Civic, Ford Escape, Other}\}.$$

The sample size is $N = 250$, of which 20 were Toyota Camrys. Thus, the frequency of E is $fr(E) = 250 - 20 = 230$, and the relative frequency of E is

$$P(E) = \frac{fr(E)}{N} = \frac{230}{250} = .92.$$

➡ **Before we go on . . .** In Example 1 you might ask how accurate the estimate of .92 is or how well it reflects *all* of the hybrid vehicles sold in the United States absent any information about national sales figures. The field of statistics provides the tools needed to say to what extent this estimated probability can be trusted. ∎

---

[9] The proportions are based on approximate actual cumulative sales through October 2011 (www.wikipedia.com).

EXAMPLE 2 Auctions on eBay

The following chart shows the results of a survey of the bid prices for 50 paintings on eBay with the highest number of bids:[10]

Bid Price	$0–$9.99	$10–$49.99	$50–$99.99	≥$100
Frequency	6	23	15	6

Consider the experiment in which a painting is chosen and the bid price is observed.

a. Find the relative frequency distribution.

b. Find the relative frequency that a painting in the survey had a bid price of less than $50.

Solution

a. The following table shows the relative frequency of each outcome, which we find by dividing each frequency by the sum $N = 50$:

Bid Price	$0–$9.99	$10–$49.99	$50–$99.99	≥$100
Rel. Frequency	$\dfrac{6}{50} = .12$	$\dfrac{23}{50} = .46$	$\dfrac{15}{50} = .30$	$\dfrac{6}{50} = .12$

b. Method 1: Computing Directly

$$E = \{\$0–\$9.99, \$10–\$49.99\}$$

Thus,

$$P(E) = \frac{fr(E)}{N} = \frac{6 + 23}{50} = \frac{29}{50} = .58.$$

Method 2: Using the Relative Frequency Distribution

Notice that we can obtain the same answer from the distribution in part (a) by simply adding the relative frequencies of the outcomes in E:

$$P(E) = .12 + .46 = .58.$$

Q: Why did we get the same result in Example 2(b) by simply adding the relative frequencies of the outcomes in E?

A: The reason can be seen by doing the calculation in the first method a slightly different way:

$$P(E) = \frac{fr(E)}{N} = \frac{6 + 23}{50}$$

$$= \frac{6}{50} + \frac{23}{50}. \qquad \text{Sum of relative frequencies of the individual outcomes}$$

This property of relative frequency distributions is discussed below.

---

[10] In the category "Art—Direct from Artist" on November 14, 2011 (www.eBay.com).

Following are some important properties of estimated probability that we can observe in Example 2.

Some Properties of Relative Frequency Distributions

Let $S = \{s_1, s_2, \ldots, s_n\}$ be a sample space, and let $P(s_i)$ be the relative frequency of the event $\{s_i\}$. Then

1. $0 \leq P(s_i) \leq 1$
2. $P(s_1) + P(s_2) + \cdots + P(s_n) = 1$
3. If $E = \{e_1, e_2, \ldots, e_r\}$, then $P(E) = P(e_1) + P(e_2) + \cdots + P(e_r)$.

In words:

1. The relative frequency of each outcome is a number between 0 and 1 (inclusive).
2. The relative frequencies of all the outcomes add up to 1.
3. The relative frequency of an event E is the sum of the relative frequencies of the individual outcomes in E.

Relative Frequency and Increasing Sample Size

A "fair" coin is one that is as likely to come up heads as it is to come up tails. In other words, we expect heads to come up 50% of the time if we toss such a coin many times. Put more precisely, we expect the relative frequency to approach .5 as the number of trials gets larger. Figure 4 shows how the relative frequency behaved for one sequence of coin tosses. For each N we have plotted what fraction of times the coin came up heads in the first N tosses.

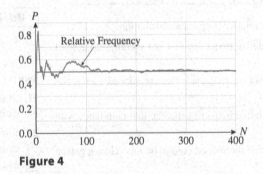

Figure 4

*This can be made more precise by the concept of a "limit" used in calculus.

Notice that the relative frequency graph meanders as N increases, sometimes getting closer to .5 and sometimes drifting away. However, the graph tends to meander within smaller and smaller distances of .5 as N increases.*

In general, this is how relative frequency seems to behave: As N gets large, the relative frequency appears to approach some fixed value. Some refer to this value as the "actual" probability, whereas others point out that there are difficulties with this notion. For instance, how can we actually determine this limit to any accuracy by experiment? How exactly is the experiment conducted? Technical and philosophical issues aside, the relative frequencies do approach a fixed value, and in the next section we will talk about how we use probability models to predict this limiting value.

Using Technology

See the Technology Guides at the end of the chapter to see how to use a TI-83/84 Plus or a spreadsheet to simulate experiments.

8.2   EXERCISES

▼ more advanced   ◆ challenging
⊤ indicates exercises that should be solved using technology

In Exercises 1–6, calculate the relative frequency P(E) using the given information.

1. $N = 100$, $fr(E) = 40$ **2.** $N = 500$, $fr(E) = 300$

3. Eight hundred adults are polled, and 640 of them support universal health-care coverage. E is the event that an adult supports universal health-care coverage. [HINT: See Example 1.]

4. Eight hundred adults are polled, and 640 of them support universal health-care coverage. E is the event that an adult does not support universal health-care coverage. [HINT: See Example 1.]

5. A die is rolled 60 times with the following result: 1, 2, and 3 each come up 8 times, and 4, 5, and 6 each come up 12 times. E is the event that the number that comes up is at most 4.

6. A die is rolled 90 times with the following result: 1 and 2 never come up, 3 and 4 each come up 30 times, and 5 and 6 each come up 15 times. E is the event that the number that comes up is at least 4.

Exercises 7–12 are based on the following table, which shows the frequency of outcomes when two distinguishable coins were tossed 4,000 times and the uppermost faces were observed. [HINT: See Example 2.]

Outcome	HH	HT	TH	TT
Frequency	1,100	950	1,200	750

7. Determine the relative frequency distribution.

8. What is the relative frequency that heads comes up at least once?

9. What is the relative frequency that the second coin lands with heads up?

10. What is the relative frequency that the first coin lands with heads up?

11. Would you judge the second coin to be fair? Give a reason for your answer.

12. Would you judge the first coin to be fair? Give a reason for your answer.

In Exercises 13–18, say whether the given distribution can be a relative frequency distribution. If your answer is no, indicate why not. [HINT: See the properties of relative frequency distributions.]

13.

Outcome	1	2	3	5
Rel. Frequency	.4	.6	0	0

14.

Outcome	A	B	C	D
Rel. Frequency	.2	.1	.2	.1

15.

Outcome	HH	HT	TH	TT
Rel. Frequency	.5	.4	.5	−.4

16.

Outcome	2	4	6	8
Rel. Frequency	25	25	25	25

17.

Outcome	−3	−2	−1	0
Rel. Frequency	.2	.3	.2	.3

18.

Outcome	HH	HT	TH	TT
Rel. Frequency	0	0	0	1

In Exercises 19 and 20, complete the given relative frequency distribution and compute the stated relative frequencies. [HINT: See the properties of relative frequency distributions.]

19.

Outcome	1	2	3	4	5
Rel. Frequency	.2	.3	.1	.1	

    a. $P(\{1, 3, 5\})$ **b.** $P(E')$ where $E = \{1, 2, 3\}$

20.

Outcome	1	2	3	4	5
Rel. Frequency	.4		.3	.1	.1

    a. $P(\{2, 3, 4\})$ **b.** $P(E')$ where $E = \{3, 4\}$

⊤ *Exercises 21–24 require the use of a calculator or computer with a random number generator.*

21. Simulate 100 tosses of a fair coin, and compute the estimated probability that heads comes up.

22. Simulate 100 throws of a fair die, and calculate the estimated probability that the result is a 6.

23. Simulate 50 tosses of two coins, and compute the estimated probability that the outcome is one head and one tail (in any order).

24. Simulate 100 throws of two fair dice, and calculate the estimated probability that the result is a double 6.

Applications

25. *Latin Music Sales: 2013* In a survey of 500 Latin music downloads in 2013, 270 were regional (Mexican/Tejano), 150 were pop-rock, 70 were tropical (salsa/merengue/

cumbia/bachata), and 10 were urban (reggaeton).[11] Calculate the following relative frequencies:

a. That a music download was regional

b. That a music download was either tropical or urban

c. That a music download was not urban [**HINT**: See Example 1.]

26. *Latin Music Sales: 2009* In a survey of 400 Latin music downloads in 2009, 200 were regional (Mexican/Tejano), 130 were pop-rock, 45 were tropical (salsa/merengue/cumbia/bachata), and 25 were urban (reggaeton).[12] Calculate the following relative frequencies:

a. That a music download was pop-rock

b. That a music download was neither tropical nor regional

c. That a music download was not regional [**HINT**: See Example 1.]

27. *Subprime Mortgages during the 2000–2008 Housing Bubble* The following chart shows the results of a survey of the status of subprime home mortgages in Texas in November 2008:[13]

Mortgage Status	Current	Past Due	In Foreclosure	Repossessed
Frequency	134	52	9	5

(The four categories are mutually exclusive; for instance, "Past Due" refers to a mortgage whose payment status is past due but is not in foreclosure, and "In Foreclosure" refers to a mortgage that is in the process of being foreclosed but not yet repossessed.)

a. Find the relative frequency distribution for the experiment of randomly selecting a subprime mortgage in Texas and determining its status.

b. What is the relative frequency that a randomly selected subprime mortgage in Texas was not current? [**HINT**: See Example 2.]

28. *Subprime Mortgages during the 2000–2008 Housing Bubble* The following chart shows the results of a survey of the status of subprime home mortgages in Florida in November 2008:[14]

Mortgage Status	Current	Past Due	In Foreclosure	Repossessed
Frequency	110	65	60	15

(The four categories are mutually exclusive; for instance, "Past Due" refers to a mortgage whose payment status is past due but is not in foreclosure, and "In Foreclosure" refers to a mortgage that is in the process of being foreclosed but not yet repossessed.)

a. Find the relative frequency distribution for the experiment of randomly selecting a subprime mortgage in Florida and determining its status.

b. What is the relative frequency that a randomly selected subprime mortgage in Florida was neither in foreclosure nor repossessed? [**HINT**: See Example 2.]

29. *Population Age in Mexico* The following table shows the results of a survey of randomly selected residents of Mexico:[15]

Age	0–14	15–29	30–64	>64
Percentage	30	27	37	6

a. Find the associated relative frequency distribution. [**HINT**: See Quick Example 3.]

b. Find the relative frequency that a resident of Mexico is *not* from 15 to 64 years old.

30. *Population Age in the United States* The following table shows the results of a survey of randomly selected U.S. residents:[16]

Age	0–14	15–29	30–64	>64
Percentage	20	21	46	13

a. Find the associated relative frequency distribution. [**HINT**: See Quick Example 3.]

b. Find the relative frequency that a resident of the United States is 30 years old or older.

31. *Motor Vehicle Safety* The following table shows crashworthiness ratings for 10 small SUVs.[17] (3 = Good, 2 = Acceptable, 1 = Marginal, 0 = Poor)

Frontal Crash Test Rating	3	2	1	0
Frequency	1	4	4	1

a. Find the relative frequency distribution for the experiment of choosing a small SUV at random and determining its frontal crash rating.

b. What is the relative frequency that a randomly selected small SUV will have a crash test rating of "Acceptable" or better?

---

[11] Based on digital revenues in 2013. Source: The Recording Industry Association of America (www.riaa.com).

[12] Based on digital revenues in 2009. Source: *Ibid.*

[13] Based on actual data in 2008. Source: Federal Reserve Bank of New York (www.newyorkfed.org/regional/subprime.html).

[14] *Ibid.*

[15] Based on population distribution in 2010. Source: Instituto Nacional de Estadística y Geografía (www.inegi.org.mx).

[16] *Ibid.* (The data for the United States was also provided by the Instituto Nacional de Estadística y Geografía.)

[17] Ratings by the Insurance Institute for Highway Safety. Sources: Oak Ridge National Laboratory: "An Analysis of the Impact of Sport Utility Vehicles in the United States," Stacy C. Davis, Lorena F. Truett (August 2000) Insurance Institute for Highway Safety (www-cta.ornl.gov/Publications/Final SUV report.pdf).

32. *Motor Vehicle Safety* The following table shows crash-worthiness ratings for 16 small cars.[18] (3 = Good, 2 = Acceptable, 1 = Marginal, 0 = Poor)

Frontal Crash Test Rating	3	2	1	0
Frequency	1	11	2	2

a. Find the relative frequency distribution for the experiment of choosing a small car at random and determining its frontal crash rating.

b. What is the relative frequency that a randomly selected small car will have a crash test rating of "Marginal" or worse?

33. *Internet Connections* The following pie chart shows the relative frequency distribution resulting from a survey of 2,000 U.S. households with Internet connections back in 2003:[19]

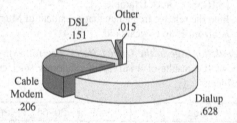

Determine the **frequency distribution**, that is, the total number of households with each type of Internet connection in the survey.

34. *Internet Connections* The following pie chart shows the relative frequency distribution resulting from a survey of 3,000 U.S. rural households with Internet connections back in 2003:[20]

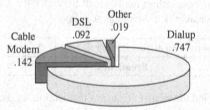

Determine the **frequency distribution**, that is, the total number of households with each type of Internet connection in the survey.

35. ▼ *Stock Market Gyrations* The following chart shows the day-by-day change in the Dow Jones Industrial Average

during 20 successive business days in October 2008 during the 2008 financial crisis:[21]

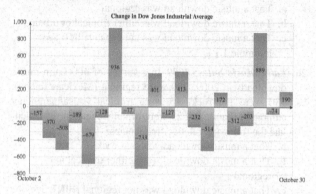

Use the chart to construct the relative frequency distribution using the following three outcomes. Surge: The Dow was up by more than 300 points; Plunge: The Dow was down by more than 300 points; Steady: The Dow changed by 300 points or less.

36. ▼ *Stock Market Gyrations* Repeat Exercise 35 using the following chart for November–December 2008:[22]

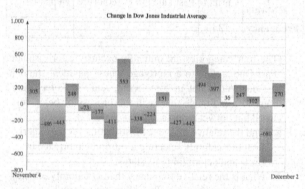

Publishing *Exercises 37–46 are based on the following table, which shows the results of a survey of 100 authors by a (fictitious) publishing company:*

	New Authors	Established Authors	Total
Successful	5	25	30
Unsuccessful	15	55	70
Total	20	80	100

Compute the relative frequencies of the given events if an author as specified is chosen at random.

37. ▼ An author is established and successful.

38. ▼ An author is unsuccessful and new.

---

[18] See footnote for Exercise 31.

[19] Based on a 2003 survey. Source: "A Nation Online: Entering the Broadband Age," U.S. Department of Commerce, September 2004 (www.ntia.doc.gov/reports/anol/index.html).

[20] *Ibid.*

[21] Source: http://finance.google.com.

[22] *Ibid.*

39. ▼ An author is a new author.

40. ▼ An author is successful.

41. ▼ An author is unsuccessful.

42. ▼ An author is established.

43. ▼ A successful author is established.

44. ▼ An unsuccessful author is established.

45. ▼ An established author is successful.

46. ▼ A new author is unsuccessful.

47. ▼ *Public Health* A random sampling of chicken in supermarkets revealed that approximately 80% was contaminated with the organism *Campylobacter*.[23] Of the contaminated chicken, 20% had the strain that is resistant to antibiotics. Construct a relative frequency distribution showing the following outcomes when chicken is purchased at a supermarket: *U:* the chicken is not infected with *Campylobacter*; *C:* the chicken is infected with nonresistant *Campylobacter*; *R:* the chicken is infected with resistant *Campylobacter*.

48. ▼ *Public Health* A random sampling of turkey in supermarkets found 58% to be contaminated with *Campylobacter*, and 84% of those to be contaminated with the strain that is resistant to antibiotics.[24] Construct a relative frequency distribution showing the following outcomes when turkey is purchased at a supermarket: *U:* the turkey is not infected with *Campylobacter*; *C:* the turkey is infected with nonresistant *Campylobacter*; and *R:* the turkey is infected with resistant *Campylobacter*.

49. ▼ *Organic Produce* A 2001 Agriculture Department study of more than 94,000 samples from more than 20 crops showed that 73% of conventionally grown foods had residues from at least one pesticide. Moreover, conventionally grown foods were six times as likely to contain multiple pesticides as organic foods. Of the organic foods tested, 23% had pesticide residues, which includes 10% with multiple pesticide residues.[25] Compute two estimated probability distributions: one for conventional produce and one for organic produce, showing the relative frequencies that a randomly selected product has no pesticide residues, has residues from a single pesticide, and has residues from multiple pesticides.

50. ▼ *Organic Produce* Repeat Exercise 49 using the following information for produce from California: 31% of conventional food and 6.5% of organic food had residues from

at least one pesticide. Assume that, as in Exercise 49, conventionally grown foods are six times as likely to contain multiple pesticides as organic foods. Also assume that 3% of the organic food has residues from multiple pesticides.

51. ▼ *Steroids Testing* A pharmaceutical company is running trials on a new test for anabolic steroids. The company uses the test on 400 athletes known to be using steroids and 200 athletes known not to be using steroids. Of those using steroids, the new test is positive for 390 and negative for 10. Of those not using steroids, the test is positive for 10 and negative for 190. What is the relative frequency of a **false negative** result (the probability that an athlete using steroids will test negative)? What is the relative frequency of a **false positive** result (the probability that an athlete not using steroids will test positive)?

52. ▼ *Lie Detectors* A manufacturer of lie detectors is testing its newest design. It asks 300 subjects to lie deliberately and another 500 to tell the truth. Of those who lied, the lie detector caught 200. Of those who told the truth, the lie detector accused 200 of lying. What is the relative frequency of the machine wrongly letting a liar go, and what is the probability that it will falsely accuse someone who is telling the truth?

53. ▣ ◆ *Public Health* Refer back to Exercise 47. Simulate the experiment of selecting chicken at a supermarket and determining the following outcomes: *U:* The chicken is not infected with *Campylobacter*; *C:* The chicken is infected with nonresistant *Campylobacter*; *R:* The chicken is infected with resistant *Campylobacter*. [HINT: Generate integers in the range 1–100. The outcome is determined by the range. For instance, if the number is in the range 1–20, regard the outcome as *U*, etc.]

54. ▣ ◆ *Public Health* Repeat Exercise 53, but use turkeys and the data given in Exercise 48.

Communication and Reasoning Exercises

55. Complete the following. The relative frequency of an event *E* is defined to be _____.

56. If two people each flip a coin 100 times and compute the relative frequency that heads comes up, they will both obtain the same result—right?

57. How many different answers are possible if you flip a coin 100 times and compute the relative frequency that heads comes up? What are the possible answers?

58. Interpret the popularity rating of the student council president as a relative frequency by specifying an appropriate experiment and also what is observed.

59. ▼ Ruth tells you that when you roll a pair of fair dice, the probability of obtaining a pair of matching numbers is 1/6. To test this claim, you roll a pair of fair dice 20 times and never once get a pair of matching numbers. This proves that either Ruth is wrong or the dice are not fair—right?

---

[23] *Campylobacter* is one of the leading causes of food poisoning in humans. Thoroughly cooking the meat kills the bacteria. Source: *New York Times*, October 20, 1997, p. A1. Publication of this article first brought *Campylobacter* to the attention of a wide audience.

[24] *Ibid.*

[25] The 10% figure is an estimate. Source: *New York Times*, May 8, 2002, p. A29.

60. ▼ Juan tells you that when you roll a pair of fair dice, the probability that the numbers add up to 7 is 1/6. To test this claim, you roll a pair of fair dice 24 times, and the numbers add up to 7 exactly four times. This proves that Juan is right—right?

61. ▼ How would you measure the relative frequency that the weather service accurately predicts the next day's high temperature?

62. ▼ Suppose that you toss a coin 100 times and get 70 heads. If you continue tossing the coin, the estimated probability of heads overall should approach 50% if the coin is fair. Will you have to get more tails than heads in subsequent tosses to "correct" for the 70 heads you got in the first 100 tosses?

8.3 Probability and Probability Models

What Is Probability?

It is understandable if you are a little uncomfortable with using relative frequency as the estimated probability because it does not always agree with what you intuitively think to be true. For instance, if you toss a fair coin (one as likely to come up heads as tails) 100 times and heads happen to come up 62 times, the experiment seems to suggest that the probability of heads is .62, even though you *know* that the "actual" probability is .50 (because the coin is fair).

Q: *So what do we mean by "actual" probability?*

A: There are various philosophical views as to exactly what we should mean by "actual" probability. For example, (finite) *frequentists* say that there is no such thing as "actual probability"—all we should really talk about is what we can actually measure: the relative frequency. *Propensitists* say that the actual probability *p* of an event is a property of the event that makes its relative frequency tend to *p* in the long run; that is, *p* will be the limiting value of the relative frequency as the number of trials in a repeated experiment gets larger and larger. (See Figure 4 in Section 8.2.) *Bayesians*, on the other hand, argue that the actual probability of an event is the degree to which we *expect* it to occur, given our knowledge about the nature of the experiment. These and other viewpoints have been debated in considerable depth in the literature.*

---

* The interested reader should consult references in the philosophy of probability. For an online summary, see, for example, the Stanford Encyclopedia of Philosophy (http://plato.stanford.edu/contents.html).

Mathematicians tend to avoid the whole debate and talk instead about *abstract* probability, or **probability distributions**, based purely on the properties of relative frequency listed in Section 8.2. Specific probability distributions can then be used as *models* in real-life situations such as flipping a coin or tossing a die, to predict (or model) relative frequency.

Probability Distribution; Probability

(Compare with the properties of relative frequency distributions in Section 8.2.)
A (finite) **probability distribution** is an assignment of a number $P(s_i)$, the **probability of** s_i, to each outcome of a finite sample space $S = \{s_1, s_2, \ldots, s_n\}$. The probabilities must satisfy

1. $0 \leq P(s_i) \leq 1$

and

2. $P(s_1) + P(s_2) + \cdots + P(s_n) = 1$.

We find the **probability of an event** E, written $P(E)$, by adding up the probabilities of the outcomes in E.

If $P(E) = 0$, we call E an **impossible event**. The empty event $\varnothing$ is always impossible, since *something* must happen.

Quick Examples

1. All the examples of estimated probability distributions in Section 8.2 are examples of probability distributions. (See the Quick Examples in that section.)

2. Let us take $S = \{H, T\}$ and make the assignments $P(H) = .5$, $P(T) = .5$. Because these numbers are between 0 and 1 and add to 1, they specify a probability distribution.

3. In Quick Example 2, we can instead make the assignments $P(H) = .2$, $P(T) = .8$. Because these numbers are between 0 and 1 and add to 1, they, too, specify a probability distribution.

4. With $S = \{H, T\}$ again, we could also take $P(H) = 1$, $P(T) = 0$, so $\{T\}$ is an impossible event.

5. The following table gives a probability distribution for the sample space $S = \{1, 2, 3, 4, 5, 6\}$:

Outcome	1	2	3	4	5	6
Probability	.3	.3	0	.1	.2	.1

It follows that

$$P(\{1, 6\}) = .3 + .1 = .4$$
$$P(\{2, 3\}) = .3 + 0 = .3$$
$$P(3) = 0. \qquad \text{\{3\} is an impossible event.}$$

The above Quick Examples included models for the experiments of flipping fair and unfair coins. In general, we have the following.

Probability Models

A **probability model** for a particular experiment is a probability distribution that predicts the relative frequency of each outcome if the experiment is performed a large number of times. (See Figure 4 at the end of Section 8.2).* Just as we think of relative frequency as *estimated probability*, we can think of modeled probability as *theoretical probability*.

Quick Examples

6. **Fair Coin Model:** (See Quick Example 2.) Flip a fair coin, and observe the side that faces up. Because we expect that heads is as likely to come up as tails, we model this experiment with the probability distribution specified by $S = \{H, T\}$, $P(H) = .5$, $P(T) = .5$. Figure 4 in Section 8.2 suggests that the relative frequency of heads

* Just how large is a "large number of times"? That depends on the nature of the experiment. For example, if you toss a fair coin 100 times, then the relative frequency of heads will be between .45 and .55 about 73% of the time. If an outcome is extremely unlikely (such as winning the lottery), you might need to repeat the experiment billions or trillions of times before the relative frequency approaches any specific number.

approaches .5 as the number of coin tosses gets large, so the fair coin model predicts the relative frequency for a large number of coin tosses quite well.

7. **Unfair Coin Model:** (See Quick Example 3.) Take $S = \{H, T\}$ and $P(H) = .2$, $P(T) = .8$. We can think of this distribution as a model for the experiment of flipping an unfair coin that is four times as likely to land with tails uppermost than heads.

8. **Fair Die Model:** Roll a fair die, and observe the uppermost number. Because we expect to roll each specific number one sixth of the time, we model the experiment with the probability distribution specified by $S = \{1, 2, 3, 4, 5, 6\}$, $P(1) = 1/6$, $P(2) = 1/6, \ldots, P(6) = 1/6$. This model predicts, for example, that the relative frequency of throwing a 5 approaches $1/6$ as the number of times you roll the die gets large.

9. Roll a pair of fair dice. (Recall that there are a total of 36 outcomes if the dice are distinguishable.) Then an appropriate model of the experiment has

$$S = \begin{Bmatrix} (1,1), \ (1,2), \ (1,3), \ (1,4), \ (1,5), \ (1,6), \\ (2,1), \ (2,2), \ (2,3), \ (2,4), \ (2,5), \ (2,6), \\ (3,1), \ (3,2), \ (3,3), \ (3,4), \ (3,5), \ (3,6), \\ (4,1), \ (4,2), \ (4,3), \ (4,4), \ (4,5), \ (4,6), \\ (5,1), \ (5,2), \ (5,3), \ (5,4), \ (5,5), \ (5,6), \\ (6,1), \ (6,2), \ (6,3), \ (6,4), \ (6,5), \ (6,6) \end{Bmatrix},$$

with each outcome being assigned a probability of $1/36$.

10. In the experiment in Quick Example 9, take E to be the event that the sum of the numbers that face up is 5, so

$$E = \{(1, 4), (2, 3), (3, 2), (4, 1)\}.$$

By the properties of probability distributions,

$$P(E) = \frac{1}{36} + \frac{1}{36} + \frac{1}{36} + \frac{1}{36} = \frac{4}{36} = \frac{1}{9}.$$

Notice that, in all of the Quick Examples above except Quick Example 7, all the outcomes are equally likely, and each outcome s has a probability of

$$P(s) = \frac{1}{\text{Total number of outcomes}} = \frac{1}{n(S)}.$$

More generally, in Quick Example 10 we saw that adding the probabilities of the individual outcomes in an event E amounted to computing the ratio (Number of favorable outcomes)/(Total number of outcomes):

$$P(E) = \frac{\text{Number of favorable outcomes}}{\text{Total number of outcomes}} = \frac{n(E)}{n(S)}.$$

Visualizing Probability for Equally Likely Outcomes

Sample Space S

$P(E) = \frac{n(E)}{n(S)} = \frac{6}{10} = .6$

Probability Model for Equally Likely Outcomes

In an experiment in which all outcomes are equally likely, we model the experiment by taking the probability of an event E to be

$$P(E) = \frac{\text{Number of favorable outcomes}}{\text{Total number of outcomes}} = \frac{n(E)}{n(S)}.$$

Note Remember that this formula will work *only* when the outcomes are equally likely. If, for example, a die is *weighted*, then the outcomes may not be equally likely, and the formula above will not give an appropriate probability model. ∎

Quick Examples

11. Toss a fair coin three times. In this case, $S = \{$HHH, HHT, HTH, HTT, THH, THT, TTH, TTT$\}$. The probability that we throw exactly two heads is

    $$P(E) = \frac{n(E)}{n(S)} = \frac{3}{8}.$$

    There are eight equally likely outcomes, and $E = \{$HHT, HTH, THH$\}$.

12. Roll a pair of fair dice. The probability that we roll a double (both dice show the same number) is

    $$P(E) = \frac{n(E)}{n(S)} = \frac{6}{36} = \frac{1}{6}. \quad E = \{(1, 1), (2, 2), (3, 3), (4, 4), (5, 5), (6, 6)\}$$

13. Randomly choose a person from a class of 40, in which 6 have red hair. If E is the event that a randomly selected person in the class has red hair, then

    $$P(E) = \frac{n(E)}{n(S)} = \frac{6}{40} = .15$$

EXAMPLE 1   Sales of Hybrid Vehicles

(Compare Example 1 in Section 8.2.) A total of 1.9 million hybrid vehicles had been sold in the United States through October of 2011. Of these, 955,000 were Toyota Prii, 205,000 were Honda Civics, 170,000 were Toyota Camrys, 105,000 were Ford Escapes, and the rest were other makes.[26]

a. What is the probability that a randomly selected hybrid vehicle sold in the United States was either a Toyota Prius or a Honda Civic?

b. What is the probability that a randomly selected hybrid vehicle sold in the United States was not a Toyota Camry?

---

[26] Source for sales data: www.wikipedia.com.

Solution

a. The experiment suggested by the question consists of randomly choosing a hybrid vehicle sold in the United States and determining its make. We are interested in the event E that the hybrid vehicle was either a Toyota Prius or a Honda Civic. So

$$S = \text{the set of hybrid vehicles sold; } n(S) = 1,900,000$$

$$E = \text{the set of Toyota Prii and Honda Civics sold;}$$
$$n(E) = 955,000 + 205,000 = 1,160,000.$$

Are the outcomes equally likely in this experiment? Yes, because we are as likely to choose one vehicle as another. Thus,

$$P(E) = \frac{n(E)}{n(S)} = \frac{1,160,000}{1,900,000} \approx .61.$$

b. Let the event F consist of those hybrid vehicles sold that were not Toyota Camrys:

$$n(F) = 1,900,000 - 170,000 = 1,730,000.$$

Hence,

$$P(F) = \frac{n(F)}{n(S)} = \frac{1,730,000}{1,900,000} \approx .91.$$

Q: *In Example 1 of Section 8.2 we had a similar example about hybrid vehicles, but we called the probabilities calculated there relative frequencies. Here, they are probabilities. What is the difference?*

A: In Example 1 of Section 8.2, the data were based on the results of a survey, or sample, of only 250 hybrid vehicles (out of a total of about 1.9 million sold in the United States) and were therefore incomplete. (A statistician would say that we were given *sample data*.) It follows that any inference we draw from the 250 surveyed, such as the probability that a hybrid vehicle sold in the United States is not a Toyota Camry, is uncertain, and this is the cue that tells us that we are working with relative frequency, or estimated probability. Think of the survey as an experiment (choosing a hybrid vehicle) repeated 250 times—exactly the setting for estimated probability.

In Example 1 above, on the other hand, the data do not describe how *some* hybrid vehicle sales are broken down into the categories described; they describe how *all 1.9 million* hybrid vehicle sales in the United States are broken down. (The statistician would say that we were given *population data* in this case, because the data describe the entire "population" of hybrid vehicles sold in the United States.)

EXAMPLE 2   Indistinguishable Dice

We recall from Section 8.1 that the sample space when we roll a pair of indistinguishable dice is

$$S = \left\{ \begin{array}{l} (1,1),\ (1,2),\ (1,3),\ (1,4),\ (1,5),\ (1,6), \\ \quad\quad (2,2),\ (2,3),\ (2,4),\ (2,5),\ (2,6), \\ \quad\quad\quad\quad (3,3),\ (3,4),\ (3,5),\ (3,6), \\ \quad\quad\quad\quad\quad\quad (4,4),\ (4,5),\ (4,6), \\ \quad\quad\quad\quad\quad\quad\quad\quad (5,5),\ (5,6), \\ \quad\quad\quad\quad\quad\quad\quad\quad\quad\quad (6,6) \end{array} \right\}.$$

Construct a probability model for this experiment.

Solution Because there are 21 outcomes, it is tempting to say that the probability of each outcome should be taken to be $1/21$. However, the outcomes are not all equally likely. For instance, the outcome $(2, 3)$ is twice as likely as $(2, 2)$, because $(2, 3)$ can occur in two ways. (It corresponds to the event $\{(2, 3), (3, 2)\}$ for distinguishable dice.) For purposes of calculating probability, it is easiest to use calculations for distinguishable dice.* Here are some examples.

* Note that any pair of real dice can be distinguished in principle because they possess slight differences, although we may regard them as indistinguishable by not attempting to distinguish them. Thus, the probabilities of events must be the same as for the corresponding events for distinguishable dice.

Outcome (Indistinguishable Dice)	$(1, 1)$	$(1, 2)$	$(2, 2)$	$(1, 3)$	$(2, 3)$	$(3, 3)$
Corresponding Event (Distinguishable Dice)	$\{(1, 1)\}$	$\{(1, 2), (2, 1)\}$	$\{(2, 2)\}$	$\{(1, 3), (3, 1)\}$	$\{(2, 3), (3, 2)\}$	$\{(3, 3)\}$
Probability	$\dfrac{1}{36}$	$\dfrac{2}{36} = \dfrac{1}{18}$	$\dfrac{1}{36}$	$\dfrac{2}{36} = \dfrac{1}{18}$	$\dfrac{2}{36} = \dfrac{1}{18}$	$\dfrac{1}{36}$

If we continue this process for all 21 outcomes, we will find that they add to 1. Figure 5 illustrates the complete probability distribution:

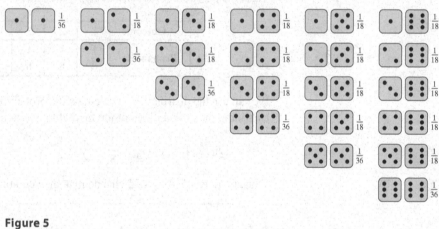

Figure 5

EXAMPLE 3   **Weighted Dice**

To impress your friends with your die-rolling skills, you have surreptitiously weighted your die in such a way that 6 is three times as likely to come up as any one of the other numbers. (All the other outcomes are equally likely.) Obtain a probability distribution for a roll of the die, and use it to calculate the probability of an even number coming up.

Solution Let us label our unknowns (there appear to be two of them):

x = probability of rolling a 6

y = probability of rolling any one of the other numbers.

We are first told that "6 is three times as likely to come up as any one of the other numbers." If we rephrase this in terms of our unknown probabilities, we get "the probability of rolling a 6 is three times the probability of rolling any one of the other numbers." In symbols,

$$x = 3y.$$

We must also use a piece of information that has not been given to us but that we know must be true: The sum of the probabilities of all the outcomes is 1:

$$x + y + y + y + y + y = 1$$

or

$$x + 5y = 1.$$

We now have two linear equations in two unknowns, and we solve for x and y. Substituting the value of x in the first equation ($x = 3y$) in the second ($x + 5y = 1$) gives

$$8y = 1$$

or

$$y = \frac{1}{8}.$$

To get x, we substitute the value of y back into either equation and find

$$x = \frac{3}{8}.$$

Thus, the probability model we seek is the one shown in the following table:

Outcome	1	2	3	4	5	6
Probability	$\frac{1}{8}$	$\frac{1}{8}$	$\frac{1}{8}$	$\frac{1}{8}$	$\frac{1}{8}$	$\frac{3}{8}$

We can use the distribution to calculate the probability of an even number coming up by adding the probabilities of the favorable outcomes:

$$P(\{2, 4, 6\}) = \frac{1}{8} + \frac{1}{8} + \frac{3}{8} = \frac{5}{8}$$

Thus, there is a $5/8 = .625$ chance that an even number will come up.

➡ **Before we go on ...** We should check that the probability distribution in Example 3 satisfies the requirements: 6 is indeed three times as likely to come up as any other number. Also, the probabilities that we calculated do add up to 1:

$$\frac{1}{8} + \frac{1}{8} + \frac{1}{8} + \frac{1}{8} + \frac{1}{8} + \frac{3}{8} = 1. \ \blacksquare$$

Probability of Unions, Intersections, and Complements

So far, all we know about computing the probability of an event E is that $P(E)$ is the sum of the probabilities of the individual outcomes in E. Suppose, though, that we do not know the probabilities of the individual outcomes in E but we do know that $E = A \cup B$, where we happen to know $P(A)$ and $P(B)$. How do we compute the probability of $A \cup B$? We might be tempted to say that $P(A \cup B)$ is $P(A) + P(B)$, but let us look at an example using the probability distribution in Quick Example 5 at the beginning of this section:

Outcome	1	2	3	4	5	6
Probability	.3	.3	0	.1	.2	.1

For A, let us take the event $\{2, 4, 5\}$, and for B, let us take $\{2, 4, 6\}$. $A \cup B$ is then the event $\{2, 4, 5, 6\}$. We know that we can find the probabilities $P(A)$, $P(B)$, and $P(A \cup B)$ by adding the probabilities of all the outcomes in these events, so

$$P(A) = P(\{2, 4, 5\}) = .3 + .1 + .2 = .6$$
$$P(B) = P(\{2, 4, 6\}) = .3 + .1 + .1 = .5$$
$$P(A \cup B) = P(\{2, 4, 5, 6\}) = .3 + .1 + .2 + .1 = .7.$$

Our first guess was wrong: $P(A \cup B) \neq P(A) + P(B)$. Notice, however, that the outcomes in $A \cap B$ are counted twice in computing $P(A) + P(B)$ but only once in computing $P(A \cup B)$:

$$P(A) + P(B) = P(\{2, 4, 5\}) + P(\{2, 4, 6\}) \qquad A \cap B = \{2, 4\}$$
$$= (.3 + .1 + .2) + (.3 + .1 + .1) \qquad P(A \cap B) \text{ counted twice}$$
$$= 1.1,$$

whereas

$$P(A \cup B) = P(\{2, 4, 5, 6\}) = .3 + .1 + .2 + .1 \qquad P(A \cap B) \text{ counted once}$$
$$= .7.$$

Thus, if we take $P(A) + P(B)$ and then subtract the surplus $P(A \cap B)$, we get $P(A \cup B)$. In symbols,

$$P(A \cup B) = P(A) + P(B) - P(A \cap B)$$
$$.7 = .6 + .5 - .4$$

(see Figure 6). We call this formula the **addition principle**. One more thing: Notice that our original guess $P(A \cup B) = P(A) + P(B)$ would have worked if we had chosen A and B with no outcomes in common; that is, if $A \cap B = \varnothing$. When $A \cap B = \varnothing$, recall that we say that A and B are mutually exclusive.

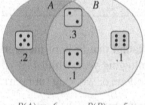

$$P(A) = .6 \qquad P(B) = .5$$
$$P(A \cap B) = .4$$
$$P(A \cup B) = .6 + .5 - .4$$

Figure 6

Visualizing the Addition Principle

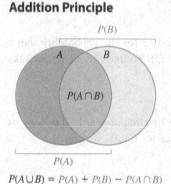

$$P(A \cup B) = P(A) + P(B) - P(A \cap B)$$

Mutually Exclusive Events

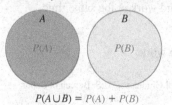

$$P(A \cup B) = P(A) + P(B)$$

Addition Principle

If A and B are any two events, then

$$P(A \cup B) = P(A) + P(B) - P(A \cap B).$$

Addition Principle for Mutually Exclusive Events

If $A \cap B = \varnothing$, we say that A and B are **mutually exclusive**, and we have

$$P(A \cup B) = P(A) + P(B). \qquad \text{Because } P(A \cap B) = 0$$

This holds true also for more than two events: If $A_1, A_2, \ldots, A_n$ are mutually exclusive events (that is, the intersection of every pair of them is empty), then

$$P(A_1 \cup A_2 \cup \cdots \cup A_n) = P(A_1) + P(A_2) + \cdots + P(A_n). \qquad \begin{array}{l}\text{Addition principle} \\ \text{for many mutually} \\ \text{exclusive events}\end{array}$$

Quick Examples

14. There is a 10% chance of rain (R) tomorrow, a 20% chance of high winds (W), and a 5% chance of both. The probability of either rain or high winds (or both) is

$$P(R \cup W) = P(R) + P(W) - P(R \cap W)$$
$$= .10 + .20 - .05 = .25.$$

15. The probability that you will be in Cairo at 6:00 am tomorrow (C) is .3, while the probability that you will be in Alexandria at 6:00 am tomorrow (A) is .2. Thus, the probability that you will be in either Cairo or Alexandria at 6:00 am tomorrow is

$$P(C \cup A) = P(C) + P(A) \qquad \text{\textit{A} and \textit{C} are mutually exclusive.}$$
$$= .3 + .2 = .5.$$

16. When a pair of fair dice is rolled, the probability of the numbers that face up adding to 7 is 6/36, the probability of their adding to 8 is 5/36, and the probability of their adding to 9 is 4/36. Thus, the probability of the numbers adding to 7, 8, or 9 is

＊The sum of the numbers that face up cannot equal two different numbers at the same time.

$$P(\{7\} \cup \{8\} \cup \{9\}) = P(7) + P(8) + P(9) \qquad \begin{array}{l}\text{The events are}\\ \text{mutually exclusive.}^*\end{array}$$
$$= \frac{6}{36} + \frac{5}{36} + \frac{4}{36} = \frac{15}{36} = \frac{5}{12}.$$

EXAMPLE 4 **School and Work**

A survey[27] conducted by the Bureau of Labor Statistics found that 68% of the high school graduating class of 2010 went on to college the following year, while 42% of the class was working. Furthermore, 92% were either in college or working (or both).

a. What percentage went on to college and work at the same time?

b. What percentage went on to college but not work?

Solution We can think of the experiment of choosing a member of the high school graduating class of 2010 at random. The sample space is the set of all these graduates.

a. We are given information about two events:

You can use the formula $P(A \cup B) = P(A) + P(B) - P(A \cap B)$ to calculate any of the four quantities in the formula if you know the other three.

  A: A graduate went on to college; $P(A) = .68$.

  B: A graduate went on to work; $P(B) = .42$.

We are also told that $P(A \cup B) = .92$. We are asked for the probability that a graduate went on to both college and work, $P(A \cap B)$. To find $P(A \cap B)$, we take advantage of the fact that the formula

$$P(A \cup B) = P(A) + P(B) - P(A \cap B)$$

can be used to calculate any one of the four quantities that appear in it as long as we know the other three. Substituting the quantities we know, we get

  $.92 = .68 + .42 - P(A \cap B)$,

so

  $P(A \cap B) = .68 + .42 - .92 = .18$.

Thus, 18% of the graduates went on to college and work at the same time.

b. We are asked for the probability of a new event:

  C: A graduate went on to college but not to work.

---

[27] Source: "College Enrollment and Work Activity of High School Graduates," U.S. Bureau of Labor Statistics (www.bls.gov/news.release/hsgec.htm).

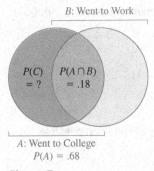

B: Went to Work

$P(C)$
$= ?$ $P(A \cap B)$
$= .18$

A: Went to College
$P(A) = .68$

Figure 7

C is the part of A outside of $A \cap B$, so $C \cup (A \cap B) = A$, and C and $A \cap B$ are mutually exclusive. (See Figure 7.)

Thus, applying the addition principle, we have

$$P(C) + P(A \cap B) = P(A).$$

From part (a) we know that $P(A \cap B) = .18$, so

$$P(C) + .18 = .68$$

giving

$$P(C) = .50.$$

In other words, 50% of the graduates went on to college but not to work.

We can use the addition principle to deduce other useful properties of probability distributions.

More Principles of Probability Distributions

The following rules hold for any sample space S and any event A:

$$P(S) = 1 \qquad \text{The probability of } \textit{something} \text{ happening is 1.}$$
$$P(\varnothing) = 0 \qquad \text{The probability of } \textit{nothing} \text{ happening is 0.}$$
$$P(A') = 1 - P(A). \qquad \text{The probability of } A \textit{ not} \text{ happening is } 1 \text{ minus the probability of } A.$$

Note We can also write the third equation as

$$P(A) = 1 - P(A')$$

or

$$P(A) + P(A') = 1. \qquad \blacksquare$$

Visualizing the Rule for Complements

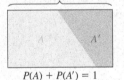

Sample Space S

A A'

$P(A) + P(A') = 1$

Quick Examples

17. There is a 10% chance of rain (R) tomorrow. Therefore, the probability that it will *not* rain is

$$P(R') = 1 - P(R) = 1 - .10 = .90.$$

18. The probability that Eric Ewing will score at least two goals is .6. Therefore, the probability that he will score at most one goal is $1 - .6 = .4$.

Q: *Can you persuade me that all of these principles are true?*

A: Let us take them one at a time. We know that $S = \{s_1, s_2, \ldots, s_n\}$ is the set of all outcomes, so

$$
\begin{aligned}
P(S) &= P(\{s_1, s_2, \ldots, s_n\}) && \text{We add the probabilities of the outcomes to} \\
&= P(s_1) + P(s_2) + \cdots + P(s_n) && \text{obtain the probability of an event.} \\
&= 1. && \text{By the definition of a probability distribution}
\end{aligned}
$$

Now, note that $S \cap \varnothing = \varnothing$, so that S and $\varnothing$ are mutually exclusive. Applying the addition principle gives

$$P(S) = P(S \cup \varnothing) = P(S) + P(\varnothing).$$

Subtracting $P(S)$ from both sides gives $0 = P(\varnothing)$.

If A is any event in S, then we can write

$$S = A \cup A',$$

where A and A' are mutually exclusive. (Why?) Thus, by the addition principle,

$$P(S) = P(A) + P(A').$$

Because $P(S) = 1$, we get

$$1 = P(A) + P(A')$$

or $P(A') = 1 - P(A)$.

EXAMPLE 5   **Subprime Mortgages during the Housing Bubble**

A home loan is either current, 30–59 days past due, 60–89 days past due, 90 or more days past due, in foreclosure, or repossessed by the lender. In November 2008 the probability that a randomly selected subprime home mortgage in California was not current was .51. The probability that a mortgage was not current, but neither in foreclosure nor repossessed, was .28.[28] Calculate the probabilities of the following events:

a. A California home mortgage was current.

b. A California home mortgage was in foreclosure or repossessed.

Solution

a. Let us write C for the event that a randomly selected subprime home mortgage in California was current. The event that the home mortgage was *not* current is its complement C', and we are given that $P(C') = .51$. We have

$$P(C) + P(C') = 1$$
$$P(C) + .51 = 1,$$

so $P(C) = 1 - .51 = .49.$

b. Take

F: A mortgage was in foreclosure or repossessed.

N: A mortgage was neither current, in foreclosure, nor repossessed.

We are given $P(N) = .28$. Further, the events F and N are mutually exclusive with union C', the set of all noncurrent mortgages. Hence,

$$P(C') = P(F) + P(N)$$
$$.51 = P(F) + .28,$$

giving

$$P(F) = .51 - .28 = .23.$$

Thus, there was a 23% chance that a subprime home mortgage was either in foreclosure or repossessed.

---

[28] Source: Federal Reserve Bank of New York (www.newyorkfed.org/regional/subprime.html).

EXAMPLE 6   **Apple Sales**

The following table shows sales, in millions of items, of Macs, iPhones, and iPads sold by Apple in 2012, 2013, and 2014:[29]

	Macs (A)	iPhones (B)	iPads (C)	Total
2012 (U)	18	125	58	201
2013 (V)	16	150	71	238
2014 (W)	19	169	68	256
Total	53	444	197	695

If one of these 695 million items sold is selected at random, find the probabilities of the following events:

a. It is a Mac.

b. It was sold in 2013.

c. It is a Mac sold in 2013.

d. Either it is a Mac or it was sold in 2013.

e. It is not a Mac.

Solution   Before answering the questions, first notice that the sample space S is the set of all items represented in the table, so S has a total of 695 million outcomes.

a. When we say that an item is being selected at random, we mean that all the outcomes are equally likely. If A is the event that the selected item is a Mac, then

$$P(A) = \frac{n(A)}{n(S)} = \frac{53}{695} \approx .076.$$

The event A is represented by the blue shaded region in the table:

	Macs (A)	iPhones (B)	iPads (C)	Total
2012 (U)	18	125	58	201
2013 (V)	16	150	71	238
2014 (W)	19	169	68	256
Total	53	444	197	695

b. If V is the event that the selected item was sold in 2013, then

$$P(V) = \frac{n(V)}{n(S)} = \frac{238}{695} \approx .342.$$

In the table, V is represented as shown:

	Macs (A)	iPhones (B)	iPads (C)	Total
2012 (U)	18	125	58	201
2013 (V)	16	150	71	238
2014 (W)	19	169	68	256
Total	53	444	197	695

---

[29] Figures are rounded. Source: Apple quarterly press releases, www.investor.apple.com.

c. The event that the selected item is a Mac sold in 2013 is the event $A \cap V$:

$$P(A \cap V) = \frac{n(A \cap V)}{n(S)} = \frac{16}{695} \approx .023.$$

In the table, $A \cap V$ is represented by the overlap of the regions representing A and V:

	Macs (A)	iPhones (B)	iPads (C)	Total
2012 (U)	18	125	58	201
2013 (V)	16	150	71	238
2014 (W)	19	169	68	256
Total	53	444	197	695

d. The event that the selected item either is a Mac or was sold in 2013 is the event $A \cup V$ and is represented by the entire blue shaded area in the table:

	Macs (A)	iPhones (B)	iPads (C)	Total
2012 (U)	18	125	58	201
2013 (V)	16	150	71	238
2014 (W)	19	169	68	256
Total	53	444	197	695

We can compute its probability in two ways:

1. Directly from the table:

$$P(A \cup V) = \frac{n(A \cup V)}{n(S)} = \frac{53 + 238 - 16}{695} \approx .396$$

2. Using the addition principle:

$$P(A \cup V) = P(A) + P(V) - P(A \cap V)$$
$$\approx .076 + .342 - .023 = .395 \quad \text{Slightly less accurate, as we rounded the three intermediate answers } P(A), P(V), \text{ and } P(A \cap V).$$

e. The event that the selected item is not a Mac is the event A'. Its probability may be computed by using the formula for the probability of the complement:

$$P(A') = 1 - P(A) \approx 1 - .076 = .924$$

FAQs

Distinguishing Probability from Relative Frequency

Q: *Relative frequency and modeled probability using equally likely outcomes have essentially the same formula: (Number of favorable outcomes)/(Total number of outcomes). How do I know whether a given probability is one or the other?*

A: Ask yourself this: Has the probability been arrived at experimentally, by performing a number of trials and counting the number of times the event occurred? If so, the probability is estimated; that is, it is the relative frequency. If, on the other hand, the probability was computed by analyzing the experiment under consideration rather than by performing actual trials of the experiment, it is a probability model.

Q: *Out of every 100 homes, 67 have broadband Internet service. Thus, the probability that a house has broadband Internet service is .67. Is this probability estimated (relative frequency) or theoretical (a probability model)?*

A: That depends on how the ratio 67 out of 100 was arrived at. If it is based on a poll of *all* homes, then the probability is theoretical. If it is based on a survey of only a *sample* of homes, it is estimated (see the Q&A following Example 1).

8.3 EXERCISES

▼ more advanced   ◆ challenging
🔢 indicates exercises that should be solved using technology

1. Complete the following probability distribution table, and then calculate the stated probabilities. [**HINT**: See Quick Example 5.]

Outcome	a	b	c	d	e
Probability	.1	.05	.6	.05	

   a. $P(\{a, c, e\})$
   b. $P(E \cup F)$, where $E = \{a, c, e\}$ and $F = \{b, c, e\}$
   c. $P(E')$, where E is as in part (b)
   d. $P(E \cap F)$, where E and F are as in part (b)

2. Repeat Exercise 1 using the following table. [**HINT**: See Quick Example 5.]

Outcome	a	b	c	d	e
Probability	.1		.65	.1	.05

In Exercises 3–8, calculate the (modeled) probability $P(E)$ using the given information, assuming that all outcomes are equally likely. [**HINT**: See Quick Examples 11–13.]

   3. $n(S) = 20, n(E) = 5$ **4.** $n(S) = 8, n(E) = 4$
   5. $n(S) = 10, n(E) = 10$ **6.** $n(S) = 10, n(E) = 0$
   7. $S = \{a, b, c, d\}, E = \{a, b, d\}$
   8. $S = \{1, 3, 5, 7, 9\}, E = \{3, 7\}$

In Exercises 9–18 an experiment is given together with an event. Find the (modeled) probability of each event, assuming that the coins and dice are distinguishable and fair and that what is observed are the faces or numbers uppermost. (Compare with Exercises 1–10 in Section 8.1.)

   9. Two coins are tossed; the result is at most one tail.
   10. Two coins are tossed; the result is one or more heads.
   11. Three coins are tossed; the result is at most one head.
   12. Three coins are tossed; the result is more tails than heads.
   13. Two dice are rolled; the numbers add to 5.
   14. Two dice are rolled; the numbers add to 9.

   15. Two dice are rolled; the numbers add to 1.
   16. Two dice are rolled; one of the numbers is even, and the other is odd.
   17. Two dice are rolled; both numbers are prime.[30]
   18. Two dice are rolled; neither number is prime.
   19. If two indistinguishable dice are rolled, what is the probability of the event $\{(4, 4), (2, 3)\}$? What is the corresponding event for a pair of distinguishable dice? [**HINT**: See Example 2.]
   20. If two indistinguishable dice are rolled, what is the probability of the event $\{(5, 5), (2, 5), (3, 5)\}$? What is the corresponding event for a pair of distinguishable dice? [**HINT**: See Example 2.]
   21. A die is weighted in such a way that each of 2, 4, and 6 is twice as likely to come up as each of 1, 3, and 5. Find the probability distribution. What is the probability of rolling less than 4? [**HINT**: See Example 3.]
   22. Another die is weighted in such a way that each of 1 and 2 is three times as likely to come up as each of the other numbers. Find the probability distribution. What is the probability of rolling an even number?
   23. A tetrahedral die has four faces, numbered 1–4. If the die is weighted in such a way that each number is twice as likely to land facing down as the next number (1 twice as likely as 2, 2 twice as likely as 3, and 3 twice as likely as 4), what is the probability distribution for the face landing down?
   24. A dodecahedral die has 12 faces, numbered 1–12. If the die is weighted in such a way that 2 is twice as likely to land facing up as 1, 3 is three times as likely to land facing up as 1, and so on, what is the probability distribution for the face landing up?

In Exercises 25–40, use the given information to find the indicated probability. [**HINT**: See Quick Examples 14–16.]

   25. $P(A) = .1, P(B) = .6, P(A \cap B) = .05$. Find $P(A \cup B)$.
   26. $P(A) = .3, P(B) = .4, P(A \cap B) = .02$. Find $P(A \cup B)$.
   27. $A \cap B = \varnothing, P(A) = .3, P(A \cup B) = .4$. Find $P(B)$.
   28. $A \cap B = \varnothing, P(B) = .8, P(A \cup B) = .8$. Find $P(A)$.

---

[30] A positive integer is prime if it is neither 1 nor a product of smaller integers.

29. $A \cap B = \varnothing$, $P(A) = .3$, $P(B) = .4$. Find $P(A \cup B)$.

30. $A \cap B = \varnothing$, $P(A) = .2$, $P(B) = .3$. Find $P(A \cup B)$.

31. $P(A \cup B) = .9$, $P(B) = .6$, $P(A \cap B) = .1$. Find $P(A)$.

32. $P(A \cup B) = 1.0$, $P(A) = .6$, $P(A \cap B) = .1$. Find $P(B)$.

33. $P(A) = .75$. Find $P(A')$.   **34.** $P(A) = .22$. Find $P(A')$.

35. A, B, and C are mutually exclusive. $P(A) = .3$, $P(B) = .4$, $P(C) = .3$. Find $P(A \cup B \cup C)$.

36. A, B, and C are mutually exclusive. $P(A) = .2$, $P(B) = .6$, $P(C) = .1$. Find $P(A \cup B \cup C)$.

37. A and B are mutually exclusive. $P(A) = .3$, $P(B) = .4$. Find $P((A \cup B)')$.

38. A and B are mutually exclusive. $P(A) = .4$, $P(B) = .4$. Find $P((A \cup B)')$.

39. $A \cup B = S$ and $A \cap B = \varnothing$. Find $P(A) + P(B)$.

40. $P(A \cup B) = .3$ and $P(A \cap B) = .1$. Find $P(A) + P(B)$.

In Exercises 41–46, determine whether the information shown is consistent with a probability distribution. If not, say why.

41. $P(A) = .2$; $P(B) = .1$; $P(A \cup B) = .4$

42. $P(A) = .2$; $P(B) = .4$; $P(A \cup B) = .2$

43. $P(A) = .2$; $P(B) = .4$; $P(A \cap B) = .2$

44. $P(A) = .2$; $P(B) = .4$; $P(A \cap B) = .3$

45. $P(A) = 0.1$; $P(B) = 0$; $P(A \cup B) = 0$

46. $P(A) = .1$; $P(B) = 0$; $P(A \cap B) = 0$

Applications

47. *Subprime Mortgages during the 2000–2008 Housing Bubble* (Compare Exercise 27 in Section 8.2.) The following chart shows the (approximate) total number of subprime home mortgages in Texas in November 2008, broken down into four categories:[31]

Mortgage Status	Current	Past Due	In Foreclosure	Repossessed	Total
Number	136,330	53,310	8,750	5,090	203,480

(The four categories are mutually exclusive; for instance, "Past Due" refers to a mortgage whose payment status is past due but is not in foreclosure, and "In Foreclosure" refers to a mortgage that is in the process of being foreclosed but not yet repossessed.)

a. Find the probability that a randomly selected subprime mortgage in Texas during November 2008 was neither in foreclosure nor repossessed. [**HINT**: See Example 1.]

b. What is the probability that a randomly selected subprime mortgage in Texas during November 2008 was not current?

48. *Subprime Mortgages during the 2000–2008 Housing Bubble* (Compare Exercise 28 in Section 8.2.) The following chart shows the (approximate) total number of subprime home mortgages in Florida in November 2008, broken down into four categories:[32]

Mortgage Status	Current	Past Due	In Foreclosure	Repossessed	Total
Number	130,400	73,260	72,380	17,000	293,040

(The four categories are mutually exclusive; for instance, "Past Due" refers to a mortgage whose payment status is past due but is not in foreclosure, and "In Foreclosure" refers to a mortgage that is in the process of being foreclosed but not yet repossessed.)

a. Find the probability that a randomly selected subprime mortgage in Florida during November 2008 was either in foreclosure or repossessed. [**HINT**: See Example 1.]

b. What is the probability that a randomly selected subprime mortgage in Florida during November 2008 was not repossessed?

49. *Ethnic Diversity* The following pie chart shows the ethnic makeup of California schools in the 2006–2007 academic year.[33]

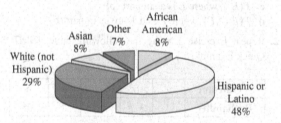

Write down the probability distribution showing the probability that a randomly selected California student in 2006–2007 belonged to one of the ethnic groups named. What is the probability that a student is neither white nor Asian?

50. *Ethnic Diversity* (Compare Exercise 49.) The following pie chart shows the ethnic makeup of California schools in the 1981–1982 academic year.[34]

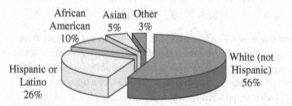

Write down the probability distribution showing the probability that a randomly selected California student in

---

[31] Data are rounded to the nearest 10 units. Source: Federal Reserve Bank of New York (www.newyorkfed.org/regional/subprime.html).

[32] *Ibid.*

[33] Source: CBEDS data collection, Educational Demographics, October 2006 (www.cde.ca.gov).

[34] *Ibid.*

1981–1982 belonged to one of the ethnic groups named. What is the probability that a student is neither Hispanic, Latino, nor African American?

51. ▼ *Internet Investments in the 1990s* The following excerpt is from an article in *The New York Times* in July 1999:[35]

> While statistics are not available for web entrepreneurs who fail, the venture capitalists that finance such Internet start-up companies have a rule of thumb. For every 10 ventures that receive financing—and there are plenty that do not—2 will be stock market successes, which means spectacular profits for early investors; 3 will be sold to other concerns, which translates into more modest profits; and the rest will fail.

   a. What is a sample space for the scenario?
   b. Write down the associated probability distribution.
   c. What is the probability that a start-up venture that receives financing will realize profits for early investors?

52. ▼ *Internet Investments in the 1990s* The following excerpt is from an article in *The New York Times* in July 1999:[36]

> Right now, the market for Web stocks is sizzling. Of the 126 initial public offerings of Internet stocks priced this year, 73 are trading above the price they closed on their first day of trading. . . . Still, 53 of the offerings have failed to live up to their fabulous first-day billings, and 17 [of these] are below the initial offering price.

   Assume that, on the first day of trading, all stocks closed higher than their initial offering price.
   a. What is a sample space for the scenario?
   b. Write down the associated probability distribution. (Round your answers to two decimal places.)
   c. What is the probability that an Internet stock purchased during the period reported ended either below its initial offering price or above the price it closed on its first day of trading? [HINT: See Example 3.]

53. ▼ *Market Share: Light Vehicles* In 2003, 25% of all light vehicles sold (SUVs, pickups, passenger cars, and minivans) in the United States were SUVs, and 15% were pickups. Moreover, a randomly chosen vehicle sold that year was five times as likely to be a passenger car as a minivan.[37] Find the associated probability distribution.

54. ▼ *Market Share: Light Vehicles* In 2000, 15% of all light vehicles (SUVs, pickups, passenger cars, and minivans)

sold in the United States were pickups, and 55% were passenger cars. Moreover, a randomly chosen vehicle sold that year was twice as likely to be an SUV as a minivan.[38] Find the associated probability distribution.

Gambling In Exercises 55–62 are detailed some of the nefarious dicing practices of the Win Some/Lose Some Casino. *In each case, find the probabilities of all the possible outcomes and also the probability that an odd number or an odd sum faces up.* [HINT: See Example 3.]

55. Some of the dice are specially designed so that 1 and 6 never come up and all the other outcomes are equally likely.

56. Other dice are specially designed so that 1 comes up half the time, 6 never comes up, and all the other outcomes are equally likely.

57. Some of the dice are cleverly weighted so that each of 2, 3, 4, and 5 is twice as likely to come up as 1 is, and 1 and 6 are equally likely.

58. Other dice are weighted so that each of 2, 3, 4, and 5 is half as likely to come up as 1 is, and 1 and 6 are equally likely.

59. ▼ Some pairs of dice are magnetized so that each pair of mismatching numbers is twice as likely to come up as each pair of matching numbers.

60. ▼ Other pairs of dice are so strongly magnetized that mismatching numbers never come up.

61. ▼ Some dice are constructed in such a way that deuce (2) is five times as likely to come up as 4 and three times as likely to come up as each of 1, 3, 5, and 6.

62. ▼ Other dice are constructed in such a way that deuce is six times as likely to come up as 4 and four times as likely to come up as each of 1, 3, 5, and 6.

63. *Astrology* The astrology software package *Turbo Kismet*[39] works by first generating random number sequences and then interpreting them numerologically. When I ran it yesterday, it informed me that there was a 1/3 probability that I would meet a tall, dark stranger this month, a 2/3 probability that I would travel this month, and a 1/6 probability that I would meet a tall, dark stranger and also travel this month. What is the probability that I will either meet a tall, dark stranger or travel this month? [HINT: See Quick Example 14.]

64. *Astrology* Another astrology software package, *Java Kismet*, is designed to help day traders choose stocks based on the position of the planets and constellations. When I ran it yesterday, it informed me that there was a .5 probability that Amazon.com will go up this afternoon, a .2 probability that Yahoo.com will go up this afternoon, and a .2 chance that

[35] Article: "Not All Hit It Rich in the Internet Gold Rush," *New York Times*, July 20, 1999, p. A1.

[36] Article: Ibid. Source for data: Comm-Scan/*New York Times*, July 20, 1999, p. A1.

[37] Source: Environmental Protection Agency/*New York Times*, June 28, 2003.

[38] *Ibid.*

[39] The name and concept were borrowed from a hilarious (as yet unpublished) novel by the science-fiction writer William Orr, who also happened to be a faculty member at Hofstra University.

both will go up this afternoon. What is the probability that either Amazon.com or Yahoo.com will go up this afternoon? [HINT: See Quick Example 14.]

65. Polls According to a *New York Times*/CBS poll released in March 2005, 61% of those polled ranked jobs or health care as the top domestic priority.[40] What is the probability that a randomly selected person polled did not rank either as the top domestic priority? [HINT: See Example 5.]

66. Polls According to *The New York Times*/CBS poll of March 2005 referred to in Exercise 65, 72% of those polled ranked neither Iraq nor North Korea as the top foreign policy issue.[41] What is the probability that a randomly selected person polled ranked either Iraq or North Korea as the top foreign policy issue? [HINT: See Example 5.]

67. Electric Car Sales In 2014 the probability that a randomly chosen electric car sold in the United States was manufactured by Tesla was .30, while the probability that it was manufactured by Nissan was .35.[42] What is the probability that a randomly chosen electric car was manufactured by neither company?

68. Hybrid Auto Sales In 2010 the probability that a randomly chosen hybrid vehicle sold in the United States was manufactured by Ford was .12, while the probability that it was manufactured by Nissan was .02.[43] What is the probability that a randomly chosen hybrid vehicle was manufactured by neither company?

Student Admissions Exercises 69–84 are based on the following table, which shows the profile, by the math section of the SAT Reasoning Test, of admitted students at UCLA for the Fall 2014 semester:[44]

SAT Reasoning Test—Math Section

	700–800	600–699	500–599	400–499	200–399	Total
Admitted	8,398	3,517	1,410	358	9	13,692
Not Admitted	16,599	18,363	13,119	6,714	1,652	56,447
Total Applicants	24,997	21,880	14,529	7,072	1,661	70,139

Determine the probabilities of the following events. (Round your answers to the nearest .01.) [HINT: Example 6.]

69. An applicant was admitted.

70. An applicant had a Math SAT below 400.

71. An applicant had a Math SAT below 400 and was admitted.

72. An applicant had a Math SAT of 700 or above and was admitted.

73. An applicant was not admitted.

74. An applicant did not have a Math SAT below 400.

75. An applicant had a Math SAT in the range 500–599 or was admitted.

76. An applicant had a Math SAT of 700 or above or was admitted.

77. An applicant neither was admitted nor had a Math SAT in the range 500–599.

78. An applicant neither had a Math SAT of 700 or above nor was admitted.

79. ▼ An applicant who had a Math SAT below 400 was admitted.

80. ▼ An applicant who had a Math SAT of 700 or above was admitted.

81. ▼ An admitted student had a Math SAT of 700 or above.

82. ▼ An admitted student had a Math SAT below 400.

83. ▼ A rejected applicant had a Math SAT below 600.

84. ▼ A rejected applicant had a Math SAT of at least 600.

85. ▼ **Social Security** According to *The New York Times*/CBS poll of March 2005 referred to in Exercise 65, 79% agreed that it should be the government's responsibility to provide a decent standard of living for the elderly, and 43% agreed that it would be a good idea to invest part of their Social Security taxes on their own. What is the smallest percentage of people who could have agreed with both statements? What is the largest percentage of people who could have agreed with both statements?

86. ▼ **Social Security** According to *The New York Times*/CBS poll of March 2005 referred to in Exercise 65, 49% agreed that Social Security taxes should be raised if necessary to keep the system afloat, and 43% agreed that it would be a good idea to invest part of their Social Security taxes on their own. What is the largest percentage of people who could have agreed with at least one of these statements? What is the smallest percentage of people who could have agreed with at least one of these statements?

87. ▼ **Greek Life** The ΤΦΦ Sorority has a tough pledging program: It requires its pledges to master the Greek alphabet forward, backward, and "sideways." During the last pledge period, two thirds of the pledges failed to learn it backward, and three quarters of them failed to learn it sideways; 5 of the 12 pledges failed to master it either backward or sideways. Because admission into the sisterhood requires both backward and sideways mastery, what fraction of the pledges were disqualified on this basis?

88. ▼ **Swords and Sorcery** Lance the Wizard has been informed that tomorrow there will be a 50% chance of encountering the evil Myrmidons and a 20% chance of meeting up with the dreadful Balrog. Moreover, Hugo the Elf has predicted that

---

[40] Source: *New York Times*, March 3, 2005, p. A20.

[41] *Ibid.*

[42] Probabilities are approximate. Source for sales data: www.wikipedia.com.

[43] *Ibid.*

[44] Source: University of California (www.admissions.ucla.edu/Prospect/Adm_fr/Frosh_Prof14.htm).

there is a 10% chance of encountering both tomorrow. What is the probability that Lance will be lucky tomorrow and encounter neither the Myrmidons nor the Balrog?

89. ▼ *Public Health* A study shows that 80% of the population was vaccinated against the Venusian flu but 2% of the vaccinated population got the flu anyway. If 10% of the total population got this flu, what percent of the population either got the vaccine or got the disease?

90. ▼ *Public Health* A study shows that 75% of the population was vaccinated against the Martian ague but 4% of this group got this disease anyway. If 10% of the total population got this disease, what is the probability that a randomly selected person neither was vaccinated nor contracted Martian ague?

Communication and Reasoning Exercises

91. Design an experiment based on rolling a fair die for which there are exactly three outcomes with the same probabilities.

92. Design an experiment based on rolling a fair die for which there are at least three outcomes with different probabilities.

93. ▼ Tony has had a losing streak at the casino: The chances of winning the game he is playing are 40%, but he has lost five times in a row. Tony argues that, because he should have won two times, the game must obviously be rigged. Comment on his reasoning.

94. ▼ Maria is on a winning streak at the casino. She has already won four times in a row and concludes that her chances of winning a fifth time are good. Comment on her reasoning.

95. Complete the following sentence. The probability of the union of two events is the sum of the probabilities of the two events if _____.

96. A friend of yours asserted at lunch today that, according to the weather forecast for tomorrow, there is a 52% chance of rain and a 60% chance of snow. "But that's impossible!" you blurted out, "the percentages add up to more than 100%." Explain why you were wrong.

97. ▼ A certain experiment is performed a large number of times, and the event E has relative frequency equal to zero. This means that it should have modeled probability zero—right? [HINT: See the definition of a probability model.]

98. ▼ (Refer to Exercise 97.) How can the modeled probability of winning the lottery be nonzero if you have never won it despite having played 600 times? [HINT: See the definition of a probability model.]

99. ▼ Explain how the addition principle for mutually exclusive events follows from the general addition principle.

100. ▼ Explain how the property $P(A') = 1 - P(A)$ follows directly from the properties of a probability distribution.

101. ◆ It is said that lightning never strikes twice in the same spot. Assuming this to be the case, what should be the modeled probability that lightning will strike a given spot during a thunderstorm? Explain. [HINT: See the definition of a probability model.]

102. ◆ A certain event has modeled probability equal to zero. This means it will never occur—right? [HINT: See the definition of a probability model.]

103. ◆ Find a formula for the probability of the union of three (not necessarily mutually exclusive) events A, B, and C.

104. ◆ Four events A, B, C, and D have the following property: If any two events have an outcome in common, that outcome is common to all four events. Find a formula for the probability of their union.

8.4 Probability and Counting Techniques

Counting Techniques Return

We saw in Section 8.3 that, when all outcomes in a sample space are equally likely, we can use the following formula to model the probability of each event.

Modeling Probability: Equally Likely Outcomes

In an experiment in which all outcomes are equally likely, the probability of an event E is given by

$$P(E) = \frac{\text{Number of favorable outcomes}}{\text{Total number of outcomes}} = \frac{n(E)}{n(S)}.$$

This formula is simple, but calculating $n(E)$ and $n(S)$ may not be. In this section we look at some examples in which we need to use the counting techniques discussed in Chapter 7.

S is the set of *all* outcomes that can occur, and has nothing to do with having green marbles.

EXAMPLE 1   Marbles

A bag contains four red marbles and two green ones. Upon seeing the bag, Suzan (who has compulsive marble-grabbing tendencies) sticks her hand in and grabs three at random. Find the probability that she will get both green marbles.

Solution According to the formula, we need to know these numbers:

- The number of elements in the sample space S
- The number of elements in the event E.

First of all, what is the sample space? The sample space is the set of all possible outcomes, and each outcome consists of a set of three marbles (in Suzan's hand). So the set of outcomes is the set of all sets of three marbles chosen from a total of six marbles (four red and two green). Thus,

$$n(S) = C(6, 3) = 20.$$

Now what about E? This is the event that Suzan gets both green marbles. We must *rephrase this as a subset of S* in order to deal with it: "E is the collection of sets of three marbles such that one is red and two are green." Thus, $n(E)$ is the *number* of such sets, which we determine using a decision algorithm.

Step 1 Choose a red marble: $C(4, 1) = 4$ possible outcomes.

Step 2 Choose the two green marbles: $C(2, 2) = 1$ possible outcome.

We get $n(E) = 4 \times 1 = 4$. Now,

$$P(E) = \frac{n(E)}{n(S)} = \frac{4}{20} = \frac{1}{5}.$$

Thus, there is a one in five chance of Suzan's getting both the green marbles.

EXAMPLE 2   Investment Lottery

After a down day on the stock market, you decide to ignore your broker's cautious advice and purchase three stocks at random from the six most active stocks listed on the New York Stock Exchange at the end of the day's trading.[45]

Symbol	Company	Price ($)	% Change
BAC	Bank of America	16.78	−1.81
KEY	KeyCorp	12.42	−7.17
GE	General Electric	28.92	−1.43
PFE	Pfizer	33.82	−2.73
VRX	Valeant Pharmaceuticals	93.77	−15.90
NYCB	New York Community Bancorp	16.52	−2.02

Find the probabilities of the following events:

a. You purchase BAC and KEY.

b. At most two of the stocks you purchase declined in value by more than 2.5%.

---

[45] Most active stocks on October 30, 2015. Source: www.nasdaq.com.

Solution First, the sample space is the set of all collections of three stocks chosen from the six. Thus,

$$n(S) = C(6, 3) = 20.$$

a. The event E of interest is the event that you purchase BAC and KEY. Thus, E is the set of all groups of three stocks that include BAC and KEY. Because there is only one more stock left to choose,

$$n(E) = C(4, 1) = 4.$$

We now have

$$P(E) = \frac{n(E)}{n(S)} = \frac{4}{20} = \frac{1}{5} = .2.$$

b. Let F be the event that at most two of the stocks you purchase declined in value by more than 2.5%. Thus, F is the set of all groups of three stocks of which at most two declined in value by more than 2.5%. To calculate $n(F)$, we use the following decision algorithm.

Alternative 1: None of the stocks declined in value by more than 2.5%.
   Step 1 Choose three stocks that did not decline in value by more than 2.5%: $C(3, 3) = 1$ possibility.

Alternative 2: One of the stocks declined in value by more than 2.5%.
   Step 1 Choose one stock that declined in value by more than 2.5%: $C(3, 1) = 3$ possibilities.
   Step 2 Choose two stocks that did not decline in value by more than 2.5%: $C(3, 2) = 3$ possibilities.
   This gives $3 \times 3 = 9$ possibilities for this alternative.

Alternative 3: Two of the stocks declined in value by more than 2.5%.
   Step 1 Choose two stocks that declined in value by more than 2.5%: $C(3, 2) = 3$ possibilities.
   Step 2 Choose one stock that did not decline in value by more than 2.5%: $C(3, 1) = 3$ possibilities.
   This gives $3 \times 3 = 9$ possibilities for this alternative.

So we have a total of $1 + 9 + 9 = 19$ possible outcomes. Thus,

$$n(F) = 19$$

and

$$P(F) = \frac{n(F)}{n(S)} = \frac{19}{20} = .95.$$

At most two of the stocks declined in value by more than 2.5%.

↑
Complementary Events
↓

At least three of the stocks declined in value by more than 2.5%.

➡ **Before we go on . . .** When we are counting the number of outcomes in an event, the calculation is sometimes easier if we look at the *complement* of that event. In the case of part (b) of Example 2, the complement of the event F is

F': At least three of the stocks you purchase declined in value by more than 2.5%.

Because there are only three stocks in your portfolio, this is the same as the event that all three stocks you purchase declined in value by more than 2.5%. The decision algorithm for $n(F')$ is far simpler:

Step 1 Choose three stocks that declined in value by more than 2.5%: $C(3, 3) = 1$ possibility.

So $n(F') = 1$, giving

$$n(F) = n(S) - n(F') = 20 - 1 = 19,$$

as we calculated above. ∎

EXAMPLE 3 **Poker Hands**

You are dealt 5 cards from a well-shuffled standard deck of 52. Find the probability that you have a full house. (Recall that a full house consists of 3 cards of one denomination and 2 of another.)

Solution The sample space S is the set of all possible 5-card hands dealt from a deck of 52. Thus,

$$n(S) = C(52, 5) = 2,598,960.$$

If the deck is thoroughly shuffled, then each of these 5-card hands is equally likely. Now consider the event E, the set of all possible 5-card hands that constitute a full house. To calculate $n(E)$, we use a decision algorithm, which we show in the following compact form:

    1. Choose first denomination.

        2. Choose three cards of that denomination.

            3. Choose second denomination.

                4. Choose two cards of that denomination.

$$n(E) = C(13, 1) \times C(4, 3) \times C(12, 1) \times C(4, 2) = 3,744$$

Thus,

$$P(E) = \frac{n(E)}{n(S)} = \frac{3,744}{2,598,960} \approx .00144.$$

In other words, there is an approximately 0.144% chance that you will be dealt a full house.

EXAMPLE 4 **More Poker Hands**

You are playing poker, and you have been dealt the following hand:

    J♠, J♦, J♥, 2♣, 10♠.

You decide to exchange the last two cards. The exchange works as follows: The two cards are discarded (not replaced in the deck), and you are dealt two new cards.

a. Find the probability that you end up with a full house.

b. Find the probability that you end up with four jacks.

c. What is the probability that you end up with either a full house or four jacks?

Solution

a. To get a full house, you must be dealt two of a kind. The sample space S is the set of all pairs of cards selected from what remains of the original deck of 52. You were dealt 5 cards originally, so there are $52 - 5 = 47$ cards left in the deck. Thus, $n(S) = C(47, 2) = 1{,}081$. The event E is the set of all pairs of cards that constitute two of a kind. Note that you cannot get two jacks because only one is left in the deck. Also, only three 2s and three 10s are left in the deck. We have

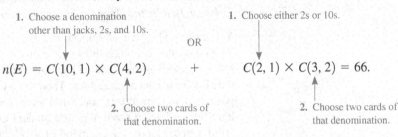

1. Choose a denomination other than jacks, 2s, and 10s.

1. Choose either 2s or 10s.

OR

$$n(E) = C(10, 1) \times C(4, 2) \qquad + \qquad C(2, 1) \times C(3, 2) = 66.$$

2. Choose two cards of that denomination.

2. Choose two cards of that denomination.

Thus,

$$P(E) = \frac{n(E)}{n(S)} = \frac{66}{1{,}081} \approx .0611.$$

b. We have the same sample space as in part (a). Let F be the set of all pairs of cards that include the missing jack of clubs. So

1. Choose the jack of clubs.

2. Choose one card from the remaining 46.

$$n(F) = C(1, 1) \times C(46, 1) = 46.$$

Thus,

$$P(F) = \frac{n(F)}{n(S)} = \frac{46}{1{,}081} \approx .0426.$$

c. We are asked to calculate the probability of the event $E \cup F$. From the addition principle we have

$$P(E \cup F) = P(E) + P(F) - P(E \cap F).$$

Because $E \cap F$ means "E and F," $E \cap F$ is the event that the pair of cards you are dealt are two of a kind and include the jack of clubs. But this is impossible because only one jack is left. Thus, $E \cap F = \varnothing$, so $P(E \cap F) = 0$. This gives us

$$P(E \cup F) = P(E) + P(F) \approx .0611 + .0426 = .1037.$$

In other words, there is slightly better than a 1 in 10 chance that you will wind up with either a full house or four of a kind, given the original hand.

➡ **Before we go on ...** A more accurate answer to part (c) of Example 4 is $(66 + 46)/1{,}081 \approx .1036$. We lost some accuracy in rounding the answers to parts (a) and (b). ∎

EXAMPLE 5   Committees

The University Senate bylaws at Hofstra University state the following:[46]

The Student Affairs Committee shall consist of one elected faculty senator, one faculty senator-at-large, one elected student senator, five student senators-at-

---

[46] As of 2011. Source: Hofstra University Senate Bylaws.

large (including one from the graduate school), two delegates from the Student Government Association, the President of the Student Government Association or his/her designate, and the President of the Graduate Student Organization. It shall be chaired by the elected student senator on the Committee and it shall be advised by the Dean of Students or his/her designate.

You are an undergraduate student, and even though you are not an elected student senator, you would very much like to serve on the Student Affairs Committee. The senators-at-large as well as the Student Government delegates are chosen by means of a random drawing from a list of candidates. There are already 13 undergraduate candidates for the position of senator-at-large and 6 candidates for Student Government delegates, and you have been offered a position on the Student Government Association by the president (who happens to be a good friend of yours), should you wish to join it. (This would make you ineligible for a senator-at-large position.) What should you do?

Solution You have two options. Option 1 is to include your name on the list of candidates for the senator-at-large position. Option 2 is to join the Student Government Association (SGA) and add your name to its list of candidates. Let us look at the two options separately.

Option 1: Add your name to the senator-at-large list.
This will result in a list of 14 undergraduates for 4 undergraduate positions. The sample space is the set of all possible outcomes of the random drawing. Each outcome consists of a set of 4 lucky students chosen from 14. Thus,

$$n(S) = C(14, 4) = 1{,}001.$$

We are interested in the probability that you are among the chosen four. Thus, E is the set of sets of four that include you:

1. Choose yourself.

2. Choose three from the remaining 13.

$$n(E) = C(1, 1) \times C(13, 3) = 286.$$

So

$$P(E) = \frac{n(E)}{n(S)} = \frac{286}{1{,}001} = \frac{2}{7} \approx .2857.$$

Option 2: Join the SGA and add your name to its list.
This results in a list of seven candidates from which two are selected. For this case, the sample space consists of all sets of two chosen from seven, so

$$n(S) = C(7, 2) = 21,$$

and

1. Choose yourself.

2. Choose one from the remaining six.

$$n(E) = C(1, 1) \times C(6, 1) = 6.$$

Thus,

$$P(E) = \frac{n(E)}{n(S)} = \frac{6}{21} = \frac{2}{7} \approx .2857.$$

In other words, the probability of being selected is exactly the same for Option 1 as it is for Option 2! Thus, you can choose either option, and you will have slightly less than a 29% chance of being selected.

8.4 EXERCISES

▼ more advanced   ◆ challenging
Ⓣ indicates exercises that should be solved using technology

Recall from Example 1 that whenever Suzan sees a bag of marbles, she grabs a handful at random. In Exercises 1–10, she has seen a bag containing four red marbles, three green ones, two white ones, and one purple one. She grabs five of them. Find the probabilities of the following events, expressing each as a fraction in lowest terms. [HINT: See Example 1.]

1. She has all the red ones.

2. She has none of the red ones.

3. She has at least one white one.

4. She has at least one green one.

5. She has two red ones and one of each of the other colors.

6. She has two green ones and one of each of the other colors.

7. She has at most one green one.

8. She has no more than one white one.

9. She does not have all the red ones.

10. She does not have all the green ones.

Dogs of the Dow   The "Dogs of the Dow" are the stocks listed on the Dow with the highest dividend yield. Exercises 11–16 are based on the following table, which shows the top ten stocks of the "Dogs of the Dow" list for 2015, based on their performance the preceding year.[47] [HINT: See Example 2.]

Symbol	Company	Price	Yield
T	AT&T	33.59	5.48%
VZ	Verizon	46.78	4.70%
CVX	Chevron	112.18	3.82%
MCD	McDonald's	93.70	3.63%
PFE	Pfizer	31.15	3.60%
GE	General Electric	25.27	3.48%
MRK	Merck	56.79	3.17%
CAT	Caterpillar	91.53	3.06%
XOM	ExxonMobil	92.45	2.99%
KO	Coca-Cola	42.22	2.89%

11. If you selected two of these stocks at random, what is the probability that both the stocks in your selection had yields of 3.75% or more?

12. If you selected three of these stocks at random, what is the probability that all three of the stocks in your selection had yields of 3.75% or more?

13. If you selected four of these stocks at random, what is the probability that your selection included the company with the highest yield and excluded the company with the lowest yield?

14. If you selected four of these stocks at random, what is the probability that your selection included KO and VZ but excluded PFE and GE?

15. ▼ If your portfolio included 100 shares of PFE and you then purchased 100 shares each of any two companies on the list at random, find the probability that you ended up with a total of 200 shares of PFE.

16. ▼ If your portfolio included 100 shares of PFE and you then purchased 100 shares each of any three companies on the list at random, find the probability that you ended up with a total of 200 shares of PFE.

17. ***Tests***   A test has three parts. Part A consists of eight true-false questions, Part B consists of five multiple-choice questions with five choices each, and Part C requires you to match five questions with five different answers one-to-one. Assuming that you make random guesses in filling out your answer sheet, what is the probability that you will earn 100% on the test? (Leave your answer as a formula.)

18. ***Tests***   A test has three parts. Part A consists of four true-false questions, Part B consists of four multiple-choice questions with five choices each, and Part C requires you to match six questions with six different answers one-to-one. Assuming that you make random choices in filling out your answer sheet, what is the probability that you will earn 100% on the test? (Leave your answer as a formula.)

Poker   In Exercises 19–24 you are asked to calculate the probability of being dealt various poker hands. (Recall that a poker player is dealt 5 cards at random from a standard deck of 52.) Express each of your answers as a decimal rounded to four decimal places unless otherwise stated. [HINT: See Example 3.]

19. **Two of a kind:** Two cards with the same denomination and three cards with other denominations (different from each other and that of the pair). Example: K♣, K♥, 2♠, 4♦, J♠

20. **Three of a kind:** Three cards with the same denomination and two cards with other denominations (different from each other and that of the three). Example: Q♣, Q♥, Q♠, 4♦, J♠

[47] Source: www.dogsofthedow.com.

21. Two pairs: Two cards with one denomination, two with another, and one with a third. Example: 3♣, 3♥, Q♠, Q♥, 10♠

22. Straight flush: Five cards of the same suit with consecutive denominations but not a royal flush. (A royal flush consists of the 10, J, Q, K, and A of one suit.) Round the answer to one significant digit. Examples: A♣, 2♣, 3♣, 4♣, 5♣, or 9♦, 10♦, J♦, Q♦, K♦, or A♥, 2♥, 3♥, 4♥, 5♥, but *not* 10♦, J♦, Q♦, K♦, A♦

23. Flush: Five cards of the same suit but not a straight flush or royal flush. Example: A♣, 5♣, 7♣, 8♣, K♣

24. Straight: Five cards with consecutive denominations but not all of the same suit. Examples: 9♦, 10♦, J♣, Q♥, K♦, and 10♥, J♦, Q♦, K♦, A♦

25. *The Monkey at the Typewriter* Suppose that a monkey is seated at a computer keyboard and randomly strikes the 26 letter keys and the space bar. Find the probability that its first 39 characters (including spaces) will be "to be or not to be that is the question". (Leave your answer as a formula.)

26. *The Cat on the Piano* A standard piano keyboard has 88 different keys. Find the probability that a cat, jumping on 4 keys in sequence and at random (possibly with repetition), will strike the first four notes of Beethoven's Fifth Symphony. (Leave your answer as a formula.)

27. *(Based on a question from the GMAT)* Tyler and Gebriella are among seven contestants from whom four semifinalists are to be selected at random. Find the probability that neither Tyler nor Gebriella is selected.

28. *(Based on a question from the GMAT)* Tyler and Gebriella are among seven contestants from whom four semifinalists are to be selected at random. Find the probability that Tyler but not Gebriella is selected.

29. ▼ *Lotteries* The *Sorry State Lottery* requires you to select five different numbers from 0 through 49. (Order is not important.) You are a Big Winner if the five numbers you select agree with those in the drawing, and you are a Small-Fry Winner if four of your five numbers agree with those in the drawing. What is the probability of being a Big Winner? What is the probability of being a Small-Fry Winner? What is the probability that you are either a Big Winner or a Small-Fry winner?

30. ▼ *Lotteries* The *Sad State Lottery* requires you to select a sequence of three different numbers from 0 through 49. (Order is important.) You are a Winner if your sequence agrees with that in the drawing, and you are a Booby Prize Winner if your selection of numbers is correct but in the wrong order. What is the probability of being a Winner? What is the probability of being a Booby Prize Winner? What is the probability that you are either a Winner or a Booby Prize Winner?

31. ▼ *Transfers* Your company is considering offering 400 employees the opportunity to transfer to its new headquarters in Ottawa, and, as personnel manager, you decide that it would be fairest if the transfer offers are decided by means of a lottery. Assuming that your company currently employs 100 managers, 100 factory workers, and 500 miscellaneous staff, find the following probabilities, leaving the answers as formulas:

a. All the managers will be offered the opportunity.

b. You will be offered the opportunity.

32. ▼ *Transfers* (Refer back to Exercise 31.) After thinking about your proposed method of selecting employees for the opportunity to move to Ottawa, you decide that it might be a better idea to select 50 managers, 50 factory workers, and 300 miscellaneous staff, all chosen at random. Find the probability that you will be offered the opportunity. (Leave your answer as a formula.)

33. ▼ *Lotteries* In a New York State daily lottery game, a sequence of three digits (not necessarily different) in the range 0–9 are selected at random. Find the probability that all three are different.

34. ▼ *Lotteries* Refer back to Exercise 33. Find the probability that two of the three digits are the same.

35. ▼ *Elimination Tournaments* In an elimination tournament the teams are arranged in opponent pairs for the first round, and the winner of each round goes on to the next until the champion emerges. What is the probability that North Carolina will beat Central Connecticut but lose to Virginia in the following (fictitious) soccer tournament? (Assume that all outcomes are equally likely.)

North Carolina

Central Connecticut

Virginia

Syracuse

36. ▼ *Elimination Tournaments* In a (fictitious) soccer tournament involving the four teams San Diego State, De Paul, Colgate, and Hofstra, find the probability that Hofstra will play Colgate in the finals and win. (Assume that all outcomes are equally likely and that the teams not listed in the first round slots are placed at random.)

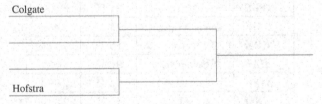

Colgate

Hofstra

Elimination Tournaments *The following diagram illustrates a 16-team tournament bracket, in which the 16 participating teams are arranged on the left under Round 1 and the winners of each round are added as the tournament progresses. The top* *team in each game is considered the "home" team, so the top-to-bottom order matters.*

Round 1   Round 2   Round 3   Round 4

(Quarter final)   (Semifinal)   (Final)

Champion

To seed *a tournament means to select which teams to play each other in the first round according to their preliminary ranking. For instance, in professional tennis and NCAA basketball the seeding is set up in the following order based on the preliminary rankings: 1 versus 16, 8 versus 9, 5 versus 12, 4 versus 13, 6 versus 11, 3 versus 14, 7 versus 10, and 2 versus 15.*[48] *Exercises 37–40 are based on various types of elimination tournaments. (Leave each answer as a formula.)*

37. In a randomly chosen seeding of a 16-team tournament, what is the probability that the top-ranked team plays the bottom-ranked team, the second-ranked team plays the second-lowest ranked team, and so on? [HINT: See Exercise 65 in Section 7.4.]

38. In a randomly chosen seeding of an 8-team tournament, what is the probability that each team plays a team with adjacent ranking? [HINT: See Exercise 66 in Section 7.4.]

39. ▼ In 2014, after the NCAA basketball 64-team tournament had already been seeded, Quicken Loans, backed by investor Warren Buffett, offered a billion dollar prize for picking all the winners.[49] An *upset* occurs when a team beats a higher-ranked team.

a. If you picked the winners completely at random, what is the probability that you would win the prize?

b. If you picked the winners completely at random, what is the probability that your choice would give 15 upsets in the first four rounds? [HINT: See Exercise 67 in Section 7.4.]

40. ▼ Refer to Exercise 39. In the 2013 NCAA playoffs there were 10 upsets in the first round, 4 in the second round, and 3 in each of the third and fourth rounds.[50] If you had picked the winners completely at random, what is the probability that your choice would have given the same number of upsets in each of the first four rounds as above?

41. ▼ *Sports* The following table shows the results of the Big Eight Conference for the 1988 college football season:[51]

Team	Won	Lost
Nebraska (NU)	7	0
Oklahoma (OU)	6	1
Oklahoma State (OSU)	5	2
Colorado (CU)	4	3
Iowa State (ISU)	3	4
Missouri (MU)	2	5
Kansas (KU)	1	6
Kansas State (KSU)	0	7

An arrangement such as the one above in which each team has a different number of wins (from 0 to 7) is called a *perfect progression.* Assuming that the "Won" score for each team is chosen at random in the range 0–7, find the probability that the results form a perfect progression.[52] (Leave your answer as a formula.)

42. ▼ *Sports* Refer back to Exercise 41. Find the probability of a perfect progression with Nebraska scoring seven wins and zero losses. (Leave your answer as a formula.)

43. ▼ *Graph Searching* A graph consists of a collection of **nodes** (the dots in the figure) connected by **edges** (line segments from one node to another). A **move on a graph** is a move from one node to another along a single edge. Find the probability of going from Start to Finish in a sequence

---

[48] Source: www.wikipedia.com, www.ncaa.com

[49] No one won the prize, and the offer was scrapped the following year as a result of a series of lawsuits and countersuits by Yahoo, SCA Promotions (a sweepstakes company), and Berkshire-Hathaway. Sources: http://abcnews.go.com/Sports/warren-buffet-backs-billion-dollar-march-madness-challenge/story?id=21615743, http://money.cnn.com/2015/03/12/news/buffett-ncaa-bracket-bet/index.html.

[50] Source: *Washington Post*, March 16, 2014 (www.washingtonpost.com).

[51] Source: On the probability of a perfect progression, *The American Statistician,* August 1991, vol. 45, no. 3, p. 214.

[52] Even if all the teams are equally likely to win each game, the chances of a perfect progression actually coming up are a little more difficult to estimate, because the number of wins by one team directly affects the number of wins by the others. For instance, it is impossible for all eight teams to show a score of seven wins and zero losses at the end of the season—someone must lose! It is, however, not too hard to come up with a counting argument to estimate the total number of win-loss scores actually possible.

of two random moves in the graph shown. (All directions are equally likely.)

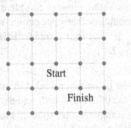

Start

Finish

44. ▼ *Graph Searching* Refer back to Exercise 43. Find the probability of going from Start to one of the Finish nodes in a sequence of two random moves in the following figure. (All directions are equally likely.)

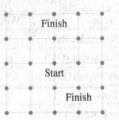

Finish

Start

Finish

45. ◆ *Product Design* Your company has patented an electronic digital padlock that a user can program with his or her own four-digit code. (Each digit can be 0 through 9, and repetitions are allowed.) The padlock is designed to open either if the correct code is keyed in or—and this is helpful for forgetful people—if exactly one of the digits is incorrect. What is the probability that a randomly chosen sequence of four digits will open a programmed padlock?

46. ◆ *Product Design* Assume that you already know the first digit of the combination for the lock described in Exercise 45. Find the probability that a random guess of the remaining three digits will open the lock. [HINT: See Example 5.]

47. ◆ *Committees* An investigatory committee in the Kingdom of Utopia consists of a chief investigator (a Royal Party member), an assistant investigator (a Birthday Party member), two at-large investigators (either party), and five ordinary members (either party). Royal Party member Larry Sifford is hoping to avoid serving on the committee unless he is the Chief Investigator and Otis Taylor, a Birthday Party member, is the Assistant Investigator. The committee is to be selected at random from a pool of 12 candidates (including Larry Sifford and Otis Taylor), half of whom are Royal Party and half of whom are Birthday Party.

a. How many different committees are possible? [HINT: See Example 5.]

b. How many committees are possible in which Larry's hopes are fulfilled? (This includes the possibility that he's not on the committee at all.)

c. What is the probability that he'll be happy with a randomly selected committee?

48. ◆ *Committees* A committee is to consist of a chair, three hagglers, and four do-nothings. The committee is formed by choosing randomly from a pool of 10 people and assigning them to the various "jobs."

a. How many different committees are possible? [HINT: See Example 5.]

b. Norman is eager to be the chair of the committee. What is the probability that he will get his wish?

c. Norman's girlfriend Norma is less ambitious and would be happy to hold any position on the committee provided that Norman is also selected as a committee member. What is the probability that she will get her wish and serve on the committee?

d. Norma does not get along with Oona (who is also in the pool of prospective members) and would be most unhappy if Oona were to chair the committee. Find the probability that all Norma's wishes will be fulfilled: She and Norman are on the committee, and it is not chaired by Oona.

Communication and Reasoning Exercises

49. What is wrong with the following argument? A bag contains two blue marbles and two red ones; two are drawn at random. Because there are four possibilities—(red, red), (blue, blue), (red, blue) and (blue, red)—the probability that both are red is 1/4.

50. What is wrong with the following argument? When we roll two indistinguishable dice, the number of possible outcomes (unordered groups of two not necessarily distinct numbers) is 21 and the number of outcomes in which both numbers are the same is 6. Hence, the probability of throwing a double is $6/21 = 2/7$.

51. ▼ Suzan grabs two marbles out of a bag of five red marbles and four green ones. She could do so in two ways: She could take them out one at a time so that there is a first and a second marble, or she could grab two at once so that there is no order. Does the method she uses to grab the marbles affect the probability that she gets two red marbles?

52. ▼ If Suzan grabs two marbles, one at a time, out of a bag of five red marbles and four green ones, find an event with a probability that depends on the order in which the two marbles are drawn.

53. Create an interesting application whose solution requires finding a probability using combinations.

54. Create an interesting application whose solution requires finding a probability using permutations.

8.5   Conditional Probability and Independence

Conditional Probability

Cyber Video Games, Inc., ran a television ad in advance of the release of its latest game, Ultimate Hockey. As Cyber Video's director of marketing, you would like to assess the ad's effectiveness, so you ask your market research team to survey video game players. The results of its survey of 800 video game players are summarized in the following table:

	Saw Ad	Did Not See Ad	Total
Purchased Game	20	70	90
Did Not Purchase Game	80	630	710
Total	100	700	800

At first glance, it looks as though potential customers are being *put off* by the ad: Only 20 people who saw the ad purchased the game, whereas 70 people purchased the game without seeing the ad at all. But let us analyze the figures a little more carefully.

First, let's restrict attention to those players who saw the ad (first column of data: "Saw Ad") and compute the estimated probability that a player *who saw the ad* purchased Ultimate Hockey.

	Saw Ad
Purchased Game	20
Did Not Purchase Game	80
Total	100

To compute this probability, we calculate

Probability that someone who saw the ad purchased the game

$$= \frac{\text{Number of people who saw the ad and bought the game}}{\text{Total number of people who saw the ad}} = \frac{20}{100} = .2.$$

In other words, 20% of game players who saw the ad went ahead and purchased the game. Let us compare this with the corresponding probability for those players who did *not* see the ad (second column of data "Did Not See Ad"):

	Did Not See Ad
Purchased Game	70
Did Not Purchase Game	630
Total	700

Probability that someone who did not see the ad purchased the game

$$= \frac{\text{Number of people who did not see the ad and purchased the game}}{\text{Total number of people who did not see the ad}} = \frac{70}{700} = .1.$$

Thus, only 10% of game players who did not see the ad purchased the game, whereas 20% of those who *did* see the ad purchased the game. Thus, it appears that the ad *was* highly persuasive: Seeing the ad appears to have made one twice as likely to purchase the game as not seeing the ad.

Here's some terminology. In this example there were two related events of importance:

A: A video game player purchased Ultimate Hockey.

B: A video game player saw the ad.

The first probability we computed was the estimated probability that a video game player purchased Ultimate Hockey *given that* he or she saw the ad. We call the latter probability the (estimated) **probability of A, given B**, and we write it as $P(A \mid B)$. We call $P(A \mid B)$ a **conditional probability**—it is the probability of A under the condition that B occurred. Put another way, it is the probability of A occurring if the sample space is reduced to just those outcomes in B:

$$P(\text{Purchased game } given \ that \text{ saw the ad}) = P(A \mid B) = .2.$$

The second probability we computed was the estimated probability that a video game player purchased Ultimate Hockey *given that* he or she did not see the ad, or the **probability of A, given B'**:

$$P(\text{Purchased game } given \ that \text{ did not see the ad}) = P(A \mid B') = .1.$$

Calculating Conditional Probabilities

How do we calculate conditional probabilities? In the example above, we used the ratio

$$P(A \mid B) = \frac{\text{Number of people who saw the ad and bought the game}}{\text{Total number of people who saw the ad}}.$$

The numerator is the frequency of $A \cap B$, and the denominator is the frequency of B:

$$P(A \mid B) = \frac{fr(A \cap B)}{fr(B)}.$$

Now, we can write this formula in another way:

$$P(A \mid B) = \frac{fr(A \cap B)}{fr(B)} = \frac{fr(A \cap B)/N}{fr(B)/N} = \frac{P(A \cap B)}{P(B)}.$$

We therefore have the following definition, which applies to general probability distributions.

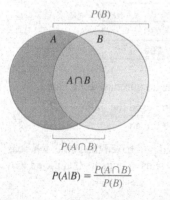

Conditional Probability

If A and B are events with $P(B) \neq 0$, then the **(conditional) probability of A given B** is

$$P(A \mid B) = \frac{P(A \cap B)}{P(B)}.$$

Quick Examples

1. If there is a 50% chance of rain (R) and a 10% chance of both rain and lightning (L), then the probability of lightning, given that it rains, is

$$P(L \mid R) = \frac{P(L \cap R)}{P(R)} = \frac{.10}{.50} = .20.$$

Here are two more ways to express the result:

- If it rains, the probability of lightning is .20.
- Assuming that it rains, there is a 20% chance of lightning.

2. Referring to the Cyber Video data at the beginning of this section, the probability that a video game player did not purchase the game (A'), given that she did not see the ad (B'), is

$$P(A'|B') = \frac{P(A' \cap B')}{P(B')} = \frac{630/800}{700/800} = \frac{9}{10} = .9.$$

Q: *Returning to the video game sales survey, how do we compute the ordinary probability of A, not "given" anything?*

A: We look at the event A that a randomly chosen game player purchased Ultimate Hockey *regardless of whether or not he or she saw the ad*. In the "Purchased Game" row we see that a total of 90 people purchased the game out of a total of 800 surveyed. Thus, the (estimated) probability of A is

$$P(A) = \frac{fr(A)}{N} = \frac{90}{800} \approx .11.$$

We sometimes refer to $P(A)$ as the **unconditional** probability of A to distinguish it from conditional probabilities such as $P(A|B)$ and $P(A|B')$.

Now let's see some more examples involving conditional probabilities.

EXAMPLE 1   **Dice**

If you roll a fair die twice and observe the numbers that face up, find the probability that the sum of the numbers is 8, given that the first number is 3.

Solution   We begin by recalling that the sample space when we roll a fair die twice is the set $S = \{(1, 1), (1, 2), \ldots, (6, 6)\}$ containing the 36 different equally likely outcomes.

The two events under consideration are

A: The sum of the numbers is 8.

B: The first number is 3.

We also need

$A \cap B$: The sum of the numbers is 8 and the first number is 3.

But this can happen in only one way: $A \cap B = \{(3, 5)\}$. From the formula, then,

$$P(A|B) = \frac{P(A \cap B)}{P(B)} = \frac{1/36}{6/36} = \frac{1}{6}.$$

➡ **Before we go on ...** There is another way to think about Example 1. When we say that the first number is 3, we are restricting the sample space to the six outcomes $(3, 1), (3, 2), \ldots, (3, 6)$, all still equally likely. Of these six, only one has a sum of 8, so the probability of the sum being 8, given that the first number is 3, is $1/6$. ■

Notes

1. Remember that, in the expression $P(A|B)$, A is the event whose probability you want, given that you know the event B has occurred.
2. From the formula, notice that $P(A|B)$ is not defined if $P(B) = 0$. Could $P(A|B)$ make any sense if the event B were impossible? ■

EXAMPLE 2   School and Work

A survey[53] of the high school graduating class of 2010, conducted by the Bureau of Labor Statistics, found that, if a graduate went on to college, there was a 40% chance that he or she would work at the same time. On the other hand, there was a 68% chance that a randomly selected graduate would go on to college. What is the probability that a graduate went to college and work at the same time?

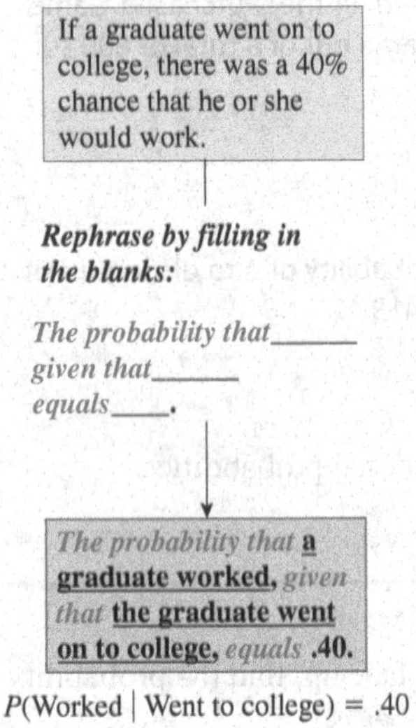

Solution To understand what the question asks and what information is given, it is helpful to rephrase everything using the standard wording "*the probability that ___* " and "*the probability that ___ given that ___.*" Now we have "The probability that a graduate worked, given that the graduate went on to college, equals .40. (See Figure 8.) The probability that a graduate went on to college is .68." The events in question are as follows:

> W: A high school graduate went on to work.
>
> C: A high school graduate went on to college.

From our rephrasing of the question we can write

$$P(W|C) = .40. \qquad P(C) = .68. \qquad \text{Find } P(W \cap C).$$

The definition

$$P(W|C) = \frac{P(W \cap C)}{P(C)}$$

can be used to find $P(W \cap C)$:

$$P(W \cap C) = P(W|C)\,P(C)$$
$$= (.40)(.68) \approx .27.$$

Thus, there is a 27% chance that a member of the high school graduating class of 2010 went on to college and work at the same time.

If a graduate went on to college, there was a 40% chance that he or she would work.

|

Rephrase by filling in the blanks:

The probability that _____ given that _____ equals ____.

↓

The probability that a graduate worked, given that the graduate went on to college, equals .40.

$P(\text{Worked} \mid \text{Went to college}) = .40$

Figure 8

The Multiplication Principle and Trees

In Example 2 we saw that the formula

$$P(A|B) = \frac{P(A \cap B)}{P(B)}$$

---

[53] Source: "College Enrollment and Work Activity of High School Graduates," U.S. Bureau of Labor Statistics (www.bls.gov/news.release/hsgec.htm).

can be used to calculate $P(A \cap B)$ if we rewrite the formula in the following form, known as the **multiplication principle for conditional probability**.

Multiplication Principle for Conditional Probability

If A and B are events, then

$$P(A \cap B) = P(A|B)\,P(B).$$

Quick Example

3. If there is a 50% chance of rain (R) and a 20% chance of lightning (L) if it rains, then the probability of both rain and lightning is

$$P(R \cap L) = P(L|R)\,P(R) = (.20)(.50) = .10.$$

The multiplication principle is often used in conjunction with **tree diagrams**. Let's return to *Cyber Video Games, Inc.*, and its television ad campaign. Its marketing survey was concerned with the following events:

A: A video game player purchased Ultimate Hockey.

B: A video game player saw the ad.

We can illustrate the various possibilities by means of the two-stage "tree" shown in Figure 9.

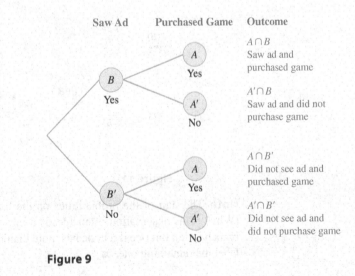

Figure 9

Consider the outcome $A \cap B$. To get there from the starting position on the left, we must first travel up to the B node. (In other words, B must occur.) Then we must travel up the branch from the B node to the A node. We are now going to associate a probability with each branch of the tree: the probability of traveling along that branch *given that we have gotten to its beginning node*. For instance, the probability of traveling up the branch from the starting position to the B node is $P(B) = 100/800 = .125$. (See the data in the survey.) The probability of going up the branch from the B node to the A node is the probability that A occurs, given that B has occurred. In other words, it is the *conditional* probability $P(A|B) = .2$.

(We calculated this probability at the beginning of the section.) The probability of the outcome $A \cap B$ can then be computed by using the multiplication principle:

$$P(A \cap B) = P(B)\,P(A\,|\,B) = (.125)(.2) = .025.$$

In other words, *to obtain the probability of the outcome $A \cap B$, we multiply the probabilities on the branches leading to that outcome* (Figure 10).

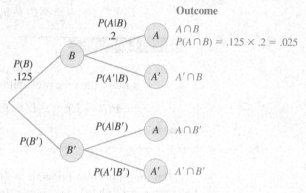

Figure 10

The same argument holds for the remaining three outcomes, and we can use the table given at the beginning of this section to calculate all the conditional probabilities shown in Figure 11.

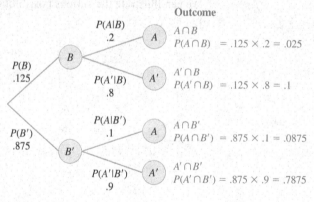

Figure 11

Note The sum of the probabilities on the branches leaving any node is always 1. (Why?) This observation often speeds things up because after we have labeled one branch (or all but one if a node has more than two branches leaving it), we can easily label the remaining one. ■

EXAMPLE 3   **Unfair Coins**

An experiment consists of tossing two coins. The first coin is fair, while the second coin is twice as likely to land with heads facing up as it is with tails facing up. Draw a tree diagram to illustrate all the possible outcomes, and use the multiplication principle to compute the probabilities of all the outcomes.

Solution A quick calculation shows that the probability distribution for the second coin is $P(\text{H}) = 2/3$ and $P(\text{T}) = 1/3$. (How did we get that?) Figure 12 shows the tree diagram and the calculations of the probabilities of the outcomes.

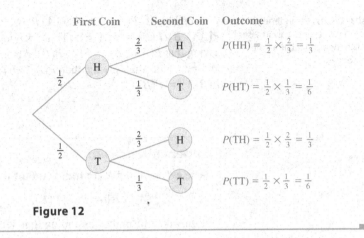

Figure 12

Independence

Let us go back once again to *Cyber Video Games, Inc.*, and its ad campaign. How did we assess the ad's effectiveness? We considered the following events:

> *A*: A video game player purchased Ultimate Hockey.

> *B*: A video game player saw the ad.

We used the survey data to calculate $P(A)$, the probability that a video game player purchased Ultimate Hockey, and $P(A|B)$, the probability that a video game player *who saw the ad* purchased Ultimate Hockey. When these probabilities are compared, one of three things can happen.

Case 1 $P(A|B) > P(A)$
This is what the survey data actually showed: A video game player was more likely to purchase Ultimate Hockey if he or she saw the ad. This indicates that the ad is effective; seeing the ad had a positive effect on a player's decision to purchase the game.

Case 2 $P(A|B) < P(A)$
If this had happened, then a video game player would have been *less* likely to purchase Ultimate Hockey if he or she saw the ad. This would have indicated that the ad had backfired; it had, for some reason, put potential customers off. In this case, just as in the first case, the event *B* would have had an effect—a negative one—on the event *A*.

Case 3 $P(A|B) = P(A)$
In this case, seeing the ad would have had absolutely no effect on a potential customer's buying Ultimate Hockey. Put another way, the probability of *A* occurring *does not depend* on whether *B* occurred or not. We say in a case like this that the events *A* and *B* are **independent**.

In general, we say that two events *A* and *B* are independent if $P(A|B) = P(A)$. When this happens, we have

$$P(A) = P(A|B) = \frac{P(A \cap B)}{P(B)},$$

so

$$P(A \cap B) = P(A)P(B).$$

* We shall discuss the independence of two events only in cases in which their probabilities are both nonzero.

Conversely, if $P(A \cap B) = P(A)P(B)$, then, assuming that $P(B) \neq 0$,* $P(A) = P(A \cap B)/P(B) = P(A|B)$. Thus, saying that $P(A) = P(A|B)$ is the same as saying that $P(A \cap B) = P(A)P(B)$. Also, we can switch A and B in this last formula and conclude that saying that $P(A \cap B) = P(A)P(B)$ is the same as saying that $P(B|A) = P(B)$.

Independent Events

The events A and B are **independent** if

$$P(A \cap B) = P(A)P(B).$$

Equivalent formulas (assuming that neither A nor B is impossible) are

$$P(A|B) = P(A)$$

and

$$P(B|A) = P(B).$$

If two events A and B are not independent, then they are **dependent**.

* See Exercises 111 and 112.

Note It can be verified* that if A and B are independent, then A' and B' are also independent, as are A and B', and A' and B. ■

The property $P(A \cap B) = P(A)P(B)$ can be extended to three or more independent events. If, for example, A, B, and C are three mutually independent events (that is, each one of them is independent of each of the other two and of their intersection), then, among other things,

$$P(A \cap B \cap C) = P(A)P(B)P(C).$$

Quick Examples

4. If A and B are independent, and if A has a probability of .2 and B has a probability of .3, then $A \cap B$ has a probability of $(.2)(.3) = .06$.

5. Let us assume that the phase of the moon has no effect on whether or not my newspaper is delivered. The probability of a full moon (M) on a randomly selected day is about .034, and the probability that my newspaper will be delivered (D) on the random day is .2. Therefore, the probability that it is a full moon and my paper is delivered is

$$P(M \cap D) = P(M)P(D) = (.034)(.2) = .0068.$$

To test for independence, calculate the three quantities $P(A)$, $P(B)$, and $P(A \cap B)$ separately, and then see if $P(A \cap B) = P(A) \cdot P(B)$.

Testing for Independence

To check whether two events A and B are independent, we compute $P(A)$, $P(B)$, and $P(A \cap B)$. If $P(A \cap B) = P(A)P(B)$, the events are independent; otherwise, they are dependent. Sometimes it is obvious that two events, by their nature, are independent, so a test is not necessary. For example, the event that a die you roll comes up 1 is clearly independent of whether or not a coin you toss comes up heads.

Quick Examples

6. Roll two distinguishable dice (one red, one green), and observe the numbers that face up.

A: The red die is even; $P(A) = \dfrac{18}{36} = \dfrac{1}{2}$.

B: The dice have the same parity*; $P(B) = \dfrac{18}{36} = \dfrac{1}{2}$.

$A \cap B$: Both dice are even; $P(A \cap B) = \dfrac{9}{36} = \dfrac{1}{4}$.

$P(A \cap B) = P(A)\,P(B)$, so A and B are independent.

7. Roll two distinguishable dice, and observe the numbers that face up.

A: The sum of the numbers is 6; $P(A) = \dfrac{5}{36}$.

B: Both numbers are odd; $P(B) = \dfrac{9}{36} = \dfrac{1}{4}$.

$A \cap B$: The sum is 6, and both are odd; $P(A \cap B) = \dfrac{3}{36} = \dfrac{1}{12}$.

$P(A \cap B) \neq P(A)\,P(B)$, so A and B are dependent.

*Two numbers have the **same parity** if both are even or both are odd. Otherwise, they have **opposite parity**.

EXAMPLE 4   Weather Prediction

According to the weather service, there is a 50% chance of rain in New York and a 30% chance of rain in Honolulu. Assuming that New York's weather is independent of Honolulu's, find the probability that it will rain in at least one of these cities.

Solution We take A to be the event that it will rain in New York and B to be the event that it will rain in Honolulu. We are asked to find the probability of $A \cup B$, the event that it will rain in at least one of the two cities. We use the addition principle:

$$P(A \cup B) = P(A) + P(B) - P(A \cap B).$$

We know that $P(A) = .50$ and $P(B) = .30$. But what about $P(A \cap B)$? Because the events A and B are independent, we can compute

$$P(A \cap B) = P(A)\,P(B)$$
$$= (.50)(.30) = .15.$$

Thus,

$$P(A \cup B) = P(A) + P(B) - P(A \cap B)$$
$$= .50 + .30 - .15$$
$$= .65.$$

So there is a 65% chance that it will rain either in New York or in Honolulu (or in both).

EXAMPLE 5   Roulette

You are playing roulette and have decided to leave all 10 of your $1 chips on black for five consecutive rounds, hoping for a sequence of five blacks, which, according to the rules, will leave you with $320. There is a 50% chance of black coming up on each spin, ignoring the complicating factor of zero or double zero. What is the probability that you will be successful?

Solution   Because the roulette wheel has no memory, each spin is independent of the others. Thus, if A_1 is the event that black comes up the first time, A_2 the event that it comes up the second time, and so on, then

$$P(A_1 \cap A_2 \cap A_3 \cap A_4 \cap A_5) = P(A_1)\,P(A_2)\,P(A_3)\,P(A_4)\,P(A_5) = \left(\frac{1}{2}\right)^5 = \frac{1}{32}.$$

The next example is a version of a well-known brain teaser that forces one to think carefully about conditional probability.

EXAMPLE 6   Legal Argument

A man was arrested for attempting to smuggle a bomb on board an airplane. During the subsequent trial, his lawyer claimed that, by means of a simple argument, she would prove beyond a shadow of a doubt that her client not only was innocent of any crime, but was in fact contributing to the safety of the other passengers on the flight. This was her eloquent argument: "Your Honor, first of all, my client had absolutely no intention of setting off the bomb. As the record clearly shows, the detonator was unarmed when he was apprehended. In addition—and your Honor is certainly aware of this—there is a small but definite possibility that there will be a bomb on any given flight. On the other hand, the chances of there being *two* bombs on a flight are so remote as to be negligible. There is in fact no record of this having *ever* occurred. Thus, because my client had already brought one bomb on board (with no intention of setting it off) and because we have seen that the chances of there being a second bomb on board were vanishingly remote, it follows that the flight was far safer as a result of his action! I rest my case." This argument was so elegant in its simplicity that the judge acquitted the defendant. Where is the flaw in the argument? (Think about this for a while before reading the solution.)

Solution   The lawyer has cleverly confused the phrases "two bombs on board" and "a second bomb on board." To pinpoint the flaw, let us take B to be the event that there is one bomb on board a given flight, and let A be the event that there are two independent bombs on board. Let us assume for argument's sake that $P(B) = 1/1,000,000 = .000001$. Then the probability of the event A is

$$(.000001)(.000001) = .000000000001.$$

This *is* vanishingly small, as the lawyer contended. It was at this point that the lawyer used a clever maneuver: She assumed in concluding her argument that the probability of having two bombs on board was the same as the probability of having a *second* bomb on board. But to say that there is a *second* bomb on board is to imply that there already is one bomb on board. This is therefore a *conditional* event: the event that there are two bombs on board, *given that there is already one bomb on board.* Thus, the probability that there is a second bomb on board is the probability that there are two bombs on board, given that there is already one bomb on board, which is

$$P(A\,|\,B) = \frac{P(A \cap B)}{P(B)} = \frac{.000000000001}{.000001} = .000001.$$

In other words, it is the same as the probability of there being a single bomb on board to begin with! Thus the man's carrying the bomb onto the plane did not improve the flight's safety at all.[*]

* If we want to be picky, there was a *slight* decrease in the probability of a second bomb because there was one less seat for a potential second bomb bearer to occupy. In terms of our analysis, this is saying that the event of one passenger with a bomb and the event of a second passenger with a bomb are not completely independent.

FAQs

Probability of what given what?

Q: *How do I tell whether a statement in an application is talking about conditional probability or unconditional probability? And if it is talking about conditional probability, how do I determine what to use as A and B in $P(A\,|\,B)$?*

A: Look carefully at the wording of the statement. If there is some kind of qualification or restriction to a smaller set than the entire sample space, then it is probably talking about conditional probability, as in the following examples:

60% of veterans vote Republican, while 40% of the entire voting population vote Republican.

Here the sample space can be taken to be the entire voting population.
Reworded (see Example 2): *The probability of voting Republican (R) is 60% given that the person is a veteran (V); $P(R\,|\,V) = .60$, whereas the probability of voting Republican is .40: $P(R) = .40$.*

The likelihood of being injured if in an accident is 80% for a driver not wearing a seatbelt but it is 50% for all drivers.

Here, the sample space can be taken to be the set of drivers involved in an accident—these are the only drivers discussed.
Reworded: *The probability of a driver being injured (I) is .80 given that the driver is not wearing a seatbelt (B); $P(I\,|\,B) = .80$ whereas, for all drivers, the probability of being injured is .50: $P(I) = .50$.*

8.5 EXERCISES

▼ more advanced   ◆ challenging
▣ indicates exercises that should be solved using technology

In Exercises 1–10, compute the indicated quantity.

1. $P(B) = .5, P(A \cap B) = .2$. Find $P(A\,|\,B)$.

2. $P(B) = .6, P(A \cap B) = .3$. Find $P(A\,|\,B)$.

3. $P(A\,|\,B) = .2, P(B) = .4$. Find $P(A \cap B)$.

4. $P(A\,|\,B) = .1, P(B) = .5$. Find $P(A \cap B)$.

5. $P(A\,|\,B) = .4, P(A \cap B) = .3$. Find $P(B)$.

6. $P(A\,|\,B) = .4, P(A \cap B) = .1$. Find $P(B)$.

7. $P(A) = .5, P(B) = .4$. A and B are independent. Find $P(A \cap B)$.

8. $P(A) = .2, P(B) = .2$. A and B are independent. Find $P(A \cap B)$.

9. $P(A) = .5, P(B) = .4$. A and B are independent. Find $P(A\,|\,B)$.

10. $P(A) = .3, P(B) = .6$. A and B are independent. Find $P(B\,|\,A)$.

In Exercises 11–16, fill in the blanks using the named events. [**HINT:** See Example 2 and the FAQ at the end of the section.]

11. 10% of all Anchovians detest anchovies (D), whereas 30% of all married Anchovians (M) detest them. $P(\_\_\_) = \_\_\_$; $P(\_\_\_\,|\,\_\_\_) = \_\_\_$

12. 95% of all music composers can read music (*M*), whereas 99% of all classical music composers (*C*) can read music. $P(\underline{\quad}) = \underline{\quad}$; $P(\underline{\quad}|\underline{\quad}) = \underline{\quad}$

13. 30% of all lawyers who lost clients (*L*) were antitrust lawyers (*A*), whereas 10% of all antitrust lawyers lost clients. $P(\underline{\quad}|\underline{\quad}) = \underline{\quad}$; $P(\underline{\quad}|\underline{\quad}) = \underline{\quad}$

14. 2% of all items bought on my auction site (*B*) were works of art (*A*), whereas only 1% of all works of art on the site were bought. $P(\underline{\quad}|\underline{\quad}) = \underline{\quad}$; $P(\underline{\quad}|\underline{\quad}) = \underline{\quad}$

15. 55% of those who go out in the midday sun (*M*) are Englishmen (*E*), whereas only 5% of those who do not go out in the midday sun are Englishmen. $P(\underline{\quad}|\underline{\quad}) = \underline{\quad}$; $P(\underline{\quad}|\underline{\quad}) = \underline{\quad}$

16. 80% of those who have a Mac now (*M*) will purchase a Mac next time (*X*), whereas 20% of those who do not have a Mac now will purchase a Mac next time. $P(\underline{\quad}|\underline{\quad}) = \underline{\quad}$; $P(\underline{\quad}|\underline{\quad}) = \underline{\quad}$

In Exercises 17–22, find the conditional probability of the indicated event when two fair dice (one red and one green) are rolled. [HINT: See Example 1.]

17. The sum is 5, given that the green one is not a 1.

18. The sum is 6, given that the green one is either 4 or 3.

19. The red one is 5, given that the sum is 6.

20. The red one is 4, given that the green one is 4.

21. The sum is 5, given that the dice have opposite parity.

22. The sum is 6, given that the dice have opposite parity.

Exercises 23–28 require the use of counting techniques from Chapter 7. A bag contains three red marbles, two green ones, one fluorescent pink one, two yellow ones, and two orange ones. Suzan grabs four at random. Find the probability of the indicated event.

23. She gets all the red ones, given that she gets the fluorescent pink one.

24. She gets all the red ones, given that she does not get the fluorescent pink one.

25. She gets none of the red ones, given that she gets the fluorescent pink one.

26. She gets one of each color other than fluorescent pink, given that she gets the fluorescent pink one.

27. She gets one of each color other than fluorescent pink, given that she gets at least one red one.

28. She gets at least two red ones, given that she gets at least one green one.

In Exercises 29–32, supply the missing quantities. [HINT: See Example 3 and the discussion preceding it.]

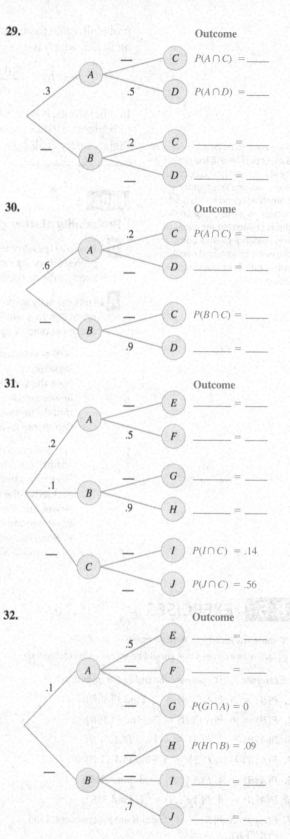

29.

Outcome

$P(A \cap C) = \underline{\quad}$

$P(A \cap D) = \underline{\quad}$

$\underline{\quad\quad} = \underline{\quad}$

$\underline{\quad\quad} = \underline{\quad}$

30.

Outcome

$P(A \cap C) = \underline{\quad}$

$\underline{\quad\quad} = \underline{\quad}$

$P(B \cap C) = \underline{\quad}$

$\underline{\quad\quad} = \underline{\quad}$

31.

Outcome

$\underline{\quad\quad} = \underline{\quad}$

$\underline{\quad\quad} = \underline{\quad}$

$\underline{\quad\quad} = \underline{\quad}$

$\underline{\quad\quad} = \underline{\quad}$

$P(I \cap C) = .14$

$P(J \cap C) = .56$

32.

Outcome

$\underline{\quad\quad} = \underline{\quad}$

$\underline{\quad\quad} = \underline{\quad}$

$P(G \cap A) = 0$

$P(H \cap B) = .09$

$\underline{\quad\quad} = \underline{\quad}$

$\underline{\quad\quad} = \underline{\quad}$

In Exercises 33–36, say whether the given pair of events are independent, mutually exclusive, or neither.

33. *A*: Your new skateboard design is a success.

   B: Your new skateboard design is a failure.

34. *A*: Your new skateboard design is a success.

   B: There is life in the Andromeda galaxy.

35. *A*: Your new skateboard design is a success.

   B: Your competitor's new skateboard design is a failure.

36. *A*: Your first coin flip results in heads.

   B: Your second coin flip results in heads.

In Exercises 37–42, two dice (one red and one green) are rolled, and the numbers that face up are observed. Test the given pair of events for independence. [HINT: See Quick Examples 6 and 7.]

37. *A*: The red die is 1, 2, or 3; *B*: The green die is even.

38. *A*: The red die is 1; *B*: The sum is even.

39. *A*: Exactly one die is 1; *B*: The sum is even.

40. *A*: Neither die is 1 or 6; *B*: The sum is even.

41. *A*: Neither die is 1; *B*: Exactly one die is 2.

42. *A*: Both dice are 1; *B*: Neither die is 2.

43. If a coin is tossed 11 times, find the probability of the sequence H, T, T, H, H, H, T, H, H, T, T. [HINT: See Example 5.]

44. If a die is rolled four times, find the probability of the sequence 4, 3, 2, 1. [HINT: See Example 5.]

Applications

45. *Personal Bankruptcy* In 2004 the probability that a person in the United States would declare personal bankruptcy was .006. The probability that a person in the United States would declare personal bankruptcy and had recently experienced a "big three" event (loss of job, medical problem, or divorce or separation) was .005.[54] What was the probability that a person had recently experienced one of the "big three" events, given that she had declared personal bankruptcy? (Round your answer to one decimal place.)

46. *Personal Bankruptcy* In 2004 the probability that a person in the United States would declare personal bankruptcy was .006. The probability that a person in the United States would declare personal bankruptcy and had recently overspent credit cards was .0004.[55] What was the probability that a person had recently overspent credit cards given that he had declared personal bankruptcy?

47. *Existing Home Sales* During the year ending April 30, 2015, there were approximately 5.0 million sales of existing homes in the United States, of which 1.2 million were sold in the West. During April 2015 there were a total of 450,000 existing homes sold in the United States, of which 110,000 were sold in the West.[56]
   a. Find the probability that a home sale in the year ending April 30, 2015, took place in the West, given that the home was sold during April of that year.
   b. Find the probability that a home sale in the year ending April 30, 2015, took place in April of that year, given that it took place in the West.

48. *Existing Home Sales* Refer to the data given in Exercise 47.
   a. Find the probability that a home sale in the year ending April 30, 2015, took place outside the West, given that the home was sold during April of that year.
   b. Find the probability that a home sale in the year ending April 30, 2015, took place in April of that year, given that it took place outside the West.

49. *Social Security* According to a *New York Times*/CBS poll released in March 2005, 79% of respondents agreed that it should be the government's responsibility to provide a decent standard of living for the elderly, and 43% agreed that it would be a good idea to invest part of their Social Security taxes on their own.[57] If agreement with one of these propositions is independent of agreement with the other, what is the probability that a person agreed with both propositions? (Round your answer to two decimal places.) [HINT: See Quick Examples 4 and 5.]

50. *Social Security* According to *The New York Times*/CBS poll of March 2005 referred to in Exercise 49, 49% of respondents agreed that Social Security taxes should be raised if necessary to keep the system afloat, and 43% agreed that it would be a good idea to invest part of their Social Security taxes on their own.[58] If agreement with one of these propositions is independent of agreement with the other, what is the probability that a person agreed with both propositions? (Round your answer to two decimal places.) [HINT: See Quick Examples 4 and 5.]

51. *Marketing* A market survey shows that 40% of the population used Brand X laundry detergent last year, 5% of the population gave up doing its laundry last year, and 4% of the population used Brand X and then gave up doing laundry last year. Are the events of using Brand X and giving up doing laundry independent? Is a user of Brand X detergent more or less likely to give up doing laundry than a randomly chosen person?

52. *Marketing* A market survey shows that 60% of the population used Brand Z computers last year, 5% of the population

---

[54] Probabilities are approximate. Source: *New York Times*, March 13, 2005, p, WK3.

[55] The .0004 figure is an estimate by the authors. Source: *Ibid.*

[56] Source: National Association of Realtors (www.realtor.org).

[57] Source: *New York Times*, March 3, 2005, p. A20.

[58] *Ibid.*

quit their jobs last year, and 3% of the population used Brand Z computers and then quit their jobs. Are the events of using Brand Z computers and quitting one's job independent? Is a user of Brand Z computers more or less likely to quit a job than a randomly chosen person?

53. **Road Safety** In 1999 the probability that a randomly selected vehicle would be involved in a deadly tire-related accident was approximately 3×10^{-6}, whereas the probability that a tire-related accident would prove deadly was .02.[59] What was the probability that a vehicle would be involved in a tire-related accident?

54. **Road Safety** In 1998 the probability that a randomly selected vehicle would be involved in a deadly tire-related accident was approximately 2.8×10^{-6}, while the probability that a tire-related accident would prove deadly was .016.[60] What was the probability that a vehicle would be involved in a tire-related accident?

Publishing Exercises 55–62 are based on the following table, which shows the results of a survey of 100 authors by a publishing company:

	New Authors	Established Authors	Total
Successful	5	25	30
Unsuccessful	15	55	70
Total	20	80	100

Compute the following conditional probabilities:

55. An author is established, given that she is successful.

56. An author is successful, given that he is established.

57. An author is unsuccessful, given that he is a new author.

58. An author is a new author, given that she is unsuccessful.

59. An author is unsuccessful, given that she is established.

60. An author is established, given that he is unsuccessful.

61. An unsuccessful author is established.

62. An established author is successful.

In Exercises 63–68, draw an appropriate tree diagram, and use the multiplication principle to calculate the probabilities of all the outcomes. [HINT: See Example 3.]

63. **Sales** Each day, there is a 40% chance that you will sell an automobile. You know that 30% of all the automobiles you sell are two-door models and the rest are four-door models.

64. **Product Reliability** You purchase Brand X memory chips one quarter of the time and Brand Y memory chips the rest of the time. Brand X memory chips have a 1% failure rate, while Brand Y memory chips have a 3% failure rate.

65. **Car Rentals** Your auto rental company rents out 30 small cars, 24 luxury sedans, and 46 slightly damaged "budget" vehicles. The small cars break down 14% of the time, the luxury sedans break down 8% of the time, and the "budget" cars break down 40% of the time.

66. **Travel** It appears that there is only a one in five chance that you will be able to take your spring vacation to the Greek Islands. If you are lucky enough to go, you will visit either Corfu (20% chance) or Rhodes. On Rhodes there is a 20% chance of meeting a tall, dark stranger, while on Corfu there is no such chance.

67. **Weather Prediction** There is a 50% chance of rain today and a 50% chance of rain tomorrow. Assuming that the event that it rains today is independent of the event that it rains tomorrow, draw a tree diagram showing the probabilities of all outcomes. What is the probability that there will be no rain today or tomorrow?

68. **Weather Prediction** There is a 20% chance of snow today and a 20% chance of snow tomorrow. Assuming that the event that it snows today is independent of the event that it snows tomorrow, draw a tree diagram showing the probabilities of all outcomes. What is the probability that it will snow by the end of tomorrow?

Education and Employment Exercises 69–78 are based on the following table, which shows U.S. employment figures for 2014, broken down by educational attainment.[61] All numbers are in millions and represent civilians aged 25 years and over. Those classed as "not in labor force" were not employed nor actively seeking employment. Round all answers to two decimal places.

	Employed	Unemployed	Not in Labor Force	Total
Less Than High School Diploma	9.9	1.0	13.2	24.1
High School Diploma Only	33.9	2.2	25.9	62.0
Some College or Associate's Degree	35.3	2.0	18.4	55.7
Bachelor's Degree or Higher	48.8	1.6	16.9	67.3
Total	127.9	6.8	74.4	209.1

69. Find the probability that a person was employed, given that the person had a bachelor's degree or higher.

70. Find the probability that a person was employed, given that the person had attained less than a high school diploma.

71. Find the probability that a person had a bachelor's degree or higher, given that the person was employed.

---

[59] The original data reported three tire-related deaths per million vehicles. Source: *New York Times* analysis of National Traffic Safety Administration crash data/Polk Company vehicle registration data/ *New York Times*, Nov. 22, 2000, p. C5.

[60] The original data reported 2.8 tire-related deaths per million vehicles. Source: *Ibid.*

[61] Source: Bureau of Labor Statistics (www.bls.gov).

72. Find the probability that a person had attained less than a high school diploma, given that the person was employed.

73. ▼ Find the probability that a person who had not completed a bachelor's degree or higher was not in the labor force.

74. ▼ Find the probability that a person who had completed at least a high school diploma was not in the labor force.

75. ▼ Find the probability that a person who had completed a bachelor's degree or higher and was in the labor force was employed.

76. ▼ Find the probability that a person who had completed less than a high school diploma and was in the labor force was employed.

77. ▼ Your friend claims that an unemployed person is more likely to have a high school diploma only than an employed person. Respond to this claim by citing actual probabilities.

78. ▼ Your friend claims that a person not in the labor force is more likely to have less than a high school diploma than an employed person. Respond to this claim by citing actual probabilities.

79. ▼ *Air Bag Safety* According to a 2000 study conducted by the Harvard School of Public Health, a child seated in the front seat who was wearing a seatbelt was 31% more likely to be killed in an accident if the car had an air bag that deployed than if it did not.[62] Let the sample space S be the set of all accidents involving a child seated in the front seat wearing a seatbelt. Let K be the event that the child was killed, and let D be the event that the air bag deployed. Fill in the missing terms and quantities: $P(\_\_|\_\_) = \_\_ \times P(\_\_|\_\_)$. [**HINT:** When we say, "A is 31% more likely than B," we mean that the probability of A is 1.31 times the probability of B.]

80. ▼ *Air Bag Safety* According to the study cited in Exercise 79, a child seated in the front seat not wearing a seatbelt was 84% more likely to be killed in an accident if the car had an air bag that deployed than if it did not.[63] Let the sample space S be the set of all accidents involving a child seated in the front seat not wearing a seatbelt. Fill in the missing terms and quantities: $P(\_\_|\_\_) = \_\_ \times P(\_\_|\_\_)$. [**HINT:** When we say, "A is 84% more likely than B," we mean that the probability of A is 1.84 times the probability of B.]

81. ▼ *Productivity* A company wishes to enhance productivity by running a one-week training course for its employees. Let T be the event that an employee participated in the course, and let I be the event that an employee's productivity improved the week after the course was run.
  a. Assuming that the course has a positive effect on productivity, how are $P(I|T)$ and $P(I)$ related?
  b. If T and I are independent, what can one conclude about the training course?

82. ▼ *Productivity* Consider the events T and I in Exercise 81.
  a. Assuming that everyone who improved took the course but that not everyone took the course, how are $P(T|I)$ and $P(T)$ related?
  b. If half the employees who improved took the course and half the employees took the course, are T and I independent?

83. ▼ *Internet Use in 2000* The following pie chart shows the percentage of the population that used the Internet in 2000, broken down further by family income and based on a survey taken in August 2000:[64]

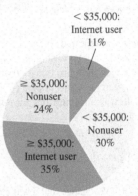

  a. Determine the probability that a randomly chosen person was an Internet user, given that his or her family income was at least $35,000.
  b. Based on the data, was a person more likely to be an Internet user if his or her family income was less than $35,000 or $35,000 or more? (Support your answer by citing the relevant conditional probabilities.)

84. ▼ *Internet Use in 2001* Repeat Exercise 83 using the following pie chart, which shows the results of a similar survey taken in September 2001:[65]

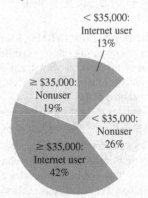

[62] The study was conducted by Dr. Segul-Gomez at the Harvard School of Public Health. Source: *New York Times*, December 1, 2000, p. F1.
[63] *Ibid.*

[64] Source: *Falling Through the Net: Toward Digital Inclusion, A Report on Americans' Access to Technology Tools*, U.S. Department of Commerce, October 2000. Available at www.ntia.doc.gov/ntiahome/fttn00/contents00.html.

[65] Source: *A Nation Online: How Americans Are Expanding Their Use of the Internet*, U.S. Department of Commerce, February 2002. Available at www.ntia.doc.gov/ntiahome/dn/index.html.

Auto Theft *Exercises 85–90 are based on the following table, which shows the probability that an owner of the given model would report his or her vehicle stolen in a 1-year period:*[66]

Model	Jeep Wrangler	Suzuki Sidekick (two-door)	Toyota Land Cruiser	Geo Tracker (two-door)	Acura Integra (two-door)
Probability	.0170	.0154	.0143	.0142	.0123
Model	Mitsubishi Montero	Acura Integra (four-door)	BMW 3-series (two-door)	Lexus GS300	Honda Accord (two-door)
Probability	.0108	.0103	.0077	.0074	.0070

In an experiment in which a vehicle is selected, consider the following events:

   R: The vehicle was reported stolen.
   J: The vehicle was a Jeep Wrangler.
   A2: The vehicle was an Acura Integra (two-door).
   A4: The vehicle was an Acura Integra (four-door).
   A: The vehicle was an Acura Integra (either two-door or four-door).

85. ▼ Fill in the blanks: $P(\_\_\_|\_\_\_) = .0170$.

86. ▼ Fill in the blanks: $P(\_\_\_|A4) = \_\_\_$.

87. ▼ Which of the following is true?
  (A) There is a 1.43% chance that a vehicle reported stolen was a Toyota Land Cruiser.
  (B) Of all the vehicles reported stolen, 1.43% of them were Toyota Land Cruisers.
  (C) Given that a vehicle was reported stolen, there is a .0143 probability that it was a Toyota Land Cruiser.
  (D) Given that a vehicle was a Toyota Land Cruiser, there was a 1.43% chance that it was reported stolen.

88. ▼ Which of the following is true?
  (A) $P(R|A) = .0123 + .0103 = .0226$
  (B) $P(R'|A2) = 1 - .0123 = .9877$
  (C) $P(A2|A) = .0123/(.0123 + .0103) \approx .544$
  (D) $P(R|A2') = 1 - .0123 = .9877$

89. ▼ It is now January, and I own a BMW 3-series and a Lexus GS300. Because I house my vehicles in different places, the event that one of my vehicles gets stolen does not depend on the event that the other gets stolen. Compute each probability to six decimal places.
  a. Both my vehicles will get stolen this year.
  b. At least one of my vehicles will get stolen this year.

90. ▼ It is now December, and I own a Mitsubishi Montero and a Jeep Wrangler. Because I house my vehicles in different places, the event that one of my vehicles gets stolen does not depend on the event that the other gets stolen. I have just returned from a 1-year trip to the Swiss Alps.
  a. What is the probability that my Montero, but not my Wrangler, has been stolen?

  b. Which is more likely: the event that my Montero was stolen or the event that *only* my Montero was stolen?

91. ▼ *Drug Tests* If 90% of the athletes who test positive for steroids in fact use them, and 10% of all athletes use steroids and test positive, what percentage of athletes test positive?

92. ▼ *Fitness Tests* If 80% of candidates for the soccer team pass the fitness test, and only 20% of all athletes are soccer team candidates who pass the test, what percentage of the athletes are candidates for the soccer team?

93. ▼ *Food Safety* According to a University of Maryland study of 200 samples of ground meats,[67] the probability that a sample was contaminated by *Salmonella* was .20. The probability that a *Salmonella*-contaminated sample was contaminated by a strain resistant to at least three antibiotics was .53. What was the probability that a ground meat sample was contaminated by a strain of *Salmonella* resistant to at least three antibiotics?

94. ▼ *Food Safety* According to the study mentioned in Exercise 93, the probability that a ground meat sample was contaminated by *Salmonella* was .20. The probability that a *Salmonella*-contaminated sample was contaminated by a strain resistant to at least one antibiotic was .84. What was the probability that a ground meat sample was contaminated by a strain of *Salmonella* resistant to at least one antibiotic?

95. ◆ *Food Safety* According to the study mentioned in Exercise 93, the probability that one of the samples was contaminated by *Salmonella* was .20. The probability that a *Salmonella*-contaminated sample was contaminated by a strain resistant to at least one antibiotic was .84, and the probability that a *Salmonella*-contaminated sample was contaminated by a strain resistant to at least three antibiotics was .53. Find the probability that a ground meat sample that was contaminated by an antibiotic-resistant strain was contaminated by a strain resistant to at least three antibiotics.

96. ◆ *Food Safety* According to the study mentioned in Exercise 93, the probability that a ground meat sample was contaminated by a strain of *Salmonella* resistant to at least three antibiotics was .11. The probability that someone infected with any strain of *Salmonella* will become seriously ill

---

[66] Data are for insured vehicles, for 1995 to 1997 models except Wrangler, which is for 1997 models only. Source: Highway Loss Data Institute/*New York Times*, March 28, 1999, p. WK3.

[67] As cited in the *New York Times*, October 16, 2001, p. A12.

is .10. What is the probability that someone eating a randomly chosen ground meat sample will not become seriously ill with a strain of *Salmonella* resistant to at least three antibiotics?

97. ▼ *Ultimate Hockey* Cyber Video Games, Inc., the makers of Ultimate Hockey (see the discussion at the beginning of this section), switched to a cheaper ad agency whose TV ad had no effect whatsoever on sales according to a survey. Unfortunately, a student intern accidentally erased some of the survey data in the table below:

	Saw Ad	Did Not See Ad	Total
Purchased Game	20	40	60
Did Not Purchase Game	180	?	?
Total	200	?	?

Calculate the missing quantities.

98. ▼ *Ultimate Hockey* (See Exercise 97.) *Cyber Video Games, Inc.*, the makers of Ultimate Hockey, switched to a more expensive ad agency whose TV ad *still* had no effect whatsoever on sales according to a survey. Unfortunately, the same student intern again erased some of the survey data in the table below:

	Saw Ad	Did Not See Ad	Total
Purchased Game	20	60	80
Did Not Purchase Game	?	180	?
Total	?	240	?

Calculate the missing quantities.

Communication and Reasoning Exercises

99. The probability of misspelling "Waner" is p and is equal to the probability of misspelling "Costenoble." If the event of misspelling one author's name is independent of the event of misspelling the other, what percentage of people can be expected to misspell both names?

100. The probability of spelling "Waner" correctly is p, and the probability of spelling "Costenoble" correctly is q. If the event of misspelling one author's name is independent of the event of correctly spelling the other, what is the probability of misspelling both names?

101. Name three events, each independent of the others, when a fair coin is tossed four times.

102. Name three pairs of independent events when a pair of distinguishable and fair dice is rolled and the numbers that face up are observed.

103. You wish to ascertain the probability of an event E, but you happen to know that the event F has occurred. Is the probability you are seeking $P(E)$ or $P(E|F)$? Give the reason for your answer.

104. Your television advertising campaign seems to have been very persuasive: 10,000 people who saw the ad purchased your product, while only 2,000 people purchased the product without seeing the ad. Explain how additional data could show that your ad campaign was, in fact, unpersuasive.

105. You are having trouble persuading your friend Iliana that conditional probability is different from unconditional probability. She just said, "Look here, Saul, the probability of throwing a double-six is 1/36, and that's that! That probability is not affected by anything, including the 'given' that the sum is larger than 7." How do you persuade her otherwise?

106. Your other friend Giuseppe is spreading rumors that the conditional probability $P(E|F)$ is always bigger than $P(E)$. Is he right? (If he is, explain why. If he is not, give an example to prove him wrong.)

107. ▼ If $A \subseteq B$ and $P(B) \neq 0$, why is $P(A|B) = \dfrac{P(A)}{P(B)}$?

108. ▼ If $B \subseteq A$ and $P(B) \neq 0$, why is $P(A|B) = 1$?

109. ▼ Your best friend thinks that it is impossible for two mutually exclusive events with nonzero probabilities to be independent. Establish whether or not he is correct.

110. ▼ Another of your friends thinks that two mutually exclusive events with nonzero probabilities can never be dependent. Establish whether or not she is correct.

111. ◆ Show that if A and B are independent, then so are A' and B' (assuming that none of these events has zero probability). [HINT: $A' \cap B'$ is the complement of $A \cup B$.]

112. ◆ Show that if A and B are independent, then so are A and B' (assuming that none of these events has zero probability). [HINT: $P(B'|A) + P(B|A) = 1$.]

8.6   Bayes' Theorem and Applications

Motivating Bayes' Theorem

Should schools test their athletes for drug use? A problem with drug testing is that there are always false positive results, so one can never be certain that an athlete who tests positive is in fact using drugs. Here is a typical scenario.

EXAMPLE 1   Steroids Testing

Gamma Chemicals advertises its anabolic steroid detection test as being 95% effective at detecting steroid use, meaning that the test will show a positive result on 95% of all anabolic steroid users. The company also states that its test has a false positive rate of 6%. This means that the probability of a nonuser testing positive is .06. Estimating that about 10% of its athletes are using anabolic steroids, *Enormous State University* begins testing its football players. The quarterback, Hugo V. Huge, tests positive and is promptly dropped from the team. Hugo claims that he is not using anabolic steroids. How confident can we be that he is not telling the truth?

Solution There are two events of interest here: the event T that a person tests positive and the event A that the person tested uses anabolic steroids. Here are the probabilities we are given:

$$P(T|A) = .95$$
$$P(T|A') = .06$$
$$P(A) = .10.$$

We are asked to find $P(A|T)$, the probability that someone who tests positive is using anabolic steroids. We can use a tree diagram to calculate $P(A|T)$. The trick to setting up the tree diagram is to use as the first branching the events with *unconditional* probabilities we know. Because the only unconditional probability we are given is $P(A)$, we use A and A' as our first branching (Figure 13). For the second branching, we use the outcomes of the drug test: positive (T) or negative (T'). The probabilities on these branches are conditional probabilities because they depend on whether or not an athlete uses steroids. (See Figure 14.) (We fill in the probabilities that are not supplied by remembering that the sum of the probabilities on the branches leaving any node must be 1.)

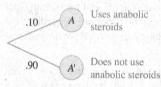

.10 — A Uses anabolic steroids

.90 — A' Does not use anabolic steroids

Figure 13

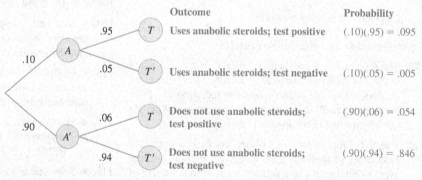

	Outcome	Probability
.95 → T	Uses anabolic steroids; test positive	$(.10)(.95) = .095$
.05 → T'	Uses anabolic steroids; test negative	$(.10)(.05) = .005$
.06 → T	Does not use anabolic steroids; test positive	$(.90)(.06) = .054$
.94 → T'	Does not use anabolic steroids; test negative	$(.90)(.94) = .846$

Figure 14

We can now calculate the probability we are asked to find:

$$P(A|T) = \frac{P(A \cap T)}{P(T)} = \frac{P(\text{Uses anabolic steroids and tests positive})}{P(\text{Tests positive})}$$

$$= \frac{P(\text{Using } A \text{ and } T \text{ branches})}{\text{Sum of } P(\text{Using branches ending in } T)}.$$

From the tree diagram, we see that $P(A \cap T) = .095$. To calculate $P(T)$, the probability of testing positive, notice that there are two outcomes on the tree diagram that reflect a positive test result. The probabilities of these events are .095 and .054. Because these two events are mutually exclusive (an athlete either uses steroids or does not, but not both), the probability of a test being positive (ignoring whether or not steroids are used) is the sum of these probabilities, .149. Thus,

$$P(A\,|\,T) = \frac{.095}{.095 + .054} = \frac{.095}{.149} \approx .64.$$

Thus, there is a 64% chance that a randomly selected athlete who tests positive, such as Hugo, is using steroids. In other words, we can be 64% confident that Hugo is lying.

➡ **Before we go on . . .** Note that the correct answer in Example 1 is 64%, *not* the 94% we might suspect from the test's false positive rating. In fact, we can't answer the question asked without knowing the percentage of athletes who actually use steroids. For instance, if *no* athletes at all use steroids, then Hugo must be telling the truth, so the test result has no significance whatsoever. On the other hand, if *all* athletes use steroids, then Hugo is definitely lying, regardless of the outcome of the test.

False positive rates are determined by testing a large number of samples known not to contain drugs and computing estimated probabilities. False negative rates are computed similarly by testing samples known to contain drugs. However, the accuracy of the tests depends also on the skill of those administering them. False positives were a significant problem when drug testing started to become common, with estimates of false positive rates for common immunoassay tests ranging from 10% to 30% on the high end,[*] but the accuracy has improved since then. Because of the possibility of false positive results, positive immunoassay tests need to be confirmed by the more expensive and much more reliable gas chromatograph/mass spectrometry (GC/MS) test. See also the National Collegiate Athletic Association's (NCAA) Drug-Testing Program handbook, available at www.ncaa.org/health-and-safety/policy/drug-testing. The section on Institutional Drug Testing addresses the problem of false positives. ■

[*] Drug Testing in the Workplace, ACLU Briefing Paper, 1996.

Bayes' Theorem Formula

The calculation we used to answer the question in Example 1 can be recast as a formula known as **Bayes' theorem**. Figure 15 shows a general form of the tree we used in Example 1.

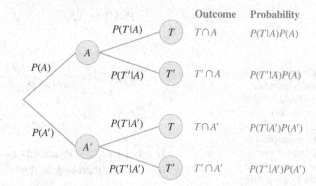

Figure 15

We calculated

$$P(A\,|\,T) = \frac{P(A \cap T)}{P(T)}$$

as follows. We first calculated the numerator $P(A \cap T)$ using the multiplication principle:

$$P(A \cap T) = P(T\,|\,A)\,P(A).$$

We then calculated the denominator $P(T)$ by using the addition principle for mutually exclusive events together with the multiplication principle:

$$P(T) = P(A \cap T) + P(A' \cap T)$$
$$= P(T|A) P(A) + P(T|A') P(A').$$

Substituting gives

$$P(A|T) = \frac{P(T|A) P(A)}{P(T|A) P(A) + P(T|A') P(A')}.$$

This is the short form of Bayes' theorem.

Bayes' Theorem (Short Form)

If A and T are events, then

Bayes' Formula

$$P(A|T) = \frac{P(T|A) P(A)}{P(T|A) P(A) + P(T|A') P(A')}.$$

Using a Tree

$$P(A|T) = \frac{P(\text{Using } A \text{ and } T \text{ branches})}{\text{Sum of } P(\text{Using branches ending in } T)}$$

Quick Examples

1. Let us calculate the probability that an athlete from Example 1 who tests positive is actually using steroids if only 5% of ESU athletes are using steroids. Thus,

$$P(T|A) = .95$$
$$P(T|A') = .06$$
$$P(A) = .05$$
$$P(A') = .95,$$

so

$$P(A|T) = \frac{P(T|A) P(A)}{P(T|A) P(A) + P(T|A') P(A')}$$
$$= \frac{(.95)(.05)}{(.95)(.05) + (.06)(.95)} \approx .45.$$

In other words, it is actually more likely that such an athlete does *not* use steroids than that he does.*

* Without knowing the results of the test, we would have said that there was a probability of $P(A) = .05$ that the athlete is using steroids. The positive test result raises the probability to $P(A|T) = .45$, but the test gives too many false positives for us to be any more than 45% certain that the athlete is actually using steroids.

Remembering the Formula

Although the formula looks complicated at first sight, it is not hard to remember if you notice the pattern. Or you could re-derive it yourself by thinking of the tree diagram.

The next example illustrates that we can use either a tree diagram or the Bayes' theorem formula.

EXAMPLE 2   **Lie Detectors**

The *Sherlock Lie Detector Company* manufactures the latest in lie detectors, and the *Count-Your-Pennies* (CYP) store chain is eager to use them to screen its employees for theft. Sherlock's advertising claims that the test misses a lie only once in every 100 instances. On the other hand, an analysis by a consumer group reveals 20% of people who are telling the truth fail the test anyway.[*] The local police department estimates that 1 out of every 200 employees has engaged in theft. When the CYP store first screened its employees, the test indicated that Prudence V. Good was lying when she claimed that she had never stolen from CYP. What is the probability that she was lying and had in fact stolen from the store?

* The reason for this is that many people show physical signs of distress when asked accusatory questions. Many people are nervous around police officers even if they have done nothing wrong.

Solution   We are asked for the probability that Prudence Good was lying, and in the preceding sentence we are told that the lie detector test showed her to be lying. So we are looking for a conditional probability: the probability that she is lying, given that the lie detector test is positive. Now we can start to give names to the events:

L: A subject is lying.
T: The test is positive (indicated that the subject was lying).

We are looking for $P(L|T)$. We know that 1 out of every 200 employees engages in theft. Let us assume that no employee admits to theft while taking a lie detector test, so the probability $P(L)$ that a test subject is lying is 1/200. We also know the false negative and false positive rates $P(T'|L)$ and $P(T|L')$.

Using a Tree Diagram   Figure 16 shows the tree diagram.

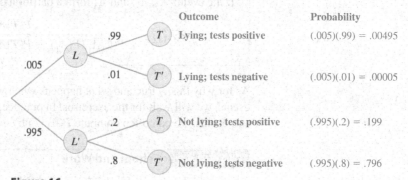

Figure 16

We see that

$$P(L|T) = \frac{P(\text{Using } L \text{ and } T \text{ branches})}{\text{Sum of } P(\text{Using branches ending in } T)}$$

$$= \frac{.00495}{.00495 + .199} \approx .024.$$

This means that there was only a 2.4% chance that Prudence Good was lying and had stolen from the store!

Using Bayes' Theorem   We have

$$P(L) = .005$$
$$P(T|L') = .2$$
$$P(T'|L) = .01,$$

from which we obtain

$$P(T|L) = .99,$$

so

$$P(L|T) = \frac{P(T|L)\,P(L)}{P(T|L)\,P(L) + P(T|L')\,P(L')} = \frac{(.99)(.005)}{(.99)(.005) + (.2)(.995)} \approx .024.$$

Expanded Form of Bayes' Theorem

We have seen the "short form" of Bayes' theorem. What is the "long form"? To motivate an expanded form of Bayes' theorem, look again at the formula we've been using:

$$P(A|T) = \frac{P(T|A)\,P(A)}{P(T|A)\,P(A) + P(T|A')\,P(A')}.$$

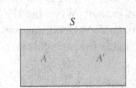

A and *A'* form a partition of *S*.

Figure 17

The events *A* and *A'* form a **partition** of the sample space *S*; that is, their union is the whole of *S*, and their intersection is empty (Figure 17).

The expanded form of Bayes' theorem applies to a partition of *S* into three or more events, as shown in Figure 18.

By saying that the events A_1, A_2, and A_3 form a partition of *S*, we mean that their union is the whole of *S* and the intersection of any two of them is empty, as in the figure. When we have a partition into three events as shown, the formula gives us $P(A_1|T)$ in terms of $P(T|A_1)$, $P(T|A_2)$, $P(T|A_3)$, $P(A_1)$, $P(A_2)$, and $P(A_3)$.

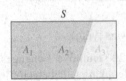

A_1, A_2, and A_3 form a partition of *S*.

Figure 18

Bayes' Theorem (Expanded Form)

If the events A_1, A_2, and A_3 form a partition of the sample space *S*, then

$$P(A_1|T) = \frac{P(T|A_1)\,P(A_1)}{P(T|A_1)\,P(A_1) + P(T|A_2)\,P(A_2) + P(T|A_3)\,P(A_3)}$$

As for why this is true and what happens when we have a partition into *four or more* events, we will wait for the exercises. In practice, as was the case with a partition into two events, we can often compute $P(A_1|T)$ by constructing a tree diagram.

EXAMPLE 3   School and Work

A survey[68] conducted by the Bureau of Labor Statistics found that approximately 27% of the high school graduating class of 2010 went on to a 2-year college, 41% went on to a 4-year college, and the remaining 32% did not go on to college. Of those who went on to a 2-year college, 52% worked at the same time, 32% of those going on to a 4-year college worked, and 78% of those who did not go on to college worked. What percentage of those working had not gone on to college?

Solution We can interpret these percentages as probabilities if we consider the experiment of choosing a member of the high school graduating class of 2010 at random. The events we are interested in are these:

R_1: A graduate went on to a 2-year college.

R_2: A graduate went on to a 4-year college.

R_3: A graduate did not go to college.

A: A graduate went on to work.

---

[68] Source: "College Enrollment and Work Activity of High School Graduates," U.S. Bureau of Labor Statistics (www.bls.gov/news.release/hsgec.htm).

The three events R_1, R_2, and R_3 partition the sample space of all graduates into three events. We are given the following probabilities:

$$P(R_1) = .27 \qquad P(R_2) = .41 \qquad P(R_3) = .32$$
$$P(A|R_1) = .52 \quad P(A|R_2) = .32 \quad P(A|R_3) = .78.$$

We are asked to find the probability that a graduate who went on to work did not go to college, so we are looking for $P(R_3|A)$. Bayes' formula for these events is

$$P(R_3|A) = \frac{P(A|R_3)P(R_3)}{P(A|R_1)P(R_1) + P(A|R_2)P(R_2) + P(A|R_3)P(R_3)}$$
$$= \frac{(.78)(.32)}{(.52)(.27) + (.32)(.41) + (.78)(.32)} \approx .48.$$

Thus, we conclude that 48% of all those working had not gone on to college.

➡ **Before we go on...** We could also solve Example 3 using a tree diagram. As before, the first branching corresponds to the events with unconditional probabilities that we know: R_1, R_2, and R_3. You should complete the tree and check that you obtain the same result as above. ■

8.6 EXERCISES

▼ more advanced   ◆ challenging

🔲 indicates exercises that should be solved using technology

In Exercises 1–8, use Bayes' theorem or a tree diagram to calculate the indicated probability. Round all answers to four decimal places. [HINT: See Quick Example 1 and Example 3.]

1. $P(A|B) = .8$, $P(B) = .2$, $P(A|B') = .3$. Find $P(B|A)$.

2. $P(A|B) = .6$, $P(B) = .3$, $P(A|B') = .5$. Find $P(B|A)$.

3. $P(X|Y) = .8$, $P(Y') = .3$, $P(X|Y') = .5$. Find $P(Y|X)$.

4. $P(X|Y) = .6$, $P(Y') = .4$, $P(X|Y') = .3$. Find $P(Y|X)$.

5. Y_1, Y_2, Y_3 form a partition of S. $P(X|Y_1) = .4$, $P(X|Y_2) = .5$, $P(X|Y_3) = .6$, $P(Y_1) = .8$, $P(Y_2) = .1$. Find $P(Y_1|X)$.

6. Y_1, Y_2, Y_3 form a partition of S. $P(X|Y_1) = .2$, $P(X|Y_2) = .3$, $P(X|Y_3) = .6$, $P(Y_1) = .3$, $P(Y_2) = .4$. Find $P(Y_1|X)$.

7. Y_1, Y_2, Y_3 form a partition of S. $P(X|Y_1) = .4$, $P(X|Y_2) = .5$, $P(X|Y_3) = .6$, $P(Y_1) = .8$, $P(Y_2) = .1$. Find $P(Y_2|X)$.

8. Y_1, Y_2, Y_3 form a partition of S. $P(X|Y_1) = .2$, $P(X|Y_2) = .3$, $P(X|Y_3) = .6$, $P(Y_1) = .3$, $P(Y_2) = .4$. Find $P(Y_2|X)$.

Applications

9. *Music Downloading* According to a study on the effect of music downloading on spending on music, 11% of all Internet users had decreased their spending on music.[69] We estimate that 40% of all music fans used the Internet at the time of the study.[70] If 20% of non–Internet users had decreased their spending on music, what percentage of those who had decreased their spending on music were Internet users? [HINT: See Examples 1 and 2.]

10. *Music Downloading* According to the study cited in Exercise 9, 36% of experienced file-sharers with broadband access had decreased their spending on music. Let us estimate that 3% of all music fans were experienced file-sharers with broadband access at the time of the study.[71] If 20% of the other music fans had decreased their spending on music, what percentage of those who had decreased their spending on music were experienced file-sharers with broadband access? [HINT: See Examples 1 and 2.]

11. *Weather* It snows in Greenland an average of once every 25 days, and when it does, glaciers have a 20% chance of growing. When it does not snow in Greenland, glaciers have only a 4% chance of growing. What is the probability that it is snowing in Greenland when glaciers are growing?

---

[69] Regardless of whether they used the Internet to download music. Source: *New York Times*, May 6, 2002, p. C6.

[70] According to the U.S. Department of Commerce, 51% of all U.S. households had computers in 2001.

[71] Around 15% of all online households had broadband access in 2001, according to a *New York Times* article (Dec. 24, 2001, p. C1).

12. **Weather** It rains in Spain an average of once every 10 days, and when it does, hurricanes have a 2% chance of happening in Hartford. When it does not rain in Spain, hurricanes have a 1% chance of happening in Hartford. What is the probability that it rains in Spain when hurricanes happen in Hartford?

13. **University Admissions** In fall 2014, 34% of applicants with a Math SAT of 700 or more were admitted by the University of California, Los Angeles (UCLA), while 12% with a Math SAT of less than 700 were admitted. Further, 36% of all applicants had a Math SAT score of 700 or more.[72] What percentage of admitted applicants had a Math SAT of 700 or more? (Round your answer to the nearest percentage point.)

14. **University Admissions** In fall 2014, 71% of rejected applicants to UCLA had a Math SAT of less than 700, while 39% of accepted applicants to UCLA had a Math SAT of less than 700. Further, 80% of all applicants were rejected.[73] What percentage of applicants with a Math SAT of less than 700 were rejected? (Round your answer to the nearest percentage point.)

15. **Side-Impact Hazard** In 2004, 45.4% of all light vehicles were cars, and the rest were light trucks or SUVs. The probability that a severe side-impact crash would prove deadly to a driver depended on the type of vehicle he or she was driving at the time, as shown in the table:[74]

Car	1.0
Light Truck or SUV	.3

What is the probability that the victim of a deadly side-impact accident was driving a car?

16. **Side-Impact Hazard** In 2004, 27.3% of all light vehicles were light trucks, and the rest were cars or SUVs. The probability that a severe side-impact crash would prove deadly to a driver depended on the type of vehicle he or she was driving at the time, as shown in the table:[75]

Light Truck	.2
Car or SUV	.7

What is the probability that the victim of a deadly side-impact accident was driving a car or SUV?

17. **Athletic Fitness Tests** Any athlete who fails the *Enormous State University*'s women's soccer fitness test is automatically dropped from the team. Last year, Mona Header failed

the test but claimed that this was due to the early hour. (The fitness test is traditionally given at 5 am on a Sunday morning.) In fact, a study by the ESU Physical Education Department suggested that 50% of athletes fit enough to play on the team would fail the soccer test, although no unfit athlete could possibly pass the test. It also estimated that 45% of the athletes who take the test are fit enough to play soccer. Assuming that these estimates are correct, what is the probability that Mona was justifiably dropped?

18. **Academic Testing** Professor Frank Nabarro insists that all senior physics majors take his notorious physics aptitude test. The test is so tough that anyone *not* going on to a career in physics has no hope of passing, whereas 60% of the seniors who do go on to a career in physics still fail the test. Further, 75% of all senior physics majors in fact go on to a career in physics. Assuming that you fail the test, what is the probability that you will not go on to a career in physics?

19. **Side-Impact Hazard** (Compare Exercise 15.) In 2004, 27.3% of all light vehicles were light trucks, 27.3% were SUVs, and 45.4% were cars. The probability that a severe side-impact crash would prove deadly to a driver depended on the type of vehicle he or she was driving at the time, as shown in the table:[76]

Light Truck	.210
SUV	.371
Car	1.000

What is the probability that the victim of a deadly side-impact accident was driving an SUV? [**HINT:** See Example 3.]

20. **Side-Impact Hazard** In 1986, 23.9% of all light vehicles were light trucks, 5.0% were SUVs, and 71.1% were cars. Refer to Exercise 19 for the probabilities that a severe side-impact crash would prove deadly. What is the probability that the victim of a deadly side-impact accident was driving a car? [**HINT:** See Example 3.]

21. **University Admissions** In fall 2008, UCLA admitted 22% of its California resident applicants, 28% of its applicants from other U.S. states, and 22% of its international student applicants. Of all its applicants, 84% were California residents, 10% were from other U.S. states, and 6% were international students.[77] What percentage of all admitted students were California residents? (Round your answer to the nearest 1%.)

22. **University Admissions** In fall 2002, UCLA admitted 26% of its California resident applicants, 18% of its applicants from other U.S. states, and 13% of its international student applicants. Of all its applicants, 86% were California residents, 11% were from other U.S. states, and 3% were international

---

[72] Percentages are rounded. Source: University of California (www.admissions.ucla.edu/Prospect/Adm_fr/Frosh_Prof14.htm).

[73] *Ibid.*

[74] A "serious" side-impact accident is defined as one in which the driver of a car would be killed. Source: National Highway Traffic Safety Administration/*New York Times*, May 30, 2004, p. BU 9.

[75] *Ibid.*

[76] *Ibid.*

[77] Source: University of California (www.admissions.ucla.edu/Prospect/Adm_fr/Frosh_Prof08.htm).

students.[78] What percentage of all admitted students were California residents? (Round your answer to the nearest 1%.)

23. **Internet Use (Historical)** In 2000, 86% of all Caucasians in the United States, 77% of all African-Americans, 77% of all Hispanics, and 85% of residents not classified into one of these groups used the Internet for email.[79] At that time, the U.S. population was 69% Caucasian, 12% African-American, and 13% Hispanic. What percentage of U.S. residents who used the Internet for email were Hispanic?

24. **Internet Use (Historical)** In 2000, 59% of all Caucasians in the United States, 57% of all African-Americans, 58% of all Hispanics, and 54% of residents not classified into one of these groups used the Internet to search for information.[80] At that time, the U.S. population was 69% Caucasian, 12% African-American, and 13% Hispanic. What percentage of U.S. residents who used the Internet for information search were African-American?

25. ▼ **Market Surveys** A *New York Times* survey of homeowners in the 1990s showed that 86% of those with swimming pools were married couples, and the other 14% were single.[81] It also showed that 15% of all homeowners had pools.
   a. Assuming that 90% of all homeowners without pools are married couples, what percentage of homes owned by married couples have pools?
   b. Would it have been more profitable for pool manufacturers to go after single homeowners or married homeowners? Explain.

26. ▼ **Crime and Preschool.** A *New York Times* survey[82] of needy and disabled youths showed that 51% of those who had no preschool education were arrested or charged with a crime by the time they were 19, whereas only 31% who had preschool education wound up in this category. The survey did not specify what percentage of the youths in the survey had preschool education, so let us take a guess at that and estimate that 20% of them had attended preschool.
   a. What percentage of the youths arrested or charged with a crime had no preschool education?
   b. What would this figure be if 80% of the youths had attended preschool? Would youths who had preschool education be more likely to arrested or charged with a crime than those who did not? Support your answer by quoting probabilities.

27. ▼ **Grade Complaints** Two of the mathematics professors at *Enormous State University* are Professor A (known for easy grading) and Professor F (known for tough grading). Last semester, roughly three quarters of Professor F's class consisted of former students of Professor A; these students apparently felt encouraged by their (utterly undeserved) high grades. (Professor F's own former students had fled in droves to Professor A's class to try to shore up their grade-point averages.) At the end of the semester, as might have been predicted, all of Professor A's former students wound up with a C– or lower. The rest of the students in the class— former students of Professor F who had decided to "stick it out"—fared better, and two thirds of them earned higher than a C–. After discovering what had befallen them, all the students who earned C– or lower got together and decided to send a delegation to the department chair to complain that their grade-point averages had been ruined by this callous and heartless beast! The contingent was to consist of 10 representatives selected at random from among them. How many of the 10 would you estimate to have been former students of Professor A?

28. ▼ **Weather Prediction** A local TV station employs Desmorelda, "Mistress of the Zodiac," as its weather forecaster. Now, when it rains, Sagittarius is in the shadow of Jupiter one-third of the time, and it rains on 4 out of every 50 days. Sagittarius falls in Jupiter's shadow on only 1 in every 5 rainless days. The powers that be at the station notice a disturbing pattern to Desmorelda's weather predictions. It seems that she always predicts that it will rain when Sagittarius is in the shadow of Jupiter. What percentage of the time is she correct? Should they replace her?

29. ▼ **Employment in the 1980s** In a 1987 survey of married couples with earnings, 95% of all husbands were employed. Of all employed husbands, 71% of their wives were also employed.[83] Noting that either the husband or wife in a couple with earnings had to be employed, find the probability that the husband of an employed woman was also employed.

30. ▼ **Employment in the 1980s** Repeat Exercise 29 in the event that 50% of all husbands were employed.

31. ▼ **Juvenile Delinquency** According to a study at the Oregon Social Learning Center, boys who had been arrested by age 14 were 17.9 times more likely to become chronic offenders than those who had not.[84] Use these data to estimate the percentage of chronic offenders who had been arrested by age 14 in a city where 0.1% of all boys have been arrested by age 14. [HINT: Use Bayes' formula rather than a tree.]

[78] Source: UCLA website, May 2002 (www.admissions.ucla.edu/Prospect/Adm_fr/Frosh_Prof.htm).

[79] Source: NTIA and ESA, U.S. Department of Commerce, using August 2000 U.S. Bureau of The Census Current Population Survey Supplement.

[80] *Ibid.*

[81] Source: "All about Swimming Pools," *New York Times*, September 13, 1992.

[82] Source: "Governors Develop Plan to Help Preschool Children," *New York Times*, August 2, 1992.

[83] Source: *Statistical Abstract of the United States*, 111th Ed., 1991, U.S. Dept. of Commerce/U.S. Bureau of Labor Statistics. Figures rounded to the nearest 1%.

[84] Based on a study by Marion S. Forgatch of 319 boys from high-crime neighborhoods in Eugene, Oregon. Source: W. Wayt Gibbs, "Seeking the Criminal Element," *Scientific American*, March 1995, pp. 101–107.

32. ▼ *Crime* According to the same study at the Oregon Social Learning Center, chronic offenders were 14.3 times more likely to commit violent offenses than people who were not chronic offenders.[85] In a neighborhood where 2 in every 1,000 residents is a chronic offender, estimate the probability that a violent offender is also a chronic offender. [HINT: Use Bayes' formula rather than a tree.]

33. ▼ *Benefits of Exercise* According to a study in *The New England Journal of Medicine*,[86] 202 of a sample of 5,990 middle-aged men had developed diabetes. It also found that men who were very active (burning about 3,500 calories daily) were half as likely to develop diabetes compared with men who were sedentary. Assume that one third of all middle-aged men are very active, and the rest are classified as sedentary. What is the probability that a middle-aged man with diabetes is very active?

34. ▼ *Benefits of Exercise* Repeat Exercise 33 assuming that only 1 in 10 middle-aged men is very active.

35. ◆ *Air Bag Safety* According to a 2000 study conducted by the Harvard School of Public Health, a child seated in the front seat who was wearing a seatbelt was 31% more likely to be killed in an accident if the car had an air bag that deployed than if it did not.[87] Air bags deployed in 25% of all accidents. For a child seated in the front seat wearing a seatbelt, what is the probability that the air bag deployed in an accident in which the child was killed? (Round your answer to two decimal places.) [HINT: When we say that "A is 31% more likely than B," we mean that the probability of A is 1.31 times the probability of B.]

36. ◆ *Air Bag Safety* According to the study cited in Exercise 35, a child seated in the front seat who was not wearing a seatbelt was 84% more likely to be killed in an accident if the car had an air bag that deployed than if it did not.[88] Air bags deployed in 25% of all accidents. For a child seated in the front seat not wearing a seatbelt, what is the probability that the air bag deployed in an accident in which the child was killed? (Round your answer to two decimal places.) [HINT: When we say that "A is 84% more likely than B," we mean that the probability of A is 1.84 times the probability of B.]

Communication and Reasoning Exercises

37. Your friend claims that the probability of *A* given *B* is the same as the probability of *B* given *A*. How would you convince him that he is wrong?

38. Complete the following sentence. To use Bayes' formula to compute $P(E|F)$, you need to be given _____.

39. ▼ Give an example in which a steroids test gives a false positive only 1% of the time, yet if an athlete tests positive, the chance that he or she has used steroids is under 10%.

40. ▼ Give an example in which a steroids test gives a false positive 30% of the time, yet if an athlete tests positive, the chance that he or she has used steroids is over 90%.

41. ▼ Use a tree to derive the expanded form of Bayes' theorem for a partition of the sample space S into three events R_1, R_2, and R_3.

42. ▼ Write down an expanded form of Bayes' theorem that applies to a partition of the sample space S into four events R_1, R_2, R_3, and R_4.

43. ◆ *Politics* The following letter appeared in *The New York Times*:[89]

> To the Editor:
>
> It stretches credulity when William Safire contends (column, Jan. 11) that 90 percent of those who agreed with his Jan. 8 column, in which he called the First Lady, Hillary Rodham Clinton, "a congenital liar," were men and 90 percent of those who disagreed were women.
>
> Assuming these percentages hold for Democrats as well as Republicans, only 10 percent of Democratic men disagreed with him. Is Mr. Safire suggesting that 90 percent of Democratic men supported him? How naive does he take his readers to be?
>
> A. D.
> New York, Jan. 12, 1996

Comment on the letter writer's reasoning.

44. ◆ *Politics* Refer back to Exercise 43. If the letter writer's conclusion was correct, what percentage of all Democrats would have agreed with Safire's column?

---

[85] See footnote for Exercise 31.

[86] As cited in an article in *New York Times* on July 18, 1991.

[87] The study was conducted by Dr. Segul-Gomez at the Harvard School of Public Health. Source: *New York Times*, December 1, 2000, p. F1.

[88] *Ibid.*

[89] The original letter appeared in *New York Times*, January 16, 1996, p. A16. We have edited the first phrase of the second paragraph slightly for clarity; the original sentence read: "Assuming the response was equally divided between Democrats and Republicans, . . . "

8.7 Markov Systems

Markov Systems, States, and Transition Probabilities

Many real-life situations can be modeled by processes that pass from state to state with given probabilities. A simple example of such a **Markov system** is the fluctuation of a gambler's fortune as he or she continues to bet. Other examples come from the study of trends in the commercial world and the study of neural networks and artificial intelligence. The mathematics of Markov systems is an interesting combination of probability and matrix arithmetic.

Here is a basic example we shall use many times: A market analyst for *Gamble Detergents* is interested in whether consumers prefer powdered laundry detergents or liquid detergents. Two market surveys taken 1 year apart revealed that 20% of powdered detergent users had switched to liquid 1 year later, while the rest were still using powder. Only 10% of liquid detergent users had switched to powder 1 year later, with the rest still using liquid.

We analyze this example as follows: Every year, a consumer may be in one of two possible **states**: He may be a powdered detergent user or a liquid detergent user. Let us number these states: A consumer is in state 1 if he uses powdered detergent and in state 2 if he uses liquid. There is a basic **time step** of 1 year. If a consumer happens to be in state 1 during a given year, then there is a probability of 20% = .2 (the chance that a randomly chosen powder user will switch to liquid) that he will be in state 2 the next year. We write

$$p_{12} = .2$$

to indicate that the probability of going *from* state 1 *to* state 2 in one time step is .2. The other 80% of the powder users are using powder the next year. We write

$$p_{11} = .8$$

* Notice that these are actually *conditional* probabilities. For instance, p_{12} is the probability that the system (the consumer in this case) will go into state 2, *given that the system* (the consumer) *is in state 1*.

to indicate that the probability of *staying* in state 1 from one year to the next is .8.* What if a consumer is in state 2? Then the probability of going to state 1 is given as 10% = .1, so the probability of remaining in state 2 is .9. Thus,

$$p_{21} = .1$$

and

$$p_{22} = .9.$$

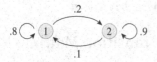

Figure 19

† Named after the Russian mathematician A.A. Markov (1856–1922), who first studied these "nondeterministic" processes.

We can picture this system as in Figure 19, which shows the **state transition diagram** for this example. The numbers p_{ij}, which appear as labels on the arrows, are the **transition probabilities**.

Markov System, States, and Transition Probabilities

A **Markov system**† (or **Markov process** or **Markov chain**) is a system that can be in one of several specified **states**. There is specified a certain **time step**, and at each step, the system will randomly change states or remain where it is. The probability of going from state i to state j is a fixed number p_{ij}, called the **transition probability**.

Quick Example

1. The Markov system depicted in Figure 19 has two states: state 1 and state 2. The transition probabilities are as follows:

$$p_{11} = \text{Probability of going from state 1 to state 1} = .8$$
$$p_{12} = \text{Probability of going from state 1 to state 2} = .2$$
$$p_{21} = \text{Probability of going from state 2 to state 1} = .1$$
$$p_{22} = \text{Probability of going from state 2 to state 2} = .9.$$

Notice that, because the system must go somewhere at each time step, the transition probabilities originating at a particular state always add up to 1. For example, in the transition diagram above, when we add the probabilities originating at state 1, we get $.8 + .2 = 1$.

The transition probabilities may be conveniently arranged in a matrix.

Transition Matrix

The **transition matrix** associated with a given Markov system is the matrix P whose ijth entry is the transition probability p_{ij}, the transition probability of going *from* state i *to* state j. In other words, the entry in position ij is the *label on the arrow going from state i to state j* in a state transition diagram.

Thus, the transition matrix for a system with two states would be set up as follows:

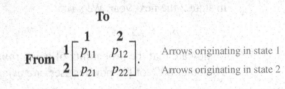

$$\text{From } \begin{array}{c} 1 \\ 2 \end{array} \begin{bmatrix} p_{11} & p_{12} \\ p_{21} & p_{22} \end{bmatrix}. \qquad \begin{array}{l} \text{Arrows originating in state 1} \\ \text{Arrows originating in state 2} \end{array}$$

Quick Example

2. In the system pictured in Figure 19, the transition matrix is

$$P = \begin{bmatrix} .8 & .2 \\ .1 & .9 \end{bmatrix}.$$

Note Notice that because the sum of the transition probabilities that originate at any state is 1, *the sum of the entries in any row of a transition matrix is* 1. ∎

Distribution Vectors and Powers of the Transition Matrix

EXAMPLE 1 **Laundry Detergent Switching**

Consider the Markov system found by *Gamble Detergents* at the beginning of this section. Suppose that 70% of consumers are now using powdered detergent, while the other 30% are using liquid.

a. What will be the distribution 1 year from now? (That is, what percentage will be using powdered and what percentage liquid detergent?)

b. Assuming that the probabilities remain the same, what will be the distribution 2 years from now? 3 years from now?

Solution

a. First, let us think of the statement that 70% of consumers are using powdered detergent as telling us a probability: The probability that a randomly chosen consumer uses powdered detergent is .7. Similarly, the probability that a randomly chosen consumer uses liquid detergent is .3. We want to find the corresponding probabilities 1 year from now. To do this, consider the tree diagram in Figure 20.

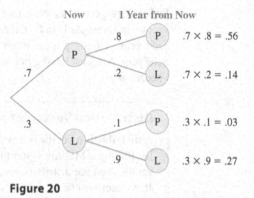

Figure 20

The first branching shows the probabilities now, and the second branching shows the (conditional) transition probabilities. So if we want to know the probability that a consumer is using powdered detergent 1 year from now, it will be

Probability of using powder after 1 year $= .7 \times .8 + .3 \times .1 = .59.$

On the other hand, we have:

Probability of using liquid after 1 year $= .7 \times .2 + .3 \times .9 = .41.$

Now, here's the crucial point: *These are exactly the same calculations as in the matrix product*

$$[.7 \quad .3]\begin{bmatrix} .8 & .2 \\ .1 & .9 \end{bmatrix} = [.59 \quad .41].$$

↑   ↑   ↑

Initial distribution   Transition matrix   Distribution after one step

Thus, to get the distribution of detergent users after 1 year, all we have to do is multiply the **initial distribution vector** $[.7 \quad .3]$ by the transition matrix P. The result is $[.59 \quad .41]$, the **distribution vector after one step**.

b. Now what about the distribution after 2 years? If we assume that the same fraction of consumers switch or stay put in the second year as in the first, we can simply repeat the calculation we did above, using the new distribution vector:

$$[.59 \quad .41]\begin{bmatrix} .8 & .2 \\ .1 & .9 \end{bmatrix} = [.513 \quad .487].$$

↑   ↑   ↑

Distribution after one step   Transition matrix   Distribution after two steps

Thus, after 2 years we can expect 51.3% of consumers to be using powdered detergent and 48.7% to be using liquid detergent. Similarly, after 3 years we have

$$[.513 \quad .487]\begin{bmatrix} .8 & .2 \\ .1 & .9 \end{bmatrix} = [.4591 \quad .5409].$$

So after 3 years, 45.91% of consumers will be using powdered detergent, and 54.09% will be using liquid. Slowly but surely, liquid detergent seems to be winning.

➡ **Before we go on ...** Note that the sum of the entries is 1 in each of the distribution vectors in Example 1. In fact, these vectors are giving the probability distributions for each year of finding a randomly chosen consumer using either powdered or liquid detergent. A vector having nonnegative entries adding up to 1 is called a **probability vector**. ∎

Distribution Vector after *m* Steps

A **distribution vector** is a probability vector giving the probability distribution for finding a Markov system in its various possible states. If v is a distribution vector, then the distribution vector one step later will be vP. The distribution m steps later will be

$$\text{Distribution after } m \text{ steps} = v \cdot P \cdot P \cdot \ldots \cdot P \ (m \text{ times}) = vP^m.$$

Quick Example

3. If $P = \begin{bmatrix} 0 & 1 \\ .5 & .5 \end{bmatrix}$ and $v = [.2 \quad .8]$, then we can calculate the following distribution vectors:

$$vP = [.2 \quad .8]\begin{bmatrix} 0 & 1 \\ .5 & .5 \end{bmatrix} = [.4 \quad .6] \qquad \text{Distribution after one step}$$

$$vP^2 = (vP)P = [.4 \quad .6]\begin{bmatrix} 0 & 1 \\ .5 & .5 \end{bmatrix} = [.3 \quad .7] \qquad \text{Distribution after two steps}$$

$$vP^3 = (vP^2)P = [.3 \quad .7]\begin{bmatrix} 0 & 1 \\ .5 & .5 \end{bmatrix} = [.35 \quad .65]. \qquad \text{Distribution after three steps}$$

What about the matrix P^m that appears above? Multiplying a distribution vector v times P^m gives us the distribution m steps later, so we can think of P^m as the m-step transition matrix. More explicitly, consider the following example.

EXAMPLE 2   Powers of the Transition Matrix

Continuing the example of detergent switching, suppose that a consumer is now using powdered detergent. What are the probabilities that the consumer will be using powdered or liquid detergent 2 years from now? What if the consumer is now using liquid detergent?

Solution To record the fact that we know that the consumer is using powdered detergent, we can take as our initial distribution vector $v = [1 \quad 0]$. To find the distribution 2 years from now, we compute vP^2. To make a point, we do the calculation slightly differently:

$$vP^2 = [1 \quad 0]\begin{bmatrix} .8 & .2 \\ .1 & .9 \end{bmatrix}\begin{bmatrix} .8 & .2 \\ .1 & .9 \end{bmatrix}$$

$$= [1 \quad 0]\begin{bmatrix} .66 & .34 \\ .17 & .83 \end{bmatrix}$$

$$= [.66 \quad .34].$$

So the probability that our consumer is using powdered detergent 2 years from now is .66, while the probability of using liquid detergent is .34. The point to notice is that these are the entries in the first row of P^2. Similarly, if we consider a consumer now using liquid detergent, we should take the initial distribution vector to be $v = \begin{bmatrix} 0 & 1 \end{bmatrix}$ and compute

$$vP^2 = \begin{bmatrix} 0 & 1 \end{bmatrix} \begin{bmatrix} .66 & .34 \\ .17 & .83 \end{bmatrix} = \begin{bmatrix} .17 & .83 \end{bmatrix}.$$

Thus, the bottom row gives the probabilities that a consumer, now using liquid detergent, will be using either powdered or liquid detergent 2 years from now.

In other words, the *ij*th entry of P^2 gives the probability that a consumer, starting in state i, will be in state j after two time steps.

What is true in Example 2 for two time steps is true for any number of time steps, which gives us the following.

Powers of the Transition Matrix

P^m $(m = 1, 2, 3, \ldots)$ is the **m-step transition matrix**. The *ij*th entry in P^m is the probability of a transition from state i to state j in m steps.

Quick Example

4. If $P = \begin{bmatrix} 0 & 1 \\ .5 & .5 \end{bmatrix}$, then

$$P^2 = P \cdot P = \begin{bmatrix} .5 & .5 \\ .25 & .75 \end{bmatrix} \qquad \text{Two-step transition matrix}$$

$$P^3 = P \cdot P^2 = \begin{bmatrix} .25 & .75 \\ .375 & .625 \end{bmatrix}. \qquad \text{Three-step transition matrix}$$

The probability of going from state 1 to state 2 in two steps = $(1, 2)$-entry of P^2 = .5.

The probability of going from state 1 to state 2 in three steps = $(1, 2)$-entry of P^3 = .75.

Steady-State Distribution Vector

What happens if we follow our laundry detergent–using consumers for many years?

EXAMPLE 3 **Long-Term Behavior**

Suppose that 70% of consumers are now using powdered detergent while the other 30% are using liquid. Assuming that the transition matrix remains valid the whole time, what will be the distribution 1, 2, 3, . . . , and 50 years later?

Solution Of course, to do this many matrix multiplications, we're best off using technology. We already did the first three calculations in an earlier example.

Distribution after 1 year: $[.7 \quad .3]\begin{bmatrix} .8 & .2 \\ .1 & .9 \end{bmatrix} = [.59 \quad .41]$

Distribution after 2 years: $[.59 \quad .41]\begin{bmatrix} .8 & .2 \\ .1 & .9 \end{bmatrix} = [.513 \quad .487]$

Distribution after 3 years: $[.513 \quad .487]\begin{bmatrix} .8 & .2 \\ .1 & .9 \end{bmatrix} = [.4591 \quad .5409]$

$\vdots$

Distribution after 48 years: $[.33333335 \quad .66666665]$

Distribution after 49 years: $[.33333334 \quad .66666666]$

Distribution after 50 years: $[.33333334 \quad .66666666]$

Thus, the distribution after 50 years is approximately $[.33333334 \quad .66666666]$.

Something interesting seems to be happening in Example 3. The distribution seems to be getting closer and closer to

$$[.333333\ldots \quad .666666\ldots] = \left[\tfrac{1}{3} \quad \tfrac{2}{3}\right].$$

Let's call this distribution vector v_∞. Notice two things about v_∞:

- v_∞ is a probability vector.
- If we calculate $v_\infty P$, we find

$$v_\infty P = \left[\tfrac{1}{3} \quad \tfrac{2}{3}\right]\begin{bmatrix} .8 & .2 \\ .1 & .9 \end{bmatrix} = \left[\tfrac{1}{3} \quad \tfrac{2}{3}\right] = v_\infty.$$

In other words,

$$v_\infty P = v_\infty.$$

We call a probability vector v with the property that $vP = v$ a **steady-state (probability) vector**.

Q: Where does the name steady-state vector come from?

A: If $vP = v$, then v is a distribution that will not change from time step to time step. In the example above, because $[1/3 \quad 2/3]$ is a steady-state vector, if 1/3 of consumers use powdered detergent and 2/3 use liquid detergent one year, then the proportions will be the same the next year. Individual consumers may still switch from year to year, but as many will switch from powder to liquid as will switch from liquid to powder, so the number using each will remain constant.

But how do we find a steady-state vector?

EXAMPLE 4 **Calculating the Steady-State Vector**

Calculate the steady-state probability vector for the transition matrix in the preceding examples:

$$P = \begin{bmatrix} .8 & .2 \\ .1 & .9 \end{bmatrix}.$$

Solution We are asked to find

$$v_\infty = [x \quad y].$$

This vector must satisfy the equation

$$v_\infty P = v_\infty$$

or

$$[x \quad y]\begin{bmatrix} .8 & .2 \\ .1 & .9 \end{bmatrix} = [x \quad y].$$

Doing the matrix multiplication gives

$$[.8x + .1y \quad .2x + .9y] = [x \quad y].$$

Equating corresponding entries gives

$$.8x + .1y = x$$
$$.2x + .9y = y$$

or

$$-.2x + .1y = 0$$
$$.2x - .1y = 0.$$

Now, these equations are really the same equation. (Do you see that?) There is one more thing we know, though: Because $[x \quad y]$ is a probability vector, its entries must add up to 1. This gives one more equation:

$$x + y = 1.$$

Taking this equation together with one of the two equations above gives us the following system:

$$x + \quad y = 1$$
$$-.2x + .1y = 0.$$

We now solve this system using any of the techniques we learned for solving systems of linear equations. We find that the solution is $x = 1/3$, and $y = 2/3$, so the steady-state vector is

$$v_\infty = [x \quad y] = [\tfrac{1}{3} \quad \tfrac{2}{3}],$$

as suggested in Example 3.

The method we just used works for any size transition matrix and can be summarized as follows.

Calculating the Steady-State Distribution Vector

To calculate the steady-state probability vector for a Markov system with transition matrix P, we solve the system of equations given by

$$x + y + z + \cdots = 1$$
$$[x \quad y \quad z \quad \cdots]P = [x \quad y \quad z \quad \cdots],$$

Using Technology

Technology can be used to compute the steady-state vector in Example 4.

TI-83/84 Plus
Define [A] as the coefficient matrix of the system of equations being solved and [B] as the column matrix of the right-hand sides.
Then compute [A]$^{-1}$[B]
[More details in the Technology Guide.]

Spreadsheet
Use the MMULT and MINVERSE commands to solve the necessary system of equations.
[More details in the Technology Guide.]

Website
www.WanerMath.com
→ Online Utilities
→ Pivot and Gauss-Jordan Tool
You can use the Pivot and Gauss-Jordan Tool to solve the system of equations that gives you the steady-state vector.

where we use as many unknowns as there are states in the Markov system. The steady-state probability vector is then

$$v_\infty = \begin{bmatrix} x & y & z & \cdots \end{bmatrix}.$$

Q : *Is there always a steady-state distribution vector?*

A : Yes, although the explanation why is more involved than we can give here.

Q : *In Example 3 we started with a distribution vector v and found that vP^m got closer and closer to v_∞ as m got larger. Does that always happen?*

A : It does if the Markov system is **regular**, as we define below, but may not for other kinds of systems. Again, we shall not prove this fact here.

Regular Markov Systems

A **regular** Markov system is one for which some power of its transition matrix P has no zero entries. If a Markov system is regular, then

1. It has a unique steady-state probability vector v_∞, and
2. If v is any probability vector whatsoever, then vP^m approaches v_∞ as m gets large. We say that the **long-term behavior** of the system is to have distribution (close to) v_∞.

Interpreting the Steady-State Vector

In a regular Markov system, the entries in the steady-state probability vector give the long-term probabilities that the system will be in the corresponding states, or the fractions of time one can expect to find the Markov system in the corresponding states.

Quick Examples

5. The system with transition matrix $P = \begin{bmatrix} .8 & .2 \\ .1 & .9 \end{bmatrix}$ is regular because $P(= P^1)$ has no zero entries.

6. The system with transition matrix $P = \begin{bmatrix} 0 & 1 \\ .5 & .5 \end{bmatrix}$ is regular because $P^2 = \begin{bmatrix} .5 & .5 \\ .25 & .75 \end{bmatrix}$ has no zero entries.

7. The system with transition matrix $P = \begin{bmatrix} 0 & 1 \\ 1 & 0 \end{bmatrix}$ is *not* regular: $P^2 = \begin{bmatrix} 1 & 0 \\ 0 & 1 \end{bmatrix}$ and $P^3 = P$ again, so the powers of P alternate between these two matrices. Thus, every power of P has zero entries. Although this system has a steady-state vector, namely, $\begin{bmatrix} .5 & .5 \end{bmatrix}$, if we take $v = \begin{bmatrix} 1 & 0 \end{bmatrix}$, then $vP = \begin{bmatrix} 0 & 1 \end{bmatrix}$ and $vP^2 = v$, so the distribution vectors vP^m just alternate between these two vectors, not approaching v_∞.

We finish with one more example.

EXAMPLE 5 **Gambler's Ruin**

A timid gambler, armed with her annual bonus of $20, decides to play roulette using the following scheme. At each spin of the wheel, she places $10 on red. If red comes up, she wins an additional $10; if black comes up, she loses her $10. For the sake of simplicity, assume that she has a probability of 1/2 of winning. (In the real game, the probability is slightly lower—a fact that many gamblers forget.) She keeps playing until she has either reached $30 or lost it all. In either case she then packs up and leaves. Model this situation as a Markov system, and find the associated transition matrix. What can we say about the long-term behavior of this system?

Solution We must first decide on the states of the system. A good choice is the gambler's financial state, the amount of money she has at any stage of the game. According to her rules, she can be broke or can have $10, $20, or $30. Thus, there are four states: $1 = \$0, 2 = \$10, 3 = \$20,$ and $4 = \$30$. Because she bets $10 each time, she moves down $10 if she loses (with probability 1/2) and up $10 if she wins (with probability also 1/2) until she reaches one of the extremes. The transition diagram is shown in Figure 21.

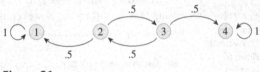

Figure 21

Note that once the system enters state 1 or state 4, it does not leave; with probability 1, it stays in the same state.* We call such states **absorbing states**. We can now write down the transition matrix:

$$P = \begin{bmatrix} 1 & 0 & 0 & 0 \\ .5 & 0 & .5 & 0 \\ 0 & .5 & 0 & .5 \\ 0 & 0 & 0 & 1 \end{bmatrix}.$$

(Notice all the 0 entries, corresponding to possible transitions that we did not draw in the transition diagram because they have 0 probability of occurring. We usually leave out such arrows.) Is this system regular? Take a look at P^2:

$$P^2 = \begin{bmatrix} 1 & 0 & 0 & 0 \\ .5 & .25 & 0 & .25 \\ .25 & 0 & .25 & .5 \\ 0 & 0 & 0 & 1 \end{bmatrix}.$$

Notice that the first and last rows haven't changed. After two steps, there is still no chance of leaving state 1 or state 4. In fact, no matter how many powers we take, no matter how many steps we look at, there will still be no way to leave either of those states, and the first and last rows will still have plenty of zeros. This system is not regular.

Nonetheless, we can try to find a steady-state probability vector. If we do this (and you should set up the system of linear equations and solve it), we find that there are infinitely many steady-state probability vectors, namely, all vectors of the form

*These states are like "Roach Motels" ("Roaches check in, but they don't check out")!

$[x \quad 0 \quad 0 \quad 1-x]$ for $0 \le x \le 1$. (You can check directly that these are all steady-state vectors.) As with a regular system, if we start with any distribution, the system will tend toward one of these steady-state vectors. In other words, eventually the gambler will either lose all her money or leave the table with $30.

But which outcome is more likely and with what probability? One way to approach this question is to try computing the distribution after many steps. The distribution that represents the gambler starting with $20 is $v = [0 \quad 0 \quad 1 \quad 0]$. Using technology, it's easy to compute vP^n for some large values of n:

$$vP^{10} \approx [.333008 \quad 0 \quad .000977 \quad .666016]$$
$$vP^{50} \approx [.333333 \quad 0 \quad 0 \quad .666667].$$

So it looks like the probability that she will leave the table with $30 is approximately 2/3, while the probability that she loses it all is 1/3.

What if she started with only $10? Then our initial distribution would be $v = [0 \quad 1 \quad 0 \quad 0]$, and

$$vP^{10} \approx [.666016 \quad .000977 \quad 0 \quad .333008]$$
$$vP^{50} \approx [.666667 \quad 0 \quad 0 \quad .333333].$$

So this time, the probability of her losing everything is about 2/3, while the probability of her leaving with $30 is 1/3. There is a way of calculating these probabilities exactly using matrix arithmetic; however, it would take us too far afield to describe it here.

➡ **Before we go on ...** Another interesting question is, How long will it take the gambler in Example 5 to get to $30 or lose it all? This is called the *time to absorption* and can also be calculated by using matrix arithmetic. ■

8.7 EXERCISES

▼ more advanced   ◆ challenging
Ⓣ indicates exercises that should be solved using technology

In Exercises 1–10, write down the transition matrix associated with each state transition diagram.

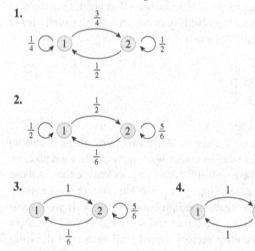

1.

2.

3.   4.

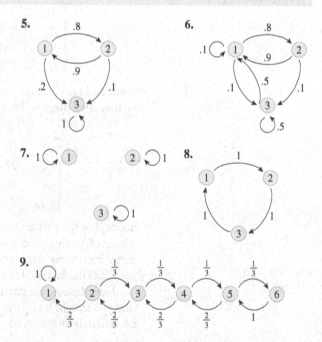

5.

6.

7.   8.

9.

10.

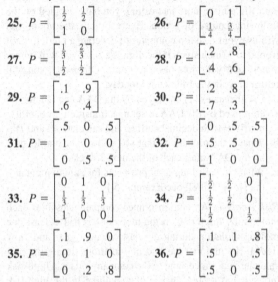

In Exercises 11–24, you are given a transition matrix P and initial distribution vector v. Find **(a)** the two-step transition matrix and **(b)** the distribution vectors after one, two, and three steps. [**HINT:** See Quick Examples 3 and 4.]

11. $P = \begin{bmatrix} .5 & .5 \\ 0 & 1 \end{bmatrix}, v = \begin{bmatrix} 1 & 0 \end{bmatrix}$

12. $P = \begin{bmatrix} 1 & 0 \\ .5 & .5 \end{bmatrix}, v = \begin{bmatrix} 0 & 1 \end{bmatrix}$

13. $P = \begin{bmatrix} .2 & .8 \\ .4 & .6 \end{bmatrix}, v = \begin{bmatrix} .5 & .5 \end{bmatrix}$

14. $P = \begin{bmatrix} \frac{1}{3} & \frac{2}{3} \\ \frac{1}{2} & \frac{1}{2} \end{bmatrix}, v = \begin{bmatrix} \frac{1}{4} & \frac{3}{4} \end{bmatrix}$

15. $P = \begin{bmatrix} \frac{1}{2} & \frac{1}{2} \\ 1 & 0 \end{bmatrix}, v = \begin{bmatrix} \frac{2}{3} & \frac{1}{3} \end{bmatrix}$

16. $P = \begin{bmatrix} 0 & 1 \\ \frac{1}{4} & \frac{3}{4} \end{bmatrix}, v = \begin{bmatrix} \frac{1}{5} & \frac{4}{5} \end{bmatrix}$

17. $P = \begin{bmatrix} \frac{3}{4} & \frac{1}{4} \\ \frac{3}{4} & \frac{1}{4} \end{bmatrix}, v = \begin{bmatrix} \frac{1}{2} & \frac{1}{2} \end{bmatrix}$

18. $P = \begin{bmatrix} \frac{2}{3} & \frac{1}{3} \\ \frac{2}{3} & \frac{1}{3} \end{bmatrix}, v = \begin{bmatrix} \frac{1}{7} & \frac{6}{7} \end{bmatrix}$

19. $P = \begin{bmatrix} .5 & .5 & 0 \\ 0 & 1 & 0 \\ 0 & .5 & .5 \end{bmatrix}, v = \begin{bmatrix} 1 & 0 & 0 \end{bmatrix}$

20. $P = \begin{bmatrix} .5 & 0 & .5 \\ 1 & 0 & 0 \\ 0 & .5 & .5 \end{bmatrix}, v = \begin{bmatrix} 0 & 1 & 0 \end{bmatrix}$

21. $P = \begin{bmatrix} 0 & 1 & 0 \\ \frac{1}{3} & \frac{1}{3} & \frac{1}{3} \\ 1 & 0 & 0 \end{bmatrix}, v = \begin{bmatrix} \frac{1}{2} & 0 & \frac{1}{2} \end{bmatrix}$

22. $P = \begin{bmatrix} \frac{1}{2} & \frac{1}{2} & 0 \\ \frac{1}{2} & \frac{1}{2} & 0 \\ \frac{1}{2} & 0 & \frac{1}{2} \end{bmatrix}, v = \begin{bmatrix} 0 & 0 & 1 \end{bmatrix}$

23. $P = \begin{bmatrix} .1 & .9 & 0 \\ 0 & 1 & 0 \\ 0 & .2 & .8 \end{bmatrix}, v = \begin{bmatrix} .5 & 0 & .5 \end{bmatrix}$

24. $P = \begin{bmatrix} .1 & .1 & .8 \\ .5 & 0 & .5 \\ .5 & 0 & .5 \end{bmatrix}, v = \begin{bmatrix} 0 & 1 & 0 \end{bmatrix}$

In Exercises 25–36, you are given a transition matrix P. Find the steady-state distribution vector. [**HINT:** See Example 4.]

25. $P = \begin{bmatrix} \frac{1}{2} & \frac{1}{2} \\ 1 & 0 \end{bmatrix}$

26. $P = \begin{bmatrix} 0 & 1 \\ \frac{1}{4} & \frac{3}{4} \end{bmatrix}$

27. $P = \begin{bmatrix} \frac{1}{3} & \frac{2}{3} \\ \frac{1}{2} & \frac{1}{2} \end{bmatrix}$

28. $P = \begin{bmatrix} .2 & .8 \\ .4 & .6 \end{bmatrix}$

29. $P = \begin{bmatrix} .1 & .9 \\ .6 & .4 \end{bmatrix}$

30. $P = \begin{bmatrix} .2 & .8 \\ .7 & .3 \end{bmatrix}$

31. $P = \begin{bmatrix} .5 & 0 & .5 \\ 1 & 0 & 0 \\ 0 & .5 & .5 \end{bmatrix}$

32. $P = \begin{bmatrix} 0 & .5 & .5 \\ .5 & .5 & 0 \\ 1 & 0 & 0 \end{bmatrix}$

33. $P = \begin{bmatrix} 0 & 1 & 0 \\ \frac{1}{3} & \frac{1}{3} & \frac{1}{3} \\ 1 & 0 & 0 \end{bmatrix}$

34. $P = \begin{bmatrix} \frac{1}{2} & \frac{1}{2} & 0 \\ \frac{1}{2} & \frac{1}{2} & 0 \\ \frac{1}{2} & 0 & \frac{1}{2} \end{bmatrix}$

35. $P = \begin{bmatrix} .1 & .9 & 0 \\ 0 & 1 & 0 \\ 0 & .2 & .8 \end{bmatrix}$

36. $P = \begin{bmatrix} .1 & .1 & .8 \\ .5 & 0 & .5 \\ .5 & 0 & .5 \end{bmatrix}$

Applications

37. *Marketing* A market survey shows that half the owners of *Sorey State Boogie Boards* became disenchanted with the product and switched to *C&T Super Professional Boards* the next surf season, while the other half remained loyal to Sorey State. On the other hand, three quarters of the C&T Boogie Board users remained loyal to C&T, while the rest switched to Sorey State. Set these data up as a Markov transition matrix, and calculate the probability that a Sorey State Board user will be using the same brand two seasons later. [**HINT:** See Example 1.]

38. *Major Switching* At *Suburban Community College*, 10% of all business majors switched to another major the next semester, while the remaining 90% continued as business majors. Of all non–business majors, 20% switched to a business major the following semester, while the rest did not. Set up these data as a Markov transition matrix, and calculate the probability that a business major will no longer be a business major in two semesters' time. [**HINT:** See Example 1.]

39. *Pest Control* In an experiment to test the effectiveness of the latest roach trap, the "Roach Resort," 50 roaches were placed in the vicinity of the trap and left there for an hour. At the end of the hour, it was observed that 30 of the roaches had "checked in," while the rest were still scurrying around. (Remember that "once a roach checks in, it never checks out.")
  a. Set up the transition matrix P for the system with decimal entries, and calculate P^2 and P^3.
  b. If a roach begins outside the "Resort," what is the probability of its "checking in" by the end of 1 hour? 2 hours? 3 hours?
  c. What do you expect to be the long-term impact on the number of roaches? [**HINT:** See Example 5.]

40. *Employment* You have worked for the Department of Administrative Affairs (DAA) for 27 years, and you still have little or no idea exactly what your job entails. To make your life a little more interesting, you have decided on the following course of action. Every Friday afternoon, you will use your desktop computer to generate a random digit from 0 to 9 (inclusive). If the digit is a zero, you will immediately quit your job, never to return. Otherwise, you will return to work the following Monday.

a. Use the states (1) employed by the DAA and (2) not employed by the DAA to set up a transition probability matrix P with decimal entries, and calculate P^2 and P^3.

b. What is the probability that you will still be employed by the DAA after each of the next 3 weeks?

c. What are your long-term prospects for employment at the DAA? [**HINT**: See Example 5.]

41. *Risk Analysis* An auto insurance company classifies each motorist as "high risk" if the motorist has had at least one moving violation during the past calendar year and "low risk" if the motorist has had no violations during the past calendar year. According to the company's data, a high-risk motorist has a 50% chance of remaining in the high-risk category the next year and a 50% chance of moving to the low-risk category. A low-risk motorist has a 10% chance of moving to the high-risk category the next year and a 90% chance of remaining in the low-risk category. In the long term, what percentage of motorists fall in each category?

42. *Debt Analysis* A credit card company classifies its cardholders as falling into one of two credit ratings: "good" and "poor." On the basis of its rating criteria, the company finds that a cardholder with a good credit rating has an 80% chance of remaining in that category the following year and a 20% chance of dropping into the poor category. A cardholder with a poor credit rating has a 40% chance of moving into the good rating the following year and a 60% chance of remaining in the poor category. In the long term, what percentage of cardholders fall in each category?

43. *Textbook Adoptions* College instructors who adopt this book are (we hope!) twice as likely to continue to use the book the following semester as they are to drop it, whereas nonusers are nine times as likely to remain nonusers the following year as they are to adopt this book.

a. Determine the probability that a nonuser will be a user in 2 years.

b. In the long term, what proportion of college instructors will be users of this book?

44. *Confidence Level* Tommy the Dunker's performance on the basketball court is influenced by his state of mind: If he scores, he is twice as likely to score on the next shot as he is to miss, whereas if he misses a shot, he is three times as likely to miss the next shot as he is to score.

a. If Tommy has missed a shot, what is the probability that he will score two shots later?

b. In the long term, what percentage of shots are successful?

45. *Debt Analysis* As the manager of a large retailing outlet, you have classified all credit customers as falling into one of the following categories: Paid Up, Outstanding 0–90 Days, Bad Debts. Based on an audit of your company's records, you have come up with the following table, which gives the probabilities that a single credit customer will move from one category to the next in the period of 1 month.

		To	
	Paid Up	**0–90 Days**	**Bad Debts**
Paid Up	.5	.5	0
From **0–90 Days**	.5	.3	.2
Bad Debts	0	.5	.5

How do you expect the company's credit customers to be distributed in the long term?

46. *Debt Analysis* Repeat Exercise 45 using the following table:

		To	
	Paid Up	**0–90 Days**	**Bad Debts**
Paid Up	.8	.2	0
From **0–90 Days**	.5	.3	.2
Bad Debts	0	.5	.5

47. ▼ ***Income Brackets*** The following diagram shows the movement of U.S. households among three income groups—affluent, middle class, and poor—over the 11-year period 1980–1991.[90]

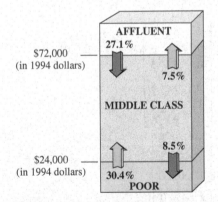

a. Use the transitions shown in the diagram to construct a transition matrix (assuming zero probabilities for the transitions between affluent and poor).

[90] The figures were based on household after-tax income. The study was conducted by G. J. Duncan of Northwestern University and T. Smeeding of Syracuse University and was based on annual surveys of the personal finances of 5,000 households since the late 1960s. (The surveys were conducted by the University of Michigan.) Source: *New York Times*, June 4, 1995, p. E4.

b. Assuming that the trend shown were to continue, what percentage of households classified as affluent in 1980 were predicted to become poor in 2002? (Give your answer to the nearest 0.1%.)

c. ⊤ According to the model, what percentage of all U.S. households will be in each income bracket in the long term? (Give your answer to the nearest 0.1%.)

48. ▼ *Income Brackets* The following diagram shows the movement of U.S. households among three income groups—affluent, middle class, and poor—over the 12-year period 1967–1979.[91]

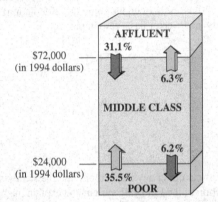

a. Use the transitions shown in the diagram to construct a transition matrix (assuming zero probabilities for the transitions between affluent and poor).

b. Assuming that the trend shown had continued, what percentage of households classified as affluent in 1967 would have been poor in 1991? (Give your answer to the nearest 0.1%.)

c. ⊤ According to the model, what percentage of all U.S. households will be in each income bracket in the long term? (Give your answer to the nearest 0.1%.)

49. ⊤ ▼ *Income Distribution* A University of Michigan study shows the following one-generation transition probabilities among four major income groups.[92]

Eldest Son's Income

		Bottom 10%	10–50%	50–90%	Top 10%
Father's Income	**Bottom 10%**	.30	.52	.17	.01
	10–50%	.10	.48	.38	.04
	50–90%	.04	.38	.48	.10
	Top 10%	.01	.17	.52	.30

In the long term, what percentage of male earners would you expect to find in each category? Why are the long-range figures not necessarily 10% in the lowest 10% income bracket, 40% in the 10–50% range, 40% in the 50–90% range, and 10% in the top 10% range? (Use technology to compute an approximation of the steady-state transition matrix.)

50. ⊤ ▼ *Income Distribution* Repeat Exercise 49, using the following data:

Eldest Son's Income

		Bottom 10%	10–50%	50–90%	Top 10%
Father's Income	**Bottom 10%**	.50	.32	.17	.01
	10–50%	.10	.48	.38	.04
	50–90%	.04	.38	.48	.10
	Top 10%	.01	.17	.32	.50

Market Share: Cell Phones *Three of the largest cellular phone companies in 2004 were* Verizon, Cingular, *and* AT&T Wireless. *Exercises 51 and 52 are based on the following figure, which shows percentages of subscribers who switched from one company to another during the third quarter of 2003:*[93]

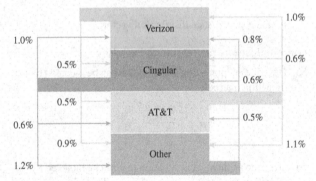

51. a. ⊤ ▼ Use the diagram to set up an associated transition matrix.

b. At the end of the third quarter of 2003, the market shares were Verizon: 29.7%, Cingular: 19.3%, AT&T: 18.1%, and Other: 32.9%. Use your Markov system to estimate the percentage shares at the *beginning* of the third quarter of 2003.

c. Using the information from part (b), estimate the market shares at the end of 2005. Which company is predicted to have gained the most in market share?

---

[91] *Ibid.*

[92] Source: Gary Solon, University of Michigan/*New York Times*, May 18, 1992, p. D5. We have adjusted some of the figures so that the probabilities add to 1; they did not do so in the original table because of rounding.

[93] Published market shares and "churn rate" (percentage drops for each company) were used to estimate the individual transition percentages. "Other" consists of Sprint, Nextel, and T-Mobile. No other cellular companies are included in this analysis. Source: The Yankee Group/*New York Times*, January 21, 2004, p. C1.

52. a. ⬛ ▼ Use the diagram to set up an associated transition matrix.

    b. At the end of the third quarter of 2003, the market shares were Verizon: 29.7%, Cingular: 19.3%, AT&T: 18.1%, Other: 32.9%. Use your Markov system to estimate the percentage shares 1 year earlier.

    c. Using the information from part (b), estimate the market shares at the end of 2010. Which company is predicted to have lost the most in market share?

53. ▼ *Dissipation* Consider the following five-state model of one-dimensional dissipation without drift:

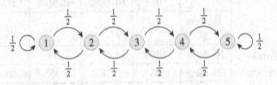

Find the steady-state distribution vector.

54. ▼ *Dissipation with Drift* Consider the following five-state model of one-dimensional dissipation with drift:

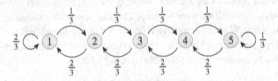

Find the steady-state distribution vector.

Communication and Reasoning Exercises

55. Describe an interesting situation that can be modeled by the transition matrix

$$P = \begin{bmatrix} .2 & .8 & 0 \\ 0 & 1 & 0 \\ .4 & .6 & 0 \end{bmatrix}.$$

56. Describe an interesting situation that can be modeled by the transition matrix

$$P = \begin{bmatrix} .8 & .1 & .1 \\ 1 & 0 & 0 \\ .3 & .3 & .4 \end{bmatrix}.$$

57. ▼ Describe some drawbacks to using Markov processes to model the behavior of the stock market with states (1) bull market and (2) bear market.

58. ▼ Can the repeated toss of a fair coin be modeled by a Markov process? If so, describe a model. If not, explain the reason.

59. ▼ Explain: If Q is a matrix whose rows are steady-state distribution vectors for P then $QP = Q$.

60. ▼ Construct a four-state Markov system so that both $[.5 \quad .5 \quad 0 \quad 0]$ and $[0 \quad 0 \quad .5 \quad .5]$ are steady-state vectors. [**HINT**: Try one in which no arrows link the first two states to the last two.]

61. ▼ Refer to the following state transition diagram, and explain in words (without doing any calculation) why the steady-state vector has a zero in position 1.

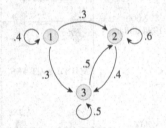

62. ▼ Without doing any calculation, find the steady-state distribution of the following system and explain the reasoning behind your claim.

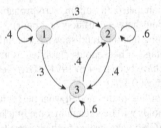

63. ◆ Construct a regular state transition diagram that possesses the steady-state vector $[.3 \quad .3 \quad .4]$.

64. ◆ Construct a regular state transition diagram that possesses the steady-state vector $[.6 \quad .3 \quad 0 \quad .1]$.

65. ◆ Show that if a Markov system has two distinct steady-state distributions v and w, then $\dfrac{v + w}{2}$ is another steady-state distribution.

66. ◆ If higher and higher powers of P approach a fixed matrix Q, explain why the rows of Q must be steady-state distributions vectors.

KEY CONCEPTS

www.WanerMath.com
Go to the Website to find a comprehensive and interactive Web-based summary of Chapter 8.

8.1 Sample Spaces and Events
Experiment, outcome, sample space [p. 548]
Event [p. 550]
The complement of an event [p. 553]
Unions of events [p. 554]
Intersections of events [p. 554]
Mutually exclusive events [p. 557]

8.2 Relative Frequency
Relative frequency or estimated probability [p. 562]
Relative frequency distribution [p. 562]
Properties of relative frequency distribution [p. 565]

8.3 Probability and Probability Models
Probability distribution, probability: $0 \leq P(s_i) \leq 1$ and $P(s_1) + \cdots + P(s_n) = 1$ [p. 570]
If $P(E) = 0$, we call E an impossible event [p. 571]
Probability models [p. 571]
Probability models for equally likely outcomes: $P(E) = n(E)/n(S)$ [p. 573]
Addition principle: $P(A \cup B) = P(A) + P(B) - P(A \cap B)$ [p. 577]
If A and B are mutually exclusive, then $P(A \cup B) = P(A) + P(B)$ [p. 577]
If S is the sample space, then $P(S) = 1$, $P(\varnothing) = 0$, and $P(A') = 1 - P(A)$ [p. 579]

8.4 Probability and Counting Techniques
Use counting techniques from Chapter 7 to calculate probability [p. 588]

8.5 Conditional Probability and Independence
Conditional probability: $P(A|B) = P(A \cap B)/P(B)$ [p. 598]

Multiplication principle for conditional probability:
$P(A \cap B) = P(A|B)P(B)$ [p. 601]
Independent events: $P(A \cap B) = P(A)P(B)$ [p. 604]

8.6 Bayes' Theorem and Applications
Bayes' theorem (short form):
$$P(A|T) = \frac{P(T|A)P(A)}{P(T|A)P(A) + P(T|A')P(A')}$$ [p. 616]
Bayes' theorem (partition of sample space into three events):
$$P(A_1|T) = \frac{P(T|A_1)P(A_1)}{P(T|A_1)P(A_1) + P(T|A_2)P(A_2) + P(T|A_3)P(A_3)}$$
[p. 618]

8.7 Markov Systems
Markov system, Markov process, states, transition probabilities [p. 623]
Transition matrix associated with a given Markov system [p. 624]
A vector having nonnegative entries adding up to 1 is called a probability vector [p. 626]
A distribution vector is a probability vector giving the probability distribution for finding a Markov system in its various possible states [p. 626]
If v is a distribution vector, then the distribution vector one step later will be vP. The distribution after m steps will be vP^m [p. 626]
P^m is the m-step transition matrix. The ijth entry in P^m is the probability of a transition from state i to state j in m steps [p. 627]
A steady-state (probability) vector is a probability vector v such that $vP = v$ [p. 628]
Calculation of the steady-state distribution vector [p. 629]
A regular Markov system, long-term behavior of a regular Markov system [p. 630]
An absorbing state is one for which the probability of staying in the state is 1 (and the probability of leaving it for any other state is 0) [p. 631]

REVIEW EXERCISES

In Exercises 1–6, say how many elements are in the sample space S, list the elements of the given event E, and compute the probability of E.

1. Three coins are tossed; the result is one or more tails.

2. Four coins are tossed; the result is fewer heads than tails.

3. Two distinguishable dice are rolled; the numbers facing up add to 7.

4. Three distinguishable dice are rolled; the numbers facing up add to 5.

5. A die is weighted so that each of 2, 3, 4, and 5 is half as likely to come up as either 1 or 6; however, 2 comes up.

6. Two indistinguishable dice are rolled; the numbers facing up add to 7.

In Exercises 7–10, calculate the relative frequency $P(E)$.

7. Two coins are tossed 50 times, and two heads come up 12 times. E is the event that at least one tail comes up.

8. Ten stocks are selected at random from a portfolio. Seven of them have increased in value since their purchase, and the rest have decreased. Eight of them are Internet stocks, and two of those have decreased in value. E is the event that a stock either has increased in value or is an Internet stock.

9. You have read 150 of the 400 novels in your home, but your sister Roslyn has read 200, of which only 50 are novels you have read as well. *E* is the event that a novel has been read by neither you nor your sister.

10. You roll two dice 10 times. Both dice show the same number 3 times, and on 2 rolls, exactly one number is odd. *E* is the event that the sum of the numbers is even.

In Exercises 11–14, calculate the probability P(E).

11. There are 32 students in categories A and B combined. Some students are in both, 24 are in A, and 24 are in B. *E* is the event that a randomly selected student (among the 32) is in both categories.

12. You roll two dice, one red and one green. Losing combinations are doubles (both dice showing the same number) and outcomes in which the green die shows an odd number and the red die shows an even number. The other combinations are winning ones. *E* is the event that you roll a winning combination.

13. The *jPlay* portable music/photo/video player and bottle opener comes in three models: A, B, and C, each with five colors to choose from, and there are equal numbers of each combination. *E* is the event that a randomly selected *jPlay* is either orange (one of the available colors), a Model A, or both.

14. The *Heavy Weather Service* predicts that for tomorrow there is a 50% chance of tornadoes, a 20% chance of a monsoon, and a 10% chance of both. What is the probability that we will be lucky tomorrow and encounter neither tornadoes nor a monsoon?

A bag contains four red marbles, two green ones, one transparent one, three yellow ones, and two orange ones. You select five at random. In Exercises 15–20, compute the probability of the given event.

15. You have selected all the red ones.

16. You have selected all the green ones.

17. All are different colors.

18. At least one is not red.

19. At least two are yellow.

20. None are yellow and at most one is red.

In Exercises 21–26, find the probability of being dealt the given type of 5-card hand from a standard deck of 52 cards. (None of these is a recognized poker hand.) Express your answer in terms of combinations.

21. **Kings and Queens:** Each of the five cards is either a king or a queen.

22. **Five Pictures:** Each card is a picture card (J, Q, K).

23. **Fives and Queens:** Three fives, the queen of spades, and one other queen.

24. **Prime Full House:** A full house (three cards of one denomination, two of another) with the face value of each card a prime number (ace = 1, J = 11, Q = 12, K = 13).

25. **Full House of Commons:** A full house (three cards of one denomination, two of another) with no royal cards (that is, no J, Q, K, or ace).

26. **Black Two Pair:** Five black cards (spades or clubs), two with one denomination, two with another, and one with a third.

Two dice, one green and one yellow, are rolled. In Exercises 27–32, find the conditional probability, and say whether the indicated pair of events is independent.

27. The sum is 5, given that the green one is not 1 and the yellow one is 1.

28. The sum is 6, given that the green one is either 1 or 3 and the yellow one is 1.

29. The yellow one is 4, given that the green one is 4.

30. The yellow one is 5, given that the sum is 6.

31. The dice have the same parity, given that both of them are odd.

32. The sum is 7, given that the dice do not have the same parity.

A poll shows that half the consumers who use Brand A switched to Brand B the following year, while the other half stayed with Brand A. Three quarters of the Brand B users stayed with Brand B the following year, while the rest switched to Brand A. Use this information to answer Exercises 33–36.

33. Give the associated Markov transition matrix, with state 1 representing using Brand A and state 2 representing using Brand B.

34. Compute the associated two- and three-step transition matrices. What is the probability that a Brand A user will be using Brand B 3 years later?

35. If two thirds of consumers are presently using Brand A and one third are using Brand B, how are these consumers distributed in 3 years' time?

36. In the long term, what fraction of the time will a user spend using each of the two brands?

Applications: OHaganBooks.com
[Try the game at www.OHaganBooks.com]

Inventory OHaganBooks.com currently operates three warehouses: one in Washington, one in California, and the new one in Texas. Book inventories are shown in the following table, which should be used for Exercises 37–42.

	Sci Fi	Horror	Romance	Other	Total
Washington	10,000	12,000	12,000	30,000	64,000
California	8,000	12,000	6,000	16,000	42,000
Texas	15,000	15,000	20,000	44,000	94,000
Total	33,000	39,000	38,000	90,000	200,000

A book is selected at random. Compute the probability of the given event.

37. That it is either a sci-fi book or stored in Texas (or both)

38. That it is a sci-fi book stored in Texas

39. That it is a sci-fi book, given that it is stored in Texas

40. That it is stored in Texas, given that it is a sci-fi book

41. That it is stored in Texas, given that it is not a sci-fi book

42. That it is not stored in Texas, given that it is a sci-fi book

Marketing *To gauge the effectiveness of the OHaganBooks .com site, you recently commissioned a survey of online shoppers. According to the results, 2% of online shoppers visited OHaganBooks.com during a 1-week period, while 5% of them visited at least one of OHaganBooks.com's two main competitors:* JungleBooks.com *and* FarmerBooks.com. *Use this information to answer Exercises 43–50.*

43. What percentage of online shoppers never visited OHaganBooks.com?

44. What percentage of online shoppers never visited either of OHaganBooks.com's main competitors?

45. Assuming that visiting OHaganBooks.com was independent of visiting a competitor, what percentage of online shoppers visited either OHaganBooks.com or a competitor?

46. Assuming that visiting OHaganBooks.com was independent of visiting a competitor, what percentage of online shoppers visited OHaganBooks.com but not a competitor?

47. Under the assumption of Exercise 45, what is the probability that an online shopper will visit none of the three sites during a week?

48. If no one who visited OHaganBooks.com ever visited any of the competitors, what is the probability that an online shopper will visit none of the three sites during a week?

49. Actually, the assumption in Exercise 45 is not what was found by the survey, because an online shopper visiting a competitor was in fact more likely to visit OHaganBooks .com than a randomly selected online shopper. Let H be the event that an online shopper visits OHaganBooks.com, and let C be the event that the shopper visits a competitor. Which is greater: $P(H \cap C)$ or $P(H)P(C)$? Why?

50. What the survey found is that 25% of online shoppers who visited a competitor also visited OHaganBooks.com. Given this information, what percentage of online shoppers visited OHaganBooks.com and neither of its competitors?

51. *Sales* According to statistics gathered by OHaganBooks .com, 2% of online shoppers visited the OHaganBooks.com website during the course of a week, and 8% of those purchased books from the company. Further, 0.5% of online shoppers who did not visit the OHaganBooks.com website during the course of a week nonetheless purchased books from the company (through mail-order catalogs and other

sites such as LemmaZorn.com). What is the probability that an online shopper who purchased books from OHaganBooks .com during a given week visited the site?

52. *Sales* Repeat Exercise 51 in the event that 1% of online shoppers visited OHaganBooks.com during the week.

53. *University Admissions* In the year when Billy-Sean O'Hagan applied to *Suburban State U*, 56% of in-state applicants were admitted, while only 15% of out-of-state applicants were admitted. Further, 72% of all applicants were in-state. What percentage of admitted applicants were in-state? (Round your answer to the nearest percentage point.)

54. *University Admissions* Billy-Sean O'Hagan had also applied to *Gigantic State U*, at which time 75% of all applicants were from the United States and 22% of those applicants were admitted. Also, 14% of the applicants from foreign countries were admitted. What percentage of admitted applicants were from the United States? (Round your answer to the nearest percentage point.)

Competition *As was mentioned earlier, OHaganBooks.com has two main competitors—JungleBooks.com and FarmerBooks .com—and no other competitors of any significance. Exercises 55–58 are based on the following table, which shows the movement of customers during July.[94] (Thus, for instance, the first row tells us that 80% of OHaganBooks.com's customers remained loyal, 10% of them went to JungleBooks.com, and the remaining 10% went to FarmerBooks.com.)*

		To		
		OHaganBooks	**JungleBooks**	**FarmerBooks**
From	**OHaganBooks**	80%	10%	10%
	JungleBooks	40%	60%	0%
	FarmerBooks	20%	0%	80%

At the beginning of July, OHaganBooks.com had an estimated market share of one fifth of all customers, while its two competitors had two fifths each.

55. Estimate the market shares each company had at the end of July.

56. Assuming that the July trends continue in August, predict the market shares of each company at the end of August.

57. Name one or more important factors that the Markov model does not take into account.

58. Assuming that the July trend were to continue indefinitely, predict the market share enjoyed by each of the three e-commerce sites.

---

[94] By a "customer" of one of the three e-commerce sites, we mean someone who purchases more at that site than at any of the two competitors' sites.

The Monty Hall Problem

Here is a famous "paradox" that even mathematicians find counterintuitive. On the game show *Let's Make a Deal*, you are shown three doors, A, B, and C, and behind one of them is the Big Prize. After you select one of them—say, door A—to make things more interesting the host (Monty Hall), who knows what is behind each door, opens one of the other doors—say, door B—to reveal that the Big Prize is not there. He then offers you the opportunity to change your selection to the remaining door, door C. Should you switch or stick with your original guess? Does it make any difference?

Most people would say that the Big Prize is equally likely to be behind door A or door C, so there is no reason to switch.* In fact, this is wrong: The prize is more likely to be behind door C! There are several ways of seeing why this is so. Here is how you might work it out using Bayes' theorem.

* This problem caused quite a stir in late 1991 when it was discussed in Marilyn vos Savant's column in *Parade* magazine. Vos Savant gave the answer that you should switch. She received about 10,000 letters in response, most of them disagreeing with her. Several of those disagreeing with her were mathematicians.

Let A be the event that the Big Prize is behind door A, let B be the event that it is behind door B, and let C be the event that it is behind door C. Let F be the event that Monty has opened door B and revealed that the prize is not there. You wish to find $P(C|F)$ using Bayes' theorem. To use that formula you need to find $P(F|A)$ and $P(A)$ and similarly for B and C. Now, $P(A) = P(B) = P(C) = 1/3$ because at the outset, the prize is equally likely to be behind any of the doors. $P(F|A)$ is the probability that Monty will open door B if the prize is actually behind door A, and this is $1/2$ because we assume that he will choose either B or C randomly in this case. On the other hand, $P(F|B) = 0$, because he will never open the door that hides the prize. Also, $P(F|C) = 1$ because if the prize is behind door C, he must open door B to keep from revealing that the prize is behind door C. Therefore,

$$P(C|F) = \frac{P(F|C)P(C)}{P(F|A)P(A) + P(F|B)P(B) + P(F|C)P(C)}$$

$$= \frac{1 \cdot \frac{1}{3}}{\frac{1}{2} \cdot \frac{1}{3} + 0 \cdot \frac{1}{3} + 1 \cdot \frac{1}{3}} = \frac{2}{3}.$$

You conclude from this that you *should* switch to door C because it is more likely than door A to be hiding the prize.

Here is a more elementary way you might work it out. Consider the tree diagram of possibilities shown in Figure 22. The top two branches of the tree give the cases in

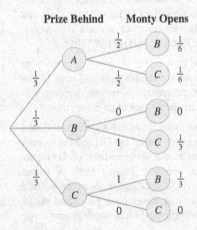

Figure 22

which the prize is behind door A, and there is a total probability of 1/3 for that case. The remaining two branches with nonzero probabilities give the cases in which the prize is behind the door that you did not choose, and there is a total probability of 2/3 for that case. Again, you conclude that you should switch your choice of doors because the one you did not choose is twice as likely as door A to be hiding the Big Prize.

EXERCISES

1. The answer you came up with, to switch to the other door, depends on the strategy Monty Hall uses in picking the door to open. Suppose that he actually picks one of doors B and C at random so that there is a chance that he will reveal the Big Prize. If he opens door B and it happens that the prize is not there, should you switch or not?

2. What if you know that Monty's strategy is always to open door B if possible (i.e., it does not hide the Big Prize) after you choose A?
   a. If he opens door B, should you switch?
   b. If he opens door C, should you switch?

3. Repeat the analysis of the original game, but suppose that the game uses four doors instead of three (and still only one prize).

4. Repeat the analysis of the original game, but suppose that the game uses 1,000 doors instead of 3 (and still only one prize).

Section 8.2

The TI-83/84 Plus has a random number generator that we can use to simulate experiments. For the following example, recall that a fair coin has probability 1/2 of coming up heads and 1/2 of coming up tails.

Example Use a simulated experiment to check the following.

a. The estimated probability of heads coming up in a toss of a fair coin approaches 1/2 as the number of trials gets large.

b. The estimated probability of heads coming up in two consecutive tosses of a fair coin approaches 1/4 as the number of trials gets large.[95]

Solution

a. Let us use 1 to represent heads and 0 to represent tails. We need to generate a list of **random binary digits** (0 or 1). One way to do this—a method that works for most forms of technology—is to generate a random number between 0 and 1 and then round it to the nearest whole number, which will be either 0 or 1.

We generate random numbers on the TI-83/84 Plus using the "rand" function. To round the number X to the nearest whole number on the TI-83/84 Plus, follow MATH → NUM, select "round," and enter round(X,0). This instruction rounds X to zero decimal places—that is, to the nearest whole number. Since we wish to round a random number, we need to enter

$$\text{round(rand,0)} \quad \text{To obtain rand,}$$
$$\text{follow } \boxed{\text{MATH}} \rightarrow \text{PRB.}$$

The result will be either 0 or 1. Each time you press ENTER, you will now get another 0 or 1. The TI-83/84 Plus can also generate a random integer directly (without the need for rounding) through the instruction

$$\text{randInt(0,1)} \quad \text{To obtain randInt,}$$
$$\text{follow } \boxed{\text{MATH}} \rightarrow \text{PRB.}$$

In general, the command randInt(m, n) generates a random integer in the range $[m, n]$. The

following sequence of 100 random binary digits was produced by using technology.[96]

0	1	0	0	1	1	0	1	0	0
0	1	0	0	0	0	0	0	1	0
1	1	0	0	0	1	0	0	1	1
1	1	1	0	1	0	0	0	1	0
1	1	1	1	1	1	1	0	0	1
1	0	1	1	1	0	0	1	1	0
0	1	0	1	1	1	0	1	1	1
1	0	0	0	0	0	0	1	1	1
1	1	1	1	0	0	1	1	1	0
1	1	1	0	1	1	0	1	0	0

If we use only the first row of data (corresponding to the first ten tosses), we find

$$P(\text{H}) = \frac{fr(1)}{N} = \frac{4}{10} = .4.$$

Using the first two rows ($N = 20$) gives

$$P(\text{H}) = \frac{fr(1)}{N} = \frac{6}{20} = .3.$$

Using all ten rows ($N = 100$) gives

$$P(\text{H}) = \frac{fr(1)}{N} = \frac{54}{100} = .54.$$

This is somewhat closer to the theoretical probability of 1/2 and supports our intuitive notion that the larger the number of trials, the more closely the estimated probability should approximate the theoretical value.[97]

b. We need to generate pairs of random binary digits and then check whether they are both 1s. Although the TI-83/84 Plus will generate a pair of random digits if you enter round(rand(2),0), it would be a lot more convenient if the calculator could tell you right away whether both digits are 1s (corresponding to two consecutive heads in a coin toss). Here is a simple way of accomplishing this. Notice that if we *add* the two random binary digits, we obtain either 0, 1, or 2, telling us the number of heads that result

---

[95] Since the set of outcomes of a pair of coin tosses is {HH, HT, TH, TT}, we expect HH to come up once in every four trials, on average.

[96] The instruction randInt(0,1,100)→L$_1$ will generate a list of 100 random 0s and 1s and store it in L$_1$, where it can be summed with Sum(L$_1$) (under 2ND LIST →MATH).

[97] Do not expect this to happen every time. Compare, for example, $P(\text{H})$ for the first five rows and for all ten rows.

from the two consecutive throws. Therefore, all we need to do is add the pairs of random digits and then count the number of times 2 comes up. A formula we can use is

```
randInt(0,1)+randInt(0,1)
```

What would be even *more* convenient would be if the result of the calculation were either 0 or 1, with 1 signifying success (two consecutive heads) and 0 signifying failure. Then we could simply add up all the results to obtain the number of times two heads occurred. To do this, we first divide the result of the previous calculation above by 2 (obtaining 0, .5, or 1, where now 1 signifies success) and then round *down* to an integer, using a function called "int":

```
int(0.5*(randInt(0,1)+randInt(0,1)))
```

Following is the result of 100 such pairs of coin tosses, with 1 signifying success (two heads) and 0 signifying failure (all other outcomes). The last column records the number of successes in each row and the total number at the end.

1	1	0	0	0	0	0	0	0	0	2
0	1	0	0	0	0	0	1	0	1	3
0	1	0	0	1	1	0	0	0	1	4
0	0	0	0	0	0	0	0	1	0	1
0	1	0	0	1	0	0	1	0	0	3
1	0	1	0	0	0	0	0	0	0	2
0	0	0	0	0	0	0	0	0	1	1
0	1	1	1	1	0	0	0	0	1	5
1	1	0	1	0	0	1	1	0	0	5
0	0	0	0	0	0	0	0	1	0	1
										27

Now, as in part (a), we can compute estimated probabilities, with D standing for the outcome "two heads":

First 10 trials: $P(D) = \dfrac{fr(1)}{N} = \dfrac{2}{10} = .2$

First 20 trials: $P(D) = \dfrac{fr(1)}{N} = \dfrac{5}{20} = .25$

First 50 trials: $P(D) = \dfrac{fr(1)}{N} = \dfrac{13}{50} = .26$

100 trials: $P(D) = \dfrac{fr(1)}{N} = \dfrac{27}{100} = .27.$

Q: *What is happening with the data? The probabilities seem to be getting less accurate as N increases!*

A: Quite by chance, exactly 5 of the first 20 trials resulted in success, which matches the theoretical probability. The figure below shows an Excel plot of estimated probability versus N (for N a multiple of 10). Notice that, as N increases, the graph seems to meander within smaller distances of .25.

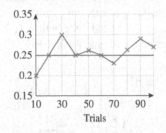

Trials

Q: *The previous techniques work fine for simulating coin tosses. What about rolls of a fair die, in which we want outcomes between 1 and 6?*

A: We can simulate a roll of a die by generating a random integer in the range 1 through 6. The following formula accomplishes this:

$$1 + \text{int}(5.99999*\text{rand}).$$

(We used 5.99999 instead of 6 to avoid the outcome 7.)

Section 8.7

Example 1 (page 624)   Consider the Markov system found by *Gamble Detergents* at the beginning of this section. Suppose that 70% of consumers are now using powdered detergent while the other 30% are using liquid. What will be the distribution 1 year from now? 2 years from now? 3 years from now?

Solution

In Chapter 5 we saw how to set up and multiply matrices. For this example we can use the matrix editor to define [A] as the initial distribution and [B] as the transition matrix. (Remember that the only names we can use are [A] through [J].)

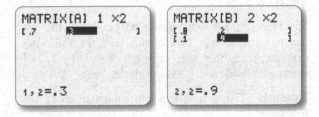

Entering [A] (obtained by pressing MATRIX 1 ENTER) will show you the initial distribution. To obtain the distribution after one step, press X MATRIX 2 ENTER , which has the effect of multiplying the previous answer by the transition matrix [B]. Now just press ENTER repeatedly to continue multiplying by the transition matrix and obtain the distribution after any number of steps. The screenshot shows the initial distribution [A] and the distributions after one, two, and three steps.

```
[A]
        [[.7 .3]]
Ans*[B]
        [[.59 .41]]
    [[.513 .487]]
  [[.4591 .5409]]
```

Example 4 (page 628) Calculate the steady-state probability vector for the transition matrix in the preceding examples.

Solution

Finding the steady-state probability vector comes down to solving a system of equations. As discussed in Chapters 4 and 5, there are several ways to use a calculator to help. The most straightforward is to use matrix inversion to solve the matrix form of the system. In this case, as in the text, the system of equations we need to solve is

$$x + y = 1$$
$$-.2x + .1y = 0.$$

We write this as the matrix equation $AX = B$ with

$$A = \begin{bmatrix} 1 & 1 \\ -.2 & .1 \end{bmatrix} \qquad B = \begin{bmatrix} 1 \\ 0 \end{bmatrix}.$$

To find $X = A^{-1}B$ using the TI-83/84 Plus, we first use the matrix editor to enter these matrices as [A] and [B], then compute $[A]^{-1}[B]$ on the Home screen.

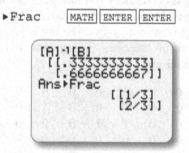

To convert the entries to fractions, we can follow this by the command.

►Frac   MATH ENTER ENTER

```
[A]⁻¹[B]
    [[.3333333333]
     [.6666666667]]
Ans►Frac
          [[1/3]
           [2/3]]
```

Spreadsheet   Technology Guide

Section 8.2

Spreadsheets have random number generators that we can use to simulate experiments. For the following example, recall that a fair coin has probability 1/2 of coming up heads and 1/2 of coming up tails.

Example Use a simulated experiment to check the following.

a. The estimated probability of heads coming up in a toss of a fair coin approaches 1/2 as the number of trials gets large.

b. The estimated probability of heads coming up in two consecutive tosses of a fair coin approaches 1/4 as the number of trials gets large.[98]

Solution

a. Let us use 1 to represent heads and 0 to represent tails. We need to generate a list of **random binary digits**

---

[98] Because the set of outcomes of a pair of coin tosses is {HH, HT, TH,TT}, we expect HH to come up once in every four trials, on average.

(0 or 1). One way to do this—a method that works for most forms of technology—is to generate a random number between 0 and 1 and then round it to the nearest whole number, which will be either 0 or 1.

In a spreadsheet, the formula RAND() gives a random number between 0 and 1.[99] The function ROUND(X,0) rounds X to zero decimal places—that is, to the nearest integer. Therefore, to obtain a random binary digit in any cell, just enter the following formula:

    =ROUND(RAND(),0)

Spreadsheets can also generate a random integer directly (without the need for rounding) through the formula

    =RANDBETWEEN(0,1)

To obtain a whole array of random numbers, just drag this formula into the cells you wish to use.

b. We need to generate pairs of random binary digits and then check whether they are both 1s. It would be convenient if the spreadsheet could tell you right away whether both digits are 1s (corresponding to two consecutive heads in a coin toss). Here is a simple way of accomplishing this. Notice that if we *add* two random binary digits, we obtain either 0, 1, or 2, telling us the number of heads that result from the two consecutive throws. Therefore, all we need to do is add pairs of random digits and then count the number of times 2 comes up. A formula we can use is

    =RANDBETWEEN(0,1)+RANDBETWEEN(0,1)

What would be even *more* convenient would be if the result of the calculation were either 0 or 1, with 1 signifying success (two consecutive heads) and 0 signifying failure. Then we could simply add up all the results to obtain the number of times two heads occurred. To do this, we first divide the result of the calculation above by 2 (obtaining 0, .5, or 1, where now 1 signifies success) and then round *down* to an integer using a function called "int":

    =INT(0.5*(RANDBETWEEN(0,1)+
    RANDBETWEEN(0,1)))

Following is the result of 100 such pairs of coin tosses, with 1 signifying success (two heads) and 0 signifying failure (all other outcomes). The last column records the number of successes in each row and the total number at the end.

1	1	0	0	0	0	0	0	0	0	2
0	1	0	0	0	0	0	1	0	1	3
0	1	0	0	1	1	0	0	0	1	4
0	0	0	0	0	0	0	0	1	0	1
0	1	0	0	1	0	0	1	0	0	3
1	0	1	0	0	0	0	0	0	0	2
0	0	0	0	0	0	0	0	0	1	1
0	1	1	1	1	0	0	0	0	1	5
1	1	0	1	0	0	1	1	0	0	5
0	0	0	0	0	0	0	0	1	0	1
										27

Now, as in part (a), we can compute estimated probabilities, with D standing for the outcome "two heads":

First 10 trials: $P(D) = \dfrac{fr(1)}{N} = \dfrac{2}{10} = .2$

First 20 trials: $P(D) = \dfrac{fr(1)}{N} = \dfrac{5}{20} = .25$

First 50 trials: $P(D) = \dfrac{fr(1)}{N} = \dfrac{13}{50} = .26$

100 trials: $P(D) = \dfrac{fr(1)}{N} = \dfrac{27}{100} = .27.$

Q: *What is happening with the data? The probabilities seem to be getting less accurate as N increases!*

A: Quite by chance, exactly 5 of the first 20 trials resulted in success, which matches the theoretical probability. The figure below shows an Excel plot of estimated probability versus N (for N a multiple of 10). Notice that, as N increases, the graph seems to meander within smaller distances of .25.

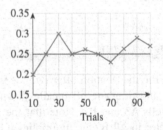

Q: *The previous techniques work fine for simulating coin tosses. What about rolls of a fair die, in which we want outcomes between 1 and 6?*

A: We can simulate a roll of a die by generating a random integer in the range 1 through 6. The following formula accomplishes this:

    =1 + INT(5.99999*RAND())

(We used 5.99999 instead of 6 to avoid the outcome 7.)

---

[99] The parentheses after RAND are necessary even though the function takes no arguments.

Section 8.7

Example 1 (page 624) Consider the Markov system found by *Gamble Detergents* at the beginning of this section. Suppose that 70% of consumers are now using powdered detergent while the other 30% are using liquid. What will be the distribution 1 year from now? 2 years from now? 3 years from now?

Solution

In your spreadsheet, enter the initial distribution vector in cells A1 and B1 and the transition matrix to the right of that, as shown.

	A	B	C	D	E
1	0.7	0.3		0.8	0.2
2				0.1	0.9

To calculate the distribution after one step, use the array formula

=MMULT(A1:B1,$D$1:$E$2)

The absolute cell references (dollar signs) ensure that the formula always refers to the same transition matrix, even if we copy it into other cells. To use the array formula, select cells A2 and B2, where the distribution vector will go, enter this formula, and then press Control+Shift+Enter.[100]

	A	B	C	D	E
1	0.7	0.3		0.8	0.2
2	=MMULT(A1:B1,$D$1:$E$2)			0.1	0.9

The result is the following, with the distribution after one step highlighted.

	A	B	C	D	E
1	0.7	0.3		0.8	0.2
2	0.59	0.41		0.1	0.9

To calculate the distribution after two steps, select cells A2 and B2, and drag the fill handle down to copy the formula to cells A3 and B3. Note that the formula now takes the vector in A2:B2 and multiplies it by the transition matrix to get the vector in A3:B3. To calculate several more steps, drag down as far as desired.

	A	B	C	D	E
1	0.7	0.3		0.8	0.2
2	0.59	0.41		0.1	0.9
3					
4					

	A	B	C	D	E
1	0.7	0.3		0.8	0.2
2	0.59	0.41		0.1	0.9
3	0.513	0.487			
4	0.4591	0.5409			

Example 4 (page 628) Calculate the steady-state probability vector for the transition matrix in the preceding examples.

Solution

Finding the steady-state probability vector comes down to solving a system of equations. As was discussed in Chapters 4 and 5, there are several ways to use Excel to help. The most straightforward is to use matrix inversion to solve the matrix form of the system. In this case, as in the text, the system of equations we need to solve is

$$x + y = 1$$
$$-.2x + .1y = 0.$$

We write this as the matrix equation $AX = B$ with

$$A = \begin{bmatrix} 1 & 1 \\ -.2 & .1 \end{bmatrix} \qquad B = \begin{bmatrix} 1 \\ 0 \end{bmatrix}.$$

We enter A in cells A1:B2, B in cells D1:D2, and the formula for $X = A^{-1}B$ in a convenient location, say, B4:B5.

	A	B	C	D
1	1	1		1
2	-0.2	0.1		0
3				
4		=MMULT(MINVERSE(A1:B2),D1:D2)		
5				

When we press Control+Shift+Enter, we see the result.

	A	B	C	D
1	1	1		1
2	-0.2	0.1		0
3				
4		0.3333333		
5		0.6666667		

If we want to see the answer in fraction rather than decimal form, we format the cells as fractions.

	A	B	C	D
1	1	1		1
2	-0.2	0.1		0
3				
4		1/3		
5		2/3		

---

[100] On a Macintosh you can also use Command+Enter.

9

RANDOM VARIABLES AND STATISTICS

CASE STUDY

Spotting Tax Fraud with Benford's Law

You are a tax fraud specialist working for the Internal Revenue Service (IRS), and you have just been handed a portion of the tax return from *Colossal Conglomerate*. The IRS suspects that the portion you were handed may be fraudulent and would like your opinion.

Is there any mathematical test, you wonder, that can point to a suspicious tax return based on nothing more than the numbers entered?

Paula Borchardt/AGE Fotostock

www.WanerMath.com

At the Website, in addition to the resources listed in the Preface, you will find:

- Histogram, Bernoulli trials, and normal distribution utilities

The following optional extra sections:

- Sampling Distributions and the Central Limit Theorem
- Confidence Intervals
- Calculus and Statistics

Introduction

Statistics is the branch of mathematics concerned with organizing, analyzing, and interpreting numerical data. For example, given the current annual incomes of 1,000 lawyers selected at random, you might wish to answer some questions: If I become a lawyer, what income am I likely to earn? Do lawyers' salaries vary widely? If so, how widely?

To answer questions like these, it helps to begin by organizing the data in the form of tables or graphs. This is the topic of the first section of the chapter. The second section describes an important class of examples that are applicable to a wide range of situations, from tossing a coin to product testing.

Once the data are organized, the next step is to apply mathematical tools for analyzing the data and answering questions like those posed above. Numbers such as the **mean** and the **standard deviation** can be computed to reveal interesting facts about the data. These numbers can then be used to make predictions about future events.

The chapter ends with a section on one of the most important distributions in statistics, the **normal distribution**. This distribution describes many sets of data and also plays an important role in the underlying mathematical theory.

9.1   Random Variables and Distributions

Random Variables

In many experiments we can assign numerical values to the outcomes. For instance, if we roll a die, each outcome has a value from 1 through 6. If you select a lawyer and ascertain his or her annual income, the outcome is again a number. We call a rule that assigns a number to each outcome of an experiment a **random variable**.

* In the language of functions (Chapter 1), a random variable is a *real-valued function* whose domain is the sample space.

Random Variable

A **random variable** X is a rule that assigns a number, or **value**, to each outcome in the sample space of an experiment.*

Quick Examples

1. Roll a die; X = The number facing up.
2. Select a mutual fund; X = The number of companies in the fund portfolio.
3. Select a computer; X = The number of gigabytes of memory it has.
4. Survey a group of 20 college students; X = The mean SAT.

Visualizing a Random Variable

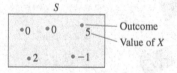

Discrete and Continuous Random Variables

A **discrete** random variable can take on only specific, isolated numerical values, such as the outcome of a roll of a die or the number of dollars in a randomly chosen bank account. A **continuous** random variable, on the other hand, can take on any values within a continuum or an interval, such as the temperature in Central Park or the height of an athlete in centimeters. Discrete random variables that can take on only finitely many values (such as the outcome of a roll of a die) are called **finite** random variables.

Quick Examples

Random Variable	Values	Type
5. Select a mutual fund; X = The number of companies in the fund portfolio.	$\{1, 2, 3, \ldots\}$	Discrete infinite
6. Take five shots at the goal during a soccer match; X = The number of times you score.	$\{0, 1, 2, 3, 4, 5\}$	Finite
7. Measure the length of an object; X = Its length in centimeters.	Any positive real number	Continuous
8. Roll a die until you get a 6; X = The number of times you roll the die.	$\{1, 2, 3, \ldots\}$	Discrete infinite
9. Bet a whole number of dollars in a race where the betting limit is $100; X = The amount you bet.	$\{0, 1, \ldots, 100\}$	Finite
10. Bet a whole number of dollars in a race where there is no betting limit; X = The amount you bet.	$\{0, 1, \ldots, 100, 101, \ldots\}$	Discrete infinite

Notes

1. In Chapter 8 the only sample spaces that we considered in detail were finite sample spaces. However, in general, sample spaces can be infinite, as in many of the experiments mentioned above.

2. There are some borderline situations. For instance, if X is the salary of a factory worker, then X is, strictly speaking, discrete. However, the values of X are so numerous and close together that in some applications it makes sense to model X as a continuous random variable. ■

For the moment we shall consider only finite random variables.

EXAMPLE 1 Finite Random Variable

Let X be the number of heads that come up when a coin is tossed three times. List the value of X for each possible outcome. What are the possible values of X?

Solution First, we describe X as a random variable:

X is the rule that assigns to each outcome the number of heads that come up.

We take as the outcomes of this experiment all possible sequences of three heads and tails. Then, for instance, if the outcome is HTH, the value of X is 2. An easy way to list the values of X for all the outcomes is by means of a table:

Outcome	HHH	HHT	HTH	HTT	THH	THT	TTH	TTT
Value of X	3	2	2	1	2	1	1	0

From the table we also see that the possible values of X are 0, 1, 2, and 3.

2 Heads (X = 2)

W Website
www.WanerMath.com
Go to the Chapter 9 Topic Summary to find an interactive simulation based on Example 1.

➡ **Before we go on ...** Remember that X is just a rule we decide on. In Example 1 we could have taken X to be a different rule, such as the number of tails or perhaps the number of heads minus the number of tails. These different rules are examples of different random variables associated with the same experiment. ■

EXAMPLE 2 **Stock Prices**

You have purchased $10,000 worth of stock in a biotech company whose newest arthritis drug is awaiting approval by the Food and Drug Administration (FDA). If the drug is approved this month, the value of the stock will double by the end of the month. If the drug is rejected this month, the stock's value will decline by 80%. If no decision is reached this month, its value will decline by 10%. Let X be the value of your investment at the end of this month. List the value of X for each possible outcome.

Solution There are three possible outcomes: the drug is approved this month, it is rejected this month, and no decision is reached. Once again, we express the random variable as a rule:

The random variable X is the rule that assigns to each outcome the value, in dollars, of your investment at the end of this month.

We can now tabulate the values of X as follows:

Outcome	Approved this month	Rejected this month	No decision
Value of X	20,000	2,000	9,000

Probability Distribution of a Finite Random Variable

Given a random variable X, it is natural to look at certain *events*—for instance, the event that $X = 2$. By this, we mean the event consisting of all outcomes that have an assigned X-value of 2. Looking once again at the chart in Example 1, with X being the number of heads that face up when a coin is tossed three times, we find the following events:

The event that $X = 0$ is {TTT}.
The event that $X = 1$ is {HTT, THT, TTH}.
The event that $X = 2$ is {HHT, HTH, THH}.
The event that $X = 3$ is {HHH}.
The event that $X = 4$ is ∅.   There are no outcomes with four heads.

Each of these events has a certain probability. For instance, the probability of the event that $X = 2$ is 3/8 because the event in question consists of three of the eight possible (equally likely) outcomes. We shall abbreviate this by writing

$$P(X = 2) = \frac{3}{8}.$$ The probability that $X = 2$ is 3/8.

Similarly,

$$P(X = 4) = 0.$$ The probability that $X = 4$ is 0.

When X is a finite random variable, the collection of the probabilities of X equaling each of its possible values is called the **probability distribution** of X. Because the probabilities in a probability distribution can be estimated or theoretical, we shall discuss both *estimated probability distributions* (or *relative frequency distributions*) and *theoretical (modeled) probability distributions* of random variables. (See the next two examples.)

Probability Distribution of a Finite Random Variable

If X is a finite random variable with values $n_1, n_2, \ldots$, then its **probability distribution** lists the probabilities that $X = n_1, X = n_2, \ldots$. The sum of these probabilities is always 1.

Visualizing the Probability Distribution of a Random Variable

If each outcome in S is equally likely, we get the probability distribution shown for the random variable X.

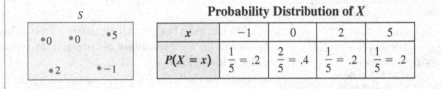

Probability Distribution of X

x	-1	0	2	5
$P(X = x)$	$\dfrac{1}{5} = .2$	$\dfrac{2}{5} = .4$	$\dfrac{1}{5} = .2$	$\dfrac{1}{5} = .2$

Here, $P(X = x)$ means "the probability that the random variable X has the specific value x."

Quick Example

11. Roll a fair die; X = the number facing up. Then the probability that any specific value of X occurs is $\frac{1}{6}$. So the probability distribution of X is the following (notice that the probabilities add up to 1):

x	1	2	3	4	5	6
$P(X = x)$	$\dfrac{1}{6}$	$\dfrac{1}{6}$	$\dfrac{1}{6}$	$\dfrac{1}{6}$	$\dfrac{1}{6}$	$\dfrac{1}{6}$

Using this probability distribution, we can calculate the probabilities of certain events; for instance,

$$P(X < 3) = \frac{1}{3} \quad \text{The event that } X < 3 \text{ is the event } \{1, 2\}.$$

$$P(1 < X < 5) = \frac{1}{2} \quad \text{The event that } 1 < X < 5 \text{ is the event } \{2, 3, 4\}.$$

Note The distinction between X (uppercase) and x (lowercase) in the tables above is important; X stands for the random variable in question, whereas x stands for a specific *value* of X (so x is always a number). Thus, if, say, $x = 2$, then $P(X = x)$ means $P(X = 2)$, the probability that X is 2. Similarly, if Y is a random variable, then $P(Y = y)$ is the probability that Y has the specific value y. ∎

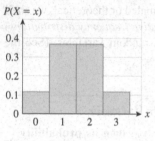

Figure 1

EXAMPLE 3 **Probability Distribution**

Let X be the number of heads that face up in three tosses of a coin. Give the probability distribution of X. What is the probability of throwing at least two heads?

Solution X is the random variable of Example 1, so its values are 0, 1, 2, and 3. The
probability distribution of X is given in the following table:

x	0	1	2	3
$P(X = x)$	$\frac{1}{8}$	$\frac{3}{8}$	$\frac{3}{8}$	$\frac{1}{8}$

Notice that the probabilities add to 1, as we might expect. From the distribution the
probability of throwing at least two heads is

$$P(X \ge 2) = P(\{2, 3\}) = \frac{3}{8} + \frac{1}{8} = \frac{1}{2}.$$

We can use a bar graph to visualize a probability distribution. Figure 1 shows the
bar graph for the probability distribution we obtained. Such a graph is sometimes
called a **histogram**.

➡ **Before we go on ...** The probabilities in the table in Example 3 are *modeled* probabilities. To obtain a similar table of relative frequencies, we would have to repeatedly
toss a coin three times and calculate the fraction of times we got 0, 1, 2, and 3 heads. ■

Note The table of probabilities in Example 3 looks like the probability distribution
associated with an experiment, as we studied in Section 8.3. In fact, the probability
distribution of a random variable is not really new. Consider the following experiment: Toss three coins, and count the number of heads. The associated probability
distribution (per Section 8.3) would be this:

Outcome	0	1	2	3
Probability	$\frac{1}{8}$	$\frac{3}{8}$	$\frac{3}{8}$	$\frac{1}{8}$

The difference is that in this chapter we are thinking of 0, 1, 2, and 3 not as the
outcomes of the experiment, but as values of the random variable X. ■

EXAMPLE 4 **Relative Frequency Distribution**

The following table shows the (fictitious) income brackets of a sample of 1,000 lawyers in their first year out of law school:

Income Bracket	$20,000–$29,999	$30,000–$39,999	$40,000–$49,999	$50,000–$59,999	$60,000–$69,999	$70,000–$79,999	$80,000–$89,999
Number	20	80	230	400	170	70	30

Think of the experiment of choosing a first-year lawyer at random (all being equally
likely), and assign to each lawyer the number X that is the midpoint of his or her
income bracket. Find the relative frequency distribution of X.

Solution Statisticians refer to the income brackets as **measurement classes**. Because
the first measurement class contains incomes that are at least $20,000 but less than

* One might argue that the midpoint should be (20,000 + 29,999)/2 = 24,999.50, but we round this to 25,000. So, technically we are using "rounded" midpoints of the measurement classes.

Using Technology

Technology can be used to automate the calculations in Example 4. Here is an outline.

TI-83/84 Plus
STAT EDIT values of x in L_1 and frequencies in L_2.
Home screen: $L_2/\text{sum}(L_2) \to L_3$
[More details in the Technology Guide.]

Spreadsheet
Headings x, Fr, and $P(X = x)$ in A1–C1
x-values and frequencies in columns A2–B8
=B2/SUM(B:B) in C2
Copy down column C.
[More details in the Technology Guide.]

Website
www.WanerMath.com
→ Online Utilities
→ Histogram Utility

Enter the x-values and frequencies as shown:

```
25000, 20
35000, 80
45000, 230
55000, 400
65000, 170
75000, 70
85000, 30
```

Make sure "Show probability distribution" is checked, and press "Results". The relative frequency distribution will appear at the bottom of the page.

$30,000, its midpoint is $25,000.* Similarly, the second measurement class has midpoint $35,000, and so on. We can rewrite the table with the midpoints as follows:

x	25,000	35,000	45,000	55,000	65,000	75,000	85,000
Frequency	20	80	230	400	170	70	30

We have used the term *frequency* rather than *number*, although it means the same thing. This table is called a **frequency table**. It is *almost* the relative frequency distribution for X except that we must replace frequencies by relative frequencies. (We did this in calculating relative frequencies in Chapter 8.) We start with the lowest measurement class. Because 20 of the 1,000 lawyers fall in this group, we have

$$P(X = 25,000) = \frac{20}{1,000} = .02.$$

We can calculate the remaining relative frequencies similarly to obtain the following distribution:

x	25,000	35,000	45,000	55,000	65,000	75,000	85,000
$P(X = x)$	.02	.08	.23	.40	.17	.07	.03

Note again the distinction between X and x: X stands for the random variable in question, whereas x stands for a specific value (25,000, 35,000, ..., or 85,000) of X.

EXAMPLE 5 **Probability Distribution: Greenhouse Gases**

The following table shows per capita emissions of greenhouse gases for the 30 countries with the highest per capita carbon dioxide emissions. (Emissions are rounded to the nearest 5 metric tons.)[1]

Country	Per Capita Emissions (metric tons)	Country	Per Capita Emissions (metric tons)
Qatar	45	Canada	15
Trinidad and Tobago	35	Russian Federation	15
Kuwait	30	Turkmenistan	10
Brunei Darussalam	25	Korea, Republic of	10
Aruba	25	Czech Republic	10
Oman	20	Finland	10
Luxembourg	20	Netherlands	10
United Arab Emirates	20	Equatorial Guinea	10
Saudi Arabia	20	Japan	10
Bahrain	20	Israel	10
United States	15	Norway	10
Kazakhstan	15	Souh Africa	10
Australia	15	Belgium	10
New Caledonia	15	Germany	10
Estonia	15	Poland	10

---

[1] Figures are based on 2011 data. Source: United Nations Millennium Development Goals Indicators, based on information from the U.S. Department of Energy's Carbon Dioxide Information Analysis Center (CDIAC) (http://mdgs.un.org).

Consider the experiment in which a country is selected at random from this list, and let X be the per capita carbon dioxide emissions for that country. Find the probability distribution of X, and graph it with a histogram. Use the probability distribution to compute $P(X \geq 20)$ (the probability that X is 20 or more), and interpret the result.

Solution The values of X are the possible emissions figures, which we can take to be 0, 5, 10, 15, ..., 45. In the table below, we first compute the frequency of each value of X by counting the number of countries that produce that per capita level of greenhouse gases. For instance, there are seven countries that have $X = 15$. Then we divide each frequency by the sample size $N = 30$ to obtain the probabilities.*

* Even though we are using the term "frequency," we are really calculating *modeled* probability based on the assumption of equally likely outcomes. In this context, the frequencies are the number of favorable outcomes for each value of X. (See the Q&A discussion at the end of Section 8.3.)

x	0	5	10	15	20	25	30	35	40	45
Frequency	0	0	13	7	5	2	1	1	0	1
$P(X = x)$	0	0	$\dfrac{13}{30}$	$\dfrac{7}{30}$	$\dfrac{5}{30}$	$\dfrac{2}{30}$	$\dfrac{1}{30}$	$\dfrac{1}{30}$	0	$\dfrac{1}{30}$

$P(X = x)$

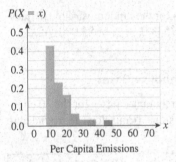

Per Capita Emissions

Figure 2

Figure 2 shows the resulting histogram.

Finally, we compute $P(X \geq 20)$, the probability of the event that X has a value of 20 or more, which is the sum of the probabilities $P(X = 20)$, $P(X = 25)$, and so on. From the table we obtain

$$P(X \geq 20) = \frac{5}{30} + \frac{2}{30} + \frac{1}{30} + \frac{1}{30} + 0 + \frac{1}{30} = \frac{10}{30} \approx .33.$$

Thus, there is an approximately 33% chance that a country randomly selected from the given list produces 20 or more metric tons per capita of carbon dioxide.

FAQs

Recognizing What to Use as a Random Variable and Deciding on Its Values

Q: *In an application, how, exactly, do I decide what to use as a random variable X?*

A: Be as systematic as possible: First, decide what the experiment is and what its sample space is. Then, on the basis of what is asked for in the application, complete the following sentence: "*X* assigns ____ to each outcome." For instance, "*X* assigns <u>the number of flavors</u> to each packet of gummy bears selected" or "*X* assigns <u>the average faculty salary</u> to each college selected."

Q: *Once I have decided what X should be, how do I decide what values to assign it?*

A: Ask yourself: What are the conceivable values I could get for *X*? Then choose a collection of values that includes all of these. For instance, if *X* is the number of heads obtained when a coin is tossed five times, then the possible values of *X* are 0, 1, 2, 3, 4, and 5. If *X* is the average faculty salary in dollars, rounded to the nearest $5,000, then possible values of *X* could be 20,000, 25,000, 30,000, and so on, up to the highest salary in your data.

9.1　EXERCISES

▼ more advanced　　◆ challenging
🔲 indicates exercises that should be solved using technology

In Exercises 1–10, classify the random variable X as finite, discrete infinite, or continuous, and indicate the values that X can take. [HINT: See Quick Examples 5–10.]

1. Roll two dice; X = the sum of the numbers facing up.

2. Open a 500-page book on a random page; X = the page number.

3. Select a stock at random; X = your profit, to the nearest dollar, if you purchase one share and sell it one year later.

4. Select an electric utility company at random; X = the exact amount of electricity, in gigawatt hours, it supplies in a year.

5. Look at the second hand of your watch; X is the time it reads in seconds.

6. Watch a soccer game; X = the total number of goals scored.

7. Watch a soccer game; X = the total number of goals scored, up to a maximum of 10.

8. Your class is given a mathematics exam worth 100 points; X is the average score, rounded to the nearest whole number.

9. According to quantum mechanics, the energy of an electron in a hydrogen atom can assume only the values $k/1$, $k/4$, $k/9$, $k/16$, . . . for a certain constant value k. X = the energy of an electron in a hydrogen atom.

10. According to classical mechanics, the energy of an electron in a hydrogen atom can assume any positive value. X = the energy of an electron in a hydrogen atom.

In Exercises 11–18, (a) say what an appropriate sample space is; (b) complete the following sentence: "X is the rule that assigns to each . . . "; and (c) list the values of X for all the outcomes. [HINT: See Example 1.]

11. X is the number of tails that come up when a coin is tossed twice.

12. X is the largest number of consecutive times heads comes up in a row when a coin is tossed three times.

13. X is the sum of the numbers that face up when two dice are rolled.

14. X is the value of the larger number when two dice are rolled.

15. X is the number of red marbles that Tonya has in her hand after she selects four marbles from a bag containing four red marbles and two green ones and then notes how many there are of each color.

16. X is the number of green marbles that Stej has in his hand after he selects four marbles from a bag containing three red marbles and two green ones and then notes how many there are of each color.

17. The mathematics final exam scores for the students in your study group are 89%, 85%, 95%, 63%, 92%, and 80%.

18. The capacities of the hard drives of your dormitory suite mates' computers are 1,000 GB, 1,500 GB, 2,000 GB, 2,500 GB, 3,000 GB, and 3,500 GB.

19. The random variable X has this probability distribution table:

x	2	4	6	8	10
$P(X = x)$	.1	.2	—	—	.1

a. Assuming that $P(X = 8) = P(X = 6)$, find each of the missing values. [HINT: See Quick Example 11.]

b. Calculate $P(X \geq 6)$ and $P(2 < X < 8)$.

20. The random variable X has the probability distribution table shown below:

x	−2	−1	0	1	2
$P(X = x)$	—	—	.4	.1	.1

a. Calculate $P(X \geq 0)$ and $P(X < 0)$. [HINT: See Quick Example 11.]

b. Assuming that $P(X = -2) = P(X = -1)$, find each of the missing values.

In Exercises 21–28, give the probability distribution for the indicated random variable, draw the corresponding histogram, and calculate the indicated probability. [HINT: See Example 3.]

21. A fair die is rolled, and X is the number facing up. Calculate $P(X < 5)$.

22. A fair die is rolled, and X is the square of the number facing up. Calculate $P(X > 9)$.

23. Three fair coins are tossed, and X is the square of the number of heads showing. Calculate $P(1 \leq X \leq 9)$.

24. Three fair coins are tossed, and X is the number of heads minus the number of tails. Calculate $P(-3 \leq X \leq -1)$.

25. A red die and a green die are rolled, and X is the sum of the numbers facing up. Calculate $P(X \neq 7)$.

26. A red die and a green die are rolled, and

$$X = \begin{cases} 0 & \text{if the numbers are the same} \\ 1 & \text{if the numbers are different.} \end{cases}$$

Calculate $P(X > 1)$.

27. ▼ A red die and a green die are rolled, and X is the larger of the two numbers facing up. Calculate $P(X \leq 3)$.

28. ▼ A red die and a green die are rolled, and X is the smaller of the two numbers facing up. Calculate $P(X \geq 4)$.

Applications

29. *2010 Income Distribution up to $100,000* The following table shows the distribution of household incomes in 2010 for a sample of 1,000 households in the United States with incomes up to $100,000:[2]

Income Bracket ($)	0–19,999	20,000–39,999	40,000–59,999	60,000–79,999	80,000–99,999
Households	240	290	180	170	120

a. Let X be the (rounded) midpoint of a bracket in which a household falls. Find the relative frequency distribution of X, and graph its histogram. [HINT: See Example 4.]

b. Shade the area of your histogram corresponding to the probability that a randomly selected U.S. household in the sample has a value of X above 50,000. What is this probability?

30. *2003 Income Distribution up to $100,000* Repeat Exercise 29, using the following data from a sample of 1,000 households in the United States in 2003:[3]

Income Bracket ($)	0–19,999	20,000–39,999	40,000–59,999	60,000–79,999	80,000–99,999
Households	270	280	200	150	100

31. *Population Age in Mexico* The following chart shows the ages of 250 randomly selected residents of Mexico:[4]

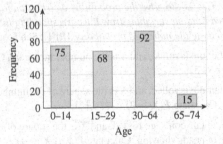

What is the associated random variable? Represent the data as a relative frequency distribution using the (rounded) midpoints of the given measurement classes. [HINT: See Example 4.]

32. *Population Age in the United States* Repeat Exercise 31, using the following chart, which shows the ages of 250 randomly selected residents of the United States:[5]

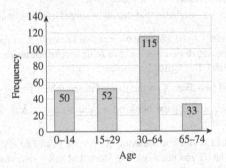

33. *Sport Utility Vehicles—Tow Ratings* The following table shows tow ratings (in pounds) for some popular sports utility vehicles in 2000:[6]

Vehicle	Tow Rating
Mercedes Grand Marquis V8	2,000
Jeep Wrangler I6	2,000
Ford Explorer V6	3,000
Dodge Dakota V6	4,000
Mitsubishi Montero V6	5,000
Ford Explorer V8	6,000
Dodge Durango V8	6,000
Dodge Ram 1500 V8	8,000
Ford Expedition V8	8,000
Hummer 2-Door Hardtop	8,000

Let X be the tow rating of a randomly chosen popular SUV from the list above.

a. What are the values of X?

b. Compute the frequency and probability distributions of X. [HINT: See Example 5.]

c. What is the probability that an SUV (from the list above) is rated to tow no more than 5,000 pounds?

34. *Housing Prices Going into the Real Estate Bubble* The following table shows the average percentage increase in the price of a house from 1980 to 2001 in nine regions of the United States:[7]

---

[2] Based on actual income distribution in 2010. Source: U.S. Census Bureau, Current Population Survey, 2010 American Community Survey (www.census.gov).

[3] Based on actual income distribution in 2003 (not adjusted for inflation). Source: U.S. Census Bureau, Current Population Survey, 2004 Annual Social and Economic Supplement (www.census.gov).

[4] Based on population distribution in 2010. Source: Instituto Nacional de Estadística y Geografía (www.inegi.org.mx).

[5] *Ibid.* (The data for the United States was also provided by the Instituto Nacional de Estadística y Geografía.)

[6] Tow ratings are for 2000 models and vary considerably within each model. Figures cited are rounded. For more detailed information, consult www.rvsafety.com/towrate2k.htm.

[7] Percentages are rounded to the nearest 25%. Source: Third Quarter 2001 House Price Index, released November 30, 2001, by the Office of Federal Housing Enterprise Oversight; available online at www.ofheo.gov/house/3q01hpi.pdf.

Region	Percent Increase
New England	300
Pacific	225
Middle Atlantic	225
South Atlantic	150
Mountain	150
West North Central	125
West South Central	75
East North Central	150
East South Central	125

Let X be the percentage increase in the price of a house in a randomly selected region.

a. What are the values of X?

b. Compute the frequency and probability distribution of X. [HINT: See Example 5.]

c. What is the probability that, in a randomly selected region, the percentage increase in the cost of a house exceeded 200%?

35. *Stock Market Gyrations* The following chart shows the day-by-day change, rounded to the nearest 100 points, in the Dow Jones Industrial Average during 20 successive business days around the start of the financial crisis in October 2008:[8]

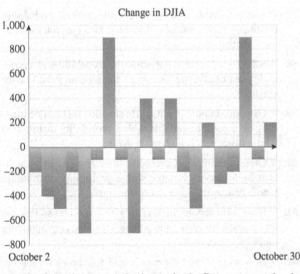

Change in DJIA

October 2   October 30

Let X be the (rounded) change in the Dow on a randomly selected day.

a. What are the values of X?

b. Compute the frequency and probability distribution of X. [HINT: See Example 5.]

c. What is the probability that, on a randomly selected day, the Dow decreased by more than 250 points?

36. *Stock Market Gyrations* Repeat Exercise 35 using the following chart for November–December 2008:[9]

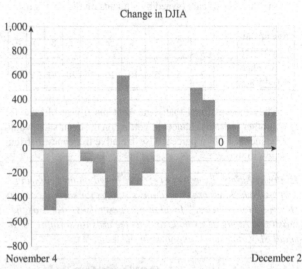

Change in DJIA

November 4   December 2

37. *Grade-Point Averages* The grade-point averages of the students in your mathematics class are

3.2, 3.5, 4.0, 2.9, 2.0, 3.3, 3.5, 2.9, 2.5, 2.0,
2.1, 3.2, 3.6, 2.8, 2.5, 1.9, 2.0, 2.2, 3.9, 4.0.

Use these raw data to construct a frequency table with the measurement classes 1.1–2.0, 2.1–3.0, 3.1–4.0, and find the probability distribution using the (rounded) midpoint values as the values of X. [HINT: See Example 5.]

38. *Test Scores* Your scores for the 20 surprise math quizzes last semester were (out of 10)

4.5, 9.5, 10.0, 3.5, 8.0, 9.5, 7.5, 6.5, 7.0, 8.0,
8.0, 8.5, 7.5, 7.0, 8.0, 9.0, 10.0, 8.5, 7.5, 8.0.

Use these raw data to construct a frequency table with the brackets 2.1–4.0, 4.1–6.0, 6.1–8.0, 8.1–10.0, and find the probability distribution using the (rounded) midpoint values as the values of X. [HINT: See Example 5.]

39. ▽ *Car Purchases* To persuade his parents to contribute to his new car fund, Carmine has spent the last week surveying the ages of 2,000 cars on campus. His findings are reflected in the following frequency table:

Age of Car (years)	0	1	2	3	4	5	6	7	8	9	10
Number of Cars	140	350	450	650	200	120	50	10	5	15	10

Carmine's jalopy is 6 years old. He would like to make the following claim to his parents: "x percent of students have cars newer than mine." Use a relative frequency distribution to find x.

[8] Source: http://finance.google.com.

[9] *Ibid.*

40. ▼ *Car Purchases* Carmine's parents, not convinced of his need for a new car, produced the following statistics showing the ages of cars owned by students on the dean's list:

Age of Car (years)	0	1	2	3	4	5	6	7	8	9	10
Number of Cars	0	2	5	5	10	10	15	20	20	20	40

They then claimed that if he kept his 6-year-old car for another year, his chances of getting on the dean's list would be increased by x percent. Use a relative frequency distribution to find x.

Highway Safety Exercises 41–50 are based on the following table, which shows crashworthiness ratings for several categories of motor vehicles.[10] *In all of these exercises, take X as the crash-test rating of a small car, Y as the crash-test rating for a small SUV, and so on, as shown in the table.*

		Overall Frontal Crash Test Rating			
	Number Tested	3 (Good)	2 (Acceptable)	1 (Marginal)	0 (Poor)
Small Cars, X	16	1	11	2	2
Small SUVs, Y	10	1	4	4	1
Medium SUVs, Z	15	3	5	3	4
Passenger Vans, U	13	3	0	3	7
Midsize Cars, V	15	3	5	0	7
Large Cars, W	19	9	5	3	2

41. Compute the relative frequency distribution for X.

42. Compute the relative frequency distribution for Y.

43. Compute $P(X \geq 2)$, and interpret the result.

44. Compute $P(Y \leq 1)$, and interpret the result.

45. Compare $P(Y \geq 2)$ and $P(Z \geq 2)$. What does the result suggest about SUVs?

46. Compare $P(V \geq 2)$ and $P(Z \geq 2)$. What does the result suggest?

47. ▼ Which of the six categories shown has the *lowest* probability of a Good rating?

48. ▼ Which of the six categories shown has the *highest* probability of a Poor rating?

49. ▼ You choose, at random, a small car and a small SUV. What is the probability that both will be rated at least 2?

---

[10] Ratings are by the Insurance Institute for Highway Safety. Sources: Oak Ridge National Laboratory: "An Analysis of the Impact of Sport Utility Vehicles in the United States," Stacy C. Davis, Lorena F. Truett (August 2000)/Insurance Institute for Highway Safety (www-cta.ornl .gov/Publications/Final SUV report.pdf, www.highwaysafety.org/ vehicle_ratings).

50. ▼ You choose, at random, a small car and a midsize car. What is the probability that both will be rated at most 1?

Exercises 51 and 52 assume familiarity with counting arguments and probability (see Section 8.4).

51. ▼ *Camping* Kent's Tents has four red tents and three green tents in stock. Karin selects four of them at random. Let X be the number of red tents she selects. Give the probability distribution, and find $P(X \geq 2)$.

52. ▼ *Camping* Kent's Tents has five green knapsacks and four yellow ones in stock. Curt selects four of them at random. Let X be the number of green knapsacks he selects. Give the probability distribution, and find $P(X \leq 2)$.

53. ◆ *Testing Your Calculator* Use your calculator or computer to generate a sequence of 100 random digits in the range 0–9, and test the random number generator for uniformness by drawing the distribution histogram.

54. ◆ *Testing Your Dice* Repeat Exercise 53, but this time, use a die to generate a sequence of 50 random numbers in the range 1–6.

Communication and Reasoning Exercises

55. Are all infinite random variables necessarily continuous? Explain.

56. Are all continuous random variables necessarily infinite? Explain.

57. If you are unable to compute the (theoretical) probability distribution for a random variable X, how can you estimate the distribution?

58. What do you expect to happen to the probabilities in a probability distribution as you make the measurement classes smaller?

59. ▼ Give an example of a real-life situation that can be modeled by a random variable with a probability distribution whose histogram is highest on the left.

60. ▼ Give an example of a real-life situation that can be modeled by a random variable with a probability distribution whose histogram is highest on the right.

61. ▼ How wide should the bars in a histogram be so that the area of each bar equals the probability of the corresponding range of values of X?

62. ▼ How wide should the bars in a histogram be so that the probability $P(a \leq X \leq b)$ equals the area of the corresponding portion of the histogram?

63. ▼ Give at least one scenario in which you might prefer to model the number of pages in a randomly selected book using a continuous random variable rather than a discrete random variable.

64. ▼ Give at least one scenario in which you might prefer to model a temperature using a discrete random variable rather than a continuous random variable.

9.2 Bernoulli Trials and Binomial Random Variables

Your electronics production plant produces video game joysticks. Unfortunately, quality control at the plant leaves much to be desired, and 10% of the joysticks the plant produces are defective. A large corporation has expressed interest in adopting your product for its new game console, and today an inspection team will be visiting to test video game joysticks as they come off the assembly line. If the team tests five joysticks, what is the probability that none will be defective? What is the probability that more than one will be defective?

In this scenario we are interested in the following, which is an example of a particular type of finite random variable called a **binomial random variable**: Think of the experiment as a sequence of five "trials" (in each trial the inspection team chooses one joystick at random and tests it) each with two possible outcomes: "success" (a defective joystick) and "failure" (a nondefective one).[*] If we now take X to be the number of successes (defective joysticks) the inspection team finds, we can recast the questions above as follows: Find $P(X = 0)$ and $P(X > 1)$.

[*] These are customary names for the two possible outcomes, and they often do not indicate actual success or failure at anything. "Success" is the label we give the outcome of interest—in this case, finding a defective joystick.

[†] Jakob Bernoulli (1654–1705) was one of the pioneers of probability theory.

Bernoulli Trial

A **Bernoulli**[†] **trial** is an experiment that has two possible outcomes, called **success** and **failure**. If the probability of success is p, then the probability of failure is $q = 1 - p$.

Visualizing a Bernoulli Trial

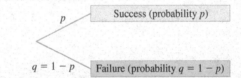

Tossing a coin three times is an example of a **sequence of independent Bernoulli trials**: a sequence of Bernoulli trials in which the outcomes in any one trial are independent (in the sense of Chapter 8) of those in any other trial and in which the probability of success is the same for all the trials.

Quick Examples

1. Roll a die, and take success to be the event that you roll a 6. Then $p = 1/6$ and $q = 5/6$. Rolling the die 10 times is then an example of a sequence of 10 independent Bernoulli trials.

2. Provide a property with flood insurance for 20 years, and take success to be the event that the property is flooded during a particular year. Observing whether or not the property is flooded each year for 20 years is then an example of 20 independent Bernoulli trials (assuming that the occurrence of flooding one year is independent of whether there was flooding in earlier years).

3. You know that 60% of all bond funds will depreciate in value next year. Take success to be the event that a randomly chosen fund depreciates next year. Then $p = .6$ and $q = .4$. Choosing five funds at random for your portfolio from a very large number of possible funds is, approximately,[§] an example of five independent Bernoulli trials.

[§] Choosing a "loser" (a fund that will depreciate next year) slightly depletes the pool of "losers" and hence slightly decreases the probability of choosing another one. However, the fact that the pool of funds is very large means that this decrease is extremely small. Hence, p is very nearly constant.

4. Suppose that E is an event in an experiment with sample space S. Then we can think of the experiment as a Bernoulli trial with two outcomes; success if E occurs and failure if E' occurs. The probability of success is then

$$p = P(E),$$ Success is the occurrence of E.

and the probability of failure is

$$q = P(E') = 1 - P(E) = 1 - p.$$ Failure is the occurrence of E'.

Repeating the experiment 30 times, say, is then an example of 30 independent Bernoulli trials.

Note Quick Example 4 tells us that Bernoulli trials are not very special kinds of experiments; in fact, we are performing a Bernoulli trial every time we repeat *any* experiment and observe whether a specific event E occurs. Thinking of an experiment in this way amounts, mathematically, to thinking of $\{E, E'\}$ as our sample space (E = success, E' = failure). ∎

Binomial Random Variable

A **binomial random variable** is one that counts the number of successes in a sequence of independent Bernoulli trials, where the number of trials is fixed.

Visualizing a Binomial Random Variable

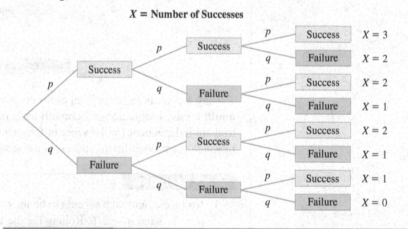

Quick Examples

5. Roll a die 10 times; X is the number of times you roll a 6.

6. Provide a property with flood insurance for 20 years; X is the number of years, during the 20-year period, during which the property is flooded (assuming that the occurrence of flooding in any year is independent of whether there was flooding in earlier years).

7. You know that 60% of all bond funds will depreciate in value next year, and you randomly select four from a very large number of possible choices; X is the number of bond funds you hold that will depreciate next year. (X is approximately binomial; see the margin note for Quick Example 3.)

| EXAMPLE 1 | **Probability Distribution of a Binomial Random Variable** |

Suppose that we have a possibly unfair coin with the probability of heads p and the probability of tails $q = 1 - p$.

a. Let X be the number of heads you get in a sequence of five tosses. Find $P(X = 2)$.

b. Let X be the number of heads you get in a sequence of n tosses. Find $P(X = x)$.

Solution

a. We are looking for the probability of getting exactly two heads in a sequence of five tosses. Let's start with a simpler question: What is the probability that we will get the sequence HHTTT?

The probability that the first toss will come up heads is p.

The probability that the second toss will come up heads is also p.

The probability that the third toss will come up tails is q.

The probability that the fourth toss will come up tails is q.

The probability that the fifth toss will come up tails is q.

The probability that the first toss will be heads *and* the second will be heads *and* the third will be tails *and* the fourth will be tails *and* the fifth will be tails equals the probability of the *intersection* of these five events. Because these are independent events, the probability of the intersection is the product of the probabilities, which is

$$p \times p \times q \times q \times q = p^2 q^3.$$

Now HHTTT is only one of several outcomes with two heads and three tails. Two others are HTHTT and TTTHH. How many such outcomes are there altogether? This is the number of "words" with two H's and three T's, and we know from Chapter 7 that the answer is $C(5, 2) = 10$.

Each of the 10 outcomes with two H's and three T's has the same probability: $p^2 q^3$. (Why?) Thus, the probability of getting one of these 10 outcomes is the probability of the union of all these (mutually exclusive) events, and we saw in Chapter 8 that this is just the sum of the probabilities. In other words, the probability we are after is

$$P(X = 2) = p^2 q^3 + p^2 q^3 + \cdots + p^2 q^3 \qquad C(5, 2) \text{ times}$$
$$= C(5, 2) p^2 q^3.$$

The structure of this formula is as follows:

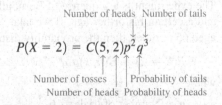

b. What we did using the numbers 5 and 2 in part (a) works as well in general. For the general case, with n tosses and x heads, replace 5 with n and replace 2 with x to get

$$P(X = x) = C(n, x) p^x q^{n-x}.$$

(Note that the exponent of q is the number of tails, which is $n - x$.)

The calculation in Example 1 applies to any binomial random variable, so we can say the following.

Probability Distribution of Binomial Random Variables

If X is the number of successes in a sequence of n independent Bernoulli trials, then

$$P(X = x) = C(n, x)p^x q^{n-x},$$

where

$n = $ Number of trials

$p = $ Probability of success

$q = $ Probability of failure $= 1 - p$.

Quick Example

8. If you roll a fair die five times, the probability of throwing exactly two 6s is

$$P(X = 2) = C(5, 2) \left(\frac{1}{6}\right)^2 \left(\frac{5}{6}\right)^3 = 10 \times \frac{1}{36} \times \frac{125}{216} \approx .1608.$$

Here, we used $n = 5$ and $p = 1/6$, the probability of rolling a 6 on one roll of the die.

EXAMPLE 2 **Aging**

By 2030 the probability that a randomly chosen resident in the United States will be 65 years old or older is projected[11] to be .2.

a. What is the probability that, in a randomly selected sample of six U.S. residents, exactly four of them will be 65 or older?

b. If X is the number of people aged 65 or older in a sample of six, construct the probability distribution of X and plot its histogram.

c. Compute $P(X \le 2)$.

d. Compute $P(X \ge 2)$.

Solution

a. The experiment is a sequence of Bernoulli trials; in each trial we select a person and ascertain his or her age. If we take "success" to mean selection of a person aged 65 or older, then the probability distribution is

$$P(X = x) = C(n, x)p^x q^{n-x},$$

where

$n = $ Number of trials $= 6$

$p = $ Probability of success $= .2$

$q = $ Probability of failure $= .8$.

---

[11] Source: U.S. Census Bureau, Decennial Census, Population Estimates and Projections (www.agingstats.gov/agingstatsdotnet/Main_Site/Data/2012_Documents/Population.aspx).

So

$$P(X = 4) = C(6, 4)(.2)^4(.8)^2$$
$$= 15 \times .0016 \times .64 = .01536.$$

b. We have already computed $P(X = 4)$. Here are all the calculations:

$$P(X = 0) = C(6, 0)(.2)^0(.8)^6$$
$$= 1 \times 1 \times .262144 = .262144$$

$$P(X = 1) = C(6, 1)(.2)^1(.8)^5$$
$$= 6 \times .2 \times .32768 = .393216$$

$$P(X = 2) = C(6, 2)(.2)^2(.8)^4$$
$$= 15 \times .04 \times .4096 = .24576$$

$$P(X = 3) = C(6, 3)(.2)^3(.8)^3$$
$$= 20 \times .008 \times .512 = .08192$$

$$P(X = 4) = C(6, 4)(.2)^4(.8)^2$$
$$= 15 \times .0016 \times .64 = .01536$$

$$P(X = 5) = C(6, 5)(.2)^5(.8)^1$$
$$= 6 \times .00032 \times .8 = .001536$$

$$P(X = 6) = C(6, 6)(.2)^6(.8)^0$$
$$= 1 \times .000064 \times 1 = .000064.$$

The probability distribution is therefore as follows:

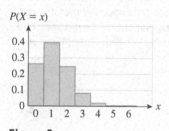

Figure 3

x	0	1	2	3	4	5	6
$P(X = x)$	.262144	.393216	.24576	.08192	.01536	.001536	.000064

Figure 3 shows its histogram.

c. $P(X \leq 2)$—the probability that the number of people selected who are at least 65 years old is either 0, 1, or 2—is the probability of the union of these events and is thus the sum of the three probabilities:

$$P(X \leq 2) = P(X = 0) + P(X = 1) + P(X = 2)$$
$$= .262144 + .393216 + .24576$$
$$= .90112.$$

d. To compute $P(X \geq 2)$, we *could* compute the sum

$$P(X \geq 2) = P(X = 2) + P(X = 3) + P(X = 4) + P(X = 5) + P(X = 6),$$

but it is far easier to compute the probability of the complement of the event,

$$P(X < 2) = P(X = 0) + P(X = 1)$$
$$= .262144 + .393216 = .65536$$

and then subtract the answer from 1:

$$P(X \geq 2) = 1 - P(X < 2)$$
$$= 1 - .65536 = .34464.$$

Using Technology

Technology can be used to replicate the histogram in Example 2.

TI-83/84 Plus
Y= screen: Y₁=6 nCr
X*0.2^X*0.8^(6-X)
[2ND] [TBLSET] Set "Indpnt" to "Ask".
[2ND] [TABLE] Enter x-values
0, 1, . . . , 6.
[More details in the Technology Guide.]

Spreadsheet
Headings x and P(X = x) in A1, B1
x-values 0, 1, . . . , 6 in A2–A8
=BINOMDIST(A2,6,.2,0)
in B2
Copy down to B6.
[More details in the Technology Guide.]

Website
www.WanerMath.com
→ Online Utilities
→ Binomial Distribution Utility
Enter $n = 6$ and $p = .2$, and press "Generate Distribution".

FAQs

Terminology and Recognizing When to Use the Binomial Distribution

Q: *What is the difference between Bernoulli trials and a binomial random variable?*

A: A Bernoulli trial is a type of experiment, whereas a binomial random variable is the resulting kind of random variable. More precisely, if your experiment consists of performing a sequence of *n* Bernoulli trials (think of throwing a dart *n* times at random points on a dartboard hoping to hit the bull's-eye), then the random variable *X* that counts the number of successes (the number of times you actually hit the bull's-eye) is a binomial random variable.

Q: *How do I recognize when a situation gives a binomial random variable?*

A: Make sure that the experiment consists of a sequence of independent Bernoulli trials, that is, a sequence of a fixed number of trials of an experiment that has two outcomes, where the outcome of each trial does not depend on the outcomes in previous trials and where the probability of success is the same for all the trials. For instance, repeatedly throwing a dart at a dartboard hoping to hit the bull's-eye does not constitute a sequence of Bernoulli trials if you adjust your aim each time depending on the outcome of your previous attempt. This dart-throwing experiment can be modeled by a sequence of Bernoulli trials if you make no adjustments after each attempt and your aim does not improve (or deteriorate) with time.

9.2 EXERCISES

▼ more advanced ◆ challenging
T indicates exercises that should be solved using technology

In Exercises 1–10, you are performing five independent Bernoulli trials with p = .1 and q = .9. Calculate the probability of the stated outcome. Check your answer using technology. [HINT: See Quick Example 8.]

1. Two successes

2. Three successes

3. No successes

4. No failures

5. All successes

6. All failures

7. At most two successes

8. At least four successes

9. At least three successes

10. At most three successes

In Exercises 11–18, X is a binomial variable with n = 6 and p = .4. Compute the given probability. Check your answer using technology. [HINT: See Example 2.]

11. $P(X = 3)$

12. $P(X = 4)$

13. $P(X \leq 2)$

14. $P(X \leq 1)$

15. $P(X \geq 5)$

16. $P(X \geq 4)$

17. $P(1 \leq X \leq 3)$

18. $P(3 \leq X \leq 5)$

In Exercises 19 and 20, graph the histogram of the given binomial distribution. Check your answer using technology.

19. $n = 5, p = \frac{1}{4}, q = \frac{3}{4}$

20. $n = 5, p = \frac{1}{3}, q = \frac{2}{3}$

In Exercises 21 and 22, graph the histogram of the given binomial distribution, and compute the given quantity, indicating the corresponding region on the graph.

21. $n = 4, p = \frac{1}{3}, q = \frac{2}{3}; P(X \leq 2)$

22. $n = 4, p = \frac{1}{4}, q = \frac{3}{4}; P(X \leq 1)$

Applications

23. *Internet Addiction* The probability that a randomly chosen person in the Netherlands connects to the Internet immediately upon waking[12] is approximately .25. What is the probability that, in a randomly selected sample of five people, two connect to the Internet immediately upon waking? [HINT: See Example 2.]

24. *Alien Retirement* The probability that a randomly chosen citizen-entity of Cygnus is of pension age[13] is approximately .8. What is the probability that, in a randomly selected sample of four citizen-entities, all of them are of pension age? [HINT: See Example 2.]

---

[12] Source: *Webwereld* November 17, 2008 (http://webwereld.nl/article/view/id/53599).

[13] The retirement age in Cygnus is 12,000 bootlags, which is equivalent to approximately 20 minutes Earth time.

25. *1990s Internet Stock Boom* According to a July 1999 article in *The New York Times*,[14] venture capitalists had this "rule of thumb": The probability that an Internet start-up company will be a "stock market success" resulting in "spectacular profits for early investors" is .2. If you were a venture capitalist who invested in 10 Internet start-up companies, what was the probability that at least 1 of them would be a stock market success? (Round your answer to four decimal places.)

26. *1990s Internet Stock Boom* According to the article cited in Exercise 25, 13.5% of Internet stocks that entered the market in 1999 ended up trading below their initial offering prices. If you were an investor who purchased five Internet stocks at their initial offering prices, what was the probability that at least four of them would end up trading at or above their initial offering price? (Round your answer to four decimal places.)

27. *Job Training* *(from the GRE Exam in Economics)* In a large on-the-job training program, half of the participants are female and half are male. In a random sample of three participants, what is the probability that an investigator will draw at least one male?

28. *Job Training* *(based on a question from the GRE Exam in Economics)* In a large on-the-job training program, half of the participants are female and half are male. In a random sample of five participants, what is the probability that an investigator will draw at least two males?

29. *Manufacturing* Your manufacturing plant produces air bags, and it is known that 10% of them are defective. Five air bags are tested.
a. Find the probability that three of them are defective.
b. Find the probability that at least two of them are defective.

30. *Manufacturing* Compute the probability distribution of the binomial variable described in Exercise 29, and use it to compute the probability that if five air bags are tested, at least one will be defective and at least one will not.

31. *Teenage Pastimes* According to a study,[15] the probability that a randomly selected teenager watched a rented video at least once during a week was .71. What is the probability that at least 8 teenagers in a group of 10 watched a rented movie at least once last week?

32. *Other Teenage Pastimes* According to the study cited in Exercise 31, the probability that a randomly selected teenager studied at least once during a week was only .52. What is the probability that less than half of the students in your study group of 10 have studied in the last week?

33. *Subprime Mortgages during the Housing Bubble* In November 2008[16] the probability that a randomly selected subprime home mortgage in Florida was in foreclosure was .24. Choose 10 subprime home mortgages at random.
a. What is the probability that exactly 5 of them were in foreclosure?
b. ▯ Use technology to generate the probability distribution for the associated binomial random variable.
c. Fill in the blank: If 10 subprime home mortgages were chosen at random, the number of them most likely to have been in foreclosure was _____.

34. *Subprime Mortgages during the Housing Bubble* In November 2008[17] the probability that a randomly selected subprime home mortgage in Texas was current in its payments was .67. Choose 10 subprime home mortgages at random.
a. What is the probability that exactly 4 of them were current?
b. ▯ Use technology to generate the probability distribution for the associated binomial random variable.
c. Fill in the blank: If 10 subprime home mortgages were chosen at random, the number of them most likely to have been current was _____.

35. ▼ *Triple Redundancy* To ensure reliable performance of vital computer systems, aerospace engineers sometimes employ the technique of "triple redundancy," in which three identical computers are installed in a space vehicle. If one of the three computers gives results different from the other two, it is assumed to be malfunctioning and is ignored. This technique will work as long as no more than one computer malfunctions. Assuming that an onboard computer is 99% reliable (that is, the probability of its failing is .01), what is the probability that at least two of the three computers will malfunction?

36. ▼ *IQ Scores* Mensa is a club for people who have high IQ scores. To qualify, your IQ must be at least 132, putting you in the top 2% of the general population. If a group of 10 people are chosen at random, what is the probability that at least 2 of them qualify for Mensa?

37. ▯ ▼ *Standardized Tests* Assume that on a standardized test of 100 questions, a person has a probability of 80% of answering any particular question correctly. Find the probability of correctly answering between 75 and 85 questions, inclusive. (Assume independence, and round your answer to four decimal places.)

38. ▯ ▼ *Standardized Tests* Assume that on a standardized test of 100 questions, a person has a probability of 80% of answering any particular question correctly. Find the probability of correctly answering at least 90 questions. (Assume independence, and round your answer to four decimal places.)

39. ▯ ▼ *Product Testing* It is known that 43% of all the ZeroFat hamburger patties produced by your factory actually contain

---

[14] "Not All Hit It Rich in the Internet Gold Rush," *New York Times*, July 20, 1999, p. A1.

[15] Sources: Rand Youth Poll/Teen-Age Research Unlimited/*New York Times*, March 14, 1998, p. D1.

[16] Source: Federal Reserve Bank of New York (www.newyorkfed.org/regional/subprime.html).

[17] *Ibid.*

more than 10 grams of fat. Compute the probability distribution for $n = 50$ Bernoulli trials.

a. What is the most likely value for the number of burgers in a sample of 50 that contain more than 10 grams of fat?

b. Complete the following sentence: There is an approximately 71% chance that a batch of 50 ZeroFat patties contains ____ or more patties with more than 10 grams of fat.

c. Compare the graphs of the distributions for $n = 50$ trials and $n = 20$ trials. What do you notice?

40. ▼ *Product Testing* It is known that 65% of all the ZeroCal hamburger patties produced by your factory actually contain more than 1,000 calories. Compute the probability distribution for $n = 50$ Bernoulli trials.

a. What is the most likely value for the number of burgers in a sample of 50 that contain more than 1,000 calories?

b. Complete the following sentence: There is an approximately 73% chance that a batch of 50 ZeroCal patties contains ____ or more patties with more than 1,000 calories.

c. Compare the graphs of the distributions for $n = 50$ trials and $n = 20$ trials. What do you notice?

41. ▼ *Quality Control* A manufacturer of light bulbs chooses bulbs at random from its assembly line for testing. If the probability of a bulb's being bad is .01, how many bulbs does the manufacturer need to test before the probability of finding at least one bad one rises to more than .5? (You may have to use trial and error to solve this.)

42. ▼ *Quality Control* A manufacturer of light bulbs chooses bulbs at random from its assembly line for testing. If the probability of a bulb's being bad is .01, how many bulbs does the manufacturer need to test before the probability of finding at least two bad ones rises to more than .5? (You may have to use trial and error to solve this.)

43. ▼ *Highway Safety* According to a study,[18] a male driver in the United States will average 562 accidents per 100 million miles. Regard an n-mile trip as a sequence of n Bernoulli trials with "success" corresponding to having an accident during a particular mile. What is the probability that a male driver will have an accident in a 1-mile trip?

44. ▼ *Highway Safety:* According to the study cited in Exercise 43, a female driver in the United States will average 611 accidents per 100 million miles. Regard an n-mile trip as a sequence of n Bernoulli trials with "success" corresponding to having an accident during a particular mile. What is the probability that a female driver will have an accident in a 1-mile trip?

45. ◆ *Mad Cow Disease* In March 2004 the U.S. Department of Agriculture announced plans to test approximately 243,000 slaughtered cows per year for mad cow disease (bovine spongiform encephalopathy).[19] When announcing the plan, the Agriculture Department stated that "by the laws of probability, that many tests should detect mad cow disease even if it is present in only 5 cows out of the 45 million in the nation."[20] Test the Department's claim by computing the probability that, if only 5 out of 45 million cows had mad cow disease, at least 1 cow would test positive in a year (assuming that the testing was done randomly).

46. ◆ *Mad Cow Disease* According to the article cited in Exercise 45, only 223,000 of the cows being tested for bovine spongiform encephalopathy were to be "downer cows," that is, cows unable to walk to their slaughter. Assuming that just one downer cow in 500,000 is infected on average, use a binomial distribution to find the probability that two or more cows would test positive in a year. Your associate claims that "by the laws of probability, that many tests should detect at least two cases of mad cow disease even if it is present in only two cows out of a million downers." Comment on that claim.

Communication and Reasoning Exercises

47. A soccer player is more likely to score on his second shot if he was successful on his first. Can we model a succession of shots a player takes as a sequence of Bernoulli trials? Explain.

48. A soccer player takes repeated shots on goal. What assumption must we make if we want to model a succession of shots by a player as a sequence of Bernoulli trials?

49. Your friend just told you that "misfortunes always occur in threes." If life is just a sequence of Bernoulli trials, is this possible? Explain.

50. Suppose an experiment consists of repeatedly (every week) checking whether your graphing calculator battery has died. Is this a sequence of Bernoulli trials? Explain.

51. In an experiment with sample space S, a certain event E has a probability p of occurring. What has this scenario to do with Bernoulli trials?

52. An experiment consists of removing a gummy bear from a bag originally containing 10 and then eating it. Regard eating a lime-flavored bear as success. Repeating the experiment five times is a sequence of Bernoulli trials—right?

53. ▼ Why is the following not a binomial random variable? Select, without replacement, five marbles from a bag containing six red marbles and two blue ones, and let X be the number of red marbles you have selected.

54. ▼ By contrast with Exercise 53, why can the following be modeled by a binomial random variable? Select, without replacement, 5 electronic components from a batch of 10,000 in which 1,000 are defective, and let X be the number of defective components you select.

[18] Data are based on a report by the National Highway Traffic Safety Administration released in January, 1996. Source for data: U.S. Department of Transportation/*New York Times*, April 9, 1999, p. F1.

[19] Source: *New York Times*, March 17, 2004, p. A19.

[20] As stated in the *New York Times* article.

9.3   Measures of Central Tendency

Mean, Median, and Mode of a Set of Data

One day you decide to measure the popularity rating of your statistics instructor, Mr. Pelogrande. Ideally, you should poll all of Mr. Pelogrande's students, which is what statisticians would refer to as the **population**. However, it would be difficult to poll all the members of the population in question. (Mr. Pelogrande teaches more than 400 students.) Instead, you decide to survey 10 of his students, chosen at random, and ask them to rate Mr. Pelogrande on a scale of 0–100. The survey results in the following set of data:

$$60, 50, 55, 0, 100, 90, 40, 20, 40, 70.$$

Such a collection of data is called a **sample**, because the 10 people polled represent only a (small) sample of Mr. Pelogrande's students. We should think of the individual scores $60, 50, 55, \ldots$ as values of a random variable: Choose one of Mr. Pelogrande's students at random, and let X be the rating the student gives to Mr. Pelogrande.

How do we distill a single measurement, or **statistic**, from this sample that would describe Mr. Pelogrande's popularity? Perhaps the most commonly used statistic is the **average**, or **mean**, which is computed by adding the scores and dividing the sum by the number of scores in the sample:

$$\text{Sample mean} = \frac{60 + 50 + 55 + 0 + 100 + 90 + 40 + 20 + 40 + 70}{10}$$

$$= \frac{525}{10} = 52.5.$$

We might then conclude, on the basis of the sample, that Mr. Pelogrande's average popularity rating is about 52.5. The usual notation for the sample mean is $\bar{x}$, and the formula that we use to compute it is

$$\bar{x} = \frac{x_1 + x_2 + \cdots + x_n}{n},$$

where $x_1, x_2, \ldots, x_n$ are the values of X in the sample.

A convenient way of writing the sum that appears in the numerator is to use **summation** or **sigma notation**. We write the sum $x_1 + x_2 + \cdots + x_n$ as

$$\sum_{i=1}^{n} x_i.$$

$\sum_{i=1}^{n}$ by itself stands for "the sum, from $i = 1$ to n."

$\sum_{i=1}^{n} x_i$ stands for "the sum of the x_i, from $i = 1$ to n."

We think of i as taking on the values $1, 2, \ldots, n$ in turn, making x_i equal $x_1, x_2, \ldots, x_n$ in turn, and we then add up these values.

Visualizing the Mean

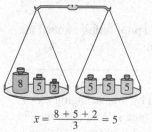

$$\bar{x} = \frac{8 + 5 + 2}{3} = 5$$

Sample and Mean

A **sample** is a sequence of values (or scores) of a random variable X. (The process of collecting such a sequence is sometimes called **sampling** X.) The **sample mean** is the average of the values, or **scores**, in the sample. To compute the sample mean, we use the following formula:

$$\bar{x} = \frac{x_1 + x_2 + \cdots + x_n}{n} = \frac{\sum_{i=1}^{n} x_i}{n}$$

or simply

$$\bar{x} = \frac{\sum_i x_i}{n}. \qquad \text{$\sum_i$ stands for "sum over all i."}^{*}$$

* In Section 1.4 we simply wrote $\sum x$ for the sum of all the x_i, but here we will use the subscripts to make it easier to interpret formulas in this and the next section.

† When we talk about *populations*, the understanding is that the underlying experiment consists of selecting a member of a given population and ascertaining the value of X.

Here, n is the **sample size** (number of scores), and $x_1, x_2, \ldots, x_n$ are the individual values.

If the sample $x_1, x_2, \ldots, x_n$ consists of all the values of X from the entire population† (for instance, the ratings given Mr. Pelogrande by *all* of his students), we refer to the mean as the **population mean**, and write it as μ (Greek "mu") instead of $\bar{x}$.

Quick Examples

1. The mean of the sample 1, 2, 3, 4, 5 is $\bar{x} = 3$.

2. The mean of the sample $-1, 0, 2$ is $\bar{x} = \dfrac{-1 + 0 + 2}{3} = \dfrac{1}{3}$.

3. The mean of the population $-3, -3, 0, 0, 1$ is

$$\mu = \frac{-3 - 3 + 0 + 0 + 1}{5} = -1.$$

Note: Sample Mean versus Population Mean Determining a population mean can be difficult or even impossible. For instance, computing the mean household income for the United States would entail recording the income of every single household in the United States. Instead of attempting to do this, we usually use sample means instead. The larger the sample used, the more accurately we expect the sample mean to approximate the population mean. Estimating how accurately a sample mean based on a given sample size approximates the population mean is possible, but we will not go into that in this book. ■

The mean $\bar{x}$ is an attempt to describe where the "center" of the sample is. It is therefore called a **measure of central tendency**. There are two other common measures of central tendency: the "middle score," or **median**, and the "most frequent score," or **mode**. These are defined as follows.

Median and Mode

The **sample median** m is the middle score (in the case of an odd-size sample), or average of the two middle scores (in the case of an even-size sample) when the scores in a sample are arranged in ascending order.

A **sample mode** is a score that appears most often in the collection. (There may be more than one mode in a sample.)

As before, we refer to the **population median** and **population mode** if the sample consists of the data from the entire population.

Visualizing the Median and Mode

Median = Middle score = 4

Mode = Most frequent score = 2

Quick Examples

4. The sample median of 2, −3, −1, 4, 2 is found by first arranging the scores in ascending order: −3, −1, 2, 2, 4 and then selecting the middle

(third) score: $m = 2$. The sample mode is also 2 because this is the score that appears most often.

5. The sample 2, 5, 6, −1, 0, 6 has median $m = (2 + 5)/2 = 3.5$ and mode 6.

The *mean* tends to give more weight to scores that are farther away from the center than does the median. For example, if you take the largest score in a collection of more than two numbers and make it larger, the mean will increase but the median will remain the same. For this reason the median is often preferred for collections that contain a wide range of scores. The mode can sometimes lie far from the center and is therefore used less often as an indication of where the "center" of a sample lies.

EXAMPLE 1	Teenage Spending in the 1990s

A 10-year survey of spending patterns of U.S. teenagers in the 1990s yielded the following figures (in billions of dollars spent in a year):[21] 90, 90, 85, 80, 80, 80, 80, 85, 90, 100. Compute and interpret the mean, median, and mode, and illustrate the data on a graph.

Solution The *mean* is given by

$$\bar{x} = \frac{\sum_i x_i}{n}$$

$$= \frac{90 + 90 + 85 + 80 + 80 + 80 + 80 + 85 + 90 + 100}{10} = \frac{860}{10} = 86.$$

Thus, spending by teenagers averaged $86 billion per year.

For the *median* we arrange the sample data in ascending order:

80, 80, 80, 80, 85, 85, 90, 90, 90, 100.

We then take the average of the two middle scores:

$$m = \frac{85 + 85}{2} = 85.$$

This means that in half the years in question, teenagers spent $85 billion or less, and in half they spent $85 billion or more.

For the *mode* we choose the score (or scores) that occurs most frequently: 80. Thus, teenagers spent $80 billion per year more often than any other amount.

The frequency histogram in Figure 4 illustrates these three measures.

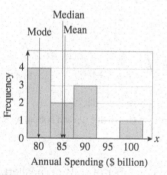

Figure 4

➡ **Before we go on . . .** There is a nice geometric interpretation of the difference between the median and mode: The median line shown in Figure 4 divides the total area of the histogram into two equal pieces, whereas the mean line passes through its "center of gravity"; if you placed the histogram on a knife-edge along the mean line, it would balance. ∎

Expected Value of a Finite Random Variable

Now, instead of looking at a sample of values of a given random variable, let us look at the probability distribution of the random variable itself and see if we can predict

[21] Spending figures are rounded, and cover the years 1988 through 1997. Source: Rand Youth Poll/Teen-Age Research Unlimited/*New York Times*, March 14, 1998, p. D1.

the sample mean without actually taking a sample. This prediction is what we call the *expected value* of the random variable.

EXAMPLE 2 **Expected Value of a Random Variable**

Suppose you roll a fair die a large number of times. What do you expect to be the average of the numbers that face up?

Solution Suppose we take a sample of n rolls of the die (where n is large). Because the probability of rolling a 1 is 1/6, we would expect that we would roll a 1 one sixth of the time, or $n/6$ times. Similarly, each other number should also appear $n/6$ times. The frequency table should then look like this:

x	1	2	3	4	5	6
Number of Times x Is Rolled (Frequency)	$\dfrac{n}{6}$	$\dfrac{n}{6}$	$\dfrac{n}{6}$	$\dfrac{n}{6}$	$\dfrac{n}{6}$	$\dfrac{n}{6}$

Note that we would not really expect the scores to be evenly distributed in practice, although for very large values of n we would expect the frequencies to vary only by a small percentage. To calculate the sample mean, we would add up all the scores and divide by the sample size. Now, the table tells us that there are $n/6$ ones, $n/6$ twos, $n/6$ threes, and so on, up to $n/6$ sixes. Adding these all up gives

$$\sum_i x_i = \frac{n}{6} \cdot 1 + \frac{n}{6} \cdot 2 + \frac{n}{6} \cdot 3 + \frac{n}{6} \cdot 4 + \frac{n}{6} \cdot 5 + \frac{n}{6} \cdot 6.$$

(Notice that we can obtain this number by multiplying the frequencies by the values of X and then adding.) Thus, the mean is

$$\bar{x} = \frac{\sum_i x_i}{n}$$

$$= \frac{\frac{n}{6} \cdot 1 + \frac{n}{6} \cdot 2 + \frac{n}{6} \cdot 3 + \frac{n}{6} \cdot 4 + \frac{n}{6} \cdot 5 + \frac{n}{6} \cdot 6}{n}$$

$$= \frac{1}{6} \cdot 1 + \frac{1}{6} \cdot 2 + \frac{1}{6} \cdot 3 + \frac{1}{6} \cdot 4 + \frac{1}{6} \cdot 5 + \frac{1}{6} \cdot 6 \quad \text{Divide top and bottom by } n.$$

$$= 3.5.$$

This is the average value we expect to get after a large number of rolls or, in short, the **expected value** of a roll of the die. More precisely, we say that this is the expected value of the random variable X whose value is the number we get by rolling a die. Notice that n, the number of rolls, does not appear in the expected value. In fact, we could redo the calculation more simply by dividing the frequencies in the table by n *before* adding. Doing this replaces the frequencies with the *probabilities*, 1/6. That is, it *replaces the frequency distribution with the probability distribution.*

x	1	2	3	4	5	6
$P(X = x)$	$\dfrac{1}{6}$	$\dfrac{1}{6}$	$\dfrac{1}{6}$	$\dfrac{1}{6}$	$\dfrac{1}{6}$	$\dfrac{1}{6}$

The expected value of X is then the sum of the products $x \cdot P(X = x)$. This is how we shall compute it from now on.

To obtain the expected value, multiply the values of X by their probabilities, and then add the results.

Expected Value of a Finite Random Variable

If X is a finite random variable that takes on the values $x_1, x_2, \ldots, x_n$, then the **expected value** of X, written $E(X)$ or μ, is

$$\mu = E(X) = x_1 \cdot P(X = x_1) + x_2 \cdot P(X = x_2) + \cdots + x_n \cdot P(X = x_n)$$

$$= \sum_i x_i \cdot P(X = x_i).$$

In Words

To compute the expected value from the probability distribution of X, we multiply the values of X by their probabilities and add up the results.

Interpretation

We interpret the expected value of X as a *prediction* of the mean of a large random sample of measurements of X; in other words, it is what we "expect" the mean of a large number of scores to be. (The larger the sample, the more accurate this prediction will tend to be.)

Quick Example

6. If X has the distribution shown,

x	-1	0	4	5
$P(X = x)$	.3	.5	.1	.1

then

$$\mu = E(X) = -1(.3) + 0(.5) + 4(.1) + 5(.1) = -.3 + 0 + .4 + .5 = .6.$$

EXAMPLE 3   Sports Injuries

According to historical data, the number of injuries that a member of the *Enormous State University* women's soccer team will sustain during a typical season is given by the following probability distribution table:

Injuries	0	1	2	3	4	5	6
Probability	.20	.20	.22	.20	.15	.01	.02

If X denotes the number of injuries sustained by a player during one season, compute $E(X)$, and interpret the result.

Solution We can compute the expected value using the following tabular approach: Take the probability distribution table, add another row in which we compute the product $xP(X = x)$, and then add these products together.

x	0	1	2	3	4	5	6	
$P(X = x)$	.20	.20	.22	.20	.15	.01	.02	**Total**
$xP(X = x)$	0	.20	.44	.60	.60	.05	.12	2.01

Using Technology

Technology can be used to compute the expected values in Example 3.

TI-83/84 Plus
STAT EDIT values of X in L_1 and probabilities in L_2.
Home screen: sum($L_1 * L_2$)
[More details in the Technology Guide.]

Spreadsheet
Headings x and $P(X = x)$ in A1, B1. x-values and probabilities in A2–B8. =A2*B2 in C2, copied down to B6. =SUM(C2:C8) in C9. [More details in the Technology Guide.]

Website
www.WanerMath.com
→ Online Utilities
→ Histogram Utility

Enter the x-values and frequencies as shown:

```
0, .2
1, .2
2, .22
3, .2
4, .15
5, .01
6, .02
```

Make sure "Show expected value and standard deviation" is checked, and press "Results". The results will appear at the bottom of the page.

The total of the entries in the bottom row is the expected value. Thus,

$$E(X) = 2.01.$$

We interpret the result as follows: If many soccer players are observed for a season, we predict that the average number of injuries each will sustain is about two.

EXAMPLE 4 Roulette

A roulette wheel (of the kind used in the United States) has the numbers 1 through 36, 0 and 00. A bet on a single number pays 35 to 1. This means that if you place a $1 bet on a single number and win (your number comes up), you get your $1 back plus $35 (that is, you gain $35). If your number does not come up, you lose the $1 you bet. What is the expected gain from a $1 bet on a single number?

Solution The probability of winning is $1/38$, so the probability of losing is $37/38$. Let X be the gain from a $1 bet. X has two possible values: $X = -1$ if you lose and $X = 35$ if you win. $P(X = -1) = 37/38$ and $P(X = 35) = 1/38$. This probability distribution and the calculation of the expected value are given in the following table:

x	-1	35	
$P(X = x)$	$\dfrac{37}{38}$	$\dfrac{1}{38}$	**Total**
$xP(X = x)$	$-\dfrac{37}{38}$	$\dfrac{35}{38}$	$-\dfrac{2}{38}$

So we expect to average a small loss of $2/38 \approx \$0.0526$ on each spin of the wheel.

➡ **Before we go on ...** Of course, you cannot actually lose the expected $0.0526 on one spin of the roulette wheel in Example 4. However, if you play many times, this is what you expect your *average* loss per bet to be. For example, if you played 100 times, you could expect to lose about $100 \times 0.0526 = \$5.26$. ∎

A betting game in which the expected value is zero is called a **fair game**. For example, if you and I flip a coin, and I give you $1 each time it comes up heads but you give me $1 each time it comes up tails, then the game is fair. Over the long run, we expect to come out even. On the other hand, a game like roulette, in which the expected value is not zero, is **biased**. Most casino games are slightly biased in favor of the house.[*] Thus, most gamblers will lose only a small amount, and many gamblers will actually win something (and return to play some more). However, when the earnings are averaged over the huge numbers of people playing, the house is guaranteed to come out ahead. This is how casinos make (lots of) money.

* Only rarely are games not biased in favor of the house. However, blackjack played without continuous shuffle machines can be beaten by card counting.

Expected Value of a Binomial Random Variable

Suppose you guess all the answers to the questions on a multiple-choice test. What score can you expect to get? This scenario is an example of a sequence of Bernoulli trials (see the preceding section), and the number of correct guesses is therefore a binomial random variable whose expected value we wish to know. There is a simple formula for the expected value of a binomial random variable.

Expected Value of a Binomial Random Variable

If X is the binomial random variable associated with n independent Bernoulli trials, each with probability p of success, then the expected value of X is

$$\mu = E(X) = np.$$

Quick Examples

7. If X is the number of successes in 20 Bernoulli trials with $p = .7$, then the expected number of successes is $\mu = E(X) = (20)(.7) = 14$.

8. If an event F in some experiment has $P(F) = .25$, the experiment is repeated 100 times, and X is the number of times F occurs, then $E(X) = (100)(.25) = 25$ is the number of times we expect F to occur.

Where does this formula come from? We *could* use the formula for expected value and compute the sum

$$E(X) = 0C(n, 0)p^0q^n + 1C(n, 1)p^1q^{n-1} + 2C(n, 2)p^2q^{n-2} + \cdots + nC(n, n)p^nq^0$$

directly (using the binomial theorem), but this is one of the many places in mathematics where a less direct approach is much easier. X is the number of successes in a sequence of n Bernoulli trials, each with probability p of success. Thus, p is the fraction of time we expect a success, so out of n trials we expect np successes. Because X counts successes, we expect the value of X to be np. (With a little more effort, this can be made into a formal proof that the sum above equals np.)

EXAMPLE 5   **Guessing on an Exam**

An exam has 50 multiple-choice questions, each having four choices. If a student randomly guesses on each question, how many correct answers can he or she expect to get?

Solution Each guess is a Bernoulli trial with probability of success 1 in 4, so $p = .25$. Thus, for a sequence of $n = 50$ trials,

$$\mu = E(X) = np = (50)(.25) = 12.5.$$

Thus, the student can expect to get about 12.5 correct answers.

Q: *Wait a minute. How can a student get a fraction of a correct answer?*

A: Remember that the expected value is the average number of correct answers a student will get if he or she guesses on a large number of such tests. Or we can say that if many students use this strategy of guessing, they will average about 12.5 correct answers each.

Estimating the Expected Value from a Sample

It is not always possible to know the probability distribution of a random variable. For instance, if we take X to be the income of a randomly selected lawyer, we could not be expected to know the probability distribution of X. However, we can still obtain a good *estimate* of the expected value of X (the average income of all lawyers) by using the relative frequency distribution based on a large random sample.

EXAMPLE 6   **Estimating an Expected Value**

The following table shows the (fictitious) incomes of a random sample of 1,000 lawyers in the United States in their first year out of law school.

Income Bracket	$20,000–$29,999	$30,000–$39,999	$40,000–$49,999	$50,000–$59,999	$60,000–$69,999	$70,000–$79,999	$80,000–$89,999
Number	20	80	230	400	170	70	30

Estimate the average of the incomes of all lawyers in their first year out of law school.

Solution We first interpret the question in terms of a random variable. Let X be the income of a lawyer selected at random from among all currently practicing first-year lawyers in the United States. We are given a sample of 1,000 values of X, and we are asked to find the expected value of X. First, we use the midpoints of the income brackets to set up a relative frequency distribution for X:

x	25,000	35,000	45,000	55,000	65,000	75,000	85,000
$P(X = x)$	.02	.08	.23	.40	.17	.07	.03

Our estimate for $E(X)$ is then

$$E(X) = \sum_i x_i \cdot P(X = x_i)$$
$$= (25,000)(.02) + (35,000)(.08) + (45,000)(.23) + (55,000)(.40)$$
$$+ (65,000)(.17) + (75,000)(.07) + (85,000)(.03) = \$54,500.$$

Thus, $E(X)$ is approximately \$54,500. That is, the average income of all currently practicing first-year lawyers in the United States is approximately \$54,500.

FAQs

Recognizing When to Compute the Mean and When to Compute the Expected Value

Q: *When am I supposed to compute the mean (add the values of X and divide by n) and when am I supposed to use the expected value formula?*

A: The formula for the mean (adding and dividing by the number of observations) is used to compute the mean of a sequence of random scores, or sampled values of X. If, on the other hand, you are given the probability distribution for X (even if it is only an estimated probability distribution), then you need to use the expected value formula.

9.3 EXERCISES

▼ more advanced   ◆ challenging
Ⓣ indicates exercises that should be solved using technology

Compute the mean, median, and mode of the data samples in Exercises 1–8. [**HINT**: See Quick Examples 1–5.]

1. $-1, 5, 5, 7, 14$

2. $2, 6, 6, 7, -1$

3. $2, 5, 6, 7, -1, -1$

4. $3, 1, 6, -3, 0, 5$

5. $\dfrac{1}{2}, \dfrac{3}{2}, -4, \dfrac{5}{4}$

6. $-\dfrac{3}{2}, \dfrac{3}{8}, -1, \dfrac{5}{2}$

7. $2.5, -5.4, 4.1, -0.1, -0.1$

8. $4.2, -3.2, 0, 1.7, 0$

9. ▼ Give a sample of six scores with mean 1 and with median ≠ mean. (Arrange the scores in ascending order.)

10. ▼ Give a sample of five scores with mean 100 and median 1. (Arrange the scores in ascending order.)

In Exercises 11–16, calculate the expected value of X for the given probability distribution. [**HINT**: See Quick Example 6.]

11.

x	0	1	2	3
$P(X = x)$	.5	.2	.2	.1

12.

x	1	2	3	4
$P(X = x)$	.1	.2	.5	.2

13.

x	10	20	30	40
$P(X = x)$	$\frac{15}{50}$	$\frac{20}{50}$	$\frac{10}{50}$	$\frac{5}{50}$

14.

x	2	4	6	8
$P(X = x)$	$\frac{1}{20}$	$\frac{15}{20}$	$\frac{2}{20}$	$\frac{2}{20}$

15.

x	-5	-1	0	2	5	10
$P(X = x)$	.2	.3	.2	.1	.2	0

16.

x	-20	-10	0	10	20	30
$P(X = x)$	.2	.4	.2	.1	0	.1

In Exercises 17–28, calculate the expected value of the given random variable X. [Exercises 23, 24, 27, and 28 assume familiarity with counting arguments and probability (see Section 8.4).] [**HINT**: See Quick Example 6.]

17. X is the number that faces up when a fair die is rolled.

18. X is a number selected at random from the set $\{1, 2, 3, 4\}$.

19. X is the number of tails that come up when a coin is tossed twice.

20. X is the number of tails that come up when a coin is tossed three times.

21. ▼ X is the higher number when two dice are rolled.

22. ▼ X is the lower number when two dice are rolled.

23. ▼ X is the number of red marbles that Suzan has in her hand after she selects four marbles from a bag containing four red marbles and two green ones.

24. ▼ X is the number of green marbles that Suzan has in her hand after she selects four marbles from a bag containing three red marbles and two green ones.

25. ▼ Twenty darts are thrown at a dartboard. The probability of hitting a bull's-eye is .1. Let X be the number of bull's-eyes hit.

26. ▼ Thirty darts are thrown at a dartboard. The probability of hitting a bull's-eye is $\frac{1}{5}$. Let X be the number of bull's-eyes hit.

27. Ⓣ ▼ Select 5 cards without replacement from a standard deck of 52, and let X be the number of queens you draw.

28. Ⓣ ▼ Select 5 cards without replacement from a standard deck of 52, and let X be the number of red cards you draw.

Applications

29. *Stock Market Gyrations* Following is a sample of the day-by-day change, rounded to the nearest 100 points, in the Dow Jones Industrial Average during 10 successive business days around the start of the financial crisis in October 2008:[22]

$$-400, -500, -200, -700, -100, 900, -100, -700, 400, -100$$

Compute the mean and median of the given sample. Fill in the blank: There were as many days with a change in the Dow above _____ points as there were with changes below that. [**HINT**: See Quick Examples 1–5.]

30. *Stock Market Gyrations* Following is a sample of the day-by-day change, rounded to the nearest 100 points, in the Dow Jones Industrial Average during 10 successive business days around the start of the financial crisis in October 2008:[23]

$$-100, 400, -200, -500, 200, -300, -200, 900, -100, 200$$

Compute the mean and median of the given sample. Fill in the blank: There were as many days with a change in the Dow above _____ points as there were with changes below that. [**HINT**: See Quick Examples 1–5.]

31. *Gold* The following figures show the price of gold per ounce, in dollars, for the 10-business-day period Dec. 7–Dec. 18, 2015:[24]

$$1,076, 1,072, 1,081, 1,071, 1,072,$$
$$1,068, 1,062, 1,075, 1,049, 1,062$$

Find the sample mean, median, and mode(s). What do your answers tell you about the price of gold?

---

[22] Source: http://finance.google.com.

[23] *Ibid.*

[24] Prices rounded to the nearest $1. Source: www.kitco.com/gold.londonfix.html.

32. *Silver* The following figures show the price of silver per ounce, in dollars, for the 10-business-day period Dec. 7–Dec. 18, 2015:[25]

14.5, 14.2, 14.3, 14.2, 14.0, 13.7, 13.7, 13.7, 14.1, 13.8

Find the sample mean, median, and mode(s). What do your answers tell you about the price of silver?

33. *Supermarkets* A survey of 52 U.S. supermarkets yielded the following relative frequency table, where X is the number of checkout lanes at a randomly chosen supermarket:[26]

x	1	2	3	4	5	6	7	8	9	10
$P(X = x)$	.01	.04	.04	.08	.10	.15	.25	.20	.08	.05

a. Compute $\mu = E(X)$, and interpret the result. [HINT: See Example 3.]
b. Which is larger: $P(X < \mu)$ or $P(X > \mu)$? Interpret the result.

34. *Video Arcades* Your company, *Sonic Video, Inc.*, has conducted research that shows the following probability distribution, where X is the number of video arcades in a randomly chosen city with more than 500,000 inhabitants:

x	0	1	2	3	4	5	6	7	8	9
$P(X = x)$	.07	.09	.35	.25	.15	.03	.02	.02	.01	.01

a. Compute $\mu = E(X)$, and interpret the result. [HINT: See Example 3.]
b. Which is larger: $P(X < \mu)$ or $P(X > \mu)$? Interpret the result.

35. *School Enrollment* The following table shows the approximate numbers of school goers in the United States (residents who attended some educational institution) in 1998, broken down by age group:[27]

Age	3–6.9	7–12.9	13–16.9	17–22.9	23–26.9	27–42.9
Population (millions)	12	24	15	14	2	5

Use the rounded midpoints of the given measurement classes to compute the probability distribution of the age X of a school goer. (Round probabilities to two decimal places.) Hence, compute the expected value of X. What information does the expected value give about residents enrolled in schools?

36. *School Enrollment* Repeat Exercise 35, using the following data from 1980:[28]

Age	3–6.9	7–12.9	13–16.9	17–22.9	23–26.9	27–42.9
Population (millions)	8	20	11	13	1	3

37. *Population Age in Mexico* The following chart shows the ages of 250 randomly selected residents of Mexico:[29]

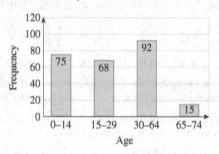

Use the relative frequency distribution based on the (rounded) midpoints of the given measurement classes to obtain an estimate of the average age of a resident in Mexico. (Round the answer to one decimal place.) [HINT: See Example 6.]

38. *Population Age in the United States* Repeat Exercise 37, using the following chart, which shows the ages of 250 randomly selected residents of the United States:[30]

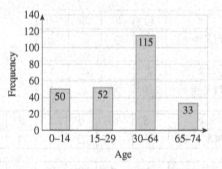

39. *2010 Income Distribution up to $100,000* The following table shows the distribution of household incomes in 2010[31] for a sample of 1,000 households in the United States with incomes up to $100,000:

Income Bracket ($)	0–19,999	20,000–39,999	40,000–59,999	60,000–79,999	80,000–99,999
Households	240	290	180	170	120

[25] Prices rounded to the nearest $0.10. Source: www.kitco.com/gold.londonfix.html.

[26] Sources: J. T. McClave, P. G. Benson, T. Sincich, *Statistics for Business and Economics*, 7th Ed. (Prentice Hall, 1998), p. 177; W. Chow et al., "A model for predicting a supermarket's annual sales per square foot," Graduate School of Management, Rutgers University.

[27] Data are approximate. Source: Statistical Abstract of the United States: 2000.

[28] *Ibid.*

[29] Based on population distribution in 2010. Source: Instituto Nacional de Estadística y Geografía (www.inegi.org.mx).

[30] *Ibid.*

[31] Based on actual income distribution in 2010. Source: U.S. Census Bureau, Current Population Survey, 2010 American Community Survey (www.census.gov).

Use this information to estimate, to the nearest $1,000, the average household income for such households. [HINT: See Example 6.]

40. *2003 Income Distribution up to $100,000* Repeat Exercise 39, using the following data[32] from a sample of 1,000 households in the United States in 2003:

Income Bracket ($)	0–19,999	20,000–39,999	40,000–59,999	60,000–79,999	80,000–99,999
Households	270	280	200	150	100

Highway Safety *Exercises 41–44 are based on the following table, which shows crashworthiness ratings for several categories of motor vehicles.[33] In all of these exercises, take X as the crash-test rating of a small car, Y as the crash-test rating for a small SUV, and so on as shown in the table.*

	Number Tested	**Overall Frontal Crash Test Rating**			
		3 (Good)	**2** (Acceptable)	**1** (Marginal)	**0** (Poor)
Small Cars X	16	1	11	2	2
Small SUVs Y	10	1	4	4	1
Medium SUVs Z	15	3	5	3	4
Passenger Vans U	13	3	0	3	7
Midsize Cars V	15	3	5	0	7
Large Cars W	19	9	5	3	2

41. ▼ Compute the probability distributions and expected values of X and Y. On the basis of the results, which of the two types of vehicles performed better in frontal crashes?

42. ▼ Compute the probability distributions and expected values of Z and V. On the basis of the results, which of the two types of vehicles performed better in frontal crashes?

43. ▣ ▼ On the basis of expected values, which of the following categories performed best in crash tests: small cars, midsize cars, or large cars?

44. ▣ ▼ On the basis of expected values, which of the following categories performed best in crash tests: small SUVs, medium SUVs, or passenger vans?

45. ▼ *Roulette* A roulette wheel has the numbers 1 through 36, 0, and 00. Half of the numbers from 1 through 36 are red,

and a bet on red pays even money (that is, if you bet $1 and win, you will get back your $1 plus another $1). How much do you expect to win with a $1 bet on red? [HINT: See Example 4.]

46. ▼ *Roulette* A roulette wheel has the numbers 1 through 36, 0, and 00. A bet on two numbers pays 17 to 1 (that is, if you bet $1 and one of the two numbers you bet comes up, you get back your $1 plus another $17). How much do you expect to win with a $1 bet on two numbers? [HINT: See Example 4.]

47. *Teenage Pastimes* According to a study,[34] the probability that a randomly selected teenager shopped at a mall at least once during a week was .63. How many teenagers in a randomly selected group of 40 would you expect to shop at a mall during the next week? [HINT: See Example 5.]

48. *Other Teenage Pastimes* According to the study referred to in Exercise 47, the probability that a randomly selected teenager played a computer game at least once during a week was .48. How many teenagers in a randomly selected group of 30 would you expect to play a computer game during the next 7 days? [HINT: See Example 5.]

49. ▼ *Manufacturing* Your manufacturing plant produces air bags, and it is known that 10% of them are defective. A random collection of 20 air bags is tested.
   a. How many of them would you expect to be defective?
   b. In how large a sample would you expect to find 12 defective air bags?

50. ▼ *Spiders* Your pet tarantula, Spider, has a .12 probability of biting an acquaintance who comes into contact with him. Next week, you will be entertaining 20 friends (all of whom will come into contact with Spider).
   a. How many guests should you expect Spider to bite?
   b. At your last party, Spider bit 6 of your guests. Assuming that Spider bit the expected number of guests, how many guests did you have?

Exercises 51 and 52 assume familiarity with counting arguments and probability (see Section 8.4).

51. ▼ *Camping* Kent's Tents has four red tents and three green tents in stock. Karin selects four of them at random. Let X be the number of red tents she selects. Give the probability distribution of X and find the expected number of red tents selected.

52. ▼ *Camping* Kent's Tents has five green knapsacks and four yellow ones in stock. Curt selects four of them at random. Let X be the number of green knapsacks he selects. Give the probability distribution of X, and find the expected number of green knapsacks selected.

---

[32] Based on actual income distribution in 2003 (not adjusted for inflation). Source: U.S. Census Bureau, Current Population Survey, 2004 Annual Social and Economic Supplement (www.census.gov).

[33] Ratings are by the Insurance Institute for Highway Safety. Sources: Oak Ridge National Laboratory: "An Analysis of the Impact of Sport Utility Vehicles in the United States," Stacy C. Davis, Lorena F. Truett, August 2000, Insurance Institute for Highway Safety (www-cta.ornl .gov/Publications/Final SUV report.pdf, www.highwaysafety.org/ vehicle_ratings).

---

[34] Source: Rand Youth Poll/Teen-Age Research Unlimited/*New York Times*, March 14, 1998, p. D1.

Elimination Tournaments *In an elimination tournament the teams are arranged in opponent pairs for the first round, and the winner of each round goes on to the next round until the champion emerges. The following diagram illustrates a 16-team tournament bracket, in which the 16 participating teams are arranged on the left under Round 1 and the winners of each round are added as the tournament progresses. The top team in each game is considered the "home" team, so the top-to-bottom order matters.*

Round 1   Round 2   Round 3   Round 4
          (Quarter final) (Semifinal) (Final)

Champion

To seed a tournament means to select which teams to play each other in the first round according to their preliminary ranking. For instance, in professional tennis and NCAA basketball the seeding is set up in the following order based on the preliminary rankings: 1 versus 16, 8 versus 9, 5 versus 12, 4 versus 13, 6 versus 11, 3 versus 14, 7 versus 10, and 2 versus 15.[35] Exercises 53–56 are based on various types of elimination tournaments.

53. Someone offers you the following bet: If a randomly chosen seeding of a 16-team tournament results in the top-ranked team playing the bottom-ranked team, the second-ranked team playing the second-lowest ranked team, and so on, you win $1 million; otherwise, you lose $1. What are your expected winnings on this bet? [HINT: See Exercise 37 in Section 8.4.]

54. Someone offers you the following bet: If a randomly chosen seeding of an 8-team tournament results in each team playing a team with adjacent ranking, you win $100; otherwise, you lose $1. What are your expected winnings on this bet? [HINT: See Exercise 38 in Section 8.4.]

55. ▼ In 2014, after the NCAA basketball 64-team tournament had already been seeded, Quicken Loans, backed by investor

Warren Buffett, offered a billion-dollar prize for picking all the winners.[36] If 50,000,000 people entered the contest by picking winners at random, how much money did Quicken Loans expect to have to pay out? [HINT: See Exercise 39 in Section 8.4.]

56. ▼ Refer to Exercise 55. An *upset* occurs when a team beats a higher-ranked team. Suppose that, on average, there are 20 upsets in the first four rounds of the NCAA tournament each year. Assuming that the higher-ranked team always has the same probability of winning and that the outcomes of the games are independent, what is the probability that the higher-ranked team will win?

57. ⊤ ▼ *Stock Portfolios* You are required to choose between two stock portfolios: *FastForward Funds* and *SolidState Securities*. Stock analysts have constructed the following probability distributions for next year's rate of return for the two funds.

FastForward Funds

Rate of Return	−0.4	−0.3	−0.2	−0.1	0	0.1	0.2	0.3	0.4
Probability	.015	.025	.043	.132	.289	.323	.111	.043	.019

SolidState Securities

Rate of Return	−0.4	−0.3	−0.2	−0.1	0	0.1	0.2	0.3	0.4
Probability	.012	.023	.050	.131	.207	.330	.188	.043	.016

Which of the two funds gives the higher expected rate of return?

58. ⊤ ▼ *Risk Management* Before making your final decision whether to invest in *FastForward Funds* or *SolidState Securities* (see Exercise 57), you consult your colleague in the risk management department of your company. She informs you that, in the event of a stock market crash, the following probability distributions for next year's rate of return would apply:

FastForward Funds

Rate of Return	−0.8	−0.7	−0.6	−0.5	−0.4	−0.2	−0.1	0	0.1
Probability	.028	.033	.043	.233	.176	.230	.111	.044	.102

SolidState Securities

Rate of Return	−0.8	−0.7	−0.6	−0.5	−0.4	−0.2	−0.1	0	0.1
Probability	.033	.036	.038	.167	.176	.230	.211	.074	.035

Which of the two funds offers the lower risk in case of a market crash?

---

[35] Source: www.wikipedia.com, www.ncaa.com.

[36] No one won the prize, and the offer was scrapped the following year as a result of a series of lawsuits and countersuits by Yahoo, SCA Promotions (a sweepstakes company), and Berkshire-Hathaway. Sources: http://abcnews.go.com/Sports/warren-buffet-backs-billion-dollar-march-madness-challenge/story?id=21615743, http://money.cnn.com/2015/03/12/news/buffett-ncaa-bracket-bet/index.html.

59. ◆ *Insurance Schemes* The *Acme Insurance Company* is launching a drive to generate greater profits, and it decides to insure racetrack drivers against wrecking their cars. The company's research shows that, on average, a racetrack driver races 4 times a year and has a 1 in 10 chance of wrecking a vehicle, worth an average of $100,000, in every race. The annual premium is $5,000, and Acme automatically drops any driver who is involved in an accident (after paying for a new car) but does not refund the premium. How much profit (or loss) can the company expect to earn from a typical driver in a year? [HINT: Use a tree diagram to compute the probabilities of the various outcomes.]

60. ◆ *Insurance* The *Blue Sky Flight Insurance Company* insures passengers against air disasters, charging a prospective passenger $20 for coverage on a single plane ride. In the event of a fatal air disaster, it pays out $100,000 to the named beneficiary. In the event of a nonfatal disaster, it pays out an average of $25,000 for hospital expenses. Given that the probability of a plane's crashing on a single trip[37] is .00000087, and assuming that a passenger involved in a plane crash has a .9 chance of being killed, determine the profit (or loss) per passenger that the insurance company expects to make on each trip. [HINT: Use a tree to compute the probabilities of the various outcomes.]

Communication and Reasoning Exercises

61. In a certain set of five scores, there are as many values above the mean as below it. It follows that
(A) The median and mean are equal.
(B) The mean and mode are equal.
(C) The mode and median are equal.
(D) The mean, mode, and median are all equal.

62. In a certain set of scores, the median occurs more often than any other score. It follows that
(A) The median and mean are equal.
(B) The mean and mode are equal.
(C) The mode and median are equal.
(D) The mean, mode, and median are all equal.

63. Your friend Charlesworth claims that the median of a collection of data is always close to the mean. Is he correct? If so, say why. If not, give an example to prove him wrong.

64. Your other friend Imogen asserts that Charlesworth is wrong and that it is the mode and the median that are always close to each other. Is she correct? If so, say why. If not, give an example to prove her wrong.

65. Must the expected number of times you hit a bull's-eye after 50 attempts always be a whole number? Explain.

66. Your statistics instructor tells you that the expected score of the upcoming midterm test is 75%. That means that 75% is the most likely score to occur—right?

67. ▼ Your grade in a recent midterm was 80%, but the class average was 83%. Most people in the class scored better than you—right?

68. ▼ Your grade in a recent midterm was 80%, but the class median was 100%. Your score was lower than the average score—right?

69. ▼ Slim tells you that the population mean is just the mean of a suitably large sample. Is he correct? Explain.

70. ▼ Explain how you can use a sample to estimate an expected value.

71. ▼ Following is an excerpt from a full-page ad by MoveOn .org in the *New York Times* criticizing President G.W. Bush:[38]

On Tax Cuts:

George Bush: ". . . Americans will keep, this year, an average of almost $1,000 more of their own money."

The Truth: Nearly half of all taxpayers get less than $100. And 31% of all taxpayers get nothing at all.

The statements referred to as "The Truth" contradict the statement attributed to President Bush—right? Explain.

72. ▼ Following is an excerpt from a five-page ad by WeissneggerForGov.org in *The Martian Enquirer* criticizing Supreme Martian Administrator, Gov. Red Davis:

On Worker Accommodation:

Gov. Red Davis: "The median size of Government worker habitats in Valles Marineris is at least 400 square feet."

Weissnegger: "The average size of a Government worker habitat in Valles Marineris is a mere 150 square feet."

The statements attributed to Weissnegger do not contradict the statement attributed to Gov. Davis—right? Explain.

73. ▼ Sonia has just told you that the expected household income in the United States is the same as the population mean of all U.S. household incomes. Clarify her statement by describing an experiment and an associated random variable X so that the expected household income is the expected value of X.

74. ▼ If X is a random variable, what is the difference between a sample mean of measurements of X and the expected value of X? Illustrate by means of an example.

---

[37] This was the probability of a passenger plane crashing per departure in 1990. (Source: National Transportation Safety Board)

[38] Source: Full-page ad in the *New York Times*, September 17, 2003, p. A25.

9.4   Measures of Dispersion

Variance and Standard Deviation of a Set of Scores

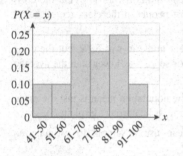

$P(X = x)$

Figure 5(a)

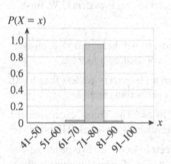

$P(X = x)$

Figure 5(b)

Your grade on a recent midterm was 68%; the class average was 72%. How do you stand in comparison with the rest of the class? If the grades were widely scattered, then your grade may be close to the mean, and a fair number of people may have done a lot worse than you (Figure 5(a)). If, on the other hand, almost all the grades were within a few points of the average, then your grade may not be much higher than the lowest grade in the class (Figure 5(b)).

This scenario suggests that it would be useful to have a way of measuring not only the central tendency of a set of scores (mean, median, or mode) but also the amount of "scatter" or "dispersion" of the data.

If the scores in our set are $x_1, x_2, \ldots, x_n$ and their mean is $\bar{x}$ (or μ in the case of a population mean), we are really interested in the distribution of the differences $x_i - \bar{x}$. We could compute the *average* of these differences, but this average will always be 0. (Why?) It is really the *sizes* of these differences that interest us, so we might try computing the average of the absolute values of the differences. This idea is reasonable, but it leads to technical difficulties that are avoided by a slightly different approach: The statistic we use is based on the average of the *squares* of the differences, as explained in the following definitions.

Population Variance and Standard Deviation

If the values $x_1, x_2, \ldots, x_n$ are all the measurements of X in the entire population, then the **population variance** is given by

$$\sigma^2 = \frac{(x_1 - \mu)^2 + (x_2 - \mu)^2 + \cdots + (x_n - \mu)^2}{n} = \frac{\sum_{i=1}^{n}(x_i - \mu)^2}{n}.$$

(Remember that μ is the symbol we use for the *population* mean.) The **population standard deviation** is the square root of the population variance:

$$\sigma = \sqrt{\sigma^2}.$$

Sample Variance and Standard Deviation

The **sample variance** of a sample $x_1, x_2, \ldots, x_n$ of n values of X is given by

$$s^2 = \frac{(x_1 - \bar{x})^2 + (x_2 - \bar{x})^2 + \cdots + (x_n - \bar{x})^2}{n - 1} = \frac{\sum_{i=1}^{n}(x_i - \bar{x})^2}{n - 1}.$$

The **sample standard deviation** is the square root of the sample variance:

$$s = \sqrt{s^2}.$$

Visualizing Small and Large Variance

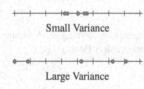

Small Variance

Large Variance

Using Technology

Technology can be used to compute means and standard deviations as follows:

TI-83/84 Plus
STAT EDIT Enter the values $x_1,\ x_2,\ \ldots,\ x_n$ in L_1
STAT CALC 1-Var Stats
ENTER
s will appear as "Sx" and σ as "σx".

Spreadsheet
Enter the values $x_1, x_2, \ldots, x_n$ in column A
=AVERAGE(A:A) computes the mean.
=STDEV(A:A) computes s.
=STDEVP(A:A) computes σ.

Quick Examples

1. The sample variance of the scores 1, 2, 3, 4, 5 is the sum of the squares of the differences between the scores and the mean $\bar{x} = 3$, divided by $n - 1 = 4$:

$$s^2 = \frac{(1-3)^2 + (2-3)^2 + (3-3)^2 + (4-3)^2 + (5-3)^2}{4}$$

$$= \frac{10}{4} = 2.5,$$

so

$$s = \sqrt{2.5} \approx 1.58.$$

2. The population variance of the scores 1, 2, 3, 4, 5 is the sum of the squares of the differences between the scores and the mean $\mu = 3$, divided by $n = 5$:

$$\sigma^2 = \frac{(1-3)^2 + (2-3)^2 + (3-3)^2 + (4-3)^2 + (5-3)^2}{5}$$

$$= \frac{10}{5} = 2,$$

so

$$\sigma = \sqrt{2} \approx 1.41.$$

Q: *The population variance is the average of the squares of the differences between the values and the mean. But why do we divide by $n - 1$ instead of n when calculating the sample variance?*

A: In real-life applications we would like the variance we calculate from a sample to approximate the variance of the whole population. In statistical terms, we would like the expected value of the sample variance s^2 to be the same as the population variance σ^2. The sample variance s^2 as we have defined it is the "unbiased estimator" of the population variance σ^2 that accomplishes this task; if, instead, we divided by n in the formula for s^2, we would, on average, tend to underestimate the population variance. (See the online text on Sampling Distributions at the Website for further discussion of unbiased estimators.) Note that as the sample size gets larger and larger, the discrepancy between the formulas for s^2 and σ^2 becomes negligible; dividing by n gives almost the same answer as dividing by $n - 1$. It is traditional, nonetheless, to use the sample variance in preference to the population variance when working with samples, and we do that here. In practice we should not try to draw conclusions about the entire population from samples so small that the difference between the two formulas matters. As one book puts it, "If the difference between n and $n - 1$ ever matters to you, then you are probably up to no good anyway—e.g., trying to substantiate a questionable hypothesis with marginal data."[*]

* W. H. Press, S. A. Teukolsky, E. T. Vetterling, and B. P. Flannery, *Numerical Recipes: The Art of Scientific Computing,* Cambridge University Press, 2007.

Here's a simple example of calculating standard deviation.

EXAMPLE 1   Income

Following is a sample of the incomes (in thousands of dollars) of eight U.S. residents selected at random:[39]

$$50, 40, 60, 20, 90, 10, 30, 20.$$

Compute the sample mean and standard deviation, rounded to one decimal place. What percentage of the scores fall within one standard deviation of the mean? What percentage fall within two standard deviations of the mean?

Solution The sample mean is

$$\bar{x} = \frac{\sum_i x_i}{n} = \frac{50 + 40 + 60 + 20 + 90 + 10 + 30 + 20}{8} = \frac{320}{8} = 40.$$

The sample variance is

$$s^2 = \frac{\sum_i (x_i - \bar{x})^2}{n - 1}$$

$$= \frac{1}{7}[(50 - 40)^2 + (40 - 40)^2 + (60 - 40)^2 + (20 - 40)^2$$

$$+ (90 - 40)^2 + (10 - 40)^2 + (30 - 40)^2 + (20 - 40)^2]$$

$$= \frac{1}{7}(100 + 0 + 400 + 400 + 2{,}500 + 900 + 100 + 400)$$

$$= \frac{4{,}800}{7}.$$

Thus, the sample standard deviation is

$$s = \sqrt{\frac{4{,}800}{7}} \approx 26.2. \qquad \text{Rounded to one decimal place}$$

To ask which scores fall "within one standard deviation of the mean" is to ask which scores fall in the interval $[\bar{x} - s, \bar{x} + s]$, or about $[40 - 26.2, 40 + 26.2] = [13.8, 66.2]$. Six out of the eight scores fall in this interval, so the percentage of scores that fall within one standard deviation of the mean is $6/8 = .75$, or 75%.

For two standard deviations, the interval in question is $[\bar{x} - 2s, \bar{x} + 2s] \approx [40 - 52.4, 40 + 52.4] = [-12.4, 92.4]$, which includes all of the scores. In other words, 100% of the scores fall within two standard deviations of the mean.

Q: *In Example 1, 75% of the scores fell within one standard deviation of the mean, and all of them fell within two standard deviations of the mean. Is this typical?*

A: Actually, the percentage of scores within a number of standard deviations of the mean depends a great deal on the way the scores are distributed. There are two useful methods for *estimating* the percentage of scores that fall within any number of standard deviations of the mean. The first method applies to any set of data and is due to P.L. Chebyshev (1821–1894), while the second applies to "nice" sets of data and is based on the "normal distribution," which we shall discuss in Section 9.5.

---

[39] The sample is roughly statistically representative of the actual income distribution in the United States in 2010 for incomes up to $100,000. (See Exercise 35.) Source for income distribution: U.S. Census Bureau (www.census.gov).

Chebyshev's Rule

For any set of data the following statements are true:

At least 3/4 of the scores fall within two standard deviations of the mean (within the interval $[\bar{x} - 2s, \bar{x} + 2s]$ for samples or $[\mu - 2\sigma, \mu + 2\sigma]$ for populations).

At least 8/9 of the scores fall within three standard deviations of the mean (within the interval $[\bar{x} - 3s, \bar{x} + 3s]$ for samples or $[\mu - 3\sigma, \mu + 3\sigma]$ for populations).

At least 15/16 of the scores fall within four standard deviations of the mean (within the interval $[\bar{x} - 4s, \bar{x} + 4s]$ for samples or $[\mu - 4\sigma, \mu + 4\sigma]$ for populations).

$$\vdots$$

At least $1 - 1/k^2$ of the scores fall within k standard deviations of the mean (within the interval $[\bar{x} - ks, \bar{x} + ks]$ for samples or $[\mu - k\sigma, \mu + k\sigma]$ for populations).

Visualizing Chebyshev's Rule

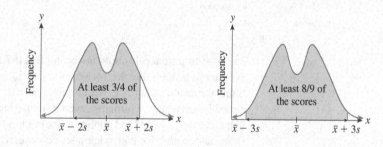

Empirical Rule*

* Unlike Chebyshev's rule, which is a precise theorem, the empirical rule is a rule of thumb that is intentionally vague about what exactly is meant by a "bell-shaped distribution" and "approximately such-and-such %." (As a result, the rule is often stated differently in different textbooks.) We will see in Section 9.5 that if the distribution is a *normal* one, the empirical rule translates to a precise statement.

For a set of data whose frequency distribution is bell-shaped and symmetric (see Figure 6), the following is true:

Approximately 68% of the scores fall within one standard deviation of the mean (within the interval $[\bar{x} - s, \bar{x} + s]$ for samples or $[\mu - \sigma, \mu + \sigma]$ for populations).

Approximately 95% of the scores fall within two standard deviations of the mean (within the interval $[\bar{x} - 2s, \bar{x} + 2s]$ for samples or $[\mu - 2\sigma, \mu + 2\sigma]$ for populations).

Approximately 99.7% of the scores fall within three standard deviations of the mean (within the interval $[\bar{x} - 3s, \bar{x} + 3s]$ for samples or $[\mu - 3\sigma, \mu + 3\sigma]$ for populations).

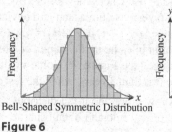
Bell-Shaped Symmetric Distribution

Not Symmetric

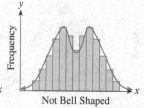
Not Bell Shaped

Figure 6

Visualizing the Empirical Rule

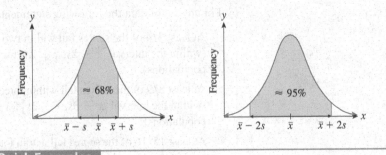

Quick Examples

3. If the mean of a sample is 20 with standard deviation $s = 2$, then at least 15/16, or 93.75%, of the scores lie within four standard deviations of the mean—that is, in the interval $[12, 28]$.

4. If the mean of a sample with a bell-shaped symmetric distribution is 20 with standard deviation $s = 2$, then approximately 95% of the scores lie in the interval $[16, 24]$.

The empirical rule could not be applied in Example 1. The distribution there is not symmetric (sketch it to see for yourself), and the fact that there were only eight scores limits the accuracy further. The empirical rule is, however, accurate in distributions that are bell shaped and symmetric, even if not perfectly so. Chebyshev's rule, on the other hand, is always valid (and applies in Example 1 in particular) but tends to be "overcautious" and in practice underestimates how much of a distribution lies in a given interval.

EXAMPLE 2 Automobile Life

The average life span of a Batmobile is 9 years, with a standard deviation of 2 years. My own Batmobile lasted less than 3 years before being condemned to the bat-junkyard.

a. Without any further knowledge about the distribution of Batmobile life spans, what can one say about the percentage of Batmobiles that last less than 3 years?

b. Refine the answer in part (a), assuming that the distribution of Batmobile life spans is bell shaped and symmetric.

Solution

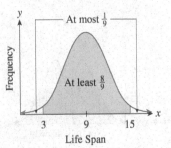

a. If we are given no further information about the distribution of Batmobile life spans, we need to use Chebyshev's rule. Because the life span of my Batmobile was more than 6 years (or three standard deviations) shorter than the mean, it lies outside the range $[\mu - 3\sigma, \mu + 3\sigma] = [3, 15]$. Because *at least* 8/9 of the life spans of all Batmobiles lie in this range, *at most* 1/9, or 11%, of the life spans lie outside this range (see Figure 7). Some of these, like the life span of my own Batmobile, are less than 3 years, while the rest are more than $\mu + 3\sigma = 15$ years.

b. Because we know more about the distribution now than we did in part (a), we can use the empirical rule and obtain sharper results. The empirical rule predicts that approximately 99.7% of the life spans of Batmobiles lie in the range

Figure 7

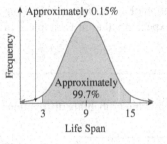

Figure 8

$[\mu - 3\sigma, \mu + 3\sigma] = [3, 15]$. Thus, approximately $1 - 99.7\% = 0.3\%$ of them lie outside that range. Because the distribution is symmetric, however, more can be said: Half of that 0.3%, or 0.15% of Batmobiles, will last longer than 15 years, while the other 0.15% are, like my own ill-fated Batmobile, doomed to a life span of less than 3 years (see Figure 8).

Variance and Standard Deviation of a Finite Random Variable

Recall that the expected value of a random variable X is a prediction of the average of a large sample of values of X. Can we similarly predict the variance of a large sample? Suppose we have a sample $x_1, x_2, \ldots, x_n$. If n is large, the sample and population variances are essentially the same, so we concentrate on the population variance, which is the average of the numbers $(x_i - \bar{x})^2$. This average can be predicted by using $E([X - \mu]^2)$, the expected value of $(X - \mu)^2$. In general, we make the following definition.

Variance and Standard Deviation of a Finite Random Variable

If X is a finite random variable taking on values $x_1, x_2, \ldots, x_n$, then the **variance** of X is

$$\sigma^2 = E([X - \mu]^2)$$
$$= (x_1 - \mu)^2 P(X = x_1) + (x_2 - \mu)^2 P(X = x_2) + \cdots + (x_n - \mu)^2 P(X = x_n)$$
$$= \sum_i (x_i - \mu)^2 P(X = x_i).$$

The **standard deviation** of X is then the square root of the variance:

$$\sigma = \sqrt{\sigma^2}.$$

To compute the variance from the probability distribution of X, first compute the expected value μ, and then compute the expected value of $(X - \mu)^2$.

Quick Example

5. The following distribution has expected value $\mu = E(X) = 2$:

x	-1	2	3	10
$P(X = x)$	.3	.5	.1	.1

The variance of X is

$$\sigma^2 = (x_1 - \mu)^2 P(X = x_1) + (x_2 - \mu)^2 P(X = x_2) + \cdots + (x_n - \mu)^2 P(X = x_n)$$
$$= (-1 - 2)^2(.3) + (2 - 2)^2(.5) + (3 - 2)^2(.1) + (10 - 2)^2(.1) = 9.2.$$

The standard deviation of X is

$$\sigma = \sqrt{9.2} \approx 3.03.$$

Note We can interpret the variance of X as the number we expect to get for the variance of a large sample of values of X, and similarly for the standard deviation. ∎

We can calculate the variance and standard deviation of a random variable using a tabular approach just as when we calculated the expected value in Example 3 in Section 9.3.

Using Technology

Technology can be used to automate the calculations of Example 3.

TI-83/84 Plus
STAT EDIT values of x in L_1, probabilities in L_2.
Home screen: $\texttt{sum}(\texttt{L}_1*\texttt{L}_2) \rightarrow \texttt{M}$
Then $\texttt{sum}((\texttt{L}_1-\texttt{M})\char`\^2*\texttt{L}_2)$
[More details in the Technology Guide.]

Spreadsheet
x-values in A2–A7, probabilities in B2–B7
$\texttt{=A2*B2}$ in C2; copy down to C7.
$\texttt{=SUM(C2:C7)}$ in C8
$\texttt{=(A2-\$C\$8)\char`\^2*B2}$ in D2; copy down to D7.
$\texttt{=SUM(D2:D7)}$ in D8
[More details in the Technology Guide.]

WW Website
www.WanerMath.com
→ Online Utilities
→ Histogram Utility
Enter the x-values and probabilities as shown:

```
10, .2
20, .2
30, .3
40, .1
50, .1
60, .1
```

Make sure "Show expected value and standard deviation" is checked, and press "Results".

EXAMPLE 3 **Variance of a Random Variable**

Compute the variance and standard deviation for the following probability distribution:

x	10	20	30	40	50	60
$P(X = x)$	.2	.2	.3	.1	.1	.1

Solution We first compute the expected value, μ, in the usual way:

x	10	20	30	40	50	60	
$P(X = x)$	.2	.2	.3	.1	.1	.1	
$xP(X = x)$	2	4	9	4	5	6	$\mu = 30$

Next, we add an extra three rows:

- a row for the differences $(x - \mu)$, which we get by subtracting μ from the values of X
- a row for the squares $(x - \mu)^2$, which we obtain by squaring the values immediately above
- a row for the products $(x - \mu)^2 P(X = x)$, which we obtain by multiplying the values in the second and the fifth rows.

x	10	20	30	40	50	60	
$P(X = x)$	.2	.2	.3	.1	.1	.1	
$xP(X = x)$	2	4	9	4	5	6	$\mu = 30$
$x - \mu$	-20	-10	0	10	20	30	
$(x - \mu)^2$	400	100	0	100	400	900	
$(x - \mu)^2 P(X = x)$	80	20	0	10	40	90	$\sigma^2 = 240$

The sum of the values in the last row is the variance. The standard deviation is then the square root of the variance:

$$\sigma = \sqrt{240} \approx 15.49.$$

Note Chebyshev's rule and the empirical rule apply to random variables just as they apply to samples and populations, as we illustrate in the following example. ∎

EXAMPLE 4 **Internet Commerce**

Your newly launched company, *CyberPromo, Inc.*, sells computer games on the Internet.

a. Statistical research indicates that the life span of an Internet marketing company such as yours is symmetrically distributed with an expected value of 30 months and standard deviation of 4 months. Complete the following sentence:

There is (at least/at most/approximately)_____ a _____ percent chance that CyberPromo will still be around for more than 3 years.

b. How would the answer to part (a) be affected if the distribution of life spans was not known to be symmetric?

Solution

a. Do we use Chebyshev's rule or the empirical rule? Because the empirical rule requires that the distribution be both symmetric and bell shaped—not just symmetric—we cannot conclude that it applies here, so we are forced to use Chebyshev's rule instead.

Let X be the life span of an Internet commerce site. The expected value of X is 30 months, and the hoped-for life span of CyberPromo, Inc., is 36 months, which is 6 months, or $6/4 = 1.5$ standard deviations, above the mean. Chebyshev's rule tells us that X is within $k = 1.5$ standard deviations of the mean at least $1 - 1/k^2$ of the time; that is,

$$P(24 \leq X \leq 36) \geq 1 - \frac{1}{k^2} = 1 - \frac{1}{1.5^2} \approx .56.$$

In other words, at least 56% of all Internet marketing companies have life spans in the range of 24 to 36 months. Thus, *at most* 44% have life spans outside this range. Because the distribution is symmetric, at most 22% have life spans longer than 36 months. Thus, we can complete the sentence as follows:

There is <u>at most</u> a <u>22</u> percent chance that CyberPromo will still be around for more than 3 years.

b. If the given distribution was not known to be symmetric, how would this affect the answer? We saw above that regardless of whether the distribution is symmetric or not, at most 44% have life spans outside the range 24 to 36 months. Because the distribution is not symmetric, we cannot conclude that at most half of the 44% have life spans longer than 36 months, and all we can say is that *no more than 44% can possibly have life spans longer than 36 years.* In other words:

There is <u>at most</u> a <u>44</u> percent chance that CyberPromo will still be around for more than 3 years.

Variance and Standard Deviation of a Binomial Random Variable

We saw that there is an easy formula for the expected value of a binomial random variable: $\mu = np$, where n is the number of trials and p is the probability of success. Similarly, there is a simple formula for the variance and standard deviation.

Variance and Standard Deviation of a Binomial Random Variable

If X is a binomial random variable associated with n independent Bernoulli trials, each with probability p of success, then the variance and standard deviation of X are given by

$$\sigma^2 = npq \quad \text{and} \quad \sigma = \sqrt{npq}$$

where $q = 1 - p$ is the probability of failure.

> ### Quick Example
>
> **6.** If X is the number of successes in 20 Bernoulli trials with $p = .7$, then the standard deviation is $\sigma = \sqrt{npq} = \sqrt{(20)(.7)(.3)} \approx 2.05$.

For values of p near $1/2$ and large values of n, a binomial distribution is bell shaped and (nearly) symmetric; hence, the empirical rule applies. One rule of thumb is that we can use the empirical rule when both $np \geq 10$ and $nq \geq 10$.[*]

* Remember that the empirical rule gives only an *estimate* of probabilities. In Section 9.5 we give a more accurate approximation that takes into account the fact that the binomial distribution is not continuous.

EXAMPLE 5   Internet Commerce

You have calculated that there is a 40% chance that a hit on your web page results in a fee paid to your company, *CyberPromo, Inc.* Your web page receives 25 hits per day. Let X be the number of hits that result in payment of the fee ("successful hits").

a. What are the expected value and standard deviation of X?

b. Complete the following: On approximately 95 out of 100 days, I will get between ___ and ___ successful hits.

Solution

a. The random variable X is binomial with $n = 25$ and $p = .4$. To compute μ and σ, we use the formulas

$$\mu = np = (25)(.4) = 10 \text{ successful hits}$$
$$\sigma = \sqrt{npq} = \sqrt{(25)(.4)(.6)} \approx 2.45 \text{ hits.}$$

b. Because $np = 10 \geq 10$ and $nq = (25)(.6) = 15 \geq 10$, we can use the empirical rule, which tells us that there is an approximately 95% probability that the number of successful hits is within two standard deviations of the mean—that is, in the interval

$$[\mu - 2\sigma, \mu + 2\sigma] = [10 - 2(2.45), 10 + 2(2.45)] = [5.1, 14.9].$$

Thus, on approximately 95 out of 100 days, I will get between <u>5.1</u> and <u>14.9</u> successful hits.

FAQs

Recognizing When to Use the Empirical Rule or Chebyshev's Rule

Q : *How do I decide whether to use Chebyshev's rule or the empirical rule?*

A : Check to see whether the probability distribution you are considering is both symmetric and bell shaped. If so, you can use the empirical rule. If not, then you must use Chebyshev's rule. Thus, for instance, if the distribution is symmetric but not known to be bell shaped, you must use Chebyshev's rule.

9.4   EXERCISES

▼ more advanced   ◆ challenging
⬛ indicates exercises that should be solved using technology

In Exercises 1–8, compute the (sample) variance and standard deviation of the given data sample. (You calculated the means in the Section 9.3 exercises. Round all answers to two decimal places.) [HINT: See Quick Examples 1 and 2.]

1. $-1, 5, 5, 7, 14$

2. $2, 6, 6, 7, -1$

3. $2, 5, 6, 7, -1, -1$

4. $3, 1, 6, -3, 0, 5$

5. $\dfrac{1}{2}, \dfrac{3}{2}, -4, \dfrac{5}{4}$

6. $-\dfrac{3}{2}, \dfrac{3}{8}, -1, \dfrac{5}{2}$

7. $2.5, -5.4, 4.1, -0.1, -0.1$

8. $4.2, -3.2, 0, 1.7, 0$

In Exercises 9–14, calculate the standard deviation of X for each probability distribution. (You calculated the expected values in the Section 9.3 exercises. Round all answers to two decimal places.) [HINT: See Quick Example 5.]

9.

x	0	1	2	3
$P(X = x)$	.5	.2	.2	.1

10.

x	1	2	3	4
$P(X = x)$	.1	.2	.5	.2

11.

x	10	20	30	40
$P(X = x)$	$\frac{3}{10}$	$\frac{2}{5}$	$\frac{1}{5}$	$\frac{1}{10}$

12.

x	2	4	6	8
$P(X = x)$	$\frac{1}{20}$	$\frac{15}{20}$	$\frac{2}{20}$	$\frac{2}{20}$

13.

x	−5	−1	0	2	5	10
$P(X = x)$	.2	.3	.2	.1	.2	0

14.

x	−20	−10	0	10	20	30
$P(X = x)$	.2	.4	.2	.1	0	.1

In Exercises 15–24, calculate the expected value, the variance, and the standard deviation of the given random variable X. (You calculated the expected values in the Section 9.3 exercises. Round all answers to two decimal places.)

15. X is the number that faces up when a fair die is rolled.

16. X is the number selected at random from the set $\{1, 2, 3, 4\}$.

17. X is the number of tails that come up when a coin is tossed twice.

18. X is the number of tails that come up when a coin is tossed three times.

19. ▼ X is the higher number when two dice are rolled.

20. ▼ X is the lower number when two dice are rolled.

21. ▼ X is the number of red marbles that Suzan has in her hand after she selects four marbles from a bag containing four red marbles and two green ones.

22. ▼ X is the number of green marbles that Suzan has in her hand after she selects four marbles from a bag containing three red marbles and two green ones.

23. ▼ Twenty darts are thrown at a dartboard. The probability of hitting a bull's-eye is .1. Let X be the number of bull's-eyes hit.

24. ▼ Thirty darts are thrown at a dartboard. The probability of hitting a bull's-eye is $\frac{1}{5}$. Let X be the number of bull's-eyes hit.

Applications

25. *Popularity Ratings* In your bid to be elected class representative, you have your election committee survey five randomly chosen students in your class and ask them to rank you on a scale of 0–10. Your rankings are 3, 2, 0, 9, 1.
   a. Find the sample mean and standard deviation. (Round your answers to two decimal places.) [HINT: See Example 1 and Quick Examples 1 and 2.]
   b. Assuming that the sample mean and standard deviation are indicative of the class as a whole, in what range does the empirical rule predict that approximately 68% of the class will rank you? What other assumptions must we make to use the rule?

26. *Popularity Ratings* Your candidacy for elected class representative is being opposed by Slick Sally. Your election committee has surveyed six of the students in your class and had them rank Sally on a scale of 0–10. The rankings were 2, 8, 7, 10, 5, 8.
   a. Find the sample mean and standard deviation. (Round your answers to two decimal places.) [HINT: See Example 1 and Quick Examples 1 and 2.]
   b. Assuming that the sample mean and standard deviation are indicative of the class as a whole, in what range does the empirical rule predict that approximately 95% of the class will rank Sally? What other assumptions must we make to use the rule?

27. *Unemployment* Following is a sample of unemployment rates (in percentage points) in the United States sampled from the period 1990–2004:[40]

$$4.2, 4.7, 5.4, 5.8, 4.9.$$

   a. Compute the mean and standard deviation of the given sample. (Round your answers to one decimal place.)
   b. Assuming that the distribution of unemployment rates in the population is symmetric and bell shaped, 95% of the time, the unemployment rate is between ____ and ____ percent.

---

[40] Sources for data: Bureau of Labor Statistics (BLS) (www.bls.gov).

28. Unemployment Following is a sample of unemployment rates among Hispanics (in percentage points) in the United States sampled from the period 1990–2004:[41]

$$7.7, 7.5, 9.3, 6.9, 8.6.$$

a. Compute the mean and standard deviation of the given sample. (Round your answers to one decimal place.)

b. Assuming that the distribution of unemployment rates in the population of interest is symmetric and bell shaped, 68% of the time, the unemployment rate is between ____ and ____ percent.

29. Stock Market Gyrations Following is a sample of the day-by-day change, rounded to the nearest 100 points, in the Dow Jones Industrial Average during 10 successive business days around the start of the financial crisis in October 2008:[42]

$$-400, -500, -200, -700, -100, 900, -100, -700, 400, -100.$$

a. Compute the mean and standard deviation of the given sample. (Round your answers to the nearest whole number.)

b. Assuming that the distribution of day-by-day changes of the Dow during financial crises is symmetric and bell shaped, then the Dow falls by more than ____ points 16% of the time. What is the percentage of times in the sample that the Dow actually fell by more than that amount? [HINT: See Example 2(b).]

30. Stock Market Gyrations Following is a sample of the day-by-day change, rounded to the nearest 100 points, in the Dow Jones Industrial Average during 10 successive business days around the start of the financial crisis in October 2008:[43]

$$-100, 400, -200, -500, 200, -300, -200, 900, -100, 200.$$

a. Compute the mean and standard deviation of the given sample. (Round your answers to the nearest whole number.)

b. Assuming that the distribution of day-by-day changes of the Dow during financial crises is symmetric and bell shaped, then the Dow rises by more than ____ points 2.5% of the time. What is the percentage of times in the sample that the Dow actually rose by more than that amount? [HINT: See Example 2(b).]

31. Sport Utility Vehicles Following are highway driving gas mileages of a selection of medium-sized sport utility vehicles (SUVs):[44]

$$17, 18, 17, 18, 21, 16, 21, 18, 16, 14, 15, 22, 17, 19, 17, 18.$$

a. Find the sample standard deviation (rounded to two decimal places).

b. In what gas mileage range does Chebyshev's inequality predict that at least 8/9 (approximately 89%) of the selection will fall?

c. What is the actual percentage of SUV models of the sample that fall in the range predicted in part (b)? Which gives the more accurate prediction of this percentage: Chebyshev's rule or the empirical rule?

32. Sport Utility Vehicles Following are the city driving gas mileages of a selection of sport utility vehicles (SUVs):[45]

$$14, 15, 14, 15, 13, 16, 12, 14, 19, 18, 16, 16, 12, 15, 15, 13.$$

a. Find the sample standard deviation (rounded to two decimal places).

b. In what gas mileage range does Chebyshev's inequality predict that at least 75% of the selection will fall?

c. What is the actual percentage of SUV models of the sample that fall in the range predicted in part (b)? Which gives the more accurate prediction of this percentage: Chebyshev's rule or the empirical rule?

33. Shopping Malls A survey of all the shopping malls in your region yields the following probability distribution, where X is the number of movie theater screens in a selected mall:

Number of Movie Screens	0	1	2	3	4
Probability	.4	.1	.2	.2	.1

Compute the expected value μ and the standard deviation σ of X. (Round answers to two decimal places.) What percentage of malls have a number of movie theater screens within two standard deviations of μ?

34. Pastimes A survey of all the students in your school yields the following probability distribution, where X is the number of movies that a selected student has seen in the past week:

Number of Movies	0	1	2	3	4
Probability	.5	.1	.2	.1	.1

Compute the expected value μ and the standard deviation σ of X. (Round answers to two decimal places.) For what percentage of students is X within two standard deviations of μ?

35. 2010 Income Distribution up to $100,000 The following table shows the distribution of household incomes in 2010[46] for a sample of 1,000 households in the United States with incomes up to $100,000:

Income ($1,000)	10	30	50	70	90
Households	240	290	180	170	120

---

[41] Sources for data: Bureau of Labor Statistics (BLS) (www.bls.gov).

[42] Source: http://finance.google.com.

[43] Ibid.

[44] Figures are the low-end of ranges for 1999 models tested. Source: Oak Ridge National Laboratory: "An Analysis of the Impact of Sport Utility Vehicles in the United States," Stacy C. Davis, Lorena F. Truett (August 2000)/Insurance Institute for Highway Safety (http://cta.ornl.gov/cta/ Publications/pdf/ORNL_TM_2000_147.pdf).

[45] Ibid.

[46] Based on actual income distribution in 2010. Source: U.S. Census Bureau, Current Population Survey, 2010 American Community Survey (www.census.gov).

Compute the expected value μ and the standard deviation σ of the associated random variable X. If we define a "lower-income" family as one whose income is more than one standard deviation below the mean and a "higher-income" family as one whose income is at least one standard deviation above the mean, what is the income gap between higher- and lower-income families in the United States? (Round your answers to the nearest $1,000.)

36. ▣ *2003 Income Distribution up to $100,000* Repeat Exercise 35, using the following data from a sample of 1,000 households in the United States in 2003:[47]

Income ($1,000)	10	30	50	70	90
Households	270	280	200	150	100

37. *Hispanic Employment: Male* The following table shows the approximate number of males of Hispanic origin employed in the United States in 2005, broken down by age group:[48]

Age	15–24.9	25–54.9	55–64.9
Employment (thousands)	16,000	13,000	1,600

  a. Use the rounded midpoints of the given measurement classes to compute the expected value and the standard deviation of the age X of a male Hispanic worker in the United States. (Round all probabilities and intermediate calculations to two decimal places.)

  b. Into what age interval does the empirical rule predict that 68% of all male Hispanic workers will fall? (Round answers to the nearest year.)

38. *Hispanic Employment: Female* Repeat Exercise 37, using the corresponding data for females of Hispanic origin:[49]

Age	15–24.9	25–54.9	55–64.9
Employment (thousands)	1,200	5,000	600

39. *Commerce* You have been told that the average life span of an Internet-based company is 2 years, with a standard deviation of 0.15 years. Further, the associated distribution is highly skewed (not symmetric). Your Internet company is now 2.6 years old. What percentage of all Internet-based companies have enjoyed a life span at least as long as yours? Your answer should contain one of the following phrases: *At least; At most; Approximately.* [HINT: See Example 2.]

40. *Commerce* You have been told that the average life span of a car-compounding service is 3 years, with a standard deviation of 0.2 years. Further, the associated distribution is symmetric but not bell shaped. Your car-compounding service is exactly 2.6 years old. What fraction of car-compounding services last at most as long as yours? Your answer should contain one of the following phrases: *At least; At most; Approximately.* [HINT: See Example 2.]

41. *Batmobiles* The average life span of a Batmobile is 9 years, with a standard deviation of 2 years.[50] Further, the probability distribution of the life spans of Batmobiles is symmetric but is not known to be bell shaped.

Because my old Batmobile has been sold as bat-scrap, I have decided to purchase a new one. According to the above information, there is

(A) at least   **(B)** at most   **(C)** approximately

a ____ percent chance that my new Batmobile will last 13 years or more.

42. *Spiderman Coupés* The average life span of a Spiderman Coupé is 8 years, with a standard deviation of 2 years. Further, the probability distribution of the life spans of Spiderman Coupés is not known to be bell shaped or symmetric. I have just purchased a brand-new Spiderman Coupé. According to the above information, there is

(A) at least   **(B)** at most   **(C)** approximately

a ____ percent chance that my new Spiderman Coupé will last for less than 4 years.

43. *Teenage Pastimes* According to a study,[51] the probability that a randomly selected teenager shopped at a mall at least once during a week was .63. Let X be the number of teenagers in a randomly selected group of 40 that will shop at a mall during the next week.

---

[47]Based on actual income distribution in 2003 (not adjusted for inflation). Source: U.S. Census Bureau, Current Population Survey, 2004 Annual Social and Economic Supplement (www.census.gov).

[48]Figures are rounded. Bounds for the age groups for the first and third categories were adjusted for computational convenience. Source: Bureau of Labor Statistics (ftp://ftp.bls.gov/pub/suppl/empsit.cpseed15.txt).

[49]*Ibid.*

[50] See Example 2.

[51] Source: Rand Youth Poll/Teen-Age Research Unlimited/*New York Times*, March 14, 1998, p. D1.

a. Compute the expected value and standard deviation of X. (Round answers to two decimal places.) [HINT: See Example 5.]

b. Fill in the missing quantity: There is an approximately 2.5% chance that ___ or more teenagers in the group will shop at a mall during the next week.

44. **Other Teenage Pastimes** According to the study referred to in Exercise 43, the probability that a randomly selected teenager played a computer game at least once during a week was .48. Let X be the number of teenagers in a randomly selected group of 30 who will play a computer game during the next 7 days.
   a. Compute the expected value and standard deviation of X. (Round answers to two decimal places.) [HINT: See Example 5.]
   b. Fill in the missing quantity: There is an approximately 16% chance that ___ or more teenagers in the group will play a computer game during the next 7 days.

45. ▼ **Teenage Marketing** In 2000, 22% of all teenagers in the United States had checking accounts.[52] Your bank, *Teen-Chex, Inc.*, is interested in targeting teenagers who do not already have a checking account.
   a. If TeenChex selects a random sample of 1,000 teenagers, what number of teenagers *without* checking accounts can it expect to find? What is the standard deviation of this number? (Round the standard deviation to one decimal place.)
   b. Fill in the missing quantities: There is an approximately 95% chance that between ___ and ___ teenagers in the sample will not have checking accounts. (Round answers to the nearest whole number.)

46. ▼ **Teenage Marketing** In 2000, 18% of all teenagers in the United States owned stocks or bonds.[53] Your brokerage company, *TeenStox, Inc.*, is interested in targeting teenagers who do not already own stocks or bonds.
   a. If TeenStox selects a random sample of 2,000 teenagers, what number of teenagers who *do not* own stocks or bonds can it expect to find? What is the standard deviation of this number? (Round the standard deviation to one decimal place.)
   b. Fill in the missing quantities: There is an approximately 99.7% chance that between ___ and ___ teenagers in the sample will not own stocks or bonds. (Round answers to the nearest whole number.)

47. ▣ ▼ **Supermarkets** A survey of supermarkets in the United States yielded the following relative frequency table, where X is the number of checkout lanes at a randomly chosen supermarket:[54]

x	1	2	3	4	5	6	7	8	9	10
P(X = x)	.01	.04	.04	.08	.10	.15	.25	.20	.08	.05

   a. Compute the mean, variance, and standard deviation (accurate to one decimal place).
   b. As financial planning manager at *Express Lane Mart*, you wish to install a number of checkout lanes that is in the range of at least 75% of all supermarkets. What is this range, according to Chebyshev's inequality? What is the *least* number of checkout lanes you should install so as to fall within this range?

48. ▣ ▼ **Video Arcades** Your company, *Sonic Video, Inc.*, has conducted research that shows the following probability distribution, where X is the number of video arcades in a randomly chosen city with more than 500,000 inhabitants:

x	0	1	2	3	4	5	6	7	8	9
P(X = x)	.07	.09	.35	.25	.15	.03	.02	.02	.01	.01

   a. Compute the mean, variance, and standard deviation (accurate to one decimal place).
   b. As CEO of Sonic Video, you wish to install a chain of video arcades in Sleepy City, U.S.A. The city council regulations require that the number of arcades be within the range shared by at least 75% of all cities. What is this range? What is the *largest* number of video arcades you should install so as to comply with this regulation?

Distribution of Wealth If we model after-tax household income by a normal distribution, then the figures of a 1995 study imply the information in the following table, which should be used for Exercises 49–60.[55] Assume that the distribution of incomes in each country is bell shaped and symmetric.

Country	United States	Canada	Switzerland	Germany	Sweden
Mean Household Income	$38,000	$35,000	$39,000	$34,000	$32,000
Standard Deviation	$21,000	$17,000	$16,000	$14,000	$11,000

49. If we define a "poor" household as one whose after-tax income is at least 1.3 standard deviations below the mean, what is the household income of a poor family in the United States?

[52] Source: Teen-Age Research Unlimited, January 25, 2001 (www .teenresearch.com).

[53] Ibid.

[54] Source: J. T. McClave, P. G. Benson, T. Sincich, *Statistics for Business and Economics*, 7th Ed. (Prentice Hall, 1998) p. 177; W. Chow et al., "A model for predicting a supermarket's annual sales per square foot," Graduate School of Management, Rutgers University.

[55] The data are rounded to the nearest $1,000 and based on a report published by the Luxembourg Income Study. The report shows after-tax income, including government benefits (such as food stamps) of households with children. Our figures were obtained from the published data by assuming a normal distribution of incomes. All data were based on constant 1991 U.S. dollars and converted foreign currencies (adjusted for differences in buying power). Source: Luxembourg Income Study/*New York Times*, August 14, 1995, p. A9.

50. If we define a "poor" household as one whose after-tax income is at least 1.3 standard deviations below the mean, what is the household income of a poor family in Switzerland?

51. If we define a "rich" household as one whose after-tax income is at least 1.3 standard deviations above the mean, what is the household income of a rich family in the United States?

52. If we define a "rich" household as one whose after-tax income is at least 1.3 standard deviations above the mean, what is the household income of a rich family in Sweden?

53. ▼ Refer to Exercise 49. Which of the five countries listed has the poorest households (i.e., the lowest cutoff for considering a household poor)?

54. ▼ Refer to Exercise 52. Which of the five countries listed has the wealthiest households (i.e., the highest cutoff for considering a household rich)?

55. ▼ Which of the five countries listed has the largest gap between rich and poor?

56. ▼ Which of the five countries listed has the smallest gap between rich and poor?

57. What percentage of U.S. families earned an after-tax income of $17,000 or less?

58. What percentage of U.S. families earned an after-tax income of $80,000 or more?

59. What was the after-tax income range of approximately 99.7% of all Germans?

60. What was the after-tax income range of approximately 99.7% of all Swedes?

⬛ Aging *Exercises 61–68 are based on the following list, which shows the percentage of aging population (residents of age 65 and older) in each of the 50 states in 1990, 2000, and 2010:*[56]

1990

4, 9, 10, 10, 10, 10, 10, 11, 11, 11, 11, 11, 11, 11, 11, 12, 12, 12, 12, 12, 12, 13, 13, 13, 13, 13, 13, 13, 13, 13, 13, 13, 13, 13, 13, 14, 14, 14, 14, 14, 14, 14, 15, 15, 15, 15, 15, 15, 18

2000

6, 9, 10, 10, 10, 11, 11, 11, 11, 11, 11, 11, 12, 12, 12, 12, 12, 12, 12, 12, 12, 12, 13, 13, 13, 13, 13, 13, 13, 13, 13, 13, 13, 13, 14, 14, 14, 14, 14, 14, 15, 15, 15, 15, 16, 18

2010

8, 9, 10, 11, 11, 11, 12, 12, 12, 12, 12, 12, 12, 13, 13, 13, 13, 13, 13, 13, 13, 13, 14, 14, 14, 14, 14, 14, 14, 14, 14, 14, 14, 14, 14, 14, 14, 14, 14, 15, 15, 15, 15, 15, 16, 16, 17

61. ⬛ Compute the population mean and standard deviation for the 2000 and 2010 data.

62. ⬛ Compute the population mean and standard deviation for the 1990 and 2000 data.

63. The answer to Exercise 61 suggests that the 2010 population was:
   (A) older on average and more diverse with respect to age
   (B) older on average and less diverse with respect to age
   (C) younger on average and more diverse with respect to age
   (D) younger on average and less diverse with respect to age than the 2000 population.

64. The answer to Exercise 62 suggests that the 1990 population was:
   (A) older on average and more diverse with respect to age
   (B) older on average and less diverse with respect to age
   (C) younger on average and more diverse with respect to age
   (D) younger on average and less diverse with respect to age than the 2000 population.

65. ⬛ Compare the actual percentage of states whose aging population in 2010 was within one standard deviation of the mean to the percentage predicted by the empirical rule. Comment on your answer.

66. ⬛ Compare the actual percentage of states whose aging population in 1990 was within one standard deviation of the mean to the percentage predicted by the empirical rule. Comment on your answer.

67. ⬛ What was the actual percentage of states whose aging population in 2010 was within two standard deviations of the mean? Does Chebyshev's rule apply to the data? Explain.

68. ⬛ What was the actual percentage of states whose aging population in 2000 was within two standard deviations of the mean? Does Chebyshev's rule apply to the data? Explain.

Electric Grid Stress *In early 2000 a Federal Energy Regulatory Commission order (FERC Order 888, first issued in 1996 and advocated by various energy companies, including* Enron*) went into effect, mandating that owners of power transmission lines make them available on the open market. The subsequent levels of stress on the electric grid are believed by many to have led to the Northeast blackout of August 14, 2003. Exercises 69–72 deal with the stress on the national electric grid before and after Order 888 went into effect.*

69. ▼ The following chart shows the approximate standard deviation of the power grid frequency, in $1/1,000$ cycles per second, taken over 6-month periods. (0.9 is the average standard deviation.)[57]

[56] Percentages are rounded and listed in ascending order. Source: U.S. Census Bureau, Census 2000 Summary File 1 (www.census.gov/prod/2001pubs/c2kbr01-10.pdf), Age and Sex Composition: 2010 (www.census.gov/prod/cen2010/briefs/c2010br-03.pdf).

[57] Source: Robert Blohm, energy consultant and adviser to the North American Electric Reliability Council/*New York Times*, August 20, 2003, p. A16.

Which of the following statements are true? (More than one may be true.)

(A) The power grid frequency was at or below the mean until late 1999.

(B) The power grid frequency was more stable in mid-1999 than in 1995.

(C) The power grid frequency was more stable in mid-2002 than in mid-1999.

(D) The greatest fluctuations in the power grid frequency occurred in 2000–2001.

(E) The power grid frequency was more stable around January 1995 than around January 1999.

70. ▼ The following chart shows the approximate monthly means of the power grid frequency, in 1/1,000 cycles per second. 0.0 represents the desired frequency of exactly 60 cycles per second.[58]

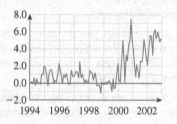

Which of the following statements are true? (More than one may be true.)

(A) Both the mean and the standard deviation show an upward trend from 2000 on.

(B) The mean, but not the standard deviation, shows an upward trend from 2000 on.

(C) The demand for electric power peaked in the second half of 2001.

(D) The standard deviation was larger in the second half of 2002 than in the second half of 1999.

(E) The mean of the monthly means in 2000 was lower than that for 2002, but the standard deviation of the monthly means was higher.

71. ▼ The following chart shows the approximate monthly means of the power grid frequency, in 1/1,000 cycles per second. 0.0 represents the desired frequency of exactly

60 cycles per second. (Note that this is the same data as in Exercise 70 but over a different period of time.)[59]

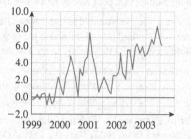

Which of the following statements are true? (More than one may be true.)

(A) Both the mean and the standard deviation show an upward trend from 2002 on.

(B) The mean, but not the standard deviation, shows an upward trend from 2002 on.

(C) The standard deviation, but not the mean, shows an upward trend from 2002 on.

(D) The standard deviation was greater in 2003 than in 2001.

(E) The mean of the monthly means in 2002 was higher than that for 2000, but the standard deviation of the monthly means was lower.

72. ▼ The following chart shows the number of transmission loading relief procedures (procedures undertaken to relieve excessive transmission loads by shifting power to other lines) per month.[60]

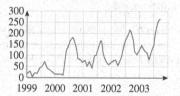

Which of the following statements are true? (More than one may be true.)

(A) Both the annual mean and the standard deviation show a significant upward trend from 2000 on.

(B) The annual mean, but not the standard deviation, shows a significant upward trend from 2000 on.

(C) The annual standard deviation, but not the mean, shows a significant upward trend from 2000 on.

(D) The standard deviation in the second half of 2000 is significantly greater than that in the first half.

(E) The standard deviation in 2000 is significantly greater than that in 2001.

[58] Source: Robert Blohm, energy consultant and adviser to the North American Electric Reliability Council/*New York Times*, August 20, 2003, p. A16.

[59] Source: Eric J. Lerner, "What's wrong with the electric grid?" *The Industrial Physicist,* Oct./Nov. 2003, American Institute of Physics (www.aip.org/tip/INPHFA/vol-9/iss-5/p8.pdf).

[60] *Ibid.*

Communication and Reasoning Exercises

73. Which is greater for a given set of data: the sample standard deviation or the population standard deviation? Explain.

74. Suppose you take larger and larger samples of a given population. Would you expect the sample and population standard deviations to get closer or farther apart? Explain.

75. In one Finite Math class, the average grade was 75, and the standard deviation of the grades was 5. In another Finite Math class, the average grade was 65, and the standard deviation of the grades was 20. What conclusions can you draw about the distributions of the grades in each class?

76. You are a manager in a precision manufacturing firm, and you must evaluate the performance of two employees. You do so by examining the quality of the parts they produce. One particular item should be 50.0 ± 0.3 mm long to be

usable. The first employee produces parts that are an average of 50.1 mm long with a standard deviation of 0.15 mm. The second employee produces parts that are an average of 50.0 mm long with a standard deviation of 0.4 mm. Which employee do you rate higher? Why? (Assume that the empirical rule applies.)

77. ▼ If a finite random variable has an expected value of 10 and a standard deviation of 0, what must its probability distribution be?

78. ▼ If the values of X in a population consist of an equal number of 1s and -1s, what is its standard deviation?

79. ◆ Find an algebraic formula for the population standard deviation of a population $\{x, y\}$ of two scores ($x \leq y$).

80. ◆ Find an algebraic formula for the sample standard deviation of a sample $\{x, y\}$ of two scores ($x \leq y$).

9.5 Normal Distributions

Continuous Random Variables

Figure 9 shows the probability distributions for the number of successes in sequences of 10 and 15 independent Bernoulli trials, each with probability of success $p = .5$.

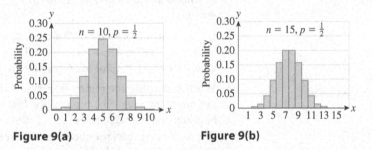

Figure 9(a)   **Figure 9(b)**

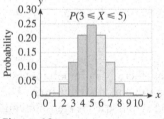

Figure 10

Because each column is 1 unit wide, its area is numerically equal to its height. Thus, the area of each rectangle can be interpreted as a probability. For example, in Figure 9(a) the area of the rectangle over $X = 3$ represents $P(X = 3)$. If we want to find $P(3 \leq X \leq 5)$, we can add up the areas of the three rectangles over 3, 4, and 5, shown shaded in Figure 10. Notice that if we add up the areas of *all* the rectangles in Figure 9(a), the total is 1 because $P(0 \leq X \leq 10) = 1$. We can summarize these observations.

Properties of the Probability Distribution Histogram

In a probability distribution histogram in which each column is 1 unit wide:

- The total area enclosed by the histogram is 1 square unit.

- $P(a \leq X \leq b)$ is the area enclosed by the rectangles lying between and including $X = a$ and $X = b$.

This discussion is motivation for considering another kind of random variable, one whose probability distribution is specified not by a bar graph, as above, but by the graph of a function.

Continuous Random Variable; Probability Density Function

A **continuous random variable** X may take on any real value whatsoever. The probabilities $P(a \leq X \leq b)$ are defined by means of a **probability density function**, a function whose graph lies above the x-axis with the total area between the graph and the x-axis being 1. The probability $P(a \leq X \leq b)$ is defined to be the area enclosed by the curve, the x-axis, and the lines $x = a$ and $x = b$ (see Figure 11).

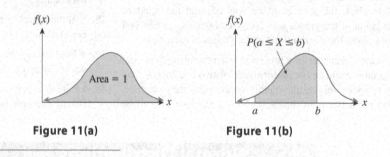

Figure 11(a)   **Figure 11(b)**

Notes

1. In Chapter 8 we defined probability distributions only for *finite* sample spaces. Because continuous random variables have infinite sample spaces, we need the definition above to give meaning to $P(a \leq X \leq b)$ if X is a continuous random variable.

2. If $a = b$, then $P(X = a) = P(a \leq X \leq a)$ is the area under the curve between the lines $x = a$ and $x = a$—no area at all! Thus, when X is a continuous random variable, $P(X = a) = 0$ for every value of a.

3. Whether we take the region in Figure 11(b) to include the boundary or not does not affect the area. The probability $P(a < X < b)$ is defined as the area strictly between the vertical lines $x = a$ and $x = b$ but is, of course, the same as $P(a \leq X \leq b)$, because the boundary contributes nothing to the area. When we are calculating probabilities associated with a continuous random variable,

$$P(a \leq X \leq b) = P(a < X \leq b) = P(a \leq X < b) = P(a < X < b). \blacksquare$$

Normal Density Functions

Among all the possible probability density functions, there is an important class of functions called **normal density functions**, or **normal distributions**. The graph of a normal density function is bell shaped and symmetric, as the following figure shows. The formula for a normal density function is rather complicated looking:

$$f(x) = \frac{1}{\sigma\sqrt{2\pi}} e^{-(x-\mu)^2/(2\sigma^2)}.$$

The quantity μ is called the **mean** and can be any real number. The quantity σ is called the **standard deviation** and can be any positive real number. The number $e = 2.7182\ldots$ is a useful constant that shows up many places in mathematics, much as the constant π does. Finally, the constant $1/(\sigma\sqrt{2\pi})$ that appears in front is there to make the total area come out to be 1. We rarely use the actual formula in computations; instead, we use tables or technology.

Normal Density Function; Normal Distribution

A **normal density function**, or **normal distribution**, is a function of the form

$$f(x) = \frac{1}{\sigma\sqrt{2\pi}}\, e^{-(x-\mu)^2/(2\sigma^2)},$$

where μ is the mean and σ is the standard deviation. Its graph is bell shaped and symmetric, and has the following form:

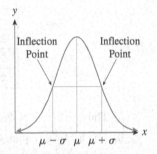

The "inflection points" are the points where the curve changes from bending in one direction to bending in another.*

* Pretend that you are driving along the curve in a car. Then the points of inflection are the points where you would change the direction in which you are steering (from left to right or from right to left).

Figure 12 shows the graphs of several normal density functions. The third of these has mean 0 and standard deviation 1, and is called the **standard normal distribution**. We use Z rather than X to refer to the standard normal variable.

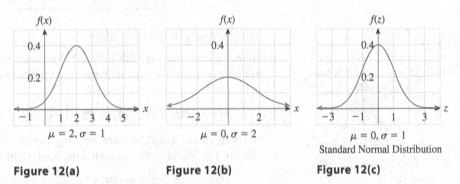

Figure 12(a)   **Figure 12(b)**   **Figure 12(c)**

Using Technology

The graphs in Figure 12 can be drawn on a TI-83/84 Plus or the Website grapher.

TI-83/84 Plus
Figure 12(a):
Y₁=normalpdf(x,2,1)
Figure 12(b):
Y₁=normalpdf(x,0,2)
Figure 12(c):
Y₁=normalpdf(x)

W **Website**
www.WanerMath.com

→ Online Utilities

→ Function Evaluator and Grapher

Figure 12(a):
normalpdf(x,2,1)
Figure 12(b):
normalpdf(x,0,2)
Figure 12(c):
normalpdf(x)

Calculating Probabilities for the Standard Normal Distribution

The standard normal distribution has $\mu = 0$ and $\sigma = 1$. The corresponding variable is called the **standard normal variable**, which we always denote by Z. Recall that to calculate the probability $P(a \le Z \le b)$, we need to find the area under the distribution curve between the vertical lines $z = a$ and $z = b$. We can use the table in the Appendix to look up these areas, or we can use technology. Here is an example.

EXAMPLE 1   **Standard Normal Distribution**

Let Z be the standard normal variable. Calculate the following probabilities:

a. $P(0 \le Z \le 2.4)$ **b.** $P(0 \le Z \le 2.43)$

c. $P(-1.37 \le Z \le 2.43)$ **d.** $P(1.37 \le Z \le 2.43)$

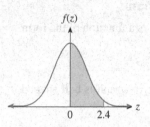

$f(z)$

0   2.4 z

Figure 13

Solution

a. We are asking for the shaded area under the standard normal curve shown in Figure 13. We can find this area, correct to four decimal places, by looking at the table in the Appendix, which lists the area under the standard normal curve from $Z = 0$ to $Z = b$ for any value of b between 0 and 3.09. To use the table, write 2.4 as 2.40, and read the entry in the row labeled 2.4 and the column labeled 0.00 ($2.4 + 0.00 = 2.40$). Here is the relevant portion of the table:

Z	0.00	0.01	0.02	0.03
2.3	.4893	.4896	.4898	.4901
→ 2.4	.4918	.4920	.4922	.4925
2.5	.4938	.4940	.4941	.4943

Thus, $P(0 \leq Z \leq 2.40) = .4918$.

b. The area we require can be read from the same portion of the table shown above. Write 2.43 as $2.4 + 0.03$, and read the entry in the row labeled 2.4 and the column labeled 0.03:

Z	0.00	0.01	0.02	0.03
2.3	.4893	.4896	.4898	.4901
→ 2.4	.4918	.4920	.4922	.4925
2.5	.4938	.4940	.4941	.4943

Thus, $P(0 \leq Z \leq 2.43) = .4925$.

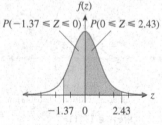

$f(z)$

$P(-1.37 \leq Z \leq 0)$ $P(0 \leq Z \leq 2.43)$

−1.37 0   2.43 z

Figure 14

c. Here, we cannot use the table directly because the range $-1.37 \leq Z \leq 2.43$ does not start at 0. But we can break the area up into two smaller areas that start or end at 0:

$$P(-1.37 \leq Z \leq 2.43) = P(-1.37 \leq Z \leq 0) + P(0 \leq Z \leq 2.43).$$

In terms of the graph, we are splitting the desired area into two smaller areas (Figure 14). We already calculated the area of the right-hand piece in part (b):

$$P(0 \leq Z \leq 2.43) = .4925.$$

For the left-hand piece, the symmetry of the normal curve tells us that

$$P(-1.37 \leq Z \leq 0) = P(0 \leq Z \leq 1.37).$$

This we can find on the table. Look at the row labeled 1.3 and the column labeled 0.07, and read

$$P(-1.37 \leq Z \leq 0) = P(0 \leq Z \leq 1.37) = .4147.$$

Thus,

$$P(-1.37 \leq Z \leq 2.43) = P(-1.37 \leq Z \leq 0) + P(0 \leq Z \leq 2.43)$$
$$= .4147 + .4925$$
$$= .9072.$$

d. The range $1.37 \leq Z \leq 2.43$ does not contain 0, so we cannot use the technique of part (c). Instead, the corresponding area can be computed as the *difference* of two areas:

$$P(1.37 \leq Z \leq 2.43) = P(0 \leq Z \leq 2.43) - P(0 \leq Z \leq 1.37)$$
$$= .4925 - .4147$$
$$= .0778.$$

Using Technology

Technology can be used to calculate the probabilities in Example 1. For instance, the calculation for part (c) is as follows:

TI-83/84 Plus
`normalcdf(-1.37,2.43)`
(`normalcdf` is in `2ND` `VARS`.)
[More details in the Technology Guide.]

Spreadsheet
`=NORMSDIST(2.43)`
`-NORMSDIST(-1.37)`
[More details in the Technology Guide.]

W Website
www.WanerMath.com
→ Online Utilities
→ Normal Distribution
   Utility

Set up as shown, and press "Calculate Probability".

Calculating Probabilities for Any Normal Distribution

Although we have tables to compute the area under the *standard* normal curve, there are no readily available tables for nonstandard distributions. For example, if $\mu = 2$ and $\sigma = 3$, then how would we calculate $P(0.5 \leq X \leq 3.2)$? The following conversion formula provides a method for doing so.

Standardizing a Normal Distribution

If X has a normal distribution with mean μ and standard deviation σ, and if Z is the standard normal variable, then

$$P(a \leq X \leq b) = P\left(\frac{a - \mu}{\sigma} \leq Z \leq \frac{b - \mu}{\sigma}\right).$$

> **Quick Example**
>
> **1.** If $\mu = 2$ and $\sigma = 3$, then
>
> $$P(0.5 \leq X \leq 3.2) = P\left(\frac{0.5 - 2}{3} \leq Z \leq \frac{3.2 - 2}{3}\right)$$
> $$= P(-0.5 \leq Z \leq 0.4) = .1915 + .1554 = .3469.$$

To completely justify the above formula requires more mathematics than we shall discuss here. However, here is the main idea: If X is normal with mean μ and standard deviation σ, then $X - \mu$ is normal with mean 0 and standard deviation still σ, while $(X - \mu)/\sigma$ is normal with mean 0 and standard deviation 1. In other words, $(X - \mu)/\sigma = Z$. Therefore,

$$P(a \leq X \leq b) = P\left(\frac{a - \mu}{\sigma} \leq \frac{X - \mu}{\sigma} \leq \frac{b - \mu}{\sigma}\right) = P\left(\frac{a - \mu}{\sigma} \leq Z \leq \frac{b - \mu}{\sigma}\right).$$

EXAMPLE 2   Quality Control

Pressure gauges manufactured by *Precision Corp.* must be checked for accuracy before being placed on the market. To test a pressure gauge, a worker uses it to measure the pressure of a sample of compressed air known to be at a pressure of exactly 50 pounds per square inch. If the gauge reading is off by more than 1% (0.5 pounds), it is rejected. Assuming that the reading of a pressure gauge under these circumstances is a normal random variable with mean 50 and standard deviation 0.4, find the percentage of gauges rejected.

Solution If X is the reading of the gauge, then X has a normal distribution with $\mu = 50$ and $\sigma = 0.4$. We are asking for $P(X < 49.5$ or $X > 50.5) = 1 - P(49.5 \leq X \leq 50.5)$. We calculate

$$P(49.5 \leq X \leq 50.5) = P\left(\frac{49.5 - 50}{0.4} \leq Z \leq \frac{50.5 - 50}{0.4}\right) \quad \text{Standardize}$$

$$= P(-1.25 \leq Z \leq 1.25)$$

$$= 2 \cdot P(0 \leq Z \leq 1.25)$$

$$= 2(.3944) = .7888.$$

So $\quad P(X < 49.5$ or $X > 50.5) = 1 - P(49.5 \leq X \leq 50.5)$

$$= 1 - .7888 = .2112.$$

In other words, about 21% of the gauges will be rejected.

In many applications we need to know the probability that a value of a normal random variable will lie within one standard deviation of the mean, or within two standard deviations, or within some number of standard deviations. To compute these probabilities, we first notice that, if X has a normal distribution with mean μ and standard deviation σ, then

$$P(\mu - k\sigma \leq X \leq \mu + k\sigma) = P(-k \leq Z \leq k)$$

by the standardizing formula. We can compute these probabilities for various values of k using the table in the Appendix, and we obtain the following results.

Probability of a Normal Distribution Being within k Standard Deviations of Its Mean

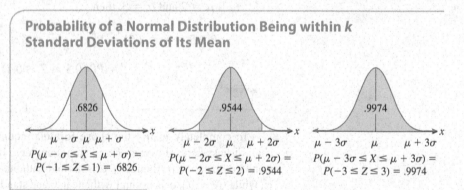

Now you can see where the empirical rule in Section 9.4 comes from! Notice also that the probabilities above are a good deal larger than the lower bounds given by Chebyshev's rule. Chebyshev's rule must work for distributions that are skew or any shape whatsoever.

EXAMPLE 3 Loans

The values of mortgage loans made by a certain bank one year were normally distributed with a mean of $120,000 and a standard deviation of $40,000.

a. What is the probability that a randomly selected mortgage loan was in the range of $40,000–$200,000?

b. You would like to state in your annual report that 50% of all mortgage loans were in a certain range with the mean in the center. What is that range?

Solution

a. We are asking for the probability that a loan was within two standard deviations ($80,000) of the mean. By the calculation done previously, this probability is .9544.

b. We look for the k such that

$$P(120,000 - k \cdot 40,000 \leq X \leq 120,000 + k \cdot 40,000) = .5$$

Because

$$P(120,000 - k \cdot 40,000 \leq X \leq 120,000 + k \cdot 40,000) = P(-k \leq Z \leq k),$$

we look in the Appendix to see for which k we have

$$P(0 \leq Z \leq k) = .25$$

so that $P(-k \leq Z \leq k) = .5$. That is, we look *inside* the table to see where 0.25 is, and find the corresponding k. We find

$$P(0 \leq Z \leq 0.67) = .2486$$

and

$$P(0 \leq Z \leq 0.68) = .2517.$$

Therefore, the k that we want is about halfway between 0.67 and 0.68—call it 0.675. This tells us that 50% of all mortgage loans were in the range

$$120,000 - 0.675 \cdot 40,000 = \$93,000$$

to

$$120,000 + 0.675 \cdot 40,000 = \$147,000.$$

Normal Approximation to a Binomial Distribution

You might have noticed that the histograms of some of the binomial distributions we have drawn (for example, those in Figure 9) have a very rough bell shape. In fact, in many cases it is possible to draw a normal curve that closely approximates a given binomial distribution.

Normal Approximation to a Binomial Distribution

If X is the number of successes in a sequence of n independent Bernoulli trials, with probability p of success in each trial, and if the range of values of X within three standard deviations of the mean lies entirely within the range 0 to n (the possible values of X), then

$$P(a \leq X \leq b) \approx P(a - 0.5 \leq Y \leq b + 0.5),$$

where Y has a normal distribution with the same mean and standard deviation as X; that is, $\mu = np$ and $\sigma = \sqrt{npq}$, where $q = 1 - p$.

Notes

1. The condition that $0 \leq \mu - 3\sigma < \mu + 3\sigma \leq n$ is satisfied if n is sufficiently large and p is not too close to 0 or 1; it ensures that most of the normal curve lies in the range 0 to n.

2. In the formula $P(a \leq X \leq b) \approx P(a - 0.5 \leq Y \leq b + 0.5)$, we assume that a and b are integers. The use of $a - 0.5$ and $b + 0.5$ is called the **continuity correction**. To see that it is necessary, think about what would happen if you wanted to approximate, say, $P(X = 2) = P(2 \leq X \leq 2)$. Should the answer be 0? ■

Figures 15 and 16 show two binomial distributions with their normal approximations superimposed and illustrate how closely the normal approximation fits the binomial distribution.

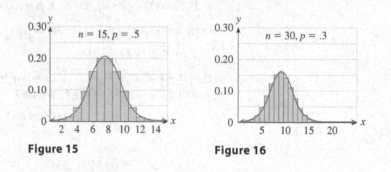

Figure 15   Figure 16

EXAMPLE 4   **Coin Tosses**

a. If you flip a fair coin 100 times, what is the probability of getting more than 55 heads or fewer than 45 heads?

b. What number of heads (out of 100) would make you suspect that the coin is not fair?

Solution

a. We are asking for

$$P(X < 45 \text{ or } X > 55) = 1 - P(45 \leq X \leq 55).$$

We *could* compute this by calculating

$$1 - [C(100, 45)(.5)^{45}(.5)^{55} + C(100, 46)(.5)^{46}(.5)^{54} + \cdots + C(100, 55)(.5)^{55}(.5)^{45}],$$

but we can much more easily *approximate* it by looking at a normal distribution with mean $\mu = 50$ and standard deviation $\sigma = \sqrt{(100)(.5)(.5)} = 5$. (Notice that three standard deviations above and below the mean is the range 35 to 65, which is well within the range of possible values for X, which is 0 to 100, so the approximation should be a good one.) Let Y have this normal distribution. Then

$$P(45 \leq X \leq 55) \approx P(44.5 \leq Y \leq 55.5)$$
$$= P(-1.1 \leq Z \leq 1.1)$$
$$= .7286.$$

Therefore,

$$P(X < 45 \text{ or } X > 55) \approx 1 - .7286 = .2714.$$

b. This is a deep question that touches on the concept of **statistical significance**: What evidence is strong enough to overturn a reasonable assumption (the assumption that the coin is fair)? Statisticians have developed sophisticated ways of answering this question, but we can look at one simple test now. Suppose we tossed a coin 100 times and got 66 heads. If the coin were fair, then $P(X > 65) \approx P(Y > 65.5) = P(Z > 3.1) \approx .001$. This is small enough to raise a reasonable doubt that the coin is fair. However, we should not be too surprised if we threw 56 heads because we can calculate $P(X > 55) \approx .1357$, which is not such a small probability. As we said, the actual tests of statistical significance are more sophisticated than this, but we shall not go into them.

9.5   EXERCISES

▼ more advanced   ◆ challenging
🔲 indicates exercises that should be solved using technology

Note: Answers for Section 9.5 were computed by using the four-digit table in the Appendix and may differ slightly from the more accurate answers generated by using technology.

In Exercises 1–8, Z is the standard normal variable. Find the indicated probabilities. [HINT: See Example 1.]

1. $P(0 \leq Z \leq 0.5)$

2. $P(0 \leq Z \leq 1.5)$

3. $P(-0.71 \leq Z \leq 0.71)$

4. $P(-1.71 \leq Z \leq 1.71)$

5. $P(-0.71 \leq Z \leq 1.34)$

6. $P(-1.71 \leq Z \leq 0.23)$

7. $P(0.5 \leq Z \leq 1.5)$

8. $P(0.71 \leq Z \leq 1.82)$

In Exercises 9–14, X has a normal distribution with the given mean and standard deviation. Find the indicated probabilities. [HINT: See Quick Example 1.]

9. $\mu = 50, \sigma = 10$, find $P(35 \leq X \leq 65)$

10. $\mu = 40, \sigma = 20$, find $P(35 \leq X \leq 45)$

11. $\mu = 50, \sigma = 10$, find $P(30 \leq X \leq 62)$

12. $\mu = 40, \sigma = 20$, find $P(30 \leq X \leq 53)$

13. $\mu = 100, \sigma = 15$, find $P(110 \leq X \leq 130)$

14. $\mu = 100, \sigma = 15$, find $P(70 \leq X \leq 80)$

15. ▼ Find the probability that a normal variable takes on values within 0.5 standard deviations of its mean.

16. ▼ Find the probability that a normal variable takes on values within 1.5 standard deviations of its mean.

17. ▼ Find the probability that a normal variable takes on values more than $\frac{2}{3}$ standard deviations away from its mean.

18. ▼ Find the probability that a normal variable takes on values more than $\frac{5}{3}$ standard deviations away from its mean.

19. ▼ Suppose X is a normal random variable with mean $\mu = 100$ and standard deviation $\sigma = 10$. Find b such that $P(100 \leq X \leq b) = .3$. [HINT: See Example 3.]

20. ▼ Suppose X is a normal random variable with mean $\mu = 10$ and standard deviation $\sigma = 5$. Find b such that $P(10 \leq X \leq b) = .4$. [HINT: See Example 3.]

21. ▼ Suppose X is a normal random variable with mean $\mu = 100$ and standard deviation $\sigma = 10$. Find a such that $P(X \geq a) = .04$.

22. ▼ Suppose X is a normal random variable with mean $\mu = 10$ and standard deviation $\sigma = 5$. Find a such that $P(X \geq a) = .03$.

23. If you roll a die 100 times, what is the approximate probability that you will roll between 10 and 15 ones, inclusive? (Round your answer to two decimal places.) [HINT: See Example 4.]

24. If you roll a die 100 times, what is the approximate probability that you will roll between 15 and 20 ones, inclusive? (Round your answer to two decimal places.) [HINT: See Example 4.]

25. If you roll a die 200 times, what is the approximate probability that you will roll fewer than 25 ones? (Round your answer to two decimal places.)

26. If you roll a die 200 times, what is the approximate probability that you will roll more than 40 ones? (Round your answer to two decimal places.)

Applications

27. *SAT Scores* SAT test scores are normally distributed with a mean of 500 and a standard deviation of 100. Find the probability that a randomly chosen test-taker will score between 450 and 550. [HINT: See Example 3.]

28. *SAT Scores* SAT test scores are normally distributed with a mean of 500 and a standard deviation of 100. Find the probability that a randomly chosen test-taker will score 650 or higher. [HINT: See Example 3.]

29. *LSAT Scores* LSAT test scores are normally distributed with a mean of 151 and a standard deviation of 7. Find the probability that a randomly chosen test-taker will score between 137 and 158.

30. *LSAT Scores* LSAT test scores are normally distributed with a mean of 151 and a standard deviation of 7. Find the probability that a randomly chosen test-taker will score 144 or lower.

31. *IQ Scores* IQ scores (as measured by the Stanford-Binet intelligence test) are normally distributed with a mean of 100 and a standard deviation of 16. What percentage of the population has an IQ score between 110 and 140? (Round your answer to the nearest percentage point.)

32. *IQ Scores* Refer to Exercise 31. What percentage of the population has an IQ score between 80 and 90? (Round your answer to the nearest percentage point.)

33. *IQ Scores* Refer to Exercise 31. Find the approximate number of people in the United States (assuming a total population of 323,000,000) with an IQ of 120 or higher.

34. *IQ Scores* Refer to Exercise 31. Find the approximate number of people in the United States (assuming a total population of 323,000,000) with an IQ of 140 or higher.

35. *SAT Scores* SAT test scores are normally distributed with a mean of 500 and a standard deviation of 100. What score would place you in the top 5% of test-takers? [HINT: See Example 3.]

36. *LSAT Scores* LSAT test scores are normally distributed with a mean of 151 and a standard deviation of 7. What score would place you in the top 2% of test-takers? [HINT: See Example 3.]

37. *Baseball* The mean batting average in major league baseball is about 0.250. If batting averages are normally distributed, the standard deviation in the averages is 0.03, and there are 250 batters, what is the expected number of batters with an average of at least 0.400?

38. *Baseball* The mean batting average in major league baseball is about 0.250. If batting averages are normally distributed, the standard deviation in the averages is 0.05, and there are 250 batters, what is the expected number of batters with an average of at least 0.400?[61]

39. *Marketing* Your pickle company rates its pickles on a scale of spiciness from 1 to 10. Market research shows that customer preferences for spiciness are normally distributed, with a mean of 7.5 and a standard deviation of 1. Assuming that you sell 100,000 jars of pickles, how many jars with a spiciness of 9 or above do you expect to sell?

40. *Marketing* Your hot sauce company rates its sauce on a scale of spiciness of 1 to 20. Market research shows that customer preferences for spiciness are normally distributed, with a mean of 12 and a standard deviation of 2.5. Assuming that you sell 300,000 bottles of sauce, how many bottles with a spiciness below 9 do you expect to sell?

Distribution of Income *If we model after-tax household income with a normal distribution, then the figures of a 1995 study imply the information in the following table, which should be used for Exercises 41–46.[62] Assume that the distribution of incomes in each country was normal, and round all percentages to the nearest whole number.*

Country	United States	Canada	Switzerland	Germany	Sweden
Mean Household Income ($)	38,000	35,000	39,000	34,000	32,000
Standard Deviation	21,000	17,000	16,000	14,000	11,000

41. What percentage of U.S. households had an income of $50,000 or more?

42. What percentage of German households had an income of $50,000 or more?

43. What percentage of Swiss households were either very wealthy (income at least $100,000) or very poor (income at most $12,000)?

---

[61] The last time that a batter ended the year with an average above 0.400 was in 1941. The batter was Ted Williams of the Boston Red Sox, and his average was 0.406. Over the years, as pitching and batting have improved, the standard deviation in batting averages has declined from around 0.05 when professional baseball began to around 0.03 by the end of the twentieth century. For a very interesting discussion of statistics in baseball and in evolution, see Stephen Jay Gould, *Full House: The Spread of Excellence from Plato to Darwin*, Random House, 1997.

[62] The data are rounded to the nearest $1,000 and are based on a report published by the Luxembourg Income Study. The report shows after-tax income, including government benefits (such as food stamps), of households with children. Our figures were obtained from the published data by assuming a normal distribution of incomes. All data were based on constant 1991 U.S. dollars and converted foreign currencies (adjusted for differences in buying power). Source: Luxembourg Income Study/*New York Times*, August 14, 1995, p. A9.

44. What percentage of Swedish households were either very wealthy (income at least $100,000) or very poor (income at most $12,000)?

45. Which country had a higher proportion of very poor families (income $12,000 or less): the United States or Canada?

46. Which country had a higher proportion of very poor families (income $12,000 or less): Canada or Switzerland?

47. ▼ *Comparing IQ Tests* IQ scores as measured by both the Stanford-Binet intelligence test and the Wechsler intelligence test have a mean of 100. The standard deviation for the Stanford-Binet test is 16, while that for the Wechsler test is 15. For which test do a smaller percentage of test-takers score less than 80? Why?

48. ▼ *Comparing IQ Tests* Referring to Exercise 47, for which test do a larger percentage of test-takers score more than 120?

49. ▼ *Product Repairs* The new copier your business bought lists a mean time between failures of 6 months, with a standard deviation of 1 month. One month after a repair, it breaks down again. Is this surprising? (Assume that the times between failures are normally distributed.)

50. ▼ *Product Repairs* The new computer your business bought lists a mean time between failures of 1 year, with a standard deviation of 2 months. Ten months after a repair, it breaks down again. Is this surprising? (Assume that the times between failures are normally distributed.)

Software Testing Exercises 51–56 are based on the following information, gathered from student testing of a statistical software package called MODSTAT.[63] Students were asked to complete certain tasks using the software, without any instructions. The results were as follows. (Assume that the time for each task is normally distributed.)

Task	Mean Time (minutes)	Standard Deviation
Task 1: Descriptive Analysis of Data	11.4	5.0
Task 2: Standardizing Scores	11.9	9.0
Task 3: Poisson Probability Table	7.3	3.9
Task 4: Areas under Normal Curve	9.1	5.5

51. Find the probability that a student will take at least 10 minutes to complete Task 1.

52. Find the probability that a student will take at least 10 minutes to complete Task 3.

53. ▼ Assuming that the time it takes a student to complete each task is independent of the others, find the probability that a student will take at least 10 minutes to complete each of Tasks 1 and 2.

54. ▼ Assuming that the time it takes a student to complete each task is independent of the others, find the probability that a student will take at least 10 minutes to complete each of Tasks 3 and 4.

55. ◆ It can be shown that if X and Y are independent normal random variables with means μ_X and μ_Y, and standard deviations σ_X and σ_Y respectively, then their sum $X + Y$ is also normally distributed and has mean $\mu = \mu_X + \mu_Y$ and standard deviation $\sigma = \sqrt{\sigma_X^2 + \sigma_Y^2}$. Assuming that the time it takes a student to complete each task is independent of the others, find the probability that a student will take at least 20 minutes to complete both Tasks 1 and 2.

56. ◆ Referring to Exercise 55, compute the probability that a student will take at least 20 minutes to complete both Tasks 3 and 4.

57. *Internet Access* In 2010, 71% of all households in the United States had Internet access.[64] Find the probability that, in a small town with 1,200 households, at least 840 had Internet access in 2010. [**HINT**: See Example 4.]

58. *Television Ratings* According to data from the Nielsen Company, there is a 1.8% chance that any television that is turned on during the time of the evening newscasts will be tuned to ABC's evening news show.[65] Your company wishes to advertise on a local station carrying ABC that serves a community with 5,000 households that regularly watch TV during this time slot. Find the approximate probability that at least 100 households will be tuned in to the show. [**HINT**: See Example 4.]

59. *Aviation* The probability of a plane crashing on a single trip in 2010 was .00000276.[66] Find the approximate probability that in 10 million flights, there will be fewer than 35 crashes.

60. *Aviation* The probability of a plane crashing on a single trip in 1990 was .00000087. Find the approximate probability that in 100 million flights, there will be more than 110 crashes.

---

[63] Data are rounded to one decimal place. Source: *Student Evaluations of MODSTAT,* by Joseph M. Nowakowski, Muskingum College, New Concord, OH, 1997.

[64] Source: *Digital Nation: Expanding Internet Usage,* National Telecommunications and Information Administration, February 2011 (www.ntia.doc.gov/data).

[65] As of November 2011. Source: The Nielsen Company via the TVbytheNumbers website (http://tvbythenumbers.zap2it.com/category/ratings/evening-news).

[66] Figures are for scheduled commercial flights. Source for this exercise and the following three: National Transportation Safety Board (www.ntsb.gov).

61. ▼ *Insurance* Your company issues flight insurance. You charge $3, and in the event of a plane crash, you will pay out $1 million to the victim or his or her family. In 2010 the probability of a plane crashing on a single trip was .00000276. If 10 people per flight buy insurance from you, what was your approximate probability of losing money over the course of 10 million flights in 2010? [HINT: First determine how many crashes there must be for you to lose money.]

62. ▼ *Insurance* Refer back to Exercise 61. What is your approximate probability of losing money over the course of 100 million flights?

63. ◆ *Polls* In a certain political poll, each person polled has a 90% probability of telling his or her real preference. Suppose that 55% of the population really prefer candidate Goode and 45% prefer candidate Slick. First find the probability that a person polled will say that he or she prefers Goode. Then find the approximate probability that, if 1,000 people are polled, more than 52% will say that they prefer Goode.

64. ◆ *Polls* In a certain political poll, each person polled has a 90% probability of telling his or her real preference. Suppose that 1,000 people are polled and 51% say that they prefer candidate Goode, while 49% say that they prefer candidate Slick. Find the approximate probability that Goode could do at least this well if, in fact, only 49% prefer Goode.

65. ◆ *IQ Scores* Mensa is a club for people with high IQs. To qualify, you must be in the top 2% of the population. One way of qualifying is by having an IQ of at least 148, as measured by the Cattell intelligence test. Assuming that scores on this test are normally distributed with a mean of 100, what is the standard deviation? [HINT: Use the table in the Appendix "backward."]

66. ◆ *SAT Scores* Another way to qualify for Mensa (see Exercise 65) is to score at least 1,250 on the SAT [combined Critical Reading (Verbal, before March 2005) and Math scores], which puts you in the top 2%. Assuming that SAT scores are normally distributed with a mean of 1,000, what is the standard deviation? (See the hint for Exercise 65.)

Communication and Reasoning Exercises

67. Under what assumptions are the estimates in the empirical rule exact?

68. If X is a continuous random variable, what values can the quantity $P(X = a)$ have?

69. Which is larger for a continuous random variable: $P(X \leq a)$ or $P(X < a)$?

70. Which of the following is greater: $P(X \leq b)$ or $P(a \leq X \leq b)$?

71. ▼ A uniform continuous distribution is one with a probability density curve that is a horizontal line. If X takes on values between the numbers a and b with a uniform distribution, find the height of its probability density curve.

72. ▼ Which would you expect to have the greater variance: the standard normal distribution or the uniform distribution taking values between -1 and 1? Explain.

73. ◆ Which would you expect to have a density curve that is higher at the mean: the standard normal distribution or a normal distribution with standard deviation 0.5? Explain.

74. ◆ Suppose students must perform two tasks: Task 1 and Task 2. Which of the following would you expect to have a smaller standard deviation?
    (A) The time it takes a student to perform both tasks if the time it takes to complete Task 2 is independent of the time it takes to complete Task 1.
    (B) The time it takes a student to perform both tasks if students will perform similarly in both tasks.
    Explain.

CHAPTER 9 REVIEW

KEY CONCEPTS

www.WanerMath.com
Go to the Website to find a comprehensive and interactive Web-based summary of Chapter 9.

9.1 Random Variables and Distributions
Random variable; discrete vs. continuous random variable [p. 648]
Probability distribution of a finite random variable [p. 651]
Using measurement classes [p. 652]

9.2 Bernoulli Trials and Binomial Random Variables
Bernoulli trial [p. 659]
Binomial random variable [p. 660]
Probability distribution of binomial random variable:
$$P(X = x) = C(n, x)p^x q^{n-x} \text{ [p. 662]}$$

9.3 Measures of Central Tendency
Sample, sample mean; population, population mean [p. 667]

Median, mode [p. 668]
Expected value of a random variable:
$$\mu = E(X) = \sum_i x_i \cdot P(X = x_i)$$
[p. 671]
Expected value of a binomial random variable: $\mu = E(X) = np$ [p. 673]

9.4 Measures of Dispersion
Population variance:
$$\sigma^2 = \frac{\sum_{i=1}^{n}(x_i - \mu)^2}{n}$$

Population standard deviation:
$$\sigma = \sqrt{\sigma^2} \text{ [p. 680]}$$
Sample variance:
$$s^2 = \frac{\sum_{i=1}^{n}(x_i - \bar{x})^2}{n - 1}$$

Sample standard deviation: $s = \sqrt{s^2}$ [p. 680]
Chebyshev's rule [p. 683]
Empirical rule [p. 683]

Variance of a random variable:
$$\sigma^2 = \sum_i (x_i - \mu)^2 P(X = x_i)$$
[p. 685]
Standard deviation of X: $\sigma = \sqrt{\sigma^2}$ [p. 685]
Variance and standard deviation of a binomial random variable:
$$\sigma^2 = npq, \sigma = \sqrt{npq} \text{ [p. 687]}$$

9.5 Normal Distributions
Probability density function [p. 696]
Normal density function; normal distribution; standard normal distribution [p. 697]
Calculating probabilities based on the standard normal distribution [p. 697]
Standardizing a normal distribution [p. 699]
Calculating probabilities based on non-standard normal distributions [p. 699]
Normal approximation to a binomial distribution [p. 701]

REVIEW EXERCISES

In Exercises 1–6, find the probability distribution for the given random variable and draw a histogram.

1. A couple has two children; X = the number of boys. (Assume an equal likelihood of a child being a boy or a girl.)

2. A couple has three children; X = the number of girls. (Assume an equal likelihood of a child being a boy or a girl.)

3. A four-sided die (with sides numbered 1 through 4) is rolled twice in succession; X = the sum of the two numbers.

4. 48.2% of Xbox players are in their teens, 38.6% are in their twenties, 11.6% are in their thirties, and the rest are in their forties; X = age of an Xbox player. (Use the midpoints of the measurement classes.)

5. From a bin that contains 20 defective joysticks and 30 good ones, 3 are chosen at random; X = the number of defective joysticks chosen. (Round all probabilities to four decimal places.)

6. Two dice are weighted so that each number 2, 3, 4, and 5 is half as likely to face up as each of 1 and 6; X = the number of 1s that face up when both are thrown.

7. Use any method to calculate the sample mean, median, and standard deviation of the following sample of scores: $-1, 2, 0, 3, 6$.

8. Use any method to calculate the sample mean, median, and standard deviation of the following sample of scores: 4, 4, 5, 6, 6.

9. Give an example of a sample of four scores with mean 1 and median 0. (Arrange them in ascending order.)

10. Give an example of a sample of six scores with sample standard deviation 0 and mean 2.

11. Give an example of a population of six scores with mean 0 and population standard deviation 1.

12. Give an example of a sample of five scores with mean 0 and sample standard deviation 1.

A die is constructed in such a way that rolling a 6 is twice as likely as rolling each other number. That die is rolled four times. Let X be the number of times a 6 is rolled. Evaluate the probabilities in Exercises 13–20.

13. $P(X = 1)$ 14. $P(X = 3)$

15. The probability that 6 comes up at most twice

16. The probability that 6 comes up at most once

17. The probability that X is more than 3

18. The probability that X is at least 2

19. $P(1 \leq X \leq 3)$ 20. $P(X \leq 3)$

21. A couple has three children; $X =$ the number of girls. (Assume an equal likelihood of a child being a boy or a girl.) Find the expected value and standard deviation of X, and complete the following sentence with the smallest possible whole number: All values of X lie within ___ standard deviations of the expected value.

22. A couple has four children; $X =$ the number of boys. (Assume only a 25% chance of a child being a boy.) Find the expected value and standard deviation of X, and complete the following sentence with the smallest possible whole number: All values of X lie within ___ standard deviations of the expected value.

23. A random variable X has the following frequency distribution:

x	-3	-2	-1	0	1	2	3
$fr(X = x)$	1	2	3	4	3	2	1

Find the probability distribution, expected value, and standard deviation of X, and complete the following sentence: 87.5% (or 14/16) of the time, X is within ___ (round to one decimal place) standard deviations of the expected value.

24. A random variable X has the following frequency distribution:

x	-4	-2	0	2	4	6
$fr(X = x)$	3	3	4	5	3	2

Find the probability distribution, expected value, and standard deviation of X, and complete the following sentence: ___ percent of the values of X lie within one standard deviation of the expected value.

25. A random variable X has expected value $\mu = 100$ and standard deviation $\sigma = 16$. Use Chebyshev's rule to find an interval in which X is guaranteed to lie with a probability of at least 90%.

26. A random variable X has a symmetric distribution and an expected value $\mu = 200$ and standard deviation $\sigma = 5$. Use Chebyshev's rule to find a value that X is guaranteed to exceed with a probability of at most 10%.

27. A random variable X has a bell-shaped symmetric distribution, with expected value $\mu = 200$ and standard deviation $\sigma = 20$. The empirical rule tells us that X has a value greater than ___ approximately 0.15% of the time.

28. A random variable X has a bell-shaped symmetric distribution, with expected value $\mu = 100$ and standard deviation $\sigma = 30$. Use the empirical rule to give an interval in which X lies approximately 95% of the time.

In Exercises 29–34 the mean and standard deviation of a normal variable X are given. Find the indicated probability.

29. X is the standard normal variable Z; $P(0 \leq X \leq 1.5)$.

30. X is the standard normal variable Z; $P(X \leq -1.5)$.

31. X is the standard normal variable Z; $P(|X| \geq 2.1)$.

32. $\mu = 100, \sigma = 16; P(80 \leq X \leq 120)$

33. $\mu = 0, \sigma = 2; P(X \leq -1)$

34. $\mu = -1, \sigma = 0.5; P(X \geq 1)$

Applications: OHaganBooks.com
[Try the game at www.OHaganBooks.com]

Marketing As a promotional gimmick, OHaganBooks.com has been selling copies of Encyclopædia Galactica *at an extremely low price that is changed each week at random in a nationally televised drawing. Exercises 35–40 are based on the following table, which gives the frequency with which each price will be chosen and summarizes the anticipated sales:*

Price	$5.50	$10	$12	$15
Frequency (weeks)	1	2	3	4
Weekly Sales	6,200	3,500	3,000	1,000

35. What is the expected value of the price of *Encyclopædia Galactica*?

36. What are the expected weekly sales of *Encyclopædia Galactica*?

37. What is the expected weekly revenue from sales of *Encyclopædia Galactica*? (Revenue = Price per copy sold × Number of copies sold.)

38. OHaganBooks.com originally paid *Duffin House* $20 per copy for the *Encyclopædia Galactica*. What is the expected weekly loss from sales of the encyclopædia? (Loss = Loss per copy sold × Number of copies sold.)

39. True or false? If X and Y are two random variables, then $E(XY) = E(X)E(Y)$. (The expected value of the product of two random variables is the product of the expected values.) Support your claim by referring to the answers of Exercises 35–37.

40. True or false? If X and Y are two random variables, then $E(X/Y) = E(X)/E(Y)$ (the expected value of the ratio of two random variables is the ratio of the expected values). Support your claim by referring to the answers of Exercises 36 and 38.

41. *Online Sales* The following table shows the number of online orders at OHaganBooks.com per million residents in 100 U.S. cities during 1 month:

Orders (per million residents)	1–2.9	3–4.9	5–6.9	7–8.9	9–10.9
Number of Cities	25	35	15	15	10

a. Let X be the number of orders per million residents in a randomly chosen U.S. city. (Use rounded midpoints of the given measurement classes.) Construct the probability distribution for X, and hence compute the expected value μ of X and standard deviation σ. (Round answers to four decimal places.)

b. What range of orders per million residents does the empirical rule predict from approximately 68% of all cities? Would you judge that the empirical rule applies? Why?

c. The actual percentage of cities from which you obtain between 3 and 8 orders per million residents is (choose the correct answer that gives the most specific information):

(A) Between 50% and 65%

(B) At least 65%

(C) At least 50%

(D) 57.5%

42. *Pollen* Marjory Duffin is planning a joint sales meeting with OHaganBooks.com in Atlanta at the end of March but is extremely allergic to pollen, so she went online to find pollen counts for the period. The following table shows the results of her search:

Pollen Count	0–1.9	2–3.9	4–5.9	6–7.9	8–9.9	10–11.9
Number of Days	3	5	7	2	1	2

a. Let X be the pollen count on a given day. (Use rounded midpoints of the given measurement classes.) Construct the probability distribution for X, and hence compute the expected value μ of X and standard deviation σ. (Round answers to four decimal places.)

b. What range of pollen counts does the empirical rule predict on approximately 95% of the days? Would you judge that the empirical rule applies? Why?

c. The actual percentage of days on which the pollen count is between 2 and 7 is (choose the correct answer that gives the most specific information):

(A) Between 50% and 60%

(B) At least 60%

(C) At most 70%

(D) Between 60% and 70%

Mac vs. Windows *On average, 5% of all hits by Mac OS users and 10% of all hits by Windows users result in orders for books at OHaganBooks.com. Due to online promotional efforts, the site traffic is approximately 10 hits per hour by Mac OS users, and 20 hits per hour by Windows users. Compute the probabilities in Exercises 43–48. (Round all answers to three decimal places.)*

43. What is the probability that exactly three Windows users will order books in the next hour?

44. What is the probability that at most three Windows users will order books in the next hour?

45. What is the probability that exactly one Mac OS user and three Windows users will order books in the next hour?

46. What assumption must you make to justify your calculation in Exercise 45?

47. How many orders for books can OHaganBooks.com expect in the next hour from Mac OS users?

48. How many orders for books can OHaganBooks.com expect in the next hour from Windows users?

Online Cosmetics *OHaganBooks.com has launched a subsidiary, GnuYou.com, which sells beauty products online. Most products sold by GnuYou.com are skin creams and hair products. Exercises 49–52 are based on the following table, which shows monthly revenues earned through sales of these products. (Assume a normal distribution. Round all answers to three decimal places.)*

Product	Skin Creams	Hair Products
Mean Monthly Revenue ($)	38,000	34,000
Standard Deviation ($)	21,000	14,000

49. What is the probability that GnuYou.com will sell *at least* $50,000 worth of skin cream next month?

50. What is the probability that GnuYou.com will sell *at most* $50,000 worth of hair products next month?

51. What is the probability that GnuYou.com will sell less than $12,000 of skin creams next month?

52. What is the probability that GnuYou.com will sell less than $12,000 of hair products next month?

53. *Intelligence* Billy-Sean O'Hagan, now a senior at *Suburban State University*, has done exceptionally well and has just joined Mensa, a club for people with high IQs. Within Mensa is a group called the Three Sigma Club because its members' IQ scores are at least three standard deviations higher than the U.S. mean. Assuming a U.S. population of 323,000,000 and assuming that IQ scores are normally distributed, how many people in the United States are qualified for the Three Sigma Club? (Round your answer to the nearest 1,000 people.)

54. *Intelligence* To join Mensa (not necessarily the Three Sigma Club), one needs an IQ of at least 132, corresponding to the top 2% of the population. Assuming that scores on this test are normally distributed with a mean of 100, what is the standard deviation? (Round your answer to the nearest whole number.)

55. *Intelligence* On the basis of information given in Exercises 53 and 54, what score must Billy-Sean have to get into the Three Sigma Club? (Assume that IQ scores are normally distributed with a mean of 100, and use the rounded standard deviation.)

56. *Intelligence* Mensa allows the results of various standardized tests to be used to gain membership. Suppose that there was such a test with a mean of 500 on which one needed to score at least 600 to be in the top 2% of the population, hence eligible to join Mensa. What would Billy-Sean need to score on this test to get into the Three Sigma Club?

Paula Borchardt/AGE Fotostock

Spotting Tax Fraud with Benford's Law[67]

You are a tax fraud specialist working for the Internal Revenue Service (IRS), and you have just been handed a portion of the tax return from *Colossal Conglomerate*. The IRS suspects that the portion you were handed may be fraudulent, and would like your opinion. Is there any mathematical test, you wonder, that can point to a suspicious tax return based on nothing more than the numbers entered?

You decide, on an impulse, to make a list of the first digits of all the numbers entered in the portion of the Colossal Conglomerate tax return (there are 625 of them). You reason that, if the tax return is an honest one, the first digits of the numbers should be uniformly distributed. More precisely, if the experiment consists of selecting a number at random from the tax return, and the random variable X is defined to be the first digit of the selected number, then X should have the following probability distribution:

x	1	2	3	4	5	6	7	8	9
$P(X = x)$	$\frac{1}{9}$	$\frac{1}{9}$	$\frac{1}{9}$	$\frac{1}{9}$	$\frac{1}{9}$	$\frac{1}{9}$	$\frac{1}{9}$	$\frac{1}{9}$	$\frac{1}{9}$

You then do a quick calculation based on this probability distribution and find an expected value of $E(X) = 5$. Next, you turn to the Colossal Conglomerate tax return data and calculate the relative frequency (estimated probability) of the actual numbers in the tax return. You find the following results:

Colossal Conglomerate Return

y	1	2	3	4	5	6	7	8	9
$P(Y = y)$	.29	.1	.04	.15	.31	.08	.01	.01	.01

It certainly does look suspicious! For one thing, the digits 1 and 5 seem to occur a lot more often than any of the other digits and roughly three times what you predicted. Moreover, when you compute the expected value, you obtain $E(Y) = 3.48$, considerably lower than the value of 5 you predicted. "Gotcha!" you exclaim.

You are about to file a report recommending a detailed audit of Colossal Conglomerate when you recall an article you once read about first digits in lists of numbers. The article dealt with a remarkable discovery in 1938 by Dr. Frank Benford, a physicist at General Electric. What Dr. Benford noticed was that the pages of logarithm tables that listed numbers starting with the digits 1 and 2 tended to be more soiled and dog-eared than the pages that listed numbers starting with higher digits—say, 8. For some reason, numbers that start with low digits seemed more prevalent than numbers that start with high digits. He subsequently analyzed more than 20,000 sets of numbers, such as tables of baseball statistics, listings of widths of rivers, half-lives of radioactive elements, street addresses, numbers in magazine articles. The result was always the same: Inexplicably, numbers that start with low digits tended to appear more frequently than those that start with high ones, numbers beginning with the digit 1 being most prevalent of all.[68] Moreover, the expected value of the first digit was not the expected 5, but 3.44.

Because the first digits in Colossal Conglomerate's return have an expected value of 3.48, very close to Benford's value, it might appear that your suspicion was groundless after all. (Back to the drawing board . . .)

Out of curiosity, you decide to investigate Benford's discovery more carefully. What you find is that Benford did more than simply observe a strange phenomenon in lists of numbers. He went further and derived the following formula for the probability distribution of first digits in lists of numbers:

$$P(X = x) = \log(1 + 1/x) \quad (x = 1, 2, \ldots, 9).$$

You compute these probabilities and find the following distribution. (The probabilities are all rounded and thus do not add to exactly 1.)

x	1	2	3	4	5	6	7	8	9
$P(X = x)$	.30	.18	.12	.10	.08	.07	.06	.05	.05

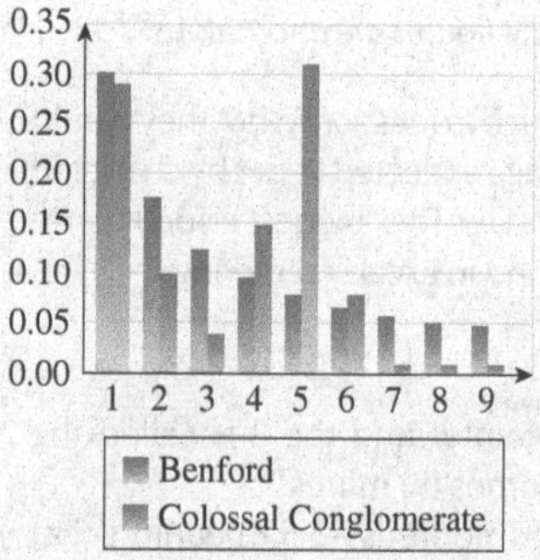

Benford
Colossal Conglomerate

Figure 17

You then enter these data along with the Colossal Conglomerate tax return data in your spreadsheet program and obtain the graph shown in Figure 17.

The graph shows something awfully suspicious happening with the digit 5. The percentage of numbers in the Colossal Conglomerate return that begin with 5 far exceeds Benford's prediction that approximately 8% of all numbers should begin with 5.

Now it seems fairly clear that you are justified in recommending Colossal Conglomerate for an audit after all.

Q: *Because no given set of data can reasonably be expected to satisfy Benford's law exactly, how can I be certain that the Colossal Conglomerate data are not simply due to chance?*

A: You can never be 100% certain. It is certainly conceivable that the tax figures just happen to result in the "abnormal" distribution in the Colossal Conglomerate tax return. However—and this is the subject of what is known as inferential statistics— there is a method for deciding whether you can be, say, "95% certain" that the anomaly reflected in the data is not due to chance. To check, you must first compute a statistic that determines how far a given set of data deviates from satisfying a theoretical prediction (Benford's law, in this case). This statistic is called a **sum-of-squares error** and is given by the following formula (reminiscent of the variance):

$$\text{SSE} = n\left[\frac{[P(y_1) - P(x_1)]^2}{P(x_1)} + \frac{[P(y_2) - P(x_2)]^2}{P(x_2)} + \cdots + \frac{[P(y_9) - P(x_9)]^2}{P(x_9)}\right].$$

Here, n is the sample size: 625 in the case of Colossal Conglomerate. The quantities $P(x_i)$ are the theoretically predicted probabilities according to Benford's Law, and the $P(y_i)$ are the probabilities in the Colossal Conglomerate return. Notice that if the Colossal Conglomerate return probabilities had exactly matched the theoretically predicted probabilities, then SSE would have been zero. Notice also the effect of multiplying by the sample size n: The larger the sample, the more likely that the

---

[68] This does not apply to all lists of numbers. For instance, a list of randomly chosen numbers between 100 and 999 will have first digits uniformly distributed between 1 and 9.

discrepancy between the $P(x_i)$ and the $P(y_i)$ is not due to chance. Substituting the numbers gives[69]

$$SSE \approx 625\left[\frac{[.29 - .30]^2}{.30} + \frac{[.1 - .18]^2}{.18} + \cdots + \frac{[.01 - .05]^2}{.05}\right]$$

$$\approx 552.$$

Q: *The value of SSE does seem quite large. But how can I use this figure in my report? I would like to say something impressive, such as "Based on the portion of the Colossal Conglomerate tax return analyzed, one can be 95% certain that the figures are anomalous."*

A: The error SSE is used by statisticians to answer exactly such a question. What they would do is compare this figure to the largest SSE we would have expected to get by chance in 95 out of 100 selections of data that *do* satisfy Benford's law. This "biggest error" is computed using a "chi-squared" distribution and can be found in Excel by entering

=CHIINV(0.05,8)

Here, the 0.05 is $1 - 0.95$, encoding the "95% certainty," and the 8 is called the "number of degrees of freedom" = number of outcomes (9) minus 1.

You now find, using Excel, that the chi-squared figure is 15.5, meaning that the largest SSE that you could have expected purely by chance is 15.5. Because Colossal Conglomerate's error is much larger at 552, you can now justifiably say in your report that there is a 95% certainty that the figures are anomalous.[70]

EXERCISES

Which of the following lists of data would you expect to follow Benford's law? If the answer is "no," give a reason.

1. Distances between cities in France, measured in kilometers
2. Distances between cities in France, measured in miles
3. The grades (0–100) in your math instructor's grade book
4. The Dow Jones averages for the past 100 years
5. Verbal SAT scores of college-bound high school seniors
6. Life spans of companies

Use technology to determine whether the given distribution of first digits fails, with 95% certainty, to follow Benford's law.

7. *Good Neighbor, Inc.*'s tax return ($n = 1,000$)

y	1	2	3	4	5	6	7	8	9
$P(Y = y)$	.31	.16	.13	.11	.07	.07	.05	.06	.04

8. *Honest Growth Funds* stockholder report ($n = 400$)

y	1	2	3	4	5	6	7	8	9
$P(Y = y)$	.28	.16	.1	.11	.07	.09	.05	.07	.07

---

[69] If you use more accurate values for the probabilities in Benford's distribution, the value is approximately 560.

[70] What this actually means is that, if you were to do a similar analysis on a large number of tax returns and you designated as "not conforming to Benford's law" all of those whose value of SSE was larger than 15.5, you would be justified in 95% of the cases.

Section 9.1

Example 3 (page 652) Let X be the number of heads that face up in three tosses of a coin. We obtained the following probability distribution of X in the text:

x	0	1	2	3
$P(X = x)$	$\frac{1}{8}$	$\frac{3}{8}$	$\frac{3}{8}$	$\frac{1}{8}$

Use technology to obtain the corresponding histogram.

Solution

1. In the TI-83/84 Plus, you can enter a list of probabilities as follows: Press [STAT], choose EDIT, and then press [ENTER]. Clear columns L_1 and L_2 if they are not already cleared. (Select the heading of a column and press [CLEAR] [ENTER] to clear it.) Enter the values of X in the column under L_1 (pressing [ENTER] after each entry), and enter the frequencies in the column under L_2.

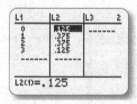

2. To graph the data as in Figure 1, first set the [WINDOW] to $0 \le X \le 4$, $0 \le Y \le 0.5$, and Xscl = 1 (the width of the bars). Then turn STAT PLOT on ([2nd] [Y=]), and configure it by selecting the histogram icon, setting Xlist = L_1 and Freq = L_2. Then hit [GRAPH].

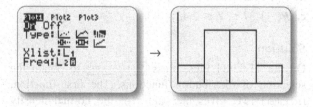

Example 4 (page 652) We obtained the following frequency table in the text:

x	25,000	35,000	45,000	55,000	65,000	75,000	85,000
Frequency	20	80	230	400	170	70	30

Find the probability distribution of X.

Solution

We need to divide each frequency by the sum. Although the computations in this example (dividing the seven frequencies by 1,000) are simple to do by hand, they could become tedious in general, so technology is helpful.

1. On the TI-83/84 Plus, press [STAT], select EDIT, enter the values of X in the L_1 list, and enter the frequencies in the L_2 list as in Example 3 (below left).

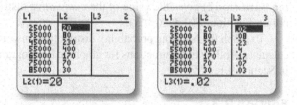

2. Then, on the Home screen, enter

$$L_2/1000 \rightarrow L_3$$

L_2 is [2ND] [2], L_3 is [2ND] [3].

or, better yet,

$$L_2/\text{sum}(L_2) \rightarrow L_3$$

Sum is found in [2ND] [STAT], under MATH.

3. After pressing [ENTER], you can now go back to the [STAT] EDIT screen, and you will find the probabilities displayed in L_3 as shown above on the right.

Section 9.2

Example 2(b) (page 662) By 2030 the probability that a randomly chosen resident in the United States will be 65 years old or older is projected to be .2. If X is the number of people aged 65 or older in a sample of 6, construct the probability distribution of X.

Solution

In the "Y=" screen, you can enter the binomial distribution formula

$$Y_1 = 6 \text{ nCr } X*0.2\char`^X*0.8\char`^(6-X)$$

directly (to get nCr, press [MATH] and select PRB), and hit [TABLE]. You can then replicate the table in the text by choosing $X = 0, 1, \ldots, 6$ (use the TBLSET screen to set "Indpnt" to "Ask" if you have not already done so).

$Y_1 = .262144$

The TI-83/84 Plus also has a built-in binomial distribution function that you can use in place of the explicit formula:

$$Y_1 = \text{binompdf}(6, 0.2, X) \quad \text{In } \boxed{\text{2ND}} \boxed{\text{VARS}}$$

The TI-83/84 Plus function binomcdf (directly following binompdf) gives the value of the *cumulative* distribution function, $P(0 \le X \le x)$.

To graph the resulting probability distribution on your calculator, follow the instructions for graphing a histogram in Section 9.1.

Section 9.3

Example 3 (page 671) According to historical data, the number of injuries that a member of the *Enormous State University* women's soccer team will sustain during a typical season is given by the following probability distribution table:

Injuries	0	1	2	3	4	5	6
Probability	.20	.20	.22	.20	.15	.01	.02

If X denotes the number of injuries sustained by a player during one season, compute $E(X)$.

Solution

To obtain the expected value of a probability distribution on the TI-83/84 Plus, press $\boxed{\text{STAT}}$, select EDIT, and then press $\boxed{\text{ENTER}}$, and enter the values of X in the L_1 list and the probabilities in the column in the L_2 list. Then, on the Home screen, you can obtain the expected value as

$\text{sum}(L_1 * L_2)$ L_1 is $\boxed{\text{2ND}}\boxed{1}$ L_2 is $\boxed{\text{2ND}}\boxed{2}$
Sum is found in $\boxed{\text{2ND}}\boxed{\text{STAT}}$, under MATH.

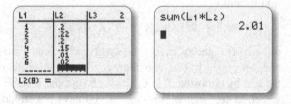

Section 9.4

Example 3 (page 686) Compute the variance and standard deviation for the following probability distribution:

x	10	20	30	40	50	60
$P(X = x)$	.2	.2	.3	.1	.1	.1

Solution

1. As in Example 3 in Section 9.3, begin by entering the probability distribution of X into columns L_1 and L_2 in the LIST screen (press $\boxed{\text{STAT}}$ and select EDIT). (See below left.)

2. Then, on the Home screen, enter

$\text{sum}(L_1 * L_2) \to M$ Stores the value of μ as M
Sum is found in $\boxed{\text{2ND}}\boxed{\text{STAT}}$, under MATH.

3. To obtain the variance, enter

$\text{sum}((L_1 - M)^2 * L_2)$ Computation of $\Sigma(x - \mu)^2 P(X = x)$

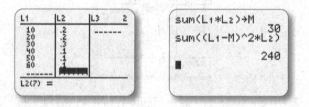

Section 9.5

Example 1(b), (c) (page 697) Let Z be the standard normal variable. Calculate the following probabilities:

b. $P(0 \le Z \le 2.43)$

c. $P(-1.37 \le Z \le 2.43)$

Solution

On the TI-83/84 Plus, press $\boxed{\text{2ND}}\boxed{\text{VARS}}$ to obtain the selection of distribution functions. The first function, normalpdf, gives the values of the normal density function (whose graph is the normal curve). The second, normalcdf, gives $P(a \le Z \le b)$. For example, to compute $P(0 \le Z \le 2.43)$, enter

$$\text{normalcdf}(0, 2.43)$$

To compute $P(-1.37 \le Z \le 2.43)$, enter

$$\texttt{normalcdf(-1.37,2.43)}$$

Example 2 (page 699)   Pressure gauges manufactured by *Precision Corp.* must be checked for accuracy before being placed on the market. To test a pressure gauge, a worker uses it to measure the pressure of a sample of compressed air known to be at a pressure of exactly 50 pounds per square inch. If the gauge reading is off by more than 1% (0.5 pounds), it is rejected. Assuming that the reading of a pressure gauge under these circumstances is a normal random variable with mean 50 and standard deviation 0.4, find the percentage of gauges rejected.

Solution

As seen in the text, we need to compute $1 - P(49.5 \le X \le 50.5)$ with $\mu = 50$ and $\sigma = 0.4$. On the TI-83/84 Plus, the built-in $\texttt{normalcdf}$ function permits us to compute $P(a \le X \le b)$ for nonstandard normal distributions as well. The format is

$$\texttt{normalcdf(a,b,}\mu\texttt{,}\sigma\texttt{)} \qquad P(a \le X \le b)$$

For example, we can compute $P(49.5 \le X \le 50.5)$ by entering

$$\texttt{normalcdf(49.5,50.5,50,0.4)}$$

Then subtract it from 1 to obtain the answer:

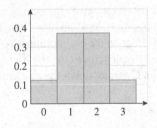

Spreadsheet Technology Guide

Section 9.1

Example 3 (page 652)   Let X be the number of heads that face up in three tosses of a coin. We obtained the following probability distribution of X in the text:

x	0	1	2	3
$P(X = x)$	$\frac{1}{8}$	$\frac{3}{8}$	$\frac{3}{8}$	$\frac{1}{8}$

Use technology to obtain the corresponding histogram.

Solution

1. In your spreadsheet, enter the values of X in one column and the probabilities in another.

	A	B
1	x	P(X=x)
2	0	0.125
3	1	0.375
4	2	0.375
5	3	0.125

2. Next, select *only* the column of probabilities (B2–B5), and then insert a column chart. The procedure for doing this depends heavily on the spreadsheet and platform you are using.

Example 4 (page 652) We obtained the following frequency table in the text:

x	25,000	35,000	45,000	55,000	65,000	75,000	85,000
Frequency	20	80	230	400	170	70	30

Find the probability distribution of X.

Solution

We need to divide each frequency by the sum. Although the computations in this example (dividing the seven frequencies by 1,000) are simple to do by hand, they could become tedious in general, so technology is helpful. Spreadsheets manipulate lists with ease. Set up your spreadsheet as shown.

	A	B	C
1	x	Fr	P(X=x)
2	25000	20	=B2/SUM(B:B)
3	35000	80	
4	45000	230	
5	55000	400	
6	65000	170	
7	75000	70	
8	85000	30	

↓

	A	B	C
1	x	Fr	P(X=x)
2	25000	20	0.02
3	35000	80	0.08
4	45000	230	0.23
5	55000	400	0.4
6	65000	170	0.17
7	75000	70	0.07
8	85000	30	0.03

The formula SUM(B:B) gives the sum of all the numerical entries in column B. You can now change the frequencies to see the effect on the probabilities. You can also add new values and frequencies to the list if you copy the formula in column C farther down the column.

Section 9.2

Example 2(b) (page 662) By 2030 the probability that a randomly chosen resident in the United States will be 65 years old or older is projected to be .2. If X is the number of people aged 65 or older in a sample of 6, construct the probability distribution of X.

Solution

You can generate the binomial distribution as follows in your spreadsheet:

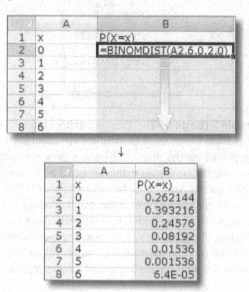

	A	B
1	x	P(X=x)
2	0	=BINOMDIST(A2,6,0.2,0)
3	1	
4	2	
5	3	
6	4	
7	5	
8	6	

↓

	A	B
1	x	P(X=x)
2	0	0.262144
3	1	0.393216
4	2	0.24576
5	3	0.08192
6	4	0.01536
7	5	0.001536
8	6	6.4E-05

The values of X are shown in column A, and the probabilities are computed in column B. The arguments of the BINOMDIST function are as follows:

BINOMDIST(x, n, p, Cumulative (0 = no, 1 = yes)).

Setting the last argument to 0 (as shown) gives $P(X = x)$. Setting it to 1 gives $P(X \leq x)$.

To graph the resulting probability distribution using your spreadsheet, insert a bar chart as in Section 9.1.

Section 9.3

Example 3 (page 671) According to historical data, the number of injuries that a member of the *Enormous State University* women's soccer team will sustain during a typical season is given by the following probability distribution table:

Injuries	0	1	2	3	4	5	6
Probability	.20	.20	.22	.20	.15	.01	.02

If X denotes the number of injuries sustained by a player during one season, compute $E(X)$.

Solution

As the method we used suggests, the calculation of the expected value from the probability distribution is particularly easy to do using a spreadsheet program such as Excel.

The following worksheet shows one way to do it. (The first two columns contain the probability distribution of X; the quantities $xP(X = x)$ are summed in cell C9.)

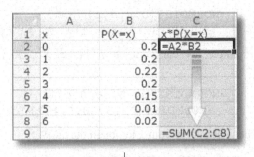

	A	B	C
1	x	P(X=x)	x*P(X=x)
2	0		0.2 =A2*B2
3	1		0.2
4	2		0.22
5	3		0.2
6	4		0.15
7	5		0.01
8	6		0.02
9			=SUM(C2:C8)

↓

	A	B	C
1	x	P(X=x)	x*P(X=x)
2	0	0.2	0
3	1	0.2	0.2
4	2	0.22	0.44
5	3	0.2	0.6
6	4	0.15	0.6
7	5	0.01	0.05
8	6	0.02	0.12
9			2.01

An alternative is to use the SUMPRODUCT function: Once we enter the first two columns above, the formula

=SUMPRODUCT(A2:A8,B2:B8)

computes the sum of the products of corresponding entries in the columns, giving us the expected value.

Section 9.4

Example 3 (page 686)   Compute the variance and standard deviation for the following probability distribution:

x	10	20	30	40	50	60
$P(X = x)$	.2	.2	.3	.1	.1	.1

Solution

As in Example 3 in Section 9.3, begin by entering the probability distribution into columns A and B, and then proceed as shown:

	A	B	C	D
1	x	P(X=x)	x*P(X=x)	(x-Mu)^2 * P(X=x)
2		10	0.2 =A2*B2	=(A2-$C$8)^2*B2
3		20	0.2	
4		30	0.3	
5		40	0.1	
6		50	0.1	
7		60	0.1	
8			=SUM(C2:C7)	=SUM(D2:D7)
9			Expected Value	Variance

The variance then appears in cell D8:

	A	B	C	D
1	x	P(X=x)	x*P(X=x)	(x-Mu)^2 * P(X=x)
2	10	0.2	2	80
3	20	0.2	4	20
4	30	0.3	9	0
5	40	0.1	4	10
6	50	0.1	5	40
7	60	0.1	6	90
8			30	240
9			Expected Value	Variance

Section 9.5

Example 1(b), (c) (page 697)   Let Z be the standard normal variable. Calculate the following probabilities:

b. $P(0 \le Z \le 2.43)$

c. $P(-1.37 \le Z \le 2.43)$

Solution

In spreadsheets the function NORMSDIST (<u>Norm</u>al <u>S</u>tandard <u>Dist</u>ribution) gives the area shown on the left in the figure below. (Tables such as the one in the Appendix give the area shown on the right.)

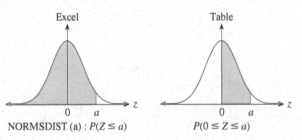

Excel
NORMSDIST (a) : $P(Z \le a)$

Table
$P(0 \le Z \le a)$

To compute a general area, $P(a \le Z \le b)$ in your spreadsheet, subtract the cumulative area to a from that to b:

=NORMSDIST(b)-NORMSDIST(a) $P(a \le Z \le b)$

In particular, to compute $P(0 \le Z \le 2.43)$, use

=NORMSDIST(2.43)-NORMSDIST(0)

and to compute $P(-1.37 \le Z \le 2.43)$, use

=NORMSDIST(2.43)-NORMSDIST(-1.37)

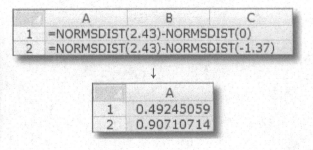

	A	B	C
1	=NORMSDIST(2.43)-NORMSDIST(0)		
2	=NORMSDIST(2.43)-NORMSDIST(-1.37)		

↓

	A
1	0.49245059
2	0.90710714

Example 2 (page 699) Pressure gauges manufactured by *Precision Corp.* must be checked for accuracy before being placed on the market. To test a pressure gauge, a worker uses it to measure the pressure of a sample of compressed air known to be at a pressure of exactly 50 pounds per square inch. If the gauge reading is off by more than 1% (0.5 pounds), it is rejected. Assuming that the reading of a pressure gauge under these circumstances is a normal random variable with mean 50 and standard deviation 0.4, find the percentage of gauges rejected.

Solution

In spreadsheets we use the function NORMDIST instead of NORMSDIST. Its format is similar to NORMSDIST but includes extra arguments as shown:

$$=\text{NORMDIST}(a,\mu,\sigma,1) \quad P(X \leq a)$$

(The last argument, set to 1, tells the spreadsheet that we want the cumulative distribution.) To compute $P(a \leq X \leq b)$, we enter the following in any vacant cell:

$$=\text{NORMDIST}(b,\mu,\sigma,1)$$
$$-\text{NORMDIST}(a,\mu,\sigma,1) \quad P(a \leq X \leq b)$$

For example, we can compute $P(49.5 \leq X \leq 50.5)$ by entering

$$=\text{NORMDIST}(50.5,50,0.4,1)$$
$$-\text{NORMDIST}(49.5,50,0.4,1)$$

We then subtract it from 1 to obtain the answer:

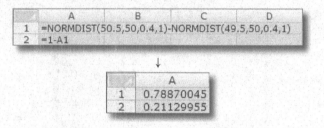

	A	B	C	D
1	=NORMDIST(50.5,50,0.4,1)-NORMDIST(49.5,50,0.4,1)			
2	=1-A1			

↓

	A
1	0.78870045
2	0.21129955

10

INTRODUCTION TO THE DERIVATIVE

CASE STUDY

Reducing Sulfur Emissions

The Environmental Protection Agency (EPA) wants to formulate a policy that will encourage utilities to reduce sulfur emissions. Its goal is to reduce annual emissions of sulfur dioxide by a total of 10 million tons from the current level of 25 million tons by imposing a fixed charge for every ton of sulfur released into the environment per year. The EPA has some data showing the marginal cost to utilities of reducing sulfur emissions. As a consultant to the EPA, you must determine the amount to be charged per ton of sulfur emissions in light of these data.

Norbert Schaefer/CORBIS/Getty Images

W **www.WanerMath.com**

At the Website, in addition to the resources listed in the Preface, you will find:

The following extra topics:

- Sketching the Graph of the Derivative
- Continuity and Differentiability

Introduction

In the world around us, everything is changing. The mathematics of change is largely about the rate of change: how fast and in which direction the change is occurring. Is the Dow Jones average going up, and if so, how fast? If I raise my prices, how many customers will I lose? If I launch this missile, how fast will it be traveling after 2 seconds, how high will it go, and where will it come down?

We have already discussed the concept of rate of change for linear functions (straight lines), where the slope measures the rate of change. But this works only because a straight line maintains a constant rate of change along its whole length. Other functions rise faster here than there—or rise in one place and fall in another—so the rate of change varies along the graph. The first achievement of calculus is to provide a systematic and straightforward way of calculating (hence the name) these rates of change. To describe a changing world, we need a language of change, and that is what calculus is.

The history of calculus is an interesting story of personalities, intellectual movements, and controversy. Credit for its invention is given to two mathematicians: Isaac Newton (1642–1727) and Gottfried Leibniz (1646–1716). Newton, an English mathematician and scientist, developed calculus first, probably in the 1660s. We say "probably" because, for various reasons, he did not publish his ideas until much later. This allowed Leibniz, a German mathematician and philosopher, to publish his own version of calculus first, in 1684. Fifteen years later, stirred up by nationalist fervor in England and on the continent, controversy erupted over who should get the credit for the invention of calculus. The debate got so heated that the Royal Society (of which Newton and Leibniz were both members) set up a commission to investigate the question. The commission decided in favor of Newton, who happened to be president of the society at the time. The consensus today is that both mathematicians deserve credit because they came to the same conclusions working independently. This is not really surprising: Both built on well-known work of other people, and it was almost inevitable that someone would put it all together at about that time.

Precalculus Review
For this chapter you should be familiar with the algebra reviewed in **Section 0.2**.

10.1 Limits: Numerical and Graphical Viewpoints

Rates of change are calculated by derivatives, but an important part of the definition of the derivative is something called a **limit**. Arguably, much of mathematics since the eighteenth century has revolved around understanding, refining, and exploiting the idea of the limit. The basic idea is easy, but getting the technicalities right is not.

Estimating Limits Numerically

Start with a very simple example: Look at the function $f(x) = 2 + x$, and ask, "What happens to $f(x)$ as x approaches 3?" The following table shows the value of $f(x)$ for values of x close to and on either side of 3:

x approaching 3 from the left→   ← x approaching 3 from the right

x	2.9	2.99	2.999	2.9999	3	3.0001	3.001	3.01	3.1
$f(x) = 2 + x$	4.9	4.99	4.999	4.9999		5.0001	5.001	5.01	5.1

We have left the entry under 3 blank to emphasize that when calculating the limit of $f(x)$ as x *approaches* 3, we are not interested in its value when x *equals* 3.

Notice from the table that the closer x gets to 3 from either side, the closer $f(x)$ gets to 5. We write this as

$$\lim_{x \to 3} f(x) = 5. \qquad \text{The limit of } f(x), \text{ as } x \text{ approaches 3, equals 5.}$$

Q: *Why all the fuss? Can't we simply substitute $x = 3$ and avoid having to use a table?*

A: This happens to work for *some* functions but not for *all* functions. The following example illustrates this point.

EXAMPLE 1 Estimating a Limit Numerically

Use a table to estimate the following limits:

a. $\lim_{x \to 2} \dfrac{x^3 - 8}{x - 2}$ **b.** $\lim_{x \to 0} \dfrac{e^{2x} - 1}{x}$

Solution

a. We cannot simply substitute $x = 2$, because the function $f(x) = \dfrac{x^3 - 8}{x - 2}$ is not defined at $x = 2$. (Why?)[*] Instead, we use a table of values as we did above, with x approaching 2 from both sides:

x approaching 2 from the left→   ← x approaching 2 from the right

x	1.9	1.99	1.999	1.9999	2	2.0001	2.001	2.01	2.1
$f(x) = \dfrac{x^3 - 8}{x - 2}$	11.41	11.9401	11.9940	11.9994		12.0006	12.0060	12.0601	12.61

We notice that as x approaches 2 from either side, $f(x)$ appears to be approaching 12. This suggests that the limit is 12, and we write

$$\lim_{x \to 2} \frac{x^3 - 8}{x - 2} = 12.$$

b. The function $g(x) = \dfrac{e^{2x} - 1}{x}$ is not defined at $x = 0$ (nor can it even be simplified to one that *is* defined at $x = 0$). In the following table we allow x to approach 0 from both sides:

x approaching 0 from the left→   ← x approaching 0 from the right

x	−0.1	−0.01	−0.001	−0.0001	0	0.0001	0.001	0.01	0.1
$g(x) = \dfrac{e^{2x} - 1}{x}$	1.8127	1.9801	1.9980	1.9998		2.0002	2.0020	2.0201	2.2140

The table suggests that $\lim_{x \to 0} \dfrac{e^{2x} - 1}{x} = 2$.

[*] However, if you factor $x^3 - 8$, you will find that $f(x)$ can be simplified to a function that *is* defined at $x = 2$. This point will be discussed (and this example redone) in Section 10.3. The function in Example 1(b) cannot be simplified by factoring.

Using Technology

To automate the computations in Example 1 using a graphing calculator or a spreadsheet, see the Technology Guides at the end of the chapter. Outline for Example 1(a):

TI-83/84 Plus
Home screen: $Y_1 = (X^3-8)/(X-2)$
2ND TBLSET Indpnt
set to Ask
2ND TABLE Enter some
values of x from the example:
1.9, 1.99, 1.999 . . .
[More details in the Technology Guide.]

Spreadsheet
Headings x, $f(x)$ in A1–B1
and again in C1–D1.
In A2–A5 enter 1.9, 1.99,
1.999, 1.9999.
In C1–C5 enter 2.1, 2.01,
2.001, 2.0001. Enter
$=(A2^3-8)/(A2-2)$
in B2, and copy down to B5.
Copy and paste the same
formula in D2–D5.
[More details in the Technology Guide.]

Website
www.WanerMath.com
Go to
  Online Utilities → Function
  Evaluator and Grapher
Enter
$(x^3-8)/(x-2)$
for y_1. For a table of values, enter
the various x-values in the Evaluator box, and press "Evaluate".

➡ **Before we go on ...** We will revisit the limit in Example 1(a) from the geometric point of view in Example 5. Although the table *suggests* that the limit in Example 1(b) is 2, it by no means establishes that fact conclusively. It is *conceivable* (though not in fact the case here) that putting $x = 0.000000087$ could result in, say, $g(x) = 426$. Using a table can only *suggest* a value for the limit. In the next two sections we shall discuss algebraic techniques to allow us to actually *calculate* limits. ∎

Before we continue, let us make a more formal definition.

Definition of a Limit

Let f be a function such that $f(x)$ is defined for values of x arbitrarily close to, but different from, a. Then, if $f(x)$ approaches the number L as x approaches (but is not equal to) a, regardless from which side, we say that $f(x)$ **approaches L as $x \to a$** ("x approaches a") or that the **limit** of $f(x)$ as $x \to a$ is L. In other words, *we can make $f(x)$ be as close to L as we like by choosing any x in the domain of f sufficiently close to (but not equal to) a on either side.* We write

$$\lim_{x \to a} f(x) = L$$

or

$$f(x) \to L \text{ as } x \to a.$$

If $f(x)$ *fails* to approach *a single fixed number* as x approaches a, then we say that $f(x)$ **has no limit** as $x \to a$, or

$$\lim_{x \to a} f(x) \textbf{ does not exist}.$$

Quick Examples

1. $\lim_{x \to 3}(2 + x) = 5$ — See discussion before Example 1.

2. $\lim_{x \to -2}(3x) = -6$ — As x approaches -2, $3x$ approaches -6.

3. $\lim_{x \to 0}(x^2 - 2x + 1)$ exists. — In fact, the limit is 1.

4. $\lim_{x \to 5} \dfrac{1}{x} = \dfrac{1}{5}$ — As x approaches 5, $\dfrac{1}{x}$ approaches $\dfrac{1}{5}$.

5. $\lim_{x \to 2} \dfrac{x^3 - 8}{x - 2} = 12$ — See Example 1. (We cannot just put $x = 2$ here.)

6. $\lim_{x \to 0} \sqrt{x} = 0$. (Even though $\sqrt{x}$ is not defined to the left of 0, it still satisfies the definition: No matter what x you choose *in the domain of the function,* you can make $\sqrt{x}$ as close as you like to zero by choosing x sufficiently close to zero.)

(For examples where the limit does not exist, see Example 2.)

Notes

1. It is important that $f(x)$ approach a *single number* regardless from which side x is approaching a. For instance, if $f(x)$ approaches 5 for $x = 1.9, 1.99, 1.999, \ldots$ but approaches 4 for $x = 2.1, 2.01, 2.001, \ldots$, then the limit as $x \to 2$ does not exist. (See Example 2 for such a situation.)

2. It may happen that $f(x)$ does not approach any fixed number at all as $x \to a$ from either side. In this case we also say that the limit does not exist. ∎

The next example includes instances in which a stated limit does not exist.

EXAMPLE 2   Limits May or May Not Exist

Do the following limits exist?

a. $\lim\limits_{x \to 0} \dfrac{1}{x^2}$ **b.** $\lim\limits_{x \to 0} \dfrac{|x|}{x}$ **c.** $\lim\limits_{x \to 2} \dfrac{1}{x-2}$ **d.** $\lim\limits_{x \to 1} \sqrt{x-1}$

Solution

a. Here is a table of values for $f(x) = \dfrac{1}{x^2}$, with x approaching 0 from both sides:

x approaching 0 from the left→   ←x approaching 0 from the right

x	-0.1	-0.01	-0.001	-0.0001	0	0.0001	0.001	0.01	0.1
$f(x) = \dfrac{1}{x^2}$	100	10,000	1,000,000	100,000,000		100,000,000	1,000,000	10,000	100

The table suggests that as x gets closer to zero on either side, $f(x)$ gets larger and larger **without bound**—that is, if you name any number, no matter how large, $f(x)$ will be even larger than that if x is sufficiently close to 0. Because $f(x)$ is not approaching any real number, we conclude that $\lim\limits_{x \to 0} \dfrac{1}{x^2}$ does not exist. Because $f(x)$ is becoming arbitrarily large, we also say that $\lim\limits_{x \to 0} \dfrac{1}{x^2}$ **diverges to** $+\infty$, or just

$$\lim_{x \to 0} \frac{1}{x^2} = +\infty.$$

Note This is not meant to imply that the limit exists; the symbol $+\infty$ does not represent any real number. We write $\lim_{x \to a} f(x) = +\infty$ to indicate two things: (1) The limit does not exist, and (2) the function gets large without bound as x approaches a. ∎

b. Here is a table of values for $f(x) = \dfrac{|x|}{x}$, with x approaching 0 from both sides:

x approaching 0 from the left→   ←x approaching 0 from the right

x	-0.1	-0.01	-0.001	-0.0001	0	0.0001	0.001	0.01	0.1
$f(x) = \dfrac{|x|}{x}$	-1	-1	-1	-1		1	1	1	1

The table suggests that $f(x)$ does not approach the same limit as x approaches 0 from both sides. There appear to be two *different* limits: the limit as we approach 0 from the left and the limit as we approach from the right. We write

$$\lim_{x \to 0^-} f(x) = -1,$$

which is read as "the limit as x approaches 0 from the left (or from below) is -1," and

$$\lim_{x \to 0^+} f(x) = 1,$$

which is read as "the limit as x approaches 0 from the right (or from above) is 1." These are called the **one-sided limits** of $f(x)$. In order for f to have a **two-sided limit**, the two one-sided limits must be equal. Because they are not, we conclude that $\lim_{x \to 0} f(x)$ does not exist.

c. Near $x = 2$ we have the following table of values for $f(x) = \dfrac{1}{x - 2}$:

x approaching 2 from the left→   ← x approaching 2 from the right

x	1.9	1.99	1.999	1.9999	2	2.0001	2.001	2.01	2.1
$f(x) = \dfrac{1}{x - 2}$	-10	-100	$-1,000$	$-10,000$		$10,000$	$1,000$	100	10

Because $f(x)$ is approaching no (single) real number as $x \to 2$, we see that $\lim_{x \to 2} \dfrac{1}{x - 2}$ does not exist. Notice also that $\dfrac{1}{x - 2}$ diverges to $+\infty$ as $x \to 2$ from the positive side (right half of the table) and to $-\infty$ as $x \to 2$ from the left (left half of the table). In other words,

$$\lim_{x \to 2^-} \frac{1}{x - 2} = -\infty, \quad \lim_{x \to 2^+} \frac{1}{x - 2} = +\infty, \quad \text{and} \quad \lim_{x \to 2} \frac{1}{x - 2} \text{ does not exist.}$$

d. The natural domain of $f(x) = \sqrt{x - 1}$ is $[1, +\infty)$, as $f(x)$ is defined only when $x \geq 1$. Thus, we cannot evaluate $f(x)$ if x is to the left of 1. Here is a table showing values to the right of 1:

← x approaching 1 from the right

x	1	1.00001	1.0001	1.001	1.01	1.1
$f(x) = \sqrt{x - 1}$		0.0032	0.0100	0.0316	0.1000	0.3162

The values suggest that

$$\lim_{x \to 1^+} \sqrt{x - 1} = 0.$$

What about $\lim_{x \to 1} \sqrt{x - 1}$? In the definition of a limit we need only worry about x *in the domain of f*, meaning values of x to the right of 1, and we just saw that the values of $f(x)$ are approaching 0 for such values. Thus,

$$\lim_{x \to 1} \sqrt{x - 1} = 0$$

as well, even though $\lim_{x \to 1^-} \sqrt{x - 1}$ does not exist, as x is not defined to the left of 1. We can also obtain this limit by substituting $x = 1$ in the formula for $f(x)$. (See the comments after the example.) To summarize,

$$\lim_{x \to 1^-} \sqrt{x - 1} \text{ does not exist,} \quad \lim_{x \to 1^+} \sqrt{x - 1} = 0, \quad \text{and} \quad \lim_{x \to 1} \sqrt{x - 1} = 0.$$

Q: *In Example 2(d) (and in some of the Quick Examples before that) we could find a limit of an algebraically specified function by simply substituting the value of x in the formula for f(x). Does this always work?*

A: Short answer: Yes, when it makes sense. If the function is specified by a *single* algebraic formula and if $x = a$ is in the domain of f, then the limit can be obtained by substituting. We will say more about this when we discuss the algebraic approach to limits in Section 10.3. Remember, however, that, by definition the limit of a function as $x \to a$ has nothing to do with its value at $x = a$ but rather is determined by its values for x *close to, but different from, a.*

Q: *If f(x) is undefined when x = a, then the limit does not exist—right?*

A: Wrong. If $f(a)$ is not defined, then the limit may or may not exist. Example 1 shows instances in which the limit *does* exist, and Example 2 shows instances in which it does not. Again, the limit of a function as $x \to a$ has nothing to do with its value at $x = a$ but rather is determined by its values for x *close to, but different from, a.*

Limits at Infinity

In another useful kind of limit we let x approach either $+\infty$ or $-\infty$, by which we mean that we let x get arbitrarily large or let x become an arbitrarily large negative number. The next example illustrates this.

EXAMPLE 3 **Limits at Infinity**

Use a table to estimate the following: **a.** $\lim_{x \to +\infty} \dfrac{2x^2 - 4x}{x^2 - 1}$ and **b.** $\lim_{x \to -\infty} \dfrac{2x^2 - 4x}{x^2 - 1}$.

Solution

a. By saying that x is "approaching $+\infty$," we mean that x is getting larger and larger without bound, so we make the following table:

					x approaching $+\infty \to$
x	10	100	1,000	10,000	100,000
$f(x) = \dfrac{2x^2 - 4x}{x^2 - 1}$	1.6162	1.9602	1.9960	1.9996	2.0000

(Note that we are approaching $+\infty$ only from the left because we can hardly approach it from the right!) What seems to be happening is that $f(x)$ is approaching 2. Thus we write

$$\lim_{x \to +\infty} f(x) = 2.$$

b. Here, x is approaching $-\infty$, so we make a similar table, this time with x assuming negative values of greater and greater magnitude (read this table from right to left):

	$\leftarrow x$ approaching $-\infty$				
x	$-100,000$	$-10,000$	$-1,000$	-100	-10
$f(x) = \dfrac{2x^2 - 4x}{x^2 - 1}$	2.0000	2.0004	2.0040	2.0402	2.4242

Once again, $f(x)$ is approaching 2. Thus, $\lim_{x \to -\infty} f(x) = 2$.

Estimating Limits Graphically

We can often estimate a limit from a graph, as the next example shows.

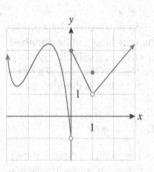

Figure 1

---

* For a visual animation of this process, look at the online tutorial for this section at the Website.

EXAMPLE 4   **Estimating Limits Graphically**

The graph of a function f is shown in Figure 1. (Recall that the solid dots indicate points on the graph and the hollow dots indicate points not on the graph.) From the graph, analyze the following limits:

a. $\lim_{x \to -2} f(x)$ **b.** $\lim_{x \to 0} f(x)$ **c.** $\lim_{x \to 1} f(x)$ **d.** $\lim_{x \to +\infty} f(x)$

Solution Since we are given only a graph of f, we must analyze these limits graphically.

a. Imagine that Figure 1 was drawn on a graphing calculator equipped with a trace feature that allows us to move a cursor along the graph and see the coordinates as we go. To simulate this, place a pencil point on the graph to the left of $x = -2$, and move it along the curve so that the x-coordinate approaches -2. (See Figure 2.) We evaluate the limit numerically by noting the behavior of the y-coordinates.*

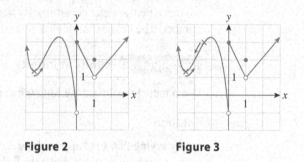

Figure 2   **Figure 3**

We can see directly from the graph that the y-coordinate approaches 2. Similarly, if we place our pencil point to the right of $x = -2$ and move it to the left, the y-coordinate will approach 2 from that side as well (Figure 3). Therefore, as x approaches -2 from either side, $f(x)$ approaches 2, so

$$\lim_{x \to -2} f(x) = 2.$$

b. This time, we move our pencil point toward $x = 0$. Referring to Figure 4, if we start from the left of $x = 0$ and approach 0 (by moving right), the y-coordinate

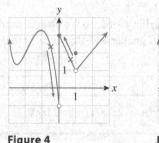

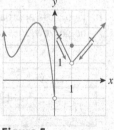
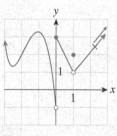

Figure 4   **Figure 5**   **Figure 6**

approaches -1. However, if we start from the right of $x = 0$ and approach 0 (by moving left), the y-coordinate approaches 3. Thus (see Example 2),

$$\lim_{x \to 0^-} f(x) = -1$$

and

$$\lim_{x \to 0^+} f(x) = 3.$$

Because these limits are not equal, we conclude that

$$\lim_{x \to 0} f(x) \text{ does not exist.}$$

In this case there is a break in the graph at $x = 0$, and we say that the function is **discontinuous** at $x = 0$ (see Section 10.2).

c. Once more, we think about a pencil point moving along the graph with the x-coordinate this time approaching $x = 1$ from the left and from the right (Figure 5). As the x-coordinate of the point approaches 1 from either side, the y-coordinate approaches 1 also. Therefore,

$$\lim_{x \to 1} f(x) = 1.$$

d. For this limit, x is supposed to approach infinity. We think about a pencil point moving along the graph farther and farther to the right, as shown in Figure 6. As the x-coordinate gets larger, the y-coordinate also gets larger and larger without bound. Thus, $f(x)$ diverges to $+\infty$:

$$\lim_{x \to +\infty} f(x) = +\infty.$$

Similarly,

$$\lim_{x \to -\infty} f(x) = +\infty.$$

➡ **Before we go on . . .** In Example 4(c), $\lim_{x \to 1} f(x) = 1$ but $f(1) = 2$ (why?). Thus, $\lim_{x \to 1} f(x) \neq f(1)$. In other words, the limit of $f(x)$ as x approaches 1 is not the same as the value of f at $x = 1$. Always keep in mind that when we evaluate a limit as $x \to a$, *we do not care about the value of the function at $x = a$. We care only about the value of $f(x)$ as x approaches a*. In other words, $f(a)$ may or may not equal $\lim_{x \to a} f(x)$. ∎

Here is a summary of the graphical method we used in Example 4, together with some additional information.

Estimating Limits Graphically

To decide whether $\lim_{x \to a} f(x)$ exists and to estimate its value if it does:

1. Draw the graph of $f(x)$ by hand or with graphing technology.

2. Position your pencil point (or the Trace cursor) on a point of the graph to the right of $x = a$.

3. Move the point *along the graph* toward $x = a$ from the right, and read the y-coordinate as you go. The value that the y-coordinate approaches (if any) is the limit $\lim_{x \to a^+} f(x)$.

4. Repeat Steps 2 and 3, this time starting from a point on the graph to the left of $x = a$ and approaching $x = a$ along the graph from the left. The value that the y-coordinate approaches (if any) is $\lim_{x \to a^-} f(x)$.

5. If the left and right limits both exist and have the same value L, then $\lim_{x \to a} f(x) = L$. Otherwise, the limit does not exist. The value $f(a)$ has no relevance whatsoever.

6. To evaluate $\lim_{x \to +\infty} f(x)$, move the pencil point toward the far right of the graph, and estimate the value the y-coordinate approaches (if any). For $\lim_{x \to -\infty} f(x)$, move the pencil point toward the far left.

7. If $x = a$ is an endpoint of the domain of f, then only a single one-sided limit can exist there and coincides with the (overall) limit. For instance, if the domain is $(-\infty, 4]$, then $\lim_{x \to 4} f(x)$ will exist if $\lim_{x \to 4^-} f(x)$ does, and they will be equal, whereas $\lim_{x \to 4^+} f(x)$ does not exist.

In the next example we see how both the numerical and graphical approaches can be used to study the same limits.

EXAMPLE 5 **Estimating Limits Numerically and Graphically**

Determine the following limits using both the numerical and graphical approaches:

a. $\lim_{x \to 2} \dfrac{x^3 - 8}{x - 2}$ (Compare Example 1(a).) **b.** $\lim_{x \to 0^+} \dfrac{1}{x}$

Solution

a. *Numerical Approach* In Example 1(a) we considered the following table of values for $f(x) = \dfrac{x^3 - 8}{x - 2}$ near $x = 2$:

x	1.9	1.99	1.999	1.9999	2	2.0001	2.001	2.01	2.1
$f(x) = \dfrac{x^3 - 8}{x - 2}$	11.41	11.9401	11.9940	11.9994		12.0006	12.0060	12.0601	12.61

suggesting that $\lim_{x \to 2} \dfrac{x^3 - 8}{x - 2} = 12$.

Graphical Approach Figure 7 shows the graph of f in this case. (Notice the open dot at $x = 2$, indicating that $f(2)$ is not defined.) The figure also shows pencil points approaching 2 from both sides, suggesting again that $\lim_{x \to 2} \dfrac{x^3 - 8}{x - 2} = 12$.

b. *Numerical Approach* Because we are asked for only the right-hand limit, we need only list values of x approaching 0 from the right:

←x approaching 0 from the right

x	0	0.0001	0.001	0.01	0.1
$f(x) = \dfrac{1}{x}$		10,000	1,000	100	10

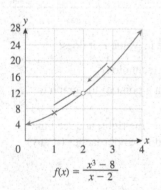

$f(x) = \dfrac{x^3 - 8}{x - 2}$

Figure 7

What seems to be happening as x approaches 0 from the right is that $f(x)$ is increasing without bound, as in Example 4(d). That is, if you name any number, no matter how large, $f(x)$ will be even larger than that if x is sufficiently close to zero. Thus, the limit diverges to $+\infty$, so

$$\lim_{x \to 0^+} \frac{1}{x} = +\infty$$

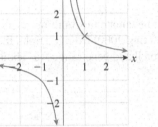

Figure 8

Graphical Approach Recall that the graph of $f(x) = \dfrac{1}{x}$ is the standard hyperbola shown in Figure 8. The figure also shows the pencil point moving so that its x-coordinate approaches 0 from the right. Because the point moves along the graph, it is forced to go higher and higher. In other words, its y-coordinate becomes larger and larger, approaching $+\infty$. Thus, we conclude that

$$\lim_{x \to 0^+} \frac{1}{x} = +\infty.$$

➡ **Before we go on ...** In Example 5 you should check that

$$\lim_{x \to 0^-} \frac{1}{x} = -\infty. \qquad \frac{1}{x} \text{ diverges to } -\infty \text{ as } x \to 0^-.$$

Also, check that

$$\lim_{x \to +\infty} \frac{1}{x} = \lim_{x \to -\infty} \frac{1}{x} = 0. \quad ■$$

Application

EXAMPLE 6 **Broadband Penetration**

Wired broadband penetration in the United States can be modeled by

$$P(t) = \frac{29.2}{1 + 9.0(1.64)^{-t}} \text{ percentage points} \qquad (t \ge 0),$$

where t is time in years since 2000.[1]

a. Estimate $\lim_{t \to +\infty} P(t)$, and interpret the answer.

b. Estimate $\lim_{t \to 0^+} P(t)$, and interpret the answer.

Solution

a. Figure 9 shows a plot of $P(t)$ for $0 \le t \le 20$. Using either the numerical or the graphical approach, we find

$$\lim_{t \to +\infty} P(t) = \lim_{t \to +\infty} \frac{29.2}{1 + 9.0(1.64)^{-t}} \approx 30.$$

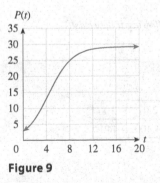

Figure 9

---

[1] See Example 2 in Section 2.4. Broadband penetration is the number of broadband installations divided by the total population. Source for data: Organization for Economic Cooperation and Development (OECD) Directorate for Science, Technology, and Industry, table of Historical Penetration Rates, December 2013, downloaded September 2014 from www.oecd.org/sti/ict/broadband.

(The actual limit is 29.2. Why?) Thus, in the long term (as t gets larger and larger), broadband penetration in the United States is expected to approach 30%; that is, the number of installations is expected to approach 30% of the total population.

b. The limit here is

$$\lim_{t\to 0^+} P(t) = \lim_{t\to 0^+} \frac{29.2}{1 + 9.0(1.64)^{-t}} \approx 2.9.$$

(Notice that in this case we can simply put $t = 0$ to evaluate this limit more precisely as 2.92.) Thus, the closer t gets to 0 (representing 2000) from the right, the closer $P(t)$ gets to 2.9%, meaning that, in 2000, broadband penetration was about 2.9% of the population.

FAQs

Determining When a Limit Does or Does Not Exist

Q: If I substitute $x = a$ in the formula for a function and find that the function is defined there, it means that $\lim_{x\to a} f(x)$ exists and equals $f(a)$—right?

A: Correct, provided that the function is specified by a *single algebraic formula** and is not, say, piecewise-defined. We shall say more about this in the next two sections.

* In a sense we will make more precise in Section 10.3.

Q: If I substitute $x = a$ in the formula for a function and find that the function is not defined there, it means that $\lim_{x\to a} f(x)$ does not exist—right?

A: Wrong. The limit may still exist, as in Example 1, or may not exist, as in Example 2. In general, whether or not $\lim_{x\to a} f(x)$ exists has nothing to do with $f(a)$ but rather is determined by the values of f when x is *very close to, but not equal to a.*

Q: Is there a quick and easy way of telling from a graph whether $\lim_{x\to a} f(x)$ exists?

A: Yes. If you cover up the portion of the graph corresponding to $x = a$ and it appears as though the visible part of the graph could be made into a continuous curve by filling in a suitable point at $x = a$, then the limit exists. (The "suitable point" need not be $(a, f(a))$.) Otherwise, it does not. Try this method with the curves in Example 4.

10.1 EXERCISES

▼ more advanced   ◆ challenging
▮ indicates exercises that should be solved using technology

In Exercises 1–4, use the given table of values to estimate, for the given value of a, each of the following if they exist:
(a) $\lim_{x\to a^-} f(x)$ (b) $\lim_{x\to a^+} f(x)$ (c) $\lim_{x\to a} f(x)$ (d) $f(a)$ *if it is defined*
[HINT: See Examples 1–3.]

1. $a = 2$; table of values:

x	1.9	1.99	1.999	1.9999	2	2.0001	2.001	2.01	2.1
$f(x)$	−5.975	−5.9975	−5.99975	−5.999975	−4	440,000	44,000	4,400	440

2. $a = -2$; table of values:

x	-2.1	-2.01	-2.001	-2.0001	-2	-1.9999	-1.999	-1.99	-1.9
$f(x)$	-1.12	-11.12	-111.12	$-1,111.12$		-0.00003	-0.00031	-0.00311	-0.03111

3. $a = -5$; table of values:

x	-5.1	-5.01	-5.001	-5.0001	-5	-4.9999	-4.999	-4.99	-4.9
$f(x)$	-3.12	-31.12	-311.12	$-3,111.12$		$-4,111.12$	-411.12	-41.12	-4.12

4. $a = 0$; table of values:

x	-0.1	-0.01	-0.001	-0.0001	0	0.0001	0.001	0.01	0.1
$f(x)$	-1.0303	-1.00303	-1.0003	-1.00003	0	1.00003	1.0003	1.00303	1.0303

In Exercises 5–34, estimate the given limit numerically if it exists. [**HINT**: See Examples 1–3.]

5. $\lim\limits_{x \to 0} \dfrac{x^2}{x+1}$

6. $\lim\limits_{x \to 0} \dfrac{x-3}{x-1}$

7. $\lim\limits_{x \to 2} \dfrac{x^2-4}{x-2}$

8. $\lim\limits_{x \to 2} \dfrac{x^2-1}{x-2}$

9. $\lim\limits_{x \to -1} \dfrac{x^2+1}{x+1}$

10. $\lim\limits_{x \to -1} \dfrac{x^2+2x+1}{x+1}$

11. $\lim\limits_{x \to 1^+} \dfrac{x-1}{\sqrt{x-1}}$

12. $\lim\limits_{x \to 3^-} \dfrac{\sqrt{3-x}}{3-x}$

13. $\lim\limits_{x \to 2^+} \dfrac{x^2+4x+3}{x+3}$

14. $\lim\limits_{x \to 2^-} \dfrac{x^2-4x+4}{x-2}$

15. $\lim\limits_{x \to 9^-} \dfrac{x-9}{\sqrt{x}-3}$

16. $\lim\limits_{x \to 25^+} \dfrac{\sqrt{x}-5}{x-25}$

17. $\lim\limits_{x \to 3^-} \dfrac{4}{(x-3)^2}$

18. $\lim\limits_{x \to 4^-} \dfrac{3}{(x-4)^{1/3}}$

19. $\lim\limits_{x \to -2^+} \dfrac{|x+2|}{(x+2)^{1/6}}$

20. $\lim\limits_{x \to -3} \dfrac{(x+3)^{2/3}}{|x+3|}$

21. $\lim\limits_{x \to +\infty} \dfrac{3x^2+10x-1}{2x^2-5x}$

22. $\lim\limits_{x \to +\infty} \dfrac{6x^2+5x+100}{3x^2-9}$

23. $\lim\limits_{x \to -\infty} \dfrac{x^5-1,000x^4}{2x^5+10,000}$

24. $\lim\limits_{x \to -\infty} \dfrac{x^6+3,000x^3+1,000,000}{2x^6+1,000x^3}$

25. $\lim\limits_{x \to +\infty} \dfrac{10x^2+300x+1}{5x+2}$

26. $\lim\limits_{x \to +\infty} \dfrac{2x^4+20x^3}{1,000x^6+6}$

27. $\lim\limits_{x \to +\infty} \dfrac{10x^2+300x+1}{5x^3+2}$

28. $\lim\limits_{x \to +\infty} \dfrac{2x^4+20x^3}{1,000x^3+6}$

29. $\lim\limits_{x \to 2} e^{x-2}$

30. $\lim\limits_{x \to +\infty} e^{-x}$

31. $\lim\limits_{x \to +\infty} xe^{-x}$

32. $\lim\limits_{x \to -\infty} xe^{x}$

33. $\lim\limits_{x \to -\infty} (x^{10}+2x^5+1)e^x$

34. $\lim\limits_{x \to +\infty} (x^{50}+x^{30}+1)e^{-x}$

In Exercises 35–48 the graph of f is given. Use the graph to compute the quantities asked for. [**HINT**: See Examples 4–5.]

35. a. $\lim\limits_{x \to 1} f(x)$ **b.** $\lim\limits_{x \to -1} f(x)$

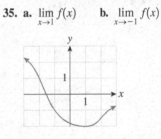

36. a. $\lim\limits_{x \to -1} f(x)$ **b.** $\lim\limits_{x \to 1} f(x)$

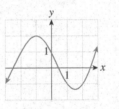

37. a. $\lim\limits_{x \to 0} f(x)$ **b.** $\lim\limits_{x \to 2} f(x)$

     c. $\lim\limits_{x \to -\infty} f(x)$ **d.** $\lim\limits_{x \to +\infty} f(x)$

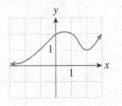

38. a. $\lim\limits_{x\to-1} f(x)$ **b.** $\lim\limits_{x\to1} f(x)$ **c.** $\lim\limits_{x\to+\infty} f(x)$ **d.** $\lim\limits_{x\to-\infty} f(x)$

39. a. $\lim\limits_{x\to2} f(x)$ **b.** $\lim\limits_{x\to0^+} f(x)$ **c.** $\lim\limits_{x\to0^-} f(x)$
d. $\lim\limits_{x\to0} f(x)$ **e.** $f(0)$ **f.** $\lim\limits_{x\to-\infty} f(x)$

40. a. $\lim\limits_{x\to3} f(x)$ **b.** $\lim\limits_{x\to1^+} f(x)$ **c.** $\lim\limits_{x\to1^-} f(x)$
d. $\lim\limits_{x\to1} f(x)$ **e.** $f(1)$ **f.** $\lim\limits_{x\to+\infty} f(x)$

41. a. $\lim\limits_{x\to-2} f(x)$ **b.** $\lim\limits_{x\to-1^+} f(x)$ **c.** $\lim\limits_{x\to-1^-} f(x)$
d. $\lim\limits_{x\to-1} f(x)$ **e.** $f(-1)$ **f.** $\lim\limits_{x\to+\infty} f(x)$

42. a. $\lim\limits_{x\to-1} f(x)$ **b.** $\lim\limits_{x\to0^+} f(x)$ **c.** $\lim\limits_{x\to0^-} f(x)$
d. $\lim\limits_{x\to0} f(x)$ **e.** $f(0)$ **f.** $\lim\limits_{x\to-\infty} f(x)$

43. a. $\lim\limits_{x\to-1^+} f(x)$ **b.** $\lim\limits_{x\to-1^-} f(x)$ **c.** $\lim\limits_{x\to-1} f(x)$ **d.** $f(-1)$

44. a. $\lim\limits_{x\to0^+} f(x)$ **b.** $\lim\limits_{x\to0^-} f(x)$ **c.** $\lim\limits_{x\to0} f(x)$ **d.** $f(0)$

45. a. $\lim\limits_{x\to-1} f(x)$ **b.** $\lim\limits_{x\to0^+} f(x)$ **c.** $\lim\limits_{x\to0^-} f(x)$
d. $\lim\limits_{x\to0} f(x)$ **e.** $f(0)$ **f.** $\lim\limits_{x\to+\infty} f(x)$

46. a. $\lim\limits_{x\to1} f(x)$ **b.** $\lim\limits_{x\to0^+} f(x)$ **c.** $\lim\limits_{x\to0^-} f(x)$
d. $\lim\limits_{x\to0} f(x)$ **e.** $f(0)$ **f.** $\lim\limits_{x\to-\infty} f(x)$

47. a. $\lim\limits_{x\to-1} f(x)$ **b.** $\lim\limits_{x\to0^+} f(x)$ **c.** $\lim\limits_{x\to0^-} f(x)$
d. $\lim\limits_{x\to0} f(x)$ **e.** $f(0)$ **f.** $f(-1)$

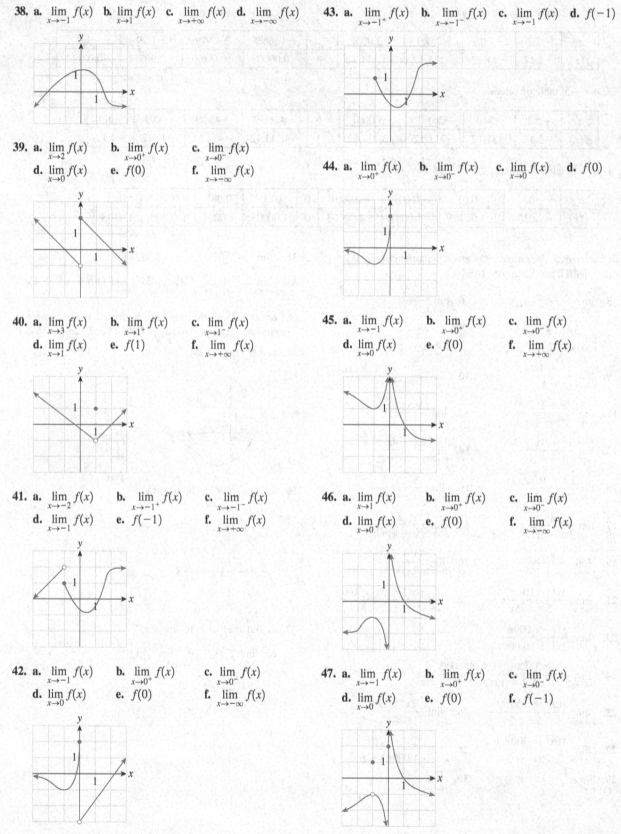

48. **a.** $\lim_{x \to 0^-} f(x)$ **b.** $\lim_{x \to 1^+} f(x)$ **c.** $\lim_{x \to 0} f(x)$
d. $\lim_{x \to 1} f(x)$ **e.** $f(0)$ **f.** $f(1)$

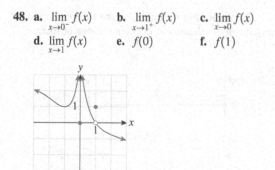

Applications

49. *Doctorates in Mexico* The annual number of PhD graduates in Mexico in the natural sciences for 1990–2012 can be approximated by

$$n(t) = 890(1 - e^{-0.05t}),$$

where t is time in years since 1990.[2] Numerically estimate $\lim_{t \to +\infty} n(t)$, and interpret the answer. [**HINT**: See Example 6.]

50. *Housing Starts* The number $s(t)$ of housing starts for single-family homes in the United States each year from 2006 through 2013 can be approximated by

$$s(t) = 500e^{0.05(x-5)^2} - 100 \text{ thousand units}$$

where t is time in years since 2006.[3] Numerically estimate $\lim_{t \to +\infty} s(t)$, and interpret the answer. [**HINT**: See Example 6.]

51. *Funding for NASA up to 1966* The percentage of the U.S. federal budget allocated to NASA from 1958 to 1966 can be modeled by

$$p(t) = \frac{4.7}{1 + 139e^{-t}} \text{ percentage points}$$

(t is time in years since 1958).[4]
a. Numerically estimate $\lim_{t \to +\infty} p(t)$, and interpret the answer. [**HINT**: See Example 6.]
b. How does your answer to part (a) compare with actual current funding for NASA?

52. *Funding for NASA up to 1966* (Compare Exercise 51.) The percentage of the U.S. federal budget allocated to NASA from 1958 to 1966 can also be modeled by

$$p(t) = \frac{4.5}{1.07^{(t-8)^2}} \text{ percentage points}$$

(t is time in years since 1958).[5]

a. Numerically estimate $\lim_{t \to +\infty} p(t)$, and interpret the answer. [**HINT**: See Example 6.]
b. How does your answer to part (a) compare with actual current funding for NASA?

53. *Scientific Research: 1983–2003* The number of research articles per year, in thousands, in the prominent journal *Physical Review* written by researchers in Europe during 1983–2003 can be modeled by

$$A(t) = \frac{7.0}{1 + 5.4(1.2)^{-t}},$$

where t is time in years ($t = 0$ represents 1983).[6] Numerically estimate $\lim_{t \to +\infty} A(t)$ and interpret the answer.

54. *Scientific Research: 1983–2003* The percentage of research articles in the prominent journal *Physical Review* written by researchers in the United States during 1983–2003 can be modeled by

$$A(t) = 25 + \frac{36}{1 + 0.6(0.7)^{-t}},$$

where t is time in years ($t = 0$ represents 1983).[7] Numerically estimate $\lim_{t \to +\infty} A(t)$, and interpret the answer.

55. *SAT Scores by Income* The following bar graph shows U.S. math SAT scores as a function of household income:[8]

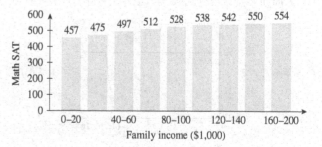

These data can be modeled by

$$S(x) = 573 - 133(0.987)^x,$$

where $S(x)$ is the average math SAT score of students whose household income is x thousand dollars per year. Numerically estimate $\lim_{x \to +\infty} S(x)$, and interpret the answer.

[5] *Ibid.*

[6] Based on data from 1983 to 2003. Source: The American Physical Society/*New York Times*, May 3, 2003, p. A1.

[7] *Ibid.*

[8] 2009 data. Source: College Board/*New York Times* http://economix .blogs.nytimes.com.

[2] Model is the authors'. Source for data: Instituto Nacional de Estadística y Geografía www.inegi.org.mx.

[3] Model is the authors'. Source of data: www.census.gov.

[4] Model is the authors'. Source of data: U.S. Office of Management and Budget/www.wikipedia.org.

56. SAT Scores by Income The following bar graph shows U.S. critical reading SAT scores as a function of household income:[9]

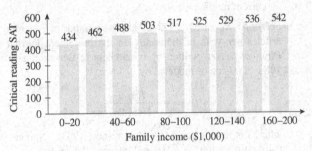

These data can be modeled by

$$S(x) = 550 - 136(0.985)^x,$$

where $S(x)$ is the average critical reading SAT score of students whose household income is x thousand dollars per year. Numerically estimate $\lim_{x \to +\infty} S(x)$, and interpret the answer.

57. Flash Crash The graph shows a rough representation of what happened to the Russell 1000 Growth Index Fund (IWF) stock price on the day of the U.S. stock market crash at 2:45 pm on May 6, 2010, the "Flash Crash" (t is the time of the day in hours, and $r(t)$ is the price of the stock in dollars).[10]

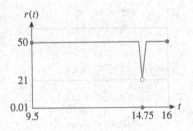

a. Compute the following (if a limit does not exist, say why):

$$\lim_{t \to 14.75^-} r(t), \quad \lim_{t \to 14.75^+} r(t), \quad \lim_{t \to 14.75} r(t), \quad r(14.75).$$

b. What do the answers to part (a) tell you about the IWF stock price?

58. Flash Crash The graph shows a rough representation of the (aggregate) market depth[11] of the stocks comprising the S&P 500 on the day of the U.S. stock market crash at 2:45 pm on

May 6, 2010, the "Flash Crash" (t is the time of the day in hours, and $m(t)$ is the market depth in millions of shares).

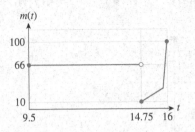

a. Compute the following (if a limit does not exist, say why):

$$\lim_{t \to 14.75^-} m(t), \quad \lim_{t \to 14.75^+} m(t), \quad \lim_{t \to 14.75} m(t), \quad m(14.75).$$

b. What do the answers to part (a) tell you about the market depth?

59. Home Prices The following graph shows the values of the home price index[12] for 2000–2014 together with a mathematical model I extrapolating the data:

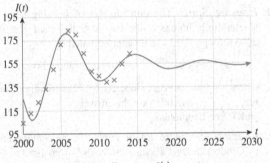

Estimate and interpret $\lim_{t \to +\infty} I(t)$.

60. Home Prices: Optimist Projection The following graph shows the values of the home price index[13] for 2000–2014 together with another mathematical model I extrapolating the data:

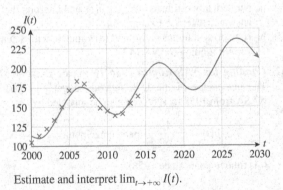

Estimate and interpret $\lim_{t \to +\infty} I(t)$.

---

[9] See footnote for Exercise 55.

[10] The actual graph can be seen at http://seekingalpha.com.

[11] The market depth of a stock is a measure of its ability to withstand relatively large market orders and is measured in orders to buy or sell the given stock. Source for data on graph: *Findings Regarding the Market Events of May 6, 2010*, U.S. Commodity Futures Trading Commission, U.S. Securities & Exchange Commission.

[12] The index is the Standard & Poor/Case-Shiller Home Price Index. Source for data: www.standardandpoors.com.

[13] *Ibid.*

61. *Electric Rates* The cost of electricity in Portland, Oregon, for residential customers increased suddenly on October 1, 2001, from around $0.06 to around $0.08 per kilowatt-hour.[14] Let $C(t)$ be this cost at time t, and take $t = 1$ to represent October 1, 2001. What does the given information tell you about $\lim_{t \to 1} C(t)$?

62. *Airline Stocks* Before the September 11, 2001 attacks, United Airlines stock was trading at around $35 per share. Immediately after the attacks, the share price dropped by $15.[15] Let $U(t)$ be this cost at time t, and take $t = 11$ to represent September 11, 2001. What does the given information tell you about $\lim_{t \to 11} U(t)$?

Foreign Trade *Annual U.S. imports from China in the years 1996–2003 can be approximated by*

$$I(t) = t^2 + 3.5t + 50 \quad (1 \le t \le 9)$$

billion dollars, where t represents time in years since 1995. Annual U.S. exports to China in the same years can be approximated by

$$E(t) = 0.4t^2 - 1.6t + 14$$

billion dollars.[16] Exercises 63 and 64 are based on these models.

63. ▼ Assuming that the trends shown in the above models continued indefinitely, numerically estimate

$$\lim_{t \to +\infty} I(t) \quad \text{and} \quad \lim_{t \to +\infty} \frac{I(t)}{E(t)},$$

interpret your answers, and comment on the results.

---

[14] Source: Portland General Electric/*New York Times*, February 2, 2002, p. C1.

[15] Stock prices are approximate.

[16] Based on quadratic regression using data from the U.S. Census Bureau Foreign Trade Division website www.census.gov/foreign-trade/sitc1/ as of December 2004.

64. ▼ Repeat Exercise 63, this time calculating

$$\lim_{t \to +\infty} E(t) \quad \text{and} \quad \lim_{t \to +\infty} \frac{E(t)}{I(t)}.$$

Communication and Reasoning Exercises

65. Describe the method of evaluating limits numerically. Give at least one disadvantage of this method.

66. Describe the method of evaluating limits graphically. Give at least one disadvantage of this method.

67. Your friend Dion, a business student, claims that the study of limits that do not exist is completely unrealistic and has nothing to do with the world of business. Give two examples from the world of business that might convince him that he is wrong.

68. Your other friend Fiona claims that the study of limits is a complete farce; all you ever need to do to find the limit as x approaches a is substitute $x = a$. Give two examples that show she is wrong.

69. ▼ What is wrong with the following statement? "Because $f(a)$ is not defined, $\lim_{x \to a} f(x)$ does not exist." Illustrate your claim with an example.

70. ▼ What is wrong with the following statement? "Because $f(a)$ is defined, $\lim_{x \to a} f(x)$ exists." Illustrate your claim with an example.

71. ◆ Give an example of a function f with $\lim_{x \to 1} f(x) = f(2)$.

72. ◆ If $S(t)$ represents the size of the universe in billions of light-years at time t years since the big bang and $\lim_{t \to +\infty} s(t) = 130{,}000$, is it possible that the universe will continue to expand forever?

73. ◆ Investigate $\lim_{x \to +\infty} x^n e^{-x}$ for some large values of n. What do you find? What do you think is the value of $\lim_{x \to +\infty} p(x)e^{-x}$ if $p(x)$ is any polynomial?

74. ◆ Investigate $\lim_{x \to -\infty} x^n e^x$ for some large values of n. What do you find? What do you think is the value of $\lim_{x \to -\infty} p(x)e^x$ if $p(x)$ is any polynomial?

10.2 Limits and Continuity

Continuous Functions

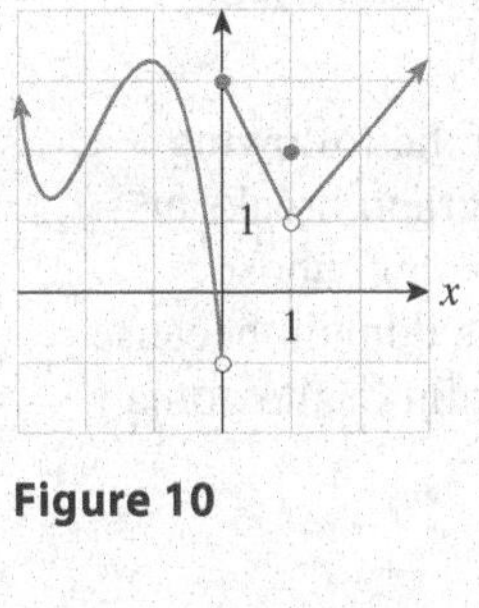

Figure 10

In Section 10.1 we saw examples of graphs that had various kinds of "breaks" or "jumps." For instance, in Example 4 we looked at the graph in Figure 10. This graph appears to have breaks, or **discontinuities**, at $x = 0$ and at $x = 1$. At $x = 0$ we saw that $\lim_{x \to 0} f(x)$ does not exist because the left- and right-hand limits are not the same. Thus, the discontinuity at $x = 0$ seems to be due to the fact that the limit does not exist there. On the other hand, at $x = 1$, $\lim_{x \to 1} f(x)$ *does* exist (it is equal to 1) but is not equal to $f(1) = 2$.

Thus, we have identified two kinds of discontinuity:

1. Points where the limit of the function does not exist $\qquad$ $x = 0$ in Figure 10 because $\lim_{x \to 0} f(x)$ does not exist.

2. Points where the limit exists but does not equal the value of the function $\qquad$ $x = 1$ in Figure 10 because $\lim_{x \to 1} f(x) = 1 \neq f(1)$.

On the other hand, there is no discontinuity at, say, $x = -2$, where we find that $\lim_{x \to -2} f(x)$ exists and equals 2 and $f(-2)$ is also equal to 2. In other words,

$$\lim_{x \to -2} f(x) = 2 = f(-2).$$

The point $x = -2$ is an example of a point where f is **continuous**. (Notice that you can draw the portion of the graph near $x = -2$ without lifting your pencil from the paper.) Similarly, f is continuous at *every* point other than $x = 0$ and $x = 1$. Here is the mathematical definition.

Continuous Function

Let f be a function, and let a be a number in the domain of f. Then f is **continuous at a** if

a. $\lim_{x \to a} f(x)$ exists and

b. $\lim_{x \to a} f(x) = f(a).$*

The function f is said to be **continuous on its domain** if it is continuous at each point in its domain.

If f is not continuous at a particular a in its domain, we say that f is **discontinuous** at a or that f has a **discontinuity** at a. Thus, a discontinuity can occur at $x = a$ if either

a. $\lim_{x \to a} f(x)$ does not exist or

b. $\lim_{x \to a} f(x)$ exists but is not equal to $f(a)$.

* If a is an isolated point in the domain of f; that is, f is defined at a but at no other points within some distance of a (for example, $f(x) = \sqrt{-x^2}$ is defined only at $x = 0$) then, even though there can be no limit at a, we regard f as continuous at a.

Quick Examples

1. The function shown in Figure 10 is continuous at $x = -1$ and $x = 2$. It is discontinuous at $x = 0$ and $x = 1$ and so is not continuous on its domain.

2. The function $f(x) = x^2$ is continuous on its domain. (Think of its graph, which contains no breaks.)

3. The function shown in Figure 11 is continuous on its domain. In particular, it is continuous at the left endpoint $x = -1$ of its domain, because $\lim_{x \to -1} f(x) = \lim_{x \to -1^+} f(x) = 1 = f(-1).$

4. The function f whose graph is shown on the left in the following figure is continuous on its domain. (Although the graph breaks at $x = 2$, that is not a point of its domain.) The function g whose graph is shown on the right is not continuous on its domain because it has a discontinuity at $x = 2$. (Here, $x = 2$ is a point of the domain of g.)

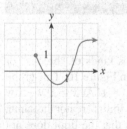

Figure 11

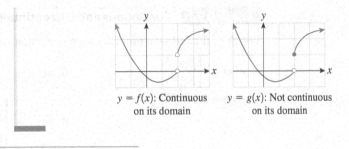

$y = f(x)$: Continuous
on its domain

$y = g(x)$: Not continuous
on its domain

Singularities

Continuity and discontinuity of a function are defined only for points in a function's domain; a function cannot be continuous at a point not in its domain, and it cannot be discontinuous there either. So if a is not in the domain of f—that is, if $f(a)$ is not defined—then it is meaningless to talk about whether f is continuous or discontinuous at a. For instance, for the function f in Quick Example 4, it is meaningless to talk about whether f is continuous or discontinuous at 2.

Q: *Wait a minute! The graph of the function f shown on the left in Quick Example 4 definitely breaks at x = 2. If that is not a point of discontinuity, then what is it?*

A: Notice that, although f is defined at values of x arbitrarily close to 2, it is not defined at x = 2, thus causing a break in its graph. We say that f has a *singularity* at 2.

Singularity

If $f(a)$ is not defined but $f(x)$ is defined for (at least some) values of x arbitrarily close to and on both sides of a, we will say that f has a **singularity at** a, or that a **is a singular point of** f.*

Quick Examples

5. Consider again the functions shown in Quick Example 4 above:

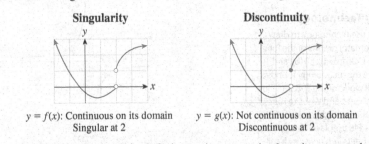

Singularity

Discontinuity

$y = f(x)$: Continuous on its domain
Singular at 2

$y = g(x)$: Not continuous on its domain
Discontinuous at 2

Although f (graph on the left) is continuous on its domain, we see that $f(2)$ is not defined, whereas $f(x)$ is defined for values of x arbitrarily close to 2. Thus, f has a singularity at 2. The function g (graph on the right) has no singularities of the type we discuss here; $f(x)$ is defined for all x.

6. $\dfrac{1}{x}$, $\dfrac{1}{x^2}$, and $\dfrac{1}{x^{1/3}}$ are all singular at 0.†

---

* In mathematics the term "singular point" or "singularity" is used quite broadly to refer to a point at which some mathematical object under consideration either is not defined or is unusual in some other manner. As a consequence, the term applies to more situations than we discuss here and has different meanings in different contexts. (See, for example, Section 12.1 for our use of the term in the context of maxima and minima.) Be aware that many people use the term "discontinuity" to apply to singular points as well, but that is contrary to the accepted definition of that term.

† What about $d(x) = \dfrac{1}{\sqrt{x}}$? A mathematician would also say that this function is singular at 0 because $f(x)$ approaches infinity as $x \to 0^+$ even though it is not defined on both sides of zero. Remember, what we call a "singularity" includes some—but not all—types of points a mathematician would call singular.

| EXAMPLE 1 | **Continuous and Discontinuous Functions** |

Which of the following functions are continuous on their domains?

a. $h(x) = \begin{cases} x + 3 & \text{if } x \le 1 \\ 5 - x & \text{if } x > 1 \end{cases}$ **b.** $k(x) = \begin{cases} x + 3 & \text{if } x \le 1 \\ 1 - x & \text{if } x > 1 \end{cases}$

c. $f(x) = \dfrac{1}{x}$ **d.** $g(x) = \begin{cases} \dfrac{1}{x} & \text{if } x \ne 0 \\ 0 & \text{if } x = 0 \end{cases}$

Solution

a. and **b.** The graphs of h and k are shown in Figure 12.

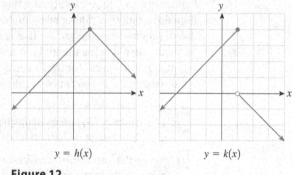

$y = h(x)$ $y = k(x)$

Figure 12

Even though the graph of h is made up of two different line segments, it is continuous at every point of its domain, including $x = 1$ because

$$\lim_{x \to 1} h(x) = 4 = h(1).$$

On the other hand, $x = 1$ is also in the domain of k, but $\lim_{x \to 1} k(x)$ does not exist. Thus, k has a discontinuity at $x = 1$ and is therefore not continuous on its domain.

c. and **d.** The graphs of f and g are shown in Figure 13.

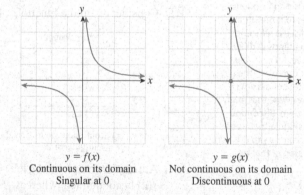

$y = f(x)$
Continuous on its domain
Singular at 0

$y = g(x)$
Not continuous on its domain
Discontinuous at 0

Figure 13

The domain of f consists of all real numbers except 0, and f is continuous at all such numbers. (Notice that 0 is not in the domain of f, so the question of continuity at 0 does not arise.) Thus, f is continuous on its domain but singular at 0, as it is not defined there but is defined at points arbitrarily close to 0.

The function g, on the other hand, has its domain expanded to include 0, so we now need to check whether g is continuous at 0. From the graph, it is easy to see that

g is discontinuous there because $\lim_{x \to 0} g(x)$ does not exist. Thus, g is not continuous on its domain because it is discontinuous at 0.

➡ **Before we go on ...** Remember: When we say that a function like $f(x) = \dfrac{1}{x}$ is continuous on its domain, we are claiming not that it is continuous *at every real number* but that it is continuous at every real number *in its domain*, so its graph can still break at any singular points. ■

EXAMPLE 2   **Continuous Except at a Point**

In each case, say what, if any, value of $f(a)$ would make f continuous at a.

a. $f(x) = \dfrac{x^3 - 8}{x - 2}; a = 2$ **b.** $f(x) = \dfrac{e^{2x} - 1}{x}; a = 0$ **c.** $f(x) = \dfrac{|x|}{x}; a = 0$

Solution

a. In Figure 14 we see the graph of $f(x) = \dfrac{x^3 - 8}{x - 2}$. The point corresponding to $x = 2$ is missing because f is not (yet) defined there. (Your graphing utility will probably miss this subtlety and render a continuous curve. See the technology note in the margin.) To turn f into a function that is continuous at $x = 2$, we need to "fill in the gap" so as to obtain a continuous curve. Since the graph suggests that the missing point is $(2, 12)$, let us define $f(2) = 12$.

Does f now become continuous if we take $f(2) = 12$? From the graph or Example 1(a) of Section 10.1,

$$\lim_{x \to 2} f(x) = \lim_{x \to 2} \frac{x^3 - 8}{x - 2} = 12,$$

which is now equal to $f(2)$. Thus, $\lim_{x \to 2} f(x) = f(2)$, showing that f is now continuous at $x = 2$.

b. In Example 1(b) of Section 10.1, we saw that

$$\lim_{x \to 0} f(x) = \lim_{x \to 0} \frac{e^{2x} - 1}{x} = 2,$$

so, as in part (a), we must define $f(0) = 2$. This is confirmed by the graph, shown in Figure 15.

c. We considered the function $f(x) = |x|/x$ in Example 2 of Section 10.1. Its graph is shown in Figure 16.

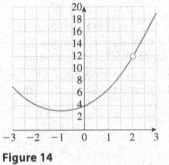

Figure 14

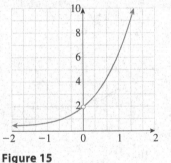

Figure 15

Using Technology

It is instructive to see how technology handles the functions in Example 2. Here are the technology formulas that will work for the TI-83/84 Plus, spreadsheets, and Website function evaluator and grapher. (In spreadsheets, replace x by a cell reference, and insert an equals sign in front of the formula.)

a. (x^3-8)/(x-2)
b. (e^(2x)-1)/x
   Spreadsheet:
   =(exp(2*A2)-1)/A2
c. abs(x)/x
In each case, compare the graph rendered by technology with the corresponding figure in Example 2.

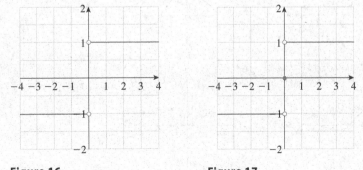

Figure 16   **Figure 17**

Now we encounter a problem: No matter how we try to fill in the gap at the singular point at $x = 0$, the result will be a discontinuous function. For example, setting $f(0) = 0$ will result in the discontinuous function shown in Figure 17. We conclude that it is impossible to assign any value to $f(0)$ to turn f into a function that is continuous at $x = 0$.

We can also see this result algebraically: In Example 2 of Section 10.1 we saw that $\lim\limits_{x \to 0} \dfrac{|x|}{x}$ does not exist. Thus, the resulting function will fail to be continuous at 0, no matter how we define $f(0)$.

Removable and Essential Singularities

The function in Example 2(a) has a singularity at 2, and the functions in Example 2(b) and 2(c) have singularities at 0. The functions in Example 2(a) and 2(b) have **removable singularities** because we can make these functions continuous at a by properly defining $f(a)$. The function in Example 2(c) has an **essential singularity** because we cannot make f continuous at $x = a$ just by defining $f(a)$ properly.

10.2 EXERCISES

▼ more advanced ◆ challenging
Ⓣ indicates exercises that should be solved using technology

In Exercises 1–14 the graph of a function f is given. Determine whether f is continuous on its domain. If it is not continuous on its domain, say why. [**HINT:** See Quick Examples 1–4.]

1.

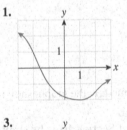

2.

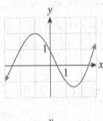

3.

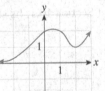

4.

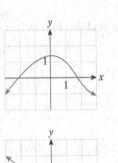

5.

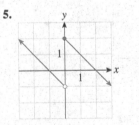

6.

7.

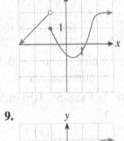

8.

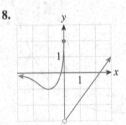

9.

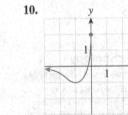

10.

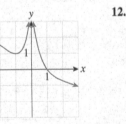

11.

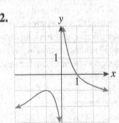

12.

13.

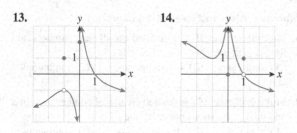

14.

(E)

(F)

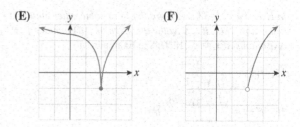

In Exercises 15 and 16, identify which (if any) of the given graphs represent functions that are continuous on their domains. [HINT: See Quick Examples 1–4.]

In Exercises 17–24, the graph of a function f is given. Determine whether, at the given point a, f is continuous, discontinuous, or singular. [HINT: See Quick Examples 5 and 6.]

15. (A)   (B)

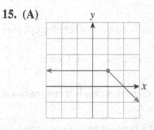

(C)   (D)

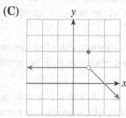

(E)   (F)

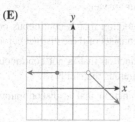

16. (A)   (B)

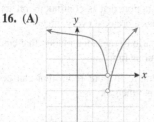

(C)   (D)

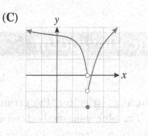

17.   18.

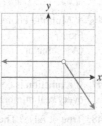

$a = -1$ $a = 0$

19.   20.

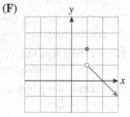

$a = -1$ $a = 0$

21.   22.

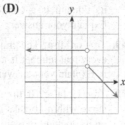

$a = 1$ $a = 2$

23.   24.

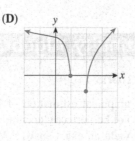

$a = 1$ $a = 2$

In Exercises 25–32, use a graph of f or some other method to determine what, if any, value to assign to $f(a)$ to make f continuous at $x = a$. [**HINT:** See Example 2.]

25. $f(x) = \dfrac{x^2 - 2x + 1}{x - 1}; a = 1$

26. $f(x) = \dfrac{x^2 + 3x + 2}{x + 1}; a = -1$

27. $f(x) = \dfrac{x}{3x^2 - x}; a = 0$ **28.** $f(x) = \dfrac{x^2 - 3x}{x + 4}; a = -4$

29. $f(x) = \dfrac{3}{3x^2 - x}; a = 0$ **30.** $f(x) = \dfrac{x - 1}{x^3 - 1}; a = 1$

31. $f(x) = \dfrac{1 - e^x}{x}; a = 0$ **32.** $f(x) = \dfrac{1 + e^x}{1 - e^x}; a = 0$

In Exercises 33–42, use a graph to determine whether the given function is continuous on its domain. If it is not continuous on its domain, list the points of discontinuity. [**HINT:** See Example 1.]

33. $f(x) = |x|$ **34.** $f(x) = \dfrac{|x|}{x}$

35. $g(x) = \dfrac{1}{x^2 - 1}$ **36.** $g(x) = \dfrac{x - 1}{x + 2}$

37. $f(x) = \begin{cases} x + 2 & \text{if } x < 0 \\ 2x - 1 & \text{if } x \geq 0 \end{cases}$

38. $f(x) = \begin{cases} 1 - x & \text{if } x \leq 1 \\ x - 1 & \text{if } x > 1 \end{cases}$

39. $h(x) = \begin{cases} \dfrac{|x|}{x} & \text{if } x \neq 0 \\ 0 & \text{if } x = 0 \end{cases}$

40. $h(x) = \begin{cases} \dfrac{1}{x^2} & \text{if } x \neq 0 \\ 2 & \text{if } x = 0 \end{cases}$

41. $g(x) = \begin{cases} x + 2 & \text{if } x < 0 \\ 2x + 2 & \text{if } x \geq 0 \end{cases}$

42. $g(x) = \begin{cases} 1 - x & \text{if } x \leq 1 \\ x + 1 & \text{if } x > 1 \end{cases}$

Communication and Reasoning Exercises

43. Multiple choice: If f is defined on all real numbers and $\lim_{x \to a} f(x)$ does not exist, then f is
(**A**) singular   (**B**) discontinuous   (**C**) continuous
at a.

44. Multiple choice: If f is defined on all real numbers except a and $\lim_{x \to a} f(x)$ does not exist, then f is
(**A**) singular   (**B**) discontinuous   (**C**) continuous
at a.

45. ▼ Multiple choice: If f is defined only at a, then f is
(**A**) singular   (**B**) discontinuous   (**C**) continuous
at a.

46. ▼ Multiple choice: If f is defined everywhere except at a, then f is
(**A**) singular   (**B**) discontinuous   (**C**) continuous
at a.

47. If a function is continuous on its domain, is it continuous at every real number? Explain.

48. True or false? The graph of a function that is continuous on its domain is a continuous curve with no breaks in it. Explain your answer.

49. True or false? The graph of a function that is continuous at every real number is a continuous curve with no breaks in it. Explain your answer.

50. True or false? If the graph of a function is a continuous curve with no breaks in it, then the function is continuous on its domain. Explain your answer.

51. ▼ Give a formula for a function that is continuous on its domain but whose graph consists of three distinct curves.

52. ▼ Give a formula for a function that is not continuous at $x = -1$ but is not discontinuous there either.

53. ▼ Draw the graph of a function that is discontinuous at every integer.

54. ▼ Draw the graph of a function that is continuous on its domain but whose graph has a break at every integer.

55. ▼ Describe a real-life scenario in the stock market that can be modeled by a discontinuous function.

56. ▼ Describe a real-life scenario in your room that can be modeled by a discontinuous function.

10.3   Limits and Continuity: Algebraic Viewpoint

Closed-Form Functions

Although numerical and graphical estimation of limits is effective, the estimates these methods yield may not be perfectly accurate. The algebraic method, when it can be used, will always yield an exact answer. Moreover, algebraic analysis of a function often enables us to take a function apart and see "what makes it tick."

Let's start with the function $f(x) = 2 + x$ and ask: What happens to $f(x)$ as x approaches 3? To answer this algebraically, notice that as x gets closer and closer to 3, the quantity $2 + x$ must get closer and closer to $2 + 3 = 5$. Hence,

$$\lim_{x \to 3} f(x) = \lim_{x \to 3}(2 + x) = 2 + 3 = 5.$$

Q : Is that all there is to the algebraic method? Just substitute $x = a$?

A : Under certain circumstances. Notice that by substituting $x = 3$, we *evaluated the function at $x = 3$.* In other words, we relied on the fact that

$$\lim_{x \to 3} f(x) = f(3).$$

In Section 10.2 we said that a function satisfying this equation is *continuous* at $x = 3$.

Thus,

If we know that the function f is continuous at a point a, we can compute $\lim_{x \to a} f(x)$ by simply substituting $x = a$ into $f(x)$.

To use this fact, we need to know how to recognize continuous functions when we see them. Geometrically, they are easy to spot: A function is continuous at $x = a$ if its graph has no break at $x = a$. Algebraically, a large class of functions are known to be continuous on their domains—those, roughly speaking, that are *specified by a single formula*.

We can be more precise: A **closed-form function** is any function that can be obtained by combining constants, powers of x, exponential functions, radicals, logarithms, absolute values, trigonometric functions (and some other functions that we do not encounter in this text) into a *single* mathematical formula by means of the usual arithmetic operations and composition of functions. (They can be as complicated as we like.)

Closed-Form Functions

A function is **written in closed form** if it is specified by combining constants, powers of x, exponential functions, radicals, logarithms, absolute values, trigonometric functions (and some other functions that we do not encounter in this text) into a *single* mathematical formula by means of the usual arithmetic operations and composition of functions. A **closed-form function** is any function that can be written in closed form.

Quick Examples

1. $3x^2 - |x| + 1$, $\dfrac{\sqrt{x^2 - 1}}{6x - 1}$, $e^{-(4x^2-1)/x}$, and $\sqrt{\log_3(x^2 - 1)}$ are written in closed form, so they are all closed-form functions.

2. $f(x) = \begin{cases} -1 & \text{if } x \le -1 \\ x^2 + x & \text{if } -1 < x \le 1 \\ 2 - x & \text{if } 1 < x \le 2 \end{cases}$ is not written in closed-form because $f(x)$ is not expressed by a *single* mathematical formula.[*]

---

* It is possible to rewrite some piecewise-defined functions in closed form (using a single formula) but not this particular function, so $f(x)$ is not a closed-form function.

What is so special about closed-form functions is the following theorem.

Theorem 10.1 Continuity of Closed-Form Functions

Every closed-form function is continuous on its domain. Thus, if f is a closed-form function and $f(a)$ is defined, then $\lim_{x \to a} f(x)$ exists, and equals $f(a)$.

Quick Example

3. $f(x) = 1/x$ is a closed-form function, and its natural domain consists of all real numbers except 0. Thus, f is continuous at every nonzero real number. That is,

$$\lim_{x \to a} \frac{1}{x} = \frac{1}{a}$$

provided that $a \neq 0$.

Mathematics majors spend a great deal of time studying the proof of this theorem. We ask you to accept it without proof.

EXAMPLE 1   Limit of a Closed-Form Function

Evaluate the following limits algebraically:

a. $\lim\limits_{x \to 1} \dfrac{x^3 - 8}{x - 2}$ **b.** $\lim\limits_{x \to 2} \dfrac{x^3 - 8}{x - 2}$

Solution

a. First, notice that $(x^3 - 8)/(x - 2)$ is a closed-form function because it is specified by a single algebraic formula. Also, $x = 1$ is in the domain of this function. Therefore, the theorem applies, and

$$\lim_{x \to 1} \frac{x^3 - 8}{x - 2} = \frac{1^3 - 8}{1 - 2} = 7.$$

b. Although $(x^3 - 8)/(x - 2)$ is a closed-form function, $x = 2$ is not in its domain. (It is a singular point.) Thus, the theorem does not apply, and we cannot obtain the limit by substitution. However—and this is the key to finding limits at singular points—*some preliminary algebraic simplification will allow us to obtain a closed-form function with $x = 2$ in its domain*. To do this, notice first that the numerator can be factored as

$$x^3 - 8 = (x - 2)(x^2 + 2x + 4).$$

Thus,

$$\frac{x^3 - 8}{x - 2} = \frac{(x - 2)(x^2 + 2x + 4)}{x - 2} = x^2 + 2x + 4.$$

Once we have canceled the offending $(x - 2)$ in the denominator, we are left with a closed-form function *with 2 in its domain.** Thus,

$$\lim_{x \to 2} \frac{x^3 - 8}{x - 2} = \lim_{x \to 2} (x^2 + 2x + 4)$$

$$= 2^2 + 2(2) + 4 = 12. \qquad \text{Substitute } x = 2.$$

* By canceling the $(x - 2)$, we have removed the singularity of $(x^3 - 8)/(x - 2)$ at $x = 2$. (See Removable and Essential Singularities in Section 10.2).

This confirms the answer we found numerically in Example 1 in Section 10.1.

➡ **Before we go on...** Notice that in Example 1(b), before simplification the substitution $x = 2$ yields

$$\frac{x^3 - 8}{x - 2} = \frac{8 - 8}{2 - 2} = \frac{0}{0}.$$

Worse than the fact that 0/0 is undefined, it also conveys absolutely no information as to what the limit might be. (The limit turned out to be 12!) We therefore call the expression 0/0 an **indeterminate form**. Once simplified, the function became $x^2 + 2x + 4$, which, upon the substitution $x = 2$, yielded 12—no longer an indeterminate form. In general, we have the following rule of thumb:

If the substitution $x = a$ yields the indeterminate form 0/0, try simplifying by the method in Example 1.

We will say more about indeterminate forms in Example 2. ∎

Q: *There is something suspicious about Example 1(b). If 2 was not in the domain before simplifying but was in the domain after simplifying, we must have changed the function—right?*

A: Correct. In fact, when we said that

$$\frac{x^3 - 8}{x - 2} = x^2 + 2x + 4,$$

Domain excludes 2   Domain includes 2

we were lying a little bit. What we really meant is that these two expressions are equal *where both are defined.* The functions $(x^3 - 8)/(x - 2)$ and $x^2 + 2x + 4$ are different functions. The difference is that $x = 2$ is a singular point of $(x^3 - 8)/(x - 2)$ but is in the domain of $x^2 + 2x + 4$. Since $\lim_{x \to 2} f(x)$ explicitly *ignores* any value that f may have at 2, this does not affect the limit. From the point of view of the limit at 2, these functions *are* equal. In general, we have the following rule.

Functions with Equal Limits

If $f(x) = g(x)$ for all x except possibly $x = a$, then

$$\lim_{x \to a} f(x) = \lim_{x \to a} g(x).$$

> **Quick Example**
>
> 4. $\dfrac{x^2 - 1}{x - 1} = x + 1$ for all x except $x = 1$.   Write $\dfrac{x^2 - 1}{x - 1}$ as $\dfrac{(x + 1)(x - 1)}{x - 1}$, and cancel the $(x - 1)$.
>
> Therefore,
>
> $$\lim_{x \to 1} \frac{x^2 - 1}{x - 1} = \lim_{x \to 1}(x + 1) = 1 + 1 = 2.$$

Q: *How do we find $\lim_{x \to a} f(x)$ when $x = a$ is a singular point of the function f and we cannot simplify the given function to make a a point of the domain?*

A: In such a case it might be necessary to analyze the function by some other method, such as numerically or graphically. However, if we do not obtain the indeterminate form $0/0$ upon substitution, we can often say what the limit is, as the following example shows.

EXAMPLE 2   **Limit of a Closed-Form Function at a Singular Point: The Determinate Form $k/0$**

Evaluate the following limits if they exist:

a. $\displaystyle\lim_{x \to 1^+} \frac{x^2 - 4x + 1}{x - 1}$ **b.** $\displaystyle\lim_{x \to 1} \frac{x^2 - 4x + 1}{x - 1}$ **c.** $\displaystyle\lim_{x \to 1} \frac{x^2 - 4x + 1}{x^2 - 2x + 1}$

Solution

a. Although the function $f(x) = \dfrac{x^2 - 4x + 1}{x - 1}$ is a closed-form function, $x = 1$ is a singular point. Notice that substituting $x = 1$ gives

$$\frac{x^2 - 4x + 1}{x - 1} = \frac{1^2 - 4 + 1}{1 - 1} = \frac{-2}{0} \qquad \text{The \textbf{determinate} form } \frac{k}{0}$$

which, although not defined, conveys important information to us: As x gets closer and closer to 1, the numerator approaches -2 and the denominator gets closer and closer to 0. Now, if we divide a number close to -2 by a number close to 0, we get a number of large absolute value; for instance,

$$\frac{-2.1}{0.0001} = -21{,}000 \qquad \text{and} \qquad \frac{-2.1}{-0.0001} = 21{,}000$$

$$\frac{-2.01}{0.00001} = -201{,}000 \qquad \text{and} \qquad \frac{-2.01}{-0.00001} = 201{,}000.$$

(Compare Example 5 of Section 10.1.) In our limit for part (a), x is approaching 1 from the right, so the denominator $x - 1$ is positive (as x is to the right of 1). Thus, we have the scenario illustrated above on the left, and we can conclude that

$$\lim_{x \to 1^+} \frac{x^2 - 4x + 1}{x - 1} = -\infty. \qquad \text{Think of this as } \frac{-2}{0^+} = -\infty.$$

b. This time, x could be approaching 1 from either side. We already have, from part (a),

$$\lim_{x \to 1^+} \frac{x^2 - 4x + 1}{x - 1} = -\infty.$$

The same reasoning we used in part (a) gives

$$\lim_{x \to 1^-} \frac{x^2 - 4x + 1}{x - 1} = +\infty \qquad \text{Think of this as } \frac{-2}{0^-} = +\infty.$$

because now the denominator is negative and still approaching zero while the numerator still approaches -2 and therefore is also negative. (See the numerical calculations above on the right.) Because the left and right limits do not agree, we conclude that

$$\lim_{x \to 1} \frac{x^2 - 4x + 1}{x - 1} \text{ does not exist.}$$

c. First notice that the denominator factors:

$$\lim_{x \to 1} \frac{x^2 - 4x + 1}{x^2 - 2x + 1} = \lim_{x \to 1} \frac{x^2 - 4x + 1}{(x - 1)^2}.$$

As x approaches 1, the numerator approaches -2 as before, and the denominator approaches 0. However, this time, the denominator $(x - 1)^2$, being a square, is ≥ 0, regardless of the side from which x is approaching 1. Thus, the entire function is negative as x approaches 1, and

$$\lim_{x \to 1} \frac{x^2 - 4x + 1}{(x - 1)^2} = -\infty. \qquad \frac{-2}{0^+} = -\infty$$

➡ **Before we go on ...** In general, the determinate forms $\dfrac{k}{0^+}$ and $\dfrac{k}{0^-}$ will always yield $\pm\infty$, with the sign depending on the sign of the overall expression as $x \to a$. (When we write the form $\dfrac{k}{0}$, we always mean $k \neq 0$.) This and other determinate forms are discussed further after Example 4.

Figure 18 shows the graphs of $\dfrac{x^2 - 4x + 1}{x - 1}$ and $\dfrac{x^2 - 4x + 1}{(x - 1)^2}$ from Example 2. You should check that the results we obtained above agree with a geometric analysis of these graphs near $x = 1$.

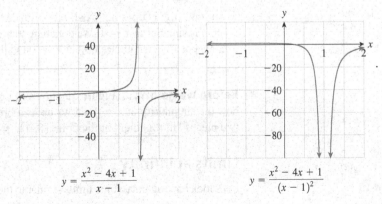

$$y = \frac{x^2 - 4x + 1}{x - 1} \qquad\qquad y = \frac{x^2 - 4x + 1}{(x - 1)^2}$$

Figure 18

Functions Not in Closed Form

We can also use algebraic techniques to analyze functions that are not given in closed form.

> **EXAMPLE 3** **Functions Not Written in Closed Form**

For which values of x are the following piecewise-defined functions continuous?

a. $f(x) = \begin{cases} x^2 + 2 & \text{if } x < 1 \\ 2x - 1 & \text{if } x \geq 1 \end{cases}$

b. $g(x) = \begin{cases} x^2 - x + 1 & \text{if } x \leq 0 \\ 1 - x & \text{if } 0 < x < 1 \\ x - 3 & \text{if } x > 1 \end{cases}$

Solution

a. The function $f(x)$ is given in closed form over the intervals $(-\infty, 1)$ and $[1, +\infty)$. At $x = 1$, $f(x)$ suddenly switches from one closed-form formula to another, so $x = 1$ is the only place where there is a potential problem with continuity. To investigate the continuity of $f(x)$ at $x = 1$, let's calculate the limit there:

$$\lim_{x \to 1^-} f(x) = \lim_{x \to 1^-} (x^2 + 2) \qquad f(x) = x^2 + 2 \text{ for } x < 1.$$
$$= (1)^2 + 2 = 3 \qquad x^2 + 2 \text{ is closed-form.}$$
$$\lim_{x \to 1^+} f(x) = \lim_{x \to 1^+} (2x - 1) \qquad f(x) = 2x - 1 \text{ for } x > 1.$$
$$= 2(1) - 1 = 1. \qquad 2x - 1 \text{ is closed-form.}$$

Because the left and right limits are different, $\lim_{x \to 1} f(x)$ does not exist, so $f(x)$ is discontinuous at $x = 1$.

b. The only potential points of discontinuity for $g(x)$ occur at $x = 0$ and $x = 1$:

$$\lim_{x \to 0^-} g(x) = \lim_{x \to 0^-} (x^2 - x + 1) = 1$$
$$\lim_{x \to 0^+} g(x) = \lim_{x \to 0^+} (1 - x) = 1.$$

Thus, $\lim_{x \to 0} g(x) = 1$. Further, $g(0) = 0^2 - 0 + 1 = 1$ from the formula, so

$$\lim_{x \to 0} g(x) = g(0),$$

which shows that $g(x)$ is continuous at $x = 0$. At $x = 1$ we have

$$\lim_{x \to 1^-} g(x) = \lim_{x \to 1^-} (1 - x) = 0$$
$$\lim_{x \to 1^+} g(x) = \lim_{x \to 1^+} (x - 3) = -2,$$

so $\lim_{x \to 1} g(x)$ does not exist. Also, notice that $x = 1$ is not in the domain of g, so $g(x)$ is singular at $x = 1$. We conclude that $g(x)$ is continuous at every real number x except at the singular point at $x = 1$ and therefore is continuous on its domain.

➡ **Before we go on ...** Figure 19 shows the graph of g from Example 3(b). Notice how the singularity at $x = 1$ shows up as a break in the graph, whereas at $x = 0$ the two pieces "fit together" at the point $(0, 1)$. ∎

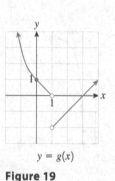

$y = g(x)$

Figure 19

Limits at Infinity

Let's look once again at some limits similar to those in Examples 3 and 6 of Section 10.1.

> [!NOTE] EXAMPLE 4   **Limits at Infinity**

Compute the following limits if they exist:

a. $\displaystyle\lim_{x\to+\infty}\frac{2x^2-4x}{x^2-1}$ **b.** $\displaystyle\lim_{x\to-\infty}\frac{2x^2-4x}{x^2-1}$

c. $\displaystyle\lim_{x\to+\infty}\frac{-x^3-4x}{2x^2-1}$ **d.** $\displaystyle\lim_{x\to+\infty}\frac{2x^2-4x}{5x^3-3x+5}$

e. $\displaystyle\lim_{t\to+\infty}(e^{0.1t}-20)$ **f.** $\displaystyle\lim_{x\to+\infty}\frac{80}{1+2.2(3.68)^{-t}}$

Solution a. and b. While calculating the values for the tables used in Example 3 in Section 10.1, you might have noticed that the highest power of x in both the numerator and denominator dominated the calculations. For instance, when $x = 100{,}000$, the term $2x^2$ in the numerator has the value of $20{,}000{,}000{,}000$, whereas the term $4x$ has the comparatively insignificant value of $400{,}000$. Similarly, the term x^2 in the denominator overwhelms the term -1. In other words, for large values of x (or negative values with large magnitude),

$$\frac{2x^2-4x}{x^2-1}\approx\frac{2x^2}{x^2}$$ Use only the highest powers top and bottom.

$$=2.$$

Therefore,

$$\lim_{x\to\pm\infty}\frac{2x^2-4x}{x^2-1}=\lim_{x\to\pm\infty}\frac{2x^2}{x^2}$$

$$=\lim_{x\to\pm\infty}2=2.$$

The procedure of using only the highest powers of x to compute the limit is stated formally and justified after this example.

c. Applying the previous technique of looking only at highest powers gives

$$\lim_{x\to+\infty}\frac{-x^3-4x}{2x^2-1}=\lim_{x\to+\infty}\frac{-x^3}{2x^2}$$ Use only the highest powers top and bottom.

$$=\lim_{x\to+\infty}\frac{-x}{2}.$$ Simplify.

As x gets large, $-x/2$ gets large in magnitude but negative, so the limit is

$$\lim_{x\to+\infty}\frac{-x}{2}=-\infty.$$ $\dfrac{-\infty}{2}=-\infty$ (See below.)

d. $\displaystyle\lim_{x\to+\infty}\frac{2x^2-4x}{5x^3-3x+5}=\lim_{x\to+\infty}\frac{2x^2}{5x^3}$ Use only the highest powers top and bottom.

$$=\lim_{x\to+\infty}\frac{2}{5x}.$$

As x gets large, $2/(5x)$ gets close to zero, so the limit is

$$\lim_{x\to+\infty}\frac{2}{5x}=0.$$ $\dfrac{2}{\infty}=0$ (See below.)

e. Here, we do not have a ratio of polynomials. However, we know that, as t becomes large and positive, so does $e^{0.1t}$ and hence also $e^{0.1t} - 20$. Thus,

$$\lim_{t \to +\infty} \left(e^{0.1t} - 20 \right) = +\infty. \qquad e^{+\infty} = +\infty \text{ (See below.)}$$

f. As $t \to +\infty$, the term $(3.68)^{-t} = \dfrac{1}{3.68^{t}}$ in the denominator, being 1 divided by a very large number, approaches zero. Hence, the denominator $1 + 2.2(3.68)^{-t}$ approaches $1 + 2.2(0) = 1$ as $t \to +\infty$. Thus,

$$\lim_{t \to +\infty} \frac{80}{1 + 2.2(3.68)^{-t}} = \frac{80}{1 + 2.2(0)} = 80. \qquad (3.68)^{-\infty} = 0 \text{ (See below.)}$$

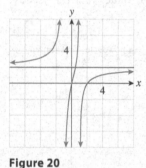

Figure 20

➡ **Before we go on ...** Let's now look at the graph of the function $\dfrac{2x^2 - 4x}{x^2 - 1}$ in Example 4(a) and 4(b). We say that the graph of f has a **horizontal asymptote** at $y = 2$ because of the limits we have just calculated. This means that the graph approaches the horizontal line $y = 2$ far to the right or left (in this case, to both the right and left). Figure 20 shows the graph of f together with the line $y = 2$. The graph reveals some additional interesting information: as $x \to 1^+$, $f(x) \to -\infty$, and as $x \to 1^-$, $f(x) \to +\infty$. Thus,

$$\lim_{x \to 1} f(x) \text{ does not exist.}$$

See whether you can determine what happens as $x \to -1$.

If you graph the functions in Example 4(d) and 4(f), you will again see a horizontal asymptote. Do the limits in Example 4(c) and 4(e) show horizontal asymptotes? ∎

It is worthwhile looking again at what we did in each of the limits in Example 4:

a. and **b.** We saw that $\dfrac{2x^2 - 4x}{x^2 - 1} \approx \dfrac{2x^2}{x^2}$, and then we canceled the x^2. Notice that, before we cancel, letting x approach $\pm\infty$ in the numerator and denominator yields the ratio ∞/∞, which, like $0/0$, is another *indeterminate form* and indicates to us that further work is needed—in this case cancellation—before we can write down the limit.

c. We obtained $\dfrac{-x^3 - 4x}{2x^2 - 1} \approx \dfrac{-x^3}{2x^2}$, which results in another indeterminate form, $-\infty/\infty$, as $x \to +\infty$. Cancellation of the x^2 gave us $\dfrac{-x}{2}$, resulting in the *determinate* form $-\infty/2 = -\infty$. (A very large number divided by 2 is again a very large number.)

d. Here, $\dfrac{2x^2 - 4x}{5x^3 - 3x + 5} \approx \dfrac{2x^2}{5x^3} = \dfrac{2}{5x}$, and the cancellation step turns the indeterminate form ∞/∞ into the determinate form $2/\infty = 0$. (Dividing 2 by a very large number yields a very small number.)

e. We reasoned that e raised to a large positive number is large and positive. Putting $t = +\infty$ gives us the determinate form $e^{+\infty} = +\infty$.

f. Here, we reasoned that 3.68 raised to a large *negative* number is close to zero. Putting $t = -\infty$ gives us the determinate form $3.68^{-\infty} = 1/3.68^{+\infty} = 1/\infty = 0$ (see part(d)).

In Example 4(a)–(d), $f(x)$ was a **rational function**: a quotient of polynomial functions. We calculated the limit of $f(x)$ at $\pm\infty$ by ignoring all powers of x in both the numerator and denominator except for the largest. Following is a theorem that justifies this procedure.

Theorem 10.2 Evaluating the Limit of a Rational Function at $\pm\infty$

If $f(x)$ has the form

$$f(x) = \frac{c_n x^n + c_{n-1}x^{n-1} + \cdots + c_1 x + c_0}{d_m x^m + d_{m-1}x^{m-1} + \cdots + d_1 x + d_0}$$

with the c_i and d_i constants ($c_n \neq 0$ and $d_m \neq 0$), then we can calculate the limit of $f(x)$ as $x \to \pm\infty$ by ignoring all powers of x except the highest in both the numerator and denominator. Thus,

$$\lim_{x \to \pm\infty} f(x) = \lim_{x \to \pm\infty} \frac{c_n x^n}{d_m x^m}.$$

Quick Examples

(See Example 4.)

5. $\displaystyle\lim_{x \to +\infty} \frac{2x^2 - 4x}{x^2 - 1} = \lim_{x \to +\infty} \frac{2x^2}{x^2} = \lim_{x \to +\infty} 2 = 2$

6. $\displaystyle\lim_{x \to +\infty} \frac{-x^3 - 4x}{2x^2 - 1} = \lim_{x \to +\infty} \frac{-x^3}{2x^2} = \lim_{x \to +\infty} \frac{-x}{2} = -\infty$

7. $\displaystyle\lim_{x \to +\infty} \frac{2x^2 - 4x}{5x^3 - 3x + 5} = \lim_{x \to +\infty} \frac{2x^2}{5x^3} = \lim_{x \to +\infty} \frac{2}{5x} = 0$

Proof Our function $f(x)$ is a polynomial of degree n divided by a polynomial of degree m. If n happens to be larger than m, then dividing the top and bottom by the largest power x^n of x gives

$$f(x) = \frac{c_n x^n + c_{n-1}x^{n-1} + \cdots + c_1 x + c_0}{d_m x^m + d_{m-1}x^{m-1} + \cdots + d_1 x + d_0}$$

$$= \frac{c_n x^n/x^n + c_{n-1}x^{n-1}/x^n + \cdots + c_1 x/x^n + c_0/x^n}{d_m x^m/x^n + d_{m-1}x^{m-1}/x^n + \cdots + d_1 x/x^n + d_0/x^n}.$$

Canceling powers of x in each term and remembering that $n > m$ leave us with

$$f(x) = \frac{c_n + c_{n-1}/x + \cdots + c_1/x^{n-1} + c_0/x^n}{d_m/x^{n-m} + d_{m-1}/x^{n-m+1} + \cdots + d_1/x^{n-1} + d_0/x^n}.$$

As $x \to \pm\infty$, all the terms shown in blue approach 0, so we can ignore them in taking the limit. (The first term in the denominator happens to approach 0 as well, but we retain it for convenience.) Thus,

$$\lim_{x \to \pm\infty} f(x) = \lim_{x \to \pm\infty} \frac{c_n}{d_m/x^{n-m}} = \lim_{x \to \pm\infty} \frac{c_n x^n}{d_m x^m},$$

as required. The cases in which n is smaller than m and $m = n$ are proved similarly by dividing top and bottom by the largest power of x in each case. ∎

Note The procedure of ignoring all but highest powers also works for arbitrary algebraic expressions involving polynomials, such as square roots of polynomials. For instance,

$$\lim_{x \to +\infty} \frac{\sqrt{25x^6 - 3x^2 + 1}}{2x^3 - 1} = \lim_{x \to +\infty} \frac{\sqrt{25x^6}}{2x^3} = \lim_{x \to +\infty} \frac{5x^3}{2x^3} = \lim_{x \to +\infty} \frac{5}{2} = \frac{5}{2}. \ \blacksquare$$

Some Determinate and Indeterminate Forms

The following summary brings these ideas together with our observations in Example 2.

Some Determinate and Indeterminate Forms

$0/0$ and $\pm\infty/\infty$ are **indeterminate**; evaluating limits in which these arise requires simplification or further analysis.* The following are **determinate** forms for any nonzero number k:

> ＊Some other indeterminate forms are $\pm\infty \cdot 0$, $\infty - \infty$, and 1^∞. (These are not discussed in this text, but see the Communication and Reasoning exercises for this section.)

$$\frac{k}{0^\pm} = \pm\infty \qquad\qquad \frac{k}{\text{Small}} = \text{Big* (See Example 2.)}$$

$$k(\pm\infty) = \pm\infty \qquad\qquad k \times \text{Big} = \text{Big*}$$

$$k \pm \infty = \pm\infty \qquad\qquad k \pm \text{Big} = \pm\text{Big}$$

$$\pm\frac{\infty}{k} = \pm\infty \qquad\qquad \frac{\text{Big}}{k} = \text{Big*}$$

$$\pm\frac{k}{\infty} = 0, \qquad\qquad \frac{k}{\text{Big}} = \text{Small}$$

and if $k > 1$, then

$$k^{+\infty} = +\infty \qquad\qquad k^{\text{Big positive}} = \text{Big}$$

$$k^{-\infty} = 0. \qquad\qquad k^{\text{Big negative}} = \text{Small}$$

---

*The sign gets switched in these forms if k is negative.

Quick Examples

8. $\displaystyle\lim_{x \to 0} \frac{60}{2x^2} = +\infty$ $\qquad\qquad$ $\dfrac{k}{0^+} = +\infty$

9. $\displaystyle\lim_{x \to -1^-} \frac{2x - 6}{x + 1} = +\infty$ $\qquad\qquad$ $\dfrac{-8}{0^-} = +\infty$

10. $\displaystyle\lim_{x \to -\infty} 3x - 5 = -\infty$ $\qquad\qquad$ $3(-\infty) - 5 = -\infty - 5 = -\infty$

11. $\displaystyle\lim_{x \to +\infty} \frac{2x}{60} = +\infty$ $\qquad\qquad$ $\dfrac{2(\infty)}{60} = \infty$

12. $\displaystyle\lim_{x \to -\infty} \frac{60}{2x} = 0$ $\qquad\qquad$ $\dfrac{60}{2(-\infty)} = 0$

13. $\displaystyle\lim_{x \to +\infty} \frac{60x}{2x} = 30$ $\qquad\qquad$ $\dfrac{\infty}{\infty}$ is indeterminate, but we can cancel.

14. $\displaystyle\lim_{x \to -\infty} \frac{60}{e^x - 1} = \frac{60}{0 - 1} = -60$ $\qquad\qquad$ $e^{-\infty} = 0$

FAQs

Strategy for Evaluating Limits Algebraically

Q: *Is there a systematic way to evaluate a limit* $\lim_{x \to a} f(x)$ *algebraically?*

A: The following approach is often successful:

Case 1: *a* is a finite number (not $\pm\infty$)

1. Decide whether *f* is a closed-form function. If it is not, then find the left and right limits at the values of *x* where the function changes from one formula to another.

2. If *f* is a closed-form function, try substituting $x = a$ in the formula for $f(x)$. Then one of the following three things may happen:

   $f(a)$ is defined. Then $\lim_{x \to a} f(x) = f(a)$.

   $f(a)$ is not defined and has the indeterminate form 0/0. Try to simplify the expression for *f* to cancel one of the terms that gives 0.

   $f(a)$ is not defined and has one of the determinate forms listed above in the above table. Use the table to determine the limit as in Quick Examples 8–14.

Case 2: $a = \pm\infty$

Remember that we can use the determinate forms $k^{+\infty} = \infty$ and $k^{-\infty} = 0$ if $k > 1$. Further, if the given function is a polynomial or ratio of polynomials, use the technique of Example 4: Focus only on the highest powers of *x*, and then simplify to obtain either a number *L*, in which case the limit exists and equals *L*, or one of the determinate forms $\pm\infty/k = \pm\infty$ or $\pm k/\infty = 0$.

There is another technique for evaluating certain difficult limits, called *l'Hospital's rule*, but this uses derivatives, so we'll have to wait until Section 11.1 to discuss it.

10.3 EXERCISES

▼ more advanced   ◆ challenging
T indicates exercises that should be solved using technology

In Exercises 1–4, complete the given sentence.

1. The closed-form function $f(x) = \dfrac{1}{x - 1}$ is continuous for all *x* except _____. [**HINT**: See Quick Example 3.]

2. The closed-form function $f(x) = \dfrac{1}{x^2 - 1}$ is continuous for all *x* except _____. [**HINT**: See Quick Example 3.]

3. The closed-form function $f(x) = \sqrt{x + 1}$ has $x = 3$ in its domain. Therefore, $\lim_{x \to 3} \sqrt{x + 1} = $ ___.
[**HINT**: See Example 1.]

4. The closed-form function $f(x) = \sqrt{x - 1}$ has $x = 10$ in its domain. Therefore, $\lim_{x \to 10} \sqrt{x - 1} = $ ___.
[**HINT**: See Example 1.]

In Exercises 5–20, determine whether the given limit leads to a determinate or indeterminate form. Evaluate the limit if it exists, or say why if not. [**HINT**: See Example 2 and Quick Examples 8–14.]

5. $\lim_{x \to 0} \dfrac{60}{x^4}$

6. $\lim_{x \to 0} \dfrac{2x^2}{x^2}$

7. $\lim_{x \to 0} \dfrac{x^3 - 1}{x^3}$

8. $\lim_{x \to 0} \dfrac{-2}{x^2}$

9. $\lim_{x \to -\infty} (-x^2 + 5)$

10. $\lim_{x \to 0} \dfrac{2x^2 + 4}{x}$

11. $\lim_{x \to +\infty} 4^{-x}$

12. $\lim_{x \to +\infty} \dfrac{60 + e^{-x}}{2 - e^{-x}}$

13. $\lim_{x \to 0} \dfrac{-x^3}{3x^3}$

14. $\lim_{x \to -\infty} 3x^2 + 6$

15. $\lim_{x \to -\infty} \dfrac{-x^3}{3x^6}$

16. $\lim_{x \to +\infty} \dfrac{-x^6}{3x^3}$

17. $\lim\limits_{x \to -\infty} \dfrac{4}{-x + 2}$

18. $\lim\limits_{x \to -\infty} e^x$

19. $\lim\limits_{x \to -\infty} \dfrac{60}{e^x - 1}$

20. $\lim\limits_{x \to -\infty} \dfrac{2}{2x^2 + 3}$

In Exercises 21–74, calculate the limit algebraically. If the limit does not exist, say why.

21. $\lim\limits_{x \to 0}(x + 1)$

[HINT: See Example 1(a).]

22. $\lim\limits_{x \to 0}(2x - 4)$

[HINT: See Example 1(a).]

23. $\lim\limits_{x \to 2} \dfrac{2 + x}{x}$

24. $\lim\limits_{x \to -1} \dfrac{4x^2 + 1}{x}$

25. $\lim\limits_{x \to -1} \dfrac{x + 1}{x}$

26. $\lim\limits_{x \to 4}(x + \sqrt{x})$

27. $\lim\limits_{x \to 8}(x - \sqrt[3]{x})$

28. $\lim\limits_{x \to 1} \dfrac{x - 2}{x + 1}$

29. $\lim\limits_{h \to 1}(h^2 + 2h + 1)$

30. $\lim\limits_{h \to 0}(h^3 - 4)$

31. $\lim\limits_{h \to 3} 2$

32. $\lim\limits_{h \to 0} -5$

33. $\lim\limits_{h \to 0} \dfrac{h^2}{h + h^2}$

[HINT: See Example 1(b).]

34. $\lim\limits_{h \to 0} \dfrac{h^2 + h}{h^2 + 2h}$

[HINT: See Example 1(b).]

35. $\lim\limits_{x \to 1} \dfrac{x^2 - 2x + 1}{x^2 - x}$

36. $\lim\limits_{x \to -1} \dfrac{x^2 + 3x + 2}{x^2 + x}$

37. $\lim\limits_{x \to 2} \dfrac{x^3 - 8}{x - 2}$

38. $\lim\limits_{x \to -2} \dfrac{x^3 + 8}{x^2 + 3x + 2}$

39. $\lim\limits_{x \to 0^+} \dfrac{1}{x^2}$ [HINT: See Example 2.]

40. $\lim\limits_{x \to 0^+} \dfrac{1}{x^2 - x}$ [HINT: See Example 2.]

41. $\lim\limits_{x \to -1} \dfrac{x^2 + 1}{x + 1}$

42. $\lim\limits_{x \to -1^-} \dfrac{x^2 + 1}{x + 1}$

43. $\lim\limits_{x \to -2^+} \dfrac{x^2 + 8}{x^2 + 3x + 2}$

44. $\lim\limits_{x \to -1} \dfrac{x^2 + 3x}{x^2 + x}$

45. $\lim\limits_{x \to -2} \dfrac{x^2 + 8}{x^2 + 3x + 2}$

46. $\lim\limits_{x \to -1} \dfrac{x^2 + 3x}{x^2 + 2x + 1}$

47. $\lim\limits_{x \to 2} \dfrac{x^2 + 8}{x^2 - 4x + 4}$

48. $\lim\limits_{x \to -1} \dfrac{x^2 + 3x}{x^2 + 3x + 2}$

49. ▼ $\lim\limits_{x \to 2^+} \dfrac{x - 2}{\sqrt{x - 2}}$

50. ▼ $\lim\limits_{x \to 3^-} \dfrac{\sqrt{3 - x}}{3 - x}$

51. ▼ $\lim\limits_{x \to 9} \dfrac{\sqrt{x} - 3}{x - 9}$

52. ▼ $\lim\limits_{x \to 4} \dfrac{x - 4}{\sqrt{x} - 2}$

53. $\lim\limits_{x \to +\infty} \dfrac{3x^2 + 10x - 1}{2x^2 - 5x}$ [HINT: See Example 4.]

54. $\lim\limits_{x \to +\infty} \dfrac{6x^2 + 5x + 100}{3x^2 - 9}$ [HINT: See Example 4.]

55. $\lim\limits_{x \to +\infty} \dfrac{x^5 - 1,000x^4}{2x^5 + 10,000}$

56. $\lim\limits_{x \to +\infty} \dfrac{x^6 + 3,000x^3 + 1,000,000}{2x^6 + 1,000x^3}$

57. $\lim\limits_{x \to +\infty} \dfrac{10x^2 + 300x + 1}{5x + 2}$

58. $\lim\limits_{x \to +\infty} \dfrac{2x^4 + 20x^3}{1,000x^3 + 6}$

59. $\lim\limits_{x \to -\infty} \dfrac{3x^2 + 10x - 1}{2x^2 - 5x}$

60. $\lim\limits_{x \to -\infty} \dfrac{6x^2 + 5x + 100}{3x^2 - 9}$

61. $\lim\limits_{x \to -\infty} \dfrac{x^5 - 1,000x^4}{2x^5 + 10,000}$

62. $\lim\limits_{x \to -\infty} \dfrac{x^6 + 3,000x^3 + 1,000,000}{2x^6 + 1,000x^3}$

63. $\lim\limits_{x \to -\infty} \dfrac{10x^2 + 300x + 1}{5x + 2}$

64. $\lim\limits_{x \to -\infty} \dfrac{2x^4 + 20x^3}{1,000x^3 + 6}$

65. $\lim\limits_{x \to -\infty} \dfrac{10x^2 + 300x + 1}{5x^3 + 2}$

66. $\lim\limits_{x \to -\infty} \dfrac{2x^4 + 20x^3}{1,000x^6 + 6}$

67. $\lim\limits_{x \to +\infty} (4e^{-3x} + 12)$

68. $\lim\limits_{x \to +\infty} \dfrac{2}{5 - 5.3e^{-3x}}$

69. $\lim\limits_{x \to +\infty} \dfrac{2}{5 - 5.3(3^{3t})}$

70. $\lim\limits_{t \to +\infty} (4.1 - 2e^{3t})$

71. $\lim\limits_{t \to +\infty} \dfrac{2^{3t}}{1 + 5.3e^{-t}}$

72. $\lim\limits_{x \to -\infty} \dfrac{4.2}{2 - 3^{2x}}$

73. $\lim\limits_{x \to -\infty} \dfrac{-3^{2x}}{2 + e^x}$

74. $\lim\limits_{x \to +\infty} \dfrac{2^{-3x}}{1 + 5.3e^{-x}}$

In Exercises 75–88, identify all singular points and points of discontinuity of the given function. [HINT: See Example 3.]

75. $f(x) = \dfrac{1}{x - 3}$

76. $f(x) = \begin{cases} \dfrac{4}{x + 1} & \text{if } x \neq -1 \\ 3 & \text{if } x = -1 \end{cases}$

77. $f(x) = \begin{cases} \dfrac{4}{(x - 5)^2} & \text{if } x \neq 5 \\ -3 & \text{if } x = 5 \end{cases}$

78. $f(x) = \dfrac{2}{x^2 - 9}$

79. $f(x) = \begin{cases} x + 2 & \text{if } x < 0 \\ 2x - 1 & \text{if } x \geq 0 \end{cases}$

80. $f(x) = \begin{cases} 2x - 1 & \text{if } x < 1 \\ -2x + 3 & \text{if } x > 1 \end{cases}$

81. $f(x) = \begin{cases} x^2 - 1 & \text{if } x < 0 \\ x^2 + 1 & \text{if } x > 0 \end{cases}$

82. $g(x) = \begin{cases} 1 - x & \text{if } x \leq 1 \\ x - 1 & \text{if } x > 1 \end{cases}$

83. $g(x) = \begin{cases} x + 2 & \text{if } x < 0 \\ 2x + 2 & \text{if } 0 \le x < 2 \\ x^2 + 2 & \text{if } x \ge 2 \end{cases}$

84. $f(x) = \begin{cases} 1 - x & \text{if } x \le 1 \\ x + 2 & \text{if } 1 < x < 3 \\ x^2 - 4 & \text{if } x \ge 3 \end{cases}$

85. ▼ $h(x) = \begin{cases} x + 2 & \text{if } x < 0 \\ 0 & \text{if } x = 0 \\ 2x + 2 & \text{if } x > 0 \end{cases}$

86. ▼ $h(x) = \begin{cases} 1 - x & \text{if } x < 1 \\ 1 & \text{if } x = 1 \\ x + 2 & \text{if } x > 1 \end{cases}$

87. ▼ $f(x) = \begin{cases} 1/x & \text{if } x < 0 \\ x & \text{if } 0 \le x \le 2 \\ 2^{x-1} & \text{if } x > 2 \end{cases}$

88. ▼ $f(x) = \begin{cases} x^3 + 2 & \text{if } x \le -1 \\ x^2 & \text{if } -1 < x < 0 \\ x & \text{if } x \ge 0 \end{cases}$

Applications

89. Processor Speeds The processor speeds, in megahertz (MHz), of Intel processors during the period 1996–2010 can be approximated by the following function of time t in years since the start of 1990:[17]

$$v(t) = \begin{cases} 400t - 2,200 & \text{if } 6 \le t < 15 \\ 3,800 & \text{if } 15 \le t \le 20. \end{cases}$$

a. Compute $\lim_{t \to 15^-} v(t)$ and $\lim_{t \to 15^+} v(t)$, and interpret each answer. [**HINT**: See Example 3.]

b. Is the function v continuous at $t = 15$? According to the model, was there any abrupt change in processor speeds during the period 1996–2010?

90. Processor Speeds The processor speeds, in megahertz (MHz), of Intel processors during the period 1970–2000 can be approximated by the following function of time t in years since the start of 1970:[18]

$$v(t) = \begin{cases} 3t & \text{if } 0 \le t < 20 \\ 174t - 3,420 & \text{if } 20 \le t \le 30. \end{cases}$$

a. Compute $\lim_{t \to 20^-} v(t)$ and $\lim_{t \to 20^+} v(t)$, and interpret each answer.

b. Is the function v continuous at $t = 20$? According to the model, was there any abrupt change in processor speeds during the period 1970–2000?

91. Movie Advertising Movie expenditures, in billions of dollars, on advertising in newspapers from 1995 to 2004 can be approximated by

$$f(t) = \begin{cases} 0.04t + 0.33 & \text{if } t \le 4 \\ -0.01t + 1.2 & \text{if } t > 4, \end{cases}$$

where t is time in years since 1995.[19]

a. Compute $\lim_{t \to 4^-} f(t)$ and $\lim_{t \to 4^+} f(t)$, and interpret each answer. [**HINT**: See Example 3.]

b. Is the function f continuous at $t = 4$? What does the answer tell you about movie advertising expenditures?

92. Movie Advertising The percentage of movie advertising as a share of newspapers' total advertising revenue from 1995 to 2004 can be approximated by

$$p(t) = \begin{cases} -0.07t + 6.0 & \text{if } t \le 4 \\ 0.3t + 17.0 & \text{if } t > 4, \end{cases}$$

where t is time in years since 1995.[20]

a. Compute $\lim_{t \to 4^-} p(t)$ and $\lim_{t \to 4^+} p(t)$, and interpret each answer. [**HINT**: See Example 3.]

b. Is the function p continuous at $t = 4$? What does the answer tell you about newspaper revenues?

93. Law Enforcement in the 1980s and 1990s The cost of fighting crime in the United States increased significantly during the period 1982–1999. Total spending on police and courts can be approximated by[21]

$P(t) = 1.745t + 29.84$ billion dollars $(2 \le t \le 19)$

$C(t) = 1.097t + 10.65$ billion dollars $(2 \le t \le 19)$,

respectively, where t is time in years since 1980. Compute

$$\lim_{t \to +\infty} \frac{P(t)}{C(t)}$$

to two decimal places, and interpret the result.

[**HINT**: See Example 4.]

94. Law Enforcement in the 1980s and 1990s Refer to Exercise 93. Total spending on police, courts, and prisons in the period 1982–1999 could be approximated by[22]

$P(t) = 1.745t + 29.84$ billion dollars $(2 \le t \le 19)$

$C(t) = 1.097t + 10.65$ billion dollars $(2 \le t \le 19)$

$J(t) = 1.919t + 12.36$ billion dollars $(2 \le t \le 19)$,

respectively, where t is time in years since 1980. Compute

$$\lim_{t \to +\infty} \frac{P(t)}{P(t) + C(t) + J(t)}$$

to two decimal places, and interpret the result. [**HINT**: See Example 4.]

---

[17] A rough model based on the fastest processors produced by Intel. Source for data: www.intel.com.

[18] Ibid.

[19] Model by the authors. Source for data: Newspaper Association of America Business Analysis and Research/*New York Times*, May 16, 2005.

[20] Ibid.

[21] Spending is adjusted for inflation and shown in 1999 dollars. Models are based on a linear regression. Source for data: Bureau of Justice Statistics/*New York Times*, February 11, 2002, p. A14.

[22] Ibid.

95. **SAT Scores by Income** The following bar graph shows U.S. math SAT scores as a function of household income:[23]

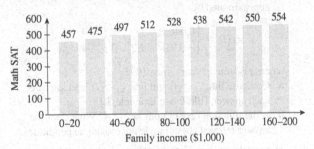

These data can be modeled by

$$S(x) = 573 - 33e^{-0.0131x},$$

where $S(x)$ is the average math SAT score of students whose household income is x thousand dollars per year. Calculate $\lim_{x \to +\infty} S(x)$, and interpret the answer.

96. **SAT Scores by Income** The following bar graph shows U.S. critical reading SAT scores as a function of household income:[24]

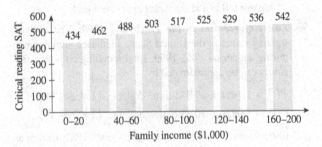

These data can be modeled by

$$S(x) = 550 - 136e^{-0.0151x},$$

where $S(x)$ is the average critical reading SAT score of students whose household income is x thousand dollars per year. Calculate $\lim_{x \to +\infty} S(x)$, and interpret the answer.

97. **Social Website Popularity** The following models approximate the popularity of Twitter and LinkedIn among social media sites from 2008 to 2013, as rated by StatCounter.com:

Twitter: $W(t) = 0.33t^2 - 2t + 8.7$ percentage points

LinkedIn: $L(t) = 0.04t^2 - 0.26t + 0.67$ percentage points.

(t is the number of years since the start of 2008.)[25] Calculate $\lim_{t \to +\infty} W(t)$ and $\lim_{t \to +\infty} \dfrac{W(t)}{L(t)}$ algebraically, interpret your answers, and comment on the results.

98. **Social Website Popularity** The following models approximate the popularity of Facebook and YouTube among social media sites from 2008 to 2013, as rated by StatCounter.com:

Facebook: $F(t) = -2t^2 + 16t + 35$ percentage points

YouTube: $Y(t) = -t^2 + 6.5t - 1.8$ percentage points.

(t is the number of years since the start of 2008.)[26] Calculate $\lim_{t \to +\infty} F(t)$ and $\lim_{t \to +\infty} \dfrac{F(t)}{Y(t)}$ algebraically, interpret your answers, and comment on the results.

99. **Acquisition of Language** The percentage $p(t)$ of children who can speak in at least single words by the age of t months can be approximated by the equation[27]

$$p(t) = 100\left(1 - \frac{12{,}200}{t^{4.48}}\right) \quad (t \geq 8.5).$$

Calculate $\lim_{t \to +\infty} p(t)$, and interpret the result. [**HINT:** See Example 4.]

100. **Acquisition of Language** The percentage $q(t)$ of children who can speak in sentences of five or more words by the age of t months can be approximated by the equation[28]

$$q(t) = 100\left(1 - \frac{5.27 \times 10^{17}}{t^{12}}\right) \quad (t \geq 30).$$

If p is the function referred to in the preceding exercise, calculate $\lim_{t \to +\infty}[p(t) - q(t)]$, and interpret the result. [**HINT:** See Example 4.]

Communication and Reasoning Exercises

101. Describe the algebraic method of evaluating limits as discussed in this section, and give at least one disadvantage of this method.

102. What is a closed-form function? What can we say about such functions?

103. Your friends Rita and Richard are arguing. Rita claims that closed-form functions cannot have points of discontinuity, but Richard retorts, "Ever heard of $f(x) = 1/x$?" On whose side (if any) of the argument should you be? Explain.

104. Your other friends, Andrew and Dorothy, are also arguing. Andrew claims that a function cannot be singular at a point of discontinuity, but Dorothy retorts, "Ever heard of $f(x) = 1/x$?" On whose side (if any) of the argument should you be? Explain.

[23] 2009 data. Source: College Board/*New York Times* http://economix .blogs.nytimes.com.

[24] *Ibid.*

[25] Percentages are based on worldwide page views. Source for data: http://gs.statcounter.com.

[26] *Ibid.*

[27] The model is the authors' and is based on data presented in the article *The Emergence of Intelligence* by William H. Calvin, *Scientific American,* October 1994, pp. 101–107.

[28] *Ibid.*

105. Why was the following marked wrong? What is the correct answer?

$$\lim_{x \to 3} \frac{x^3 - 27}{x - 3} = \frac{0}{0} \text{ undefined} \quad \text{✗ WRONG!}$$

106. Why was the following marked wrong? What is the correct answer?

$$\lim_{x \to 1^-} \frac{x - 1}{x^2 - 2x + 1} = \frac{0}{0} = 0 \quad \text{✗ WRONG!}$$

107. ▼ Your friend Karin tells you that $f(x) = 1/(x - 2)^2$ cannot be a closed-form function because it is not continuous at $x = 2$. Comment on her assertion.

108. ▼ Give an example of a function f specified by means of algebraic formulas such that the domain of f consists of all real numbers and f is not continuous at $x = 2$. Is f a closed-form function?

109. Give examples of two limits that lead to two different indeterminate forms but where both limits exist.

110. Give examples of two limits: one that leads to a determinate form and another that leads to an indeterminate form but where neither limit exists.

111. ▼ (Compare Exercise 73 in Section 10.1.) Which indeterminate form results from $\lim\limits_{x \to +\infty} \dfrac{p(x)}{e^x}$ if $p(x)$ is a polynomial? Numerically or graphically estimate these limits for various polynomials $p(x)$. What does this suggest about limits that result in $\dfrac{p(\infty)}{e^\infty}$?

112. ▼ (Compare Exercise 74 in Section 10.1.) Which indeterminate form results from $\lim\limits_{x \to -\infty} p(x)e^x$ if $p(x)$ is a polynomial? What does this suggest about the limits that result in $p(-\infty)e^{-\infty}$?

113. ▼ What is wrong with the following statement? If $f(x)$ is specified algebraically and $f(a)$ is defined, then $\lim_{x \to a} f(x)$ exists and equals $f(a)$. How can it be corrected?

114. ▼ What is wrong with the following statement? If $f(x)$ is specified algebraically and $f(a)$ is not defined, then $\lim_{x \to a} f(x)$ does not exist.

115. ▼ Give the formula for a function that is continuous everywhere except at two points.

116. ▼ Give the formula for a function that is continuous everywhere except at three points.

117. ◆ *The Indeterminate Form $\infty - \infty$* An indeterminate form not mentioned in Section 10.3 is $\infty - \infty$. Give examples of three limits that lead to this indeterminate form and where the first limit exists and equals 5, the second limit diverges to $+\infty$, and the third limit exists and equals -5.

118. ◆ *The Indeterminate Form 1^∞* An indeterminate form not mentioned in Section 10.3 is 1^∞. Give examples of three limits that lead to this indeterminate form and where the first limit exists and equals 1, the second limit exists and equals e, and the third limit diverges to $+\infty$. [HINT: For the third, consider modifying the second.]

10.4 Average Rate of Change

Change and Average Rate of Change

Calculus is the mathematics of change, inspired largely by observation of continuously changing quantities around us in the real world. As an example, the Consumer Price Index (CPI) C increased from 227 points in January 2012 to 234 points in January 2014.[29] As we saw in Chapter 1, the **change** in this index can be measured as the difference:

$$\Delta C = \text{Second value} - \text{First value} = 234 - 227 = 7 \text{ points.}$$

(The fact that the CPI increased is reflected in the positive sign of the change.) The kind of question we will concentrate on is *how fast* the CPI was changing. Because C increased by 7 points in 2 years, we say that it averaged a $7/2 = 3.5$ point rise each year. (It actually rose 3 points the first year and 4 points the second, giving an average rise of 3.5 points each year.)

Alternatively, we might want to measure this rate in points per month rather than points per year. Because C increased by 7 points in 24 months, it increased at an average rate of $7/24 \approx 0.292$ points per month.

---

[29] Figures are approximate. Source: Bureau of Labor Statistics, www.bls.gov.

In both cases we obtained the average rate of change by dividing the change by the corresponding length of time:

$$\text{Average rate of change} = \frac{\text{Change in } C}{\text{Change in time}} = \frac{7}{2} = 3.5 \text{ points per year}$$

$$\text{Average rate of change} = \frac{\text{Change in } C}{\text{Change in time}} = \frac{7}{24} \approx 0.292 \text{ points per month.}$$

EXAMPLE 1 **Standard & Poor's 500**

The following table lists the approximate value of Standard & Poor's 500 stock market index (S&P) during the period 2008–2014 ($t = 8$ represents 2008):[30]

Year t (year)	8	9	10	11	12	13	14
S&P Index $S(t)$ (points)	1,400	900	1,150	1,300	1,300	1,400	1,800

a. What was the average rate of change in the S&P over the 4-year period 2010–2014 (the period $10 \le t \le 14$ or $[10, 14]$ in interval notation), over the 2-year period 2008–2010 (the period $8 \le t \le 10$ or $[8, 10]$), and over the period $[8, 13]$?

b. Graph the values shown in the table. How are the rates of change reflected in the graph?

Solution

a. During the 4-year period $[10, 14]$ the S&P changed as follows:

Start of the period ($t = 10$):	$S(10) = 1{,}150$
End of the period ($t = 14$):	$S(14) = 1{,}800$

Change during the period $[10, 14]$: $S(14) - S(10) = 650$

Thus, the S&P increased by 650 points in 4 years, giving an average rate of change of $650/4 = 162.5$ points per year. We can write the calculation this way:

$$\text{Average rate of change of } S = \frac{\text{Change in } S}{\text{Change in } t}$$

$$= \frac{\Delta S}{\Delta t}$$

$$= \frac{S(14) - S(10)}{14 - 10}$$

$$= \frac{1{,}800 - 1{,}150}{14 - 10} = \frac{650}{4} = 162.5 \text{ points per year.}$$

Interpreting the result: During the period 2010–2014 (or $[10, 14]$ in interval notation) the S&P increased at an average rate of 162.5 points per year.

Similarly, the average rate of change during the period 2008–2010 (or $[8, 10]$) was

$$\text{Average rate of change of } S = \frac{\Delta S}{\Delta t} = \frac{S(10) - S(8)}{10 - 8} = \frac{1{,}150 - 1{,}400}{10 - 8}$$

$$= \frac{-250}{2} = -125 \text{ points per year.}$$

---

[30] The values are approximate values at the start of the given year. Source: http://finance.google.com.

Interpreting the result: During the period 2008–2010 the S&P *decreased* at an average rate of 125 points per year.

Finally, during the period 2008–2013 (or $[8, 13]$) the average change was

$$\text{Average rate of change of } S = \frac{\Delta S}{\Delta t} = \frac{S(13) - S(8)}{13 - 8} = \frac{1,400 - 1,400}{13 - 8}$$

$$= \frac{0}{5} = 0 \text{ points per year.}$$

Interpreting the result: During the period 2008–2013 the average rate of change of the S&P was zero points per year (even though its value did fluctuate during that period).

b. In Chapter 1 we saw that the rate of change of a quantity that changes linearly with time is measured by the slope of its graph. However, the S&P index does not change linearly with time. Figure 21 shows the data plotted two different ways: (a) as a bar chart and (b) as a piecewise linear graph. Bar charts are more commonly used in the media, but Figure 21(b) illustrates the changing index more clearly.

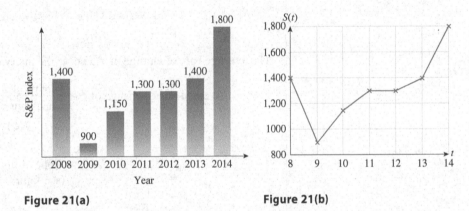

Figure 21(a)   **Figure 21(b)**

We saw in part (a) that the average rate of change of S over the interval $[8, 10]$ is the ratio

$$\text{Average rate of change of } S = \frac{\Delta S}{\Delta t} = \frac{S(10) - S(8)}{10 - 8} = -125 \text{ points per year.}$$

Notice that this rate of change is also the slope of the line through P and Q shown in Figure 22, and we can estimate this slope directly from the graph as shown.

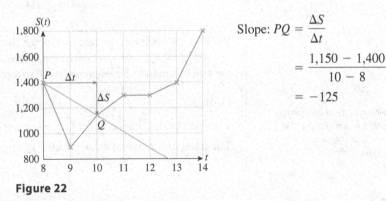

$$\text{Slope: } PQ = \frac{\Delta S}{\Delta t}$$

$$= \frac{1,150 - 1,400}{10 - 8}$$

$$= -125$$

Figure 22

Average rate of change as slope: The average rate of change of the S&P over the interval $[8, 10]$ is the slope of the line passing through the points on the graph where $t = 8$ and $t = 10$.

Similarly, the average rates of change of the S&P over the other intervals considered here are the slopes of the lines through pairs of corresponding points.

Formulas for Change and Average Rate of Change

Here is the formal definition of the average rate of change of a function over an interval.

Change and Average Rate of Change of f over $[a, b]$: Difference Quotient

The **change** in $f(x)$ over the interval $[a, b]$ is

$$
\begin{aligned}
\text{Change in } f &= \Delta f \\
&= \text{Second value} - \text{First value} \\
&= f(b) - f(a).
\end{aligned}
$$

The **average rate of change** of $f(x)$ over the interval $[a, b]$ is

$$
\begin{aligned}
\text{Average rate of change of } f &= \frac{\text{Change in } f}{\text{Change in } x} \\
&= \frac{\Delta f}{\Delta x} = \frac{f(b) - f(a)}{b - a} \\
&= \text{Slope of line through points } P \text{ and } Q \\
&\quad \text{(see figure).}
\end{aligned}
$$

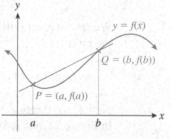

Average rate of change = Slope of PQ

We also call this average rate of change the **difference quotient** of f over the interval $[a, b]$. (It is the *quotient* of the *differences* $f(b) - f(a)$ and $b - a$.) A line through two points of a graph such as P and Q is called a **secant line** of the graph.

Units

The units of the change Δf in f are the units of $f(x)$.

The units of the average rate of change of f are units of $f(x)$ per unit of x.*

---

* The average rate of change is a slope, so it is measured in the same units as the slope: units of y (or $f(x)$) per unit of x.

> ### Quick Example
>
> 1. If $f(3) = -1$ billion dollars, $f(5) = 0.5$ billion dollars, and x is measured in years, then the change and average rate of change of f over the interval $[3, 5]$ are given by
>
> $$\text{Change in } f = f(5) - f(3) = 0.5 - (-1) = 1.5 \text{ billion dollars}$$
>
> $$\text{Average rate of change} = \frac{f(5) - f(3)}{5 - 3} = \frac{0.5 - (-1)}{2}$$
>
> $$= 0.75 \text{ billion dollars per year.}$$

Alternative Formula: Average Rate of Change of f over $[a, a + h]$

(Replace b in the formula for the average rate of change by $a + h$.) The average rate of change of f over the interval $[a, a + h]$ is

$$\text{Average rate of change of } f = \frac{f(a + h) - f(a)}{h}. \quad \text{Replace } b \text{ by } a + h.$$

In Example 1 we saw that the average rate of change of a quantity can be estimated directly from a graph. Here is an example that further illustrates the graphical approach.

EXAMPLE 2 **Carbon Dioxide Concentration**

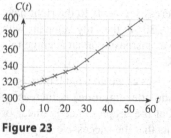

Figure 23

Figure 23 shows the annual mean carbon dioxide concentration measured at Mauna Loa Observatory in Hawaii, in parts per million (ppm), every 5 years from 1960 through 2015. ($t = 0$ represents 1960.)[31]

a. Use the graph to estimate the average rate of change of $C(t)$ with respect to t over the interval $[20, 40]$, and interpret the result.

b. Over which 10-year period(s) in the represented years was the carbon dioxide concentration increasing at an average rate of 1.5 ppm per year?

c. Multiple choice: For the period of time under consideration, carbon dioxide concentration was

   (A) increasing at a constant or increasing rate.

   (B) increasing at a constant or decreasing rate.

   (C) decreasing at a constant or increasing rate.

   (D) decreasing at a constant or decreasing rate.

---

[31] Figures are approximate. Source: U.S. Department of Commerce/National Oceanic and Atmospheric Administration (NOAA) Earth System Research Laboratory, data downloaded from www.esrl.noaa.gov/gmd/ccgg/trends/ on March 13, 2011.

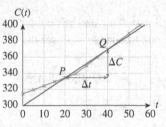

Figure 24

Solution

a. The average rate of change of C over the interval $[20, 40]$ is given by the slope of the line through the points P and Q shown in Figure 24. From the figure,

$$\text{Average rate of change of } C = \frac{\Delta C}{\Delta t} = \text{slope } PQ \approx \frac{370 - 335}{40 - 20} = \frac{35}{20} = 1.75.$$

Thus, the rate of change of C over the interval $[20, 40]$ is approximately 1.75.

Q : *How do we interpret the result?*

A : A clue is given by the units of the average rate of change: units of C per unit of t. The units of C are parts per million (ppm) of carbon dioxide, and the units of t are years. Thus, the average rate of change of C is measured in parts per million of carbon dioxide per year, and we can now interpret the result as follows.

Interpreting the average rate of change: The annual mean carbon dioxide concentration was increasing at an average rate of 1.75 ppm per year from 1980 ($t = 20$) to 2000 ($t = 40$).

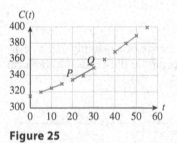

Figure 25

b. The rates of change of carbon dioxide concentration over successive 10-year periods in the represented years are given by the slopes of line segments through pairs of points 10 units apart on the t-axis in the graph in Figure 23. Figure 25 shows three such line segments. We are looking for such a segment whose slope is 1.5. Referring to Figure 25, notice that the segment PQ has the desired slope:

$$\text{Slope } PQ = \frac{350 - 335}{30 - 20} = \frac{15}{10} = 1.5.$$

Segments to the left of PQ all have slope 1, whereas segments to the right have slope 2. Thus, the segment corresponding to $[20, 30]$ is the only segment with slope 1.5, so the carbon dioxide concentration was increasing at an average rate of 1.5 ppm per year during the period 1980–1990.

c. Looking again at Figure 23, notice that the graph rises as we go from left to right; that is, the value of the function (carbon dioxide concentration) is increasing with increasing t. At the same time, the fact that the graph either is linear or bends up (is concave up) with increasing t tells us that the successive slopes are constant or increasing, so this fact applies to the average rates of change as well (choice (A)).

➡ **Before we go on . . .** Notice in Example 2 that we do not get exact answers from a graph; the best we can do is *estimate* the rates of change: Was the exact answer to part (a) closer to 1.74 or 1.76? Two people can reasonably disagree about results read from a graph, and you should bear this in mind when you check the answers to the exercises. ∎

Perhaps the most sophisticated way to compute the average rate of change of a quantity is through the use of a mathematical formula or model for the quantity in question.

Average Rate of Change of a Function Specified Algebraically

EXAMPLE 3 **Average Rate of Change from a Formula**

You are a commodities trader, and you monitor the price of gold on the spot market very closely during an active morning. Suppose you find that the price of an ounce of gold can be approximated by the function

$$G(t) = 5t^2 - 85t + 1,762 \qquad (7.5 \le t \le 10.5),$$

where t is time in hours. (See Figure 26; $t = 8$ represents 8:00 am.)

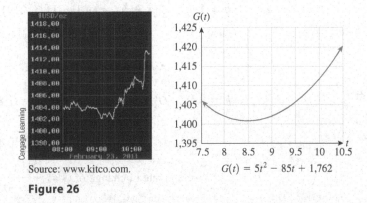

Source: www.kitco.com.

$G(t) = 5t^2 - 85t + 1,762$

Figure 26

Looking at the graph on the right, we can see that the price of gold was falling at the beginning of the time period, but by $t = 8.5$ the fall had slowed to a stop, whereupon the market turned around, and the price began to rise more and more rapidly toward the end of the period. What was the average rate of change of the price of gold over the $1\frac{1}{2}$-hour period starting at 8:00 am (the interval $[8, 9.5]$ on the t-axis)?

Solution We have

$$\text{Average rate of change of } G \text{ over } [8, 9.5] = \frac{\Delta G}{\Delta t} = \frac{G(9.5) - G(8)}{9.5 - 8}.$$

From the formula for $G(t)$ we find

$$G(9.5) = 5(9.5)^2 - 85(9.5) + 1,762 = 1,405.75$$
$$G(8) = 5(8)^2 - 85(8) + 1,762 = 1,402.$$

Thus, the average rate of change of G is given by

$$\frac{G(9.5) - G(8)}{9.5 - 8} = \frac{1,405.75 - 1,402}{1.5} = \frac{3.75}{1.5} = \$2.50 \text{ per hour.}$$

In other words, the price of gold increased at an average rate of \$2.50 per hour over the $1\frac{1}{2}$-hour period.

Using Technology

See the Technology Guides at the end of the chapter for detailed instructions on how to calculate the average rate of change of the function in Example 3 using a TI-83/84 Plus or a spreadsheet. Here is an outline:

TI-83/84 Plus
Y_1=5X^2-85X+1762
Home screen: $(Y_1(9.5) - Y_1(8))/(9.5-8)$
[More details in the Technology Guide.]

Spreadsheet
Headings t, $G(t)$, Rate of Change in A1–C1
t-values 8, 9.5 in A2–A3
=5*A2^2-85*A2+1762
in B2, copied down to B3
= (B3-B2)/(A3-A2) in C2.
[More details in the Technology Guide.]

EXAMPLE 4 **Rates of Change over Shorter Intervals**

Continuing with Example 3, use technology to compute the average rate of change of

$$G(t) = 5t^2 - 85t + 1,762 \qquad (7.5 \le t \le 10.5)$$

over the intervals $[8, 8 + h]$, where $h = 1, 0.1, 0.01, 0.001$, and 0.0001. What do the answers tell you about the price of gold?

Solution We use the "alternative" formula

$$\text{Average rate of change of } G \text{ over } [a, a + h] = \frac{G(a + h) - G(a)}{h},$$

so

$$\text{Average rate of change of } G \text{ over } [8, 8 + h] = \frac{G(8 + h) - G(8)}{h}.$$

Let us calculate this average rate of change for some of the values of h listed:

$h = 1$: $\quad G(8 + h) = G(8 + 1) = G(9) = 5(9)^2 - 85(9) + 1{,}762 = 1{,}402$

$$G(8) = 5(8)^2 - 85(8) + 1{,}762 = 1{,}402$$

$$\text{Average rate of change of } G = \frac{G(9) - G(8)}{1} = \frac{1{,}402 - 1{,}402}{1} = 0$$

$h = 0.1$: $\quad G(8 + h) = G(8 + 0.1) = G(8.1) = 5(8.1)^2 - 85(8.1) + 1{,}762$

$$= 1{,}401.55$$

$$G(8) = 5(8)^2 - 85(8) + 1{,}762 = 1{,}402$$

$$\text{Average rate of change of } G = \frac{G(8.1) - G(8)}{0.1} = \frac{1{,}401.55 - 1{,}402}{0.1} = \frac{-0.45}{0.1}$$

$$= -4.5$$

Using Technology

Example 4 is the kind of example
in which the use of technology
can make a huge difference. See
the Technology Guides at the end
of the chapter to find out how to
do the above computations
almost effortlessly using a
TI-83/84 Plus or a spreadsheet.
Here is an outline:

TI-83/84 Plus
Y₁=5X^2-85X+1762
Home screen:
(Y₁(8+1)-Y₁(8))/1
(Y₁(8+0.1)-Y₁(8))/0.1
(Y₁(8+0.01)-Y₁(8))/0.01
etc.
[More details in the Technology
Guide.]

Spreadsheet
Headings a, h, t, G(t), Rate of
Change in A1–E1
8 in A2, 1 in B2,
=A2 in C2, =A2+B2 in C3
=5*C2^2-85*C2+1762 in D2;
copy down to D3
= (D3-D2)/(C3-C2) in E2.
[More details in the Technology
Guide.]

$h = 0.01$: $\quad G(8 + h) = G(8 + 0.01) = G(8.01) = 5(8.01)^2 - 85(8.01) + 1{,}762$

$$= 1{,}401.9505$$

$$G(8) = 5(8)^2 - 85(8) + 1{,}762 = 1{,}402$$

$$\text{Average rate of change of } G = \frac{G(8.01) - G(8)}{0.01} = \frac{1{,}401.9505 - 1{,}402}{0.01} = \frac{-0.0495}{0.01}$$

$$= -4.95$$

Continuing in this way, we get the values in the following table:

h	1	0.1	0.01	0.001	0.0001
Avg. Rate of Change $\dfrac{G(8 + h) - G(8)}{h}$	0	-4.5	-4.95	-4.995	-4.9995

Each value is an average rate of change of G. For example, the value corresponding
to $h = 0.01$ is -4.95, which tells us the following:

*Over the interval $[8, 8.01]$ the price of gold was decreasing at an average rate
of $4.95 per hour.*

In other words, during the first one hundredth of an hour (or 36 seconds) starting at
$t = 8{:}00$ am, the price of gold was decreasing at an average rate of $4.95 per hour.
Put another way, in those 36 seconds, the price of gold decreased at a rate that, if
continued, would have produced a decrease of $4.95 in the price of gold during the
next hour. We will return to this example at the beginning of Section 10.5.

FAQs

Recognizing When and How to Compute the Average Rate of Change and How to Interpret the Answer

Q: *How do I know, by looking at the wording of a problem, that it is asking for an average rate of change?*

A: If a problem does not ask for an average rate of change directly, it might do so indirectly, as in "On average, how fast is quantity *q* increasing?"

Q: *If I know that a problem calls for computing an average rate of change, how should I compute it? By hand or by using technology?*

A: All the computations can be done by hand, but when hand calculations are not called for, using technology might save time.

Q: *Lots of problems ask us to "interpret" the answer. How do I do that for questions involving average rates of change?*

A: The *units* of the average rate of change are often the key to interpreting the results:

The units of the average rate of change of $f(x)$ are units of $f(x)$ per unit of x.

Thus, for instance, if $f(x)$ is the cost, in dollars, of a trip of x miles in length and the average rate of change of f is calculated to be 10, then the units of the average rate of change are dollars per mile, so we can interpret the answer by saying that the cost of a trip rises an average of $10 for each additional mile.

10.4 EXERCISES

▼ more advanced   ◆ challenging

T indicates exercises that should be solved using technology

In Exercises 1–18, calculate the average rate of change of the given function over the given interval. Where appropriate, specify the units of measurement. [**HINT**: See Example 1.]

1. Interval: $[1, 3]$

x	0	1	2	3
$f(x)$	3	5	2	−1

2. Interval: $[0, 2]$

x	0	1	2	3
$f(x)$	−1	3	2	1

3. Interval: $[-3, -1]$

x	−3	−2	−1	0
$f(x)$	−2.1	0	−1.5	0

4. Interval: $[-1, 1]$

x	−2	−1	0	1
$f(x)$	−1.5	−0.5	4	6.5

5. Interval: $[2, 6]$

t (months)	2	4	6
$R(t)$ ($ million)	20.2	24.3	20.1

6. Interval: $[1, 3]$

x (kilos)	1	2	3
$C(x)$ (£)	2.20	3.30	4.00

7. Interval: $[5, 5.5]$

p ($)	5.00	5.50	6.00
$q(p)$ (items)	400	300	150

8. Interval: $[0.1, 0.2]$

t (hours)	0	0.1	0.2
$D(t)$ (miles)	0	3	6

9. Interval: $[2, 5]$ [**HINT:** See Example 2.]

Apple Computer Stock Price ($)

10. Interval: $[1, 5]$ [**HINT:** See Example 2.]

Cisco Systems Stock Price ($)

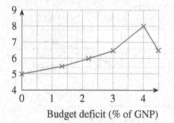

11. Interval: $[0, 4]$

Unemployment (%)

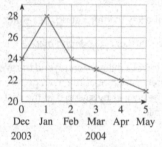

Budget deficit (% of GNP)

12. Interval: $[0, 4]$

Inflation (%)

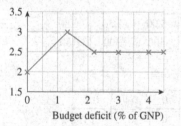

Budget deficit (% of GNP)

13. $f(x) = x^2 - 3; [1, 3]$ [**HINT:** See Example 3.]

14. $f(x) = 2x^2 + 4; [-1, 2]$ [**HINT:** See Example 3.]

15. $f(x) = 2x + 4; [-2, 0]$ **16.** $f(x) = \dfrac{1}{x}; [1, 4]$

17. $f(x) = \dfrac{x^2}{2} + \dfrac{1}{x}; [2, 3]$ **18.** $f(x) = 3x^2 - \dfrac{x}{2}; [3, 4]$

In Exercises 19–24, calculate the average rate of change of the given function f over the intervals $[a, a + h]$, *where* $h = 1, 0.1,$ $0.01, 0.001,$ *and* $0.0001.$ *(Technology is recommended for the cases* $h = 0.01, 0.001,$ *and* $0.0001.$*)* [**HINT:** See Example 4.]

19. $f(x) = 2x^2; a = 0$ **20.** $f(x) = \dfrac{x^2}{2}; a = 1$

21. $f(x) = \dfrac{1}{x}; a = 2$ **22.** $f(x) = \dfrac{2}{x}; a = 1$

23. $f(x) = x^2 + 2x; a = 3$ **24.** $f(x) = 3x^2 - 2x; a = 0$

Applications

25. *World Military Expenditure* The following table shows total military and arms trade expenditure in 2000, 2005, and 2010:[32]

Year t (year since 2000)	0	6	12
Military Expenditure $C(t)$ ($ billion)	1,100	1,450	1,750

Compute and interpret the average rate of change of $C(t)$ **(a)** over the period 2006–2012 (that is, $[6, 12]$) and **(b)** over the period $[0, 12]$. Be sure to state the units of measurement. [**HINT:** See Example 1.]

26. *Education Expenditure* The following table shows education expenditure in the United States as a percentage of total federal spending in 2009, 2015, and 2019:[33]

Year t (year since 2000)	9	15	19
Percentage $P(t)$	25	27	26

Compute and interpret the average rate of change of $P(t)$ **(a)** over the period 2009–2019 (that is, $[9, 19]$) and **(b)** over the period $[15, 19]$. Be sure to state the units of measurement.

27. *Crude Oil Production: Mexico* The following table shows daily crude oil production by Pemex, Mexico's national oil company, for 2008–2013:[34]

Year t (year since 2008)	0	1	2	3	4	5
Daily Production $p(t)$ (million barrels)	3.16	2.97	2.95	2.94	2.91	2.92

---

[32] Figures are rounded. Source: www.globalissues.org/article/75/world-military-spending.

[33] Figures are rounded and figures from 2014 on are projections. Source: www.usgovernmentspending.com.

[34] 2013 figure based on data through March. Source: www.pemex.com, March 2013.

a. Compute the average rate of change of $p(t)$ over the period 2010–2013. Interpret the result. [HINT: See Example 1.]

b. Which of the following is true? From 2008 to 2013 the three-year average rate of change of oil production by Pemex

    (**A**) increased in value.

    (**B**) decreased in value.

    (**C**) increased then decreased in value.

    (**D**) decreased then increased in value.

    [HINT: See Example 2.]

28. *Offshore Crude Oil Production: Mexico* The following table shows daily offshore crude oil production by Pemex, Mexico's national oil company, for 2008–2013:[35]

Year t (year since 2008)	0	1	2	3	4	5
Daily Offshore Production $s(t)$ (million barrels)	2.25	2.01	1.94	1.90	1.90	1.90

a. Use the data in the table to compute the average rate of change of $s(t)$ over the period 2008–2013. Interpret the result.

b. Which of the following is true? From 2008 to 2013 the two-year average rate of change of offshore crude oil production of Pemex

    (**A**) increased in value.

    (**B**) decreased in value.

    (**C**) increased then decreased in value.

    (**D**) decreased then increased in value.

29. *Subprime Mortgages during the Housing Crisis* The following graph shows the approximate percentage $P(t)$ of mortgages issued in the United States that were subprime (normally classified as risky):[36]

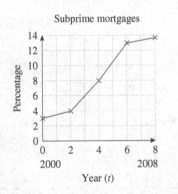

Subprime mortgages

a. Use the graph to estimate, to one decimal place, the average rate of change of $P(t)$ with respect to t over the interval $[0, 6]$, and interpret the result.

b. Over which 2-year period(s) was the average rate of change of $P(t)$ the greatest? [HINT: See Example 2.]

30. *Subprime Mortgage Debt during the Housing Crisis* The following graph shows the approximate value $V(t)$ of subprime (normally classified as risky) mortgage debt outstanding in the United States:[37]

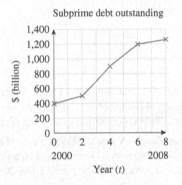

Subprime debt outstanding

a. Use the graph to estimate, to one decimal place, the average rate of change of $V(t)$ with respect to t over the interval $[2, 6]$, and interpret the result.

b. Over which 2-year period(s) was the average rate of change of $V(t)$ the least? [HINT: See Example 2.]

31. *Immigration to Ireland* The following graph shows the approximate number (in thousands) of people who immigrated to Ireland during the period 2010–2014 (t is time in years since 2010):[38]

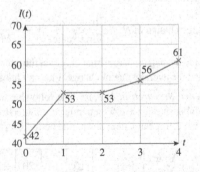

During which 2-year interval(s) was the magnitude of the average rate of change of $I(t)$ (**a**) greatest (**b**) least? Interpret your answers by referring to the rates of change.

[35] See footnote for Exercise 27.

[36] Sources: Mortgage Bankers Association, UBS.

[37] Source: Data 360 www.data360.org.

[38] Source: European Migration Network Ireland, http://emn.ie.

32. **Emigration from Ireland** The following graph shows the approximate number (in thousands) of people who emigrated from Ireland during the period 2010–2014 (*t* is time in years since 2010):[39]

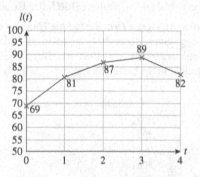

During which 2-year interval(s) was the magnitude of the average rate of change of *E*(*t*) (a) greatest (b) least? Interpret your answers by referring to the rates of change.

33. ▼ **Science Research in the United States** The following table shows the number of science research articles authored by U.S researchers during the period 1980–2010:[40]

Year *t* (year since 1980)	0	5	10	15	20	25	30
Articles *N*(*t*) (thousands)	170	200	220	260	252	290	340

a. Find the interval(s) over which the average rate of change of *N* was the greatest. What was that rate of change? Interpret your answer.

b. The **percentage change of *N* over the interval [*a*, *b*]** is defined to be

$$\text{Percentage change of } N = \frac{\text{Change in } N}{\text{First value}} = \frac{N(b) - N(a)}{N(a)}.$$

Compute the percentage change of *N* over the interval [0, 30] and also the average rate of change. Interpret the answers.

34. ▼ **Science Research in Europe** The following table shows the number of science research articles authored by researchers in the European Union during the period 1980–2010:[41]

Year *t* (year since 1980)	0	5	10	15	20	25	30
Articles *N*(*t*) (thousands)	140	170	190	260	300	340	430

a. Find the interval(s) over which the average rate of change of *N* was the least positive. What was that rate of change? Interpret your answer.

b. The **percentage change of *N* over the interval [*a*, *b*]** is defined to be

$$\text{Percentage change of } N = \frac{\text{Change in } N}{\text{First value}} = \frac{N(b) - N(a)}{N(a)}.$$

Compute the percentage change of *N* over the interval [10, 30] and also the average rate of change. Interpret the answers.

35. **College Basketball: Men** The following chart shows the number of NCAA men's college basketball teams in the United States during the period 2000–2010:[42]

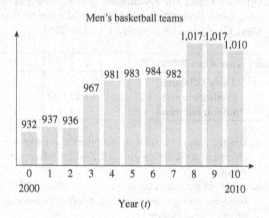

a. On average, how fast was the number of men's college basketball teams growing over the 4-year period beginning in 2002?

b. By inspecting the chart, determine whether the 3-year average rates of change increased or decreased beginning in 2005. [HINT: See Example 2.]

36. **College Basketball: Women** The following chart shows the number of NCAA women's college basketball teams in the United States during the period 2000–2010:[43]

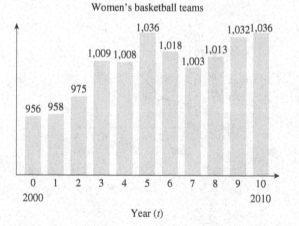

---

[39] See footnote for Exercise 31.

[40] 1980 data estimated. Source: www.sciencewatch.com.

[41] Ibid.

[42] 2010 figure is an estimate. Source: www.census.gov.

[43] Ibid.

a. On average, how fast was the number of women's college basketball teams growing over the 4-year period beginning in 2004?

b. By inspecting the graph, find the 3-year period over which the average rate of change was largest.

37. *Funding for the Arts* State governments in the United States spend between $1 and $2 per person on the arts and culture each year. The following chart shows the data for 2002–2010, together with the regression line:[44]

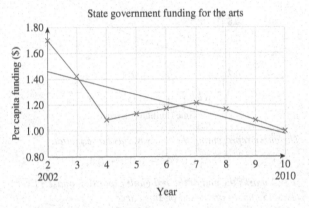

State government funding for the arts

a. Over the period $[2, 6]$ the average rate of change of state government funding for the arts was

(A) less than

(B) greater than

(C) approximately equal to

the rate predicted by the regression line.

b. Over the period $[3, 10]$ the average rate of change of state government funding for the arts was

(A) less than

(B) greater than

(C) approximately equal to

the rate predicted by the regression line.

c. Over the period $[4, 8]$ the average rate of change of state government funding for the arts was

(A) less than

(B) greater than

(C) approximately equal to

the rate predicted by the regression line.

d. Estimate, to two significant digits, the average rate of change of per capita state government funding for the arts over the period $[2, 10]$. (Be careful to state the units of measurement.) How does it compare to the slope of the regression line?

38. *Funding for the Arts* The U.S. federal government spends between $6 and $7 per person on the arts and culture each year. The following chart shows the data for 2002–2010, together with the regression line:[45]

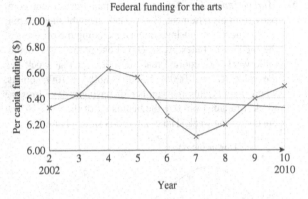

Federal funding for the arts

a. Over the period $[4, 10]$ the average rate of change of federal government funding for the arts was

(A) less than

(B) greater than

(C) approximately equal to

the rate predicted by the regression line.

b. Over the period $[2, 7]$ the average rate of change of federal government funding for the arts was

(A) less than

(B) greater than

(C) approximately equal to

the rate predicted by the regression line.

c. Over the period $[3, 10]$ the average rate of change of federal government funding for the arts was

(A) less than

(B) greater than

(C) approximately equal to

the rate predicted by the regression line.

d. Estimate, to one significant digit, the average rate of change of per capita federal government funding for the arts over the period $[2, 10]$. (Be careful to state the units of measurement.) How does it compare to the slope of the regression line?

39. ▼ *Market Volatility during the Dot-Com Boom* A volatility index generally measures the extent to which a market undergoes sudden changes in value. The volatility of the S&P 500 (as measured by one such index) was decreasing at an average rate of 0.2 points per year during 1991–1995 and was increasing at an average rate of about 0.3 points per year during 1995–1999. In 1995 the volatility of the S&P was 1.1.[46] Use this information to give a rough sketch of the volatility of the S&P 500 as a function of time, showing its values in 1991 and 1999.

40. ▼ *Market Volatility during the Dot-Com Boom* The volatility (see Exercise 39) of the NASDAQ had an average rate of change of 0 points per year during 1992–1995, and increased at an average rate of 0.2 points per year during 1995–1998. In 1995 the volatility of the NASDAQ was 1.1.[47] Use this information to give a rough sketch of the volatility of the NASDAQ as a function of time.

[44] Figures are in constant 2008 dollars, and the 2010 figure is the authors' estimate. Source: *Americans for the Arts* www.artsusa.org.

[45] *Ibid.*

[46] Source for data: Sanford C. Bernstein Company/*New York Times*, March 24, 2000, p. C1.

[47] *Ibid.*

41. *Market Index* Joe Downs runs a small investment company from his basement. Every week, he publishes a report on the success of his investments, including the progress of the Joe Downs Index. At the end of one particularly memorable week, he reported that the index for that week had the value $I(t) = 1{,}000 + 1{,}500t - 800t^2 + 100t^3$ points, where t represents the number of business days into the week; t ranges from 0 at the beginning of the week to 5 at the end of the week. The graph of I is shown below:

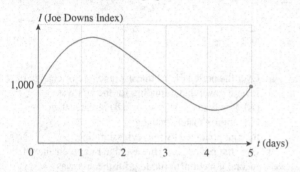

I (Joe Downs Index)

On average, how fast and in which direction was the index changing over the first two business days (the interval $[0, 2]$)? [**HINT:** See Example 3.]

42. *Market Index* Refer to the Joe Downs Index in Exercise 41. On average, how fast and in which direction was the index changing over the last three business days (the interval $[2, 5]$)? [**HINT:** See Example 3.]

43. *Crude Oil Prices* The price per barrel of crude oil in constant 2008 dollars can be approximated by

$$P(t) = 0.45t^2 - 12t + 105 \text{ dollars} \quad (0 \le t \le 28),$$

where t is time in years since the start of 1980.[48]
a. What, in constant 2008 dollars, was the average rate of change of the price of oil from the start of 1981 ($t = 1$) to the start of 2006 ($t = 26$)? [**HINT:** See Example 3.]
b. Your answer to part (a) is quite small. Can you conclude that the price of oil hardly changed at all over the 25-year period 1981–2006? Explain.

44. *Median Home Prices* The median home price in the United States over the period January 2010–January 2015 can be approximated by

$$P(t) = 4.5t^2 - 15t + 180 \text{ thousand dollars} \quad (0 \le t \le 5),$$

where t is time in years since the start of 2010.[49]
a. What was the average rate of change of the median home price from the start of 2012 to the start of 2014?
b. What, if anything, does your answer to part (a) say about the median home price in 2013? Explain.

End of the Earth In 5 billion years the Sun will have run out of hydrogen fuel and begin to expand into a red giant, eventually engulfing the Earth and causing it to spiral into the core of

the Sun 7.5 billion years from now. The following graph[50] shows the expanding radius of the red giant Sun (in red) and the radius of the Earth's orbit about the Sun (in green) during its final three and a half million years of existence. The radii are measured in astronomical units (AU; one AU is the current radius of the Earth's orbit around the Sun, approximately 93 million miles), and time is measured in millions of years.

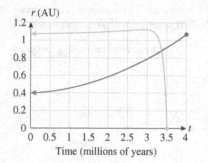

Time (millions of years)

The curve representing the Sun's radius has equation

$$r = 0.037t^2 + 0.02t + 0.4.$$

($t = 4$ marks the end of the red giant expansion phase.) Exercises 45 and 46 are based on this curve.

45. a. Calculate the rate of change of the radius of the Sun over the successive intervals $[0, 1]$, $[1, 2]$, $[2, 3]$, $[3, 4]$.
b. The successive rates of change are a linear function of t. What is the slope of that linear function? How fast will the *rate of change* of the Sun's radius be increasing in the final 4 million years?

46. a. Calculate the rate of change of the radius of the Sun over the successive intervals $[0, 2]$, $[1, 3]$, $[2, 4]$.
b. The successive rates of change are a linear function of t. What is the slope of that linear function? How fast will the *rate of change* of the Sun's radius be increasing in the final 4 million years?

47. *The 2003 SARS Outbreak* In the early stages of the SARS (severe acute respiratory syndrome) epidemic in 2003 the number of reported cases could be approximated by

$$A(t) = 167(1.18)^t \quad (0 \le t \le 20)$$

t days after March 17, 2003 (the first day for which statistics were reported by the World Health Organization).
a. What was the average rate of change of $A(t)$ from March 17 to March 23? Interpret the result.
b. Which of the following is true? For the first 20 days of the epidemic, the number of reported cases
(A) increased at a faster and faster rate.
(B) increased at a slower and slower rate.
(C) decreased at a faster and faster rate.

---

[48] Source for data: www.inflationdata.com.
[49] Source for data: www.zillow.com.

[50] The actual astrophysical models, of which the curves shown here are merely rough graphical representations, are described in "Distant Future of the Sun and Earth Revisited" by Klaus-Peter Schröder and Robert C. Smith, *Monthly Notices of the Royal Astronomical Society* **386** (1) (2008): 155–163.

(D) decreased at a slower and slower rate.
[HINT: See Example 2.]

48. *The 2003 SARS Outbreak* A few weeks into the SARS (severe acute respiratory syndrome) epidemic in 2003, the number of reported cases could be approximated by

$$A(t) = 1,804(1.04)^t \quad (0 \le t \le 30)$$

t days after April 1, 2003.

a. What was the average rate of change of $A(t)$ from April 19 ($t = 18$) to April 29? Interpret the result.

b. Which of the following is true? During the 30-day period beginning April 1, the number of reported cases

(A) increased at a faster and faster rate.

(B) increased at a slower and slower rate.

(C) decreased at a faster and faster rate.

(D) decreased at a slower and slower rate.

[HINT: See Example 2.]

49. *The 2014 Ebola Outbreak* In the first 6 months of the 2014 Ebola outbreak, the total number of reported cases could be approximated by

$$C(t) = 95.9e^{0.72t} \quad (0 \le t \le 6),$$

where t is time in months since April 1, 2014.[51]

a. Calculate the average rates of change of $C(t)$ over the successive 2-month periods $[0, 2], [1, 3], [2, 4], [3, 5]$, and $[4, 6]$. (Round answers to two decimal places.)

b. What kind of model would best describe the successive rates of change obtained in part (a): linear, quadratic, or exponential? What does your answer tell you about the 2014 Ebola outbreak?

50. *The 2014 Ebola Outbreak* Repeat Exercise 49 using the following model for the total number of reported deaths from Ebola:

$$D(t) = 90.52e^{0.60t} \quad (0 \le t \le 6),$$

where t is time in months since April 1, 2014.[52]

51. ▼ *Ecology* Increasing numbers of manatees ("sea sirens") have been killed by boats off the Florida coast. The following graph shows the relationship between the number of boats registered in Florida and the number of manatees killed each year:

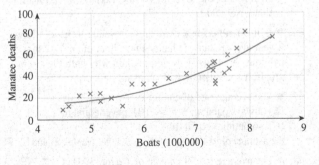

Boats (100,000)

The regression curve shown is given by

$$f(x) = 3.55x^2 - 30.2x + 81 \text{ manatees}$$
$$(4.5 < x < 8.5),$$

where x is the number of boats (in hundreds of thousands) registered in Florida in a particular year and $f(x)$ is the number of manatees killed by boats in Florida that year.[53]

a. Compute the average rate of change of f over the intervals $[5, 6]$ and $[7, 8]$.

b. What does the answer to part (a) tell you about the manatee deaths per boat?

52. ▼ *Ecology* Refer to Exercise 51.

a. Compute the average rate of change of f over the intervals $[5, 7]$ and $[6, 8]$.

b. Had we used a linear model instead of a quadratic one, how would the two answers in part (a) be related to each other?

53. ▮▼ *SAT Scores by Income* The math SAT score of a high school graduate can be approximated by

$$S(x) = 573 - 133(0.987)^x \text{ points on the math SAT test,}$$

where x is the household income of the student in thousands of dollars per year.[54]

a. Use technology to complete the following table, which shows the average rate of change of S over successive intervals of length 40. (Round all answers to two decimal places.) [HINT: See Example 4.]

Interval	[0, 40]	[40, 80]	[80, 120]	[120, 160]	[160, 200]
Avg. Rate of Change of S					

b. Interpret your answer for the interval $[40, 80]$, being sure to indicate the direction of change and the units of measurement.

c. Multiple choice: As her household income rises, a student's SAT score

(A) increases.

(B) decreases.

(C) increases, then decreases.

(D) decreases, then increases.

d. Multiple choice: As the household income increases, the effect on a student's SAT score is

(A) more pronounced.

(B) less pronounced.

---

[51] Exponential model is the authors'. Source for data: Wikipedia/Centers for Disease Control and Prevention/WHO.

[52] *Ibid.*

[53] Regression model is based on data from 1976 to 2000. Sources for data: Florida Department of Highway Safety & Motor Vehicles, Florida Marine Institute/*New York Times*, February 12, 2002, p. F4.

[54] The model is the authors'. Source for data: College Board/*New York Times* http://economix.blogs.nytimes.com.

54. ▣ ▼ *SAT Scores by Income* Repeat Exercise 53 using the following model for the critical reading SAT score of a high school graduate:

$S(x) = 550 - 136(0.985)^x$ points on the critical reading SAT test,

where x is the household income of the student in thousands of dollars per year.[55]

Communication and Reasoning Exercises

55. Describe three ways we have used to determine the average rate of change of f over an interval $[a, b]$. Which of the three ways is *least* precise? Explain.

56. If f is a linear function of x with slope m, what is its average rate of change over any interval $[a, b]$?

57. Is the average rate of change of a function over $[a, b]$ affected by the values of the function between a and b? Explain.

58. If the average rate of change of a function over $[a, b]$ is zero, this means that the function is constant over that interval—right?

59. Sketch the graph of a function whose average rate of change over $[0, 3]$ is negative but whose average rate of change over $[1, 3]$ is positive.

60. Sketch the graph of a function whose average rate of change over $[0, 2]$ is positive but whose average rate of change over $[0, 1]$ is negative.

61. ▼ If the rate of change of quantity A is 2 units of quantity A per unit of quantity B, and the rate of change of quantity B is 3 units of quantity B per unit of quantity C, what is the rate of change of quantity A with respect to quantity C?

62. ▼ If the rate of change of quantity A is 2 units of quantity A per unit of quantity B, what is the rate of change of quantity B with respect to quantity A?

63. ▼ A certain function f has the property that its average rate of change over the interval $[1, 1 + h]$ (for positive h) increases as h decreases. Which of the following graphs could be the graph of f?

(A)   **(B)**

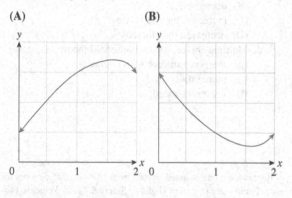

(C)

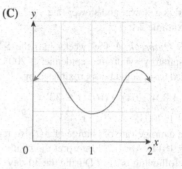

64. ▼ A certain function f has the property that its average rate of change over the interval $[1, 1 + h]$ (for positive h) decreases as h decreases. Which of the following graphs could be the graph of f?

(A)   **(B)**

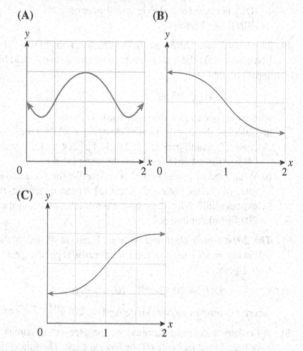

(C)

65. ▼ Is it possible for a company's revenue to have a negative 3-year average rate of growth but a positive average rate of growth in 2 of the 3 years? (If not, explain; if so, illustrate with an example.)

66. ▼ Is it possible for a company's revenue to have a larger 2-year average rate of change than either of the 1-year average rates of change? (If not, explain why with the aid of a graph; if so, illustrate with an example.)

67. ◆ The average rate of change of f over $[1, 3]$ is
(A) always equal to   **(B)** never equal to
(C) sometimes equal to
the average of its average rates of change over $[1, 2]$ and $[2, 3]$.

68. ◆ The average rate of change of f over $[1, 4]$ is
(A) always equal to   **(B)** never equal to
(C) sometimes equal to
the average of its average rates of change over $[1, 2]$, $[2, 3]$, and $[3, 4]$.

10.5 The Derivative: Numerical and Graphical Viewpoints

Instantaneous Rate of Change of a Function

In Example 4 of Section 10.4 we looked at the average rate of change of the function $G(t) = 5t^2 - 85t + 1{,}762$ approximating the price of gold on the spot market over smaller and smaller intervals of time. We obtained the following table showing the average rates of change of G over the intervals $[8, 8 + h]$ for successively smaller values of h:

h getting smaller; interval $[8, 8 + h]$ getting smaller →

h	1	0.1	0.01	0.001	0.0001
Avg. Rate of Change over $[8, 8 + h]$	0	−4.5	−4.95	−4.995	−4.9995

Rate of change approaching −$5 per hour →

The average rates of change of the price of gold over smaller and smaller periods of time, starting at the instant $t = 8$ (8:00 am), appear to be getting closer and closer to −$5 per hour. As we look at these shrinking periods of time, we are getting closer to looking at what happens at the *instant* $t = 8$. So it seems reasonable to say that the average rates of change are approaching the **instantaneous rate of change** at $t = 8$, which the table suggests is −$5 per hour. This is how fast the price of gold was changing *exactly* at 8:00 am.

At $t = 8$ the instantaneous rate of change of $G(t)$ is −5.

We express this fact mathematically by writing $G'(8) = -5$ (which we read as "G prime of 8 equals −5"). Thus,

$G'(8) = -5$ *means that, at $t = 8$, the instantaneous rate of change of $G(t)$ is −5.*

The process of letting h get smaller and smaller is called taking the **limit** as h approaches 0 (as you recognize if you've done the sections on limits). As in the sections on limits, we write $h \to 0$ as shorthand for "h approaches 0." Thus, taking the limit of the average rates of change as $h \to 0$ gives us the instantaneous rate of change.

Q : *All these intervals $[8, 8 + h]$ are intervals to the right of 8. What about small intervals to the left of 8, such as $[7.9, 8]$?*

A : We can compute the average rate of change of our function for such intervals by choosing h to be negative ($h = -0.1, -0.01$, etc.) and using the same difference quotient formula we used for positive h:

$$\text{Average rate of change of } G \text{ over } [8 + h, 8] = \frac{G(8) - G(8 + h)}{8 - (8 + h)}.$$

Here are the results we get using negative h:

h getting closer to 0; interval $[8 + h, 8]$ getting smaller →

h	−1	−0.1	−0.01	−0.001	−0.0001
Avg. Rate of Change over $[8 + h, 8]$	−10	−5.5	−5.05	−5.005	−5.0005

Rate of change approaching −$5 per hour →

Notice that the average rates of change are again getting closer and closer to −5 as h approaches 0, suggesting once again that the instantaneous rate of change is −$5 per hour.

* For instance, a is not allowed to be an endpoint of the domain of f. A point a that satisfies the given requirement is called an **interior point** of the domain of f.

Instantaneous Rate of Change of $f(x)$ at $x = a$: Derivative

Assume that $f(x)$ is defined for all x in some open interval about $x = a$.* The **instantaneous rate of change** of $f(x)$ at $x = a$ is defined as

$$f'(a) = \lim_{h \to 0} \frac{f(a+h) - f(a)}{h},$$

f prime of a equals the limit, as h approaches 0, of the ratio $\frac{f(a+h) - f(a)}{h}$.

assuming that the limit exists. The quantity $f'(a)$ is also called the **derivative of $f(x)$ at $x = a$.** Finding the derivative of f is called **differentiating f.**

Note For $f'(a)$ to exist, two requirements need to be met:

1. a must be an interior point of the domain of f (see the side note above), and
2. the above limit must exist (and be finite).

When $f'(a)$ exists, we say that f is **differentiable at a**; otherwise, f is **not differentiable at a.** ∎

Units

The units of $f'(a)$ are the same as the units of the average rate of change: units of f per unit of x.

Quick Examples

1. If $f(x) = 5x^2 - 85x + 1,762$, then the two tables above suggest that

$$f'(8) = \lim_{h \to 0} \frac{f(8+h) - f(8)}{h} = -5.$$

2. If $f(t)$ is the number of insects in your dorm room at time t hours, and you know that $f(3) = 5$ and $f'(3) = 8$, this means that, at time $t = 3$ hours, there are five insects in your room, and this number is growing at an instantaneous rate of eight insects per hour.

Important Notes

1. Sections 10.1–10.3 discuss limits in some detail. If you have not (yet) covered those sections, you can trust to your intuition.
2. The formula for the derivative tells us that the instantaneous rate of change is the limit of the average rates of change $[f(a+h) - f(a)]/h$ over smaller and smaller intervals. Thus, the value of $f'(a)$ can be approximated by computing the average rate of change for smaller and smaller values of h, both positive and negative.
3. As we noted above, if a happens to be an endpoint of the domain of f, then a is not an interior point of the domain of f, and so f is not differentiable at a.
4. In this section we will only *approximate* derivatives. In Section 10.6 we will begin to see how we find the *exact* values of derivatives.

5. $f'(a)$ is a number we can calculate, or at least approximate, for various values of a, as we have done in the earlier example. Since $f'(a)$ depends on the value of a, we can think of f' as *a function of a*. (We return to this idea at the end of this section.) An old name for f' is "the function *derived from f*," which has been shortened to the *derivative* of f.

6. It is because f' is a function that we sometimes refer to $f'(a)$ as "the derivative of *f evaluated at a*" or the "derivative of $f(x)$ evaluated at $x = a$."

7. If the average rates of change $[f(a + h) - f(a)]/h$ approach one number on the intervals using positive h and another number on the intervals using negative h, then $\lim_{h \to 0}[f(a + h) - f(a)]/h$ does not exist, so f is not differentiable at a. It is comforting to know that all polynomials and exponential functions *are* differentiable at every point, although many common functions are not; for example, neither $f(x) = |x|$ nor $f(x) = x^{1/3}$ is differentiable at 0 (see Section 11.1). ∎

EXAMPLE 1   **Instantaneous Rate of Change: Numerically and Graphically**

The air temperature one spring morning, t hours after 7:00 am, was given by the function $f(t) = 50 + 0.1t^4$ degrees Fahrenheit ($0 \le t \le 4$).

a. How fast was the temperature rising at 9:00 am?

b. How is the instantaneous rate of change of temperature at 9:00 am reflected in the graph of temperature vs. time?

Solution

a. We are being asked to find the instantaneous rate of change of the temperature at $t = 2$, so we need to find $f'(2)$. To do this, we examine the average rates of change

$$\frac{f(2 + h) - f(2)}{h} \qquad \text{Average rate of change = Difference quotient}$$

for values of h approaching 0. Calculating the average rate of change over $[2, 2 + h]$ for $h = 1, 0.1, 0.01, 0.001,$ and 0.0001, we get the following values (rounded to four decimal places):*

* We can quickly compute these values using technology as in Example 4 in Section 10.4. (See the Technology Guides at the end of the chapter.)

h	1	0.1	0.01	0.001	0.0001
Avg. Rate of Change over $[2, 2 + h]$	6.5	3.4481	3.2241	3.2024	3.2002

Here are the values we get using negative values of h:

h	-1	-0.1	-0.01	-0.001	-0.0001
Avg. Rate of Change over $[2 + h, 2]$	1.5	2.9679	3.1761	3.1976	3.1998

The average rates of change are clearly approaching the number 3.2, so we can say that $f'(2) = 3.2$. Thus, at 9:00 in the morning, the temperature was rising at the rate of 3.2 degrees per hour.

b. We saw in Section 10.4 that the average rate of change of f over an interval is the slope of the secant line through the corresponding points on the graph of f. Figure 27 illustrates this for the intervals $[2, 2 + h]$ with $h = 1, 0.5$, and 0.1.

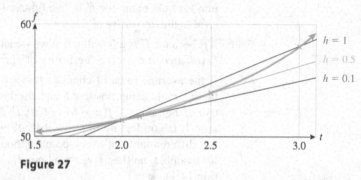

Figure 27

All three secant lines pass though the point $(2, f(2)) = (2, 51.6)$ on the graph of f. Each of them passes through a second point on the curve (the second point is different for each secant line), and this second point gets closer and closer to $(2, 51.6)$ as h gets closer to 0. What seems to be happening is that the secant lines are getting closer and closer to a line that just touches the curve at $(2, 51.6)$: the **tangent line** at $(2, 51.6)$, shown in Figure 28.

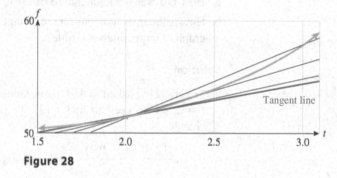

Figure 28

Q: What is the slope of this tangent line?

A: Because the slopes of the secant lines are getting closer and closer to 3.2, and because the secant lines are approaching the tangent line, the tangent line must have slope 3.2. In other words,

At the point on the graph where $x = 2$, the slope of the tangent line is $f'(2)$.

Q: What is the difference between $f(2)$ and $f'(2)$?

A: An important question. Briefly, $f(2)$ is the *value of f* when $t = 2$, while $f'(2)$ is the *rate at which f is changing* when $t = 2$. Here,

$$f(2) = 50 + 0.1(2)^4 = 51.6 \text{ degrees.}$$

Thus, at 9:00 am ($t = 2$) the temperature was 51.6 degrees. On the other hand,

$$f'(2) = 3.2 \text{ degrees per hour.} \qquad \text{Units of slope are units of } f \text{ per unit of } t.$$

This means that, at 9:00 am ($t = 2$) the temperature was increasing at a rate of 3.2 degrees per hour.

Secant and Tangent Lines

Because we have been talking about tangent lines, we should say more about what they *are*. A tangent line to a *circle* is a line that touches the circle in just one point. A tangent line gives the circle "a glancing blow," as shown in Figure 29. For a smooth curve other than a circle, a tangent line may touch the curve at more than one point or pass through it (Figure 30).

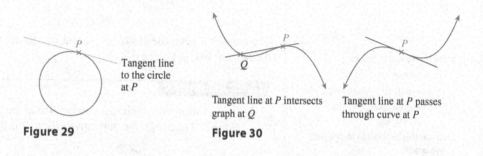

Tangent line
to the circle
at P

Figure 29

Tangent line at P intersects
graph at Q

Tangent line at P passes
through curve at P

Figure 30

However, all tangent lines have the following interesting property in common: If we focus on a small portion of the curve very close to the point P—in other words, if we zoom in to the graph near the point P—the curve will appear almost straight and almost indistinguishable from the tangent line (Figure 31).[*]

[*] For a simulation of what is happening in Figure 31, go to the Website and follow

Everything
→ Section 10.5 Practice/Visualize
→ Zooming In on a Curve

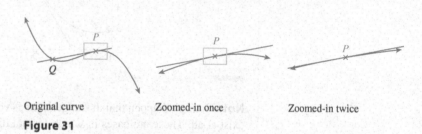

Original curve

Zoomed-in once

Zoomed-in twice

Figure 31

You can check this property by zooming in on the curve shown in Figures 27 and 28 in Example 1 near the point where $x = 2$.

Secant and Tangent Lines

The *slope of the secant line* through the points on the graph of f where $x = a$ and $x = a + h$ is given by the average rate of change, or difference quotient:

$$m_{sec} = \text{Slope of secant} = \text{Average rate of change} = \frac{f(a + h) - f(a)}{h}.$$

The *slope of the tangent line* through the point on the graph of f where $x = a$ is given by the instantaneous rate of change, or derivative:

$$m_{tan} = \text{Slope of tangent} = \text{Instantaneous rate of change} = \text{Derivative}$$

$$= f'(a) = \lim_{h \to 0} \frac{f(a + h) - f(a)}{h},$$

assuming that the derivative exists.

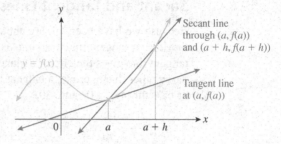

The smaller h gets, the closer the secant line in the figure above gets to being the tangent line at $(a, f(a))$.*

* On the Website, follow

Everything

→ Section 10.5 Practice/Visualize

→ Visualize the Derivative Graphically

to see this process in an interactive graph.

Quick Example

3. In the following graph, the tangent line at the point where $x = 2$ has slope 3. Therefore, the derivative at $x = 2$ is 3. That is, $f'(2) = 3$.

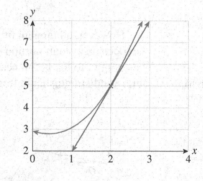

Note It might happen that the tangent line is vertical at some point or does not exist at all. These are cases in which f is not differentiable at the given point. (See Section 10.6 for examples.) ∎

We can now give a more precise definition of what we mean by the tangent line to a point P on the graph of f at a given point: The **tangent line** to the graph of f at the point $P(a, f(a))$ is the straight line passing through P with slope $f'(a)$.

Quick Approximation of the Derivative

Q: *Do we always need to make tables of difference quotients as above in order to calculate an approximate value for the derivative? That seems like a large amount of work just to get an approximation.*

* In fact, no matter how small the value we decide to use for h, it is possible to craft a function f for which the difference quotient at a is not even close to $f'(a)$.

A: We can usually *approximate* the value of the derivative by using a single, small value of h. In the example above, the value $h = 0.0001$ would have given a pretty good approximation. The problems with using a fixed value of h are that (1) we do not get an *exact* answer, only an *approximation* of the derivative, and (2) how good an approximation it is depends on the function we're differentiating.* However, with most of the functions we'll be considering, setting $h = 0.0001$ does give us a good approximation.

Calculating a Quick Approximation of the Derivative

When f is differentiable at a, we can calculate an approximate value of $f'(a)$ by using the formula

$$f'(a) \approx \frac{f(a + h) - f(a)}{h} \qquad \text{Rate of change over } [a, a + h]$$

with a small value of h. The value $h = 0.0001$ works for most examples we encounter. (Students of numerical methods study the question of exactly how accurate this approximation is.)

Alternative Formula: The Balanced Difference Quotient

The following alternative formula, which measures the rate of change of f over the interval $[a - h, a + h]$, often gives a more accurate result and is the one used in many calculators:

$$f'(a) \approx \frac{f(a + h) - f(a - h)}{2h}. \qquad \text{Rate of change over } [a - h, a + h]$$

Notes

1. If f is a linear function, both approximations give the slope (the exact value of the derivative) regardless of the choice of $h \neq 0$.
2. If f is a quadratic function, the *balanced* difference quotient gives the exact value of the derivative regardless of the choice of $h \neq 0$.* ∎

* To see why this is true, we would need to know some of the material that we study in the next chapter.

EXAMPLE 2   **Quick Approximation of the Derivative**

a. Calculate an approximate value of $f'(1.5)$ if $f(x) = x^2 - 4x$.

b. Find the equation of the tangent line at the point on the graph where $x = 1.5$.

Solution

a. We shall compute both the ordinary difference quotient and the balanced difference quotient.

Ordinary Difference Quotient: When we use $h = 0.0001$, the ordinary difference quotient is

$$\begin{aligned}
f'(1.5) &\approx \frac{f(1.5 + 0.0001) - f(1.5)}{0.0001} \qquad \text{Ordinary difference quotient} \\
&= \frac{f(1.5001) - f(1.5)}{0.0001} \\
&= \frac{(1.5001^2 - 4 \times 1.5001) - (1.5^2 - 4 \times 1.5)}{0.0001} = -0.9999.
\end{aligned}$$

This answer is accurate to 0.0001; in fact, $f'(1.5) = -1$.

Graphically, we can picture this approximation as follows: Zoom in on the curve using the window $1.5 \leq x \leq 1.5001$, and measure the slope of the secant line joining both ends of the curve segment. Figure 32 shows close-up views of the curve and tangent line near the point P in which we are interested, the third view being the zoomed-in view used for this approximation. Notice that in the

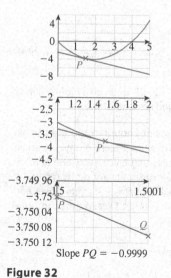

Slope $PQ = -0.9999$

Figure 32

bottom window the tangent line and curve are indistinguishable. Also, the point P in which we are interested is on the left edge of the window.

Balanced Difference Quotient: For the balanced difference quotient, we get

$$
\begin{aligned}
f'(1.5) &\approx \frac{f(1.5 + 0.0001) - f(1.5 - 0.0001)}{2(0.0001)} \qquad \text{Balanced difference quotient} \\
&= \frac{f(1.5001) - f(1.4999)}{0.0002} \\
&= \frac{(1.5001^2 - 4 \times 1.5001) - (1.4999^2 - 4 \times 1.4999)}{0.0002} = -1.
\end{aligned}
$$

This balanced difference quotient gives the exact answer in this case. (Recall that the balanced difference quotient always gives the exact derivative for a quandratic function.) Graphically, it is as though we have zoomed in using a window that puts the point P in the *center* of the screen (Figure 33) rather than at the left edge.

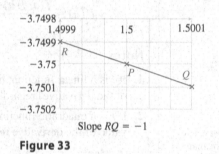

Slope $RQ = -1$

Figure 33

Using Technology

See the Technology Guides at the end of the chapter to find out how to calculate the quick approximations to the derivative in Example 2 using a TI-83/84 Plus or a spreadsheet. Here is an outline:

TI-83/84 Plus
Y₁=X^2-4*X
Home screen:
(Y₁(1.5001)-Y₁(1.5))/
0.0001
(Y₁(1.5001)-
Y₁(1.4999))/0.0002
[More details in the Technology Guide.]

Spreadsheet
Headings a, h, x, f(x), Diff Quotient, Balanced Diff Quotient in A1–F1
1.5 in A2, 0.0001 in B2,
=A2-B2 in C2, =A2 in C3,
=A2+B2 in C4
=C2^2-4*C2 in D2; copy down to D4
=(D3-D2)/(C3-C2) in E2
=(D4-D2)/(C4-C2) in E3
[More details in the Technology Guide.]

b. We find the equation of the tangent line from a point on the line and its slope, as we did in Chapter 1:

• **Point** $(1.5, f(1.5)) = (1.5, -3.75)$.
• **Slope** $m = f'(1.5) = -1$.   Slope of the tangent line = Derivative

The equation is

$$y = mx + b,$$

where $m = -1$ and $b = y_1 - mx_1 = -3.75 - (-1)(1.5) = -2.25$. Thus, the equation of the tangent line is

$$y = -x - 2.25.$$

Q: *Why can't we simply use h = 0.000 000 000 000 000 000 01 for an incredibly accurate approximation to the instantaneous rate of change and be done with it?*

A: This approach would certainly work if you were patient enough to do the (thankless) calculation by hand! However, doing it with the help of technology—even an ordinary calculator—will cause problems: The issue is that calculators and spreadsheets represent numbers with a maximum number of significant digits (15 in the case of Excel). As the value of h gets smaller, the value of $f(a + h)$ gets closer and closer to the value of $f(a)$. For example, if $f(x) = 50 + 0.1x^4$, Excel might compute

$$
\begin{aligned}
&f(2 + 0.000\,000\,000\,000\,1) - f(2) \\
&= 51.600\,000\,000\,000\,3 - 51.6 \qquad \text{Rounded to 15 digits} \\
&= 0.000\,000\,000\,000\,3,
\end{aligned}
$$

and the corresponding difference quotient would be 3, not 3.2 as it should be. If h gets even smaller, Excel will not be able to distinguish between $f(a + h)$ and $f(a)$ at all, in which case it will compute 0 for the rate of change. This loss in accuracy when subtracting two very close numbers is called **subtractive error**.

Thus, there is a trade-off in lowering the value of h: Smaller values of h yield *mathematically* more accurate approximations of the derivative, but if h gets too small, subtractive error becomes a problem and decreases the accuracy of computations that use technology.

Leibniz *d* Notation

We introduced the notation $f'(x)$ for the derivative of f at x, but there is another interesting notation. We have written the average rate of change as

$$\text{Average rate of change} = \frac{\Delta f}{\Delta x}. \qquad \frac{\text{Change in } f}{\text{Change in } x}$$

As we use smaller and smaller values for Δx, we approach the instantaneous rate of change, or derivative, for which we also have the notation df/dx, due to Leibniz:

$$\text{Instantaneous rate of change} = \lim_{\Delta x \to 0} \frac{\Delta f}{\Delta x} = \frac{df}{dx}.$$

That is, df/dx is just another notation for $f'(x)$. Do not think of df/dx as an actual quotient of two numbers: Remember that we use an actual quotient $\Delta f/\Delta x$ only to *approximate* the value of df/dx.

In Example 3 we apply the quick approximation method of estimating the derivative.

EXAMPLE 3   Velocity

My friend Eric, an enthusiastic baseball player, claims that he can "probably" throw a ball upward at a speed of 100 feet per second (ft/sec).[*] Our physicist friends tell us that its height s (in feet) t seconds later would be $s = 100t - 16t^2$. Find its average velocity over the interval $[2, 3]$ and its instantaneous velocity exactly 2 seconds after Eric throws it.

Solution The graph of the ball's height as a function of time is shown in Figure 34. Asking for the velocity is really asking for the rate of change of height with respect to time. (Why?) Consider average velocity first. To compute the **average velocity** of the ball from time 2 to time 3, we first compute the change in height:

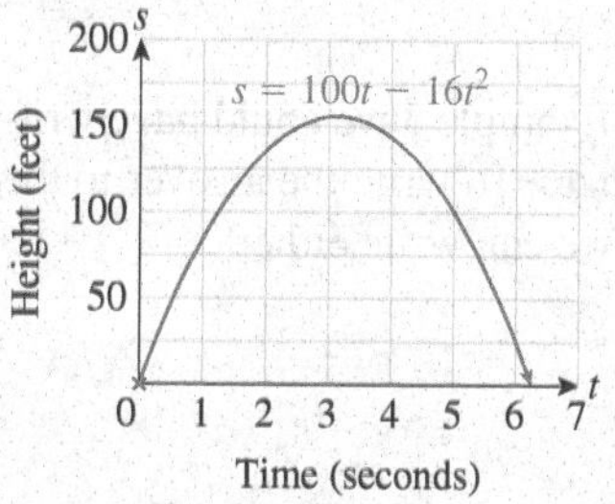

$$\Delta s = s(3) - s(2) = 156 - 136 = 20 \text{ feet}.$$

Since it rises 20 feet in $\Delta t = 1$ second, we use the defining formula *speed = distance/time* to get the average velocity:

$$\text{Average velocity} = \frac{\Delta s}{\Delta t} = \frac{20}{1} = 20 \text{ ft/sec}$$

from time $t = 2$ to $t = 3$. This is just the difference quotient, so we have the following:

The average velocity is the average rate of change of height.

To get the **instantaneous velocity** at $t = 2$, we find the instantaneous rate of change of height. In other words, we need to calculate the derivative ds/dt at $t = 2$.

[*] Eric's claim is difficult to believe; 100 ft/sec corresponds to around 68 mph, and professional pitchers can throw *forward* at about 100 mph.

Figure 34

Which approximation should we use? Because s is a quadratic function of t, we know that the balanced quick approximation will give us the exact derivative, so this is the approximation we choose:

$$\frac{ds}{dt} \approx \frac{s(2 + 0.0001) - s(2 - 0.0001)}{2(0.0001)}$$

$$= \frac{s(2.0001) - s(1.9999)}{0.0002}$$

$$= \frac{100(2.0001) - 16(2.0001)^2 - (100(1.9999) - 16(1.9999)^2)}{0.0002}$$

$$= 36 \text{ ft/sec.}$$

The instantaneous velocity at $t = 2$ is exactly 36 ft/sec.

➡ **Before we go on ...** If we repeat the calculation in Example 3 at time $t = 5$, we get

$$\frac{ds}{dt} = -60 \text{ ft/sec.}$$

The negative sign tells us that the ball is *falling* at a rate of 60 feet per second at time $t = 5$. (How does the fact that it is falling at $t = 5$ show up on the graph?) ∎

Example 3 gives another interpretation of the derivative.

Average and Instantaneous Velocity

For an object moving in a straight line with position $s(t)$ at time t, the **average velocity** from time t to time $t + h$ is the average rate of change of position with respect to time:

$$v_{avg} = \frac{s(t + h) - s(t)}{h} = \frac{\Delta s}{\Delta t}.$$

Average velocity =
Average rate of change of position

The **instantaneous velocity** at time t is

$$v = \lim_{h \to 0} \frac{s(t + h) - s(t)}{h} = \frac{ds}{dt}.$$

Instantaneous velocity =
Instantaneous rate of change of position

In other words, *instantaneous velocity is the derivative of position with respect to time.*

Here is one last comment on Leibniz notation. In Example 3 we could have written the velocity either as s' or as ds/dt, as we chose to do. To write the answer to the question, that the velocity at $t = 2$ sec was 36 ft/sec, we can write either

$$s'(2) = 36$$

or

$$\left.\frac{ds}{dt}\right|_{t=2} = 36.$$

The notation "$|_{t=2}$" is read "evaluated at $t = 2$." Similarly, if $y = f(x)$, we can write the instantaneous rate of change of f at $x = 5$ either in functional notation as

$$f'(5) \qquad \text{The derivative of } f, \text{ evaluated at } x = 5$$

or in Leibniz notation as

$$\left.\frac{dy}{dx}\right|_{x=5}.$$ The derivative of y, evaluated at $x = 5$

The latter notation is obviously more cumbersome than the functional notation $f'(5)$, but the notation dy/dx has compensating advantages. You should practice using both notations.

The Derivative Function

The derivative $f'(x)$ is a number we can calculate, or at least approximate, for various values of x. Because $f'(x)$ depends on the value of x, we may think of f' as a function of x. This function is the **derivative function**.

Derivative Function

If f is a function, its **derivative function** f' is the function whose value $f'(x)$ is the derivative of f at x. Its domain is the set of all x at which f is differentiable. Equivalently, f' associates to each x the slope of the tangent to the graph of the function f at x, or the rate of change of f at x. The formula for the derivative function is

$$f'(x) = \lim_{h \to 0} \frac{f(x + h) - f(x)}{h}.$$ Derivative function

---

Quick Examples

4. Let $f(x) = 3x - 1$. The graph of f is a straight line that has slope 3 everywhere. In other words, $f'(x) = 3$ for every choice of x; that is, f' is a constant function.

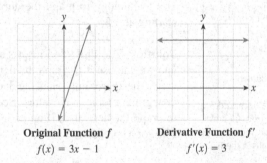

Original Function f
$f(x) = 3x - 1$

Derivative Function f'
$f'(x) = 3$

5. Given the graph of a function f, we can get a rough sketch of the graph of f' by estimating the slope of the tangent to the graph of f at several points, as illustrated below.*

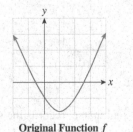

Original Function f
$y = f(x)$

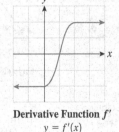

Derivative Function f'
$y = f'(x)$

* This method is discussed in detail on the Website at

Online Text → Sketching the Graph of the Derivative

For x between -2 and 0 the graph of f is linear with slope -2. As x increases from 0 to 2, the slope increases from -2 to 2. For x larger than 2 the graph of f is linear with slope 2. (Notice that, when $x = 1$, the graph of f has a horizontal tangent, so $f'(1) = 0$.)

6. Look again at the graph on the left in Quick Example 5. When $x < 1$, the derivative $f'(x)$ is negative, so the graph has negative slope and f is **decreasing**; its values are going down as x increases. When $x > 1$, the derivative $f'(x)$ is positive, so the graph has positive slope and f is **increasing**; its values are going up as x increases.

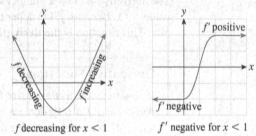

f decreasing for $x < 1$ $\qquad$ f' negative for $x < 1$
f increasing for $x > 1$ $\qquad$ f' positive for $x > 1$

The following example shows how we can use technology to graph the (approximate) derivative of a function, where it exists.

Using Technology

See the Technology Guides at the end of the chapter to find out how to obtain a table of values of and graph the derivative in Example 4 using a TI-83/84 Plus or a spreadsheet. Here is an outline:

TI-83/84 Plus
Y_1=-2X^2+6X+5
Y_2=nDeriv(Y_1,X,X)
[More details in the Technology Guide.]

Spreadsheet
Value of h in E2
Values of x from A2 down increasing by h
-2*A2^2+6*A2+5 from B2 down
=(B3-B2)/$E$2 from C2 down
Insert scatter chart using columns A and C. [More details in the Technology Guide.]

Website
www.WanerMath.com
Web grapher:
Online Utilities→ Function Evaluator and Grapher
Enter
deriv(-2*x^2+6*x+5) for y_1. Alternatively, enter
-2*x^2+6*x+5 for y_1 and deriv(y1) for y_2.
Excel grapher:
Online Utilities→ Excel First and Second Derivative Graphing Utility Function: -2*x^2+6*x+5

EXAMPLE 4 ▮ **Graphing the Derivative with Technology**

Use technology to graph the derivative of $f(x) = -2x^2 + 6x + 5$ for values of x starting at -5.

Solution The TI-83/84 Plus has a built-in function that approximates the derivative, and we can use it to graph the derivative of a function. In a spreadsheet we need to create the approximation using one of the quick approximation formulas, and we can then graph a table of its values. See the technology note in the margin to find out how to graph the derivative (Figure 35) using the Website graphing utility, the TI-83/84 Plus, or a spreadsheet.

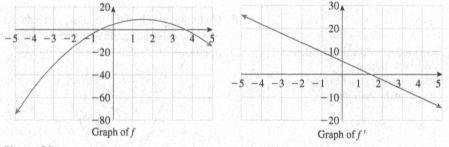

Graph of f $\qquad\qquad\qquad$ Graph of f'

Figure 35

We said that f' records the slope of (the tangent line to) the function f at each point. Notice that the graph of f' confirms that the slope of the graph of f is decreasing as x increases from -5 to 5. Note also that the graph of f reaches a high point at

$x = 1.5$ (the vertex of the parabola). At that point, the slope of the tangent is zero; that is, $f'(1.5) = 0$, as we see in the graph of f'.

EXAMPLE 5 ▮ **An Application: Broadband Penetration**

Wired broadband penetration in the United States can be modeled by

$$P(t) = \frac{29.238}{1 + 8.998(1.638)^{-x}} \quad (0 \le t \le 14),$$

where t is time in years since 2000.[56] Graph both P and its derivative, and determine when broadband penetration was growing most rapidly.

Solution Using one of the methods in Example 4, we obtain the graphs shown in Figure 36.

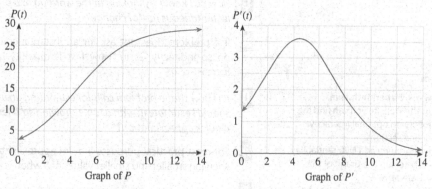

Graph of P Graph of P'

Figure 36

From the graph on the right, we see that P' reaches a peak somewhere between $t = 4$ and $t = 5$ (sometime during 2004). Recalling that P' measures the *slope* of the graph of P, we can conclude that the graph of P is steepest between $t = 4$ and $t = 5$, indicating that, according to the model, broadband penetration was growing most rapidly sometime during 2004. Notice that this is not so easy to see directly on the graph of P.

　　To determine the point of maximum growth more accurately, we can zoom in on the graph of P' using the range $4.0 \le t \le 5.0$ (Figure 37).

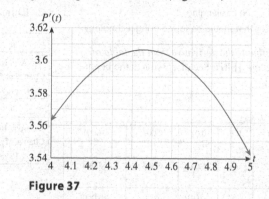

Figure 37

---

[56] Broadband penetration is the number of broadband installations divided by the total population. Source for data: Organisation for Economic Co-operation and Development (OECD) Directorate for Science, Technology, and Industry, table of Historical Penetration Rates, December 2013, downloaded September 2014 from www.oecd.org/sti/ict/broadband. Model is extrapolated to the range shown.

We can now see that P' reaches its highest point around $t = 4.45$, so we conclude that broadband penetration was growing most rapidly in mid-2004.

➡ **Before we go on . . .** Besides helping us to determine the point of maximum growth, the graph of P' in Example 5 gives us a great deal of additional information. As just one example, in Figure 37 we can see that the maximum value of P' is about 3.61, indicating that broadband penetration grew at a fastest rate of about 3.61 percentage points per year. ■

FAQs

Recognizing When and How to Compute the Instantaneous Rate of Change

Q: How do I know, by looking at the wording of a problem, that it is asking for an instantaneous rate of change?

A: If a problem does not ask for an instantaneous rate of change directly, it might do so indirectly, as in "How fast is quantity q increasing?" or "Find the rate of increase of q."

Q: If I know that a problem calls for estimating an instantaneous rate of change, how should I estimate it: with a table showing smaller and smaller values of h or by using a quick approximation?

A: For most practical purposes a quick approximation is accurate enough. Use a table showing smaller and smaller values of h when you would like to check the accuracy.

Q: Which should I use in computing a quick approximation: the balanced difference quotient or the ordinary difference quotient?

A: In general, the balanced difference quotient gives a more accurate answer.

10.5 EXERCISES

▽ more advanced   ◆ challenging
Ⓣ indicates exercises that should be solved using technology

In Exercises 1–4, estimate the derivative from the table of average rates of change. [**HINT**: See discussion at the beginning of the section.]

1. Estimate $f'(5)$.

h	1	0.1	0.01	0.001	0.0001
Avg. Rate of Change of f over $[5, 5 + h]$	12	6.4	6.04	6.004	6.0004
h	−1	−0.1	−0.01	−0.001	−0.0001
Avg. Rate of Change of f over $[5 + h, 5]$	3	5.6	5.96	5.996	5.9996

2. Estimate $g'(7)$.

h	1	0.1	0.01	0.001	0.0001
Avg. Rate of Change of g over $[7, 7 + h]$	4	4.8	4.98	4.998	4.9998
h	−1	−0.1	−0.01	−0.001	−0.0001
Avg. Rate of Change of g over $[7 + h, 7]$	5	5.3	5.03	5.003	5.0003

3. Estimate $r'(-6)$.

h	1	0.1	0.01	0.001	0.0001
Avg. Rate of Change of r over $[-6, -6+h]$	−5.4	−5.498	−5.4998	−5.499982	−5.49999822
h	−1	−0.1	−0.01	−0.001	−0.0001
Avg. Rate of Change of r over $[-6+h, -6]$	−7.52	−6.13	−5.5014	−5.5000144	−5.500001444

4. Estimate $s'(0)$.

h	1	0.1	0.01	0.001	0.0001
Avg. Rate of Change of s over $[0, h]$	−2.52	−1.13	−0.6014	−0.6000144	−0.6000001444
h	−1	−0.1	−0.01	−0.001	−0.0001
Avg. Rate of Change of s over $[h, 0]$	−0.4	−0.598	−0.5998	−0.599982	−0.59999822

Consider the functions in Exercises 5–8 as representing the value of an ounce of palladium in U.S. dollars as a function of the time t in days.[57] *Find the average rates of change of $R(t)$ over the time intervals $[t, t + h]$, where t is as indicated and h = 1, 0.1, and 0.01 days. Hence, estimate the instantaneous rate of change of R at time t, specifying the units of measurement. (Use smaller values of h to check your estimates.)* [HINT: See Example 1.]

5. $R(t) = 60 + 50t - t^2;\ t = 5$

6. $R(t) = 60t - 2t^2;\ t = 3$

7. $R(t) = 270 + 20t^3;\ t = 1$

8. $R(t) = 200 + 50t - t^3;\ t = 2$

In Exercises 9–12 the function gives the cost to manufacture x items. Find the average cost per unit of manufacturing h more items (i.e., the average rate of change of the total cost) at a production level of x, where x is as indicated and h = 10 and 1. Hence, estimate the instantaneous rate of change of the total cost at the given production level x, specifying the units of measurement. (Use smaller values of h to check your estimates.) [HINT: See Example 1.]

9. $C(x) = 10,000 + 5x - \dfrac{x^2}{10,000};\ x = 1,000$

10. $C(x) = 20,000 + 7x - \dfrac{x^2}{20,000};\ x = 10,000$

11. $C(x) = 15,000 + 100x + \dfrac{1,000}{x};\ x = 100$

12. $C(x) = 20,000 + 50x + \dfrac{10,000}{x};\ x = 100$

In Exercises 13–16 the graph of a function is shown together with the tangent line at a point P. Estimate the derivative of f at the corresponding x value. [HINT: See Quick Example 3.]

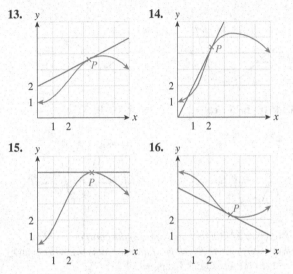

13. **14.**

15. **16.**

In Exercises 17–22, say at which labeled point the slope of the tangent is (a) greatest and (b) least (in the sense that −7 is less than 1). [HINT: See Quick Example 3.]

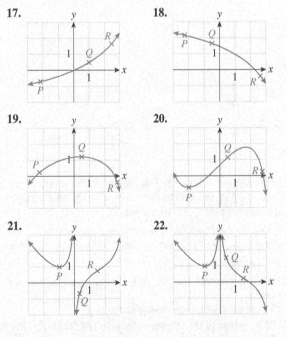

17. **18.**

19. **20.**

21. **22.**

---

[57] Palladium was trading at around $290 in August 2008.

In each of Exercises 23–26, three slopes are given. For each slope, determine at which of the labeled points on the graph the tangent line has that slope.

23. a. 0 **b.** 4 **c.** −1   **24. a.** 0 **b.** 1 **c.** −1

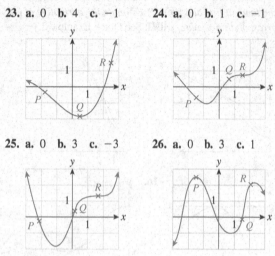

25. a. 0 **b.** 3 **c.** −3   **26. a.** 0 **b.** 3 **c.** 1

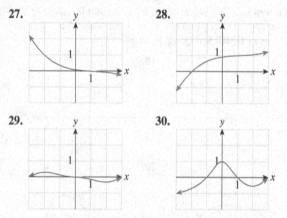

In Exercises 27–30, find the approximate coordinates of all points (if any) where the slope of the tangent is (a) 0, (b) 1, and (c) −1. [HINT: See Quick Example 3.]

27.

28.

29.

30.

31. Complete the following: The tangent to the graph of the function f at the point where $x = a$ is the line passing through the point _____ with slope _____ .

32. Complete the following: The difference quotient for f at the point where $x = a$ gives the slope of the _____ line that passes through _____ .

33. Which is correct? The derivative function assigns to each value x
 (A) the average rate of change of f at x.
 (B) the slope of the tangent to the graph of f at $(x, f(x))$.
 (C) the rate at which f is changing over the interval $[x, x + h]$ for $h = 0.0001$.
 (D) the balanced difference quotient $[f(x + h) − f(x − h)]/(2h)$ for $h \approx 0.0001$.

34. Which is correct? The derivative function $f'(x)$ tells us
 (A) the slope of the tangent line at each of the points $(x, f(x))$.
 (B) the approximate slope of the tangent line at each of the points $(x, f(x))$.
 (C) the slope of the secant line through $(x, f(x))$ and $(x + h, f(x + h))$ for $h = 0.0001$.
 (D) the slope of a certain secant line through each of the points $(x, f(x))$.

35. ▼ Let f have the graph shown.

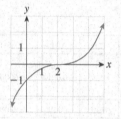

 a. The average rate of change of f over the interval $[2, 4]$ is
  (A) greater than $f'(2)$.   **(B)** less than $f'(2)$.
  (C) approximately equal to $f'(2)$.
 b. The average rate of change of f over the interval $[−1, 1]$ is
  (A) greater than $f'(0)$.   **(B)** less than $f'(0)$.
  (C) approximately equal to $f'(0)$.
 c. Over the interval $[0, 2]$ the instantaneous rate of change of f is
  (A) increasing.   **(B)** decreasing.   **(C)** neither.
 d. Over the interval $[0, 4]$ the instantaneous rate of change of f is
  (A) increasing, then decreasing.
  (B) decreasing, then increasing.
  (C) always increasing.
  (D) always decreasing.
 e. When $x = 4$, $f(x)$ is
  (A) approximately 0 and increasing at a rate of about 0.7 units per unit of x.
  (B) approximately 0 and decreasing at a rate of about 0.7 units per unit of x.
  (C) approximately 0.7 and increasing at a rate of about 1 unit per unit of x.
  (D) approximately 0.7 and increasing at a rate of about 3 units per unit of x.

36. ▼ A function f has the following graph.

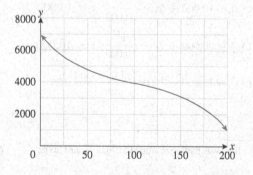

a. The average rate of change of f over $[0, 200]$ is
- **(A)** greater than
- **(B)** less than
- **(C)** approximately equal to

the instantaneous rate of change at $x = 100$.

b. The average rate of change of f over $[0, 200]$ is
- **(A)** greater than
- **(B)** less than
- **(C)** approximately equal to

the instantaneous rate of change at $x = 150$.

c. Over the interval $[0, 50]$ the instantaneous rate of change of f is
- **(A)** increasing, then decreasing.
- **(B)** decreasing, then increasing.
- **(C)** always increasing.
- **(D)** always decreasing.

d. Over the interval $[0, 200]$ the instantaneous rate of change of f is
- **(A)** always positive. **(B)** always negative.
- **(C)** negative, positive, and then negative.

e. $f'(100)$ is
- **(A)** greater than $f'(25)$. **(B)** less than $f'(25)$.
- **(C)** approximately equal to $f'(25)$.

In Exercises 37–40, use a quick approximation to estimate the derivative of the given function at the indicated point. [**HINT:** See Example 2(a).]

37. $f(x) = 1 - 2x; x = 2$ **38.** $f(x) = \dfrac{x}{3} - 1; x = -3$

39. $f(x) = \dfrac{x^2}{4} - \dfrac{x^3}{3}; x = -1$ **40.** $f(x) = \dfrac{x^2}{x} + \dfrac{x}{4}; x = 2$

In Exercises 41–48, estimate the indicated derivative by any method. [**HINT:** See Example 2.]

41. $g(t) = \dfrac{1}{t^5}$; estimate $g'(1)$

42. $s(t) = \dfrac{1}{t^3}$; estimate $s'(-2)$

43. $y = 4x^2$; estimate $\left.\dfrac{dy}{dx}\right|_{x=2}$

44. $y = 1 - x^2$; estimate $\left.\dfrac{dy}{dx}\right|_{x=-1}$

45. $s = 4t + t^2$; estimate $\left.\dfrac{ds}{dt}\right|_{t=-2}$

46. $s = t - t^2$; estimate $\left.\dfrac{ds}{dt}\right|_{t=2}$

47. $R = \dfrac{1}{P}$; estimate $\left.\dfrac{dR}{dp}\right|_{p=20}$

48. $R = \sqrt{p}$; estimate $\left.\dfrac{dR}{dp}\right|_{p=400}$

*In Exercises 49–54, **(a)** use any method to estimate the slope of the tangent to the graph of the given function at the point with the given x-coordinate, and **(b)** find an equation of the tangent line in part (a). In each case, sketch the curve together with the appropriate tangent line.* [**HINT:** See Example 2(b).]

49. $f(x) = x^3; x = -1$ **50.** $f(x) = x^2; x = 0$

51. $f(x) = x + \dfrac{1}{x}; x = 2$ **52.** $f(x) = \dfrac{1}{x^2}; x = 1$

53. $f(x) = \sqrt{x}; x = 4$ **54.** $f(x) = 2x + 4; x = -1$

In Exercises 55–58, estimate the given quantity.

55. $f(x) = e^x$; estimate $f'(0)$

56. $f(x) = 2e^x$; estimate $f'(1)$

57. $f(x) = \ln x$; estimate $f'(1)$

58. $f(x) = \ln x$; estimate $f'(2)$

In Exercises 59–64, match the graph of f to the graph of f'. (The graphs of f' are shown after Exercise 64.)

59. ▼ **60.** ▼

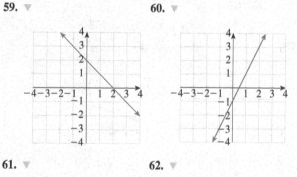

61. ▼ **62.** ▼

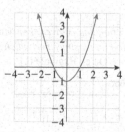
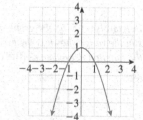

63. ▼ **64.** ▼

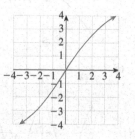
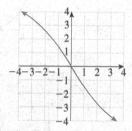

Graphs of derivatives for Exercises 59–64:

(A)   **(B)**

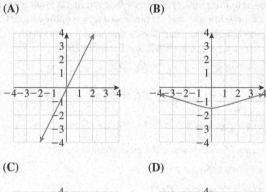

(C)   **(D)**

 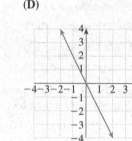

(E)   **(F)**

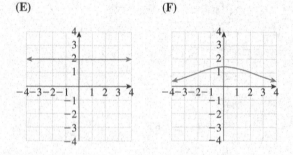

In Exercises 65–68 the graph of a function is given. For which x in the range shown is the function increasing? For which x is the function decreasing? [**HINT:** See Quick Example 6.]

65.   **66.**

67.   **68.**

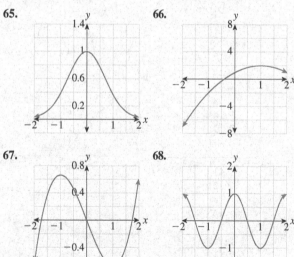

In Exercises 69–72 the graph of the derivative of a function is given. For which x is the (original) function increasing? For which x is the (original) function decreasing? [**HINT:** See Quick Example 6.]

69.   **70.**

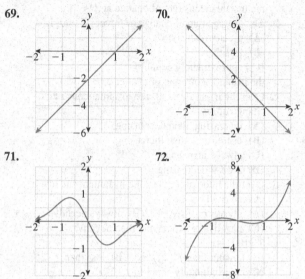

71.   **72.**

⏹ *In Exercises 73 and 74, use technology to graph the derivative of the given function for the given range of values of x. Then use your graph to estimate all values of x (if any) where the tangent line to the graph of the given function is horizontal. Round answers to one decimal place.* [**HINT:** See Example 4.]

73. $f(x) = x^4 + 2x^3 - 1;$ $-2 \le x \le 1$

74. $f(x) = -x^3 - 3x^2 - 1;$ $-3 \le x \le 1$

⏹ *In Exercises 75 and 76, use the method of Example 4 to list approximate values of $f'(x)$ for x in the given range. Graph $f(x)$ together with $f'(x)$ for x in the given range.*

75. $f(x) = \dfrac{x + 2}{x - 3};$ $4 \le x \le 5$

76. $f(x) = \dfrac{10x}{x - 2};$ $2.5 \le x \le 3$

Applications

77. *Temperatures on Mars* The air temperature one chilly spring morning at your time-share condominium at the base of Olympus Mons, *t* hours after 6:00 am, was given by the function $f(t) = -5t^2 + 50t - 80$ degrees Fahrenheit $(0 \le t \le 4)$.[58] What was the temperature at 7:00 am, and how fast was it rising? (Use the method of Example 1(a).)

---

[58] The average temperature on Mars is around $-80°$F but can get considerably warmer near the equator.

Olympus Mons

78. *Temperatures on Venus* The air temperature one balmy summer evening at your summer resort near Maxwell Montes, t hours after 5:00 pm, was given by the function $f(t) = 880 + 2t^2 - 20t$ degrees Fahrenheit ($0 \le t \le 4$).[59] What was the temperature at 8:00 pm, and how fast was it dropping? (Use the method of Example 1(a).)

Maxwell Montes

79. *Demand* Suppose the demand for a new brand of sneakers is given by

$$q = \frac{5,000,000}{p},$$

where p is the price per pair of sneakers in dollars and q is the number of pairs of sneakers that can be sold at price p. Find $q(100)$, and estimate $q'(100)$. Interpret your answers. [**HINT:** See Example 1.]

80. *Demand* Suppose the demand for an old brand of TV is given by

$$q = \frac{100,000}{p + 10},$$

where p is the price per TV set in dollars and q is the number of TV sets that can be sold at price p. Find $q(190)$, and estimate $q'(190)$. Interpret your answers. [**HINT:** See Example 1.]

81. *Oil Imports from Mexico* The following graph shows approximate daily oil imports to the United States from Mexico.[60] Also shown is the tangent line at the point corresponding to year 2011.

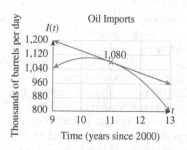

a. Estimate the slope of the tangent line shown on the graph. What does the graph tell you about oil imports from Mexico in 2011? [**HINT:** Identify two points on the tangent line. Then see Quick Example 3.]

b. According to the graph, is the rate of change of oil imports from Mexico increasing, decreasing, or increasing then decreasing? Why?

82. *Oil Production in Mexico* The following graph shows approximate daily oil production by Pemex, Mexico's national oil company.[61] Also shown is the tangent line at the point corresponding to year 2010.

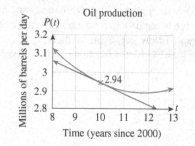

a. Estimate the slope of the tangent line shown on the graph. What does the graph tell you about oil production by Pemex in 2010? [**HINT:** Identify two points on the tangent line. Then see Quick Example 3.]

b. According to the graph, is the rate of change of oil production by Pemex increasing or decreasing over the range $[8, 11]$? Why?

83. ▼ ***Prison Population*** The following curve is a model of the total U.S. prison population as a function of time in years.[62]

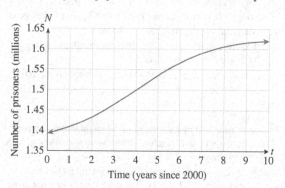

---

[59] The average temperature on Venus is around 860°F.

[60] Model based on data from the Department of Energy. Source for data: U.S. Energy Information Administration, www.eia.gov.

[61] Model based on company data. Source for data: www.pemex.com.

[62] Source: Bureau of Justice Statistics http://bjs.ojp.usdoj.gov.

a. Which is correct? Over the period $[5, 10]$ the instantaneous rate of change of N is

(A) increasing.   (B) decreasing.

b. Which is correct? The instantaneous rate of change of prison population at $t = 4$ was

(A) less than   (B) greater than

(C) approximately equal to

the average rate of change over the interval $[0, 10]$.

c. Which is correct? Over the period $[0, 10]$ the instantaneous rate of change of N is

(A) increasing, then decreasing.

(B) decreasing, then increasing.

(C) always increasing.

(D) always decreasing.

d. According to the model, the U.S. prison population was increasing fastest around what year?

e. Roughly estimate the instantaneous rate of change of N at $t = 4$ by using a balanced difference quotient with $h = 1.5$. Interpret the result.

84. ▼ *Demand for Freon 12* The demand for chlorofluorocarbon-12 (CFC-12)—the ozone-depleting refrigerant commonly known as Freon 12[63]—has been declining significantly in response to regulation and concern about the ozone layer. The graph below represents a model for the projected demand for CFC-12 as a function of time in years.[64]

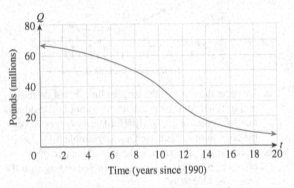

Time (years since 1990)

a. Which is correct? Over the period $[12, 20]$ the instantaneous rate of change of Q is

(A) increasing.   (B) decreasing.

b. Which is correct? The instantaneous rate of change of demand for Freon 12 at $t = 10$ was

(A) less than   (B) greater than

(C) approximately equal to

the average rate of change over the interval $[0, 20]$.

c. Which is correct? Over the period $[0, 20]$ the instantaneous rate of change of Q is

(A) increasing, then decreasing.

(B) decreasing, then increasing.

(C) always increasing.

(D) always decreasing.

d. According to the model, the demand for Freon 12 was decreasing most rapidly around what year?

e. Roughly estimate the instantaneous rate of change of Q at $t = 13$ by using a balanced difference quotient with $h = 5$. Interpret the result.

85. *Velocity* If a stone is dropped from a height of 400 feet, its height after t seconds is given by $s = 400 - 16t^2$.

a. Find its average velocity over the period $[2, 4]$.

b. Estimate its instantaneous velocity at time $t = 4$.

[HINT: See Example 3.]

86. *Velocity* If a stone is thrown down at 120 ft/s from a height of 1,000 feet, its height after t seconds is given by $s = 1,000 - 120t - 16t^2$.

a. Find its average velocity over the period $[1, 3]$.

b. Estimate its instantaneous velocity at time $t = 3$.

[HINT: See Example 3.]

87. *Crude Oil Prices* The price per barrel of crude oil in constant 2008 dollars can be approximated by

$$P(t) = 0.45t^2 - 12t + 105 \text{ dollars} \quad (0 \le t \le 28),$$

where t is time in years since the start of 1980.[65]

a. Compute the average rate of change of $P(t)$ over the interval $[0, 28]$, and interpret your answer.

[HINT: See Example 3 of Section 10.4.]

b. Estimate the instantaneous rate of change of $P(t)$ at $t = 0$ and interpret your answer. [HINT: See Example 2(a).]

c. The answers to part (a) and part (b) have opposite signs. What does this indicate about the price of oil?

88. *Median Home Prices* The median home price in the United States over the period January 2010–January 2015 can be approximated by

$$P(t) = 4.5t^2 - 15t + 180 \text{ thousand dollars} \quad (0 \le t \le 5),$$

where t is time in years since the start of 2010.[66]

a. Compute the average rate of change of $P(t)$ over the interval $[1, 5]$, and interpret your answer.

[HINT: See Example 3 of Section 10.4.]

b. Estimate the instantaneous rate of change of $P(t)$ at $t = 1$, and interpret your answer.

[HINT: See Example 2(a).]

c. The answers to parts (a) and (b) have opposite sign. What does this indicate about the median home price?

---

[63] The name given to it by DuPont. Freon 12 (dichlorodifluoromethane) is distinct from Freon 22 (chlorodifluoromethane, also registered by DuPont; see Exercise 73 in Section 2.2).

[64] Source for data: The Automobile Consulting Group (*New York Times*, December 26, 1993, p. F23). The exact figures were not given, and the chart is a reasonable facsimile of the chart that appeared in the *New York Times*.

[65] Source for data: www.inflationdata.com.

[66] Source for data: www.zillow.com.

89. The 2003 SARS Outbreak In the early stages of the SARS (severe acute respiratory syndrome) epidemic in 2003, the number of reported cases could be approximated by

$$A(t) = 167(1.18)^t \quad (0 \le t \le 20)$$

t days after March 17, 2003 (the first day in which statistics were reported by the World Health Organization).
a. What, approximately, was the instantaneous rate of change of $A(t)$ on March 27 ($t = 10$)? Interpret the result.
b. Which of the following is true? For the first 20 days of the epidemic, the instantaneous rate of change of the number of cases
(A) increased. (B) decreased.
(C) increased and then decreased.
(D) decreased and then increased.

90. The 2003 SARS Outbreak A few weeks into the SARS (severe acute respiratory syndrome) epidemic in 2003, the number of reported cases could be approximated by

$$A(t) = 1,804(1.04)^t \quad (0 \le t \le 30)$$

t days after April 1, 2003.
a. What, approximately, was the instantaneous rate of change of $A(t)$ on April 21 ($t = 20$)? Interpret the result.
b. Which of the following is true? During April the instantaneous rate of change of the number of cases
(A) increased. (B) decreased.
(C) increased and then decreased.
(D) decreased and then increased.

91. The 2014 Ebola Outbreak In the first 6 months of the 2014 Ebola outbreak, the total number of reported cases could be approximated by

$$C(t) = 95.9e^{0.72t} \quad (0 \le t \le 6),$$

where t is time in months since April 1, 2014.[67] Estimate $C(5)$ and $\left.\dfrac{dC}{dt}\right|_{t=5}$, and interpret your answers.

92. The 2014 Ebola Outbreak In the first 6 months of the 2014 Ebola outbreak, the total number of reported deaths from Ebola could be approximated by

$$D(t) = 90.52e^{0.60t} \quad (0 \le t \le 6),$$

where t is time in months since April 1, 2014.[68] Estimate $D(5)$ and $\left.\dfrac{dD}{dt}\right|_{t=5}$, and interpret your answers

93. Early Internet Services On January 1, 1996, America Online was the biggest online service provider, with 4.5 million subscribers, and was adding new subscribers at a rate of 60,000 per week.[69] If $A(t)$ is the number of America Online subscribers t weeks after January 1, 1996, what do the given data tell you about values of the function A and its derivative? [HINT: See Quick Example 2.]

94. Early Internet Services On January 1, 1996, Prodigy was the third-biggest online service provider, with 1.6 million subscribers, but was losing subscribers.[70] If $P(t)$ is the number of Prodigy subscribers t weeks after January 1, 1996, what do the given data tell you about values of the function P and its derivative? [HINT: See Quick Example 2.]

95. ▼ Learning to Speak Let $p(t)$ represent the percentage of children who are able to speak at the age of t months.
a. It is found that $p(10) = 60$ and $\left.\dfrac{dp}{dt}\right|_{t=10} = 18.2$. What does this mean?[71] [HINT: See Quick Example 2.]
b. As t increases, what happens to p and $\dfrac{dp}{dt}$?

96. ▼ Learning to Read Let $p(t)$ represent the percentage of children in your class who learned to read at the age of t years.
a. Assuming that everyone in your class could read by the age of 7, what does this tell you about $p(7)$ and $\left.\dfrac{dp}{dt}\right|_{t=7}$? [HINT: See Quick Example 2.]
b. Assuming that 25.0% of the people in your class could read by the age of 5 and that 25.3% of them could read by the age of 5 years and 1 month, estimate $\left.\dfrac{dp}{dt}\right|_{t=5}$. Remember to give its units.

97. Subprime Mortgages during the Housing Crisis (Compare Exercise 29 in Section 10.4.) The percentage of mortgages issued in the United States during the period 2000–2009 that were subprime (normally classified as risky) can be approximated by

$$A(t) = \frac{15}{1 + 8.6(1.8)^{-t}} \quad (0 \le t \le 9),$$

where t is the number of years since the start of 2000.[72]
a. Estimate $A(6)$ and $A'(6)$. (Round answers to two significant digits.) What do the answers tell you about subprime mortgages?
b. ⬛ Graph the extrapolated function and its derivative for $0 \le t \le 16$, and use your graphs to describe how the derivative behaves as t becomes large. (Express this behavior in terms of limits if you have studied the sections on limits.) What does this tell you about subprime mortgages? [HINT: See Example 5.]

---

[67] Exponential model is the authors'. Source for data: Wikipedia/Centers for Disease Control and Prevention/WHO.
[68] Ibid.
[69] Source: Information and Interactive Services Report/*New York Times*, January 2, 1996, p. C14.
[70] Ibid.
[71] Based on data presented in the article *The Emergence of Intelligence* by William H. Calvin, *Scientific American*, October 1994, pp. 101–107.
[72] Sources: Mortgage Bankers Association, UBS.

98. *Subprime Mortgage Debt during the Housing Crisis* (Compare Exercise 30 in Section 10.4.) The value of subprime (normally classified as risky) mortgage debt outstanding in the United States during the period 2000–2009 can be approximated by

$$A(t) = \frac{1{,}350}{1 + 4.2(1.7)^{-t}} \text{ billion dollars} \quad (0 \le t \le 9),$$

where t is the number of years since the start of 2000.[73]

a. Estimate $A(7)$ and $A'(7)$. (Round answers to three significant digits.) What do the answers tell you about subprime mortgages?

b. ⊞ Graph the function and its derivative, and use your graphs to estimate when, to the nearest year, $A'(t)$ is greatest. What does this tell you about subprime mortgages? [HINT: See Example 5.]

99. ⊞ ▼ *Embryo Development* The oxygen consumption of a turkey embryo increases from the time the egg is laid through the time the turkey chick hatches. In a brush turkey, the oxygen consumption (in milliliters per hour) can be approximated by

$$c(t) = -0.0012t^3 + 0.12t^2 - 1.83t + 3.97 \quad (20 \le t \le 50),$$

where t is the time (in days) since the egg was laid.[74] (An egg will typically hatch at around $t = 50$.) Use technology to graph $c'(t)$, and use your graph to answer the following questions. [HINT: See Example 5.]

a. Over the interval $[20, 32]$ the derivative c' is
(A) increasing, then decreasing.
(B) decreasing, then increasing.
(C) decreasing.   **(D)** increasing.

b. When, to the nearest day, is the oxygen consumption increasing at the fastest rate?

c. When, to the nearest day, is the oxygen consumption increasing at the slowest rate?

100. ⊞ ▼ *Embryo Development* The oxygen consumption of a galliform bird embryo increases from the time the egg is laid through the time the chick hatches. In a typical galliform bird the oxygen consumption (in milliliters per hour) can be approximated by

$$c(t) = -0.0027t^3 + 0.14t^2 - 0.89t + 0.15 \quad (8 \le t \le 30),$$

where t is the time (in days) since the egg was laid.[75] (An egg will typically hatch at around $t = 28$.) Use technology to graph $c'(t)$, and use your graph to answer the following questions. [HINT: See Example 5.]

a. Over the interval $[8, 30]$ the derivative c' is
(A) increasing, then decreasing.
(B) decreasing, then increasing.
(C) decreasing.   **(D)** increasing.

b. When, to the nearest day, is the oxygen consumption increasing the fastest?

c. When, to the nearest day, is the oxygen consumption increasing at the slowest rate?

The next two exercises are applications of Einstein's Special Theory of Relativity and relate to objects that are moving extremely fast. In science fiction terminology a speed of warp 1 is the speed of light—about 3×10^8 meters per second. (For instance, a speed of warp 0.8 corresponds to 80% of the speed of light—about 2.4×10^8 meters per second.)

101. ◆ *Lorentz Contraction* According to Einstein's Special Theory of Relativity, a moving object appears to get shorter to a stationary observer as its speed approaches the speed of light. If a spaceship that has a length of 100 meters at rest travels at a speed of warp p, its length in meters, as measured by a stationary observer, is given by

$$L(p) = 100\sqrt{1 - p^2}$$

with domain $[0, 1)$. Estimate $L(0.95)$ and $L'(0.95)$. What do these figures tell you?

102. ◆ *Time Dilation* Another prediction of Einstein's Special Theory of Relativity is that, to a stationary observer, clocks (as well as all biological processes) in a moving object appear to go more and more slowly as the speed of the object approaches that of light. If a spaceship travels at a speed of warp p, the time it takes for an onboard clock to register 1 second, as measured by a stationary observer, will be given by

$$T(p) = \frac{1}{\sqrt{1 - p^2}} \text{ seconds}$$

with domain $[0, 1)$. Estimate $T(0.95)$ and $T'(0.95)$. What do these figures tell you?

Communication and Reasoning Exercises

103. In which, if any, of the following cases is f differentiable at a? (There may be none or more than one.)

(A) $a = 2$; domain of f: all real numbers;
$$\lim_{h \to 0^+} \frac{f(2 + h) - f(2)}{h} = 3,$$
$$\lim_{h \to 0^-} \frac{f(2 + h) - f(2)}{h} = 5$$

(B) $a = 0$; domain of f: $(0, 2)$;
$$\lim_{h \to 0} \frac{f(1 + h) - f(1)}{h} = 3$$

(C) $a = 3$; domain of f: $[0, 3]$;
$$\lim_{h \to 0} \frac{f(3 + h) - f(3)}{h} = 5$$

(D) $a = 0$; domain of f: all real numbers;
$$\lim_{h \to 0} \frac{f(h) - f(0)}{h} = +\infty$$

---

[73] Source: Data 360 www.data360.org.

[74] The model approximates graphical data published in the article *The Brush Turkey* by Roger S. Seymour, *Scientific American*, December 1991, pp. 108–114.

[75] *Ibid.*

104. In which, if any, of the following cases is f differentiable at a? (There may be none or more than one.)

(A) $a = 4$; domain of f: all real numbers except 5;

$$\lim_{h \to 0^+} \frac{f(4 + h) - f(4)}{h} = 5,$$

$$\lim_{h \to 0^-} \frac{f(4 + h) - f(4)}{h} = 5$$

(B) $a = 0$; domain of f: $[0, 2)$;

$$\lim_{h \to 0} \frac{f(h) - f(0)}{h} = 3$$

(C) $a = 4$; domain of f: all real numbers except 4;

$$\lim_{h \to 0} \frac{f(4 + h) - f(4)}{h} = 5$$

(D) $a = 0$; domain of f: $(-0.0001, 0.0001)$;

$$\lim_{h \to 0} \frac{f(h) - f(0)}{h} = 30$$

105. Explain why we cannot put $h = 0$ in the approximation

$$f'(x) \approx \frac{f(x + h) - f(x)}{h}$$

for the derivative of f.

106. The balanced difference quotient

$$f'(a) \approx \frac{f(a + 0.0001) - f(a - 0.0001)}{0.0002}$$

is the average rate of change of f on what interval?

107. Let $H(t)$ represent the number of *Handbook* members in millions t years after its inception in 2020. It is found that $H(10) = 50$ and $H'(10) = -6$. This means that, in 2030 (multiple choice),

(A) there were 6 million members and this number was decreasing at a rate of 50 million per year.

(B) there were -6 million members and this number was increasing at a rate of 50 million per year.

(C) membership had dropped by 6 million since the previous year but was now increasing at a rate of 50 million per year.

(D) there were 50 million members and this number was decreasing at a rate of 6 million per year.

(E) there were 50 million members and membership had dropped by 6 million since the previous year.

108. Let $F(t)$ represent the net earnings of *Footbook, Inc.* in millions of dollars t years after its inception in 3020. It is found that $F(100) = -10$ and $F'(100) = 60$. This means that, in 3120 (multiple choice),

(A) Footbook lost $10 million, but its net earnings were increasing at a rate of $60 million per year.

(B) Footbook earned $60 million, but its earnings were decreasing at a rate of $10 million per year.

(C) Footbook's net earnings had increased by $60 million since the year before, but it still lost $10 million.

(D) Footbook earned $10 million, but its net earnings were decreasing at a rate of $60 million per year.

(E) Footbook's net earnings had decreased by $10 million since the year before, but it still earned $60 million.

109. It is now 8 months since the Garden City lacrosse team won the national championship, and sales of team paraphernalia, while still increasing, have been leveling off. What does this tell you about the derivative of the sales curve?

110. Having been soundly defeated in the national lacrosse championships, Brakpan High has been faced with decreasing sales of its team paraphernalia. However, while still decreasing, sales appear to be bottoming out. What does this tell you about the derivative of the sales curve?

111. ▼ Company A's profits are given by $P(0) = \$1$ million and $P'(0) = -\$1$ million/month. Company B's profits are given by $P(0) = -\$1$ million and $P'(0) = \$1$ million per month. In which company would you rather invest? Why?

112. ▼ Company C's profits are given by $P(0) = \$1$ million and $P'(0) = \$0.5$ million/month. Company D's profits are given by $P(0) = \$0.5$ million and $P'(0) = \$1$ million per month. In which company would you rather invest? Why?

113. ▼ During the 1-month period starting last January 1, your company's profits increased at an average rate of change of $4 million per month. On January 1, profits were increasing at an instantaneous rate of $5 million per month. Which of the following graphs could represent your company's profits? Why?

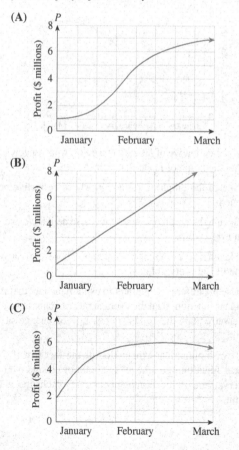

114. ▼ During the 1-month period starting last January 1, your company's sales increased at an average rate of change of $3,000 per month. On January 1, sales were changing at an instantaneous rate of −$1,000 per month. Which of the following graphs could represent your company's sales? Why?

(A)

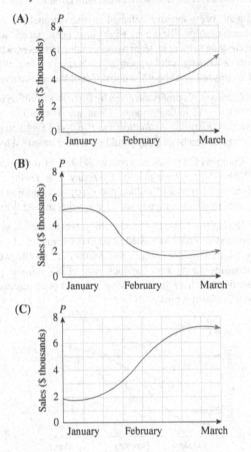

(B)

(C)

115. ▼ If the derivative of f is zero at a point, what do you know about the graph of f near that point?

116. ▼ Sketch the graph of a function whose derivative never exceeds 1.

117. ▼ Sketch the graph of a function whose derivative exceeds 1 at every point.

118. ▼ Sketch the graph of a function whose derivative is exactly 1 at every point.

119. ▼ Use the difference quotient to explain the fact that if f is a linear function, then the average rate of change over any interval equals the instantaneous rate of change at any point.

120. ▼ Give a numerical explanation of the fact that if f is a linear function, then the average rate of change over any interval equals the instantaneous rate of change at any point.

121. ◆ Consider the following values of the function f from Exercise 1:

h	0.1	0.01	0.001	0.0001
Avg. Rate of Change of f over $[5, 5+h]$	6.4	6.04	6.004	6.0004
h	−0.1	−0.01	−0.001	−0.0001
Avg. Rate of Change of f over $[5+h, 5]$	5.6	5.96	5.996	5.9996

Does the table suggest that the instantaneous rate of change of f is
(A) increasing   (B) decreasing
as x increases toward 5?

122. ◆ Consider the following values of the function g from Exercise 2:

h	0.1	0.01	0.001	0.0001
Avg. Rate of Change of g over $[7, 7+h]$	4.8	4.98	4.998	4.9998
h	−0.1	−0.01	−0.001	−0.0001
Avg. Rate of Change of g over $[7+h, 7]$	5.3	5.03	5.003	5.0003

Does the table suggest that the instantaneous rate of change of g is
(A) increasing   (B) decreasing
as x increases toward 7?

123. ▼ Sketch the graph of a function whose derivative is never zero but decreases as x increases.

124. ▼ Sketch the graph of a function whose derivative is never negative but is zero at exactly two points.

125. ◆ Here is the graph of the derivative f' of a function f. Give a rough sketch of the graph of f, given that $f(0) = 0$.

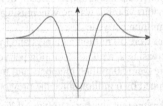

126. ◆ Here is the graph of the derivative f' of a function f. Give a rough sketch of the graph of f, given that $f(0) = 0$.

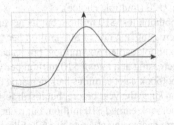

127. ◆ Professor Talker of the physics department drove a 60-mile stretch of road in exactly 1 hour. The speed limit along that stretch was 55 mph. Which of the following must be correct?
     (A) He exceeded the speed limit at no point of the journey.
     (B) He exceeded the speed limit at some point of the journey.
     (C) He exceeded the speed limit throughout the journey.
     (D) He traveled slower than the speed limit at some point of the journey.

128. ◆ Professor Silent, another physics professor, drove a 50-mile stretch of road in exactly 1 hour. The speed limit along that stretch was 55 mph. Which of the following must be correct?

(A) She exceeded the speed limit at no point of the journey.
(B) She exceeded the speed limit at some point of the journey.
(C) She traveled slower than the speed limit throughout the journey.
(D) She traveled slower than the speed limit at some point of the journey.

129. ◆ Draw the graph of a function f with the property that the balanced difference quotient gives a more accurate approximation of $f'(1)$ than the ordinary difference quotient.

130. ◆ Draw the graph of a function f with the property that the balanced difference quotient gives a less accurate approximation of $f'(1)$ than the ordinary difference quotient.

10.6   The Derivative: Algebraic Viewpoint

Calculating the Derivative Algebraically

In Section 10.5 we saw how to estimate the derivative of a function using numerical and graphical approaches. In this section we use an algebraic approach that will give us the *exact value* of the derivative rather than just an approximation, when the function is specified algebraically.

This algebraic approach is quite straightforward: Instead of subtracting numbers to estimate the average rate of change over smaller and smaller intervals, we subtract algebraic expressions. Our starting point is the definition of the derivative in terms of the difference quotient:

$$f'(a) = \lim_{h \to 0} \frac{f(a + h) - f(a)}{h}.$$

EXAMPLE 1   **Calculating the Derivative at a Point Algebraically**

Let $f(x) = x^2$. Use the definition of the derivative to compute $f'(3)$ algebraically.

Solution   Substituting $a = 3$ into the definition of the derivative, we get

$$f'(3) = \lim_{h \to 0} \frac{f(3 + h) - f(3)}{h} \qquad \text{Formula for the derivative}$$

$$= \lim_{h \to 0} \frac{\overbrace{(3 + h)^2}^{f(3+h)} - \overbrace{3^2}^{f(3)}}{h} \qquad \text{Substitute for } f(3) \text{ and } f(3 + h).$$

$$= \lim_{h \to 0} \frac{(9 + 6h + h^2) - 9}{h} \qquad \text{Expand } (3 + h)^2.$$

$$= \lim_{h \to 0} \frac{6h + h^2}{h} \qquad \text{Cancel the 9.}$$

$$= \lim_{h \to 0} \frac{h(6 + h)}{h} \qquad \text{Factor out } h.$$

$$= \lim_{h \to 0} (6 + h). \qquad \text{Cancel the } h.$$

Now we let h approach 0. As h gets closer and closer to 0, the sum $6 + h$ clearly gets closer and closer to $6 + 0 = 6$. Thus,

$$f'(3) = \lim_{h \to 0}(6 + h) = 6. \qquad \text{As } h \to 0, (6 + h) \to 6.$$

(Calculations of limits like this are discussed and justified more fully in Sections 10.2 and 10.3.)

➡ **Before we go on . . .** We did the following calculation in Example 1: If $f(x) = x^2$, then $f'(3) = 6$. In other words, the tangent to the graph of $y = x^2$ at the point $(3, 9)$ has slope 6 (Figure 38). ∎

There is nothing very special about $a = 3$ in Example 1. Let's try to compute $f'(x)$ for general x.

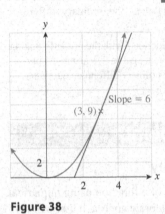

Figure 38

| EXAMPLE 2 | **Calculating the Derivative Function Algebraically** |

Let $f(x) = x^2$.

a. Use the definition of the derivative to compute $f'(x)$ algebraically.

b. Use the answer to evaluate $f'(3)$.

Solution

a. Once again, our starting point is the definition of the derivative in terms of the difference quotient:

$$f'(x) = \lim_{h \to 0}\frac{f(x + h) - f(x)}{h} \qquad \text{Formula for the derivative}$$

$$= \lim_{h \to 0}\frac{\overbrace{(x + h)^2}^{f(x+h)} - \overbrace{x^2}^{f(x)}}{h} \qquad \text{Substitute for } f(x) \text{ and } f(x + h).$$

$$= \lim_{h \to 0}\frac{(x^2 + 2xh + h^2) - x^2}{h} \qquad \text{Expand } (x + h)^2.$$

$$= \lim_{h \to 0}\frac{2xh + h^2}{h} \qquad \text{Cancel the } x^2.$$

$$= \lim_{h \to 0}\frac{h(2x + h)}{h} \qquad \text{Factor out } h.$$

$$= \lim_{h \to 0}(2x + h). \qquad \text{Cancel the } h.$$

Now we let h approach 0. As h gets closer and closer to 0, the sum $2x + h$ clearly gets closer and closer to $2x + 0 = 2x$. Thus,

$$f'(x) = \lim_{h \to 0}(2x + h) = 2x.$$

This is the derivative function.

b. Now that we have a *formula* for the derivative of f, we can obtain $f'(a)$ for any value of a we choose by simply evaluating f' there. For instance,

$$f'(3) = 2(3) = 6$$

as we saw in Example 1.

➡ **Before we go on . . .** The graphs of $f(x) = x^2$ and $f'(x) = 2x$ from Example 2 are familiar. Their graphs are shown in Figure 39.

When $x < 0$, the parabola slopes downward, which is reflected in the fact that the derivative $2x$ is negative there. When $x > 0$, the parabola slopes upward, which is reflected in the fact that the derivative is positive there. The parabola has a horizontal tangent line at $x = 0$, reflected in the fact that $2x = 0$ there. ■

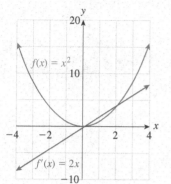

Figure 39

EXAMPLE 3 **More Computations of Derivative Functions**

Compute the derivative $f'(x)$ for each of the following functions:

a. $f(x) = x^3$ **b.** $f(x) = 2x^2 - x$ **c.** $f(x) = \dfrac{1}{x}$

Solution

a. $f'(x) = \lim\limits_{h \to 0} \dfrac{f(x + h) - f(x)}{h}$ — Formula for the derivative

$$= \lim\limits_{h \to 0} \frac{\overbrace{(x + h)^3}^{f(x+h)} - \overbrace{x^3}^{f(x)}}{h}$$ — Substitute for $f(x)$ and $f(x + h)$.

$$= \lim\limits_{h \to 0} \frac{(x^3 + 3x^2h + 3xh^2 + h^3) - x^3}{h}$$ — Expand $(x + h)^3$.

$$= \lim\limits_{h \to 0} \frac{3x^2h + 3xh^2 + h^3}{h}$$ — Cancel the x^3.

$$= \lim\limits_{h \to 0} \frac{h(3x^2 + 3xh + h^2)}{h}$$ — Factor out h.

$$= \lim\limits_{h \to 0} (3x^2 + 3xh + h^2)$$ — Cancel the h.

$$= 3x^2.$$ — Let h approach 0.

b. $f'(x) = \lim\limits_{h \to 0} \dfrac{f(x + h) - f(x)}{h}$ — Formula for the derivative

$$= \lim\limits_{h \to 0} \frac{\overbrace{(2(x + h)^2 - (x + h))}^{f(x+h)} - \overbrace{(2x^2 - x)}^{f(x)}}{h}$$ — Substitute for $f(x)$ and $f(x + h)$.

$$= \lim\limits_{h \to 0} \frac{(2x^2 + 4xh + 2h^2 - x - h) - (2x^2 - x)}{h}$$ — Expand.

$$= \lim\limits_{h \to 0} \frac{4xh + 2h^2 - h}{h}$$ — Cancel the $2x^2$ and x.

$$= \lim\limits_{h \to 0} \frac{h(4x + 2h - 1)}{h}$$ — Factor out h.

$$= \lim\limits_{h \to 0} (4x + 2h - 1)$$ — Cancel the h.

$$= 4x - 1.$$ — Let h approach 0.

c. $f'(x) = \lim\limits_{h \to 0} \dfrac{f(x+h) - f(x)}{h}$ Formula for the derivative

$= \lim\limits_{h \to 0} \dfrac{\left[\overbrace{\dfrac{1}{x+h}}^{f(x+h)} - \overbrace{\dfrac{1}{x}}^{f(x)} \right]}{h}$ Substitute for $f(x)$ and $f(x+h)$.

$= \lim\limits_{h \to 0} \dfrac{\left[\dfrac{x - (x+h)}{(x+h)x} \right]}{h}$ Subtract the fractions.

$= \lim\limits_{h \to 0} \dfrac{1}{h} \left[\dfrac{x - (x+h)}{(x+h)x} \right]$ Division by h = Multiplication by $1/h$.

$= \lim\limits_{h \to 0} \left[\dfrac{-h}{h(x+h)x} \right]$ Simplify.

$= \lim\limits_{h \to 0} \left[\dfrac{-1}{(x+h)x} \right]$ Cancel the h.

$= \dfrac{-1}{x^2}$.   Let h approach 0.

In Example 4 we redo Example 3 of Section 10.5, this time getting an exact, rather than approximate, answer.

EXAMPLE 4   **Velocity**

My friend Eric, an enthusiastic baseball player, claims that he can "probably" throw a ball upward at a speed of 100 feet per second (ft/sec). Our physicist friends tell us that its height s (in feet) t seconds later would be $s(t) = 100t - 16t^2$. Find the ball's instantaneous velocity function and its velocity exactly 2 seconds after Eric throws it.

Solution The instantaneous velocity function is the derivative ds/dt, which we calculate as follows:

$$\frac{ds}{dt} = \lim_{h \to 0} \frac{s(t+h) - s(t)}{h}.$$

Let us compute $s(t+h)$ and $s(t)$ separately:

$$s(t) = 100t - 16t^2$$
$$s(t+h) = 100(t+h) - 16(t+h)^2$$
$$= 100t + 100h - 16(t^2 + 2th + h^2)$$
$$= 100t + 100h - 16t^2 - 32th - 16h^2.$$

Therefore,

$$\frac{ds}{dt} = \lim_{h \to 0} \frac{s(t + h) - s(t)}{h}$$

$$= \lim_{h \to 0} \frac{100t + 100h - 16t^2 - 32th - 16h^2 - (100t - 16t^2)}{h}$$

$$= \lim_{h \to 0} \frac{100h - 32th - 16h^2}{h}$$

$$= \lim_{h \to 0} \frac{h(100 - 32t - 16h)}{h}$$

$$= \lim_{h \to 0} (100 - 32t - 16h)$$

$$= 100 - 32t \text{ ft/sec.}$$

Thus, the velocity exactly 2 seconds after Eric throws it is

$$\left. \frac{ds}{dt} \right|_{t=2} = 100 - 32(2) = 36 \text{ ft/sec.}$$

This verifies the accuracy of the approximation we made in Section 10.5.

➡ **Before we go on...** From the derivative function in Example 4 we can now describe the behavior of the velocity of the ball: Immediately on release ($t = 0$) the ball is traveling at 100 feet per second upward. The ball then slows down; precisely, it loses 32 feet per second of speed every second. When, exactly, does the velocity become zero, and what happens after that? ■

Q: *Do we always have to calculate the limit of the difference quotient to find a formula for the derivative function?*

A: As it turns out, no. In Section 11.1 we will start to look at shortcuts for finding derivatives that allow us to bypass the definition of the derivative in many cases.

A Function Not Differentiable at a Point

Recall from Section 10.5 that a function is **differentiable** at a point a if $f'(a)$ exists; that is, if the difference quotient $[f(a + h) - f(a)]/h$ approaches a fixed value as h approaches 0. In Section 10.5 we mentioned that the function $f(x) = |x|$ is not differentiable at $x = 0$. In Example 5 we find out why.

EXAMPLE 5 **A Function Not Differentiable at 0**

Numerically, graphically, and algebraically investigate the differentiability of the function $f(x) = |x|$ at the points **(a)** $x = 1$ and **(b)** $x = 0$.

Solution

a. We compute

$$f'(1) = \lim_{h \to 0} \frac{f(1 + h) - f(1)}{h}$$

$$= \lim_{h \to 0} \frac{|1 + h| - 1}{h}.$$

Numerically, we can make tables of the values of the average rate of change $(|1 + h| - 1)/h$ for h positive or negative and approaching 0:

h	1	0.1	0.01	0.001	0.0001
Avg. Rate of Change over $[1, 1 + h]$	1	1	1	1	1

h	-1	-0.1	-0.01	-0.001	-0.0001
Avg. Rate of Change over $[1 + h, 1]$	1	1	1	1	1

From these tables it appears that $f'(1)$ is equal to 1. We can verify that algebraically: For h that is sufficiently small, $1 + h$ is positive (even if h is negative), and so

$$f'(1) = \lim_{h \to 0} \frac{1 + h - 1}{h}$$

$$= \lim_{h \to 0} \frac{h}{h} \qquad \text{Cancel the 1s.}$$

$$= \lim_{h \to 0} 1 \qquad \text{Cancel the } h.$$

$$= 1.$$

Graphically, we are seeing the fact that the tangent line at the point $(1, 1)$ has slope 1 because the graph is a straight line with slope 1 near that point (Figure 40).

b. $f'(0) = \lim_{h \to 0} \frac{f(0 + h) - f(0)}{h}$

$$= \lim_{h \to 0} \frac{|0 + h| - 0}{h}$$

$$= \lim_{h \to 0} \frac{|h|}{h}$$

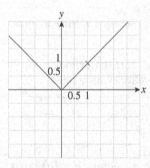

Figure 40

If we make tables of values in this case we get the following:

h	1	0.1	0.01	0.001	0.0001
Avg. Rate of Change over $[0, 0 + h]$	1	1	1	1	1

h	-1	-0.1	-0.01	-0.001	-0.0001
Avg. Rate of Change over $[0 + h, 0]$	-1	-1	-1	-1	-1

For the limit and hence the derivative $f'(0)$ to exist, the average rates of change should approach the same number for both positive and negative h. Because they do not, f is not differentiable at $x = 0$. We can verify this conclusion algebraically: If h is positive, then $|h| = h$, and so the ratio $|h|/h$ is 1, regardless of how small h is. Thus, according to the values of the difference quotients with $h > 0$, the limit should be 1. On the other hand, if h is negative, then $|h| = -h$ (positive), and so $|h|/h = -1$, meaning that the limit should be -1. Because the limit cannot be both -1 and 1 (it must be a single number for the derivative to exist), we conclude that $f'(0)$ does not exist.

To see what is happening graphically, take a look at Figure 41, which shows zoomed-in views of the graph of f near $x = 0$.

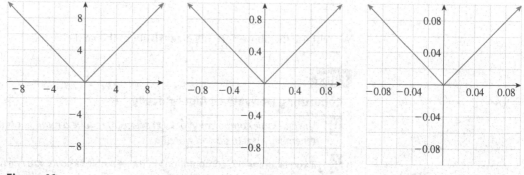

Figure 41

No matter what scale we use to view the graph, it has a sharp corner at $x = 0$ and hence has no tangent line there. Since there is no tangent line at $x = 0$, the function is not differentiable there.

➡ **Before we go on...** Notice that $|x| = \begin{cases} -x & \text{if } x < 0 \\ x & \text{if } x \geq 0 \end{cases}$ is an example of a piecewise-linear function whose graph comes to a point at $x = 0$. In general, if $f(x)$ is any piecewise-linear function whose graph comes to a point at $x = a$, it will be non-differentiable at $x = a$ for the same reason that $|x|$ fails to be differentiable at $x = 0$.

If we repeat the computation in Example 5(a) using any nonzero value for a in place of 1, we see that f is differentiable there as well. If a is positive, we find that $f'(a) = 1$, and if a is negative, $f'(a) = -1$. In other words, the derivative function is

$$f'(x) = \begin{cases} -1 & \text{if } x < 0 \\ 1 & \text{if } x > 0. \end{cases}$$

Immediately to the left of $x = 0$, we see that $f'(x) = -1$; immediately to the right, $f'(x) = 1$; and when $x = 0$, $f'(x)$ is not defined. ∎

Q: *So does that mean there is no single formula for the derivative of $|x|$?*

A: Actually, there is a convenient formula. Consider the ratio $\dfrac{|x|}{x}$. If x is positive, then $|x| = x$, so $\dfrac{|x|}{x} = \dfrac{x}{x} = 1$. On the other hand, if x is negative, then $|x| = -x$, so $\dfrac{|x|}{x} = \dfrac{-x}{x} = -1$. In other words,

$$\frac{|x|}{x} = \begin{cases} -1 & \text{if } x < 0 \\ 1 & \text{if } x > 0, \end{cases}$$

which is exactly the formula we obtained for $f'(x)$. We have therefore obtained a convenient closed-form formula for the derivative of $|x|$!

Derivative of $|x|$

If $f(x) = |x|$, then $f'(x) = \dfrac{|x|}{x}$.

Note that $|x|/x$ is not defined if $x = 0$, reflecting the fact that $f'(x)$ does not exist when $x = 0$.

We will use the above formula extensively in the next chapter.

FAQs

Computing Derivatives Algebraically

Q: *The algebraic computation of $f'(x)$ seems to require a number of steps. How do I remember what to do and when?*

A: If you examine the computations in the examples above, you will find the following pattern:

1. Write out the formula for $f'(x)$ as the limit of the difference quotient, and then substitute $f(x + h)$ and $f(x)$.

2. Expand and simplify the *numerator* of the expression but not the denominator.

3. After simplifying the numerator, factor out an h to cancel with the h in the denominator. If h does not factor out of the numerator, you might have made an error. (A frequent error is a wrong sign.)

4. After canceling the h, you should be able to see what the limit is by letting $h \to 0$.

10.6 EXERCISES

▼ more advanced   ◆ challenging
🔢 indicates exercises that should be solved using technology

In Exercises 1–14, compute $f'(a)$ algebraically for the given value of a. [HINT: See Example 1.]

1. $f(x) = x^2 + 1; a = 2$

2. $f(x) = x^2 - 3; a = 1$

3. $f(x) = 3x - 4; a = -1$

4. $f(x) = -2x + 4; a = -1$

5. $f(x) = 3x^2 + x; a = 1$

6. $f(x) = 2x^2 + x; a = -2$

7. $f(x) = 2x - x^2; a = -1$

8. $f(x) = -x - x^2; a = 0$

9. $f(x) = x^3 + 2x; a = 2$

10. $f(x) = x - 2x^3; a = 1$

11. $f(x) = -\dfrac{1}{x}; a = 1$ [HINT: See Example 3.]

12. $f(x) = \dfrac{2}{x}; a = 5$ [HINT: See Example 3.]

13. ▼ $f(x) = mx + b; a = 43$

14. ▼ $f(x) = \dfrac{x}{k} - b \quad (k \neq 0); a = 12$

In Exercises 15–28, compute the derivative function $f'(x)$ algebraically. (Notice that the functions are the same as those in Exercises 1–14.) [HINT: See Examples 2 and 3.]

15. $f(x) = x^2 + 1$ **16.** $f(x) = x^2 - 3$

17. $f(x) = 3x - 4$ **18.** $f(x) = -2x + 4$

19. $f(x) = 3x^2 + x$ **20.** $f(x) = 2x^2 + x$

21. $f(x) = 2x - x^2$ **22.** $f(x) = -x - x^2$

23. $f(x) = x^3 + 2x$

24. $f(x) = x - 2x^3$

25. ▼ $f(x) = -\dfrac{1}{x}$

26. ▼ $f(x) = \dfrac{2}{x}$

27. ▼ $f(x) = mx + b$

28. ▼ $f(x) = \dfrac{x}{k} - b \quad (k \neq 0)$

In Exercises 29–38, compute the indicated derivative.

29. $R(t) = -0.3t^2; R'(2)$

30. $S(t) = 1.4t^2; S'(-1)$

31. $U(t) = 5.1t^2 + 5.1; U'(3)$

32. $U(t) = -1.3t^2 + 1.1; U'(4)$

33. $U(t) = -1.3t^2 - 4.5t; U'(1)$

34. $U(t) = 5.1t^2 - 1.1t; U'(1)$

35. $L(r) = 4.25r - 5.01; L'(1.2)$

36. $L(r) = -1.02r + 5.7; L'(3.1)$

37. ▼ $q(p) = \dfrac{2.4}{p} + 3.1; q'(2)$

38. ▼ $q(p) = \dfrac{1}{0.5p} - 3.1; q'(2)$

In Exercises 39–44, find the equation of the tangent to the graph at the indicated point. [**HINT**: Compute the derivative algebraically; then see Example 2(b) of Section 10.5.]

39. ▼ $f(x) = x^2 - 3; a = 2$ **40.** ▼ $f(x) = x^2 + 1; a = 2$

41. ▼ $f(x) = -2x - 4; a = 3$ **42.** ▼ $f(x) = 3x + 1; a = 1$

43. ▼ $f(x) = x^2 - x; a = -1$ **44.** ▼ $f(x) = x^2 + x; a = -1$

Applications

45. *Velocity* If a stone is dropped from a height of 400 feet, its height after t seconds is given by $s = 400 - 16t^2$. Find its instantaneous velocity function and its velocity at time $t = 4$. [**HINT**: See Example 4.]

46. *Velocity* If a stone is thrown down at 120 feet per second from a height of 1,000 feet, its height after t seconds is given by $s = 1{,}000 - 120t - 16t^2$. Find its instantaneous velocity function and its velocity at time $t = 3$. [**HINT**: See Example 4.]

47. *Oil Imports from Mexico* Daily crude oil imports to the United States from Mexico for 2009–2013 could be approximated by

$$I(t) = -39t^2 + 800t - 3{,}000 \text{ thousand barrels}$$
$$(9 \leq t \leq 13),$$

where t is time in years since the start of 2000.[76] Find the derivative function $\dfrac{dI}{dt}$. At what rate were oil imports changing at the start of 2012 ($t = 12$)? [**HINT**: See Example 4.]

48. *Oil Production in Mexico* Daily crude oil production by Pemex, Mexico's national oil company, for 2008–2013 could be approximated by

$$P(t) = 0.017t^2 - 0.4t + 5.23 \text{ million barrels} \quad (8 \leq t \leq 13),$$

where t is time in years since the start of 2000.[77] Find the derivative function $\dfrac{dP}{dt}$. At what rate was oil production changing at the start of 2010 ($t = 10$)? [**HINT**: See Example 4.]

49. *Bottled Water Sales* The following chart shows the amount of bottled water sold in the United States for the period 2007–2014:[78]

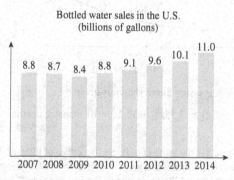

Bottled water sales in the U.S.
(billions of gallons)

The function

$$R(t) = 0.08t^2 - 0.26t + 8.8 \text{ billion gallons} \quad (0 \leq t \leq 7)$$

gives a good approximation, where t is time in years since 2007. Find the derivative function $R'(t)$. According to the model, how fast were annual sales of bottled water changing in 2012?

50. *Bottled Water Sales* The following chart shows annual per capita sales of bottled water in the United States for the period 2007–2014:[79]

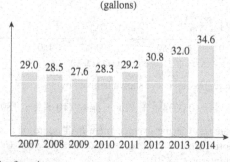

Per capita bottled water sales in the U.S.
(gallons)

The function

$$R(t) = 0.25t^2 - t + 29 \text{ gallons} \quad (0 \leq t \leq 7)$$

---

[76] Source: U.S. Energy Information Administration, www.eia.gov.

[77] Source: www.pemex.com.

[78] The 2014 figure is a projection. Source: Beverage Marketing Corporation/www.bottledwater.org.

[79] *Ibid.*

gives a good approximation, where t is time in years since 2007. Find the derivative function $R'(t)$. According to the model, how fast were per capita sales of bottled water changing in 2011?

51. ▼ *Ecology* Increasing numbers of manatees have been killed by boats off the Florida coast. The following graph shows the relationship between the number of boats registered in Florida and the number of manatees killed each year.

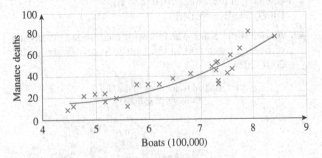

Boats (100,000)

The regression curve shown is given by

$$f(x) = 3.55x^2 - 30.2x + 81 \text{ manatee deaths}$$
$$(4.5 \leq x \leq 8.5),$$

where x is the number of boats (hundreds of thousands) registered in Florida in a particular year and $f(x)$ is the number of manatees killed by boats in Florida that year.[80] Compute and interpret $f'(8)$.

52. ▼ *SAT Scores by Income* The following graph shows U.S. math SAT scores as a function of parents' income level.[81]

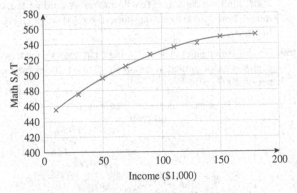

Income ($1,000)

The regression curve shown is given by

$$f(x) = -0.0034x^2 + 1.2x + 444 \quad (10 \leq x \leq 180),$$

where $f(x)$ is the average math SAT score of a student whose parents earn x thousand dollars per year. Compute and interpret $f'(30)$.

53. ▼ *Television Advertising* The cost, in thousands of dollars, of a 30-second television ad during the Super Bowl in the years 1970–2010 can be approximated by the following piecewise-linear function ($t = 0$ represents 1970):[82]

$$C(t) = \begin{cases} 31.1t + 78 & \text{if } 0 \leq t < 20 \\ 90t - 1{,}100 & \text{if } 20 \leq t \leq 40. \end{cases}$$

a. Is C a continuous function of t? Why? [**HINT:** See Example 4 of Section 10.3.]

b. Is C a differentiable function of t? Compute $\lim_{t \to 20^-} C'(t)$ and $\lim_{t \to 20^+} C'(t)$, and interpret the results. [**HINT:** See the "Before we go on" discussion after Example 5.]

54. ▼ *Television Advertising* (Compare Exercise 53.) The cost, in thousands of dollars, of a 30-second television ad during the Super Bowl in the years 1980–2010 can be approximated by the following piecewise-linear function ($t = 0$ represents 1980):[83]

$$C(t) = \begin{cases} 43.9t + 222 & \text{if } 0 \leq t \leq 20 \\ 140t - 1{,}700 & \text{if } 20 < t \leq 30. \end{cases}$$

a. Is C a continuous function of t? Why? [**HINT:** See Example 4 of Section 10.3.]

b. Is C a differentiable function of t? Compute $\lim_{t \to 20^-} C'(t)$ and $\lim_{t \to 20^+} C'(t)$, and interpret the results. [**HINT:** See the "Before we go on" discussion after Example 5.]

Communication and Reasoning Exercises

55. Of the three methods (numerical, graphical, and algebraic) we can use to estimate the derivative of a function at a given value of x, which is always the most accurate? Explain.

56. Explain why we cannot put $h = 0$ in the formula

$$f'(a) = \lim_{h \to 0} \frac{f(a + h) - f(a)}{h}$$

for the derivative of f.

57. You just got your derivatives test back, and you can't understand why that teacher of yours deducted so many points for what you thought was your best work:

$$\lim_{h \to 0} \frac{f(x + h) - f(x)}{h}$$
$$= \lim_{h \to 0} \frac{f(x) + h - f(x)}{h}$$
$$= \lim_{h \to 0} \frac{h}{h} \qquad \text{Canceled the } f(x)$$
$$= 1. \qquad\qquad \times \ \textit{WRONG} \ -10$$

What was wrong with your answer? (There may be more than one error.)

[80] Regression model is based on data from 1976–2000. Sources for data: Florida Department of Highway Safety & Motor Vehicles, Florida Marine Institute/*New York Times*, February 12, 2002, p. F4.

[81] Regression model is based on 2009 data. Source: College Board/*New York Times* http://economix.blogs.nytimes.com.

[82] Source: http://en.wikipedia.org/wiki/Super_Bowl_advertising.

[83] *Ibid.*

58. Your friend just got his derivatives test back and can't understand why that teacher of his deducted so many points for the following:

$$\lim_{h \to 0} \frac{f(x + h) - f(x)}{h}$$

$$= \lim_{h \to 0} \frac{f(x) + f(h) - f(x)}{h}$$

$$= \lim_{h \to 0} \frac{f(h)}{h} \qquad \text{Canceled the } f(x).$$

$$= \lim_{h \to 0} \frac{f(\cancel{h})}{\cancel{h}} \qquad \text{Now cancel the } h.$$

$$= f. \qquad\qquad \text{✗ WRONG } -50$$

What was wrong with his answer? (There may be more than one error.)

59. Your other friend just got her derivatives test back and can't understand why that teacher of hers took off so many points for the following:

$$\lim_{h \to 0} \frac{f(x + h) - f(x)}{h}$$

$$= \lim_{h \to 0} \frac{f(x + \cancel{h}) - f(x)}{\cancel{h}} \qquad \text{Now cancel the } h.$$

$$= \lim_{h \to 0} f(x) - f(x) \qquad \text{Cancel the } f(x).$$

$$= 0. \qquad\qquad \text{✗ WRONG } -15$$

What was wrong with her answer? (There may be more than one error.)

60. Your third friend just got her derivatives test back and can't understand why that teacher of hers took off so many points for the following:

$$\lim_{h \to 0} \frac{f(x + h) - f(x)}{h}$$

$$= \lim_{h \to 0} \frac{f(x) + h - f(x)}{h}$$

$$= \lim_{h \to 0} \frac{f(x) + \cancel{h} - f(x)}{\cancel{h}} \qquad \text{Now cancel the } h.$$

$$= \lim_{h \to 0} f(x) - f(x) \qquad \text{Cancel the } f(x).$$

$$= 0. \qquad\qquad \text{✗ WRONG } -25$$

What was wrong with her answer? (There may be more than one error.)

61. Your friend Muffy claims that, because the balanced difference quotient is more accurate, it would be better to use that instead of the usual difference quotient when computing the derivative algebraically. Comment on this advice.

62. Use the balanced difference quotient formula,

$$f'(a) = \lim_{h \to 0} \frac{f(a + h) - f(a - h)}{2h},$$

to compute $f'(3)$ when $f(x) = x^2$. What do you find?

63. ▼ A certain function f has the property that $f'(a)$ does not exist. How is that reflected in the attempt to compute $f'(a)$ algebraically?

64. ▼ One cannot put $h = 0$ in the formula

$$f'(a) = \lim_{h \to 0} \frac{f(a + h) - f(a)}{h}$$

for the derivative of f. (See Exercise 56.) However, in the last step of each of the computations in the text, we are effectively setting $h = 0$ when taking the limit. What is going on here?

CHAPTER 10 REVIEW

KEY CONCEPTS

www.WanerMath.com
Go to the Website to find a comprehensive and interactive Web-based summary of Chapter 10.

10.1 Limits: Numerical and Graphical Viewpoints

$\lim_{x \to a} f(x) = L$ means that $f(x)$ approaches L as x approaches a [p. 722]

What it means for a limit to exist [p. 723]

Limits at infinity [p. 725]

Estimating limits graphically [p. 726]

Interpreting limits in real-world situations [p. 729]

10.2 Limits and Continuity

f is continuous at a if $\lim_{x \to a} f(x)$ exists and $\lim_{x \to a} f(x) = f(a)$ [p. 736]

Discontinuous, continuous on domain [p. 736]

Discontinuities and singularities [p. 737]

Determining whether a given function is continuous [p. 738]

10.3 Limits and Continuity: Algebraic Viewpoint

Closed-form function [p. 743]

Limits of closed form functions [p. 744]

Simplifying to obtain limits [p. 744]

The indeterminate form 0/0 [p. 745]

The determinate form $k/0$ [p. 746]

Limits of piecewise-defined functions [p. 748]

Limits at infinity [p. 749]

Determinate and indeterminate forms [p. 752]

10.4 Average Rate of Change

Average rate of change of $f(x)$ over $[a, b]$: $\dfrac{\Delta f}{\Delta x} = \dfrac{f(b) - f(a)}{b - a}$ [p. 760]

Average rate of change as slope of the secant line [p. 760]

Computing the average rate of change from a graph [p. 760]

Computing the average rate of change from a formula [p. 763]

Computing the average rate of change over short intervals $[a, a + h]$ [p. 763]

10.5 The Derivative: Numerical and Graphical Viewpoints

Instantaneous rate of change of $f(x)$ (derivative of f at a);

$f'(a) = \lim_{h \to 0} \dfrac{f(a + h) - f(a)}{h}$ [p. 774]

The derivative as slope of the tangent line [p. 777]

Quick approximation of the derivative [p. 779]

$\dfrac{d}{dx}$ Notation [p. 781]

The derivative as velocity [p. 781]

Average and instantaneous velocity [p. 782]

The derivative function [p. 783]

Graphing the derivative function with technology [p. 784]

10.6 The Derivative: Algebraic Viewpoint

Derivative at the point $x = a$:

$f'(a) = \lim_{h \to 0} \dfrac{f(a + h) - f(a)}{h}$ [p. 797]

Derivative function:

$f'(x) = \lim_{h \to 0} \dfrac{f(x + h) - f(x)}{h}$ [p. 798]

Examples of the computation of $f'(x)$ [p. 799]

$f(x) = |x|$ is not differentiable at $x = 0$ [p. 801]

REVIEW EXERCISES

⊤ indicates exercises that should be solved using technology

In Exercises 1–4, numerically *estimate whether the limit exists.* If the limit does exist, give its approximate value.

1. $\lim_{x \to 3} \dfrac{x^2 - x - 6}{x - 3}$

2. $\lim_{x \to 3} \dfrac{x^2 - 2x - 6}{x - 3}$

3. $\lim_{x \to -1} \dfrac{|x + 1|}{x^2 - x - 2}$

4. $\lim_{x \to -1} \dfrac{|x + 1|}{x^2 + x - 2}$

In Exercises 5 and 6 the graph of a function f is shown. Graphically determine whether the given limits exist. If a limit does exist, give its approximate value.

5.

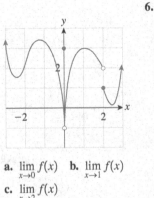

a. $\lim_{x \to 0} f(x)$ **b.** $\lim_{x \to 1} f(x)$

c. $\lim_{x \to 2} f(x)$

6.

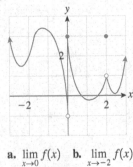

a. $\lim_{x \to 0} f(x)$ **b.** $\lim_{x \to -2} f(x)$

c. $\lim_{x \to 2} f(x)$

In Exercises 7–30, calculate the limit algebraically. If the limit does not exist, say why.

7. $\lim\limits_{x \to -2} \dfrac{x^2}{x - 3}$

8. $\lim\limits_{x \to 3} \dfrac{x^2 - 9}{2x - 6}$

9. $\lim\limits_{x \to -2} \dfrac{x^2 - 4}{x^3 + 2x^2}$

10. $\lim\limits_{x \to -1} \dfrac{x^2 - 9}{2x - 6}$

11. $\lim\limits_{x \to 0} \dfrac{x}{2x^2 - x}$

12. $\lim\limits_{x \to 1} \dfrac{x^2 - 9}{x - 1}$

13. $\lim\limits_{x \to -1} \dfrac{x^2 + 3x}{x^2 - x - 2}$

14. $\lim\limits_{x \to -1^+} \dfrac{x^2 + 1}{x^2 + 3x + 2}$

15. $\lim\limits_{x \to 8} \dfrac{x^2 - 6x - 16}{x^2 - 9x + 8}$

16. $\lim\limits_{x \to 4} \dfrac{x^2 + 3x}{x^2 - 8x + 16}$

17. $\lim\limits_{x \to 4} \dfrac{x^2 + 8}{x^2 - 2x - 8}$

18. $\lim\limits_{x \to 6} \dfrac{x^2 - 5x - 6}{x^2 - 36}$

19. $\lim\limits_{x \to 1/2} \dfrac{x^2 + 8}{4x^2 - 4x + 1}$

20. $\lim\limits_{x \to 1/2} \dfrac{x^2 + 3x}{2x^2 + 3x - 1}$

21. $\lim\limits_{x \to +\infty} \dfrac{10x^2 + 300x + 1}{5x^3 + 2}$

22. $\lim\limits_{x \to +\infty} \dfrac{2x^4 + 20x^3}{1{,}000x^6 + 6}$

23. $\lim\limits_{x \to -\infty} \dfrac{x^2 - x - 6}{x - 3}$

24. $\lim\limits_{x \to +\infty} \dfrac{x^2 - x - 6}{4x^2 - 3}$

25. $\lim\limits_{t \to +\infty} \dfrac{-5}{5 + 5.3(3^{2t})}$

26. $\lim\limits_{t \to +\infty} \left(3 + \dfrac{2}{e^{4t}}\right)$

27. $\lim\limits_{x \to +\infty} \dfrac{2}{5 + 4e^{-3x}}$

28. $\lim\limits_{x \to +\infty} (4e^{3x} + 12)$

29. $\lim\limits_{t \to +\infty} \dfrac{1 + 2^{-3t}}{1 + 5.3e^{-t}}$

30. $\lim\limits_{x \to -\infty} \dfrac{8 + 0.5^x}{2 - 3^{2x}}$

In Exercises 31–34, find the average rate of change of the given function over the interval $[a, a + h]$ for $h = 1, 0.01,$ and 0.001. (Round answers to four decimal places.) Then estimate the slope of the tangent line to the graph of the function at a.

31. $f(x) = \dfrac{1}{x + 1}$; $a = 0$

32. $f(x) = x^x$; $a = 2$

33. $f(x) = e^{2x}$; $a = 0$

34. $f(x) = \ln(2x)$; $a = 1$

In Exercises 35–38 you are given the graph of a function with four points marked. Determine at which (if any) of these points the derivative of the function is (a) −1, (b) 0, (c) 1, and (d) 2.

35.

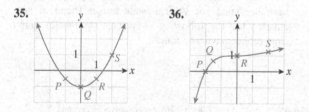

36.

37.

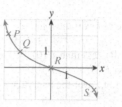

38.

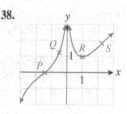

39. Let f have the graph shown.

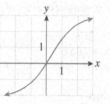

Select the correct answer.

a. The average rate of change of f over the interval $[0, 2]$ is
  (A) greater than $f'(0)$.
  (B) less than $f'(0)$.
  (C) approximately equal to $f'(0)$.

b. The average rate of change of f over the interval $[-1, 1]$ is
  (A) greater than $f'(0)$.
  (B) less than $f'(0)$.
  (C) approximately equal to $f'(0)$.

c. Over the interval $[0, 2]$ the instantaneous rate of change of f is
  (A) increasing.
  (B) decreasing.
  (C) neither increasing nor decreasing.

d. Over the interval $[-2, 2]$ the instantaneous rate of change of f is
  (A) increasing, then decreasing.
  (B) decreasing, then increasing.
  (C) approximately constant.

e. When $x = 2$, $f(x)$ is
  (A) approximately 1 and increasing at a rate of about 2.5 units per unit of x.
  (B) approximately 1.2 and increasing at a rate of about 1 unit per unit of x.
  (C) approximately 2.5 and increasing at a rate of about 0.5 units per unit of x.
  (D) approximately 2.5 and increasing at a rate of about 2.5 units per unit of x.

40. Let f have the graph shown.

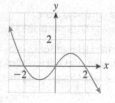

Select the correct answer.

a. The average rate of change of f over the interval $[0, 1]$ is
(A) greater than $f'(0)$.   **(B)** less than $f'(0)$.
(C) approximately equal to $f'(0)$.

b. The average rate of change of f over the interval $[0, 2]$ is
(A) greater than $f'(1)$.   **(B)** less than $f'(1)$.
(C) approximately equal to $f'(1)$.

c. Over the interval $[-2, 0]$ the instantaneous rate of change of f is
(A) increasing.   **(B)** decreasing.
(C) neither increasing nor decreasing.

d. Over the interval $[-2, 2]$ the instantaneous rate of change of f is
(A) increasing, then decreasing.
(B) decreasing, then increasing.
(C) approximately constant.

e. When $x = 0$, $f(x)$ is
(A) approximately 0 and increasing at a rate of about 1.5 units per unit of x.
(B) approximately 0 and decreasing at a rate of about 1.5 units per unit of x.
(C) approximately 1.5 and neither increasing nor decreasing.
(D) approximately 0 and neither increasing nor decreasing.

In Exercises 41–44, use the definition of the derivative to calculate the derivative of the given function algebraically.

41. $f(x) = x^2 + x$ **42.** $f(x) = 3x^2 - x + 1$

43. $f(x) = 1 - \dfrac{2}{x}$ **44.** $f(x) = \dfrac{1}{x} + 1$

⊤ *In Exercises 45–48, use technology to graph the derivative of the given function. In each case, choose a range of x-values and y-values that shows the interesting features of the graph.*

45. $f(x) = 10x^5 + \dfrac{1}{2}x^4 - x + 2$

46. $f(x) = \dfrac{10}{x^5} + \dfrac{1}{2x^4} - \dfrac{1}{x} + 2$

47. $f(x) = 3x^3 + 3\sqrt[3]{x}$

48. $f(x) = \dfrac{2}{x^{2.1}} - \dfrac{x^{0.1}}{2}$

Applications: OHaganBooks.com
[Try the game at www.OHaganBooks.com]

49. *Stock Investments* OHaganBooks.com CEO John O'Hagan has terrible luck with stocks. The following graph shows the value of *Fly-By-Night Airlines* stock that he bought acting on

a "hot tip" from Marjory Duffin (CEO of *Duffin House* publishers and a close business associate):

Fly-by-night stock

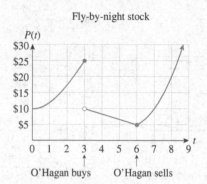

a. Compute $P(3)$, $\lim_{t \to 3^-} P(t)$ and $\lim_{t \to 3^+} P(t)$. Does $\lim_{t \to 3} P(t)$ exist? Interpret your answers in terms of Fly-By-Night stock.
b. Is P continuous at $t = 6$? Is P differentiable at $t = 6$? Interpret your answers in terms of Fly-By-Night stock.

50. *Stock Investments* John O'Hagan's golf partner Juan Robles seems to have had better luck with his investment in *Gapple Computer, Inc.* stocks as shown in the following graph:

Gapple Inc. Stock

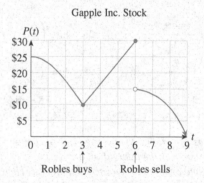

a. Compute $P(6)$, $\lim_{t \to 6^-} P(t)$ and $\lim_{t \to 6^+} P(t)$. Does $\lim_{t \to 6} P(t)$ exist? Interpret your answers in terms of Gapple stock.
b. Is P continuous at $t = 3$? Is P differentiable at $t = 3$? Interpret your answers in terms of Gapple stock.

51. *Real Estate* Marjory Duffin has persuaded John O'Hagan to consider investing a portion of OHaganBooks.com profits in real estate, now that the real estate market seems to have bottomed out. A real-estate broker friend of hers emailed her the following (somewhat optimistic) graph from brokersadvocacy.com:[84]

---

[84] Authors' note: As of March 2016, brokersadvocacy.com is unregistered.

Home price index

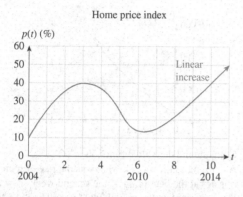

Here, $p(t)$ is the home price percentage over the 2003 level.
a. Assuming that the trend shown in the graph continues indefinitely, estimate $\lim_{t\to 3} p(t)$ and $\lim_{t\to +\infty} p(t)$, and interpret the results.
b. Estimate $\lim_{t\to +\infty} p'(t)$, and interpret the result.

52. *Advertising Costs* OHaganBooks.com has (on further advice from Marjory Duffin) mounted an aggressive online marketing strategy. The following graph shows the weekly cost of this campaign for the 6-week period since the start of July (t is time in weeks):

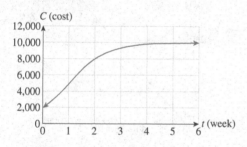

a. Assuming that the trend shown in the graph continues indefinitely, estimate $\lim_{t\to 2} C(t)$ and $\lim_{t\to +\infty} C(t)$, and interpret the results.
b. Estimate $\lim_{t\to +\infty} C'(t)$, and interpret the result.

53. *Sales* Since the start of July, OHaganBooks.com has seen its weekly sales increase, as shown in the following table:

Week	1	2	3	4	5	6
Sales (books)	6,500	7,000	7,200	7,800	8,500	9,000

a. What was the average rate of increase of weekly sales over this entire period?
b. During which 1-week interval(s) did the rate of increase of sales exceed the average rate?
c. During which 2-week interval(s) did the weekly sales rise at the highest average rate, and what was that average rate?

54. *Rising Sea Level* Marjory Duffin recently purchased a beachfront condominium in New York and is now in a panic, having just seen some disturbing figures about rising sea levels (sea levels as measured in New York relative to the 1900 level).[85]

Year Since 1900	0	25	50	75	100	125
Sea Level (mm)	0	60	140	240	310	390

a. What was the average rate of increase of the sea level over this entire period?
b. During which 25-year interval(s) did the rate of increase of the sea level exceed the average rate?
c. Marjory Duffin's condominium is about 2 meters above sea level. Using the average rate of change from part (a), estimate how long she has before the sea rises to her condominium.

55. *Real Estate* The following graph (see Exercise 51) shows the home price index chart emailed to Marjory Duffin by a real-estate broker:

Home price index

Use the graph to answer the following questions:
a. What was the average rate of change of the index over the 10-year period beginning 2004?
b. What was the average rate of change of the index over the period $[3, 10]$?
c. Which of the following is correct? Over the period $[4, 6]$
   (A) the rate of change of the index increased.
   (B) the rate of change of the index increased and then decreased.
   (C) the rate of change of the index decreased.
   (D) the rate of change of the index decreased and then increased.

---

[85] The 2025 level is a projection. Source: New England Integrated Science & Assessment, www.neisa.unh.edu/Climate/index.html.

56. *Advertising Costs* The following graph (see Exercise 52) shows the weekly cost of OHaganBooks.com's online ad campaign for the 6-week period since the start of July (*t* is time in weeks).

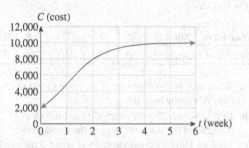

C (cost)

Use the graph to answer the following questions:

a. What was the average rate of change of cost over the entire 6-week period?

b. What was the average rate of change of cost over the period $[2, 6]$?

c. Which of the following is correct? Over the period $[2, 6]$

(A) the rate of change of cost increased and the cost increased.

(B) the rate of change of cost decreased and the cost increased.

(C) the rate of change of cost increased and the cost decreased.

(D) the rate of change of cost decreased and the cost decreased.

57. *Sales* OHaganBooks.com fits the curve

$$w(t) = 36t^2 + 250t + 6{,}240 \quad (0 \le t \le 6)$$

to its weekly sales figures from Exercise 53, as shown in the following graph:

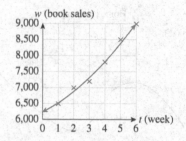

w (book sales)

a. Compute the derivative function $w'(t)$.

b. According to the model, what was the rate of increase of sales at the beginning of the second week ($t = 1$)?

c. If we extrapolate the model, what would be the rate of increase of weekly sales at the beginning of the eighth week ($t = 7$)?

58. *Sea Levels* Marjory Duffin fit the curve

$$s(t) = 0.002t^2 + 3t - 6.4 \quad (0 \le t \le 125)$$

to her sea level figures from Exercise 54, as shown in the following graph:

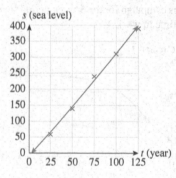

s (sea level)

a. Compute the derivative function $s'(t)$.

b. According to the model, what was the rate of increase of the sea level in 2000 ($t = 100$)?

c. If we extrapolate the model, what would be the rate of increase of the sea level in 2100 ($t = 200$)?

CASE STUDY

Reducing Sulfur Emissions

The Environmental Protection Agency (EPA) wishes to formulate a policy that will encourage utilities to reduce sulfur emissions. Its goal is to reduce annual emissions of sulfur dioxide by a total of 10 million tons from the current level of 25 million tons by imposing a fixed charge for every ton of sulfur released into the environment per year. As a consultant to the EPA, you must determine the amount to be charged per ton of sulfur emissions.

You would like first to know the cost to the utility industry of reducing sulfur emissions. In other words, you would like to have a cost function of the form

$$C(q) = \text{Cost of removing } q \text{ tons of sulfur dioxide.}$$

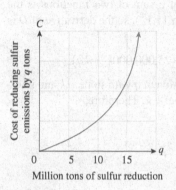

Cost of reducing sulfur emissions by q tons

Million tons of sulfur reduction

Figure 42

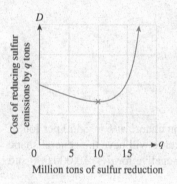

Cost of reducing sulfur emissions by q tons

Million tons of sulfur reduction

Figure 43

Unfortunately, you do not have such a function handy. You do, however, have the following data, which show the *marginal* cost (that is, the *rate of change* of cost) to the utility industry of reducing sulfur emissions at several levels of reduction.[86]

Reduction q (tons)	8,000,000	10,000,000	12,000,000
Marginal Cost $C'(q)$ ($/ton)	270	360	779

The table tells you that $C'(8,000,000) = \$270$ per ton, $C'(10,000,000) = \$360$ per ton, and $C'(12,000,000) = \$779$ per ton. Recalling that $C'(q)$ is the slope of the tangent to the graph of the cost function, you can see from the table that this slope is positive and increasing as q increases, so the graph of the cost function has the general shape shown in Figure 42.

Notice that the slope (additional cost) is increasing as you move to the right, so the utility industry has no cost incentive to reduce emissions further, as it costs the industry significantly more per ton for each additional ton of sulfur it removes. What you would like—if the goal of reducing total emissions by 10 million tons is to be reached—is that, somehow, the imposition of a fixed charge for every ton of sulfur dioxide released will *alter* the form of the cost curve so that it has the general shape shown in Figure 43. In this ideal curve, the cost D to utilities is lowest at a reduction level of 10 million tons, so if the utilities act to minimize cost, they can be expected to reduce emissions by 10 million tons, which is exactly the EPA goal! From the graph, you can see that the tangent line to the curve at the point where $q = 10$ million tons is horizontal, and thus has zero slope: $D'(10,000,000) = \$0$ per ton. Further, the slope $D'(q)$ is negative for values of q to the left of 10 million tons and positive for values to the right.

So how much should the EPA charge per ton of sulfur released into the environment? Suppose the EPA charges $\$k$ per ton, so that

Emission charge to utilities $= k \times$ Sulfur emissions.

It is your job to calculate k. Because you are working with q as the independent variable, you decide that it would be best to formulate the emission charge as a function of q. However, q represents the amount by which sulfur emissions have been reduced from the original 25 million tons, that is, the amount by which sulfur emissions are *lower than* the original 25 million tons:

$$q = 25,000,000 - \text{Sulfur emissions}.$$

Thus, the total annual emission charge to the utilities is

$$k \times \text{Sulfur emissions} = k(25,000,000 - q) = 25,000,000k - kq.$$

This results in a total cost to the utilities of

Total cost = Cost of reducing emissions + Emission charge
$$D(q) = C(q) + 25,000,000k - kq.$$

---

[86] These figures were produced in a computerized study of reducing sulfur emissions from the 1980 level by the given amounts. Source: Congress of the United States, Congressional Budget Office, *Curbing Acid Rain: Cost, Budget and Coal Market Effects* (Washington, DC: U.S. Government Printing Office, 1986): xx, xxii, 23, 80.

*This statement makes intuitive sense: For instance, if C is changing at a rate of 3 units per second and D is changing at a rate of 2 units per second, then their sum is changing at a rate of 3 + 2 = 5 units per second.

You now recall from calculus that the derivative of a sum of two functions is the sum of their derivatives (you will see why in Section 11.1*), so the derivative of D is given by

$$D'(q) = \text{Derivative of } C + \text{Derivative of } (25{,}000{,}000k - kq).$$

The function $y = 25{,}000{,}000k - kq$ is a linear function of q with slope $-k$ and intercept $25{,}000{,}000k$. Thus, its derivative is just its slope: $-k$. Therefore,

$$D'(q) = C'(q) - k.$$

Remember that you want

$$D'(10{,}000{,}000) = 0.$$

Thus,

$$C'(10{,}000{,}000) - k = 0.$$

Referring to the table, you see that

$$360 - k = 0$$

or

$$k = \$360 \text{ per ton.}$$

In other words, all you need to do is set the emission charge at $k = \$360$ per ton of sulfur emitted. Further, to ensure that the resulting curve will have the general shape shown in Figure 43, you would like to have $D'(q)$ negative for $q < 10{,}000{,}000$ and positive for $q > 10{,}000{,}000$. To check this, write

$$D'(q) = C'(q) - k$$
$$= C'(q) - 360$$

and refer to the table to obtain

$$D'(8{,}000{,}000) = 270 - 360 = -90 < 0 \quad \checkmark$$

and

$$D'(12{,}000{,}000) = 779 - 360 = 419 > 0. \quad \checkmark$$

Thus, based on the given data, the resulting curve will have the shape you require. You therefore inform the EPA that an annual emissions charge of $360 per ton of sulfur released into the environment will create the desired incentive: to reduce sulfur emissions by 10 million tons per year.

One week later, you are informed that this charge would be unrealistic because the utilities cannot possibly afford such a cost. You are asked whether there is an alternative plan that accomplishes the 10-million-ton reduction goal and yet is cheaper to the utilities by $5 billion per year. You then look at your expression for the emission charge

$$25{,}000{,}000k - kq$$

and notice that, if you decrease this amount by $5 billion, the derivative will not change at all because it will still have the same slope (only the intercept is affected). Therefore, you propose the following revised formula for the emission charge:

$$25{,}000{,}000k - kq - 5{,}000{,}000{,}000 = 25{,}000{,}000(360) - 360q - 5{,}000{,}000{,}000$$
$$= 4{,}000{,}000{,}000 - 360q.$$

At the expected reduction level of 10 million tons, the total amount paid by the utilities will then be

$$4,000,000,000 - 360(10,000,000) = \$400,000,000.$$

Thus, your revised proposal is the following: Impose an annual emissions charge of $360 per ton of sulfur released into the environment, and hand back $5 billion in the form of subsidies. The effect of this policy will be to cause the utilities industry to reduce sulfur emissions by 10 million tons per year and will result in $400 million in annual revenues to the government.

Notice that this policy also provides an incentive for the utilities to search for cheaper ways to reduce emissions. For instance, if they lowered costs to the point at which they could achieve a reduction level of 12 million tons, they would have a total emission charge of

$$4,000,000,000 - 360(12,000,000) = -\$320,000,000.$$

The fact that this is negative means that the government would be paying the utilities industry $320 million more in annual subsidies than the industry is paying in per ton emission charges.

EXERCISES

1. Excluding subsidies, what should the annual emission charge be if the goal is to reduce sulfur emissions by 8 million tons?

2. Excluding subsidies, what should the annual emission charge be if the goal is to reduce sulfur emissions by 12 million tons?

3. What is the *marginal emission charge* (derivative of emission charge) in your revised proposal (as stated before the exercise set)? What is the relationship between the marginal cost of reducing sulfur emissions before emissions charges are implemented and the marginal emission charge, at the optimal reduction under your revised proposal?

4. We said that the revised policy provided an incentive for utilities to find cheaper ways to reduce emissions. How would $C(q)$ have to change to make 12 million tons the optimum reduction?

5. What change in $C(q)$ would make 8 million tons the optimum reduction?

6. If the scenario in Exercise 5 took place, what would the EPA have to do to make 10 million tons the optimal reduction once again?

7. Because of intense lobbying by the utility industry, you are asked to revise the proposed policy so that the utility industry will pay no charge if sulfur emissions are reduced by the desired 10 million tons. How can you accomplish this?

8. Suppose that instead of imposing a fixed charge per ton of emission, you decide to use a sliding scale, so that the total charge to the industry for annual emissions of x tons will be $\$kx^2$ for some k. What must k be to again make 10 million tons the optimum reduction? [**HINT**: The derivative of kx^2 is $2kx$.]

Section 10.1

Example 1 (page 721) Use a table to estimate the following limits.

a. $\lim\limits_{x \to 2} \dfrac{x^3 - 8}{x - 2}$ **b.** $\lim\limits_{x \to 0} \dfrac{e^{2x} - 1}{x}$

Solution

On the TI-83/84 Plus, use the table feature to automate these computations as follows:

1. Define $Y_1 = (X^3 - 8) / (X - 2)$ for part (a) or $Y_1 = (e^{(2X)} - 1) / X$ for part (b).

2. Press 2ND TABLE to list its values for the given values of x. (If the calculator does not allow you to enter values of x, press 2ND TBLSET, and set Indpnt to Ask).

   Here is the table showing some of the values for part (a):

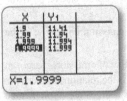

3. For part (b), use $Y_1 = (e^{(2X)} - 1) / X$ and values of x approaching 0 from either side.

Section 10.4

Example 3 (page 763) The price of an ounce of gold can be approximated by the function

$$G(t) = 5t^2 - 85t + 1{,}762 \quad (7.5 \le t \le 10.5)$$

where t is time in hours. ($t = 8$ represents 8:00 am.) What was the average rate of change of the price of gold over the $1\frac{1}{2}$-hour period starting at 8:00 am (the interval $[8, 9.5]$ on the t-axis)?

Solution

On the TI-83/84 Plus:

1. Enter the function G as Y_1 (using X for t):

$$Y_1 = 5X^2 - 85X + 1762$$

2. Now find the average rate of change over $[8, 9.5]$ by evaluating the following on the Home screen:

$$(Y_1(9.5) - Y_1(8)) / (9.5 - 8)$$

As shown on the screen, the average rate of change is 2.5.

Example 4 (page 763) Continuing with Example 3, use technology to compute the average rate of change of

$$G(t) = 5t^2 - 85t + 1{,}762 \quad (7.5 \le t \le 10.5)$$

over the intervals $[8, 8 + h]$, where $h = 1, 0.1, 0.01, 0.001,$ and 0.0001.

Solution

1. As in Example 3, enter the function G as Y_1 (using X for t):

$$Y_1 = 5X^2 - 85X + 1762$$

2. Now find the average rate of change for $h = 1$ by evaluating, on the Home screen,

$$(Y_1(8+1) - Y_1(8)) / 1$$

   which gives 0.

3. To evaluate for $h = 0.1$, recall the expression using 2ND ENTER and then change the 1, both places it occurs, to 0.1, getting

$$(Y_1(8+0.1) - Y_1(8)) / 0.1$$

   which gives -4.95.

4. Continuing, we can evaluate the average rate of change for all the desired values of h:

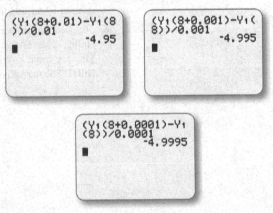

Section 10.5

Example 2 (page 779) Calculate an approximate value of $f'(1.5)$ if $f(x) = x^2 - 4x$, and then find the equation of the tangent line at the point on the graph where $x = 1.5$.

Solution

1. In the TI-83/84 Plus, enter the function f as Y_1:

$$Y_1 = X^2 - 4 * X$$

2. Go to the Home screen to compute the approximations:

$$(Y_1(1.5001) - Y_1(1.5))/0.0001$$

Usual difference quotient

$$(Y_1(1.5001) - Y_1(1.4999))/0.0002$$

Balanced difference quotient

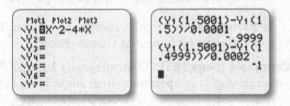

From the display on the right, we find that the difference quotient quick approximation is -0.9999 and the balanced difference quotient quick approximation is -1, which is in fact the exact value of $f'(1.5)$. See the discussion in the text for the calculation of the equation of the tangent line.

Example 4 (page 784) Use technology to graph the derivative of $f(x) = -2x^2 + 6x + 5$ for values of x in starting at -5.

Solution

On the TI-83/84 Plus, the easiest way to obtain quick approximations of the derivative of a given function is to use the built-in nDeriv function, which calculates balanced difference quotients.

1. On the Y= screen, first enter the function:

$$Y_1 = -2X^2 + 6X + 5$$

2. Then set

$$Y_2 = nDeriv(Y_1, X, X)$$ For nDeriv press [MATH] [8]

which is the TI-83/84 Plus's approximation of $f'(x)$ (see figure on the left below). Alternatively, we can enter the balanced difference quotient directly:

$$Y_2 = (Y_1(X+0.001) - Y_1(X-0.001))/0.002$$

(The TI-83/84 Plus uses $h = 0.001$ by default in the balanced difference quotient when calculating nDeriv, but this can be changed by giving a value of h as a fourth argument, such as nDeriv(Y_1, X, X, 0.0001).) To see a table of approximate values of the derivative, we press [2ND] [TABLE] and choose a collection of values for x (shown on the right below):

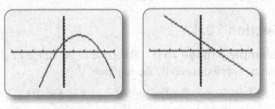

Here, Y_1 shows the value of f, and Y_2 shows the values of f'.

To graph the function or its derivative, we can graph Y_1 or Y_2 in a window showing the given domain $[-5, 5]$:

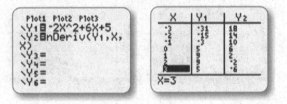

Graph of f Graph of f'

Section 10.1

Example 1 (page 721)   Use a table to estimate the following limits.

a. $\lim\limits_{x \to 2} \dfrac{x^3 - 8}{x - 2}$ **b.** $\lim\limits_{x \to 0} \dfrac{e^{2x} - 1}{x}$

Solution

1. Set up your spreadsheet to duplicate the table in part (a) as follows:

	A	B	C	D
1	x	f(x)	x	f(x)
2	1.9	=(A2^3-8)/(A2-2)	2.1	
3	1.99		2.01	
4	1.999		2.001	
5	1.9999		2.0001	

↓

	A	B	C	D
1	x	f(x)	x	f(x)
2	1.9	11.41	2.1	12.61
3	1.99	11.9401	2.01	12.0601
4	1.999	11.994001	2.001	12.006001
5	1.9999	11.99940001	2.0001	12.00060001

(The formula in cell B2 is copied to columns B and D, as indicated by the shading.) The values of $f(x)$ will be calculated in columns B and D.

2. For part (b), use the formula $=(\text{EXP}(2*\text{A2})-1)/\text{A2}$ in cell B2, and in columns A and C, use values of x approaching 0 from either side.

Section 10.4

Example 3 (page 763)   The price of an ounce of gold can be approximated by the function

$$G(t) = 5t^2 + 85t + 1{,}762 \quad (7.5 \le t \le 10.5)$$

where t is time in hours. ($t = 8$ represents 8:00 am.) What was the average rate of change of the price of gold over the $1\frac{1}{2}$-hour period starting at 8:00 am (the interval $[8, 9.5]$ on the t-axis)?

Solution

To use a spreadsheet to compute the average rate of change of G:

1. Start with two columns, one for values of t and one for values of $G(t)$, which you enter using the formula for G:

   $=5*\text{A2}^2-85*\text{A2}+1762$

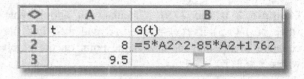

	A	B
1	t	G(t)
2	8	=5*A2^2-85*A2+1762
3	9.5	

2. Next, calculate the average rate of change as shown here:

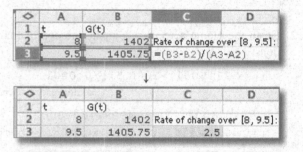

	A	B	C	D
1	t	G(t)		
2	8	1402	Rate of change over [8, 9.5]:	
3	9.5	1405.75	=(B3-B2)/(A3-A2)	

↓

	A	B	C	D
1	t	G(t)		
2	8	1402	Rate of change over [8, 9.5]:	
3	9.5	1405.75	2.5	

In Example 4 we describe another, more versatile Excel template for computing rates of change.

Example 4 (page 763)   Continuing with Example 3, use technology to compute the average rate of change of

$$G(t) = 5t^2 + 85t + 1{,}762 \quad (7.5 \le t \le 10.5)$$

over the intervals $[8, 8 + h]$, where $h = 1$, 0.1, 0.01, 0.001, and 0.0001.

Solution

The template we can use to compute the rates of change is an extension of what we used in Example 3:

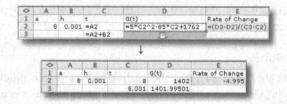

	A	B	C	D	E
1	a	h	t	G(t)	Rate of Change
2	8	0.001	=A2	=5*C2^2-85*C2+1762	=(D3-D2)/(C3-C2)
3			=A2+B2		

↓

	A	B	C	D	E
1	a	h	t	G(t)	Rate of Change
2	8	0.001		1402	-4.995
3			8.001	1401.99501	

1. Column C contains the values $t = a$ and $t = a + h$ we are using for the independent variable.

2. The formula in cell E2 is the average-rate-of-change formula $\Delta G/\Delta t$. Entering the different values $h = 1$, 0.1, 0.01, 0.001, and 0.0001 in cell B2 gives the results shown in Example 4.

Section 10.5

Example 2 (page 779) Calculate an approximate value of $f'(1.5)$ if $f(x) = x^2 - 4x$, and then find the equation of the tangent line at the point on the graph where $x = 1.5$.

Solution

You can compute both the difference quotient and the balanced difference quotient approximations in a spreadsheet using the following extension of the worksheet in Example 4 in Section 10.4:

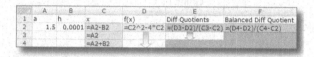

Notice that we get two difference quotients in column E. The first uses $h = -0.0001$, while the second uses $h = 0.0001$ and is the one we use for our quick approximation. The balanced quotient is their average (column F). The results are as follows:

From the results shown above, we find that the difference quotient quick approximation is -0.9999 and that the balanced difference quotient quick approximation is -1, which is in fact the exact value of $f'(1.5)$. See the discussion in the text for the calculation of the equation of the tangent line.

Example 4 (page 784) Use technology to graph the derivative of $f(x) = -2x^2 + 6x + 5$ for values of x starting at -5.

Solution

1. Start with a table of values for the function f:

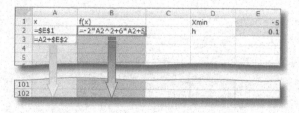

2. Next, compute approximate derivatives in column C:

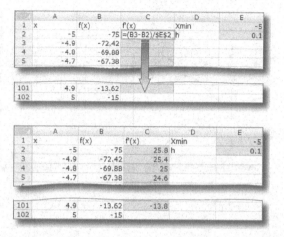

You cannot paste the difference quotient formula into cell C102. (Why?) Notice that this worksheet uses the ordinary difference quotients, $[f(x + h) - f(x)]/h$. If you prefer, you can use balanced difference quotients $[f(x + h) - f(x - h)]/(2h)$, in which case cells C2 and C102 would both have to be left blank.

We now graph the function and the derivative on different graphs as follows:

1. First, graph the function f in the usual way, using columns A and B.

2. Make a copy of this graph, and click on it once. Columns A and B should be outlined, indicating that these are the columns used in the graph.

3. By dragging from the center of the bottom edge of the box, move the column B box over to column C as shown:

	A	B	C
96	4.4	-7.32	-11.8
97	4.5	-8.5	-12.2
98	4.6	-9.72	-12.6
99	4.7	-10.98	-13
100	4.8	-12.28	-13.4
101	4.9	-13.62	-13.8
102	5	-15	

↓

	A	B	C
96	4.4	-7.32	-11.8
97	4.5	-8.5	-12.2
98	4.6	-9.72	-12.6
99	4.7	-10.98	-13
100	4.8	-12.28	-13.4
101	4.9	-13.62	-13.8
102	5	-15	

The graph will then show the derivative (columns A and C):

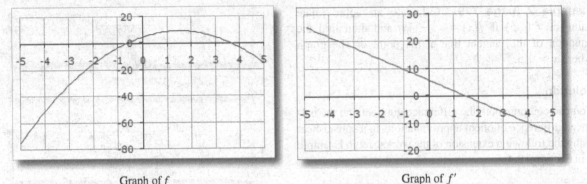

Graph of f Graph of f'

11

TECHNIQUES OF DIFFERENTIATION WITH APPLICATIONS

CASE STUDY

Projecting Market Growth

It is 2010, and you are on the board of directors at *Fullcourt Academic Press*. The sales director of the high school division has just burst into your office with a proposal for an expansion strategy based on the assumption that the number of graduates from private high schools in the United States will grow at a rate of at least 4,000 per year through the year 2015. Because the figures actually appear to be leveling off, you are suspicious about this estimate. You would like to devise a model that predicts this trend before tomorrow's scheduled board meeting.

How do you go about doing this?

Yuri Arcurs/Shutterstock.com

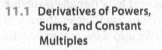

www.WanerMath.com

At the Website, in addition to the resources listed in the Preface, you will find:

The following extra topic:

- Linear Approximation and Error Estimation

821

Introduction

In Chapter 10 we studied the concept of the derivative of a function, and we saw some of the applications for which derivatives are useful. However, computing the derivative of a function algebraically, from the definition, seemed to be a time-consuming process, forcing us to restrict attention to fairly simple functions.

In this chapter we develop shortcut techniques that will allow us to write down the derivative of a function directly without having to calculate any limit. These techniques will also enable us to differentiate any closed-form function—that is, any function, no matter how complicated, that can be specified by a formula involving powers, radicals, absolute values, exponents, and logarithms. (In Chapter 16 we will discuss how to add trigonometric functions to this list.) We also show how to find the derivatives of functions that are only specified *implicitly*—that is, functions for which we are not given an explicit formula for y in terms of x but only an equation relating x and y.

Precalculus Review
For this chapter you should be familiar with the algebra reviewed in **Sections 0.3 and 0.4**.

11.1 Derivatives of Powers, Sums, and Constant Multiples

Shortcut Rules

Up to this point we have approximated derivatives using difference quotients, and we have done exact calculations using the definition of the derivative as the limit of a difference quotient. While exact calculations are preferable, the calculation of a derivative as a limit is often tedious, so it would be useful to have a quicker method, or shortcut. We discuss the first of the shortcut rules in this section. By the end of this chapter we will be able to find fairly quickly the derivative of almost any function we can write.

The Power Rule

If you look at Examples 2 and 3 in Section 10.6, you may notice a pattern:

$$f(x) = x^2 \implies f'(x) = 2x$$
$$f(x) = x^3 \implies f'(x) = 3x^2.$$

This pattern generalizes to any power of x.

Theorem 11.1 The Power Rule

If n is any constant and $f(x) = x^n$, then

$$f'(x) = nx^{n-1}.$$

Quick Examples

1. If $f(x) = x^2$, then $f'(x) = 2x^1 = 2x$.
2. If $f(x) = x^3$, then $f'(x) = 3x^2$.
3. If $f(x) = x$, rewrite* as $f(x) = x^1$, so $f'(x) = 1x^0 = 1$.
4. If $f(x) = 1$, rewrite as $f(x) = x^0$, so $f'(x) = 0x^{-1} = 0$.

∗ To use the power rule, we rewrite expressions like this in power form: constant times x^n. See Section 0.2 in the Precalculus Review to brush up on negative and fractional exponents. Pay particular attention to radical, positive exponent, and power forms.

W Website
www.WanerMath.com
At the Website you can find a proof of the power rule by following:

Everything

→ Chapter 11

→ Proof of the Power Rule

The proof of the power rule involves first studying the case when n is a positive integer and then studying the cases of other types of exponents (negative integer, rational number, irrational number). You can find a proof at the Website.

EXAMPLE 1 **Using the Power Rule for Negative and Fractional Exponents**

Calculate the derivatives of the following:

a. $f(x) = \dfrac{1}{x}$ **b.** $f(x) = \dfrac{1}{x^2}$ **c.** $f(x) = \sqrt{x}$

Solution

a. Rewrite the function in power form as $f(x) = x^{-1}$. Then $f'(x) = (-1)x^{-2} = -\dfrac{1}{x^2}$.

b. Rewrite the function in power form as $f(x) = x^{-2}$. Then $f'(x) = (-2)x^{-3} = -\dfrac{2}{x^3}$.

c. Rewrite the function in power form as $f(x) = x^{0.5}$. Then $f'(x) = 0.5x^{-0.5} = \dfrac{0.5}{x^{0.5}}$.

Alternatively, rewrite $f(x)$ as $x^{1/2}$, so that $f'(x) = \dfrac{1}{2}x^{-1/2} = \dfrac{1}{2x^{1/2}} = \dfrac{1}{2\sqrt{x}}$.

Table 1 Table of Derivative Formulas

$f(x)$	$f'(x)$
1	0
x	1
x^2	$2x$
x^3	$3x^2$
x^n	nx^{n-1}
$\dfrac{1}{x}$	$-\dfrac{1}{x^2}$
$\dfrac{1}{x^2}$	$-\dfrac{2}{x^3}$
$\sqrt{x}$	$\dfrac{1}{2\sqrt{x}}$

Caution

We cannot apply the power rule to terms in the denominators or under square roots. For example:

1. The derivative of $\dfrac{1}{x^2}$ is **NOT** $\dfrac{1}{2x}$; it is $-\dfrac{2}{x^3}$.   See Example 1(b).

2. The derivative of $\sqrt{x^3}$ is **NOT** $\sqrt{3x^2}$; it is $1.5x^{0.5}$.   Rewrite $\sqrt{x^3}$ as $x^{3/2}$ or $x^{1.5}$, and apply the power rule.

Some of the derivatives in Example 1 are very useful to remember, so we summarize them in Table 1. We suggest that you add to this table as you learn more derivatives. It is *extremely* helpful to remember the derivatives of common functions such as $1/x$ and $\sqrt{x}$, even though they can be obtained by using the power rule as in the above example.

Another Notation: Differential Notation

Here is a useful notation based on the d notation we discussed in Section 10.5. **Differential notation** is based on an abbreviation for the phrase "the derivative with respect to x." For example, we learned that if $f(x) = x^3$, then $f'(x) = 3x^2$. When we say $f'(x) = 3x^2$, we mean the following:

The derivative of x^3 with respect to x equals $3x^2$.

You may wonder why we sneaked in the words "with respect to x." All this means is that the variable of the function is x and not any other variable.[*] Because we

---

[*] This may seem odd in the case of $f(x) = x^3$ because there are no other variables to worry about. But in expressions like st^3 that involve variables other than x, it is necessary to specify just what the variable of the function is. This is the same reason that we write $f(x) = x^3$ rather than just $f = x^3$.

use the phrase "the derivative with respect to x" often, we use the following abbreviation.

Differential Notation; Differentiation

$\dfrac{d}{dx}$ means "the derivative with respect to x."

Thus, $\dfrac{d}{dx}[f(x)]$ is the same thing as $f'(x)$, the derivative of $f(x)$ with respect to x. If y is a function of x, then the derivative of y with respect to x is

$$\frac{d}{dx}(y) \quad \text{or, more compactly,} \quad \frac{dy}{dx}.$$

To **differentiate** a function $f(x)$ with respect to x means to take its derivative with respect to x.

Quick Examples

In Words	Formula
5. The derivative with respect to x of x^3 is $3x^2$.	$\dfrac{d}{dx}(x^3) = 3x^2$
6. The derivative with respect to t of $\dfrac{1}{t}$ is $-\dfrac{1}{t^2}$.	$\dfrac{d}{dt}\left(\dfrac{1}{t}\right) = -\dfrac{1}{t^2}$
7. If $y = x^4$, then $\dfrac{dy}{dx} = 4x^3$.	
8. If $u = \dfrac{1}{t^2}$, then $\dfrac{du}{dt} = -\dfrac{2}{t^3}$.	

Notes

1. $\dfrac{dy}{dx}$ is Leibniz's notation for the derivative we discussed in Section 10.5. (See the discussion before Example 3 there.)

2. Leibniz notation illustrates units nicely: Units of $\dfrac{dy}{dx}$ are units of y per unit of x.

3. We can (and often do!) use different kind of brackets or parentheses in Leibniz notation; for instance, $\dfrac{d}{dx}[x^3]$, $\dfrac{d}{dx}(x^3)$, and $\dfrac{d}{dx}\{x^3\}$ all mean the same thing (and equal $3x^2$). ∎

The Rules for Sums and Constant Multiples

We can now find the derivatives of more complicated functions, such as polynomials, using the following rules. If f and g are functions and if c is a constant, we saw in Section 1.2 how to obtain the **sum**, $f + g$, **difference**, $f - g$, and **constant multiple**, cf.

Theorem 11.2 Derivatives of Sums, Differences, and Constant Multiples

If f and g are any two differentiable functions and if c is any constant, then the sum, $f + g$, the difference, $f - g$, and the constant multiple, cf, are differentiable, and

$$[f \pm g]'(x) = f'(x) \pm g'(x) \qquad \text{Sum rule}$$

$$[cf]'(x) = cf'(x). \qquad \text{Constant multiple rule}$$

In Words:

- The derivative of a sum is the sum of the derivatives, and the derivative of a difference is the difference of the derivatives.
- The derivative of c times a function is c times the derivative of the function.

Differential Notation:

$$\frac{d}{dx}[f(x) \pm g(x)] = \frac{d}{dx}f(x) \pm \frac{d}{dx}g(x)$$

$$\frac{d}{dx}[cf(x)] = c\frac{d}{dx}f(x)$$

Quick Examples

9. $\dfrac{d}{dx}(x^2 - x^4) = \dfrac{d}{dx}(x^2) - \dfrac{d}{dx}(x^4) = 2x - 4x^3$

10. $\dfrac{d}{dx}(7x^3) = 7\dfrac{d}{dx}(x^3) = 7(3x^2) = 21x^2$

    In other words, we multiply the coefficient (7) by the exponent (3) and then decrease the exponent by 1.

11. $\dfrac{d}{dx}(12x) = 12\dfrac{d}{dx}(x) = 12(1) = 12$

    In other words, the derivative of a constant times x is that constant.

12. $\dfrac{d}{dx}(-x^{0.5}) = \dfrac{d}{dx}[(-1)x^{0.5}] = (-1)\dfrac{d}{dx}(x^{0.5}) = (-1)(0.5)x^{-0.5}$

    $= -0.5x^{-0.5}$

13. $\dfrac{d}{dx}(12) = \dfrac{d}{dx}[12(1)] = 12\dfrac{d}{dx}(1) = 12(0) = 0.$

    In other words, the derivative of a constant is zero.

14. If my company earns twice as much (annual) revenue as yours and the derivative of your revenue function is the upper curve shown in the margin, then the derivative of my revenue function is the lower curve.

15. Suppose that a company's revenue R and cost C are changing with time. Then so is the profit, $P(t) = R(t) - C(t)$, and the rate of change of the profit is

    $$P'(t) = R'(t) - C'(t).$$

    In words: *The derivative of the profit is the derivative of revenue minus the derivative of cost.*

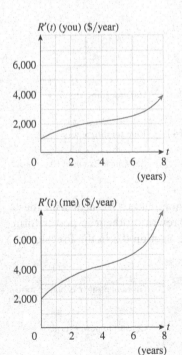

Proof of the Sum Rule

By the definition of the derivative of a function,

$$\frac{d}{dx}[f(x) + g(x)] = \lim_{h \to 0} \frac{[f(x + h) + g(x + h)] - [f(x) + g(x)]}{h}$$

$$= \lim_{h \to 0} \frac{[f(x + h) - f(x)] + [g(x + h) - g(x)]}{h}$$

$$= \lim_{h \to 0} \left[\frac{f(x + h) - f(x)}{h} + \frac{g(x + h) - g(x)}{h} \right]$$

$$= \lim_{h \to 0} \frac{f(x + h) - f(x)}{h} + \lim_{h \to 0} \frac{g(x + h) - g(x)}{h}$$

$$= \frac{d}{dx}[f(x)] + \frac{d}{dx}[g(x)].$$

The next-to-last step uses a property of limits: The limit of a sum is the sum of the limits. Think about why this should be true. The last step uses the definition of the derivative again (and the fact that the functions are differentiable).

The proofs of the rules for differences and constant multiples are similar.

EXAMPLE 2   **Combining the Sum and Constant Multiple Rules and Dealing with x in the Denominator**

Find the derivatives of the following:

a. $f(x) = 3x^2 + 2x - 4$ **b.** $f(x) = \dfrac{2x}{3} - \dfrac{6}{x} + \dfrac{2}{3x^{0.2}} - \dfrac{x^4}{2}$

c. $f(x) = \dfrac{|x|}{4} + \dfrac{1}{2\sqrt{x}}$

Solution

a. $\dfrac{d}{dx}(3x^2 + 2x - 4) = \dfrac{d}{dx}(3x^2) + \dfrac{d}{dx}(2x - 4)$ Rule for sums

$$= \frac{d}{dx}(3x^2) + \frac{d}{dx}(2x) - \frac{d}{dx}(4) \qquad \text{Rule for differences}$$

$$= 3(2x) + 2(1) - 0 \qquad \text{See Quick Example 10.}$$

$$= 6x + 2$$

b. Notice that f has x and powers of x in the denominator. We deal with these terms the same way we did in Example 1, by rewriting them in power form (that is, in the form constant $\times$ power of x; see Section 0.2 in the Precalculus Review):

$$f(x) = \frac{2x}{3} - \frac{6}{x} + \frac{2}{3x^{0.2}} - \frac{x^4}{2} \qquad \text{Given in positive exponent form}$$

$$= \frac{2}{3}x - 6x^{-1} + \frac{2}{3}x^{-0.2} - \frac{1}{2}x^4. \qquad \text{Convert to power form.}$$

We are now ready to take the derivative:

$$f'(x) = \frac{2}{3}(1) - 6(-1)x^{-2} + \frac{2}{3}(-0.2)x^{-1.2} - \frac{1}{2}(4x^3)$$

$$= \frac{2}{3} + 6x^{-2} - \frac{0.4}{3}x^{-1.2} - 2x^3 \qquad \text{Answer in power form.}$$

$$= \frac{2}{3} + \frac{6}{x^2} - \frac{0.4}{3x^{1.2}} - 2x^3. \qquad \text{Answer in positive exponent form.}$$

c. Rewrite $f(x)$ using power form as follows:

$$f(x) = \frac{|x|}{4} + \frac{1}{2\sqrt{x}} \qquad \text{Given in radical form}$$

$$= \frac{1}{4}|x| + \frac{1}{2}x^{-1/2}. \qquad \text{Convert to power form.}$$

Now recall from the end of Section 10.6 that the derivative of $|x|$ is $\dfrac{|x|}{x}$. Thus,

$$f'(x) = \frac{1}{4}\frac{|x|}{x} + \frac{1}{2}\left(\frac{-1}{2}x^{-3/2}\right)$$

$$= \frac{|x|}{4x} - \frac{1}{4}x^{-3/2} \qquad \text{Simplify.}$$

$$= \frac{|x|}{4x} - \frac{1}{4x^{3/2}}. \qquad \text{Answer in positive exponent form.}$$

Notice that in Example 2(a) we had three terms in the expression for $f(x)$, not just two. By applying the rule for sums and differences twice, we saw that the derivative of a sum or difference of three terms is the sum or difference of the derivatives of the terms. (One of those terms had zero derivative, so the final answer had only two terms.) In fact, the derivative of a sum or difference of any number of terms is the sum or difference of the derivatives of the terms. Put another way, to take the derivative of a sum or difference of any number of terms, we take derivatives term by term.

Note Nothing forces us to use only x as the independent variable when taking derivatives (although it is traditional to give x preference). For instance, part (a) in Example 2 can be rewritten as

$$\frac{d}{dt}(3t^2 + 2t - 4) = 6t + 2 \qquad \frac{d}{dt} \text{ means "derivative with respect to } t\text{."}$$

or

$$\frac{d}{du}(3u^2 + 2u - 4) = 6u + 2. \qquad \frac{d}{du} \text{ means "derivative with respect to } u\text{."} \qquad \blacksquare$$

In the preceding examples we saw instances of the following important facts. (Think about these graphically to see why they must be true.)

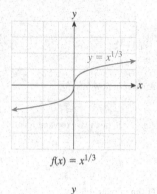

$f(x) = x^{1/3}$

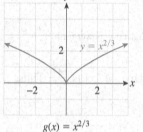

$g(x) = x^{2/3}$

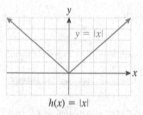

$h(x) = |x|$

Figure 1

The Derivative of a Constant Times x and the Derivative of a Constant

If c is any constant, then:

Rule

$$\frac{d}{dx}(cx) = c$$

$$\frac{d}{dx}(c) = 0$$

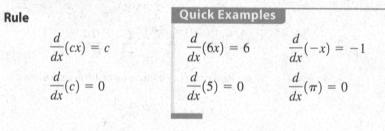

Quick Examples

$$\frac{d}{dx}(6x) = 6 \qquad \frac{d}{dx}(-x) = -1$$

$$\frac{d}{dx}(5) = 0 \qquad \frac{d}{dx}(\pi) = 0$$

In Section 10.5 we pointed out that, by definition, the derivative of a function cannot exist at an endpoint of its domain. Thus, for instance, $f(x) = \sqrt{x}$ and $g(x) = x^{1/4}$ are not differentiable at the endpoint $x = 0$ of their domains. In Example 5 of Section 10.6 we saw that $h(x) = |x|$ also fails to be differentiable at $x = 0$, even though $x = 0$ is not an endpoint of its domain (the domain of h is the set of all real numbers). In the next example we see how to spot the nondifferentiability at a point of this and other functions simply by looking at the formulas for their derivatives.

EXAMPLE 3 **Functions Not Differentiable at a Point**

Find the natural domains of the derivatives of $f(x) = x^{1/3}$, $g(x) = x^{2/3}$, and $h(x) = |x|$.

Solution Let's look at the derivatives of the three functions given:

$$f(x) = x^{1/3}, \quad \text{so} \quad f'(x) = \frac{1}{3}x^{-2/3} = \frac{1}{3x^{2/3}}$$

$$g(x) = x^{2/3}, \quad \text{so} \quad g'(x) = \frac{2}{3}x^{-1/3} = \frac{2}{3x^{1/3}}$$

$$h(x) = |x|, \quad \text{so} \quad h'(x) = \frac{|x|}{x}.$$

The derivatives of all three functions are defined only for nonzero values of x, and their natural domains consist of all real numbers except 0. Thus, the derivatives f', g', and h' do not exist at $x = 0$. In other words, these functions are not differentiable at $x = 0$. If we look at Figure 1, we notice why these functions fail to be differentiable at $x = 0$: The graph of f has a vertical tangent line at 0. Because a vertical line has undefined slope, the derivative is undefined at that point. The graphs of g and h come to a sharp point at 0, where it is not meaningful to speak about the slope of the tangent line; therefore, the derivatives of g and h are not defined there. (In the case of g, where the sharp point is called a *cusp*, a vertical tangent line would seem appropriate, but as in the case of f, its slope is undefined.)

You can also detect this nondifferentiability by computing some difference quotients numerically, as we did for h in Section 10.6.

Applications

EXAMPLE 4   **Gold Price**

You are a commodities trader, and you monitor the price of gold on the spot market very closely during an active morning. Suppose you find that the price of an ounce of gold can be approximated by the function

$$G(t) = 5t^2 - 85t + 1{,}762 \qquad (7.5 \le t \le 10.5),$$

where t is time in hours. (See Figure 2. $t = 8$ represents 8:00 am.)

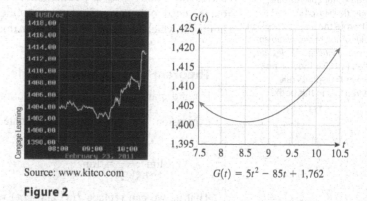

Source: www.kitco.com

$$G(t) = 5t^2 - 85t + 1{,}762$$

Figure 2

a. According to the model, how fast was the price of gold changing at 8:00 am?

b. According to the model, the price of gold

   (A) increased at a faster and faster rate
   (B) increased at a slower and slower rate
   (C) decreased at a faster and faster rate
   (D) decreased at a slower and slower rate

   between 7:30 and 8:30 am.

Solution

a. Differentiating the given function with respect to t gives

   $$G'(t) = 10t - 85.$$

   Because 8:00 am corresponds to $t = 8$, we obtain

   $$G'(8) = 10(8) - 85 = -5.$$

   The units of the derivative are dollars per hour, so we conclude that, at 8:00 am, the price of gold was dropping at a rate of $5 per hour.

b. From the graph we can see that, between 7:30 and 8:30 am (the interval $[7.5, 8.5]$), the price of gold was decreasing. Also from the graph we see that the slope of the tangent becomes less and less negative as t increases, so the price of gold is decreasing at a slower and slower rate (choice (D)).

   We can also see this algebraically from the derivative, $G'(t) = 10t - 85$: For values of t less than 8.5, $G'(t)$ is negative; that is, the rate of change of G is negative, so the price of gold is decreasing. Further, as t increases, $G'(t)$ becomes less and less negative, so the price of gold is decreasing at a slower and slower rate, confirming that choice (D) is the correct one.

An Application to Limits: L'Hospital's Rule

The limits that caused us some trouble in Sections 10.1–10.3 are those of the form $\lim_{x \to a} f(x)$ in which substituting $x = a$ gave us an indeterminate form, such as

$$\lim_{x \to 2} \frac{x^3 - 8}{x - 2} \qquad \text{Substituting } x = 2 \text{ yields } \tfrac{0}{0}.$$

$$\lim_{x \to +\infty} \frac{2x - 4}{x - 1}. \qquad \text{Substituting } x = +\infty \text{ yields } \tfrac{\infty}{\infty}.$$

L'Hospital's rule* gives us an alternative way of computing limits such as these without the need to do any preliminary simplification. It also allows us to compute some limits for which algebraic simplification does not work.

* Guillaume François Antoine, Marquis de l'Hospital (1661–1704) wrote the first textbook on calculus, *Analyse des infiniment petits pour l'intelligence des lignes courbes*, in 1692. The rule now known as l'Hospital's rule appeared first in this book.

Theorem 11.3 L'Hospital's Rule

If f and g are two differentiable functions such that substituting $x = a$ in the expression $\dfrac{f(x)}{g(x)}$ gives the indeterminate form $\dfrac{0}{0}$ or $\dfrac{\infty}{\infty}$, then

$$\lim_{x \to a} \frac{f(x)}{g(x)} = \lim_{x \to a} \frac{f'(x)}{g'(x)}.$$

That is, we can replace $f(x)$ and $g(x)$ with their *derivatives* and try again to take the limit.

Quick Examples

16. Substituting $x = 2$ in $\dfrac{x^3 - 8}{x - 2}$ yields $\dfrac{0}{0}$. Therefore, l'Hospital's rule applies, and

$$\lim_{x \to 2} \frac{x^3 - 8}{x - 2} = \lim_{x \to 2} \frac{3x^2}{1} = \frac{3(2)^2}{1} = 12.$$

17. Substituting $x = +\infty$ in $\dfrac{2x - 4}{x - 1}$ yields $\dfrac{\infty}{\infty}$. Therefore, l'Hospital's rule applies, and

$$\lim_{x \to +\infty} \frac{2x - 4}{x - 1} = \lim_{x \to +\infty} \frac{2}{1} = 2.$$

---

† A proof of l'Hospital's rule can be found in most advanced calculus textbooks.

The proof of l'Hospital's rule is beyond the scope of this text.[†]

EXAMPLE 5 Applying L'Hospital's Rule

Check whether l'Hospital's rule applies to each of the following limits. If it does, use it to evaluate the limit. Otherwise, use some other method to evaluate the limit.

a. $\displaystyle \lim_{x \to 1} \frac{x^2 - 2x + 1}{4x^3 - 3x^2 - 6x + 5}$ **b.** $\displaystyle \lim_{x \to +\infty} \frac{2x^2 - 4x}{5x^3 - 3x + 5}$

c. $\displaystyle \lim_{x \to 1} \frac{x - 1}{x^3 - 3x^2 + 3x - 1}$ **d.** $\displaystyle \lim_{x \to 1} \frac{x}{x^3 - 3x^2 + 3x - 1}$

Solution

a. Setting $x = 1$ yields

$$\frac{1 - 2 + 1}{4 - 3 - 6 + 5} = \frac{0}{0}.$$

Therefore, l'Hospital's rule applies, and

$$\lim_{x \to 1} \frac{x^2 - 2x + 1}{4x^3 - 3x^2 - 6x + 5} = \lim_{x \to 1} \frac{2x - 2}{12x^2 - 6x - 6}.$$

We are left with a closed-form function. However, we cannot substitute $x = 1$ to find the limit because the function $(2x - 2)/(12x^2 - 6x - 6)$ is still not defined at $x = 1$. In fact, if we set $x = 1$, we again get $0/0$. Thus, l'Hospital's rule applies again, and

$$\lim_{x \to 1} \frac{2x - 2}{12x^2 - 6x - 6} = \lim_{x \to 1} \frac{2}{24x - 6}.$$

Once again we have a closed-form function, but this time it is defined when $x = 1$, giving

$$\frac{2}{24 - 6} = \frac{1}{9}.$$

Thus,

$$\lim_{x \to 1} \frac{x^2 - 2x + 1}{4x^3 - 3x^2 - 6x + 5} = \frac{1}{9}.$$

b. Setting $x = +\infty$ yields ∞/∞, so

$$\lim_{x \to +\infty} \frac{2x^2 - 4x}{5x^3 - 3x + 5} = \lim_{x \to +\infty} \frac{4x - 4}{15x^2 - 3}.$$

Setting $x = +\infty$ again yields ∞/∞, so we can apply the rule again to obtain

$$\lim_{x \to +\infty} \frac{4x - 4}{15x^2 - 3} = \lim_{x \to +\infty} \frac{4}{30x}.$$

Note that we cannot apply l'Hospital's rule a third time because setting $x = +\infty$ yields the *determinate* form $4/\infty = 0$. (See the discussion at the end of Section 10.3.) Thus, the limit is 0.

c. Setting $x = 1$ yields $0/0$, so, by l'Hospital's rule,

$$\lim_{x \to 1} \frac{x - 1}{x^3 - 3x^2 + 3x - 1} = \lim_{x \to 1} \frac{1}{3x^2 - 6x + 3}.$$

We are left with a closed-form function that is still not defined at $x = 1$. Further, l'Hospital's rule no longer applies because putting $x = 1$ yields the determinate form $1/0$. To investigate this limit, we refer to the discussion at the end of Section 10.3 and find

$$\lim_{x \to 1} \frac{1}{3x^2 - 6x + 3} = \lim_{x \to 1} \frac{1}{3(x - 1)^2} = +\infty. \qquad \frac{1}{0^-} = +\infty$$

d. Setting $x = 1$ in the expression yields the determinate form $1/0$, so l'Hospital's rule does not apply here. Using the methods of Section 10.3 again, we find that the limit does not exist.

Using the Rules and Recognizing when a Function Is Not Differentiable

Q: *I would like to say that the derivative of $5x^2 - 8x + 4$ is just $10x - 8$ without having to go through all that stuff about derivatives of sums and constant multiples. Can I simply forget about all the rules and write down the answer?*

A: We developed the rules for sums and constant multiples precisely for that reason: so that we could simply write down a derivative without having to think about it too hard. So you are perfectly justified in simply writing down the derivative without going through the rules, but bear in mind that what you are really doing is applying the power rule, the rule for sums, and the rule for multiples over and over.

Q: *Is there a way of telling from its formula whether a function f is not differentiable at a point?*

A: Here are some indicators to look for in the formula for f:

- The absolute value of some expression; f may not be differentiable at points where that expression is zero.

  Example: $f(x) = 3x^2 - |x - 4|$ is not differentiable at $x = 4$.

- A fractional power smaller than 1 of some expression; f may not be differentiable at points where that expression is zero.

  Example: $f(x) = (x^2 - 16)^{2/3}$ is not differentiable at $x = \pm 4$.

11.1 EXERCISES

▼ more advanced   ◆ challenging
Ⓣ indicates exercises that should be solved using technology

*In Exercises 1–10, use the shortcut rules to **mentally** calculate the derivative of the given function.* [**HINT:** See Examples 1 and 2.]

1. $f(x) = x^5$

2. $f(x) = x^4$

3. $f(x) = 2x^{-2}$

4. $f(x) = 3x^{-1}$

5. $f(x) = -x^{0.25}$

6. $f(x) = -x^{-0.5}$

7. $f(x) = 2x^4 + 3x^3 - 1$

8. $f(x) = -x^3 - 3x^2 - 1$

9. $f(x) = -x + \dfrac{1}{x} + 1$

10. $f(x) = \dfrac{1}{x} + \dfrac{1}{x^2}$

In Exercises 11–16, obtain the derivative dy/dx, and state the rules that you use. [**HINT:** See Examples 1 and 2.]

11. $y = 10$

12. $y = x^3$

13. $y = x^2 + x$

14. $y = x - 5$

15. $y = 4x^3 + 2x - 1$

16. $y = 4x^{-1} - 2x - 10$

In Exercises 17–40, find the derivative of the given function. [**HINT:** See Examples 1 and 2.]

17. $f(x) = x^2 - 3x + 5$

18. $f(x) = 3x^3 - 2x^2 + x$

19. $f(x) = x + x^{0.5}$

20. $f(x) = x^{0.5} + 2x^{-0.5}$

21. $g(x) = x^{-2} - 3x^{-1} - 2$

22. $g(x) = 2x^{-1} + 4x^{-2}$

23. $g(x) = \dfrac{1}{x} - \dfrac{1}{x^2}$

24. $g(x) = \dfrac{1}{x^2} + \dfrac{1}{x^3}$

25. $h(x) = \dfrac{2}{x^{0.4}}$

26. $h(x) = -\dfrac{1}{2x^{0.2}}$

27. $h(x) = \dfrac{1}{x^2} + \dfrac{2}{x^3}$

28. $h(x) = \dfrac{2}{x} - \dfrac{2}{x^3} + \dfrac{1}{x^4}$

29. $r(x) = \dfrac{2}{3x} - \dfrac{1}{2x^{0.1}}$

30. $r(x) = \dfrac{4}{3x^2} + \dfrac{1}{x^{3.2}}$

31. $r(x) = \dfrac{2x}{3} - \dfrac{x^{0.1}}{2} + \dfrac{4}{3x^{1.1}} - 2$

32. $r(x) = \dfrac{4x^2}{3} + \dfrac{x^{3.2}}{6} - \dfrac{2}{3x^2} + 4$

33. $t(x) = |x| + \dfrac{1}{x}$

34. $t(x) = 3|x| - \sqrt{x}$

35. $s(x) = \sqrt{x} + \dfrac{1}{\sqrt{x}}$

36. $s(x) = x + \dfrac{7}{\sqrt{x}}$

[**HINT:** For Exercises 37–38, first expand the given function.]

37. ▼ $s(x) = x\left(x^2 - \dfrac{1}{x}\right)$

38. ▼ $s(x) = x^{-1}\left(x - \dfrac{2}{x}\right)$

[HINT: For Exercises 39–40, first rewrite the given function.]

39. ▼ $t(x) = \dfrac{x^2 - 2x^3}{x}$ **40.** ▼ $t(x) = \dfrac{2x + x^2}{x}$

In Exercises 41–46, evaluate the given expression.

41. $\dfrac{d}{dx}(2x^{1.3} - x^{-1.2})$ **42.** $\dfrac{d}{dx}(2x^{4.3} + x^{0.6})$

43. ▼ $\dfrac{d}{dx}[1.2(x - |x|)]$ **44.** ▼ $\dfrac{d}{dx}[4(x^2 + 3|x|)]$

45. ▼ $\dfrac{d}{dt}(at^3 - 4at)$ (*a* constant)

46. ▼ $\dfrac{d}{dt}(at^2 + bt + c)$ (*a, b, c* constant)

In Exercises 47–52, find the indicated derivative.

47. $y = \dfrac{x^{10.3}}{2} + 99x^{-1}; \dfrac{dy}{dx}$ **48.** $y = \dfrac{x^{1.2}}{3} - \dfrac{x^{0.9}}{2}; \dfrac{dy}{dx}$

49. $s = 2.3 + \dfrac{2.1}{t^{1.1}} - \dfrac{t^{0.6}}{2}; \dfrac{ds}{dt}$ **50.** $s = \dfrac{2}{t^{1.1}} + t^{-1.2}; \dfrac{ds}{dt}$

51. ▼ $V = \dfrac{4}{3}\pi r^3; \dfrac{dV}{dr}$ **52.** ▼ $A = 4\pi r^2; \dfrac{dA}{dr}$

In Exercises 53–58, find the slope of the tangent to the graph of the given function at the indicated point. [HINT: Recall that the slope of the tangent to the graph of f at x = a is f'(a).]

53. $f(x) = x^3; (-1, -1)$ **54.** $g(x) = x^4; (-2, 16)$

55. $f(x) = 1 - 2x; (2, -3)$ **56.** $f(x) = \dfrac{x}{3} - 1; (-3, -2)$

57. $g(t) = \dfrac{1}{t^5}; (1, 1)$ **58.** $s(t) = \dfrac{1}{t^3}; \left(-2, -\dfrac{1}{8}\right)$

In Exercises 59–64, find the equation of the tangent line to the graph of the given function at the point with the indicated x-coordinate. In each case, sketch the curve together with the appropriate tangent line.

59. ▼ $f(x) = x^3; x = -1$ **60.** ▼ $f(x) = x^2; x = 0$

61. ▼ $f(x) = x + \dfrac{1}{x}; x = 2$ **62.** ▼ $f(x) = \dfrac{1}{x^2}; x = 1$

63. ▼ $f(x) = \sqrt{x}; x = 4$ **64.** ▼ $f(x) = 2x + 4; x = -1$

In Exercises 65–70, find all values of x (if any) where the tangent line to the graph of the given equation is horizontal. [HINT: The tangent line is horizontal when its slope is zero.]

65. ▼ $y = 2x^2 + 3x - 1$ **66.** ▼ $y = -3x^2 - x$

67. ▼ $y = 2x + 8$ **68.** ▼ $y = -x + 1$

69. ▼ $y = x + \dfrac{1}{x}$ **70.** ▼ $y = x - \sqrt{x}$

71. ◆ Write out the proof that $\dfrac{d}{dx}(x^4) = 4x^3$.

72. ◆ Write out the proof that $\dfrac{d}{dx}(x^5) = 5x^4$.

In Exercises 73–76, determine whether f is differentiable at the given point. If f'(a) exists, give its value. [HINT: See Example 3.]

73. $f(x) = x - x^{1/3}$ **a.** $a = 1$ **b.** $a = 0$

74. $f(x) = 2x + x^{4/3}$ **a.** $a = 8$ **b.** $a = 0$

75. $f(x) = x^{5/4} - 1$ **a.** $a = 16$ **b.** $a = 0$

76. $f(x) = x^{1/5} + 5$ **a.** $a = 1$ **b.** $a = 0$

In Exercises 77–88, say whether l'Hospital's rule applies. If it does, use it to evaluate the given limit. If not, use some other method.

77. $\displaystyle\lim_{x \to 1} \dfrac{x^2 - 2x + 1}{x^2 - x}$ **78.** $\displaystyle\lim_{x \to -1} \dfrac{x^2 + 3x + 2}{x^2 + x}$

79. $\displaystyle\lim_{x \to 2} \dfrac{x^3 - 8}{x - 2}$ **80.** $\displaystyle\lim_{x \to 0} \dfrac{x^3 + 8}{x^2 + 3x + 2}$

81. $\displaystyle\lim_{x \to 1} \dfrac{x^2 + 3x + 2}{x^2 + x}$ **82.** $\displaystyle\lim_{x \to -2} \dfrac{x^3 + 8}{x^2 + 3x + 2}$

83. $\displaystyle\lim_{x \to -\infty} \dfrac{3x^2 + 10x - 1}{2x^2 - 5x}$ **84.** $\displaystyle\lim_{x \to -\infty} \dfrac{6x^2 + 5x + 100}{3x^2 - 9}$

85. $\displaystyle\lim_{x \to -\infty} \dfrac{10x^2 + 300x + 1}{5x + 2}$ **86.** $\displaystyle\lim_{x \to -\infty} \dfrac{2x^4 + 20x^3}{1,000x^3 + 6}$

87. $\displaystyle\lim_{x \to -\infty} \dfrac{x^3 - 100}{2x^2 + 500}$ **88.** $\displaystyle\lim_{x \to -\infty} \dfrac{x^2 + 30x}{2x^6 + 10x}$

Applications

89. *Crude Oil Prices* The price per barrel of crude oil in the period 1980–2013, in constant 2014 dollars, can be approximated by

$$P(t) = 0.27t^2 - 8.6t + 93 \text{ dollars} \quad (0 \le t \le 33),$$

where *t* is time in years since the start of 1980.[1] Find $P'(t)$ and $P'(30)$. What does the second answer tell you about the price of crude oil? [HINT: See Example 2.]

90. *Median Home Prices* The median home price in the United States over the period January 2010–January 2015 can be approximated by

$$P(t) = 4.5t^2 - 15t + 180 \text{ thousand dollars} \quad (0 \le t \le 5),$$

where *t* is time in years since the start of 2010.[2] Find $P'(t)$ and $P'(1)$. What does the second answer tell you about home prices? [HINT: See Example 2.]

---

[1] Source for data: http://inflationdata.com/Inflation/Inflation_Rate/Historical_Oil_Prices_Table.asp, March 6, 2014.

[2] Source for data: www.zillow.com.

91. Food versus Education The following equation shows the approximate relationship between the percentage y of total personal consumption spent on food and the corresponding percentage x spent on education.[3]

$$y = \frac{18.8}{x^{1.05}} \text{ percentage points} \quad (0.69 \le x \le 2.42)$$

According to the model, spending on food is decreasing at a rate of _____ percentage points per 1 percentage point increase in spending on education when 2.0% of total consumption is spent on education. (Your answer should be rounded to two significant digits.) [HINT: See Example 2(b).]

92. Food versus Recreation The following equation shows the approximate relationship between the percentage y of total personal consumption spent on food and the corresponding percentage x spent on recreation.[4]

$$y = \frac{688}{x^{1.99}} \text{ percentage points} \quad (4.83 \le x \le 9.35)$$

According to the model, spending on food is decreasing at a rate of _____ percentage points per 1 percentage point increase in spending on recreation when 6.0% of total consumption is spent on recreation. (Your answer should be rounded to two significant digits.) [HINT: See Example 2(b).]

93. Velocity If a stone is dropped from a height of 400 feet, its height s after t seconds is given by $s(t) = 400 - 16t^2$, with s in feet.
  a. Compute $s'(t)$, and hence find the stone's velocity at times $t = 0, 1, 2, 3,$ and 4 seconds.
  b. When does the stone reach the ground, and how fast is it traveling when it hits the ground? [HINT: It reaches the ground when $s(t) = 0.$]

94. Velocity If a stone is thrown down at 120 ft/sec from a height of 1,000 feet, its height s after t seconds is given by $s(t) = 1{,}000 - 120t - 16t^2$, with s in feet.
  a. Compute $s'(t)$, and hence find the stone's velocity at times $t = 0, 1, 2, 3,$ and 4 seconds.
  b. When does the stone reach the ground, and how fast is it traveling when it hits the ground? [HINT: It reaches the ground when $s(t) = 0.$]

95. Velocity The height of a soccer ball kicked by Javier "Chicharito" Hernández on Mars is given by $h(t) = 76t - 1.9t^2$ meters, where t is time in seconds after he kicks the ball.[5]

  a. When the ball reaches its highest point, $h'(t)$ must equal zero. Why is this true, and at what value of t does this occur?
  b. How high does the ball go?

96. Velocity The height of a basketball thrown by Chris Paul on Neptune is given by $h(t) = v_0 t - 5.6t^2$ meters, where t is time in seconds after he throws the ball up at v_0 m/sec.[6]
  a. When the ball reaches its highest point, $h'(t)$ must equal zero (see Exercise 95). Give a formula for the value of t when this occurs.
  b. How fast would he need to throw it up in order for it to reach its highest point in half a second? How high would it get?

97. GE Net Income 2009–2013 The annual net income of General Electric for the period 2009–2013 could be approximated by[7]

$$P(t) = -0.39t^2 + 5.2t - 4.1 \text{ billion dollars} \quad (4 \le t \le 8),$$

where t is time in years since 2005.

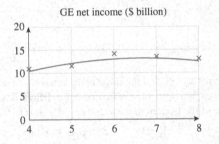

GE net income ($ billion)

  a. Compute $P'(t)$. How fast was GE's annual net income changing in 2011? (Be careful to give correct units of measurement.)
  b. According to the model, GE's annual net income
    (A) increased at a faster and faster rate
    (B) increased at a slower and slower rate
    (C) decreased at a faster and faster rate
    (D) decreased at a slower and slower rate
    during the first 2 years shown (the interval $[4, 6]$). Justify your answer in two ways: geometrically, reasoning entirely from the graph, and algebraically, reasoning from the derivative of P. [HINT: See Example 4.]

98. GE Net Income 2007–2011 The annual net income of General Electric for the period 2007–2011 could be approximated by[8]

$$P(t) = 1.6t^2 - 15t + 46 \text{ billion dollars} \quad (2 \le t \le 6),$$

where t is time in years since 2005.

---

[3] Model based on historical data from 1929–2013. Source for data: U.S. Bureau of Economic Analysis (www.bea.gov), August 2014.
[4] Ibid.
[5] The equation is quite accurate in the thin atmosphere of Mars, assuming Chicharito were to venture there and kick the ball hard enough.
[6] The equation is quite accurate if we ignore resistance due to atmospheric drag on Neptune, assuming Chris Paul were to venture there.
[7] Source for data: www.wikinvest.com.
[8] Ibid.

GE net income ($ billion)

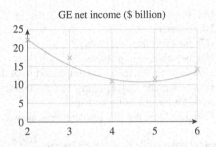

a. Compute $P'(t)$. How fast was GE's annual net income changing in 2008? (Be careful to give correct units of measurement.)

b. According to the model, GE's annual net income
  (A) increased at a faster and faster rate
  (B) increased at a slower and slower rate
  (C) decreased at a faster and faster rate
  (D) decreased at a slower and slower rate
during the first 2 years shown (the interval $[2, 4]$). Justify your answer in two ways: geometrically, reasoning entirely from the graph, and algebraically, reasoning from the derivative of P. [**HINT**: See Example 4.]

99. *Ecology* Increasing numbers of manatees ("sea sirens") have been killed by boats off the Florida coast. The following graph shows the relationship between the number of boats registered in Florida and the number of manatees killed each year.

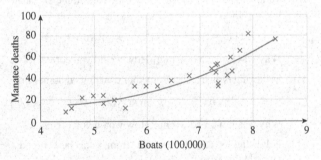

Boats (100,000)

The regression curve shown is given by

$$f(x) = 3.55x^2 - 30.2x + 81 \quad (4.5 \le x \le 8.5),$$

where x is the number of boats (hundreds of thousands) registered in Florida in a particular year and $f(x)$ is the number of manatees killed by boats in Florida that year.[9]

a. Find $f'(x)$, and use your formula to compute $f'(8)$, stating its units of measurement. What does the answer say about manatee deaths?

b. Is $f'(x)$ increasing or decreasing with increasing x? Interpret the answer. [**HINT**: See Example 4.]

100. *SAT Scores by Income* The following graph shows U.S. math SAT scores as a function of parents' income level.[10]

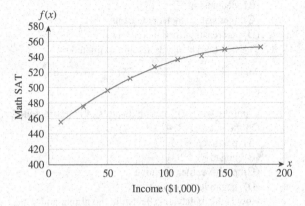

Income ($1,000)

The regression curve shown is given by

$$f(x) = -0.0034x^2 + 1.2x + 444 \quad (10 \le x \le 180),$$

where $f(x)$ is the average math SAT score of a student whose parents earn x thousand dollars per year.

a. Find $f'(x)$, and use your formula to compute $f'(100)$, stating its units of measurement. What does the answer say about math SAT scores?

b. Does $f'(x)$ increase or decrease with increasing x? What does your answer say about math SAT scores? [**HINT**: See Example 4.]

101. ▼ *Market Share: Smartphones* The following graph shows the approximate market shares, in percentage points, of smartphones using Google's Android operating system and Apple's iOS operating system, from the second quarter of 2011 to 2014. (t is time in years and $t = 0$ represents the second quarter of 2010.)[11]

Market share (%)

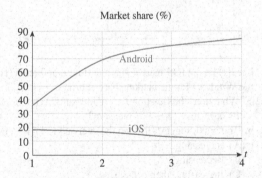

Let $A(t)$ be the Android market share at time t, and let $I(t)$ be the iOS market share at time t.

a. What does the function $A - I$ measure? What does its derivative $(A - I)'$ measure?

[9] Regression model is based on data from 1976 to 2000. Sources for data: Florida Department of Highway Safety & Motor Vehicles, Florida Marine Institute/*New York Times*, February 12, 2002, p. F4.

[10] Regression model is based on 2009 data. Source: College Board/*New York Times*, http://economix.blogs.nytimes.com.

[11] Source for data: IDC, www.idc.com.

b. The graph suggests that, on the interval $[1, 4]$, $A - I$ is
- **(A)** increasing.
- **(B)** decreasing.
- **(C)** increasing, then decreasing.
- **(D)** decreasing, then increasing.

c. The two market shares are approximated by

Android: $A(t) = 3.0t^3 - 29t^2 + 100t - 38$

iOS: $I(t) = -2.3t + 21$.

Compute $(A - I)'$, stating its units of measurement. On the interval $[1, 4]$, $(A - I)'$ is
- **(A)** positive.
- **(B)** negative.
- **(C)** positive, then negative.
- **(D)** negative, then positive.

How is this behavior reflected in the graph, and what does it mean about the market shares of the Android and iOS operating systems?

d. Compute $(A - I)'(3)$. Interpret your answer.

102. ▼ *Market Share: Smartphones* The following graph shows the approximate market shares, in percentage points, of smartphones using Apple's iOS operating system and Microsoft's Windows Phone operating system, from the second quarter of 2011 to 2014. (t is time in years and $t = 0$ represents the second quarter of 2010.)[12]

Market share (%)

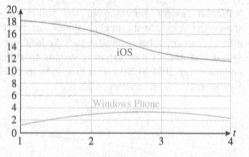

Let $I(t)$ be the iOS market share at time t, and let $W(t)$ be the Windows Phone market share at time t.

a. What does the function $I - W$ measure? What does its derivative $(I - W)'$ measure?

b. The graph suggests that, on the interval $[1, 4]$, $I - W$ is
- **(A)** increasing.
- **(B)** decreasing.
- **(C)** increasing, then decreasing.
- **(D)** decreasing, then increasing.

c. The two market shares are approximated by

iOS: $I(t) = 0.7t^3 - 5.2t^2 + 8.9t + 14$

Windows Phone: $W(t) = -0.7t^2 + 3.9t - 2$.

Compute $(I - W)'$, stating its units of measurement. On the interval $[1, 4]$, $(I - W)'$ is

- **(A)** positive.
- **(B)** negative.
- **(C)** positive, then negative.
- **(D)** negative, then positive.

How is this reflected in the graph, and what does it mean about the market shares of the iOS and Windows Phone operating systems?

d. Compute $(I - W)'(2)$. Interpret your answer.

Communication and Reasoning Exercises

103. What instructions would you give to a fellow student who wanted to accurately graph the tangent line to the curve $y = 3x^2$ at the point $(-1, 3)$?

104. What instructions would you give to a fellow student who wanted to accurately graph a line at right angles to the curve $y = 4/x$ at the point where $x = 0.5$?

105. Consider $f(x) = x^2$ and $g(x) = 2x^2$. How do the slopes of the tangent lines of f and g at the same x compare?

106. Consider $f(x) = x^3$ and $g(x) = x^3 + 3$. How do the slopes of the tangent lines of f and g compare?

107. Suppose $g(x) = -f(x)$. How do the derivatives of f and g compare?

108. Suppose $g(x) = f(x) - 50$. How do the derivatives of f and g compare?

109. Following is an excerpt from your best friend's graded homework:

$$3x^4 + 11x^5 = 12x^3 + 55x^4. \qquad ✗ \; WRONG \; -8$$

Why was it marked wrong? How would you correct it?

110. Following is an excerpt from your own graded homework:

$$x^n = nx^{n-1}. \qquad ✗ \; WRONG \; -10$$

Why was it marked wrong? How would you correct it?

111. Following is another excerpt from your best friend's graded homework:

$$y = \frac{1}{2x} = 2x^{-1}, \text{ so } \frac{dy}{dx} = -2x^{-2}. \qquad ✗ \; WRONG \; -5$$

Why was it marked wrong? How would you correct it?

112. Following is an excerpt from your second best friend's graded homework:

$$f(x) = \frac{3}{4x^2}; f'(x) = \frac{3}{8x}. \qquad ✗ \; WRONG \; -10$$

Why was it marked wrong? How would you correct it?

113. Following is an excerpt from your worst enemy's graded homework:

$$f(x) = 4x^2; f'(x) = (0)(2x) = 0. \qquad ✗ \; WRONG \; -6$$

Why was it marked wrong? How would you correct it?

---

[12] See footnote for Exercise 101.

114. Following is an excerpt from your second worst enemy's graded homework:

$$f(x) = \frac{3}{4x}; \; f'(x) = \frac{0}{4} = 0. \qquad \chi \; \textit{WRONG} \; -10$$

Why was it marked wrong? How would you correct it?

115. One of the questions in your last calculus test was "**Question 1(a)** Give the definition of the derivative of a function f." Following is your answer and the grade you received:

$$nx^{n-1}. \qquad \chi \; \textit{WRONG} \; -10$$

Why was it marked wrong? What is the correct answer?

116. ▼ How would you respond to an acquaintance who says, "I finally understand what the derivative is: It is nx^{n-1}! Why weren't we taught that in the first place instead of the difficult way using limits?"

117. ▼ Sketch the graph of a function whose derivative is undefined at exactly two points but that has a tangent line at all but one point.

118. ▼ Sketch the graph of a function that has a tangent line at each of its points but whose derivative is undefined at exactly two points.

11.2 A First Application: Marginal Analysis

Marginal Cost, Revenue, and Profit

In Chapter 1 we considered linear *cost functions* of the form $C(x) = mx + b$, where C is the total cost, x is the number of items, and m and b are constants. The slope m is the *marginal cost*. It measures the *cost of one more item*. Notice that the derivative of $C(x) = mx + b$ is $C'(x) = m$. In other words, for a linear cost function *the marginal cost is the derivative of the cost function*.

In general, we make the following definition.

Marginal Cost

Recall from Section 1.2 that a **cost function** C specifies the total cost as a function of the number of items x, so $C(x)$ is the total cost of x items. The **marginal cost function** is the derivative C' of the cost function C. Thus, $C'(x)$ measures the rate of change of cost with respect to x.

Units
The units of marginal cost are units of cost (dollars, say) per item.

Interpretation
We interpret $C'(x)$ as the approximate cost of one more item.[*]

* See Example 1 below.

Quick Example

1. If $C(x) = 400x + 1{,}000$ dollars, then the marginal cost function is $C'(x) = \$400$ per item (a constant).

EXAMPLE 1   Marginal Cost

Suppose that the cost in dollars to manufacture portable music players is given by

$$C(x) = 150{,}000 + 20x - 0.0001x^2,$$

† The term $0.0001x^2$ may reflect a cost saving for high levels of production, such as a bulk discount in the cost of electronic components.

where x is the number of music players manufactured.[†] Find the marginal cost function C', and use it to estimate the cost of manufacturing the 50,001st music player.

Solution Because

$$C(x) = 150,000 + 20x - 0.0001x^2,$$

the marginal cost function is

$$C'(x) = 20 - 0.0002x.$$

The units of $C'(x)$ are units of C (dollars) per unit of x (music players). Thus, $C'(x)$ is measured in dollars per music player.

The cost of the 50,001st music player is the amount by which the total cost would rise if we increased production from 50,000 music players to 50,001. Thus, we need to know the rate at which the total cost rises as we increase production. This rate of change is measured by the derivative, or marginal cost, which we just computed. At $x = 50,000$ we get

$$C'(50,000) = 20 - 0.0002(50,000) = \$10 \text{ per music player.}$$

In other words, we estimate that the 50,001st music player will cost approximately \$10.

⇒ **Before we go on...** In Example 1 the marginal cost is really only an *approximation* to the cost of the 50,001st music player:

$$C'(50,000) \approx \frac{C(50,001) - C(50,000)}{1} \qquad \text{Set } h = 1 \text{ in the definition of the derivative.}$$

$$= C(50,001) - C(50,000)$$

$$= \text{cost of the 50,001st music player.}$$

The exact cost of the 50,001st music player is

$$C(50,001) - C(50,000) = [150,000 + 20(50,001) - 0.0001(50,001)^2]$$
$$-[150,000 + 20(50,000) - 0.0001(50,000)^2]$$
$$= \$9.9999.$$

So the marginal cost is a good approximation to the actual cost.

Graphically, we are using the tangent line to approximate the cost function near a production level of 50,000. Figure 3 shows the graph of the cost function together with the tangent line at $x = 50,000$. Notice that the tangent line is essentially indistinguishable from the graph of the function for some distance on either side of 50,000.

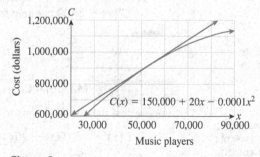

Figure 3

Notes

1. In general, the difference quotient $[C(x + h) - C(x)]/h$ gives the **average cost per item** to produce h more items at a current production level of x items. (Why?)

2. Notice that $C'(x)$ is much easier to calculate than $[C(x + h) - C(x)]/h$. (Try it in this example.) ∎

We can extend the idea of marginal cost to include other functions we discussed in Section 1.2, like revenue and profit.

Marginal Revenue and Profit

Recall that a **revenue** or **profit function** specifies the total revenue R or profit P as a function of the number of items x. The derivatives, R' and P', of these functions are called the **marginal revenue** and **marginal profit** functions. They measure the rate of change of revenue and profit with respect to the number of items.

Units

The units of marginal revenue and profit are the same as those of marginal cost: dollars (or euros, pesos, etc.) per item.

Interpretation

We interpret $R'(x)$ and $P'(x)$ as the approximate revenue and profit from the sale of one more item.

EXAMPLE 2   **Marginal Revenue and Profit**

You operate an iPad refurbishing service. (A typical refurbished iPad might have a custom color case with blinking lights and a personalized logo.) The cost to refurbish x iPads in a month is calculated to be

$$C(x) = 0.25x^2 + 40x + 1,000 \text{ dollars.}$$

You charge customers $80 per iPad for the work.

a. Calculate the marginal revenue and profit functions. Interpret the results.

b. Compute the revenue and profit, and also the marginal revenue and profit, if you have refurbished 20 units this month. Interpret the results.

c. For which value of x is the marginal profit zero? Interpret your answer.

Solution

a. We first calculate the revenue and profit functions:

$$\begin{aligned} R(x) &= 80x & \text{Revenue} = \text{Price} \times \text{Quantity} \\ P(x) &= R(x) - C(x) & \text{Profit} = \text{Revenue} - \text{Cost} \\ &= 80x - (0.25x^2 + 40x + 1,000) \\ &= -0.25x^2 + 40x - 1,000. \end{aligned}$$

The marginal revenue and profit functions are then the derivatives:

Marginal revenue $= R'(x) = 80$

Marginal profit $= P'(x) = -0.5x + 40.$

Interpretation: $R'(x)$ gives the approximate revenue from the refurbishing of one more item, and $P'(x)$ gives the approximate profit from the refurbishing of one more item. Thus, if x iPads have been refurbished in a month, you will earn a revenue of $80 and make a profit of approximately $(-0.5x + 40)$ if you refurbish one more that month.

Notice that the marginal revenue is a constant, so you earn the same revenue ($80) for each iPad you refurbish. However, the marginal profit, $(-0.5x + 40)$, decreases as x increases, so your additional profit is about 50¢ less for each additional iPad you refurbish.

b. From part (a) the revenue, profit, marginal revenue, and marginal profit functions are

$$R(x) = 80x$$
$$P(x) = -0.25x^2 + 40x - 1,000$$
$$R'(x) = 80$$
$$P'(x) = -0.5x + 40.$$

Because you have refurbished 20 iPads this month, $x = 20$, so

$R(20) = 80(20) = \$1,600$	Total revenue from 20 iPads
$P(20) = -0.25(20)^2 + 40(20) - 1,000 = -\$300$	Total profit from 20 iPads
$R'(20) = \$80$ per unit	Approximate revenue from the 21st iPad
$P'(20) = -0.5(20) + 40 = \$30$ per unit.	Approximate profit from the 21st iPad

Interpretation: If you refurbish 20 iPads in a month, you will earn a total revenue of $1,600 and a profit of $-$300 (indicating a loss of $300). Refurbishing one more iPad that month will earn you an additional revenue of $80 and an additional profit of about $30.

c. The marginal profit is zero when $P'(x) = 0$:

$$-0.5x + 40 = 0$$

$$x = \frac{40}{0.5} = 80 \text{ iPads.}$$

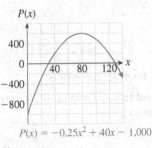

$P(x) = -0.25x^2 + 40x - 1,000$

Figure 4

Thus, if you refurbish 80 iPads in a month, refurbishing one more will get you (approximately) zero additional profit. To understand this further, let us take a look at the graph of the profit function, shown in Figure 4. Notice that the graph is a parabola (the profit function is quadratic) with vertex at the point $x = 80$, where $P'(x) = 0$, so the profit is a maximum at this value of x.

➡ **Before we go on . . .** In general, setting $P'(x) = 0$ and solving for x will always give the exact values of x for which the profit peaks as in Figure 4, assuming that there is such a value. We recommend that, when finding the maximum profit in other examples, you graph the profit function to check whether the profit is indeed a maximum at such a point. ■

EXAMPLE 3   **Marginal Product**

A consultant determines that the number (or quantity) of precision widgets that *Precision Manufacturers* can produce annually is given by

$$Q(n) = 20,000n - 100n^2 - n^3 \quad (10 \le n \le 50),$$

where n is the number of assembly-line workers it employs.

a. Compute $Q'(n)$. $Q'(n)$ is called the **marginal product of labor** at the employment level of n assembly-line workers. What are its units?

b. Calculate $Q(20)$ and $Q'(20)$, and interpret the results.

c. Precision widgets sell for $5 each, and Precision Manufacturers currently employs 20 assembly-line workers. How much more revenue will Precision Manufacturers receive annually if it hires one more assembly-line worker?

Solution

a. Taking the derivative gives

$$Q'(n) = 20{,}000 - 200n - 3n^2.$$

The units of $Q'(n)$ are widgets per worker.

b. Substituting into the formula for $Q(n)$, we get

$$Q(20) = 20{,}000(20) - 100(20)^2 - (20)^3 = 352{,}000 \text{ widgets.}$$

Thus, Precision Manufacturers will produce 352,000 precision widgets annually if it employs 20 assembly-line workers. On the other hand,

$$Q'(20) = 20{,}000 - 200(20) - 3(20)^2 = 14{,}800 \text{ widgets per worker.}$$

Thus, at an employment level of 20 assembly-line workers, annual production is increasing at a rate of 14,800 widgets per additional worker. In other words, if the company were to employ one more assembly-line worker, its annual production would increase by about 14,800 precision widgets.

c. If Precision Manufacturers hires one more worker, its annual production will rise by about 14,800 widgets. If each of these sells for $5, then its annual revenue would rise by $5 \times 14{,}800 = \$74{,}000$.

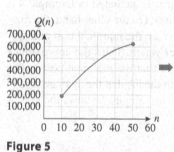

$Q(n)$

Figure 5

* You might even say that it's a marginal economic theory.

➡ **Before we go on . . .** Figure 5 shows the graph of Q from Example 3. As you can see from the graph or from the fact that $Q'(n)$ decreases with increasing n, the marginal product of labor is decreasing: Each new worker increases production by less than the previous one did. This is a common feature known as *diminishing marginal returns*.

In Example 3(c), what would be a reasonable amount for Precision Manufacturers to pay its new worker? *Marginal productivity ethics* says that the worker should be paid his or her marginal productivity, $74,000 annually in this case, as this is the worker's worth to the company, but this argument is not widely accepted.* ∎

Average Cost

EXAMPLE 4 **Average Cost**

Suppose the cost to manufacture watches is given by

$$C(x) = 1{,}000 + 125x - 0.6x^2 + 0.001x^3 \text{ dollars} \qquad (0 \le x \le 400)$$

when x watches are manufactured in a day.

a. Find the average cost per watch if 200 watches are manufactured in a day.

b. Find a formula for the average cost per watch if x watches are manufactured in a day. This function of x is called the **average cost function**, $\overline{C}(x)$.

Solution

a. The total cost of manufacturing 200 watches is given by

$$C(200) = 1,000 + 125(200) - 0.6(200)^2 + 0.001(200)^3$$
$$= \$10,000.$$

Because 200 watches cost a total of $10,000 to manufacture, the average cost of manufacturing one watch is

$$\overline{C}(200) = \frac{10,000}{200} = \$50.00 \text{ per watch.}$$

Thus, if 200 watches are manufactured in a day, each watch costs the manufacturer an average of $50.00 to manufacture.

b. If we replace 200 by x, we get the general formula for the average cost of manufacturing x watches:

$$\overline{C}(x) = \frac{C(x)}{x}$$

$$= \frac{1}{x}(1,000 + 125x - 0.6x^2 + 0.001x^3)$$

$$= \frac{1,000}{x} + 125 - 0.6x + 0.001x^2. \qquad \text{Average cost function}$$

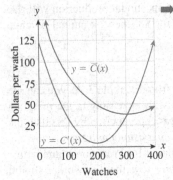

Figure with y-axis "Dollars per watch" (25, 50, 75, 100, 125) and x-axis "Watches" (0, 100, 200, 300, 400), showing $y = \overline{C}(x)$ and $y = C'(x)$.

Figure 6

➡ **Before we go on ...** Average cost and marginal cost convey different but related information. The average cost $\overline{C}(200) = \$50.00$ that we calculated in Example 4 is the cost per item of manufacturing the first 200 watches. On the other hand, the marginal cost function is $C'(x) = 125 - 1.2x + 0.003x^2$, so the marginal cost at a production level of 200 watches is $C'(200) = \$5.00$ per watch. Thus, the approximate cost of manufacturing the 201st watch is $5.00. Note that the marginal cost at this production level is lower than the average cost, which means that the average cost to manufacture watches is going down. (Think about why.) Figure 6 shows the graphs of the marginal and average cost functions. ■

To summarize, we have the following.

Average Cost

Given a cost function C, the **average cost** of the first x items is given by

$$\overline{C}(x) = \frac{C(x)}{x}.$$

The average cost is distinct from the **marginal cost** $C'(x)$, which tells us the approximate cost of the *next* item.

Quick Example

2. For the cost function $C(x) = 20x + 100$ dollars,

Marginal cost $= C'(x) = \$20$ per additional item

$$\text{Average cost} = \overline{C}(x) = \frac{C(x)}{x} = \frac{20x + 100}{x} = \$\left(20 + \frac{100}{x}\right) \text{ per item.}$$

11.2 EXERCISES

▼ more advanced   ◆ challenging
▨ indicates exercises that should be solved using technology

In Exercises 1–4, for each cost function, find the marginal cost at the given production level x, and state the units of measurement. (All costs are in dollars.) [HINT: See Example 1.]

1. $C(x) = 10,000 + 5x - 0.0001x^2$; $x = 1,000$

2. $C(x) = 20,000 + 7x - 0.00005x^2$; $x = 10,000$

3. $C(x) = 15,000 + 100x + \dfrac{1,000}{x}$; $x = 100$

4. $C(x) = 20,000 + 50x + \dfrac{10,000}{x}$; $x = 100$

In Exercises 5 and 6, find the marginal cost, marginal revenue, and marginal profit functions, and find all values of x for which the marginal profit is zero. Interpret your answer.
[HINT: See Example 2.]

5. $C(x) = 4x$; $R(x) = 8x - 0.001x^2$

6. $C(x) = 5x^2$; $R(x) = x^3 + 7x + 10$

7. ▼ A certain cost function has the following graph:

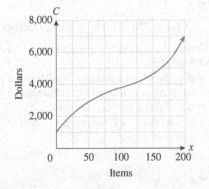

a. The associated marginal cost is
   (A) increasing, then decreasing.
   (B) decreasing, then increasing.

   (C) always increasing.
   (D) always decreasing.

b. The marginal cost is least at approximately
   (A) $x = 0$.   **(B)** $x = 50$.
   (C) $x = 100$.   **(D)** $x = 150$.

c. The cost of 50 items is
   (A) approximately $20 and increasing at a rate of about $3,000 per item.
   (B) approximately $0.50 and increasing at a rate of about $3,000 per item.
   (C) approximately $3,000 and increasing at a rate of about $20 per item.
   (D) approximately $3,000 and increasing at a rate of about $0.50 per item.

8. ▼ A certain cost function has the following graph:

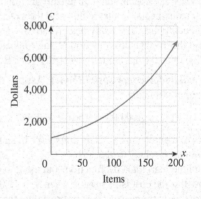

a. The associated marginal cost is
   (A) increasing, then decreasing.
   (B) decreasing, then increasing.
   (C) always increasing.
   (D) always decreasing.

b. When $x = 100$, the marginal cost is
   (A) greater than the average cost.
   (B) less than the average cost.
   (C) approximately equal to the average cost.

c. The cost of 150 items is
   (A) approximately $4,400 and increasing at a rate of about $40 per item.
   (B) approximately $40 and increasing at a rate of about $4,400 per item.
   (C) approximately $4,400 and increasing at a rate of about $1 per item.
   (D) approximately $1 and increasing at a rate of about $4,400 per item.

Applications

9. **Advertising Costs** The cost, in thousands of dollars, of airing x television commercials during a Super Bowl game is given by[13]

$$C(x) = 20 + 4{,}000x + 0.05x^2.$$

   a. Find the marginal cost function, and use it to estimate how fast the cost is increasing when $x = 4$. Compare this with the exact cost of airing the fifth commercial. [HINT: See Example 1.]
   b. Find the average cost function $\overline{C}$, and evaluate $\overline{C}(4)$. What does the answer tell you? [HINT: See Example 2.]

10. **Marginal Cost and Average Cost** The cost of producing x teddy bears per day at the *Cuddly Companion Co.* is calculated by the company's marketing staff to be given by the formula

$$C(x) = 100 + 40x - 0.001x^2.$$

   a. Find the marginal cost function, and use it to estimate how fast the cost is going up at a production level of 100 teddy bears. Compare this with the exact cost of producing the 101st teddy bear. [HINT: See Example 1.]
   b. Find the average cost function $\overline{C}$, and evaluate $\overline{C}(100)$. What does the answer tell you? [HINT: See Example 4.]

11. **Marginal and Average Cost: iPhones** Assume that it costs Apple approximately

$$C(x) = 400{,}000 + 160x + 0.001x^2$$

   dollars to manufacture x 32GB iPhone 6's in an hour at the Foxconn Technology Group.[14]
   a. Find the marginal cost function, and use it to estimate how fast the cost is increasing when $x = 10{,}000$. Compare this with the exact cost of producing the 10,001st iPhone.

b. Find the average cost function $\overline{C}$ and the average cost to produce the first 10,000 iPhones.
c. Using your answers to parts (a) and (b), determine whether the average cost is rising or falling at a production level of 10,000 iPhones.

12. **Marginal and Average Cost: PlayStation 4's** Assume that it costs Sony approximately

$$C(x) = 800{,}000 + 340x + 0.0005x^2$$

   dollars to manufacture x PlayStation 4's in an hour.[15]
   a. Find the marginal cost function, and use it to estimate how fast the cost is increasing when $x = 60{,}000$. Compare this with the exact cost of producing the 60,001st PlayStation 4.
   b. Find the average cost function $\overline{C}(x)$ and the average cost to produce the first 60,000 PlayStation 4's.
   c. Using your answers to parts (a) and (b), determine whether the average cost is rising or falling at a production level of 60,000 PlayStation 4's.

13. **Marginal Revenue and Profit** Your college newspaper, *The Collegiate Investigator*, sells for 90¢ per copy. The cost of producing x copies of an edition is given by

$$C(x) = 70 + 0.10x + 0.001x^2 \text{ dollars.}$$

   a. Calculate the marginal revenue and profit functions. [HINT: See Example 2.]
   b. Compute the revenue and profit, and also the marginal revenue and profit, if you have produced and sold 500 copies of the latest edition. Interpret the results.
   c. For which value of x is the marginal profit zero? Interpret your answer.

14. **Marginal Revenue and Profit** The Audubon Society at *Enormous State University* (ESU) is planning its annual fund-raising "Eatathon." The society will charge students $1.10 per serving of pasta. The society estimates that the total cost of producing x servings of pasta at the event will be

$$C(x) = 350 + 0.10x + 0.002x^2 \text{ dollars.}$$

   a. Calculate the marginal revenue and profit functions. [HINT: See Example 2.]
   b. Compute the revenue and profit, and also the marginal revenue and profit, if you have produced and sold 200 servings of pasta. Interpret the results.
   c. For which value of x is the marginal profit zero? Interpret your answer.

---

[13] The cost of a 30-second ad during the 2014 Super Bowl game was an estimated $4 million. This explains the coefficient of x in the cost function. Source: "Who Bought What in Super Bowl XLVII," *Advertising Age*, Feb. 3, 2014, http://adage.com/.

[14] Not the actual cost equation; the authors do not know Apple's actual cost equation. The average costs given by this model are in rough agreement with the actual cost for one of the 2014 models. Source for cost data: http://time.com.

[15] Not the actual cost equation; the authors do not know Sony's actual cost equation. The average costs given by this model are in rough agreement with the actual cost to manufacture a PlayStation 4 in 2013. Source for estimate of marginal cost: VentureBeat (http://venturebeat.com).

15. *Marginal Profit* Suppose $P(x)$ represents the profit in dollars on the sale of x Blu-ray discs. If $P(1,000) = 3,000$ and $P'(1,000) = -3$, what do these values tell you about the profit?

16. *Marginal Loss* An automobile retailer calculates that its loss in dollars on the sale of *Type M* cars is given by $L(50) = 5,000$ and $L'(50) = -200$ where $L(x)$ represents the loss on the sale of x Type M cars. What do these values tell you about losses?

17. *Marginal Profit* Your monthly profit (in dollars) from selling magazines is given by

$$P = 5x + \sqrt{x}$$

where x is the number of magazines you sell in a month. If you are currently selling 50 magazines per month, find your profit and your marginal profit. Interpret your answers.

18. *Marginal Profit* Your monthly profit (in dollars) from your newspaper route is given by

$$P = 2n - \sqrt{n}$$

where n is the number of subscribers on your route. If you currently have 100 subscribers, find your profit and your marginal profit. Interpret your answers.

19. ▼ ***Marginal Revenue: Pricing Tuna*** Assume that the demand equation for tuna in a small coastal town is given by

$$p = \frac{20,000}{q^{1.5}} \quad (200 \le q \le 800),$$

where p is the price (in dollars) per pound of tuna and q is the number of pounds of tuna that can be sold at the price p in one month.[16]
a. Calculate the price that the town's fishery should charge for tuna to produce a demand of 400 pounds of tuna per month.
b. Calculate the monthly revenue R as a function of the number of pounds of tuna q.
c. Calculate the revenue and marginal revenue (derivative of the revenue with respect to q) at a demand level of 400 pounds per month, and interpret the results.
d. If the town fishery's monthly tuna catch amounted to 400 pounds of tuna and the price is at the level in part (a), would you recommend that the fishery raise or lower the price of tuna to increase its revenue?

20. ▼ ***Marginal Revenue: Pricing Tuna*** Repeat Exercise 19, assuming a demand equation of

$$p = \frac{60}{q^{0.5}} \quad (200 \le q \le 800).$$

21. *Marginal Product* A car wash firm calculates that its daily production (in number of cars washed) depends on the number n of workers it employs according to the formula

$$P = 40n - 0.05n^2 \text{ cars.}$$

Calculate the marginal product of labor at an employment level of 50 workers, and interpret the result. [**HINT:** See Example 3.]

22. *Marginal Product* Repeat Exercise 21 using the formula

$$P = -10n + 2.5n^2 - 0.0005n^4.$$

[**HINT:** See Example 3.]

23. *Average and Marginal Cost* The daily cost to manufacture generic trinkets for gullible tourists is given by the cost function

$$C(x) = -0.001x^2 + 0.3x + 500 \text{ dollars}$$

where x is the number of trinkets.
a. As x increases, the marginal cost
   (A) increases. (B) decreases. (C) increases, then decreases. (D) decreases, then increases.
b. As x increases, the average cost
   (A) increases. (B) decreases. (C) increases, then decreases. (D) decreases, then increases.
c. The marginal cost is
   (A) greater than (B) equal to (C) less than
   the average cost when $x = 100$. [**HINT:** See Example 4.]

24. *Average and Marginal Cost* Repeat Exercise 23, using the following cost function for imitation oil paintings (x is the number of "oil paintings" manufactured):

$$C(x) = 0.1x^2 - 3.5x + 500 \text{ dollars.}$$

[**HINT:** See Example 4.]

25. *Advertising Cost* Your company is planning to air a number of television commercials during the ABC Television Network's presentation of the Academy Awards. ABC is charging your company $1.9 million per 30-second spot.[17] Additional fixed costs (development and personnel costs) amount to $500,000, and the network has agreed to provide a discount of $100,000\sqrt{x}$ for x television spots.
a. Write down the cost function C, marginal cost function C', and average cost function $\overline{C}$.
b. Compute $C'(3)$ and $\overline{C}(3)$. (Round all answers to three significant digits.) Use these two answers to say whether the average cost is increasing or decreasing as x increases.

---

[16] Notice that here we have specified p as a function of q and not the other way around as we did in Section 1.2. Economists frequently specify demand curves this way.

[17] ABC charged up to $1.9 million for a 30-second spot during the 2014 Academy Awards presentation. Source: "Oscar Ad Prices Hit All-Time High as ABC Sells Out 2014 Telecast," *Variety*, October 30, 2013, http://variety.com.

26. *Housing Costs* The cost C of building a house is related to the number k of carpenters used and the number x of electricians used by the formula[18]

$$C = 15,000 + 50k^2 + 60x^2.$$

a. Assuming that 10 carpenters are currently being used, find the cost function C, marginal cost function C', and average cost function $\bar{C}$, all as functions of x.

b. Use the functions you obtained in part (a) to compute $C'(15)$ and $\bar{C}(15)$. Use these two answers to say whether the average cost is increasing or decreasing as the number of electricians increases.

27. ▼ *Emission Control* The cost of controlling emissions at a firm rises rapidly as the amount of emissions reduced increases. Here is a possible model:

$$C(q) = 4,000 + 100q^2$$

where q is the reduction in emissions (in pounds of pollutant per day) and C is the daily cost (in dollars) of this reduction.

a. If a firm is currently reducing its emissions by 10 pounds each day, what is the marginal cost of reducing emissions further?

b. Government clean-air subsidies to the firm are based on the formula

$$S(q) = 500q$$

where q is again the reduction in emissions (in pounds per day) and S is the subsidy (in dollars). At what reduction level does the marginal cost surpass the marginal subsidy?

c. Calculate the net cost function, $N(q) = C(q) - S(q)$, given the cost function and subsidy above, and find the value of q that gives the lowest net cost. What is this lowest net cost? Compare your answer to that for part (b), and comment on what you find.

28. ▼ *Taxation Schemes* To raise revenues during the recent recession, the governor of your state proposed the following taxation formula:

$$T(i) = 0.001i^{0.5},$$

where i represents total annual income earned by an individual in dollars and $T(i)$ is the income tax rate as a percentage of total annual income. (Thus, for example, an income of $50,000 per year would be taxed at about 22%, while an income of double that amount would be taxed at about 32%.)[19]

a. Calculate the after-tax (net) income $N(i)$ an individual can expect to earn as a function of income i.

b. Calculate an individual's marginal after-tax income at income levels of $100,000 and $500,000.

c. At what income does an individual's marginal after-tax income become negative? What is the after-tax income at that level, and what happens at higher income levels?

d. What do you suspect is the most anyone can earn after taxes? (See the footnote.)

29. ▼ *Fuel Economy* Your Porsche's gas mileage (in miles per gallon) is given as a function $M(x)$ of speed x in miles per hour. It is found that

$$M'(x) = \frac{3,600x^{-2} - 1}{(3,600x^{-1} + x)^2}.$$

Estimate $M'(10)$, $M'(60)$, and $M'(70)$. What do the answers tell you about your car?

30. ▼ *Marginal Revenue* The estimated marginal revenue for sales of ESU soccer team T-shirts is given by

$$R'(p) = \frac{(8 - 2p)e^{-p^2 + 8p}}{10,000,000}$$

where p is the price (in dollars) that the soccer players charge for each shirt. Estimate $R'(3)$, $R'(4)$, and $R'(5)$. What do the answers tell you?

31. ◆ *Marginal Cost* (from the GRE Economics Test) In a multiplant firm in which the different plants have different and continuous cost schedules, if costs of production for a given output level are to be minimized, which of the following is essential?

(A) Marginal costs must equal marginal revenue.

(B) Average variable costs must be the same in all plants.

(C) Marginal costs must be the same in all plants.

(D) Total costs must be the same in all plants.

(E) Output per worker per hour must be the same in all plants.

32. ◆ *Study Time* (from the GRE economics test) A student has a fixed number of hours to devote to study and is certain of the relationship between hours of study and the final grade for each course. Grades are given on a numerical scale (0 to 100), and each course is counted equally in computing the grade average. To maximize his or her grade average, the student should allocate these hours to different courses so that

(A) the grade in each course is the same.

(B) the marginal product of an hour's study (in terms of final grade) in each course is zero.

(C) the marginal product of an hour's study (in terms of final grade) in each course is equal, although not necessarily equal to zero.

(D) the average product of an hour's study (in terms of final grade) in each course is equal.

(E) the number of hours spent in study for each course is equal.

---

[18] Based on an exercise in *Introduction to Mathematical Economics* by A. L. Ostrosky, Jr., and J. V. Koch (Waveland Press, Prospect Heights, Illinois, 1979).

[19] This model has the following interesting feature: An income of $1 million per year would be taxed at 100%, leaving the individual penniless!

33. ◆ *Marginal Product (from the GRE Economics Test)* Assume that the marginal product of an additional senior professor is 50% higher than the marginal product of an additional junior professor and that junior professors are paid one half the amount that senior professors receive. With a fixed overall budget, a university that wishes to maximize its quantity of output from professors should do which of the following?
    (A) Hire equal numbers of senior professors and junior professors.
    (B) Hire more senior professors and junior professors.
    (C) Hire more senior professors and discharge junior professors.
    (D) Discharge senior professors and hire more junior professors.
    (E) Discharge all senior professors and half of the junior professors.

34. ◆ *Marginal Product (based on a question from the GRE Economics Test)* Assume that the marginal product of an additional senior professor is twice the marginal product of an additional junior professor and that junior professors are paid two thirds the amount that senior professors receive. With a fixed overall budget, a university that wishes to maximize its quantity of output from professors should do which of the following?
    (A) Hire equal numbers of senior professors and junior professors.
    (B) Hire more senior professors and junior professors.
    (C) Hire more senior professors and discharge junior professors.
    (D) Discharge senior professors and hire more junior professors.
    (E) Discharge all senior professors and half of the junior professors.

Communication and Reasoning Exercises

35. The marginal cost of producing the 1,001st item is
    (A) equal to
    (B) approximately equal to
    (C) always slightly greater than
    (D) always slightly less than
    the actual cost of producing the 1,001st item.

36. For the cost function $C(x) = mx + b$ the marginal cost of producing the 1,001st item is
    (A) equal to
    (B) approximately equal to
    (C) always slightly greater than
    (D) always slightly less than
    the actual cost of producing the 1,001st item.

37. What is a cost function? Carefully explain the difference between *average cost* and *marginal cost* in terms of (a) their mathematical definition, (b) graphs, and (c) interpretation.

38. The cost function for your grand piano manufacturing plant has the property that $\overline{C}(1,000) = \$3,000$ per unit and $C'(1,000) = \$2,500$ per unit. Will the average cost increase or decrease if your company manufactures a slightly larger number of pianos? Explain your reasoning.

39. Give an example of a cost function for which the marginal cost function is the same as the average cost function.

40. Give an example of a cost function for which the marginal cost function is always less than the average cost function.

41. If the average cost to manufacture one grand piano increases as the production level increases, which is greater, the marginal cost or the average cost?

42. If your analysis of a manufacturing company yielded positive marginal profit but negative profit at the company's current production levels, what would you advise the company to do?

43. ▽ If the marginal cost is decreasing, is the average cost necessarily decreasing? Explain.

44. ▽ If the average cost is decreasing, is the marginal cost necessarily decreasing? Explain.

45. ◆ If a company's marginal average cost is zero at the current production level, positive for a slightly higher production level, and negative for a slightly lower production level, what should you advise the company to do?

46. ◆ The **acceleration** of cost is defined as the derivative of the marginal cost function: that is, the derivative of the derivative—or *second derivative*—of the cost function. What are the units of acceleration of cost, and how does one interpret this measure?

11.3 The Product and Quotient Rules

Motivating the Product Rule

We know how to find the derivatives of functions that are sums of powers, such as polynomials. In general, if a function is a sum or difference of functions whose derivatives we know, then we know how to find its derivative. But what about *products and quotients* of functions whose derivatives we know? For instance, how do we calculate the derivative of something like $x^2/(x + 1)$? The derivative of $x^2/(x + 1)$ is not, as one might suspect, $2x/1 = 2x$. That calculation is based on an assumption that the derivative of a quotient is the quotient of the derivatives. But it is easy to see that this assumption is false. For instance, the derivative of $1/x$ is not $0/1 = 0$, but $-1/x^2$. Similarly, the derivative of a product is almost never the product of the derivatives. For instance, the derivative of $x = 1 \cdot x$ is not $0 \cdot 1 = 0$, but 1.

To identify the correct method of computing the derivatives of products and quotients, let's look at a simple example. We know that the daily revenue resulting from the sale of q items per day at a price of p dollars per item is given by the product, $R = pq$ dollars. Suppose you are currently selling wall posters on campus. At this time your daily sales are 50 posters, and sales are increasing at a rate of 4 per day. Furthermore, you are currently charging $10 per poster, and you are also raising the price at a rate of $2 per day. Let's use this information to estimate how fast your daily revenue is increasing. In other words, let us estimate the rate of change, dR/dt, of the revenue R.

There are two contributions to the rate of change of daily revenue: the increase in daily sales and the increase in the unit price. We have

$\dfrac{dR}{dt}$ due to increasing price: $2 per day $\times$ 50 posters = $100 per day

$\dfrac{dR}{dt}$ due to increasing sales: $10 per poster $\times$ 4 posters per day = $40 per day.

Thus, we estimate the daily revenue to be increasing at a rate of $100 + $40 = $140 per day. Let us translate what we have said into symbols:

$\dfrac{dR}{dt}$ due to increasing price: $\dfrac{dp}{dt} \times q$

$\dfrac{dR}{dt}$ due to increasing sales: $p \times \dfrac{dq}{dt}$.

Thus, the rate of change of revenue is given by

$$\frac{dR}{dt} = \frac{dp}{dt}q + p\frac{dq}{dt}.$$

Because $R = pq$, we have discovered the following rule for differentiating a product:

$$\frac{d}{dt}(pq) = \frac{dp}{dt}q + p\frac{dq}{dt}.$$

The derivative of a product is the derivative of the first times the second, plus the first times the derivative of the second.

This rule and a similar rule for differentiating quotients are given next, and also a discussion of how these results are proved rigorously.

Product and Quotient Rules

Product Rule

If f and g are differentiable functions of x, then so is their product fg, and

$$\frac{d}{dx}[f(x)g(x)] = f'(x)g(x) + f(x)g'(x).$$

Product Rule in Words

The derivative of a product is the derivative of the first times the second, plus the first times the derivative of the second.

> ### Quick Example
>
> 1. Let $f(x) = x^2$ and $g(x) = 3x - 1$. Because f and g are both differentiable functions of x, so is their product fg, and its derivative is
>
> $$\frac{d}{dx}[x^2(3x - 1)] = \underset{\text{Derivative of first}}{2x} \cdot \underset{\text{Second}}{(3x - 1)} + \underset{\text{First}}{x^2} \cdot \underset{\text{Derivative of second}}{(3)}.$$

Quotient Rule

If f and g are differentiable functions of x, then so is their quotient f/g, and

$$\frac{d}{dx}\left(\frac{f(x)}{g(x)}\right) = \frac{f'(x)g(x) - f(x)g'(x)}{[g(x)]^2}.$$

provided that $g(x) \neq 0.^{*}$

＊ If $g(x)$ is zero, then the quotient $f(x)/g(x)$ is not defined in the first place.

Quotient Rule in Words

The derivative of a quotient is the derivative of the top times the bottom, minus the top times the derivative of the bottom, all over the bottom squared.

> ### Quick Example
>
> 2. Let $f(x) = x^3$ and $g(x) = x^2 - 1$. Because f and g are both differentiable functions of x, so is their quotient f/g, and its derivative is
>
> $$\frac{d}{dx}\left(\frac{x^3}{x^2 - 1}\right) = \frac{\overset{\text{Derivative of top}}{3x^2}\overset{\text{Bottom}}{(x^2 - 1)} - \overset{\text{Top}}{x^3} \cdot \overset{\text{Derivative of bottom}}{2x}}{\underset{\text{Bottom squared}}{(x^2 - 1)^2}},$$
>
> provided that $x \neq 1$ or -1.

Notes

1. Don't try to remember the rules by the symbols we have used, but remember them in words. (The slogans are easy to remember, even if the terms are not precise.)

2. One more time: *The derivative of a product is* NOT *the product of the derivatives, and the derivative of a quotient is* NOT *the quotient of the derivatives.* To find the derivative of a product, you must use the product rule, and to find the derivative of a quotient, you must use the quotient rule.[†] ∎

† Leibniz made this mistake at first, too, so you would be in good company if you forgot to use the product or quotient rule.

Q: *Wait a minute! The expression $2x^3$ is a product, and we already know that its derivative is $6x^2$. Where did we use the product rule?*

A: To differentiate functions such as $2x^3$, we have used the rule from Section 11.1:

The derivative of c times a function is c times the derivative of the function.

However, the product rule gives us the same result:

Derivative of first   Second   First   Derivative of second

$$\frac{d}{dx}(2x^3) = (0)(x^3) \quad + \quad (2)(3x^2) = 6x^2 \qquad \text{Product rule}$$

$$\frac{d}{dx}(2x^3) = (2)(3x^2) = 6x^2. \qquad \begin{array}{l}\text{Derivative of a constant}\\ \text{times a function}\end{array}$$

We do not recommend that you use the product rule to differentiate functions such as $2x^3$. Continue to use the simpler rule when one of the factors is a constant.

Derivation of the Product Rule

Website
www.WanerMath.com
The quotient rule can be proved in a very similar way. Go to the Website and follow the path
Everything
→ Chapter 11
→ Proof of Quotient Rule

Before we look at more examples of using the product and quotient rules, let's see why the product rule is true. To calculate the derivative of the product $f(x)g(x)$ of two differentiable functions, we go back to the definition of the derivative:

$$\frac{d}{dx}[f(x)g(x)] = \lim_{h \to 0} \frac{f(x + h)g(x + h) - f(x)g(x)}{h}.$$

We now rewrite this expression so that we can evaluate the limit. Notice that the numerator reflects a simultaneous change in f [from $f(x)$ to $f(x + h)$] and g [from $g(x)$ to $g(x + h)$]. To separate the two effects, we add and subtract a quantity in the numerator that reflects a change in only one of the functions:

$$\frac{d}{dx}[f(x)g(x)] = \lim_{h \to 0} \frac{f(x + h)g(x + h) - f(x)g(x)}{h}$$

$$= \lim_{h \to 0} \frac{f(x + h)g(x + h) - f(x)g(x + h) + f(x)g(x + h) - f(x)g(x)}{h} \qquad \begin{array}{l}\text{We subtracted and}\\ \text{added the quan-}\\ \text{tity}^* f(x)g(x + h).\end{array}$$

$$= \lim_{h \to 0} \frac{[f(x + h) - f(x)]g(x + h) + f(x)[g(x + h) - g(x)]}{h} \qquad \text{Common factors}$$

$$= \lim_{h \to 0} \left(\frac{f(x + h) - f(x)}{h}\right)g(x + h) + \lim_{h \to 0} f(x)\left(\frac{g(x + h) - g(x)}{h}\right) \qquad \text{Limit of sum}$$

$$= \lim_{h \to 0} \left(\frac{f(x + h) - f(x)}{h}\right)\lim_{h \to 0} g(x + h) + \lim_{h \to 0} f(x)\lim_{h \to 0}\left(\frac{g(x + h) - g(x)}{h}\right). \qquad \text{Limit of product}$$

* Adding an appropriate form of zero is an age-old mathematical ploy.

Now we already know the following four limits:

$$\lim_{h \to 0} \frac{f(x + h) - f(x)}{h} = f'(x) \qquad \text{Definition of derivative of } f; f \text{ is differentiable.}$$

$$\lim_{h \to 0} \frac{g(x + h) - g(x)}{h} = g'(x) \qquad \text{Definition of derivative of } g; g \text{ is differentiable.}$$

$$\lim_{h \to 0} g(x + h) = g(x) \qquad \text{If } g \text{ is differentiable, it must be continuous.}^\dagger$$

$$\lim_{h \to 0} f(x) = f(x). \qquad \text{Limit of a constant}$$

† For a proof of the fact that, if g is differentiable, it must be continuous, go to the Website and follow the path
Everything
→ Chapter 11
→ Continuity and Differentiability

Putting these limits into the one we're calculating, we get

$$\frac{d}{dx}[f(x)g(x)] = f'(x)g(x) + f(x)g'(x)$$

which is the product rule.

EXAMPLE 1   Using the Product Rule

Compute the following derivatives:

a. $\dfrac{d}{dx}[(x^{3.2} + 1)(1 - x)]$ Simplify the answer.

b. $\dfrac{d}{dx}[(x + 1)(x^2 + 1)(x^3 + 1)]$ Do not expand the answer.

c. $\dfrac{d}{dx}\left(\dfrac{x|x|}{2}\right)$

Solution

a. We can do the calculation in two ways:

Using the Product Rule:

$$\dfrac{d}{dx}[(x^{3.2} + 1)(1 - x)] = \overset{\text{Derivative of first}}{(3.2x^{2.2})}\overset{\text{Second}}{(1 - x)} + \overset{\text{First}}{(x^{3.2} + 1)}\overset{\text{Derivative of second}}{(-1)}$$

$$= 3.2x^{2.2} - 3.2x^{3.2} - x^{3.2} - 1 \qquad \text{Expand the answer.}$$

$$= -4.2x^{3.2} + 3.2x^{2.2} - 1$$

Not Using the Product Rule: First, expand the given expression:

$$(x^{3.2} + 1)(1 - x) = -x^{4.2} + x^{3.2} - x + 1.$$

Thus,

$$\dfrac{d}{dx}[(x^{3.2} + 1)(1 - x)] = \dfrac{d}{dx}(-x^{4.2} + x^{3.2} - x + 1)$$

$$= -4.2x^{3.2} + 3.2x^{2.2} - 1.$$

In this example the product rule saves us little or no work, but in later sections we shall see examples that can be done in no other way. Learn how to use the product rule now!

b. Here we have a product of *three* functions, not just two. We can find the derivative by using the product rule twice:

$$\dfrac{d}{dx}[(x + 1)(x^2 + 1)(x^3 + 1)]$$

$$= \dfrac{d}{dx}(x + 1) \cdot [(x^2 + 1)(x^3 + 1)] + (x + 1) \cdot \dfrac{d}{dx}[(x^2 + 1)(x^3 + 1)]$$

$$= (1)(x^2 + 1)(x^3 + 1) + (x + 1)[(2x)(x^3 + 1) + (x^2 + 1)(3x^2)]$$

$$= (1)(x^2 + 1)(x^3 + 1) + (x + 1)(2x)(x^3 + 1) + (x + 1)(x^2 + 1)(3x^2).$$

We can see here a more general product rule:

$$(fgh)' = f'gh + fg'h + fgh'.$$

Notice that every factor has a chance to contribute to the rate of change of the product. There are similar formulas for products of four or more functions.

c. First write $\dfrac{x|x|}{2}$ as $\dfrac{1}{2}x|x|$.

$$\dfrac{d}{dx}\left(\dfrac{1}{2}x|x|\right) = \dfrac{1}{2}\dfrac{d}{dx}(x|x|) \qquad \text{Constant multiple rule}$$

$$= \dfrac{1}{2}\left((1)\cdot|x| + x\cdot\dfrac{|x|}{x}\right) \qquad \text{Recall that } \dfrac{d}{dx}|x| = \dfrac{|x|}{x}.$$

$$= \dfrac{1}{2}(|x| + |x|) \qquad \text{Cancel the } x.$$

$$= \dfrac{1}{2}(2|x|) = |x| \qquad \text{See the note.}^{*}$$

* Notice that we have found a function whose derivative is $|x|$, namely, $x|x|/2$. Notice also that the derivation we gave assumes that $x \neq 0$ because we divided by x in the third step. However, one can verify, using the definition of the derivative as a limit, that $x|x|/2$ is differentiable at $x = 0$ as well and that its derivative at $x = 0$ is 0, implying that the formula $\dfrac{d}{dx}(x|x|/2) = |x|$ is valid for all values of x, including 0.

EXAMPLE 2 Using the Quotient Rule

Compute the derivatives:

a. $\dfrac{d}{dx}\left(\dfrac{1 - 3.2x^{-0.1}}{x + 1}\right)$ **b.** $\dfrac{d}{dx}\left[\dfrac{(x + 1)(x + 2)}{x - 1}\right]$

Solution

Derivative of top   Bottom   Top   Derivative of bottom

a. $\dfrac{d}{dx}\left(\dfrac{1 - 3.2x^{-0.1}}{x + 1}\right) = \dfrac{(0.32x^{-1.1})(x + 1) - (1 - 3.2x^{-0.1})(1)}{(x + 1)^2}$

Bottom squared

$$= \dfrac{0.32x^{-0.1} + 0.32x^{-1.1} - 1 + 3.2x^{-0.1}}{(x + 1)^2} \qquad \text{Expand the numerator.}$$

$$= \dfrac{3.52x^{-0.1} + 0.32x^{-1.1} - 1}{(x + 1)^2}$$

b. Here we have both a product and a quotient. Which rule do we use: the product or the quotient rule? Here is a way to decide. Think about how we would calculate, step by step, the value of $(x + 1)(x + 2)/(x - 1)$ for a specific value of x—say $x = 11$. Here is how we would probably do it:

1. Calculate $(x + 1)(x + 2) = (11 + 1)(11 + 2) = 156$.

2. Calculate $x - 1 = 11 - 1 = 10$.

3. Divide 156 by 10 to get 15.6.

Now ask: *What was the last operation we performed?* The last operation we performed was division, so we can regard the whole expression as a *quotient*—that is, as $(x + 1)(x + 2)$ *divided by* $(x - 1)$. Therefore, we should use the quotient rule.

The first thing the quotient rule tells us to do is to take the derivative of the numerator. Now, the numerator is a product, so we must use the product rule to take its derivative. Here is the calculation:

$$\frac{d}{dx}\left[\frac{(x+1)(x+2)}{x-1}\right] = \frac{\overbrace{[(1)(x+2)+(x+1)(1)]}^{\text{Derivative of top}}\overbrace{(x-1)}^{\text{Bottom}} - \overbrace{[(x+1)(x+2)]}^{\text{Top}}\overbrace{(1)}^{\substack{\text{Derivative} \\ \text{of bottom}}}}{\underbrace{(x-1)^2}_{\text{Bottom squared}}}$$

$$= \frac{(2x+3)(x-1)-(x+1)(x+2)}{(x-1)^2}$$

$$= \frac{x^2-2x-5}{(x-1)^2}.$$

What is important is to determine the *order of operations* and, in particular, to determine the last operation to be performed. Pretending to do an actual calculation reminds us of the order of operations; we call this technique the **calculation thought experiment**.

⟹ **Before we go on ...** We used the quotient rule in Example 2 because the function was a quotient; we used the product rule to calculate the derivative of the numerator because the numerator was a product. Get used to this: Differentiation rules usually must be used in combination.

Here is another way we could have done this problem. Our calculation thought experiment could have taken the following form:

1. Calculate $(x+1)/(x-1) = (11+1)/(11-1) = 1.2$.
2. Calculate $x+2 = 11+2 = 13$.
3. Multiply 1.2 by 13 to get 15.6.

We would have then regarded the expression as a *product*—the product of the factors $(x+1)/(x-1)$ and $(x+2)$—and used the product rule instead. We can't escape the quotient rule, however: We need to use it to take the derivative of the first factor, $(x+1)/(x-1)$. Try this approach for practice, and check that you get the same answer. ∎

Calculation Thought Experiment

The **calculation thought experiment** is a technique to determine whether to treat an algebraic expression as a product, quotient, sum, or difference. Given an expression, consider the steps you would use in computing its value. If the last operation is multiplication, treat the expression as a product; if the last operation is division, treat the expression as a quotient; and so on.

Quick Examples

3. $(3x^2-4)(2x+1)$ can be computed by first calculating the expressions in parentheses and then multiplying. Because the last step is multiplication, we can treat the expression as a product.

4. $\dfrac{2x - 1}{x}$ can be computed by first calculating the numerator and denominator and then dividing one by the other. Because the last step is division, we can treat the expression as a quotient.

5. $x^2 + (4x - 1)(x + 2)$ can be computed by first calculating x^2, then calculating the product $(4x - 1)(x + 2)$, and finally adding the two answers. Thus, we can treat the expression as a sum.

6. $(3x^2 - 1)^5$ can be computed by first calculating the expression in parentheses and then raising the answer to the fifth power. Thus, we can treat the expression as a power. (We shall see how to differentiate powers of expressions in Section 11.4.)

7. The expression $(x + 1)(x + 2)/(x - 1)$ can be treated as either a quotient or a product: We can write it as a quotient: $\dfrac{(x + 1)(x + 2)}{x - 1}$ or as a product: $(x + 1)\left(\dfrac{x + 2}{x - 1}\right)$. (See Example 2(b).)

EXAMPLE 3   Using the Calculation Thought Experiment

Find $\dfrac{d}{dx}\left[6x^2 + 5\left(\dfrac{x}{x - 1}\right)\right]$.

Solution The calculation thought experiment tells us that the expression we are asked to differentiate can be treated as a *sum*. Because the derivative of a sum is the sum of the derivatives, we get

$$\frac{d}{dx}\left[6x^2 + 5\left(\frac{x}{x - 1}\right)\right] = \frac{d}{dx}(6x^2) + \frac{d}{dx}\left[5\left(\frac{x}{x - 1}\right)\right].$$

In other words, we must take the derivatives of $6x^2$ and $5\left(\dfrac{x}{x - 1}\right)$ separately and then add the answers. The derivative of $6x^2$ is $12x$. There are two ways of taking the derivative of $5\left(\dfrac{x}{x - 1}\right)$: We could first multiply the expression $\left(\dfrac{x}{x - 1}\right)$ by 5 to get $\left(\dfrac{5x}{x - 1}\right)$ and then take its derivative using the quotient rule, or we could pull the 5 out, as we do next:

$$\frac{d}{dx}\left[6x^2 + 5\left(\frac{x}{x - 1}\right)\right] = \frac{d}{dx}(6x^2) + \frac{d}{dx}\left[5\left(\frac{x}{x - 1}\right)\right] \qquad \text{Derivative of sum}$$

$$= 12x + 5\frac{d}{dx}\left(\frac{x}{x - 1}\right) \qquad \text{Constant} \times \text{Function}$$

$$= 12x + 5\left(\frac{(1)(x - 1) - (x)(1)}{(x - 1)^2}\right) \qquad \text{Quotient rule}$$

$$= 12x + 5\left(\frac{-1}{(x - 1)^2}\right)$$

$$= 12x - \frac{5}{(x - 1)^2}.$$

Application

In the next example we return to a scenario similar to the one discussed at the start of this section.

EXAMPLE 4 **Applying the Product and Quotient Rules: Revenue and Average Cost**

Sales of your newly launched miniature wall posters for college dorms, *iMiniPosters,* are really taking off. (Those old-fashioned large wall posters no longer fit in today's downsized college dorm rooms.) Monthly sales to students at the start of this year were 1,500 iMiniPosters, and since that time, sales have been increasing by 300 posters each month, even though the price you charge has also been going up.

a. The price you charge for iMiniPosters is given by

$$p(t) = 10 + 0.05t^2 \text{ dollars per poster,}$$

where t is time in months since the start of January of this year. Find a formula for the monthly revenue, and then compute its rate of change at the beginning of March.

b. The number of students who purchase iMiniPosters in a month is given by

$$n(t) = 800 + 0.2t,$$

where t is as in part (a). Find a formula for the average number of posters each student buys, and hence estimate the rate at which this number was growing at the beginning of March.

Solution

a. To compute monthly revenue as a function of time t, we use

$$R(t) = p(t)q(t). \quad \text{Revenue = Price} \times \text{Quantity}$$

We already have a formula for $p(t)$. The function $q(t)$ measures sales, which were 1,500 posters per month at time $t = 0$ and were rising by 300 per month:

$$q(t) = 1,500 + 300t.$$

Therefore, the formula for revenue is

$$R(t) = p(t)q(t)$$
$$R(t) = (10 + 0.05t^2)(1,500 + 300t).$$

Rather than expanding this expression, we shall leave it as a product so that we can use the product rule in computing its rate of change:

$$R'(t) = p'(t)q(t) + p(t)q'(t)$$
$$= [0.10t][1,500 + 300t] + [10 + 0.05t^2][300].$$

Because the beginning of March corresponds to $t = 2$, we have

$$R'(2) = [0.10(2)][1,500 + 300(2)] + [10 + 0.05(2)^2][300]$$
$$= (0.2)(2,100) + (10.2)(300) = \$3,480 \text{ per month.}$$

Therefore, your monthly revenue was increasing at a rate of \$3,480 per month at the beginning of March.

b. The average number of posters sold to each student is

$$k(t) = \frac{\text{Number of posters}}{\text{Number of students}} = \frac{q(t)}{n(t)} = \frac{1{,}500 + 300t}{800 + 0.2t}.$$

The rate of change of $k(t)$ is computed with the quotient rule:

$$k'(t) = \frac{q'(t)n(t) - q(t)n'(t)}{n(t)^2}$$

$$= \frac{(300)(800 + 0.2t) - (1{,}500 + 300t)(0.2)}{(800 + 0.2t)^2}$$

so

$$k'(2) = \frac{(300)[800 + 0.2(2)] - [1{,}500 + 300(2)](0.2)}{[800 + 0.2(2)]^2}$$

$$= \frac{(300)(800.4) - (2{,}100)(0.2)}{800.4^2} \approx 0.37 \text{ posters per student per month.}$$

Therefore, the average number of posters sold to each student was increasing at a rate of about 0.37 posters per student per month.

11.3 EXERCISES

▼ more advanced ◆ challenging
Ⓣ indicates exercises that should be solved using technology

In Exercises 1–12:
(a) Calculate the derivative of the given function without using either the product rule or the quotient rule.
(b) Use the product rule or the quotient rule to find the derivative. Check that you obtain the same answer.
[**HINT:** See Quick Examples 1 and 2.]

1. $f(x) = 3x$ **2.** $f(x) = 2x^2$

3. $g(x) = x \cdot x^2$ **4.** $g(x) = x \cdot x$

5. $h(x) = x(x + 3)$ **6.** $h(x) = x(1 + 2x)$

7. $r(x) = 100x^{2.1}$ **8.** $r(x) = 0.2x^{-1}$ **9.** $s(x) = \frac{2}{x}$

10. $t(x) = \frac{x}{3}$ **11.** $u(x) = \frac{x^2}{3}$ **12.** $s(x) = \frac{3}{x^2}$

In Exercises 13–28, calculate $\frac{dy}{dx}$. Simplify your answer.

[**HINT:** See Examples 1 and 2.]

13. $y = 3x(4x^2 - 1)$ **14.** $y = 3x^2(2x + 1)$

15. $y = x^3(1 - x^2)$ **16.** $y = x^5(1 - x)$

17. $y = (2x + 3)^2$ **18.** $y = (4x - 1)^2$

19. $y = \frac{4x}{5x - 2}$ **20.** $y = \frac{3x}{-3x + 2}$

21. $y = \frac{2x + 4}{3x - 1}$ **22.** $y = \frac{3x - 9}{2x + 4}$

23. $y = \frac{|x|}{x}$ **24.** $y = \frac{x}{|x|}$

25. $y = \frac{|x|}{x^2}$ **26.** $y = \frac{x^2}{|x|}$

27. $y = x\sqrt{x}$ **28.** $y = x^2\sqrt{x}$

In Exercises 29–56, calculate $\frac{dy}{dx}$. You need not expand your answers. [**HINT:** See Examples 1 and 2.]

29. $y = (x + 1)(x^2 - 1)$

30. $y = (4x^2 + x)(x - x^2)$

31. $y = (2x^{0.5} + 4x - 5)(x - x^{-1})$

32. $y = (x^{0.7} - 4x - 5)(x^{-1} + x^{-2})$

33. $y = (2x^2 - 4x + 1)^2$

34. $y = (2x^{0.5} - x^2)^2$

35. $y = \left(\frac{x}{3.2} + \frac{3.2}{x}\right)(x^2 + 1)$

36. $y = \left(\frac{x^{2.1}}{7} + \frac{2}{x^{2.1}}\right)(7x - 1)$

37. $y = x^2(2x + 3)(7x + 2)$ [**HINT:** See Example 1(b).]

38. $y = x(x^2 - 3)(2x^2 + 1)$ [**HINT:** See Example 1(b).]

39. $y = (5.3x - 1)(1 - x^{2.1})(x^{-2.3} - 3.4)$

40. $y = (1.1x + 4)(x^{2.1} - x)(3.4 - x^{-2.1})$

41. ▼ $y = (\sqrt{x} + 1)\left(\sqrt{x} + \dfrac{1}{x^2}\right)$

42. ▼ $y = (4x^2 - \sqrt{x})\left(\sqrt{x} - \dfrac{2}{x^2}\right)$

43. $y = \dfrac{2x^2 + 4x + 1}{3x - 1}$ **44.** $y = \dfrac{3x^2 - 9x + 11}{2x + 4}$

45. $y = \dfrac{x^2 - 4x + 1}{x^2 + x + 1}$ **46.** $y = \dfrac{x^2 + 9x - 1}{x^2 + 2x - 1}$

47. $y = \dfrac{x^{0.23} - 5.7x}{1 - x^{-2.9}}$ **48.** $y = \dfrac{8.43x^{-0.1} - 0.5x^{-1}}{3.2 + x^{2.9}}$

49. ▼ $y = \dfrac{\sqrt{x} + 1}{\sqrt{x} - 1}$ **50.** ▼ $y = \dfrac{\sqrt{x} - 1}{\sqrt{x} + 1}$

51. ▼ $y = \dfrac{\left(\dfrac{1}{x} + \dfrac{1}{x^2}\right)}{x + x^2}$ **52.** ▼ $y = \dfrac{\left(1 - \dfrac{1}{x^2}\right)}{x^2 - 1}$

53. $y = \dfrac{(x + 3)(x + 1)}{3x - 1}$ [HINT: See Example 2(b).]

54. $y = \dfrac{x}{(x - 5)(x - 4)}$ [HINT: See Example 2(b).]

55. $y = \dfrac{(x + 3)(x + 1)(x + 2)}{3x - 1}$

56. $y = \dfrac{3x - 1}{(x - 5)(x - 4)(x - 1)}$

In Exercises 57–62, compute the indicated derivatives.

57. $\dfrac{d}{dx}[(x^2 + x)(x^2 - x)]$ **58.** $\dfrac{d}{dx}[(x^2 + x^3)(x + 1)]$

59. $\dfrac{d}{dx}[(x^3 + 2x)(x^2 - x)]\Big|_{x=2}$

60. $\dfrac{d}{dx}[(x^2 + x)(x^2 - x)]\Big|_{x=1}$

61. $\dfrac{d}{dt}[(t^2 - t^{0.5})(t^{0.5} + t^{-0.5})]\Big|_{t=1}$

62. $\dfrac{d}{dt}[(t^2 + t^{0.5})(t^{0.5} - t^{-0.5})]\Big|_{t=1}$

In Exercises 63–70, use the calculation thought experiment to say whether the expression is written as a sum, difference, scalar multiple, product, or quotient. Then use the appropriate rules to find its derivative. [HINT: See Quick Examples 3–7 and Example 3.]

63. $y = x^4 - (x^2 + 120)(4x - 1)$

64. $y = x^4 - \dfrac{x^2 + 120}{4x - 1}$ **65.** $y = x + 1 + 2\left(\dfrac{x}{x + 1}\right)$

66. $y = (x + 2) - 4(x^2 - x)\left(x + \dfrac{1}{x}\right)$

(Do not simplify the answer.)

67. $y = (x + 2)\left(\dfrac{x}{x + 1}\right)$ (Do not simplify the answer.)

68. $y = \dfrac{(x + 2)x}{x + 1}$ (Do not simplify the answer.)

69. $y = (x + 1)(x - 2) - 2\left(\dfrac{x}{x + 1}\right)$

70. $y = \dfrac{x + 2}{x + 1} + (x + 1)(x - 2)$

In Exercises 71–76, find the equation of the line tangent to the graph of the given function at the point with the indicated x-coordinate.

71. $f(x) = (x^2 + 1)(x^3 + x);\ x = 1$

72. $f(x) = (x^{0.5} + 1)(x^2 + x);\ x = 1$

73. $f(x) = \dfrac{x + 1}{x + 2};\ x = 0$ **74.** $f(x) = \dfrac{\sqrt{x} + 1}{\sqrt{x} + 2};\ x = 4$

75. $f(x) = \dfrac{x^2 + 1}{x};\ x = -1$ **76.** $f(x) = \dfrac{x}{x^2 + 1};\ x = 1$

Applications

77. Revenue The monthly sales of *Sunny Electronics'* new sound system are given by $q(t) = 2,000t - 100t^2$ units per month, t months after its introduction. The price Sunny charges is $p(t) = 1,000 - t^2$ dollars per sound system, t months after introduction. Find the rate of change of monthly sales, the rate of change of the price, and the rate of change of monthly revenue 5 months after the introduction of the sound system. Interpret your answers. [HINT: See Example 4(a).]

78. Revenue The monthly sales of *Sunny Electronics'* new *iSun* media player is given by $q(t) = 2,000t - 100t^2$ units per month, t months after its introduction. The price Sunny charges is $p(t) = 100 - t^2$ dollars per iSun, t months after introduction. Find the rate of change of monthly sales, the rate of change of the price, and the rate of change of monthly revenue 6 months after the introduction of the iSun. Interpret your answers. [HINT: See Example 4(a).]

79. Saudi Oil Revenues The price of crude oil during the period 2000–2010 can be approximated by

$$P(t) = 6t + 18 \text{ dollars per barrel} \quad (0 \le t \le 10)$$

in year t, where $t = 0$ represents 2000. Saudi Arabia's crude oil production over the same period can be approximated by[20]

$$Q(t) = -0.036t^2 + 0.62t + 8 \text{ million barrels per day}$$
$$(0 \le t \le 10).$$

Use these models to estimate Saudi Arabia's daily oil revenue and also its rate of change in 2008. (Round your answers to the nearest $1 million.)

---

[20] Sources for data: Oil price: InflationData.com www.inflationdata .com, Production: Energy Bulletin www.energybulletin.net.

80. *Russian Oil Revenues* The price of crude oil during the period 2000–2010 can be approximated by

$$P(t) = 6t + 18 \text{ dollars per barrels} \quad (0 \le t \le 10)$$

in year t, where $t = 0$ represents 2000. Russia's crude oil production over the same period can be approximated by[21]

$$Q(t) = -0.08t^2 + 1.2t + 5.5 \text{ million barrels per day}$$
$$(0 \le t \le 10).$$

Use these models to estimate Russia's daily oil revenue and also its rate of change in 2005. (Round your answers to the nearest \$1 million.)

81. *Revenue* Dorothy Wagner is currently selling 20 "I ♥ Calculus" T-shirts per day, but sales are dropping at a rate of 3 per day. She is currently charging \$7 per T-shirt, but to compensate for dwindling sales, she is increasing the unit price by \$1 per day. How fast, and in what direction, is her daily revenue currently changing?

82. *Pricing Policy* Let us turn Exercise 81 around a little: Dorothy Wagner is currently selling 20 "I ♥ Calculus" T-shirts per day, but sales are dropping at a rate of 3 per day. She is currently charging \$7 per T-shirt, and she wishes to increase her daily revenue by \$10 per day. At what rate should she increase the unit price to accomplish this (assuming that the price increase does not affect sales)?

83. *Bus Travel* Thoroughbred Bus Company finds that its monthly costs for one particular year were given by $C(t) = 10{,}000 + t^2$ dollars after t months. After t months the company had $P(t) = 1{,}000 + t^2$ passengers per month. How fast is its cost per passenger changing after 6 months? [HINT: See Example 4(b).]

84. *Bus Travel* Thoroughbred Bus Company finds that its monthly costs for one particular year were given by $C(t) = 100 + t^2$ dollars after t months. After t months the company had $P(t) = 1{,}000 + t^2$ passengers per month. How fast is its cost per passenger changing after 6 months? [HINT: See Example 4(b).]

85. *Fuel Economy* Your muscle car's gas mileage (in miles per gallon) is given as a function $M(x)$ of speed x in miles per hour, where

$$M(x) = \frac{3{,}000}{x + 3{,}600x^{-1}}.$$

Calculate $M'(x)$ and then $M'(10)$, $M'(60)$, and $M'(70)$. What do the answers tell you about your car?

86. *Fuel Economy* Your used Chevy's gas mileage (in miles per gallon) is given as a function $M(x)$ of speed x in miles per hour, where

$$M(x) = \frac{4{,}000}{x + 3{,}025x^{-1}}.$$

Calculate $M'(x)$, and hence determine *the sign* of each of the following: $M'(40)$, $M'(55)$, and $M'(60)$. Interpret your results.

87. ▼ *Oil Imports from Mexico* Daily oil production in Mexico and daily U.S. oil imports from Mexico during 2009–2013 could be approximated by

$$P(t) = 3.1 - 0.014t \text{ million barrels} \quad (9 \le t \le 13)$$
$$I(t) = 1.7 - 0.063t \text{ million barrels} \quad (9 \le t \le 13),$$

where t is time in years since the start of 2000.[22]

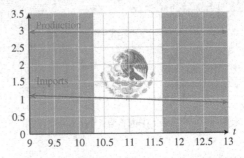

a. What are represented by the functions $P(t) - I(t)$ and $I(t)/P(t)$?

b. Compute $\dfrac{d}{dt}\left[\dfrac{I(t)}{P(t)}\right]\Big|_{t=11}$ to two significant digits. What does the answer tell you about oil imports from Mexico?

88. ▼ *Oil Imports from Mexico* Daily oil production in Mexico and daily U.S. oil imports from Mexico during 2000–2004 could be approximated by

$$P(t) = 3.0 + 0.13t \text{ million barrels} \quad (0 \le t \le 4)$$
$$I(t) = 1.4 + 0.06t \text{ million barrels} \quad (0 \le t \le 4),$$

where t is time in years since the start of 2000.[23]

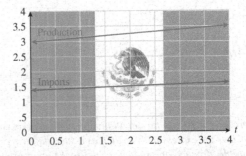

a. What are represented by the functions $P(t) - I(t)$ and $I(t)/P(t)$?

b. Compute $\dfrac{d}{dt}\left[\dfrac{I(t)}{P(t)}\right]\Big|_{t=3}$ to two significant digits. What does the answer tell you about oil imports from Mexico?

[21] See footnote for Exercise 79.

[22] Source for data: Energy Information Administration (http://tonto.eia.doe.gov)/Pemex.

[23] *Ibid.*

89. ▼ *Military Spending* The annual cost per active-duty armed service member in the United States was projected to increase from $160,000 in 2014 to $165,000 in 2018. In 2014 there were 1.36 million armed service personnel, and this number was projected to decrease to 1.32 million in 2018.[24] Use linear models for annual cost and personnel to estimate, to the nearest $10 million, the projected rate of change of total military personnel costs in 2016.

90. ▼ *Military Spending in the 1990s* The annual cost per active-duty armed service member in the United States increased from $80,000 in 1995 to $90,000 in 2000. In 1990 there were 2 million armed service personnel and this number decreased to 1.5 million in 2000.[25] Use linear models for annual cost and personnel to estimate, to the nearest $10 million, the rate of change of total military personnel costs in 1995.

91. ▼ *Biology—Reproduction* The Verhulst model for population growth specifies the reproductive rate of an organism as a function of the total population according to the following formula:

$$R(p) = \frac{r}{1 + kp},$$

where p is the total population in thousands of organisms, r and k are constants that depend on the particular circumstances and the organism being studied, and $R(p)$ is the reproduction rate in thousands of organisms per hour.[26] If $k = 0.125$ and $r = 45$, find $R'(p)$ and then $R'(4)$. Interpret the result.

92. ▼ *Biology—Reproduction* Another model, the predator satiation model for population growth, specifies that the reproductive rate of an organism as a function of the total population varies according to the following formula:

$$R(p) = \frac{rp}{1 + kp},$$

where p is the total population in thousands of organisms, r and k are constants that depend on the particular circumstances and the organism being studied, and $R(p)$ is the reproduction rate in new organisms per hour.[27] Given that $k = 0.2$ and $r = 0.08$, find $R'(p)$ and $R'(2)$. Interpret the result.

93. ▼ *Embryo Development* Bird embryos consume oxygen from the time the egg is laid through the time the chick hatches. For a typical galliform bird egg, the oxygen consumption (in milliliters) t days after the egg was laid can be approximated by[28]

$$C(t) = -0.016t^4 + 1.1t^3 - 11t^2 + 3.6t \quad (15 \le t \le 30).$$

(An egg will usually hatch at around $t = 28$.) Suppose that at time $t = 0$ you have a collection of 30 newly laid eggs and that the number of eggs decreases linearly to zero at time $t = 30$ days. How fast is the total oxygen consumption of your collection of embryos changing after 25 days? (Round your answers to two significant digits.) Comment on the result. [**HINT:** Total oxygen consumption = Oxygen consumption per egg × Number of eggs.]

94. ▼ *Embryo Developmen* Turkey embryos consume oxygen from the time the egg is laid through the time the chick hatches. For a brush turkey the oxygen consumption (in milliliters) t days after the egg was laid can be approximated by[29]

$$C(t) = -0.0071t^4 + 0.95t^3 - 22t^2 + 95t \quad (25 \le t \le 50).$$

(An egg will typically hatch at around $t = 50$.) Suppose that at time $t = 0$ you have a collection of 100 newly laid eggs and that the number of eggs decreases linearly to zero at time $t = 50$ days. How fast is the total oxygen consumption of your collection of embryos changing after 40 days? (Round your answer to two significant digits.) Interpret the result. [**HINT:** Total oxygen consumption = Oxygen consumption per egg × Number of eggs.]

Communication and Reasoning Exercises

95. If f and g are functions of time, and at time $t = 3$, f equals 5 and is rising at a rate of 2 units per second, and g equals 4 and is rising at a rate of 5 units per second, then the product fg equals ____ and is rising at a rate of ____ units per second.

96. If f and g are functions of time, and at time $t = 2$, f equals 3 and is rising at a rate of 4 units per second, and g equals 5 and is rising at a rate of 6 units per second, then fg equals ____ and is rising at a rate of ____ units per second.

97. If f and g are functions of time, and at time $t = 3$, f equals 5 and is rising at a rate of 2 units per second, and g equals 4 and is rising at a rate of 5 units per second, then f/g equals ____ and is changing at a rate of ____ units per second.

98. If f and g are functions of time, and at time $t = 2$, f equals 3 and is rising at a rate of 4 units per second, and g equals 5 and is rising at a rate of 6 units per second, then f/g equals ____ and is changing at a rate of ____ units per second.

[24] Annual costs in constant 2014 dollars. Source: *Long-Term Implications of the 2014 Future Years Defense Program*, Congressional Budget Office, November 2013, www.cbo.gov/sites/default/files/cbofiles/attachments/44683-FYDP.pdf.

[25] Annual costs are adjusted for inflation. Sources: Department of Defense, Stephen Daggett, military analyst, Congressional Research Service/*New York Times*, April 19, 2002, p. A21.

[26] Source: *Mathematics in Medicine and the Life Sciences* by F. C. Hoppensteadt and C. S. Peskin (Springer-Verlag, New York, 1992) pp. 20–22.

[27] *Ibid.*

[28] The model is derived from graphical data published in the article "The Brush Turkey" by Roger S. Seymour, *Scientific American*, December, 1991, pp. 108–114.

[29] *Ibid.*

99. You have come across the following in a newspaper article: "Revenues of HAL Home Heating Oil Inc. are rising by \$4.2 million per year. This is due to an annual increase of 70¢ per gallon in the price HAL charges for heating oil and an increase in sales of 6 million gallons of oil per year." Comment on this analysis.

100. Your friend says that because average cost is obtained by dividing the cost function by the number of units x, it follows that the derivative of average cost is the same as marginal cost because the derivative of x is 1. Comment on this analysis.

101. ▼ Find a demand function $q(p)$ such that, at a price per item of $p = \$100$ revenue will rise if the price per item is increased.

102. ▼ What must be true about a demand function $q(p)$ so that, at a price per item of $p = \$100$, revenue will decrease if the price per item is increased?

103. ▼ You and I are both selling a steady 20 T-shirts per day. The price I am getting for my T-shirts is increasing twice as fast as yours, but your T-shirts are currently selling for twice the price of mine. Whose revenue is increasing faster: yours, mine, or neither? Explain.

104. ▼ You and I are both selling T-shirts for a steady \$20 per shirt. Sales of my T-shirts are increasing at twice the rate of yours, but you are currently selling twice as many as I am. Whose revenue is increasing faster: yours, mine, or neither? Explain.

105. ◆ *Marginal Product (from the GRE Economics Test)* Which of the following statements about average product and marginal product is correct?
(A) If average product is decreasing, marginal product must be less than average product.
(B) If average product is increasing, marginal product must be increasing.
(C) If marginal product is decreasing, average product must be less than marginal product.
(D) If marginal product is increasing, average product must be decreasing.
(E) If marginal product is constant over some range, average product must be constant over that range.

106. ◆ *Marginal Cost (based on a question from the GRE Economics Test)* Which of the following statements about average cost and marginal cost is correct?
(A) If average cost is increasing, marginal cost must be increasing.
(B) If average cost is increasing, marginal cost must be decreasing.
(C) If average cost is increasing, marginal cost must be more than average cost.
(D) If marginal cost is increasing, average cost must be increasing.
(E) If marginal cost is increasing, average cost must be larger than marginal cost.

11.4 The Chain Rule

Introducing the Chain Rule

We can now find the derivatives of expressions involving powers of x combined using addition, subtraction, multiplication, and division, but we still cannot take the derivative of an expression like $(3x + 1)^{0.5}$. For this we need one more rule. The function $h(x) = (3x + 1)^{0.5}$ is not a sum, difference, product, or quotient. To find out what it is, we can use the calculation thought experiment and think about the last operation we would perform in calculating $h(x)$.

1. Calculate $3x + 1$.

2. Take the 0.5 power (square root) of the answer.

The last operation is "take the 0.5 power." We do not yet have a rule for finding the derivative of the 0.5 power of a quantity other than x.

There is a way to build $h(x) = (3x + 1)^{0.5}$ out of two simpler functions: $u(x) = 3x + 1$ (the function that corresponds to the first step in the calculation above) and $f(x) = x^{0.5}$ (the function that corresponds to the second step):

$$h(x) = (3x + 1)^{0.5}$$
$$= [u(x)]^{0.5} \qquad u(x) = 3x + 1$$
$$= f(u(x)). \qquad f(x) = x^{0.5}$$

We say that h is the **composite** of f and u. We read $f(u(x))$ as "f of u of x."

To compute $h(1)$, say, we first compute $3 \cdot 1 + 1 = 4$ and then take the square root of 4, giving $h(1) = 2$. To compute $f(u(1))$, we follow exactly the same steps: First compute $u(1) = 4$, and then compute $f(u(1)) = f(4) = 2$. We always compute $f(u(x))$ from the inside out: Given x, first compute $u(x)$ and then compute $f(u(x))$.

Now, f and u are functions *whose derivatives we know.* The *chain rule* allows us to use our knowledge of the derivatives of f and u to find the derivative of $f(u(x))$. For the purposes of stating the rule, let us avoid some of the nested parentheses by abbreviating $u(x)$ as u. Thus, we write $f(u)$ instead of $f(u(x))$ and remember that u is a function of x.

Chain Rule

If f is a differentiable function of u and u is a differentiable function of x, then the composite $f(u)$ is a differentiable function of x, and

$$\frac{d}{dx}[f(u)] = f'(u)\frac{du}{dx}. \qquad \text{Chain rule}$$

In words: *The derivative of f(quantity) is the derivative of f, evaluated at that quantity, times the derivative of the quantity.*

Quick Examples

In the Quick Examples that follow, u, "the quantity," is some (unspecified) differentiable function of x.

1. Take $f(u) = u^2$. Then

$$\frac{d}{dx}(u^2) = 2u\frac{du}{dx}. \qquad \text{Because } f'(u) = 2u$$

The derivative of a quantity squared is two times the quantity, times the derivative of the quantity.

2. Take $f(u) = u^{0.5}$. Then

$$\frac{d}{dx}(u^{0.5}) = 0.5u^{-0.5}\frac{du}{dx}. \qquad \text{Because } f'(u) = 0.5u^{-0.5}$$

The derivative of a quantity raised to the 0.5 is 0.5 times the quantity raised to the -0.5, times the derivative of the quantity.

To motivate the chain rule, let us see why it is true in the special case when $f(u) = u^3$, where the chain rule tells us that

$$\frac{d}{dx}(u^3) = 3u^2\frac{du}{dx}. \qquad \text{Chain rule with } f(u) = u^3$$

But we could have done this using the product rule instead:

$$\frac{d}{dx}(u^3) = \frac{d}{dx}(u \cdot u \cdot u) = \frac{du}{dx} \cdot u \cdot u + u \cdot \frac{du}{dx} \cdot u + u \cdot u \cdot \frac{du}{dx} = 3u^2\frac{du}{dx},$$

which gives us the same result.[*]

* A similar argument works for $f(u) = u^n$, where $n = 2, 3, 4, \ldots$. For the case of a general differentiable function f the proof of the chain rule is beyond the scope of this book, but you can find one on the Website by following the path

Everything
→ Chapter 11
→ Proof of Chain Rule

Using the Chain Rule

As Quick Examples 1 and 2 illustrate, for every power of a function u whose derivative we know, we now get a generalized differentiation rule. The following table gives more examples.

Original Rule	Generalized Rule	In Words
$\dfrac{d}{dx}(x^2) = 2x$	$\dfrac{d}{dx}(u^2) = 2u\dfrac{du}{dx}$	*The derivative of a quantity squared is twice the quantity, times the derivative of the quantity.*
$\dfrac{d}{dx}(x^3) = 3x^2$	$\dfrac{d}{dx}(u^3) = 3u^2\dfrac{du}{dx}$	*The derivative of a quantity cubed is 3 times the quantity squared, times the derivative of the quantity.*
$\dfrac{d}{dx}\left(\dfrac{1}{x}\right) = -\dfrac{1}{x^2}$	$\dfrac{d}{dx}\left(\dfrac{1}{u}\right) = -\dfrac{1}{u^2}\dfrac{du}{dx}$	*The derivative of 1 over a quantity is negative 1 over the quantity squared, times the derivative of the quantity.*
Power Rule	**Generalized Power Rule**	**In Words**
$\dfrac{d}{dx}(x^n) = nx^{n-1}$	$\dfrac{d}{dx}(u^n) = nu^{n-1}\dfrac{du}{dx}$	*The derivative of a quantity raised to the n is n times the quantity raised to the n − 1, times the derivative of the quantity.*
$\dfrac{d}{dx}|x| = \dfrac{|x|}{x}$	$\dfrac{d}{dx}|u| = \dfrac{|u|}{u}\dfrac{du}{dx}$	*The derivative of the absolute value of a quantity is the absolute value of the quantity divided by the quantity, times the derivative of the quantity.*

EXAMPLE 1   **Using the Chain Rule**

Compute the following derivatives:

a. $\dfrac{d}{dx}[(2x^2 + x)^3]$ **b.** $\dfrac{d}{dx}[(x^3 + x)^{100}]$ **c.** $\dfrac{d}{dx}\sqrt{3x + 1}$ **d.** $\dfrac{d}{dx}|4x^2 - x|$

Solution

a. Using the calculation thought experiment, we see that the last operation we would perform in calculating $(2x^2 + x)^3$ is that of *cubing*. Thus, we think of $(2x^2 + x)^3$ as *a quantity cubed*. There are two similar methods we can use to calculate its derivative.

Method 1: Using the formula We think of $(2x^2 + x)^3$ as u^3, where $u = 2x^2 + x$. By the formula,

$$\frac{d}{dx}(u^3) = 3u^2\frac{du}{dx}. \qquad \text{Generalized power rule}$$

Now substitute for u:

$$\frac{d}{dx}[(2x^2 + x)^3] = 3(2x^2 + x)^2\frac{d}{dx}(2x^2 + x)$$

$$= 3(2x^2 + x)^2(4x + 1).$$

Method 2: Using the verbal form If we prefer to use the verbal form, we get the following:

The derivative of $(2x^2 + x)$ cubed is three times $(2x^2 + x)$ squared, times the derivative of $(2x^2 + x)$.

In symbols,

$$\frac{d}{dx}[(2x^2 + x)^3] = 3(2x^2 + x)^2(4x + 1),$$

as we obtained above.

b. First, the calculation thought experiment: If we were computing $(x^3 + x)^{100}$, the last operation we would perform would be *raising a quantity to the power* 100. Thus, we are dealing with *a quantity raised to the power* 100, so we must again use the generalized power rule. According to the verbal form of the generalized power rule, the derivative of a quantity raised to the power 100 is 100 times that quantity to the power 99, times the derivative of that quantity. In symbols,

$$\frac{d}{dx}[(x^3 + x)^{100}] = 100(x^3 + x)^{99}(3x^2 + 1).$$

c. We first rewrite the expression $\sqrt{3x + 1}$ as $(3x + 1)^{0.5}$ and then use the generalized power rule as in parts (a) and (b):

The derivative of a quantity raised to the 0.5 is 0.5 times the quantity raised to the −0.5, times the derivative of the quantity.

Thus,

$$\frac{d}{dx}\sqrt{3x + 1} = \frac{d}{dx}[(3x + 1)^{0.5}]$$
$$= 0.5(3x + 1)^{-0.5} \cdot 3$$
$$= 1.5(3x + 1)^{-0.5}$$
$$= \frac{1.5}{\sqrt{3x + 1}}.$$

d. The calculation thought experiment tells us that $|4x^2 - x|$ is the absolute value of a quantity, so we use the generalized rule for absolute values (above):

$$\frac{d}{dx}|u| = \frac{|u|}{u}\frac{du}{dx}, \quad \text{or, in words,}$$

The derivative of the absolute value of a quantity is the absolute value of the quantity divided by the quantity times the derivative of the quantity.

Thus,

$$\frac{d}{dx}|4x^2 - x| = \frac{|4x^2 - x|}{4x^2 - x} \cdot (8x - 1). \qquad \frac{d}{dx}|u| = \frac{|u|}{u}\frac{du}{dx}$$

➡ **Before we go on...** The following are examples of common errors in solving Example 1(b):

$$\text{“}\frac{d}{dx}[(x^3 + x)^{100}] = 100(3x^2 + 1)^{99}\text{”} \qquad \text{✗ WRONG!}$$

$$\text{“}\frac{d}{dx}[(x^3 + x)^{100}] = 100(x^3 + x)^{99}.\text{”} \qquad \text{✗ WRONG!}$$

Remember that the generalized power rule says that the derivative of a quantity to the power 100 is 100 times *that same quantity* raised to the power 99, *times the derivative of that quantity.* ∎

Q: *It seems that there are now two formulas for the derivative of an nth power:*

1. $\dfrac{d}{dx}(x^n) = nx^{n-1}$ **2.** $\dfrac{d}{dx}(u^n) = nu^{n-1}\dfrac{du}{dx}$.

Which one do I use?

A: Formula 1 is actually a special case of Formula 2: Formula 1 is the original power rule, which applies only to a power of x. For instance, it applies to x^{10}, but it does not apply to $(2x + 1)^{10}$ because the quantity that is being raised to a power is not x. Formula 2 applies to a power of any *function of* x, such as $(2x + 1)^{10}$. It can even be used in place of the original power rule. For example, if we take $u = x$ in Formula 2, we obtain

$$\frac{d}{dx}(x^n) = nx^{n-1}\frac{dx}{dx}$$

$$= nx^{n-1}. \qquad \text{The derivative of } x \text{ with respect to } x \text{ is } 1.$$

Thus, the generalized power rule really *is* a generalization of the original power rule, as its name suggests.

EXAMPLE 2 **More Examples Using the Chain Rule**

Find: **a.** $\dfrac{d}{dx}[(2x^5 + x^2 - 20)^{-2/3}]$ **b.** $\dfrac{d}{dx}\left(\dfrac{1}{\sqrt{x+2}}\right)$ **c.** $\dfrac{d}{dx}\left(\dfrac{1}{x^2 + x}\right)$

Solution Each of the given functions is, or can be rewritten as, a power of a function whose derivative we know. Thus, we can use the method of Example 1.

a. $\dfrac{d}{dx}[(2x^5 + x^2 - 20)^{-2/3}] = -\dfrac{2}{3}(2x^5 + x^2 - 20)^{-5/3}(10x^4 + 2x)$

b. $\dfrac{d}{dx}\left(\dfrac{1}{\sqrt{x+2}}\right) = \dfrac{d}{dx}(x+2)^{-1/2} = -\dfrac{1}{2}(x+2)^{-3/2}\cdot 1 = -\dfrac{1}{2(x+2)^{3/2}}$

c. $\dfrac{d}{dx}\left(\dfrac{1}{x^2 + x}\right) = \dfrac{d}{dx}(x^2 + x)^{-1} = -(x^2 + x)^{-2}(2x + 1) = -\dfrac{2x + 1}{(x^2 + x)^2}$

➡ **Before we go on . . .** In Example 2(c) we could have used the quotient rule instead of the generalized power rule. We can think of the quantity $1/(x^2 + x)$ in two different ways using the calculation thought experiment:

1. As 1 divided by something—in other words, as a quotient

2. As something raised to the -1 power

Of course, we get the same derivative using either approach. ■

We now look at some more complicated examples.

EXAMPLE 3 **Harder Examples Using the Chain Rule**

Find $\dfrac{dy}{dx}$ in each case:

a. $y = [(x + 1)^{-2.5} + 3x]^{-3}$ **b.** $y = (x + 10)^3\sqrt{1 - x^2}$

Solution

a. The calculation thought experiment tells us that the last operation we would perform in calculating y is raising the quantity $[(x + 1)^{-2.5} + 3x]$ to the power -3. Thus, we use the generalized power rule.

$$\frac{dy}{dx} = -3[(x + 1)^{-2.5} + 3x]^{-4}\frac{d}{dx}[(x + 1)^{-2.5} + 3x]$$

We are not yet done; we must still find the derivative of $(x + 1)^{-2.5} + 3x$. Finding the derivative of a complicated function in several steps helps to keep the problem manageable. Continuing, we have

$$\frac{dy}{dx} = -3[(x + 1)^{-2.5} + 3x]^{-4}\frac{d}{dx}[(x + 1)^{-2.5} + 3x]$$

$$= -3[(x + 1)^{-2.5} + 3x]^{-4}\left(\frac{d}{dx}[(x + 1)^{-2.5}] + \frac{d}{dx}(3x)\right). \quad \text{Derivative of a sum}$$

Now we have two derivatives left to calculate. The second of these we know to be 3, and the first is the derivative of a quantity raised to the -2.5 power. Thus,

$$\frac{dy}{dx} = -3[(x + 1)^{-2.5} + 3x]^{-4}[-2.5(x + 1)^{-3.5} \cdot 1 + 3].$$

b. The expression $(x + 10)^3\sqrt{1 - x^2}$ is a product, so we use the product rule:

$$\frac{d}{dx}[(x + 10)^3\sqrt{1 - x^2}] = \left(\frac{d}{dx}[(x + 10)^3]\right)\sqrt{1 - x^2} + (x + 10)^3\left(\frac{d}{dx}\sqrt{1 - x^2}\right)$$

$$= 3(x + 10)^2\sqrt{1 - x^2} + (x + 10)^3\frac{1}{2\sqrt{1 - x^2}}(-2x)$$

$$= 3(x + 10)^2\sqrt{1 - x^2} - \frac{x(x + 10)^3}{\sqrt{1 - x^2}}.$$

Application

The next example builds on Example 3 from Section 11.2.

EXAMPLE 4   **Marginal Product and Profit**

A consultant determines that *Precision Manufacturers'* annual profit (in dollars) is given by

$$P = 1,000Q^{0.5} + 5Q,$$

where Q is the number of precision widgets it sells each year. The consultant also informs Precision's management that the number of precision widgets the company can manufacture each year depends on the number n of assembly-line workers it employs according to the equation

$$Q = 20,000n - 100n^2 - n^3.$$

Use the chain rule to find the marginal profit $\dfrac{dP}{dn}$ at an employment level of 20 workers, and interpret the answer.

* Try it yourself before going on.

Solution We could calculate the marginal profit by substituting the expression for Q in the expression for P to obtain P as a function of n and then finding dP/dn.* Alternatively—and this will simplify the calculation—we can apply the chain rule directly to the given situation. To see how the chain rule applies, notice that P is a function of Q, where Q in turn is given as a function of n. By the chain rule,

$$\frac{dP}{dn} = P'(Q)\frac{dQ}{dn} \qquad \text{Chain rule}$$

$$= \frac{dP}{dQ}\frac{dQ}{dn}. \qquad \text{Notice how the "quantities" } dQ \text{ appear to cancel.}$$

We need to calculate the two derivatives:

$$\frac{dP}{dQ} = 500Q^{-0.5} + 5$$

and

$$\frac{dQ}{dn} = 20{,}000 - 200n - 3n^2.$$

The derivative we want, dP/dn, is the product of the two derivatives above, each evaluated at an employment level of 20 workers ($n = 20$). For the second we can just substitute $n = 20$ to obtain

† We also calculated this in Example 3 in Section 11.2.

$$\left.\frac{dQ}{dn}\right|_{n=20} = 20{,}000 - 200(20) - 3(20)^2 = 14{,}800.^†$$

For the first, we need the value of Q that corresponds to $n = 20$:

$$Q(20) = 20{,}000(20) - 100(20)^2 - (20)^3 = 352{,}000$$

so

$$\left.\frac{dP}{dQ}\right|_{n=20} = \left.\frac{dP}{dQ}\right|_{Q=352{,}000} = 500(352{,}000^{-0.5}) + 5 \approx 5.8427.$$

Multiplying the two answers gives

$$\left.\frac{dP}{dn}\right|_{n=20} = \left.\frac{dP}{dQ}\right|_{n=20} \cdot \left.\frac{dQ}{dn}\right|_{n=20} \approx (5.8427) \cdot (14{,}800)$$

$$\approx \$86{,}000 \text{ per worker.} \qquad \text{Rounded to two significant digits}$$

This means that, at a production level of 20 workers, adding more workers will increase Precision Manufacturers' annual profit by approximately \$86,000 per worker.

Recall that dP/dQ is the marginal profit per widget and that dQ/dn is the marginal product of labor. Their product, dP/dn, is the marginal profit *per worker*.

The Chain Rule in Differential Notation

The equation

$$\frac{dP}{dn} = \frac{dP}{dQ}\frac{dQ}{dn}$$

in the example above is an appealing way of writing the chain rule because it suggests that the "quantities" dQ cancel. In general, we can write the chain rule as follows.

Chain Rule: Differential Notation

If y is a differentiable function of u, and u is a differentiable function of x, then

$$\frac{dy}{dx} = \frac{dy}{du}\frac{du}{dx}.$$ The terms du cancel.

Notice how the units of measurement also cancel:

$$\frac{\text{Units of } y}{\text{Units of } x} = \frac{\text{Units of } y}{\cancel{\text{Units of } u}}\frac{\cancel{\text{Units of } u}}{\text{Units of } x}.$$

Quick Examples

3. If $y = u^3$, where $u = 4x + 1$, then

$$\frac{dy}{dx} = \frac{dy}{du}\frac{du}{dx} = 3u^2 \cdot 4 = 12u^2 = 12(4x + 1)^2.$$

4. If $q = 43p^2$, where p (and hence q also) is a differentiable function of t, then

$$\frac{dq}{dt} = \frac{dq}{dp}\frac{dp}{dt}$$

$$= 86p\frac{dp}{dt}.$$ p is not specified, so we leave dp/dt as is.

5. Suppose that a company's weekly revenue R depends on the unit price p, which in turn depends on weekly sales q (by means of a demand equation). Then, if

$$\left.\frac{dR}{dp}\right|_{q=1,000} = \$40 \text{ per } \$1 \text{ increase in price}$$

and

$$\left.\frac{dp}{dq}\right|_{q=1,000} = -\$20 \text{ per additional item sold per week,}$$

the corresponding marginal revenue is

$$\left.\frac{dR}{dq}\right|_{q=1,000} = \left.\frac{dR}{dp}\right|_{q=1,000}\left.\frac{dp}{dq}\right|_{q=1,000} = (40)(-20)$$

$$= -\$800 \text{ per additional item sold.*}$$

* Notice that the units of measurement are Revenue per item = Revenue per \$1 price increase × Price increase per additional item.

Look again at the way the terms du appeared to cancel in the differential formula $\frac{dy}{dx} = \frac{dy}{du}\frac{du}{dx}$. In fact, the chain rule tells us more.

Manipulating Derivatives in Differential Notation

1. Suppose y is a function of x. Then, thinking of x as a function of y (as, for instance, when we can solve for x)[†] we have

$$\frac{dx}{dy} = \frac{1}{\left(\dfrac{dy}{dx}\right)}, \text{ provided that } \frac{dy}{dx} \neq 0.$$ Notice again how $\frac{dy}{dx}$ behaves like a fraction.

† The notion of "thinking of x as a function of y" will be made more precise in Section 11.6.

Quick Example

6. In the demand equation $q = -0.2p - 8$ we have $\dfrac{dq}{dp} = -0.2$. Therefore,

$$\frac{dp}{dq} = \frac{1}{\left(\dfrac{dq}{dp}\right)} = \frac{1}{-0.2} = -5.$$

2. Suppose x and y are functions of t. Then, thinking of y as a function of x (as, for instance, when we can solve for t as a function of x, and hence obtain y as a function of x), we have

$$\frac{dy}{dx} = \frac{dy/dt}{dx/dt}.$$ The terms dt appear to cancel.

Quick Example

7. If $x = 3 - 0.2t$ and $y = 6 + 6t$, then

$$\frac{dy}{dx} = \frac{dy/dt}{dx/dt} = \frac{6}{-0.2} = -30.$$

To see why the above formulas work, notice that the second formula,

$$\frac{dy}{dx} = \frac{\left(\dfrac{dy}{dt}\right)}{\left(\dfrac{dx}{dt}\right)},$$

can be written as

$$\frac{dy}{dx}\frac{dx}{dt} = \frac{dy}{dt},$$ Multiply both sides by $\dfrac{dx}{dt}$.

which is just the differential form of the chain rule. For the first formula, use the second formula with y playing the role of t:

$$\frac{dy}{dx} = \frac{dy/dy}{dx/dy} = \frac{1}{dx/dy}.$$ $\dfrac{dy}{dy} = \dfrac{d}{dy}(y) = 1$

FAQs

Using the Chain Rule

Q: How do I decide whether or not to use the chain rule when taking a derivative?

A: Use the calculation thought experiment (Section 11.3): Given an expression, consider the steps you would use in computing its value.

- If the last step is *raising a quantity to a power*, as in $\left(\dfrac{x^2-1}{x+4}\right)^4$, then the first step to use is the chain rule (in the form of the generalized power rule):

$$\frac{d}{dx}\left(\frac{x^2-1}{x+4}\right)^4 = 4\left(\frac{x^2-1}{x+4}\right)^3 \frac{d}{dx}\left(\frac{x^2-1}{x+4}\right).$$

Then use the appropriate rules to finish the computation. You may need to again use the calculation thought experiment to decide on the next step (here, the quotient rule):

$$= 4\left(\frac{x^2-1}{x+4}\right)^3 \frac{(2x)(x+4)-(x^2-1)(1)}{(x+4)^2}.$$

- If the last step is *division*, as in $\dfrac{(x^2-1)}{(3x+4)^4}$, then the first step to use is the quotient rule:

$$\frac{d}{dx}\frac{(x^2-1)}{(3x+4)^4} = \frac{(2x)(3x+4)^4-(x^2-1)\dfrac{d}{dx}(3x+4)^4}{(3x+4)^8}.$$

Then use the appropriate rules to finish the computation (here, the chain rule):

$$= \frac{(2x)(3x+4)^4-(x^2-1)[4(3x+4)^3(3)]}{(3x+4)^8}.$$

- If the last step is *multiplication, addition, subtraction, or multiplication by a constant*, then the first rule to use is the product rule or the rule for sums, differences, or constant multiples as appropriate.

Q: *Every time I compute a derivative, I leave something out. How do I make sure I am really done when taking the derivative of a complicated-looking expression?*

A: Until you are an expert at taking derivatives, the key is to use one rule at a time and write out each step rather than trying to compute the derivative in a single step. To illustrate this, try computing the derivative of $(x+10)^3\sqrt{1-x^2}$ in Example 3(b) in two ways: First try to compute it in a single step, and then compute it by writing out each step as shown in the example. How do your results compare? For more practice, try Exercises 103 and 104 in this section.

11.4 EXERCISES

▼ more advanced   ◆ challenging
Ⓣ indicates exercises that should be solved using technology

In Exercises 1–50, calculate the derivative of the function. [HINT: See Example 1.]

1. $f(x)=(2x+1)^2$ **2.** $f(x)=(3x-1)^2$

3. $f(x)=(x-1)^{-1}$ **4.** $f(x)=(2x-1)^{-2}$

5. $f(x)=(2-x)^{-2}$ **6.** $f(x)=(1-x)^{-1}$

7. $f(x)=(2x+1)^{0.5}$ **8.** $f(x)=(-x+2)^{1.5}$

9. $f(x)=\dfrac{1}{3x-1}$ **10.** $f(x)=\dfrac{1}{(x+1)^2}$

11. $f(x)=(x^2+2x)^4$ **12.** $f(x)=(x^3-x)^3$

13. $f(x)=(2x^2-2)^{-1}$ **14.** $f(x)=(2x^3+x)^{-2}$

15. $g(x)=(x^2-3x-1)^{-5}$ **16.** $g(x)=(2x^2+x+1)^{-3}$

17. $h(x)=\dfrac{1}{(x^2+1)^3}$ **18.** $h(x)=\dfrac{1}{(x^2+x+1)^2}$

[HINT: See Example 2.]   [HINT: See Example 2.]

19. $r(x) = (0.1x^2 - 4.2x + 9.5)^{1.5}$

20. $r(x) = (0.1x - 4.2x^{-1})^{0.5}$

21. $r(s) = (s^2 - s^{0.5})^4$ **22.** $r(s) = (2s + s^{0.5})^{-1}$

23. $f(x) = \sqrt{1 - x^2}$ **24.** $f(x) = \sqrt{x + x^2}$

25. $f(x) = |3x - 6|$ **26.** $f(x) = |-5x + 1|$

    [**HINT:** See Example 1(d).]   [**HINT:** See Example 1(d).]

27. $f(x) = |-x^3 + 5x|$ **28.** $f(x) = |x - x^4|$

29. $h(x) = 2[(x + 1)(x^2 - 1)]^{-1/2}$ [**HINT:** See Example 3.]

30. $h(x) = 3[(2x - 1)(x - 1)]^{-1/3}$ [**HINT:** See Example 3.]

31. $h(x) = (3.1x - 2)^2 - \dfrac{1}{(3.1x - 2)^2}$

32. $h(x) = \left(3.1x^2 - 2 - \dfrac{1}{3.1x - 2}\right)^2$

33. $f(x) = [(6.4x - 1)^2 + (5.4x - 2)^3]^2$

34. $f(x) = (6.4x - 3)^{-2} + (4.3x - 1)^{-2}$

35. $f(x) = (x^2 - 3x)^{-2}(1 - x^2)^{0.5}$

36. $f(x) = (3x^2 + x)(1 - x^2)^{0.5}$

37. $s(x) = \left(\dfrac{2x + 4}{3x - 1}\right)^2$ **38.** $s(x) = \left(\dfrac{3x - 9}{2x + 4}\right)^3$

39. $g(z) = \left(\dfrac{z}{1 + z^2}\right)^3$ **40.** $g(z) = \left(\dfrac{z^2}{1 + z}\right)^2$

41. $f(x) = [(1 + 2x)^4 - (1 - x)^2]^3$

42. $f(x) = [(3x - 1)^2 + (1 - x)^5]^2$

43. $f(x) = (3x - 1)|3x - 1|$

44. $f(x) = |(x - 3)^{1/3}|$

45. $f(x) = |x - (2x - 3)^{1/2}|$

46. $f(x) = (3 - |3x - 1|)^{-2}$

47. ▼ $r(x) = (\sqrt{2x + 1} - x^2)^{-1}$

48. ▼ $r(x) = (\sqrt{x + 1} + \sqrt{x})^3$

49. ▼ $f(x) = (1 + (1 + (1 + 2x)^3)^3)^3$

50. ▼ $f(x) = 2x + (2x + (2x + 1)^3)^3$

In Exercises 51–66, compute the indicated derivative using the chain rule. [**HINT:** See Quick Examples 3, 6, and 7.]

51. $y = u^2, u = x + 2; \dfrac{dy}{dx}$ **52.** $y = u^3, u = x - 1; \dfrac{dy}{dx}$

53. $y = x^2 + x, x = 2t - 1; \dfrac{dy}{dt}$

54. $y = x^3 - x, x = 1 - 4t; \dfrac{dy}{dt}$

55. $y = 3x - 2; \dfrac{dx}{dy}$ **56.** $y = 8x + 4; \dfrac{dx}{dy}$

57. $y = x^2, x \geq 0; \dfrac{dx}{dy}$ **58.** $y = \sqrt[3]{x}; \dfrac{dx}{dy}$

59. $x = 2 + 3t, y = -5t; \dfrac{dy}{dx}$

60. $x = 1 - t/2, y = 4t - 1; \dfrac{dy}{dx}$

61. $x = t^2, y = 6t + 1, t \geq 0; \dfrac{dy}{dx}$

62. $x = t^3, y = -2t + 2; \dfrac{dy}{dx}$

63. $y = 3x^2 - 2x; \dfrac{dx}{dy}\Big|_{x=1}$ **64.** $y = 3x - \dfrac{2}{x}; \dfrac{dx}{dy}\Big|_{x=2}$

65. $x = t^2 + 2t, y = t^3; \dfrac{dy}{dx}\Big|_{t=1}$

66. $x = 2t^3 + t, y = t^2 + 1; \dfrac{dy}{dx}\Big|_{t=2}$

In Exercises 67–74, find the indicated derivative. In each case the independent variable is a (unspecified) differentiable function of t. [**HINT:** See Quick Example 4.]

67. $y = x^{100} + 99x^{-1}$. Find $\dfrac{dy}{dt}$.

68. $y = x^{0.5}(1 + x)$. Find $\dfrac{dy}{dt}$.

69. $s = \dfrac{1}{r^3} + r^{0.5}$. Find $\dfrac{ds}{dt}$.   **70.** $s = r + r^{-1}$. Find $\dfrac{ds}{dt}$.

71. $V = \dfrac{4}{3}\pi r^3$. Find $\dfrac{dV}{dt}$.   **72.** $A = 4\pi r^2$. Find $\dfrac{dA}{dt}$.

73. ▼ $y = x^3 + \dfrac{1}{x}, x = 2$ when $t = 1, \dfrac{dx}{dt}\Big|_{t=1} = -1$

Find $\dfrac{dy}{dt}\Big|_{t=1}$.

74. ▼ $y = \sqrt{x} + \dfrac{1}{\sqrt{x}}, x = 9$ when $t = 1, \dfrac{dx}{dt}\Big|_{t=1} = -1$

Find $\dfrac{dy}{dt}\Big|_{t=1}$.

Applications

75. Crude Oil Prices The price per barrel of crude oil in the period 1980–2013, in constant 2014 dollars, can be approximated by

$$P(t) = 0.27(t - 1980)^2 - 8.6(t - 1980) + 93 \text{ dollars}$$
$$(1980 \leq t \leq 2013),$$

where t is the year.[30] Find $P'(t)$ and $P'(2010)$. What does the second answer tell you about the price of crude oil?

---

[30] Source for data: http://inflationdata.com/Inflation/Inflation_Rate/Historical_Oil_Prices_Table.asp, March 6, 2014.

76. Median Home Prices The median home price in the United States over the period January 2010–January 2015 can be approximated by

$$P(t) = 4.5(t - 2010)^2 - 15(t - 2010) + 180 \text{ thousand dollars}$$
$$(2010 \le t \le 2015),$$

where t is the year.[31] Find $P'(t)$ and $P'(2011)$. What does the second answer tell you about home prices?

77. Marginal Profit Your monthly profit (in dollars) from selling magazines is given by

$$P = 5x + \sqrt{2x + 10},$$

where x is the number of magazines you sell in a month. If you are currently selling 50 magazines per month, find your profit and your marginal profit. Interpret your answers.

78. Marginal Profit Your monthly profit (in dollars) from your newspaper route is given by

$$P = 2n - \sqrt{3n + 100},$$

where n is the number of subscribers on your route. If you currently have 100 subscribers, find your profit and your marginal profit. Interpret your answers.

79. Fuel Economy (You saw this exercise in Section 11.3. This time, use the chain rule to calculate the derivative.) Your muscle car's gas mileage (in miles per gallon) is given as a function $M(x)$ of speed x in miles per hour, where

$$M(x) = \frac{3,000}{x + 3,600x^{-1}}.$$

Calculate $M'(x)$ and then $M'(10)$, $M'(60)$, and $M'(70)$. What do the answers tell you about your car?

80. Fuel Economy (You saw this exercise in Section 11.3. This time, use the chain rule to calculate the derivative.) Your used Chevy's gas mileage (in miles per gallon) is given as a function $M(x)$ of speed x in miles per hour, where

$$M(x) = \frac{4,000}{x + 3,025x^{-1}}.$$

Calculate $M'(x)$, and hence determine the sign of each of the following: $M'(40)$, $M'(55)$, and $M'(60)$. Interpret your results.

81. Marginal Profit *Paramount Electronics* has an annual profit given by

$$P = -100,000 + 5,000q - 0.25q^2 \text{ dollars},$$

where q is the number of laptop computers it sells each year. The number of laptop computers it can make and sell each year depends on the number n of electrical engineers Paramount employs, according to the equation

$$q = 30n + 0.01n^2.$$

Use the chain rule to find $\left.\dfrac{dP}{dn}\right|_{n=10}$, and interpret the result. [**HINT:** See Example 4.]

82. Marginal Profit Refer back to Exercise 81. The average profit $\overline{P}$ per computer is given by dividing the total profit P by q:

$$\overline{P} = -\frac{100,000}{q} + 5,000 - 0.25q \text{ dollars}.$$

Determine the **marginal average profit**, $d\overline{P}/dn$, at an employee level of 10 engineers. Interpret the result. [**HINT:** See Example 4.]

83. Food versus Education The percentage y (of total personal consumption) an individual spends on food is approximately

$$y = 35x^{-0.25} \text{ percentage points} \quad (6.5 \le x \le 17.5),$$

where x is the percentage the individual spends on education.[32] An individual finds that she is spending

$$x = 7 + 0.2t$$

percent of her personal consumption on education, where t is time in months since January 1. Use direct substitution to express the percentage y as a function of time t (do not simplify the expression), and then use the chain rule to estimate how fast the percentage she spends on food is changing on November 1. Be sure to specify the units. [**HINT:** See Example 3(a).]

84. Food versus Recreation The percentage y (of total personal consumption) an individual spends on food is approximately

$$y = 33x^{-0.63} \text{ percentage points} \quad (2.5 \le x \le 4.5),$$

where x is the percentage the individual spends on recreation.[33] A college student finds that he is spending

$$x = 3.5 + 0.1t$$

percent of his personal consumption on recreation, where t is time in months since January 1. Use direct substitution to express the percentage y as a function of time t (do not simplify the expression) and then use the chain rule to estimate how fast the percentage he spends on food is changing on November 1. Be sure to specify the units. [**HINT:** See Example 3(a).]

85. Marginal Revenue The weekly revenue from the sale of rubies at *Royal Ruby Retailers* is increasing at a rate of $40 per $1 increase in price, and the price is decreasing at a rate of $0.75 per additional ruby sold. What is the marginal revenue? (Be sure to state the units of measurement.) Interpret the result. [**HINT:** See Quick Example 5.]

---

[31] Source for data: www.zillow.com.

[32] Model based on historical and projected data from 1908–2010. Sources: Historical data, Bureau of Economic Analysis; projected data, Bureau of Labor Statistics/*New York Times*, December 1, 2003, p. C2.

[33] *Ibid.*

86. *Marginal Revenue* The weekly revenue from the sale of emeralds at *Eduardo's Emerald Emporium* is decreasing at a rate of €500 per €1 increase in price, and the price is decreasing at a rate of €0.45 per additional emerald sold. What is the marginal revenue? (Be sure to state the units of measurement.) Interpret the result. [HINT: See Quick Example 5.]

87. *Crime Statistics* The murder rate in large cities (over 1 million residents) can be related to that in smaller cities (500,000–1,000,000 residents) by the following linear model:[34]

$$y = 1.5x - 1.9 \quad (15 \le x \le 25),$$

where y is the murder rate (in murders per 100,000 residents each year) in large cities and x is the murder rate in smaller cities. During the period 1991–1998 the murder rate in small cities was decreasing at an average rate of 2 murders per 100,000 residents each year. Use the chain rule to estimate how fast the murder rate was changing in larger cities during that period. (Show how you used the chain rule in your answer.)

88. *Crime Statistics* Following is a quadratic model relating the murder rates described in Exercise 87:

$$y = 0.1x^2 - 3x + 39 \quad (15 \le x \le 25).$$

In 1996 the murder rate in smaller cities was approximately 22 murders per 100,000 residents each year and was decreasing at a rate of approximately 2.5 murders per 100,000 residents each year. Use the chain rule to estimate how fast the murder rate was changing for large cities. (Show how you used the chain rule in your answer.)

89. *Existing Home Sales* The following graph shows the approximate value of home prices and existing home sales in 2006–2010 as a percentage change from 2003, together with quadratic approximations:[35]

Home prices and sales of existing homes

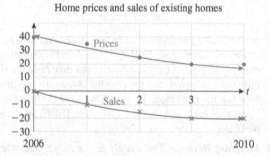

2006　　　　　　　　　　　　　　2010

The quadratic approximations are given by

Home prices: $P(t) = t^2 - 10t + 41 \quad (0 \le t \le 4)$
Existing home sales: $S(t) = 1.5t^2 - 11t \quad (0 \le t \le 4)$,

[34] The model is a linear regression model. Source for data: Federal Bureau of Investigation, Supplementary Homicide Reports/*New York Times*, May 29, 2000, p. A12.

[35] Sources: Standard & Poors/Bloomberg Financial Markets/*New York Times*, September 29, 2007, p. C3. Projection is the authors'.

where t is time in years since the start of 2006. Use the chain rule to estimate $\left.\dfrac{dS}{dP}\right|_{t=2}$. What does the answer tell you about home sales and prices? [HINT: See Quick Examples 6 and 7.]

90. *Existing Home Sales Leading to the Financial Crisis* The following graph shows the approximate value of home prices and existing home sales in 2004–2007 (the 3 years prior to the 2008 economic crisis) as a percentage change from 2003, together with quadratic approximations:[36]

Home prices and sales of existing homes

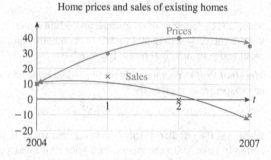

2004　　　　　　　　　　　　　　2007

The quadratic approximations are given by

Home prices: $P(t) = -6t^2 + 27t + 10 \quad (0 \le t \le 3)$
Existing home sales: $S(t) = -4t^2 + 4t + 11 \quad (0 \le t \le 3)$,

where t is time in years since the start of 2004. Use the chain rule to estimate $\left.\dfrac{dS}{dP}\right|_{t=2}$. What does the answer tell you about home sales and prices? [HINT: See Quick Examples 6 and 7.]

91. ▼ *Pollution* An offshore oil well is leaking oil and creating a circular oil slick. If the radius of the slick is growing at a rate of 2 miles per hour, find the rate at which the area is increasing when the radius is 3 miles. (The area of a disc of radius r is $A = \pi r^2$.) [HINT: See Quick Example 4.]

92. ▼ *Mold* A mold culture in a dorm refrigerator is circular and growing. The radius is growing at a rate of 0.3 centimeters per day. How fast is the area growing when the culture is 4 centimeters in radius? (The area of a disc of radius r is $A = \pi r^2$.) [HINT: See Quick Example 4.]

93. ▼ *Budget Overruns* The Pentagon is planning to build a new spherical satellite. As is typical in these cases, the specifications keep changing, so the size of the satellite keeps growing. In fact, the radius of the planned satellite is growing 0.5 feet per week. Its cost will be $1,000 per cubic foot. At the point when the plans call for a satellite 10 feet in radius, how fast is the cost growing? (The volume of a solid sphere of radius r is $V = \frac{4}{3}\pi r^3$.)

94. ▼ *Soap Bubbles* The soap bubble I am blowing has a radius that is growing at a rate of 4 centimeters per second.

[36] *Ibid.*

How fast is the surface area growing when the radius is 10 centimeters? (The surface area of a sphere of radius r is $S = 4\pi r^2$.)

95. ▣ ▼ *Revenue Growth* The demand for the Cyberpunk II arcade video game is modeled by the logistic curve

$$q(t) = \frac{10,000}{1 + 0.5e^{-0.4t}},$$

where $q(t)$ is the total number of units sold t months after its introduction.

a. Use technology to estimate $q'(4)$.
b. Assume that the manufacturers of Cyberpunk II sell each unit for $800. What is the company's marginal revenue dR/dq?
c. Use the chain rule to estimate the rate at which revenue is growing 4 months after the introduction of the video game.

96. ▣ ▼ *Information Highway* The amount of information transmitted each month in the early years of the Internet (1988–1994) can be modeled by the equation

$$q(t) = \frac{2e^{0.69t}}{3 + 1.5e^{-0.4t}} \quad (0 \le t \le 6),$$

where q is the amount of information transmitted each month in billions of data packets and t is the number of years since the start of 1988.[37]

a. Use technology to estimate $q'(2)$.
b. Assume that it costs $5 to transmit a million packets of data. What is the marginal cost $C'(q)$?
c. How fast was the cost increasing at the start of 1990?

Money Stock Exercises 97–100 are based on the following demand function for money (taken from a question on the GRE Economics Test):

$$M_d = 2 \times y^{0.6} \times r^{-0.3} \times p,$$

where

M_d = *demand for nominal money balances (money stock)*
y = *real income*
r = *an index of interest rates*
p = *an index of prices.*

These exercises also use the idea of ***percentage rate of growth***:

$$\text{Percentage rate of growth of } M = \frac{\text{Rate of growth of } M}{M}$$

$$= \frac{dM/dt}{M}.$$

97. ◆ (From the GRE Economics Test) If the interest rate and price level are to remain constant while real income grows at 5% per year, the money stock must grow at what percent per year?

98. ◆ (From the GRE Economics Test) If real income and price level are to remain constant while the interest rate grows at 5% per year, the money stock must change by what percent per year?

99. ◆ (From the GRE Economics Test) If the interest rate is to remain constant while real income grows at 5% per year and the price level rises at 5% per year, the money stock must grow at what percent per year?

100. ◆ (From the GRE Economics Test) If real income grows by 5% per year, the interest rate grows by 2% per year, and the price level drops by 3% per year, the money stock must change by what percent per year?

Communication and Reasoning Exercises

101. Complete the following: The derivative of 1 over a glob is -1 over . . . .

102. Complete the following: The derivative of the square root of a glob is 1 over . . . .

103. Say why the following was marked wrong, and give the correct answer.

$$\frac{d}{dx}[(3x^3 - x)^3] = 3(9x^2 - 1)^2 \qquad ✗ \;\; WRONG!$$

104. Say why the following was marked wrong, and give the correct answer.

$$\frac{d}{dx}\left[\left(\frac{3x^2 - 1}{2x - 2}\right)^3\right] = 3\left(\frac{3x^2 - 1}{2x - 2}\right)^2\left(\frac{6x}{2}\right) \qquad ✗ \;\; WRONG!$$

105. Name two major errors in the following graded test question, and give the correct answer.

$$\frac{d}{dx}\left[\left(\frac{3x^2 - 1}{2x - 2}\right)^3\right] = 3\left(\frac{6x}{2}\right)^2 \qquad ✗ \;\; WRONG! \; SEE \; ME!$$

106. Name two major errors in the following graded test question, and give the correct answer.

$$\frac{d}{dx}[(3x^3 - x)(2x + 1)]^4 = 4[(9x^2 - 1)(2)]^3$$
$$✗ \;\; WRONG! \; SEE \; ME!$$

107. ▼ Formulate a simple procedure for deciding whether to apply first the chain rule, the product rule, or the quotient rule when finding the derivative of a function.

108. ▼ Give an example of a function f with the property that calculating $f'(x)$ requires use of the following rules in the given order: (1) the chain rule, (2) the quotient rule, and (3) the chain rule.

109. ◆ Give an example of a function f with the property that calculating $f'(x)$ requires use of the chain rule five times in succession.

110. ◆ What can you say about the composite of two linear functions, and what can you say about its derivative?

---

[37] This is the authors' model, based on figures published in the *New York Times*, Nov. 3, 1993.

11.5   Derivatives of Logarithmic and Exponential Functions

Derivative of $\ln x$ and $\log_b x$

At this point we know how to take the derivative of any algebraic expression in x (involving powers, radicals, and so on). We now turn to the derivatives of logarithmic and exponential functions.

Derivative of the Natural Logarithm

$$\frac{d}{dx}(\ln x) = \frac{1}{x}$$ Recall that $\ln x = \log_e x$.

Quick Examples

1. $\dfrac{d}{dx}(3 \ln x) = 3 \cdot \dfrac{1}{x} = \dfrac{3}{x}$ Derivative of a constant times a function

2. $\dfrac{d}{dx}(x \ln x) = 1 \cdot \ln x + x \cdot \dfrac{1}{x}$ Product rule, because $x \ln x$ is a product

   $= \ln x + 1.$

The above simple formula works only for the natural logarithm (the logarithm with base e). For logarithms with bases other than e we have the following:

Derivative of the Logarithm with Base b

$$\frac{d}{dx}(\log_b x) = \frac{1}{x \ln b}$$ Notice that, if $b = e$, we get the same formula as previously.

Quick Examples

3. $\dfrac{d}{dx}(\log_3 x) = \dfrac{1}{x \ln 3} \approx \dfrac{1}{1.0986x}$

4. $\dfrac{d}{dx}[\log_2(x^4)] = \dfrac{d}{dx}(4 \log_2 x)$ We used the logarithm identity $\log_b(x^r) = r \log_b x$.

   $= 4 \cdot \dfrac{1}{x \ln 2} \approx \dfrac{4}{0.6931x}$

Derivation of the formulas $\dfrac{d}{dx}(\ln x) = \dfrac{1}{x}$ and $\dfrac{d}{dx}(\log_b x) = \dfrac{1}{x \ln b}$

To compute $\dfrac{d}{dx}(\ln x)$, we need to use the definition of the derivative. We also use properties of the logarithm to help evaluate the limit:

$$\frac{d}{dx}(\ln x) = \lim_{h \to 0} \frac{\ln(x + h) - \ln x}{h} \qquad \text{Definition of the derivative}$$

$$= \lim_{h \to 0} \frac{1}{h}[\ln(x + h) - \ln x] \qquad \text{Algebra}$$

$$= \lim_{h \to 0} \frac{1}{h} \ln\left(\frac{x + h}{x}\right) \qquad \text{Properties of the logarithm}$$

$$= \lim_{h \to 0} \frac{1}{h} \ln\left(1 + \frac{h}{x}\right) \qquad \text{Algebra}$$

$$= \lim_{h \to 0} \ln\left(1 + \frac{h}{x}\right)^{1/h} \qquad \text{Properties of the logarithm}$$

which we rewrite as

$$\lim_{h \to 0} \ln\left[\left(1 + \frac{1}{(x/h)}\right)^{x/h}\right]^{1/x}.$$

As $h \to 0^+$, the quantity x/h gets large and positive, so the quantity in brackets approaches e (see the definition of e in Section 2.2), which leaves us with

$$\ln[e]^{1/x} = \frac{1}{x} \ln e = \frac{1}{x}$$

which is the derivative we are after.[*] What about the limit as $h \to 0^-$? We will glide over that case and leave it for the interested reader to pursue.[†]

The rule for the derivative of $\log_b x$ follows from the fact that $\log_b x = \ln x / \ln b$.

Derivatives of Logarithms of Functions

If we were to take the derivative of the natural logarithm of a *quantity* (a function of x) rather than just x, we would need to use the chain rule.

* We actually used the fact that the logarithm function is continuous when we took the limit.

† Here is an outline of the argument for negative h. Because x must be positive for $\ln x$ to be defined, we find that $x/h \to -\infty$ as $h \to 0^-$, so we must consider the quantity $(1 + 1/m)^m$ for large *negative m*. It turns out the limit is still e (check it numerically!), so the computation above still works.

Derivatives of Logarithms of Functions

Original Rule	Generalized Rule	In Words
$\dfrac{d}{dx} \ln x = \dfrac{1}{x}$	$\dfrac{d}{dx} \ln u = \dfrac{1}{u}\dfrac{du}{dx}$	*The derivative of the natural logarithm of a* quantity *is 1 over that* quantity, *times the derivative of that* quantity.
$\dfrac{d}{dx} \log_b x = \dfrac{1}{x \ln b}$	$\dfrac{d}{dx} \log_b u = \dfrac{1}{u \ln b}\dfrac{du}{dx}$	*The derivative of the log to base b of a* quantity *is 1 over the product of* $\ln b$ *and that* quantity, *times the derivative of that* quantity.

§ If we were to evaluate $\ln(x^2 + 1)$, the last operation we would perform would be to take the natural logarithm of a quantity. Thus, the calculation thought experiment tells us that we are dealing with ln *of a quantity*, so we need the generalized logarithm rule as stated above.

Quick Examples

5. $\dfrac{d}{dx} \ln(x^2 + 1) = \dfrac{1}{x^2 + 1}\dfrac{d}{dx}(x^2 + 1) \qquad u = x^2 + 1$ (See the margin note.[§])

$$= \frac{1}{x^2 + 1}(2x) = \frac{2x}{x^2 + 1}$$

6. $\dfrac{d}{dx}\log_2(x^3 + x) = \dfrac{1}{(x^3 + x)\ln 2}\dfrac{d}{dx}(x^3 + x)$ $u = x^3 + x$

$$= \dfrac{1}{(x^3 + x)\ln 2}(3x^2 + 1) = \dfrac{3x^2 + 1}{(x^3 + x)\ln 2}$$

EXAMPLE 1   **More Derivatives of Logarithms of Functions**

Compute the following derivatives:

a. $\dfrac{d}{dx}\ln\sqrt{x + 1}$ **b.** $\dfrac{d}{dx}\ln[(1 + x)(2 - x)]$ **c.** $\dfrac{d}{dx}\ln|x|$

Solution

a. The calculation thought experiment tells us that we have the natural logarithm of a quantity, so

$$\dfrac{d}{dx}\ln\sqrt{x + 1} = \dfrac{1}{\sqrt{x + 1}}\dfrac{d}{dx}\sqrt{x + 1} \qquad \dfrac{d}{dx}\ln u = \dfrac{1}{u}\dfrac{du}{dx}$$

$$= \dfrac{1}{\sqrt{x + 1}}\cdot\dfrac{1}{2\sqrt{x + 1}} \qquad \dfrac{d}{dx}\sqrt{u} = \dfrac{1}{2\sqrt{u}}\dfrac{du}{dx}$$

$$= \dfrac{1}{2(x + 1)}.$$

Q: *What happened to the square root?*

A: As with many problems involving logarithms, we could have done this one differently and much more easily if we had simplified the expression $\ln\sqrt{x + 1}$ using the properties of logarithms *before* differentiating. Doing this, we get the following.

Part (a) redone by simplifying first:

$$\ln\sqrt{x + 1} = \ln(x + 1)^{1/2} = \dfrac{1}{2}\ln(x + 1). \qquad \text{Simplify the logarithm first.}$$

Thus,

$$\dfrac{d}{dx}\ln\sqrt{x + 1} = \dfrac{d}{dx}\left[\dfrac{1}{2}\ln(x + 1)\right]$$

$$= \dfrac{1}{2}\left(\dfrac{1}{x + 1}\right)\cdot 1 = \dfrac{1}{2(x + 1)}.$$

A *lot* easier!

b. This time, we simplify the expression $\ln[(1 + x)(2 - x)]$ before taking the derivative:

$$\ln[(1 + x)(2 - x)] = \ln(1 + x) + \ln(2 - x). \qquad \text{Simplify the logarithm first.}$$

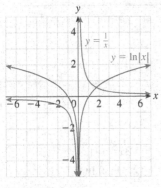

Figure 7(a)

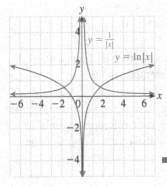

Figure 7(b)

Thus,

$$\frac{d}{dx}\ln[(1+x)(2-x)] = \frac{d}{dx}\ln(1+x) + \frac{d}{dx}\ln(2-x)$$

$$= \frac{1}{1+x} - \frac{1}{2-x}. \qquad \frac{d}{dx}\ln u = \frac{1}{u}\frac{du}{dx}$$

For practice, try doing this calculation without simplifying first. What other differentiation rule do you need to use?

c. Before we start, we note that $\ln x$ is defined only for positive values of x, so its domain is the set of positive real numbers. The domain of $\ln|x|$, on the other hand, is the set of *all* nonzero real numbers. For example, $\ln|-2| = \ln 2 \approx 0.6931$. For this reason, $\ln|x|$ often turns out to be more useful than the ordinary logarithm function.

$$\frac{d}{dx}\ln|x| = \frac{1}{|x|}\frac{d}{dx}|x| \qquad \frac{d}{dx}\ln u = \frac{1}{u}\frac{du}{dx}$$

$$= \frac{1}{|x|}\frac{|x|}{x} \qquad \text{Recall that } \frac{d}{dx}|x| = \frac{|x|}{x}.$$

$$= \frac{1}{x}$$

➡ **Before we go on ...** Figure 7(a) shows the graphs of $y = \ln|x|$ and $y = 1/x$. Figure 7(b) shows the graphs of $y = \ln|x|$ and $y = 1/|x|$. You should be able to see from these graphs why the derivative of $\ln|x|$ is $1/x$ and not $1/|x|$. ∎

This last example, in conjunction with the chain rule, gives us the following formulas.

Derivatives of Logarithms of Absolute Values

Original Rule	Generalized Rule	In Words
$\dfrac{d}{dx}\ln|x| = \dfrac{1}{x}$	$\dfrac{d}{dx}\ln|u| = \dfrac{1}{u}\dfrac{du}{dx}$	*The derivative of the natural logarithm of the absolute value of a* quantity *is 1 over that* quantity, *times the derivative of that* quantity.
$\dfrac{d}{dx}\log_b|x| = \dfrac{1}{x\ln b}$	$\dfrac{d}{dx}\log_b|u| = \dfrac{1}{u\ln b}\dfrac{du}{dx}$	*The derivative of the log to base b of the absolute value of a* quantity *is 1 over the product of* $\ln b$ *and that* quantity, *times the derivative of that* quantity.

Note Compare the above formulas with those in the box that precedes Example 1. They tell us that we can simply ignore the absolute values in $\ln|u|$ or $\log_b|u|$ when taking the derivative. ∎

Quick Examples

7. $\dfrac{d}{dx} \ln|x^2 - 1| = \dfrac{1}{x^2 - 1} \dfrac{d}{dx}(x^2 - 1)$ $u = x^2 - 1$

$\qquad = \dfrac{1}{x^2 - 1}(2x) = \dfrac{2x}{x^2 - 1}$

8. $\dfrac{d}{dx} \log_2|x^3 + x| = \dfrac{1}{(x^3 + x)\ln 2} \dfrac{d}{dx}(x^3 + x)$ $u = x^3 + x$

$\qquad = \dfrac{1}{(x^3 + x)\ln 2}(3x^2 + 1) = \dfrac{3x^2 + 1}{(x^3 + x)\ln 2}$

Derivatives of Exponential Functions

We now turn to the derivatives of *exponential* functions—that is, functions of the form $f(x) = b^x$. We begin by showing how *not* to differentiate them.

Caution The derivative of b^x is *not* xb^{x-1}. The power rule applies only to *constant* exponents. In this case the exponent is decidedly *not* constant, so the power rule does not apply. ■

The following shows the correct way of differentiating b^x, beginning with a special case.

Derivative of e^x

$$\frac{d}{dx} e^x = e^x$$

Quick Examples

9. $\dfrac{d}{dx}(3e^x) = 3\dfrac{d}{dx}e^x = 3e^x$ Constant multiple rule

10. $\dfrac{d}{dx}\left(\dfrac{e^x}{x}\right) = \dfrac{e^x x - e^x(1)}{x^2}$ Quotient rule

$\qquad = \dfrac{e^x(x - 1)}{x^2}$

* There is another—very simple—function that is its own derivative. What is it?

Thus, e^x has the amazing property that its derivative is itself!* For bases other than e we have the following generalization.

Derivative of b^x

If b is any positive number, then

$$\frac{d}{dx}b^x = b^x \ln b.$$

Note that if $b = e$, we obtain the previous formula.

Quick Example

11. $\dfrac{d}{dx}3^x = 3^x \ln 3$

Derivation of the Formula $\dfrac{d}{dx}e^x = e^x$

*This shortcut is an example of a technique called *logarithmic differentiation*, which is occasionally useful. We will see it again in Section 11.6.

To find the derivative of e^x, we use a shortcut.* Write $g(x) = e^x$. Then

$$\ln g(x) = x.$$

Take the derivative of both sides of this equation to get

$$\frac{g'(x)}{g(x)} = 1$$

or

$$g'(x) = g(x) = e^x.$$

In other words, the exponential function with base e is its own derivative. The rule for exponential functions with other bases follows from the equality $b^x = e^{x \ln b}$ (why?) and the chain rule. (Try it.)

Derivatives of Exponentials of Functions

If we were to take the derivative of e raised to a *quantity*, not just x, we would need to use the chain rule, as follows.

Derivatives of Exponentials of Functions

Original Rule	Generalized Rule	In Words
$\dfrac{d}{dx}e^x = e^x$	$\dfrac{d}{dx}e^u = e^u\dfrac{du}{dx}$	*The derivative of e raised to a quantity is e raised to that quantity, times the derivative of that quantity.*
$\dfrac{d}{dx}b^x = b^x \ln b$	$\dfrac{d}{dx}b^u = b^u \ln b\dfrac{du}{dx}$	*The derivative of b raised to a quantity is b raised to that quantity, times $\ln b$, times the derivative of that quantity.*

* The calculation thought experiment tells us that we have e raised to a quantity.

Quick Examples

12. $\dfrac{d}{dx}e^{x^2+1} = e^{x^2+1}\dfrac{d}{dx}(x^2+1)$ $u = x^2 + 1$ (See margin note.*)

$\qquad\qquad = e^{x^2+1}(2x) = 2x\,e^{x^2+1}$

13. $\dfrac{d}{dx}2^{3x} = 2^{3x}\ln 2\dfrac{d}{dx}(3x)$ $u = 3x$

$\qquad\qquad = 2^{3x}(\ln 2)(3) = (3\ln 2)2^{3x}$

14. $\dfrac{d}{dt}30e^{1.02t} = 30e^{1.02t}(1.02) = 30.6e^{1.02t}$ $u = 1.02t$

15. If \$1,000 is invested in an account earning 5% per year compounded continuously, then the rate of change of the account balance after t years is

$$\frac{d}{dt}(1{,}000e^{0.05t}) = 1{,}000(0.05)e^{0.05t} = 50e^{0.05t} \text{ dollars per year.}$$

Applications

EXAMPLE 2   **Epidemics**

In the early stages of the AIDS epidemic during the 1980s the number of cases in the United States was increasing by about 50% every 6 months. By the start of 1983 there were approximately 1,600 AIDS cases in the United States.[38] Had this trend continued, how many new cases per year would have been occurring by the start of 1993?

Solution To find the answer, we must first model this exponential growth using the methods of Chapter 2. Referring to Example 4 of Section 2.2, we find that t years after the start of 1983 the number of cases is

$$A = 1{,}600(2.25)^t.$$

We are asking for the number of new cases each year. In other words, we want the rate of change, dA/dt:

$$\frac{dA}{dt} = 1{,}600(2.25)^t \ln 2.25 \text{ cases per year.}$$

At the start of 1993, $t = 10$, so the number of new cases per year is

$$\left.\frac{dA}{dt}\right|_{t=10} = 1{,}600(2.25)^{10} \ln 2.25 \approx 4{,}300{,}000 \text{ cases per year.}$$

➡ **Before we go on...** In Example 2 the figure for the number of new cases per year is so large because we assumed that exponential growth—the 50% increase every 6 months—would continue. A more realistic model for the spread of a disease is the logistic model. (See Section 2.4 as well as the next example.) ∎

---

[38] Data based on regression of 1982–1986 figures. Source for data: Centers for Disease Control and Prevention. HIV/AIDS Surveillance Report, 2000;12 (No. 2).

EXAMPLE 3 **Sales Growth**

The sales of the *Cyberpunk II* video game can be modeled by the logistic curve

$$q(t) = \frac{10{,}000}{1 + 0.5e^{-0.4t}}$$

where $q(t)$ is the total number of units sold t months after its introduction. How fast is the game selling 2 years after its introduction?

Solution We are asked for $q'(24)$. We can find the derivative of $q(t)$ using the quotient rule, or we can first write

$$q(t) = 10{,}000(1 + 0.5e^{-0.4t})^{-1}$$

and then use the generalized power rule:

$$q'(t) = -10{,}000(1 + 0.5e^{-0.4t})^{-2}(0.5e^{-0.4t})(-0.4)$$

$$= \frac{2{,}000e^{-0.4t}}{(1 + 0.5e^{-0.4t})^2}.$$

Thus,

$$q'(24) = \frac{2{,}000e^{-0.4(24)}}{(1 + 0.5e^{-0.4(24)})^2} \approx 0.135 \text{ units per month.}$$

So after 2 years, sales are quite slow.

Application to Limits

We can now apply l'Hospital's rule and the derivatives of exponential functions to evaluate some limits of a kind we computed numerically in the exercises in Section 10.1.

EXAMPLE 4 **Exponential Functions and L'Hospital's Rule**

Evaluate the following limits using l'Hospital's rule:

a. $\displaystyle\lim_{x \to +\infty} \frac{x}{e^x}$ **b.** $\displaystyle\lim_{x \to -\infty} (x^2 + 2x)e^x$

Solution

a. This limit has the indeterminate form ∞/∞, so we can try to apply l'Hospital's rule:

$$\lim_{x \to +\infty} \frac{x}{e^x} = \lim_{x \to +\infty} \frac{1}{e^x} = 0. \qquad \text{Apply l'Hospital's rule: } \frac{d}{dx}(x) = 1, \frac{d}{dx}e^x = e^x$$

b. We first rewrite the limit as a quotient:

$$\lim_{x \to -\infty} (x^2 + 2x)e^x = \lim_{x \to -\infty} \frac{x^2 + 2x}{e^{-x}}.$$

Because $x \to -\infty$, this has the indeterminate form ∞/∞, so we can apply l'Hospital's rule:

$$\lim_{x \to -\infty} \frac{x^2 + 2x}{e^{-x}} = \lim_{x \to -\infty} \frac{2x + 2}{-e^{-x}} \qquad \text{Still indeterminate}$$

$$= \lim_{x \to -\infty} \frac{2}{e^{-x}} \qquad \text{Apply l'Hospital's rule again.}$$

$$= 0.$$

11.5 EXERCISES

▼ more advanced   ◆ challenging
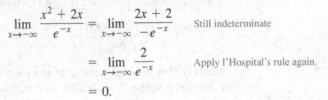 indicates exercises that should be solved using technology

In Exercises 1–66, find the derivative of the function.
[HINT: See Quick Examples 5–14.]

1. $f(x) = \ln(x - 1)$ **2.** $f(x) = \ln(x + 3)$

3. $g(x) = \ln|x^2 + 3|$ **4.** $g(x) = \ln|2x - 4|$

5. $f(x) = \log_2 x$ **6.** $f(x) = \log_3 x$

7. $h(x) = \log_2(x + 1)$ **8.** $h(x) = \log_3(x^2 + x)$

9. $r(t) = \log_3(t + 1/t)$ **10.** $r(t) = \log_3(t + \sqrt{t})$

11. $h(x) = e^{x+3}$ **12.** $h(x) = e^{x^2}$

13. $h(x) = e^{x^2 - x + 1}$ **14.** $h(x) = e^{2x^2 - x + 1/x}$

15. $r(x) = (e^{2x-1})^2$ **16.** $r(x) = (e^{2x^2})^3$

17. $g(x) = 4^x$ **18.** $g(x) = 5^x$

19. $h(x) = 2^{x^2-1}$ **20.** $h(x) = 3^{x^2-x}$

21. $f(x) = (x^2 + 1)\ln x$ **22.** $f(x) = (4x^2 - x)\ln x$

23. $f(x) = (x^2 + 1)^5 \ln x$ **24.** $f(x) = (x + 1)^{0.5}\ln x$

25. $g(x) = \ln|2x^2 + 1|$ **26.** $g(x) = \ln|x^2 - x|$

27. $g(x) = \ln(x^2 - 2.1x^{0.3})$ **28.** $g(x) = \ln(x - 3.1x^{-1})$

29. $h(x) = \ln[(-2x + 1)(x + 1)]$ **[HINT: See Example 1(b).]**

30. $h(x) = \ln[(3x + 1)(-x + 1)]$ **[HINT: See Example 1(b).]**

31. $h(x) = \ln\left(\dfrac{3x + 1}{4x - 2}\right)$ **32.** $h(x) = \ln\left(\dfrac{9x}{4x - 2}\right)$

33. $r(x) = \ln\left|\dfrac{(x + 1)(x - 3)}{-2x - 9}\right|$

34. $r(x) = \ln\left|\dfrac{-x + 1}{(3x - 4)(x - 9)}\right|$

35. $s(x) = \ln[(4x - 2)^{1.3}]$ **36.** $s(x) = \ln[(x - 8)^{-2}]$

   [HINT: See Example 1(a).]   **[HINT: See Example 1(a).]**

37. $s(x) = \ln\left|\dfrac{(x + 1)^2}{(3x - 4)^3(x - 9)}\right|$

38. $s(x) = \ln\left|\dfrac{(x + 1)^2(x - 3)^4}{2x + 9}\right|$

39. $f(x) = (\ln|x|)^2$ **40.** $f(x) = \dfrac{1}{\ln|x|}$

41. $r(x) = \ln(x^2) - [\ln(x - 1)]^2$

42. $r(x) = (\ln(x^2))^2$

43. $f(x) = xe^x$ **44.** $f(x) = 2e^x - x^2 e^x$

45. $r(x) = \ln(x + 1) + 3x^3 e^x$

46. $r(x) = \ln|x + e^x|$

47. $f(x) = e^x \ln|x|$ **48.** $f(x) = e^x \log_2|x|$

49. $s(x) = x^2 e^{2x-1}$ **50.** $s(x) = \dfrac{e^{4x-1}}{x^3 - 1}$

51. $v(x) = 3^{2x+1} + e^{3x+1}$ **52.** $v(x) = e^{2x} 4^{2x}$

53. $u(x) = \dfrac{3^{x^2}}{x^2 + 1}$ **54.** $u(x) = (x^2 + 1)4^{x^2-1}$

55. $g(x) = \dfrac{e^x + e^{-x}}{e^x - e^{-x}}$ **56.** $g(x) = \dfrac{1}{e^x + e^{-x}}$

57. ▼ $g(x) = e^{3x-1}e^{x-2}e^x$ **58.** ▼ $g(x) = e^{-x+3}e^{2x-1}e^{-x+11}$

59. ▼ $f(x) = \dfrac{1}{x \ln x}$ **60.** ▼ $f(x) = \dfrac{e^{-x}}{xe^x}$

61. ▼ $f(x) = [\ln(e^x)]^2 - \ln[(e^x)^2]$

62. ▼ $f(x) = e^{\ln x} - e^{2\ln(x^2)}$

63. ▼ $f(x) = \ln|\ln x|$ **64.** ▼ $f(x) = \ln|\ln|\ln x||$

65. ▼ $s(x) = \ln\sqrt{\ln x}$ **66.** ▼ $s(x) = \sqrt{\ln(\ln x)}$

In Exercises 67–72, find the equation of the straight line described. Use graphing technology to check your answers by plotting the given curve together with the tangent line.

67. Tangent to $y = e^x \log_2 x$ at the point $(1, 0)$

68. Tangent to $y = e^x + e^{-x}$ at the point $(0, 2)$

69. Tangent to $y = \ln\sqrt{2x + 1}$ at the point where $x = 0$

70. Tangent to $y = \ln\sqrt{2x^2 + 1}$ at the point where $x = 1$

71. At right angles to $y = e^{x^2}$ at the point where $x = 1$

72. At right angles to $y = \log_2(3x + 1)$ at the point where $x = 1$

In Exercises 73–78, use l'Hospital's rule to find the limits. [**HINT**: See Example 4.]

73. $\lim\limits_{x \to +\infty} \dfrac{x + 2}{e^x}$

74. $\lim\limits_{x \to +\infty} \dfrac{x^2 + x + 1}{e^x}$

75. $\lim\limits_{x \to -\infty} \dfrac{2x + 3}{e^{-2x}}$

76. $\lim\limits_{x \to -\infty} \dfrac{x^2 - 2x + 1}{e^{-3x}}$

77. $\lim\limits_{x \to 0} \dfrac{e^x - 1}{x}$

78. $\lim\limits_{x \to 0} \dfrac{e^x - 1 - x}{x^2}$

Applications

79. *Research and Development: Industry* The total spent on research and development by industry in the United States during 2002–2012 can be approximated by

$$S(t) = 29 \ln t + 164 \text{ billion dollars} \quad (2 \le t \le 12),$$

where t is the year since 2000.[39] What was the total spent in 2010 ($t = 10$), and how fast was it increasing? [**HINT**: See Quick Examples 1 and 2.]

80. *Research and Development: Federal* The total spent on research and development by the federal government in the United States during 2002–2012 can be approximated by

$$S(t) = 3.1 \ln t + 22 \text{ billion dollars} \quad (2 \le t \le 12),$$

where t is the year since 2000.[40] What was the total spent in 2005 ($t = 5$), and how fast was it increasing? [**HINT**: See Quick Examples 1 and 2.]

81. *Research and Development: Industry* (Refer to Exercise 79.) The function $S(t)$ in Exercise 79 can also be written (approximately) as

$$S(t) = 29 \ln(286t + 2,860) \text{ billion dollars} \quad (-8 \le t \le 2),$$

where this time t is the year since 2010. Use this alternative formula to estimate the amount spent in 2010 and its rate of change, and check your answers by comparing them with those in Exercise 79.

82. *Research and Development: Federal* (Refer to Exercise 80.) The function $S(t)$ in Exercise 80 can also be written (approximately) as

$$S(t) = 3.1 \ln(1{,}210t + 12{,}100) \text{ billion dollars} \quad (-8 \le t \le 2),$$

where this time t is the year since 2010. Use this alternative formula to estimate the amount spent in 2005 and its rate of change, and check your answers by comparing them with those in Exercise 80.

83. ▼ *Carbon Dating* The age in years of a specimen that originally contained 10 grams of carbon 14 is given by

$$y = \log_{0.999879}(0.1x),$$

where x is the amount of carbon 14 it currently contains. Compute $\dfrac{dy}{dx}\bigg|_{x=5}$, and interpret your answer. [**HINT**: For the calculation, see Quick Examples 3 and 4.]

84. ▼ *Iodine Dating* The age in years of a specimen that originally contained 10 grams of iodine 131 is given by

$$y = \log_{0.999567}(0.1x),$$

where x is the amount of iodine 131 it currently contains. Compute $\dfrac{dy}{dx}\bigg|_{x=8}$, and interpret your answer. [**HINT**: For the calculation, see Quick Examples 3 and 4.]

85. *New York City Housing Costs: Downtown* The average price of a two-bedroom apartment in downtown New York City during the real estate boom from 1994 to 2004 can be approximated by

$$p(t) = 0.33e^{0.16t} \text{ million dollars} \quad (0 \le t \le 10),$$

where t is time in years. ($t = 0$ represents 1994.)[41] What was the average price of a two-bedroom apartment in downtown New York City in 2003, and how fast was the price increasing? (Round your answers to two significant digits.) [**HINT**: See Quick Example 14.]

86. *New York City Housing Costs: Uptown* The average price of a two-bedroom apartment in uptown New York City during the real estate boom from 1994 to 2004 can be approximated by

$$p(t) = 0.14e^{0.10t} \text{ million dollars} \quad (0 \le t \le 10),$$

where t is time in years. ($t = 0$ represents 1994.)[42] What was the average price of a two-bedroom apartment in uptown New York City in 2002, and how fast was the price increasing? (Round your answers to two significant digits.) [**HINT**: See Quick Example 14.]

---

[39] Constant 2005 dollars; excludes federal funding; 2012 data is preliminary. Source: National Science Foundation, National Center for Science and Engineering Statistics, December 2013, *National Patterns of R&D Resources: 2011–12 Data Update*. NSF 14-304 (www.nsf.gov/statistics/nsf14304).

[40] Constant 2005 dollars; excludes federal funding to industry and non-profit organizations; 2012 data is preliminary. Source: National Science Foundation, National Center for Science and Engineering Statistics, December 2013, *National Patterns of R&D Resources: 2011–12 Data Update*. NSF 14-304 (www.nsf.gov/statistics/nsf14304).

[41] Model is based on an exponential regression. Source for data: Miller Samuel/*New York Times*, March 28, 2004, p. RE 11.

[42] *Ibid.*

87. *Big Brother* The following chart shows the total number of wiretaps authorized each year by U.S. state and federal courts from 1990 to 2013. ($t = 0$ represents 1990.)[43]

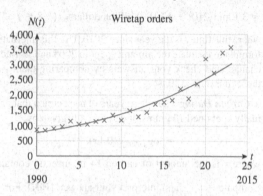

These data can be approximated by the model

$$N(t) = 770e^{0.060t} \quad (0 \leq t \leq 23).$$

a. Find $N(15)$ and $N'(15)$. Be sure to state the units of measurement. To how many significant digits should we round the answers? Why?

b. The number of people whose communications are intercepted averages around 100 per wiretap order. What does the answer to part (a) tell you about the number of people whose communications were intercepted?[44]

c. According to the model, the number of wiretap orders each year (choose one)
   (A) increased at a linear rate
   (B) decreased at a quadratic rate
   (C) increased at an exponential rate
   (D) increased at a logarithmic rate
   over the period shown.

88. *Big Brother* The following chart shows the total number of wiretaps authorized each year by U.S. state courts from 1990 to 2013. ($t = 0$ represents 1990.)[45]

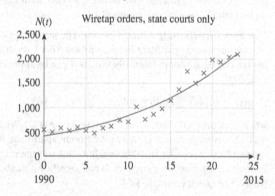

These data can be approximated by the model

$$N(t) = 410e^{0.071t} \quad (0 \leq t \leq 23).$$

a. Find $N(20)$ and $N'(20)$. Be sure to state the units of measurement. To how many significant digits should we round the answers? Why?

b. The number of people whose communications are intercepted averages around 100 per wiretap order. What does the answer to part (a) tell you about the number of people whose communications were intercepted?[46]

c. According to the model, the number of wiretap orders each year (choose one)
   (A) increased at a linear rate
   (B) decreased at a quadratic rate
   (C) increased at an exponential rate
   (D) increased at a logarithmic rate
   over the period shown.

89. *Investments* If $10,000 is invested in a savings account offering 4% per year, compounded continuously, how fast is the balance growing after 3 years? [HINT: See Quick Example 15.]

90. *Investments* If $20,000 is invested in a savings account offering 3.5% per year, compounded continuously, how fast is the balance growing after 3 years? [HINT: See Quick Example 15.]

91. *Investments* If $10,000 is invested in a savings account offering 4% per year, compounded semiannually, how fast is the balance growing after 3 years?

92. *Investments* If $20,000 is invested in a savings account offering 3.5% per year, compounded semiannually, how fast is the balance growing after 3 years?

93. *The 2003 SARS Outbreak* In the early stages of the deadly SARS (severe acute respiratory syndrome) epidemic in 2003, the number of cases was increasing by about 18% each day.[47] On March 17, 2003 (the first day for which statistics were reported by the World Health Organization), there were 167 cases. Find an exponential model that predicts the number of people infected t days after March 17, 2003, and use it to estimate how fast the epidemic was spreading on March 31, 2003. (Round your answer to the nearest whole number of new cases per day.) [HINT: See Example 2.]

94. *The 2003 SARS Outbreak* A few weeks into the deadly SARS (severe acute respiratory syndrome) epidemic in 2003, the number of cases was increasing by about 4% each day.[48] On April 1, 2003, there were 1,804 cases. Find an exponential model that predicts the number $A(t)$ of people infected t days after April 1, 2003, and use it to estimate

[43] Source for data: Wiretap Reports, Administrative Office of the United States Courts, www.uscourts.gov/Statistics/WiretapReports/wiretap-report-2013.aspx.

[44] Assume that there is no significant overlap between the people whose communications are intercepted in different wiretap orders.

[45] See footnote 41.

[46] See footnote 44.

[47] Source: World Health Organization, www.who.int.

[48] *Ibid.*

how fast the epidemic was spreading on April 30, 2003. (Round your answer to the nearest whole number of new cases per day.) [**HINT:** See Example 2.]

95. ▼ *The 2014 Ebola Outbreak* In the first 6 months of the 2014 Ebola outbreak, the total number of reported cases was increasing exponentially with a monthly growth constant of 72%.[49] There were about 100 cases as of April 1, 2014. Find an exponential model in the form $C(t) = Ae^{rt}$ for the number of cases t months after April 1, 2014, and use it to estimate how fast the number of cases was increasing on August 1, 2014. (Round your answer to the nearest 10 new cases per month.)

96. ▼ *The 2014 Ebola Outbreak* In the first 6 months of the 2014 Ebola outbreak, the total number of reported deaths was increasing exponentially with a monthly growth constant of 60%.[50] There were about 90 deaths as of April 1, 2014. Find an exponential model in the form $D(t) = Ae^{rt}$ for the number of deaths t months after April 1, 2014, and use it to estimate how fast the number of deaths was increasing on October 1, 2014. (Round your answer to the nearest 10 new deaths per month.)

97. ▼ *SAT Scores by Income* The following bar graph shows U.S. math SAT scores as a function of household income:[51]

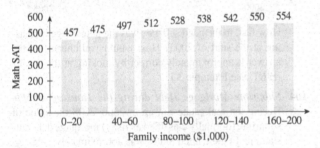

a. Which of the following best models the data (C is a constant)?

(**A**) $S(x) = C - 133e^{-0.0131x}$

(**B**) $S(x) = C + 133e^{-0.0131x}$

(**C**) $S(x) = C + 133e^{0.0131x}$

(**D**) $S(x) = C - 133e^{0.0131x}$

($S(x)$ is the average math SAT score of students whose household income is x thousand dollars per year.)

b. Use $S'(x)$ to predict how a student's math SAT score is affected by a $1,000 increase in parents' income for a student whose parents earn $45,000.

c. Does $S'(x)$ increase or decrease as x increases? Interpret your answer.

98. *SAT Scores by Income* The following bar graph shows U.S. critical reading SAT scores as a function of household income:[52]

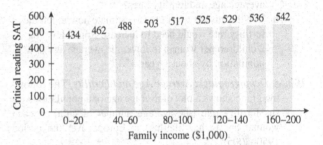

a. Which of the following best models the data (C is a constant)?

(**A**) $S(x) = C + \dfrac{1}{136e^{0.015x}}$

(**B**) $S(x) = C - 136e^{0.015x}$

(**C**) $S(x) = C - \dfrac{136}{e^{0.015x}}$

(**D**) $S(x) = C - \dfrac{e^{0.015x}}{136}$

($S(x)$ is the average critical reading SAT score of students whose household income is x thousand dollars per year.)

b. Use $S'(x)$ to predict how a student's critical reading SAT score is affected by a $1,000 increase in parents' income for a student whose parents earn $45,000.

c. Does $S'(x)$ increase or decrease as x increases? Interpret your answer.

99. ▼ *Demographics: Average Age and Fertility* The following graph shows a plot of average age of a population versus fertility rate (the average number of children each woman has in her lifetime) in the United States and Europe over the period 1950–2005:[53]

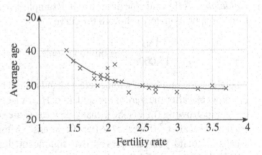

The equation of the accompanying curve is

$$a = 28.5 + 120(0.172)^x \quad (1.4 \le x \le 3.7),$$

[49] Exponential model is the authors'. Source for data: Wikipedia/Centers for Disease Control and Prevention/WHO.

[50] *Ibid.*

[51] 2009 data. Source: College Board/*New York Times,* http://economix.blogs.nytimes.com.

[52] *Ibid.*

[53] The separate data for Europe and the United States are collected in the same graph. 2005 figures are estimates. Source: United Nations World Population Division/*New York Times,* June 29, 2003, p. 3.

where a is the average age (in years) of the population and x is the fertility rate.

a. Compute $a'(2)$. What does the answer tell you about average age and fertility rates?

b. Use the answer to part (a) to estimate how much the fertility rate would need to increase from a level of 2 children per woman to lower the average age of a population by about 1 year.

100. ▼ Demographics: Average Age and Fertility The following graph shows a plot of average age of a population versus fertility rate (the average number of children each woman has in her lifetime) in Europe over the period 1950–2005:[54]

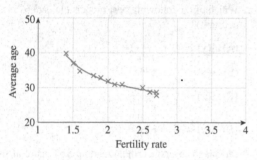

The equation of the accompanying curve is

$$g = 27.6 + 128(0.181)^x \quad (1.4 \le x \le 3.7),$$

where g is the average age (in years) of the population and x is the fertility rate.

a. Compute $g'(2.5)$. What does the answer tell you about average age and fertility rates?

b. Referring to the model that combines the data for Europe and the United States in Exercise 99, which population's average age is affected more by a changing fertility rate at the level of 2.5 children per woman?

101. Epidemics A flu epidemic described in Example 1 in Section 2.4 approximately followed the curve

$$P = \frac{150}{1 + 15,000e^{-0.35t}} \text{ million people,}$$

where P is the number of people infected and t is the number of weeks after the start of the epidemic. How fast is the epidemic growing (that is, how many new cases are there each week) after 20 weeks? After 30 weeks? After 40 weeks? (Round your answers to two significant digits.) [HINT: See Example 3.]

102. Epidemics Another epidemic follows the curve

$$P = \frac{200}{1 + 20,000e^{-0.549t}} \text{ million people,}$$

where P is the number of people infected and t is in years. How fast is the epidemic growing after 10 years? After 20 years? After 30 years? (Round your answers to two significant digits.) [HINT: See Example 3.]

103. Subprime Mortgages during the Housing Bubble During the real estate run-up in 2000–2008 the percentage of mortgages issued in the United States that were subprime (normally classified as risky) could be approximated by

$$A(t) = \frac{15.0}{1 + 8.6e^{-0.59t}} \text{ percent} \quad (0 \le t \le 8)$$

t years after the start of 2000.[55]

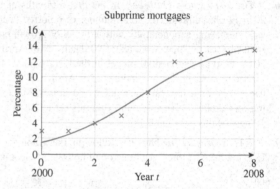

How fast, to the nearest 0.1%, was the percentage increasing at the start of 2003? How would you check that the answer is approximately correct by looking at the graph? [HINT: See Example 3.]

104. Subprime Mortgage Debt during the Housing Bubble During the real estate run-up in 2000–2008 the value of subprime (normally classified as risky) mortgage debt outstanding in the United States was approximately

$$A(t) = \frac{1,350}{1 + 4.2e^{-0.53t}} \text{ billion dollars} \quad (0 \le t \le 8)$$

t years after the start of 2000.[56]

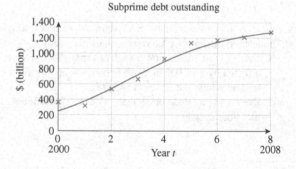

[54] All European countries including the Russian Federation. 2005 figures are estimates. Source: See footnote for Exercise 99.

[55] 2009 figure is an estimate. Sources: Mortgage Bankers Association, UBS.

[56] 2008–2009 figures are estimates. Source: www.data360.org.

How fast, to the nearest $1 billion, was subprime mortgage debt increasing at the start of 2005? How would you check that the answer is approximately correct by looking at the graph? [**HINT**: See Example 3.]

105. *Subprime Mortgages during the Housing Bubble* (Compare Exercise 103.) During the real estate run-up in 2000–2008 the percentage of mortgages issued in the United States that were subprime (normally classified as risky) could be approximated by

$$A(t) = \frac{15.0}{1 + 8.6(1.8)^{-t}} \text{ percent} \quad (0 \le t \le 8)$$

t years after the start of 2000.[57]

a. How fast, to the nearest 0.1%, was the percentage increasing at the start of 2003?

b. Compute $\lim_{t \to +\infty} A(t)$ and $\lim_{t \to +\infty} A'(t)$. What do the answers tell you about subprime mortgages?

106. *Subprime Mortgage Debt during the Housing Bubble* (Compare Exercise 104.) During the real estate run-up in 2000–2008 the value of subprime (normally classified as risky) mortgage debt outstanding in the United States could be approximated by

$$A(t) = \frac{1{,}350}{1 + 4.2(1.7)^{-t}} \text{ billion dollars} \quad (0 \le t \le 8)$$

t years after the start of 2000.[58]

a. How fast, to the nearest $1 billion, was subprime mortgage debt increasing at the start of 2005?

b. Compute $\lim_{t \to +\infty} A(t)$ and $\lim_{t \to +\infty} A'(t)$. What do the answers tell you about subprime mortgages?

107. ▼ *Population Growth* The population of Lower Anchovia was 4,000,000 at the start of 2010 and was doubling every 10 years. How fast was it growing per year at the start of 2010? (Round your answer to three significant digits.) [**HINT**: Use the method of Example 2 of Section 2.2 to obtain an exponential model for the population.]

108. ▼ *Population Growth* The population of Upper Anchovia was 3,000,000 at the start of 2011 and doubling every 7 years. How fast was it growing per year at the start of 2011? (Round your answer to three significant digits.) [**HINT**: Use the method of Example 2 of Section 2.2 to obtain an exponential model for the population.]

109. ▼ *Radioactive Decay* Plutonium 239 has a half-life of 24,400 years. How fast is a lump of 10 grams decaying after 100 years?

110. ▼ *Radioactive Decay* Carbon 14 has a half-life of 5,730 years. How fast is a lump of 20 grams decaying after 100 years?

111. ◆ *Cellphone Revenues* The number of cellphone subscribers in China for the period 2000–2005 was projected to follow the equation[59]

$$N(t) = 39t + 68 \text{ million subscribers}$$

in year t. ($t = 0$ represents 2000.) The average annual revenue per cellphone user was $350 in 2000. Assuming that, because of competition, the revenue per cellphone user decreases exponentially with an annual decay constant of 10%, give a formula for the annual revenue in year t. Hence, project the annual revenue and its rate of change in 2002. Round all answers to the nearest billion dollars or billion dollars per year.

112. ◆ *Cellphone Revenues* The annual revenue for cellphone use in China for the period 2000–2005 was projected to follow the equation[60]

$$R(t) = 14t + 24 \text{ billion dollars}$$

in year t. ($t = 0$ represents 2000.) At the same time, there were approximately 68 million subscribers in 2000. Assuming that the number of subscribers increases exponentially with an annual growth constant of 10%, give a formula for the annual revenue per subscriber in year t. Hence, project to the nearest dollar the annual revenue per subscriber and its rate of change in 2002. (Be careful with units!)

Communication and Reasoning Exercises

113. Complete the following: The derivative of e raised to a glob is . . . .

114. Complete the following: The derivative of the natural logarithm of a glob is . . . .

115. Complete the following: The derivative of 2 raised to a glob is . . . .

116. Complete the following: The derivative of the base 2 logarithm of a glob is . . . .

117. What is wrong with the following?

$$\frac{d}{dx} \ln|3x + 1| = \frac{3}{|3x + 1|} \qquad \text{✗ WRONG!}$$

118. What is wrong with the following?

$$\frac{d}{dx} 2^{2x} = (2)2^{2x} \qquad \text{✗ WRONG!}$$

119. What is wrong with the following?

$$\frac{d}{dx} 3^{2x} = (2x)3^{2x-1} \qquad \text{✗ WRONG!}$$

---

[57] 2009 figure is an estimate. Sources: Mortgage Bankers Association, UBS.

[58] 2008–2009 figures are estimates. Source: www.data360.org.

[59] Based on a regression of projected figures (coefficients are rounded). Source: Intrinsic Technology/*New York Times*, Nov. 24, 2000, p. C1.

[60] Not allowing for discounting due to increased competition. Source: *Ibid.*

120. What is wrong with the following?

$$\frac{d}{dx}\ln(3x^2 - 1) = \frac{1}{6x} \quad ✗ \; WRONG!$$

121. ▼ The number N of music downloads on campus is growing exponentially with time. Can $N'(t)$ grow linearly with time? Explain.

122. ▼ The number N of graphing calculators sold on campus is decaying exponentially with time. Can $N'(t)$ grow with time? Explain.

*The **percentage rate of change** or **fractional rate of change** of a function is defined to be the ratio $f'(x)/f(x)$. (It is customary to express this as a percentage when speaking about percentage rate of change.)*

123. ◆ Show that the fractional rate of change of the exponential function e^{kx} is equal to the growth constant k, which is often called its **fractional growth rate**.

124. ◆ Show that the fractional rate of change of $f(x)$ is the rate of change of $\ln(f(x))$.

125. ◆ Let $A(t)$ represent a quantity growing exponentially. Show that the percentage rate of change, $A'(t)/A(t)$, is constant.

126. ◆ Let $A(t)$ be the amount of money in an account that pays interest that is compounded some number of times per year. Show that the percentage rate of growth, $A'(t)/A(t)$, is constant. What might this constant represent?

11.6 Implicit Differentiation

Implicit Functions

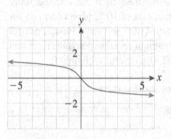

Figure 8

Consider the equation $y^5 + y + x = 0$, whose graph is shown in Figure 8. How did we obtain this graph? We did not solve for y as a function of x; that is impossible. In fact, we solved for x in terms of y to find points to plot. Nonetheless, the graph in Figure 8 is the graph of a function because it passes the vertical line test: Every vertical line crosses the graph no more than once, so for each value of x there is no more than one corresponding value of y. Because we cannot solve for y explicitly in terms of x, we say that the equation $y^5 + y + x = 0$ determines y as an **implicit function** of x.

Now, suppose we want to find the slope of the tangent line to this curve at, say, the point $(2, -1)$ (which, you should check, is a point on the curve). In the following example we find, surprisingly, that it is possible to obtain a formula for dy/dx without having to first solve the equation for y.

Implicit Differentiation

EXAMPLE 1 **Implicit Differentiation**

Find $\dfrac{dy}{dx}$, given that $y^5 + y + x = 0$.

Solution We use the chain rule and a little cleverness. Think of y as a function of x and take the derivative with respect to x of both sides of the equation:

$$y^5 + y + x = 0 \qquad \text{Original equation}$$

$$\frac{d}{dx}(y^5 + y + x) = \frac{d}{dx}(0) \qquad \text{Derivative with respect to } x \text{ of both sides}$$

$$\frac{d}{dx}(y^5) + \frac{d}{dx}(y) + \frac{d}{dx}(x) = 0 \qquad \text{Derivative rules}$$

Now we must be careful. The derivative *with respect to* x of y^5 is *not* $5y^4$. Rather, because y is a function of x, we must use the chain rule, which tells us that

$$\frac{d}{dx}(y^5) = 5y^4\frac{dy}{dx}.$$

Thus, we get

$$5y^4 \frac{dy}{dx} + \frac{dy}{dx} + 1 = 0.$$

We want to find dy/dx, so we *solve for it*:

$$\left(5y^4 + 1\right)\frac{dy}{dx} = -1 \qquad \text{Isolate } dy/dx \text{ on one side.}$$

$$\frac{dy}{dx} = -\frac{1}{5y^4 + 1}. \qquad \text{Divide both sides by } 5y^4 + 1.$$

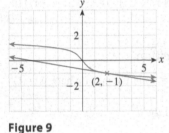

Figure 9

➡ **Before we go on . . .** Note that we should not expect to obtain dy/dx as an explicit function of x if y was not an explicit function of x to begin with. For example, the formula we found for dy/dx in Example 1 is not a function of x because there is a y in it. However, the result is still useful because we can evaluate the derivative at any point on the graph. For instance, at the point $(2, -1)$ on the graph we get

$$\frac{dy}{dx} = -\frac{1}{5y^4 + 1} = -\frac{1}{5(-1)^4 + 1} = -\frac{1}{6}.$$

Thus, the slope of the tangent line to the curve $y^5 + y + x = 0$ at the point $(2, -1)$ is $-1/6$. Figure 9 shows the graph and this tangent line. ∎

This procedure we just used—differentiating an equation to find dy/dx without first solving the equation for y—is called **implicit differentiation**.

In Example 1 we were given an equation in x and y that determined y as an (implicit) function of x, even though we could not solve for y. But an equation in x and y need not always determine y as a function of x. Consider, for example, the equation

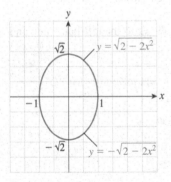

Figure 10

$$2x^2 + y^2 = 2.$$

Solving for y yields $y = \pm\sqrt{2 - 2x^2}$. The $\pm$ sign reminds us that for some values of x there are two corresponding values for y. We can graph this equation by superimposing the graphs of

$$y = \sqrt{2 - 2x^2} \quad \text{and} \quad y = -\sqrt{2 - 2x^2}.$$

The graph, an *ellipse*, is shown in Figure 10. The graph of $y = \sqrt{2 - 2x^2}$ constitutes the top half of the ellipse, and the graph of $y = -\sqrt{2 - 2x^2}$ constitutes the bottom half.

EXAMPLE 2 **Slope of Tangent Line**

Refer to Figure 10. Find the slope of the tangent line to the ellipse $2x^2 + y^2 = 2$ at the point $(1/\sqrt{2}, 1)$.

Solution Because $(1/\sqrt{2}, 1)$ is on the top half of the ellipse in Figure 10, we *could* differentiate the function $y = \sqrt{2 - 2x^2}$ to obtain the result, but it is actually easier to apply implicit differentiation to the original equation.

$$2x^2 + y^2 = 2 \qquad \text{Original equation}$$

$$\frac{d}{dx}(2x^2 + y^2) = \frac{d}{dx}(2) \qquad \text{Derivative with respect to } x \text{ of both sides}$$

$$4x + 2y\frac{dy}{dx} = 0$$

$$2y\frac{dy}{dx} = -4x \qquad \text{Solve for } dy/dx.$$

$$\frac{dy}{dx} = -\frac{4x}{2y} = -\frac{2x}{y}$$

To find the slope at $(1/\sqrt{2}, 1)$, we now substitute for x and y:

$$\left.\frac{dy}{dx}\right|_{(1/\sqrt{2},\, 1)} = -\frac{2/\sqrt{2}}{1} = -\sqrt{2}.$$

Thus, the slope of the tangent to the ellipse at the point $(1/\sqrt{2}, 1)$ is $-\sqrt{2} \approx -1.414$.

EXAMPLE 3   **Tangent Line for an Implicit Function**

Find the equation of the tangent line to the curve $\ln y = xy$ at the point where $y = 1$.

Solution First, we use implicit differentiation to find dy/dx:

$$\frac{d}{dx}(\ln y) = \frac{d}{dx}(xy) \qquad \text{Take } d/dx \text{ of both sides.}$$

$$\frac{1}{y}\frac{dy}{dx} = (1)y + x\frac{dy}{dx}. \qquad \text{Chain rule on left, product rule on right}$$

To solve for dy/dx, we bring all the terms containing dy/dx to the left-hand side and all terms not containing it to the right-hand side:

$$\frac{1}{y}\frac{dy}{dx} - x\frac{dy}{dx} = y \qquad \text{Bring the terms with } dy/dx \text{ to the left.}$$

$$\frac{dy}{dx}\left(\frac{1}{y} - x\right) = y \qquad \text{Factor out } dy/dx.$$

$$\frac{dy}{dx}\left(\frac{1 - xy}{y}\right) = y$$

$$\frac{dy}{dx} = y\left(\frac{y}{1 - xy}\right) = \frac{y^2}{1 - xy}. \qquad \text{Solve for } dy/dx.$$

The derivative gives the slope of the tangent line, so we want to evaluate the derivative at the point where $y = 1$. However, the formula for dy/dx requires values for both x and y. We get the value of x by substituting $y = 1$ in the original equation:

$$\ln y = xy$$

$$\ln 1 = x \cdot 1. \qquad \text{Substitute } y = 1.$$

But $\ln 1 = 0$, so $x = 0$ for this point. Thus,

$$\left.\frac{dy}{dx}\right|_{(0,\, 1)} = \frac{1^2}{1 - (0)(1)} = 1.$$

Therefore, the tangent line is the line through $(x, y) = (0, 1)$ with slope 1, which is

$$y = x + 1.$$

➡ **Before we go on...** Example 3 presents an instance of an implicit function in which it is simply not possible to solve for y. Try it. ∎

Logarithmic Differentiation

Sometimes, it is easiest to differentiate a complicated function of x by first taking the logarithm and then using implicit differentiation—a technique called **logarithmic differentiation**.

EXAMPLE 4   **Logarithmic Differentiation**

Find $\dfrac{d}{dx}\left[\dfrac{(x + 1)^{10}(x^2 + 1)^{11}}{(x^3 + 1)^{12}}\right]$ without using the product or quotient rules.

Solution Write

$$y = \frac{(x + 1)^{10}(x^2 + 1)^{11}}{(x^3 + 1)^{12}},$$

and then take the natural logarithm of both sides:

$$\ln y = \ln\left[\frac{(x + 1)^{10}(x^2 + 1)^{11}}{(x^3 + 1)^{12}}\right].$$

We can use properties of the logarithm to simplify the right-hand side:

$$\ln y = \ln(x + 1)^{10} + \ln(x^2 + 1)^{11} - \ln(x^3 + 1)^{12}$$
$$= 10\ln(x + 1) + 11\ln(x^2 + 1) - 12\ln(x^3 + 1).$$

Now we can find $\dfrac{dy}{dx}$ using implicit differentiation:

$$\frac{1}{y}\frac{dy}{dx} = \frac{10}{x + 1} + \frac{22x}{x^2 + 1} - \frac{36x^2}{x^3 + 1} \qquad \text{Take } d/dx \text{ of both sides.}$$

$$\frac{dy}{dx} = y\left(\frac{10}{x + 1} + \frac{22x}{x^2 + 1} - \frac{36x^2}{x^3 + 1}\right) \qquad \text{Solve for } dy/dx.$$

$$= \frac{(x + 1)^{10}(x^2 + 1)^{11}}{(x^3 + 1)^{12}}\left(\frac{10}{x + 1} + \frac{22x}{x^2 + 1} - \frac{36x^2}{x^3 + 1}\right). \qquad \text{Substitute for } y.$$

➡ **Before we go on...** Redo Example 4 using the product and quotient rules (and the chain rule) instead of logarithmic differentiation, and compare the answers. Compare also the amount of work involved in both methods. ∎

Application

Productivity usually depends on both labor and capital. Suppose, for example, that you are managing a surfboard manufacturing company. You can measure its productivity by counting the number of surfboards the company makes each year. As a measure of labor, you can use the number of employees, and as a measure of capital you can use its operating budget. The so-called *Cobb-Douglas* model uses a function of the form

$$P = Kx^a y^{1-a}, \qquad \text{Cobb-Douglas model for productivity}$$

where P stands for the number of surfboards made each year, x is the number of employees, and y is the operating budget. The numbers K and a are constants that depend on the particular situation studied, with a between 0 and 1.

EXAMPLE 5 **Cobb-Douglas Production Function**

The surfboard company you own has the Cobb-Douglas production function

$$P = x^{0.3} y^{0.7},$$

where P is the number of surfboards it produces per year, x is the number of employees, and y is the daily operating budget (in dollars). Assume that the production level P is constant.

a. Find $\dfrac{dy}{dx}$.

b. Evaluate this derivative at $x = 30$ and $y = 10{,}000$, and interpret the answer.

Solution

a. We are given the equation $P = x^{0.3} y^{0.7}$, in which P is constant. We find $\dfrac{dy}{dx}$ by implicit differentiation.

$$0 = \frac{d}{dx}(x^{0.3} y^{0.7}) \qquad\qquad d/dx \text{ of both sides}$$

$$0 = 0.3x^{-0.7} y^{0.7} + x^{0.3}(0.7)y^{-0.3}\frac{dy}{dx} \qquad \text{Product and chain rules}$$

$$-0.7x^{0.3} y^{-0.3}\frac{dy}{dx} = 0.3x^{-0.7} y^{0.7} \qquad \text{Bring term with } dy/dx \text{ to left.}$$

$$\frac{dy}{dx} = -\frac{0.3x^{-0.7} y^{0.7}}{0.7x^{0.3} y^{-0.3}} \qquad\qquad \text{Solve for } dy/dx.$$

$$= -\frac{3y}{7x}. \qquad\qquad\qquad \text{Simplify.}$$

b. Evaluating this derivative at $x = 30$ and $y = 10{,}000$ gives

$$\left.\frac{dy}{dx}\right|_{x=30,\, y=10{,}000} = -\frac{3(10{,}000)}{7(30)} \approx -143.$$

To interpret this result, first look at the units of the derivative: We recall that the units of dy/dx are units of y per unit of x. Because y is the daily budget, its units are dollars; because x is the number of employees, its units are employees. Thus,

$$\left.\frac{dy}{dx}\right|_{x=30,\, y=10{,}000} \approx -\$143 \text{ per employee.}$$

Next, recall that dy/dx measures the rate of change of y as x changes. Because the answer is negative, the daily budget to maintain production at the fixed level is decreasing by approximately $143 per additional employee at an employment level of 30 employees and a daily operating budget of $10,000. In other words, increasing the workforce by one worker will result in a savings of approximately $143 per day. Roughly speaking, *a new employee is worth $143 per day* at the current levels of employment and production.

11.6 EXERCISES

▼ more advanced   ◆ challenging

⊤ indicates exercises that should be solved using technology

In Exercises 1–10, find dy/dx, using implicit differentiation. In each case, compare your answer with the result obtained by first solving for y as a function of x and then taking the derivative. [**HINT**: See Example 1.]

1. $2x + 3y = 7$
2. $4x - 5y = 9$

3. $x^2 - 2y = 6$
4. $3y + x^2 = 5$

5. $2x + 3y = xy$
6. $x - y = xy$

7. $e^x y = 1$
8. $e^x y - y = 2$

9. $y \ln x + y = 2$
10. $\dfrac{\ln x}{y} = 2 - x$

In Exercises 11–30, find the indicated derivative using implicit differentiation. [**HINT**: See Example 1.]

11. $x^2 + y^2 = 5; \dfrac{dy}{dx}$
12. $2x^2 - y^2 = 4; \dfrac{dy}{dx}$

13. $x^2 y - y^2 = 4; \dfrac{dy}{dx}$
14. $xy^2 - y = x; \dfrac{dy}{dx}$

15. $3xy - \dfrac{y}{3} = \dfrac{2}{x}; \dfrac{dy}{dx}$
16. $\dfrac{xy}{2} - y^2 = 3; \dfrac{dy}{dx}$

17. $x^2 - 3y^2 = 8; \dfrac{dx}{dy}$
18. $(xy)^2 + y^2 = 8; \dfrac{dx}{dy}$

19. $p^2 - pq = 5p^2 q^2; \dfrac{dp}{dq}$
20. $q^2 - pq = 5p^2 q^2; \dfrac{dp}{dq}$

21. $xe^y - ye^x = 1; \dfrac{dy}{dx}$
22. $x^2 e^y - y^2 = e^x; \dfrac{dy}{dx}$

23. ▼ $e^{st} = s^2; \dfrac{ds}{dt}$
24. ▼ $e^{s^2 t} - st = 1; \dfrac{ds}{dt}$

25. ▼ $\dfrac{e^x}{y^2} = 1 + e^y; \dfrac{dy}{dx}$
26. ▼ $\dfrac{x}{e^y} + xy = 9y; \dfrac{dy}{dx}$

27. ▼ $\ln(y^2 - y) + x = y; \dfrac{dy}{dx}$
28. ▼ $\ln(xy) - x \ln y = y; \dfrac{dy}{dx}$

29. ▼ $\ln(xy + y^2) = e^y; \dfrac{dy}{dx}$
30. ▼ $\ln(1 + e^{xy}) = y; \dfrac{dy}{dx}$

*In Exercises 31–42, use implicit differentiation to find (**a**) the slope of the tangent line and (**b**) the equation of the tangent line at the indicated point on the graph. (Round answers to four decimal places as needed.) If only the x-coordinate is given, you must also find the y-coordinate.* [**HINT**: See Examples 2 and 3.]

31. $4x^2 + 2y^2 = 12, (1, -2)$
32. $3x^2 - y^2 = 11, (-2, 1)$

33. $2x^2 - y^2 = xy, (-1, 2)$
34. $2x^2 + xy = 3y^2, (-1, -1)$

35. $x^2 y - y^2 + x = 1, (1, 0)$

36. $(xy)^2 + xy - x = 8, (-8, 0)$

37. $xy - 2,000 = y, x = 2$
38. $x^2 - 10xy = 200, x = 10$

39. ▼ $\ln(x + y) - x = 3x^2, x = 0$

40. ▼ $\ln(x - y) + 1 = 3x^2, x = 0$

41. ▼ $e^{xy} - x = 4x, x = 3$
42. ▼ $e^{-xy} + 2x = 1, x = -1$

In Exercises 43–52, use logarithmic differentiation to find dy/dx. Do not simplify the result. [**HINT**: See Example 4.]

43. $y = \dfrac{2x + 1}{4x - 2}$
44. $y = (3x + 2)(8x - 5)$

45. $y = \dfrac{(3x + 1)^2}{4x(2x - 1)^3}$
46. $y = \dfrac{x^2(3x + 1)^2}{(2x - 1)^3}$

47. $y = (8x - 1)^{1/3}(x - 1)$
48. $y = \dfrac{(3x + 2)^{2/3}}{3x - 1}$

49. $y = (x^3 + x)\sqrt{x^3 + 2}$
50. $y = \sqrt{\dfrac{x - 1}{x^2 + 2}}$

51. ▼ $y = x^x$
52. ▼ $y = x^{-x}$

Applications

53. *Productivity* The number of CDs per hour that *Snappy Hardware* can manufacture at its plant is given by

$$P = x^{0.6} y^{0.4},$$

where x is the number of workers at the plant and y is the monthly budget (in dollars). Assume that P is constant, and compute $\dfrac{dy}{dx}$ when $x = 100$ and $y = 200,000$. Interpret the result. [**HINT**: See Example 5.]

54. Productivity The number of cellphone accessory kits (neon lights, matching covers, and earbuds) per day that *USA Cellular Makeover, Inc.*, can manufacture at its plant in Cambodia is given by

$$P = x^{0.5}y^{0.5},$$

where x is the number of workers at the plant and y is the monthly budget (in dollars). Assume that P is constant, and compute $\dfrac{dy}{dx}$ when $x = 200$ and $y = 100,000$. Interpret the result. [**HINT:** See Example 5.]

55. Demand The demand equation for soccer tournament T-shirts is

$$xy - 2,000 = y,$$

where y is the number of T-shirts the *Enormous State University* soccer team can sell at a price of $\$x$ per shirt. Find $\dfrac{dy}{dx}\Big|_{x=5}$, and interpret the result.

56. Cost Equations The cost y (in cents) of producing x gallons of *Ectoplasm* hair gel is given by the cost equation

$$y^2 - 10xy = 200.$$

Evaluate $\dfrac{dy}{dx}$ at $x = 1$, and interpret the result.

57. Housing Costs[61] The cost C (in dollars) of building a house is related to the number k of carpenters used and the number e of electricians used by the formula

$$C = 15,000 + 50k^2 + 60e^2.$$

If the cost of the house is fixed at $\$200,000$, find $\dfrac{dk}{de}\Big|_{e=15}$, and interpret your result.

58. Employment An employment research company estimates that the value of a recent MBA graduate to an accounting company is

$$V = 3e^2 + 5g^3,$$

where V is the value of the graduate, e is the number of years of prior business experience, and g is the graduate school grade-point average. If V is fixed at 200, find $\dfrac{de}{dg}$ when $g = 3.0$, and interpret the result.

59. ▼ Grades[62] A productivity formula for a student's performance on a difficult English examination is

$$g = 4tx - 0.2t^2 - 10x^2 \quad (t < 30),$$

where g is the score the student can expect to obtain, t is the number of hours of study for the examination, and x is the student's grade-point average.

[61] Based on an exercise in *Introduction to Mathematical Economics* by A. L. Ostrosky Jr., and J. V. Koch (Waveland Press, Springfield, Illinois, 1979).
[62] *Ibid.*

a. For how long should a student with a 3.0 grade-point average study to score 80 on the examination?

b. Find $\dfrac{dt}{dx}$ for a student who earns a score of 80, evaluate it when $x = 3.0$, and interpret the result.

60. ▼ Grades Repeat Exercise 59 using the following productivity formula for a basket-weaving examination:

$$g = 10tx - 0.2t^2 - 10x^2 \quad (t < 10).$$

Comment on the result.

Exercises 61 and 62 are based on the following demand function for money (taken from a question on the GRE Economics Test):

$$M_d = (2) \times (y)^{0.6} \times (r)^{-0.3} \times (p),$$

where

M_d = *demand for nominal money balances (money stock)*
y = *real income*
r = *an index of interest rates*
p = *an index of prices.*

61. ♦ Money Stock If real income grows while the money stock and the price level remain constant, the interest rate must change at what rate? (First find dr/dy, then find dr/dt; your answers will be expressed in terms of r, y, and dy/dt.)

62. ♦ Money Stock If real income grows while the money stock and the interest rate remain constant, the price level must change at what rate?

Communication and Reasoning Exercises

63. Fill in the missing terms: The equation $x = y^3 + y - 3$ specifies ___ as a function of ___ and ___ as an implicit function of ___.

64. Fill in the missing terms: When $x \neq 0$ in the equation $xy = x^3 + 4$, it is possible to specify ___ as a function of ___. However, ___ is only an implicit function of ___.

65. ▼ Use logarithmic differentiation to give another proof of the product rule.

66. ▼ Use logarithmic differentiation to give a proof of the quotient rule.

67. ▼ If y is given explicitly as a function of x by an equation $y = f(x)$, compare finding dy/dx by implicit differentiation to finding it explicitly in the usual way.

68. ▼ Explain why one should not expect dy/dx to be a function of x if y is not a function of x.

69. ♦ If y is a function of x and $dy/dx \neq 0$ at some point, regard x as an implicit function of y and use implicit differentiation to obtain the equation

$$\frac{dx}{dy} = \frac{1}{dy/dx}.$$

70. ♦ If you are given an equation in x and y such that dy/dx is a function of x only, what can you say about the graph of the equation?

CHAPTER 11 REVIEW

KEY CONCEPTS

www.WanerMath.com
Go to the Website to find a comprehensive and interactive Web-based summary of Chapter 11.

11.1 Derivatives of Powers, Sums, and Constant Multiples

Power Rule: If n is any constant and $f(x) = x^n$, then $f'(x) = nx^{n-1}$. [p. 822]

Using the power rule for negative and fractional exponents [p. 823]

Sums, differences, and constant multiples [p. 825]

Combining the rules [p. 826]

$\dfrac{d}{dx}(cx) = c$, $\dfrac{d}{dx}(c) = 0$ [p. 828]

$f(x) = x^{1/3}$, $g(x) = x^{2/3}$, and $h(x) = |x|$ are not differentiable at $x = 0$ [p. 828]

L'Hospital's rule [p. 830]

11.2 A First Application: Marginal Analysis

Marginal cost function $C'(x)$ [p. 837]

Marginal revenue and profit functions $R'(x)$ and $P'(x)$ [p. 839]

What it means when the marginal profit is zero [p. 840]

Marginal product [p. 840]

Average cost of the first x items:

$\overline{C}(x) = \dfrac{C(x)}{x}$ [p. 842]

11.3 The Product and Quotient Rules

Product rule: $\dfrac{d}{dx}[f(x)g(x)] =$

$f'(x)g(x) + f(x)g'(x)$ [p. 848]

Quotient rule: $\dfrac{d}{dx}\left[\dfrac{f(x)}{g(x)}\right] =$

$\dfrac{f'(x)g(x) - f(x)g'(x)}{[g(x)]^2}$ [p. 849]

Using the product rule [p. 851]

Using the quotient rule [p. 852]

Calculation thought experiment [p. 853]

Application to revenue and average cost [p. 855]

11.4 The Chain Rule

Chain rule: $\dfrac{d}{dx}[f(u)] = f'(u)\dfrac{du}{dx}$ [p. 861]

Generalized power rule:

$\dfrac{d}{dx}(u^n) = nu^{n-1}\dfrac{du}{dx}$ [p. 862]

Using the chain rule [p. 862]

Application to marginal product and profit [p. 865]

Chain rule in differential notation:

$\dfrac{dy}{dx} = \dfrac{dy}{du}\dfrac{du}{dx}$ [p. 867]

Manipulating derivatives in differential notation [p. 867]

11.5 Derivatives of Logarithmic and Exponential Functions

Derivative of the natural logarithm:

$\dfrac{d}{dx}\ln x = \dfrac{1}{x}$ [p. 874]

Derivative of logarithm with base b:

$\dfrac{d}{dx}\log_b x = \dfrac{1}{x \ln b}$ [p. 874]

Derivatives of logarithms of functions:

$\dfrac{d}{dx}\ln u = \dfrac{1}{u}\dfrac{du}{dx}$

$\dfrac{d}{dx}\log_b u = \dfrac{1}{u \ln b}\dfrac{du}{dx}$ [p. 875]

Derivatives of logarithms of absolute values:

$\dfrac{d}{dx}\ln|x| = \dfrac{1}{x}$ $\quad$ $\dfrac{d}{dx}\ln|u| = \dfrac{1}{u}\dfrac{du}{dx}$

$\dfrac{d}{dx}\log_b|x| = \dfrac{1}{x \ln b}$

$\dfrac{d}{dx}\log_b|u| = \dfrac{1}{u \ln b}\dfrac{du}{dx}$ [p. 877]

Derivative of e^x: $\dfrac{d}{dx}e^x = e^x$ [p. 878]

Derivative of b^x: $\dfrac{d}{dx}b^x = b^x \ln b$ [p. 879]

Derivatives of exponential functions [p. 879]

Application to epidemics [p. 880]

Application to sales growth (logistic function) [p. 881]

Application to limits (l'Hospital's rule) [p. 881]

11.6 Implicit Differentiation

Implicit function of x [p. 888]

Implicit differentiation [p. 888]

Using implicit differentiation [p. 889]

Finding a tangent line [p. 890]

Logarithmic differentiation [p. 891]

Application: Cobb-Douglas production function [p. 892]

REVIEW EXERCISES

In Exercises 1–32, find the derivative of the given function.

1. $f(x) = 10x^5 + \dfrac{1}{2}x^4 - x + 2$

2. $f(x) = \dfrac{10}{x^5} + \dfrac{1}{2x^4} - \dfrac{1}{x} + 2$

3. $f(x) = 3x^3 + 3\sqrt[3]{x}$

4. $f(x) = \dfrac{2}{x^{2.1}} - \dfrac{x^{0.1}}{2}$

5. $f(x) = x + \dfrac{1}{x^2}$

6. $f(x) = 2x - \dfrac{1}{x}$

7. $f(x) = \dfrac{4}{3x} - \dfrac{2}{x^{0.1}} + \dfrac{x^{1.1}}{3.2} - 4$

8. $f(x) = \dfrac{4}{x} + \dfrac{x}{4} - |x|$

9. $f(x) = e^x(x^2 - 1)$

10. $f(x) = \dfrac{x^2 + 1}{x^2 - 1}$

11. $f(x) = \dfrac{|x| + 1}{3x^2 + 1}$

12. $f(x) = (|x| + x)(2 - 3x^2)$

13. $f(x) = (4x - 1)^{-1}$

14. $f(x) = (x + 7)^{-2}$

15. $f(x) = (x^2 - 1)^{10}$

16. $f(x) = \dfrac{1}{(x^2 - 1)^{10}}$

17. $f(x) = [2 + (x + 1)^{-0.1}]^{4.3}$

18. $f(x) = [(x + 1)^{0.1} - 4x]^{-5.1}$

19. $f(x) = e^{2x+1}$

20. $f(x) = e^{4x-5}$

21. $t(x) = 3^{2x-4}$

22. $t(x) = 4^{-x+5}$

23. $f(x) = e^x(x^2 + 1)^{10}$

24. $f(x) = \left[\dfrac{x - 1}{3x + 1}\right]^3$

25. $f(x) = \dfrac{3^x}{x - 1}$

26. $f(x) = 4^{-x}(x + 1)$

27. $f(x) = e^{x^2-1}$

28. $f(x) = (x^2 + 1)e^{x^2-1}$

29. $g(x) = \ln|3x - 1|$

30. $g(x) = \ln|5 - 9x|$

31. $f(x) = \ln(x^2 - 1)$

32. $f(x) = \dfrac{\ln(x^2 - 1)}{x^2 - 1}$

In Exercises 33–40, find all values of x (if any) where the tangent line to the graph of the given equation is horizontal.

33. $y = -3x^2 + 7x - 1$

34. $y = 5x^2 - 2x + 1$

35. $y = \dfrac{x}{2} + \dfrac{2}{x}$

36. $y = \dfrac{x^2}{2} - \dfrac{8}{x^2}$

37. $y = x - e^{2x-1}$

38. $y = e^{x^2}$

39. $y = \dfrac{x}{x + 1}$

40. $y = \sqrt{x}(x - 1)$

In Exercises 41–46, find dy/dx for the given equation.

41. $x^2 - y^2 = x$

42. $2xy + y^2 = y$

43. $e^{xy} + xy = 2$

44. $\ln\left(\dfrac{y}{x}\right) = y$

45. $y = \dfrac{(2x - 1)^4(3x + 4)}{(x + 1)(3x - 1)^3}$

46. $y = x^{x-1}3^x$

In Exercises 47–52, find the equation of the tangent line to the graph of the given equation at the specified point.

47. $y = (x^2 - 3x)^{-2};\ x = 1$

48. $y = (2x^2 - 3)^{-3};\ x = -1$

49. $y = x^2e^{-x};\ x = -1$

50. $y = \dfrac{x}{1 + e^x};\ x = 0$

51. $xy - y^2 = x^2 - 3;\ (-1, 1)$

52. $\ln(xy) + y^2 = 1;\ (-1, -1)$

In Exercises 53–56, find the limit.

53. $\displaystyle\lim_{x \to +\infty} \dfrac{x^2}{e^{x^2}}$

54. $\displaystyle\lim_{x \to -\infty} xe^x$

55. $\displaystyle\lim_{x \to 0} \dfrac{x^2}{e^{x^2} - 1}$

56. $\displaystyle\lim_{x \to 0} \dfrac{x^3}{e^x - 1 - x - x^2/2}$

Applications: OHaganBooks.com
[Try the game at www.OHaganBooks.com]

57. Sales OHaganBooks.com fits the cubic curve

$$w(t) = -3.7t^3 + 74.6t^2 + 135.5t + 6{,}300 \quad (0 \le t \le 6)$$

to its weekly sales figures (see Chapter 10 Review Exercise 57; *t* is time in weeks), as shown in the following graph:

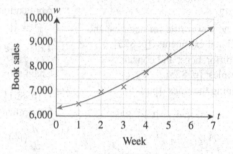

a. According to the cubic model, what was the rate of increase of sales at the beginning of the second week ($t = 1$)? (Round your answer to the nearest unit.)

b. If we extrapolate the model, what would be the rate of increase of weekly sales at the beginning of the eighth week ($t = 7$)?

c. Graph the function *w* for $0 \le t \le 20$. Would it be realistic to use the function to predict sales through week 20? Why?

d. By examining the graph, say why the choice of a quadratic model would result in radically different long-term predictions of sales.

58. Rising Sea Level Marjory Duffin is still toying with various models to fit to the New York sea level figures she had seen after purchasing a beachfront condominium in New York (see Chapter 10 Review Exercise 58). Following is a cubic curve she obtained using regression:

$$L(t) = -0.0001t^3 + 0.02t^2 + 2.2t \text{ mm.}$$

(*t* is time in years since 1900.) The curve and data are shown in the following graph:

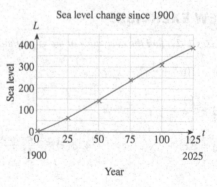

a. According to the cubic model, what was the rate at which the sea level was rising in 2000 ($t = 100$)? (Round your answer to two significant digits.)

b. If we extrapolate the model, what would be the rate at which the sea level is rising in 2025 ($t = 125$)?

c. Graph the function L for $0 \le t \le 200$. Why is it not realistic to use the function to predict the sea level through 2100?

d. James Stewart, a summer intern at *Duffin House Publishers*, differs. As he puts it, "The cubic curve came from doing regression on the actual data, and thus reflects the actual trend of the data. We can't argue against reality!" Comment on this assertion.

59. *Cost* As OHaganBooks.com's sales increase, so do its costs. If we take into account volume discounts from suppliers and shippers, the weekly cost of selling x books is

$$C(x) = -0.00002x^2 + 3.2x + 5,400 \text{ dollars.}$$

a. What is the marginal cost at a sales level of 8,000 books per week?

b. What is the average cost per book at a sales level of 8,000 books per week?

c. What is the marginal average cost ($d\bar{C}/dx$) at a sales level of 8,000 books per week?

d. Interpret the results of parts (a)–(c).

60. *Cost* OHaganBooks.com has been experiencing a run of bad luck with its summer college intern program in association with PCU (*Party Central University*), begun as a result of a suggestion by Marjory Duffin over dinner one evening. The frequent errors in filling orders, charges from movie download sites and dating sites, and beverages spilled on computer equipment have resulted in an estimated weekly cost to the company of

$$C(x) = 25x^2 - 5.2x + 4,000 \text{ dollars,}$$

where x is the number of college interns employed.

a. What is the marginal cost at a level of 10 interns?

b. What is the average cost per intern at a level of 10 interns?

c. What is the marginal average cost at a level of 10 interns?

d. Interpret the results of parts (a)–(c).

61. *Revenue* At the moment, OHaganBooks.com is selling 1,000 books per week, and its sales are rising at a rate of 200 books per week. Also, it is now selling all its books for $20 each, but its price is dropping at a rate of $1 per week.

a. At what rate is OHaganBooks.com's weekly revenue rising or falling?

b. John O'Hagan would like to see the company's weekly revenue increase at a rate of $5,000 per week. At what rate would sales have to have been increasing to accomplish that goal, assuming that all the other information is as given above?

62. *Revenue* Because of ongoing problems with its large college intern program in association with PCU (see Exercise 60), OHaganBooks.com has arranged to transfer its interns to its competitor *JungleBooks.com* (whose headquarters happens to be across the road) for a small fee. At the moment, it is transferring 5 students per week, and this number is rising at a rate of 4 students per week. Also, it is now charging JungleBooks $400 per intern, but this amount is decreasing at a rate of $20 per week.

a. At what rate is OHaganBooks.com's weekly revenue from this transaction rising or falling?

b. Flush with success of the transfer program, John O'Hagan would like to see the company's resulting revenue increase at a rate of $3,900 per week. At what rate would the transfer of interns have to increase to accomplish that goal, assuming all the other information is as given above?

63. *Percentage Rate of Change of Revenue* The percentage rate of change of a quantity Q is Q'/Q. Why is the percentage rate of change of revenue always equal to the sum of the percentage rates of change of unit price and weekly sales?

64. *P/E Ratios* At the beginning of last week, OHaganBooks.com stock was selling for $100 per share, rising at a rate of $50 per year. Its earnings amounted to $1 per share, rising at a rate of $0.10 per year. At what rate was its price-to-earnings (P/E) ratio, the ratio of its stock price to its earnings per share, rising or falling?

65. *P/E Ratios* Refer to Exercise 64. Jay Campbell, who recently invested in OHaganBooks.com stock, would have liked to see the P/E ratio increase at a rate of 100 points per year. How fast would the stock have to have been rising, assuming that all the other information is as given in Exercise 64?

66. *Percentage Rate of Change of P/E Ratios* Refer to Exercise 64. The percentage rate of change of a quantity Q is Q'/Q. Why is the percentage rate of change of the P/E ratio always equal to the percentage rate of change of unit price minus the percentage rate of change of earnings?

67. *Sales* OHaganBooks.com decided that the cubic curve in Exercise 57 was not suitable for extrapolation, so instead it tried

$$s(t) = 6,000 + \frac{4,500}{1 + e^{-0.55(t-4.8)}},$$

as shown in the following graph:

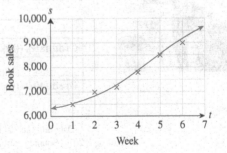

Week

a. Compute $s'(t)$, and use the answer to estimate the rate of increase of weekly sales at the beginning of the seventh week ($t = 6$). (Round your answer to the nearest unit.)

b. Compute $\lim_{t \to +\infty} s'(t)$, and interpret the answer.

68. Rising Sea Level Upon some reflection, Marjory Duffin decided that the curve in Exercise 58 was not suitable for extrapolation, so instead she tried

$$L(t) = \frac{418}{1 + 17.2e^{-0.041t}} \quad (0 \le t \le 125)$$

(t is time in years since 1900), as shown in the following graph:

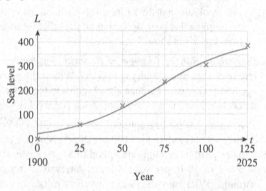

Year

a. Compute $L'(t)$, and use the answer to estimate the rate at which the sea level was rising in 2000 ($t = 100$). (Round your answer to two decimal places.)

b. Compute $\lim_{t \to +\infty} L'(t)$, and interpret the answer.

69. Website Activity The number of hits on OHaganBooks.com's website was 1,000 per day at the beginning of the year, and was growing at a rate of 5% per week. If this growth rate continued for the whole year (52 weeks), find the rate of increase (in hits per day per week) at the end of the year.

70. Website Activity The number of hits on *ShadyDownload.net* during the summer intern program at OHaganBooks.com was 100 per day at the beginning of the intern program, and was growing at a rate of 15% per day. If this growth rate continued for the duration of the whole summer intern program (85 days), find the rate of increase (in hits per day per day) at the end of the program.

71. Demand and Revenue The price p that OHaganBooks.com charges for its latest leather-bound gift edition of *The Complete Larry Potter* is related to the demand q in weekly sales by the equation

$$250pq + q^2 = 13,500,000.$$

Suppose the price is set at $50, which would make the demand 1,000 copies per week.

a. Using implicit differentiation, compute the rate of change of demand with respect to price, and interpret the result. (Round the answer to two decimal places.)

b. Use the result of part (a) to compute the rate of change of revenue with respect to price. Should the price be raised or lowered to increase revenue?

72. Demand and Revenue The price p that OHaganBooks.com charges for its latest leather-bound gift edition of *Lord of the Fields* is related to the demand q in weekly sales by the equation

$$100pq + q^2 = 5,000,000.$$

Suppose the price is set at $40, which would make the demand 1,000 copies per week.

a. Using implicit differentiation, compute the rate of change of demand with respect to price, and interpret the result. (Round the answer to two decimal places.)

b. Use the result of part (a) to compute the rate of change of revenue with respect to price. Should the price be raised or lowered to increase revenue?

CASE STUDY **Projecting Market Growth**

It is 2010, and you are on the board of directors at *Fullcourt Academic Press,* a major textbook supplier to private schools, and various expansion strategies will be discussed at tomorrow's board meeting. TJM, the sales director of the high school division, has just burst into your office with his last-minute proposal based on data showing the number of private high school graduates in the United States each year over the past 18 years:[63]

Year t	1995	1996	1997	1998	1999	2000	2001	2002	2003
Graduates (thousands)	245	254	265	273	279	279	285	296	301
Year t	2004	2005	2006	2007	2008	2009	2010	2011	2012
Graduates (thousands)	307	307	307	314	314	315	315	316	316

[63] Data through 2011 are National Center for Educational Statistics actual and projected data as of April 2010. Source: National Center for Educational Statistics (http://nces.ed.gov).

TJM asserts that, despite the unspectacular numbers in the past few years, the long-term trend appears to support a basic premise of his proposal for an expansion strategy: that the number of high school seniors in private schools in the United States will be growing at a rate of about 4,000 per year through 2015. He points out that the rate of increase predicted by the regression line is approximately 4,080 students per year, supporting his premise.

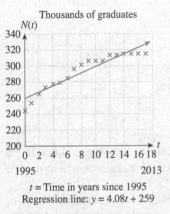

Thousands of graduates

t = Time in years since 1995
Regression line: $y = 4.08t + 259$

Figure 11

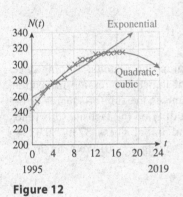

Figure 12

To decide whether to support TJM's proposal at tomorrow's board meeting, you would like first to determine whether the linear regression prediction of around 4,000 students per year is reasonable, especially in view of the more recent figures. You open your spreadsheet and graph the data with the regression line (Figure 11). The data suggest that the number of graduates began to level off (in the language of calculus, the *derivative appears to be decreasing*) toward the end of the period. Moreover, you recall reading somewhere that the numbers of students in the lower grades have also begun to level off, so it is safe to predict that the slowing of growth in the senior class will continue over the next few years, contrary to what TJM has claimed. To make a meaningful prediction, you would really need some precise data about numbers in the lower grades, but the meeting is tomorrow, and you would like a quick and easy way of extrapolating the data by "extending the curve to the right."

It would certainly be helpful if you had a mathematical model of the data in Figure 11 that you could use to project the current trend. But what kind of model should you use? The linear model is no good because it does not show any change in the derivative (the derivative of a linear function is constant). In addition, best-fit polynomial and exponential functions do not accurately reflect the leveling off, as you realize after trying to fit a few of them (Figure 12).

You then recall that a logistic curve can model the leveling-off property you desire, so you try a model of the form

$$N(t) = \frac{M}{1 + Ab^{-t}}.$$

Figure 13 shows the best-fit logistic curve, which has a sum-of-squares error (SSE) of around 109. (See Section 1.4 or any of the regression examples in Chapter 2 for a discussion of SSE.)

$$N(t) = \frac{323.9}{1 + 0.3234(1.186)^{-t}} \qquad \text{SSE} \approx 109$$

Its graph shows the leveling off and also gives more reasonable long-term predictions.

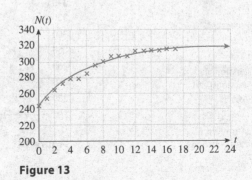

Figure 13

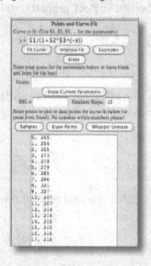

The rate of increase of high school students—pertinent to TJM's report—is given by the derivative, $N'(t)$:

$$N(t) = \frac{M}{1 + Ab^{-t}}$$

$$N'(t) = -\frac{M}{(1 + Ab^{-t})^2}\frac{d}{dt}(1 + Ab^{-t})$$

$$= \frac{M Ab^{-t}\ln b}{(1 + Ab^{-t})^2}.$$

The rate of increase in the number of high school students in 2015 ($t = 20$) is given by

$$N'(20) = \frac{(323.9)(0.3234)(1.186)^{-20}\ln 1.186}{(1 + 0.3234(1.186)^{-20})^2}$$

$$\approx 0.577 \text{ thousand students per year,}$$

or about 580 students per year—far less than the optimistic estimate of 4,000 in the proposal! Therefore, TJM's prediction is suspect, and further research will have to be done before the board can even consider the proposal.

To reassure yourself, you decide to look for another kind of S-shaped model as a backup. After flipping through a calculus book, you stumble across a function that is slightly more general than the one you have:

$$N(t) = \frac{M}{1 + Ab^{-t}} + C \qquad \text{Shifted logistic curve}^*$$

The added term C has the effect of shifting the graph up C units. Turning once again to your calculus book (see the discussion of logistic regression in Section 2.4), you see that a best-fit curve is one that minimizes the sum-of-squares error, and you find the best-fit curve by again using the utility on the Website (this time, with the model $1/(1+\$2*\$3^{\wedge}(-x))+\$4$ and initial guess 323.9, 0.3234, 1.186, 0; that is, keeping the current values and setting $c = 0$). You obtain the model

$$N(t) = \frac{135.5}{1 + 1.192(1.268)^{-t}} + 184.6. \qquad \text{SSE} \approx 100$$

The value of SSE has decreased only slightly, and, as seen in Figure 14, the shifted logistic curve seems almost identical to the unshifted curve but does seem to level off slightly faster. (Compare the portions of the two curves on the extreme right.)

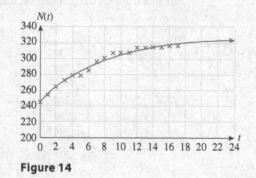

Figure 14

You decide to use the shifted model to obtain another estimate of the projected rate of change in 2015. As the two models differ by a constant, their derivatives are given by the same formula, so you compute

$$N'(20) = \frac{(135.5)(1.192)(1.268)^{-20} \ln 1.268}{(1 + 1.192(1.268)^{-20})^2}$$

$$\approx 0.325 \text{ thousand students per year,}$$

or about 325 students per year, even less than the prediction of the logistic model.

Q: *Why do the two models give very different predictions of the rate of change in 2015?*

A: The long-term prediction in any logistic model is highly sensitive to small changes in the data and/or the model. This is one reason why using regression curve-fitting models to make long-term projections can be a risky undertaking.

Q: *Then what is the point of using any model to project in the first place?*

A: Projections are always tricky, as we cannot foresee the future. But a *good* model is not merely one that seems to fit the data well, but rather a model whose structure is based on the situation being modeled. For instance, a *good* model of student graduation rates should take into account such factors as the birth rate, current school populations at all levels, and the relative popularity of private schools over public schools. It is by using models of this kind that the National Center for Educational Statistics is able to make the projections shown in the data above. (And even those turned out to be overestimates.)

EXERCISES

1. In 1994 there were 246,000 private high school graduates. What do the two logistic models (unshifted and shifted) "predict" for 1994? (Round your answer to the nearest 1,000.) Which gives the better prediction?

2. What is the long-term prediction of each of the two models? (Round your answer to the nearest 1,000.)

3. Find $\lim_{t \to +\infty} N'(t)$ for both models, and interpret the results.

4. ▆ You receive a last-minute memo from TJM to the effect that, sorry, the 2011 and 2012 figures are not accurate. Use technology to re-estimate M, A, b, and C for the shifted logistic model in the absence of this data and obtain new estimates for the 2011 and 2012 data. What does the new model predict the rate of change in the number of high school seniors will be in 2015?

5. ▆ *Another Model* Using the original data, find the best-fit shifted logistic curve of the form

$$N(t) = c + b\frac{a(t - m)}{1 + a|t - m|}. \qquad (a, b, c, m \text{ constant})$$

Its graph is shown in the margin.

(Use the model $1+$2*$3*(x-$4)/(1+$3*abs(x-$4))$ and start with the following values: $a = 0.05$, $b = 160$, $c = 250$, $m = 5$; that is, input $250, 160, 0.05, 5$ in the "Guess" field.) Graph the data together with the model. What is SSE? Is the model as accurate a fit as the model used in the text? What does this model predict will be the growth rate of the number of high school graduates in 2015? Comment on the answer. (Round the coefficients in the model and all answers to four decimal places.)

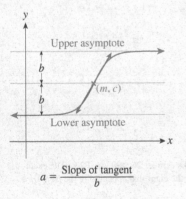

6. ▣ *Demand for Freon* The demand for chlorofluorocarbon-12 (CFC-12)—the ozone-depleting refrigerant commonly known as Freon 12 (the name given to it by DuPont)—declined significantly in response to regulation and concern about the ozone layer. The chart below shows values and projections given in 1999 of the demand for CFC-12 for the period 1994–2005:[64]

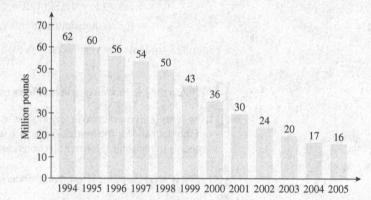

a. Use technology to obtain the best-fit equation of the form

$$N(t) = c + b\frac{a(t - m)}{1 + a|t - m|}, \quad (a, b, c, m \text{ constant})$$

where t is the number of years since 1990. Use your function to estimate the total demand for CFC-12 from the start of the year 2000 to the start of 2010. (Start with the following values: $a = 1$, $b = -25$, $c = 35$, and $m = 10$, and round your answers to four decimal places.)

b. According to your model, how fast was the demand for Freon 12 declining in 2000?

---

[64] Source: The Automobile Consulting Group (*New York Times,* December 26, 1993, p. F23). The exact figures were not given, and the chart is a reasonable facsimile of the chart that appeared in the *New York Times.*

12

FURTHER APPLICATIONS OF THE DERIVATIVE

CASE STUDY

Production Lot Size Management

Your publishing company is planning the production of its latest best seller, which it predicts will sell 100,000 copies each month over the coming year. The book will be printed in several batches of the same number, evenly spaced throughout the year. Each print run has a setup cost of $5,000, a single book costs $1 to produce, and monthly storage costs for books awaiting shipment average 1¢ per book.

To meet the anticipated demand at minimum total cost to your company, how many print runs should you plan?

SERDAR/Alamy Stock Photo

www.WanerMath.com

At the Website, in addition to the resources listed in the Preface, you will find:

The following extra topic:

• Linear Approximation and Error Estimation

Introduction

In this chapter we begin to see the power of calculus as an optimization tool. In Chapter 2 we saw how to price an item to get the largest revenue when the demand function is linear. Using calculus, we can handle nonlinear functions, which are much more general. In Section 12.1 we show how calculus can be used to solve the problem of finding the values of a variable that lead to a maximum or minimum value of a given function. In Section 12.2 we show how this helps us in various real-world applications.

Another theme in this chapter is that calculus can help us to draw and understand the graph of a function. By the time you have completed the material in Section 12.1, you will be able to locate and sketch some of the important features of a graph, such as where it rises and where it falls. In Section 12.3 we look at the *second derivative,* the derivative of the derivative function, and what it tells us about how the graph *curves.* We also see how the second derivative is used to model the notion of *acceleration.* In Section 12.4 we put a number of ideas together that help to explain what you see in a graph (drawn, for example, using graphing technology) and to locate its most important points.

We also include sections on related rates and elasticity of demand. The first of these (Section 12.5) examines further the concept of the derivative as a rate of change. The second (Section 12.6) returns to the problem of optimizing revenue based on the demand equation, looking at it in a new way that leads to an important idea in economics: elasticity.

Precalculus Review
For this chapter you should be familiar with the algebra reviewed in **Sections 0.5 and 0.6**.

12.1 Maxima and Minima

Relative Extrema

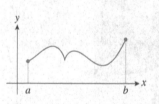

Figure 1

Figure 1 shows the graph of a function f whose domain is the closed interval $[a, b]$. A mathematician sees lots of interesting things going on here. There are hills and valleys and even a small chasm (called a *cusp*) near the center. For many purposes the important features of this curve are the highs and lows. Suppose, for example, that you know that the price of the stock of a certain company will follow this graph during the course of a week. Although you would certainly make a handsome profit if you bought at time a and sold at time b, your best strategy would be to follow the old adage to "buy low and sell high," buying at all the lows and selling at all the highs.

Figure 2 shows the graph once again with the highs and lows marked. There are names for these points: the highs (at the x-values p, r, and b) are referred to as **relative maxima**, and the lows (at the x-values a, q, and s) are referred to as **relative minima**. Collectively, these highs and lows are referred to as **relative extrema**. (A point of language: The singular forms of the plurals *minima, maxima,* and *extrema* are *minimum, maximum,* and *extremum.*)

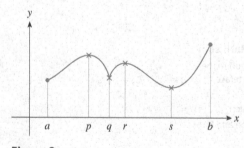

Figure 2

Why do we refer to these points as relative extrema? Take a look at the point corresponding to $x = r$. It is the highest point of the graph *compared to other points nearby*. If you were an extremely nearsighted mountaineer standing at the point where $x = r$, you would *think* that you were at the highest point of the graph, not being able to see the distant peaks at $x = p$ and $x = b$.

Let's translate into mathematical terms. We are talking about the heights of various points on the curve. The height of the curve at $x = r$ is $f(r)$, so we are saying that $f(r)$ is greater than or equal to $f(x)$ for every x near r. In other words, *$f(r)$ is the greatest value that $f(x)$ has for all choices of x between $r - h$ and $r + h$ for some (possibly small) h.* (See Figure 3.)

We can phrase the formal definition as follows.

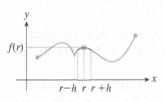

Figure 3

Relative Extrema: Definition

f has a **relative maximum** at r if there is some interval $(r - h, r + h)$ (even a very small one) for which $f(r) \geq f(x)$ for all x in $(r - h, r + h)$ for which $f(x)$ is defined.

f has a **relative minimum** at r if there is some interval $(r - h, r + h)$ (even a very small one) for which $f(r) \leq f(x)$ for all x in $(r - h, r + h)$ for which $f(x)$ is defined.

The relative maxima and minima are collectively referred to as **relative extrema**. If f has a relative extremum at r, then the corresponding point $(r, f(r))$ on the graph of f is also referred to as a relative maximum or relative minimum as the case may be.

Quick Examples

In Figure 2, f has the following relative extrema:

1. Relative maxima at p and r.

2. A relative maximum at b. (See Figure 4.) Note that $f(x)$ is not defined for $x > b$. However, $f(b) \geq f(x)$ for every x in the interval $(b - h, b + h)$ *for which $f(x)$ is defined*—that is, for every x in $(b - h, b]$.*

3. Relative minima at a, q, and s.

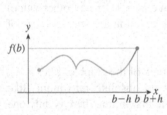

Figure 4

* Our definition of relative extremum allows f to have a relative extremum at an endpoint of its domain; the definitions used in some books do not. In view of examples like the stock market investing strategy mentioned above, we find it more useful to allow endpoints as relative extrema.

Absolute Extrema

Looking carefully at Figure 2, we can see that the lowest point on the whole graph is where $x = s$ and the highest point is where $x = b$. This means that $f(s)$ is the least value of f on the whole domain of f (the interval $[a, b]$) and $f(b)$ is the greatest value. We call these the *absolute* minimum and maximum.

Absolute Extrema: Definition

f has an **absolute maximum** at r if $f(r) \geq f(x)$ for every x in the domain of f.

f has an **absolute minimum** at r if $f(r) \leq f(x)$ for every x in the domain of f.

As with relative extrema, if f has an *absolute* extremum at r, then the corresponding point $(r, f(r))$ on the graph of f is also referred to as an absolute maximum or absolute minimum as the case may be.

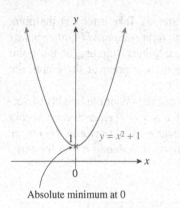

Absolute minimum at 0

Figure 5

> ### Quick Examples
>
> 4. In Figure 2, f has an absolute maximum at b and an absolute minimum at s.
> 5. If $f(x) = x^2 + 1$, then $f(x) \geq f(0)$ for every real number x. Therefore, f has an absolute minimum at 0. (See Figure 5.) Put another way, $(0, 1)$ is an absolute minimum on the graph of f.
> 6. Generalizing (5), every quadratic function $f(x) = ax^2 + bx + c$ has an absolute extremum at its vertex $-b/(2a)$, an absolute minimum if $a > 0$, and an absolute maximum if $a < 0$.

A little terminology: If the point (a, b) on the graph of f represents a maximum (or minimum) of f, we will sometimes say that f **has a maximum (or minimum) value of b at a**. Thus, in Quick Example 5 we could have said any of the following:

"f has an absolute minimum value of 1 at 0."

"f has an absolute minimum at $(0, 1)$."

"f has an absolute minimum at 0."

Note If f has an absolute extremum at r, then it automatically satisfies the requirement for a *relative* extremum there as well; take $h = 1$ (or any other value) in the definition of relative extremum. Thus, absolute extrema are special types of relative extrema. ∎

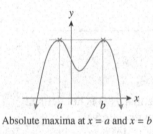

Absolute maxima at $x = a$ and $x = b$

Figure 6

Some functions have no absolute extrema at all (think of the graph of $f(x) = x$), while others might have an absolute minimum but no absolute maximum (like $f(x) = x^2$), or vice versa. When f does have an absolute maximum, there is only one absolute maximum *value* of f, but this value may occur at different values of x and similarly for absolute minima. (See Figure 6.)

Q: At how many different values of x can f take on its absolute maximum value?

A: An extreme case is that of a constant function; because we use $\geq$ in the definition of absolute maximum, a constant function has an absolute maximum (and minimum) at every point in its domain.

Locating Extrema

Now, how do we go about locating extrema? In many cases we can get a good idea by using graphing technology to zoom in on a maximum or minimum and approximate its coordinates. However, calculus gives us a way to find the exact locations of the extrema and at the same time to understand why the graph of a function behaves the way it does. In fact, it is often best to combine the powers of graphing technology with those of calculus, as we shall see.

In Figure 7 we see the graph from Figure 1 once more, but we have labeled each extreme point as one of three types. Notice that two extrema occur at endpoints of the domain and the others at interior points.* Let us look first at the extrema occurring at

* Recall from Section 10.5 that an interior point of the domain is a point a such that there is some open interval about a still in the domain. If the domain is a closed interval, an interior point is just a point other than an endpoint.

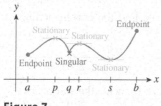

Figure 7

interior points: At the points labeled "Stationary," the tangent lines to the graph are horizontal and so have slope 0, so f' (which gives the slope) is 0. Any time $f'(x) = 0$, we say that f has a **stationary point** at x because the rate of change of f is zero there. We call an extremum that occurs at a stationary point a **stationary extremum**. In general, to find the exact location of each stationary point, we need to solve the equation $f'(x) = 0$. Note that stationary points are always interior points, as f' is defined only at interior points. (See the definition of the derivative in Section 10.5.)

There is a relative minimum in Figure 7 at $x = q$, but there is no horizontal tangent there; in fact, there is no tangent line at all. In the language of calculus, $f'(q)$ is not defined. (Recall a similar situation with the graph of $f(x) = |x|$ at $x = 0$.) We will say that the derivative f' has a **singular point** at q, and we call an extremum that occurs at a singular point a **singular extremum**. The interior points x of the domain of f that are either stationary points of f (i.e., $f'(x) = 0$) or singular points of f' (i.e., $f'(x)$ is not defined) we call collectively the **critical points** of f.

The remaining two extrema are at the **endpoints** of the domain (remember that we do allow relative extrema at endpoints). As we see in the figure, they are (almost) always either relative maxima or relative minima.

We bring all the above information together in Figure 8.

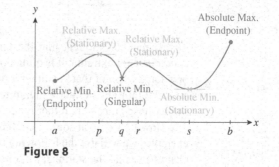

Figure 8

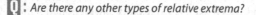

Q : *Are there any other types of relative extrema?*

A : No; relative extrema of a function always occur at critical points or endpoints. (A rigorous proof is beyond the scope of this book.)*

Locating Candidates for Extrema

If f is a real-valued function, then its extrema occur among the following types of points:

1. **Stationary Points:** points in the interior of the domain where the derivative is zero. To locate stationary points, set $f'(x) = 0$ and solve for x.

2. **Singular Points:**[†] points in the interior of the domain where the derivative is not defined. To locate singular points, find interior points x where $f'(x)$ is *not* defined but $f(x)$ *is* defined.

3. **Endpoints:** These are the endpoints, if any, of the domain. Recall that closed intervals contain endpoints but open intervals do not. If the domain of f is an open interval or the whole real line, then there are no endpoints.

* Here is an outline of the argument. Suppose f has a maximum, say, at $x = a$, at some interior point of its domain. Then either f is differentiable there, or it is not. If it is not, then we have a singular point. If f is differentiable at $x = a$, then consider the slope of the secant line through the points where $x = a$ and $x = a + h$ for small positive h. Because f has a maximum at $x = a$, it is falling (or level) to the right of $x = a$, so the slope of this secant line must be ≤ 0. Thus, we must have $f'(a) \leq 0$ in the limit as $h \to 0$. On the other hand, if h is small and *negative*, then the corresponding secant line must have slope ≥ 0 because f is also falling (or level) as we move left from $x = a$, and so $f'(a) \geq 0$. Because $f'(a)$ is both ≥ 0 and ≤ 0, it must be zero, so we have a stationary point at $x = a$.

† In the context of maxima and minima, "singular point" will be understood to refer to a singular point *of the derivative f'*, that is, a point in the interior of the domain where f' is undefined. ("Singular point" has another meaning in the context of limits, where it refers to a singular point of f; see the definition in Section 10.2.) When the context is not clear, we will say "singular point of f" or "singular point of f'" as the case may be.

Once we have a candidate for an extremum of f, we find the corresponding point (x, y) on the graph of f using $y = f(x)$.

Quick Examples

7. **Stationary Points:** Let $f(x) = x^3 - 12x$. Then to locate the stationary points, set $f'(x) = 0$ and solve for x. This gives $3x^2 - 12 = 0$, so f has stationary points at $x = \pm 2$. The corresponding points on the graph are $(-2, f(-2)) = (-2, 16)$ and $(2, f(2)) = (2, -16)$.

8. **Singular Points:** Let $f(x) = 3(x - 1)^{1/3}$. Then $f'(x) = (x - 1)^{-2/3} = 1/(x - 1)^{2/3}$. $f'(1)$ is not defined, although $f(1)$ *is* defined. Thus, the (only) singular point occurs at $x = 1$. The corresponding singular point on the graph is $(1, f(1)) = (1, 0)$.

9. **Endpoints:** Let $f(x) = 1/x$, with domain $(-\infty, 0) \cup [1, +\infty)$. Then the only endpoint in the domain of f occurs at $x = 1$. The corresponding endpoint on the graph is $(1, 1)$. The natural domain of $1/x$, on the other hand, has no endpoints.

Remember, though, that the three types of points we identify above are only *candidates* for extrema. It is quite possible, as we shall see, to have a stationary point or a singular point that is neither a maximum nor a minimum. (It is also possible for an endpoint to be neither a maximum nor a minimum, but this occurs only in functions whose graphs are rather bizarre—see Exercise 65.)

Now let's look at some examples of finding maxima and minima. In all of these examples we will use the following procedure: First, we find the derivative, which we examine to find the stationary points and singular points. Next, we make a table listing the x-coordinates of the critical points and endpoints, together with their y-coordinates. We use this table to make a rough sketch of the graph. From the table and rough sketch we usually have enough data to be able to say where the extreme points are and what kind they are.

EXAMPLE 1 Maxima and Minima

Find the relative and absolute maxima and minima of

$$f(x) = x^2 - 2x$$

on the interval $[0, 4]$.

Solution We first calculate $f'(x) = 2x - 2$. We use this derivative to locate the critical points (stationary and singular points).

Stationary Points To locate the stationary points, we solve the equation $f'(x) = 0$, or

$$2x - 2 = 0,$$

getting $x = 1$. The domain of the function is $[0, 4]$, so $x = 1$ is in the interior of the domain. Thus, the only candidate for a stationary relative extremum occurs when $x = 1$.

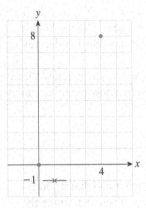

Figure 9

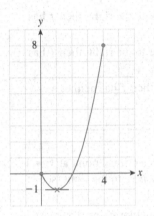

Figure 10

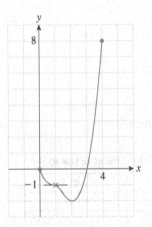

Figure 11

*Why "first" derivative test? To distinguish it from a test based on the **second derivative** of a function, which we shall discuss in Section 12.3.

Singular Points We look for interior points where the derivative is not defined. However, the derivative is $2x - 2$, which is defined for every x. Thus, there are no singular points and hence no candidates for singular relative extrema.

Endpoints The domain is $[0, 4]$, so the endpoints occur when $x = 0$ and $x = 4$.

We record these values of x in a table, together with the corresponding y-coordinates (values of f):

x	0	1	4
$f(x) = x^2 - 2x$	0	-1	8

This gives us three points on the graph, $(0, 0)$, $(1, -1)$, and $(4, 8)$, which we plot in Figure 9. We remind ourselves that the point $(1, -1)$ is a stationary point of the graph by drawing in a part of the horizontal tangent line. Connecting these points must give us a graph something like that in Figure 10.

From Figure 10 we can see that f has the following extrema:

x	$y = x^2 - 2x$	Classification
0	0	Relative maximum (endpoint)
1	-1	Absolute minimum (stationary point)
4	8	Absolute maximum (endpoint)

➡ **Before we go on . . .**

Q: *How can we be sure that the graph in Example 1 doesn't look like Figure 11?*

A: *If it did, there would be another critical point somewhere between $x = 1$ and $x = 4$. But we already know that there aren't any other critical points. The table we made listed all of the possible extrema; there can be no more.*

■

First Derivative Test

The **first derivative test*** gives another, very systematic, way of checking whether a critical point is a maximum or minimum. To motivate the first derivative test, consider again the critical point $x = 1$ in Example 1. If we look at some values of $f'(x)$ to the left and right of the critical point, we obtain the information shown in the following table:

	Point to the Left	Critical Point	Point to the Right
x	0.5	1	2
$f'(x) = 2x - 2$	-1	0	2
Direction of Graph	↘	→	↗

At $x = 0.5$ (to the left of the critical point) we see that $f'(0.5) = -1 < 0$, so the graph has negative slope and f is decreasing. We note this with the downward pointing arrow. At $x = 2$ (to the right of the critical point) we find $f'(2) = 2 > 0$, so the graph has positive slope and f is increasing. In fact, because $f'(x) = 0$ only at $x = 1$, we know that $f'(x) < 0$ for all x in $(0, 1)$, and we can say that f is decreasing on the interval $(0, 1)$. Similarly, f is increasing on $(1, 4)$.

So starting at $x = 0$, the graph of f goes down until we reach $x = 1$, and then it goes back up, telling us that $x = 1$ must be a minimum. Notice how the minimum is suggested by the arrows to the left and right.

First Derivative Test for Extrema

Suppose that c is a critical point of the continuous function f and that its derivative is defined for x close to, and on both sides of, $x = c$. Then, determine the sign of the derivative to the left and right of $x = c$.

1. If $f'(x)$ is positive to the left of $x = c$ and negative to the right, then f has a maximum at $x = c$.

2. If $f'(x)$ is negative to the left of $x = c$ and positive to the right, then f has a minimum at $x = c$.

3. If $f'(x)$ has the same sign on both sides of $x = c$, then f has neither a maximum nor a minimum at $x = c$.

Quick Examples

10. In Example 1 we saw that $f(x) = x^2 - 2x$ has a critical point at $x = 1$ with $f'(x)$ negative to the left of $x = 1$ and positive to the right (see the table). Therefore, f has a minimum at $x = 1$.

11. Here is a graph showing a function f with a singular point at $x = 1$:

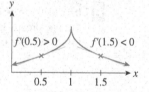

The graph gives us the information shown in the table:

	Point to the Left	Critical Point	Point to the Right
x	0.5	1	2
$f'(x)$	+	Undefined	−
Direction of Graph	↗		↘

Since $f'(x)$ is positive to the left of $x = 1$ and negative to the right, we see that f has a maximum at $x = 1$. (Notice again how this is suggested by the direction of the arrows.)

EXAMPLE 2   **Unbounded Interval**

Find all extrema of $f(x) = 3x^4 - 4x^3$ on $[-1, \infty)$.

Solution We first calculate $f'(x) = 12x^3 - 12x^2$.

Stationary Points We solve the equation $f'(x) = 0$, which is

$$12x^3 - 12x^2 = 0 \text{ or }$$
$$12x^2(x - 1) = 0.$$

There are two solutions, $x = 0$ and $x = 1$, and both are in the domain. These are our candidates for the x-coordinates of stationary extrema.

Singular Points There are no interior points where $f'(x)$ is not defined, so there are no singular points.

Endpoints The domain is $[-1, \infty)$, so there is one endpoint, at $x = -1$.

We record these points in a table with the corresponding y-coordinates:

x	-1	0	1
$f(x) = 3x^4 - 4x^3$	7	0	-1

We will illustrate three methods we can use to determine which are minima, which are maxima, and which are neither:

1. Plot these points, and sketch the graph by hand.

2. Use the first derivative test.

3. Use technology to help us.

Use the method you find most convenient.

Using a Hand Plot: If we plot these points by hand, we obtain Figure 12(a), which suggests Figure 12(b).

We can't be sure what happens to the right of $x = 1$. Does the curve go up, or does it go down? To find out, let's plot a "test point" to the right of $x = 1$. Choosing $x = 2$, we obtain $y = 3(2)^4 - 4(2)^3 = 16$, so $(2, 16)$ is another point on the graph. Thus, it must turn upward to the right of $x = 1$, as shown in Figure 13.

From the graph, we find that f has the following extrema:

A relative (endpoint) maximum at $(-1, 7)$

An absolute (stationary) minimum at $(1, -1)$

Using the First Derivative Test: List the critical points in a table, and add additional points as necessary so that each critical point has a noncritical point on either side. Then compute the derivative at each of these points, and draw an arrow to indicate the direction of the graph, suggesting the shape of the curve in Figure 13.

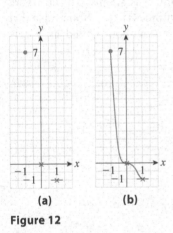

(a)   (b)

Figure 12

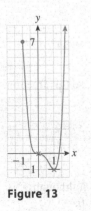

Figure 13

x	-0.5	0	0.5	1	2
$f'(x) = 12x^3 - 12x^2$	-1.5	0	-1.5	0	48
Direction of Graph	↘	→	↘	→	↗

Critical Point and Critical Point headers span over the $x = 0$ and $x = 1$ columns respectively.

The first derivative test tells us that the function has a relative maximum at $x = -1$, neither a maximum nor a minimum at $x = 0$, and a relative minimum at $x = 1$. Deciding which of these extrema are absolute and which are relative requires us to compute y-coordinates and plot the corresponding relative extrema on the graph by hand, as we did in the first method.

Using Technology

If we use technology to show the graph, we should choose the viewing window so that it contains the three interesting points we found: $x = -1$, $x = 0$, and $x = 1$. Again, we can't be sure yet what happens to the right of $x = 1$; does the graph go up or down from that point? If we set the viewing window to an interval of $[-1, 2]$ for x and $[-2, 8]$ for y, we will leave enough room to the right of $x = 1$ and below $y = -1$ to see what the graph will do. The result will be something like Figure 14.

Now we can tell what happens to the right of $x = 1$: the function increases. We know that it cannot later decrease again because if it did, there would have to be another critical point where it turns around, and we found that there are no other critical points.

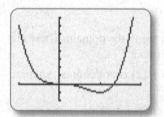

Figure 14

⟹ **Before we go on ...** Notice that the stationary point at $x = 0$ in Example 2 is neither a relative maximum nor a relative minimum. It is simply a place where the graph of f flattens out for a moment before it continues to fall. Notice also that f has no absolute maximum because $f(x)$ increases without bound as x gets large. ∎

EXAMPLE 3 **Singular Point**

Find all extrema of $f(t) = t^{2/3}$ on $[-1, 1]$.

Solution First, $f'(t) = \dfrac{2}{3}t^{-1/3}$.

Stationary Points We need to solve

$$\frac{2}{3}t^{-1/3} = 0.$$

We can rewrite this equation without the negative exponent:

$$\frac{2}{3t^{1/3}} = 0.$$

Now, the only way a fraction can equal 0 is if the numerator is 0, so this fraction can never equal 0. Thus, there are no stationary points.

Singular Points The derivative

$$f'(t) = \frac{2}{3t^{1/3}}$$

is not defined for $t = 0$. Also, 0 is in the interior of the domain of f (although f' is not defined at $t = 0$, f itself is). Thus, f has a singular point at $t = 0$.

Endpoints There are two endpoints: -1 and 1.

We now put these three points in a table with the corresponding y-coordinates:

t	-1	0	1
$f(t)$	1	0	1

Using a Hand Plot: The derivative, $f'(t) = 2/(3t^{1/3})$, is not defined at the singular point $t = 0$. To help us sketch the graph, let's use limits to investigate what happens to the derivative as we approach 0 from either side:

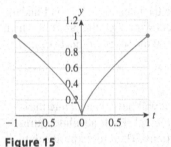

$$\lim_{t \to 0^-} f'(t) = \lim_{t \to 0^-} \frac{2}{3t^{1/3}} = -\infty$$

$$\lim_{t \to 0^+} f'(t) = \lim_{t \to 0^+} \frac{2}{3t^{1/3}} = +\infty.$$

Thus, the graph decreases very steeply, approaching $t = 0$ from the left, and then rises very steeply as it leaves to the right. It would make sense to say that the tangent line at $x = 0$ is vertical, as seen in Figure 15.

Figure 15

From this graph we find the following extrema for f:

An absolute (endpoint) maximum at $(-1, 1)$

An absolute (singular) minimum at $(0, 0)$

An absolute (endpoint) maximum at $(1, 1)$.

Notice that the absolute maximum value of f is achieved at two values of t: $t = -1$ and $t = 1$.

First Derivative Test: Here is the corresponding table for the first derivative test:

t	-0.5	0	0.5
$f'(t) = \dfrac{2}{3t^{1/3}}$	$-\dfrac{2}{3(0.5)^{1/3}}$	Undefined	$\dfrac{2}{3(0.5)^{1/3}}$
Direction of Graph	$\searrow$	$\updownarrow$	$\nearrow$

(We drew a vertical arrow at $t = 0$ to indicate a vertical tangent.) Again, notice how the arrows suggest the shape of the curve in Figure 15, and the first derivative test confirms that we have a minimum at $t = 0$.

Using Technology
Because there is only one critical point, at $t = 0$, it is clear from this table that f must decrease from $t = -1$ to $t = 0$ and then increase from $t = 0$ to $t = 1$. To graph f using technology, choose a viewing window with an interval of $[-1, 1]$ for t and $[0, 1]$ for y. The result will be something like Figure 15.*

＊Many graphing calculators will give you only the right-hand half of the graph shown in Figure 15 because fractional powers of negative numbers are not, in general, real numbers. To obtain the whole curve, enter the formula as Y= (x^2)^(1/3), a fractional power of the nonnegative function x^2.

In Examples 1 and 3 we could have found the absolute maxima and minima without doing any graphing. In Example 1, after finding the critical points and endpoints, we created the following table:

x	0	1	4
$f(x)$	0	-1	8

From this table we can see that f must decrease from its value of 0 at $x = 0$ to -1 at $x = 1$, and then increase to 8 at $x = 4$. The value of 8 must be the largest value it takes on, and the value of -1 must be the smallest, on the interval $[0, 4]$. Similarly, in Example 3 we created the following table:

t	-1	0	1
$f(t)$	1	0	1

From this table we can see that the largest value of f on the interval $[-1, 1]$ is 1 and the smallest value is 0. We are taking advantage of the following fact, the proof of which uses some deep and beautiful mathematics (alas, beyond the scope of this book).

Extreme Value Theorem

If f is *continuous* on a *closed interval* $[a, b]$, then it will have an absolute maximum and an absolute minimum value on that interval. Each absolute extremum must occur at either an endpoint or a critical point. Therefore, the absolute maximum is the largest value in a table of the values of f at the endpoints and critical points, and the absolute minimum is the smallest value.

Quick Example

12. The function $f(x) = 3x - x^3$ on the interval $[0, 2]$ has one critical point at $x = 1$. The values of f at the critical point and the endpoints of the interval are given in the following table:

	Endpoint	Critical Point	Endpoint
x	0	1	2
$f(x)$	0	2	-2

From this table we can say that the absolute maximum value of f on $[0, 2]$ is 2, which occurs at $x = 1$, and the absolute minimum value of f is -2, which occurs at $x = 2$.

As we can see in Example 2 and the following examples, if the domain is not a closed interval, then f may not have an absolute maximum and minimum, and a table of values as above is of little help in determining whether it does.

EXAMPLE 4 Domain Not a Closed Interval

Find all extrema of $f(x) = x + \dfrac{1}{x}$.

Solution Because no domain is specified, we take the domain to be as large as possible. The function is not defined at $x = 0$ but is defined at all other points, so we take its domain to be $(-\infty, 0) \cup (0, +\infty)$. We calculate

$$f'(x) = 1 - \frac{1}{x^2}.$$

Stationary Points Setting $f'(x) = 0$, we solve

$$1 - \frac{1}{x^2} = 0$$

to find $x = \pm 1$. Calculating the corresponding values of f, we get the two stationary points $(1, 2)$ and $(-1, -2)$.

Singular Points The only value of x for which $f'(x)$ is not defined is $x = 0$, but then f is not defined there either, so there are no singular points in the domain.

Endpoints The domain, $(-\infty, 0) \cup (0, +\infty)$, has no endpoints.

From this scant information it is hard to tell what f does. If we are sketching the graph by hand, or using the first derivative test, we will need to plot additional "test points" to the left and right of the stationary points $x = \pm 1$. Instead, we will use technology to draw the graph:

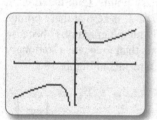

Figure 16

Using Technology

For the technology approach, let's choose a viewing window with an interval of $[-3, 3]$ for x and $[-4, 4]$ for y, which should leave plenty of room to see how f behaves near the stationary points. The result is something like Figure 16.

From this graph we can see that f has

a relative (stationary) maximum at $(-1, -2)$,

a relative (stationary) minimum at $(1, 2)$.

Curiously, the relative maximum is lower than the relative minimum! Notice also that, because of the break in the graph at $x = 0$, the graph did not need to rise to get from $(-1, -2)$ to $(1, 2)$.

So far, we have been solving the equation $f'(x) = 0$ to obtain our candidates for stationary extrema. However, it is often not easy—or even possible—to solve equations analytically. In the next example, we show a way around this problem by using graphing technology.

EXAMPLE 5 **Ⓣ Finding Approximate Extrema Using Technology**

Graph the function $f(x) = (x - 1)^{2/3} - \dfrac{x^2}{2}$ with domain $[-2, +\infty)$. Also graph its derivative and hence locate and classify all extrema of f, with coordinates accurate to two decimal places.

Solution In Example 4 of Section 10.5 we saw how to draw the graphs of functions and their derivatives using technology. Note that the technology formula to use for the graph of f is

```
((x-1)^2)^(1/3)-0.5*x^2
```

instead of

```
(x-1)^(2/3)-0.5*x^2
```

(Why?)

Figure 17 shows the resulting graphs of f and f'.

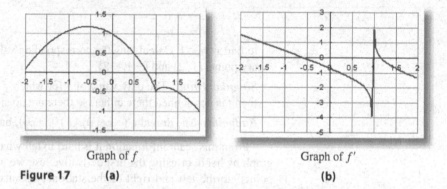

Graph of f Graph of f'

Figure 17   (a)   (b)

If we extend Xmax beyond $x = 2$, we find that the graph continues downward, apparently without any further interesting behavior.

Stationary Points The graph of f shows two stationary points, both maxima, at around $x = -0.6$ and $x = 1.2$. Notice that the graph of f' is zero at these points. Moreover, it is easier to locate these values accurately on the graph of f' because it is easier to pinpoint where a graph crosses the x-axis than to locate a stationary point. Zooming in to the stationary point at $x \approx -0.6$ results in Figure 18.

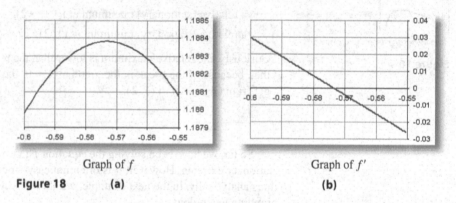

Graph of f Graph of f'

Figure 18   (a)   (b)

From the graph of f we can see that the stationary point is somewhere between -0.58 and -0.57. The graph of f' shows more clearly that the zero of f', hence the stationary point of f, lies somewhat closer to -0.57 than to -0.58. Thus, the stationary point occurs at $x \approx -0.57$, rounded to two decimal places.

In a similar way we find the second stationary point at $x \approx 1.18$.

Singular Points Going back to Figure 17, we notice what appears to be a cusp (singular point) at the relative minimum around $x = 1$, and this is confirmed by a glance at the graph of f', which seems to take a sudden jump at that value. Zooming in closer suggests that the singular point occurs at exactly $x = 1$. In fact, we can calculate

$$f'(x) = \frac{2}{3(x - 1)^{1/3}} - x.$$

From this formula we see clearly that $f'(x)$ is defined everywhere except at $x = 1$.

Endpoints The only endpoint in the domain is $x = -2$, which gives a relative minimum.

Thus, we have found the following approximate extrema for f:

A relative (endpoint) minimum at $(-2, 0.08)$

An absolute (stationary) maximum at $(-0.57, 1.19)$

A relative (singular) minimum at $(1, -0.5)$

A relative (stationary) maximum at $(1.18, -0.38)$

12.1 EXERCISES

▼ more advanced ♦ challenging

🔲 indicates exercises that should be solved using technology

In Exercises 1–12, locate and classify all extrema in each graph. (By classifying the extrema, we mean listing whether each extremum is a relative or absolute maximum or minimum.) Also, locate any stationary points or singular points that are not relative extrema. [HINT: See the box titled "Locating Candidates for Extrema."]

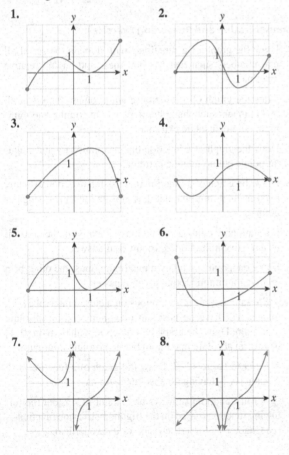

1.

2.

3.

4.

5.

6.

7.

8.

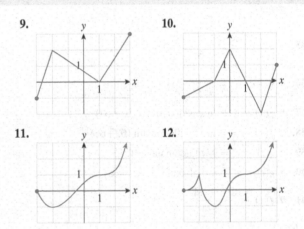

9.

10.

11.

12.

In Exercises 13–44, find the exact location of all the relative and absolute extrema of the given function. [HINT: See Example 1.]

13. $f(x) = x^2 - 4x + 1$ with domain $[0, 3]$

14. $f(x) = 2x^2 - 2x + 3$ with domain $[0, 3]$

15. $g(x) = x^3 - 12x$ with domain $[-4, 4]$

16. $g(x) = 2x^3 - 6x + 3$ with domain $[-2, 2]$

17. $f(t) = t^3 + t$ with domain $[-2, 2]$

18. $f(t) = -2t^3 - 3t$ with domain $[-1, 1]$

19. $h(t) = 2t^3 + 3t^2$ with domain $[-2, +\infty)$
[HINT: See Example 2.]

20. $h(t) = t^3 - 3t^2$ with domain $[-1, +\infty)$
[HINT: See Example 2.]

21. $f(x) = x^4 - 4x^3$ with domain $[-1, +\infty)$

22. $f(x) = 3x^4 - 2x^3$ with domain $[-1, +\infty)$

23. $g(t) = \frac{1}{4}t^4 - \frac{2}{3}t^3 + \frac{1}{2}t^2$ with domain $(-\infty, +\infty)$

24. $g(t) = 3t^4 - 16t^3 + 24t^2 + 1$ with domain $(-\infty, +\infty)$

25. $h(x) = (x - 1)^{2/3}$ with domain $[0, 2]$ [HINT: See Example 3.]

26. $h(x) = (x + 1)^{2/5}$ with domain $[-2, 0]$
[HINT: See Example 3.]

27. $k(x) = \frac{2x}{3} + (x + 1)^{2/3}$ with domain $(-\infty, 0]$

28. $k(x) = \dfrac{2x}{5} - (x-1)^{2/5}$ with domain $[0, +\infty)$

29. ▼ $f(t) = \dfrac{t^2 + 1}{t^2 - 1}; -2 \le t \le 2, t \ne \pm 1$

30. ▼ $f(t) = \dfrac{t^2 - 1}{t^2 + 1}$ with domain $[-2, 2]$

31. ▼ $f(x) = \sqrt{x}(x - 1); x \ge 0$

32. ▼ $f(x) = \sqrt{x}(x + 1); x \ge 0$

33. ▼ $g(x) = x^2 - 4\sqrt{x}$

34. ▼ $g(x) = \dfrac{1}{x} - \dfrac{1}{x^2}$

35. ▼ $g(x) = \dfrac{x^3}{x^2 + 3}$

36. ▼ $g(x) = \dfrac{x^3}{x^2 - 3}$

37. ▼ $f(x) = x - \ln x$ with domain $(0, +\infty)$

38. ▼ $f(x) = x - \ln x^2$ with domain $(0, +\infty)$

39. ▼ $g(t) = e^t - t$ with domain $[-1, 1]$

40. ▼ $g(t) = e^{-t^2}$ with domain $(-\infty, +\infty)$

41. ▼ $f(x) = \dfrac{2x^2 - 24}{x + 4}$

42. ▼ $f(x) = \dfrac{x - 4}{x^2 + 20}$

43. ▼ $f(x) = xe^{1-x^2}$

44. ▼ $f(x) = x \ln x$ with domain $(0, +\infty)$

In Exercises 45–48, use graphing technology and the method in Example 5 to find the x-coordinates of the critical points, accurate to two decimal places. Find all relative and absolute maxima and minima. [**HINT:** See Example 5.]

45. ⬚ $y = x^2 + \dfrac{1}{x - 2}$ with domain $(-3, 2) \cup (2, 6)$

46. ⬚ $y = x^2 - 10(x - 1)^{2/3}$ with domain $(-4, 4)$

47. ⬚ $f(x) = (x - 5)^2(x + 4)(x - 2)$ with domain $[-5, 6]$

48. ⬚ $f(x) = (x + 3)^2(x - 2)^2$ with domain $[-5, 5]$

In Exercises 49–56 the graph of the derivative of a function f is shown. Determine the x-coordinates of all stationary and singular points of f, and classify each as a relative maximum, a relative minimum, or neither. (Assume that $f(x)$ is defined and continuous everywhere in $[-3, 3]$.) [**HINT:** See Example 5.]

49. ▼

50. ▼

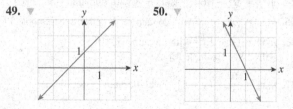

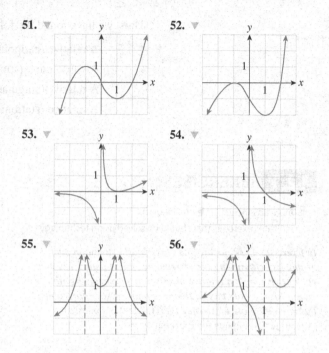

51. ▼

52. ▼

53. ▼

54. ▼

55. ▼

56. ▼

Communication and Reasoning Exercises

57. Draw the graph of a function f with domain the set of all real numbers such that f is not linear and has no relative extrema.

58. Draw the graph of a function g with domain the set of all real numbers such that g has a relative maximum and minimum but no absolute extrema.

59. Draw the graph of a function that has stationary and singular points but no relative extrema.

60. Draw the graph of a function that has relative, not absolute, maxima and minima but has no stationary or singular points.

61. If a stationary point is not a relative maximum, then must it be a relative minimum? Explain your answer.

62. If one endpoint is a relative maximum, must the other be a relative minimum? Explain your answer.

63. ▼ We said that if f is continuous on a closed interval $[a, b]$, then it will have an absolute maximum and an absolute minimum. Draw the graph of a function with domain $[0, 1]$ having an absolute maximum but no absolute minimum.

64. ▼ Refer to Exercise 63. Draw the graph of a function with domain $[0, 1]$ having no absolute extrema.

65. ⬚ ▼ Must endpoints always be extrema? Consider the following function (based on the trigonometric sine function— see Chapter 16 for a discussion of its properties):

$$f(x) = \begin{cases} x \sin\left(\dfrac{1}{x}\right) & \text{if } x > 0 \\ 0 & \text{if } x = 0. \end{cases}$$

Technology formula:
`x*sin(1/x)`

Graph this function using the technology formula above for $0 \le x \le h$, choosing smaller and smaller values of h, and decide whether f has either a relative maximum or relative minimum at the endpoint $x = 0$. Explain your answer. [Note: Very few graphers can draw this curve accurately; the grapher on the Website does a good job (you can increase the number of points to plot for more beautiful results), the grapher that comes with Mac computers is probably among the best, while the TI-83/84 Plus is probably among the worst.]

66. ▮ ▼ Refer to Exercise 65, and consider the function

$$f(x) = \begin{cases} x^2 \sin\left(\dfrac{1}{x}\right) & \text{if } x \ne 0 \\ 0 & \text{if } x = 0. \end{cases}$$

Technology formula:
`x^2*sin(1/x)`

Graph this function using the technology formula above for $-h \le x \le h$, choosing smaller and smaller values of h, and decide **(a)** whether $x = 0$ is a stationary point and **(b)** whether f has either a relative maximum or a relative minimum at $x = 0$. Explain your answers. [**HINT:** For part (a), use technology to estimate the derivative at $x = 0$.]

12.2 Applications of Maxima and Minima

In many applications we would like to find the largest or smallest possible value of some quantity—for instance, the greatest possible profit or the lowest cost. We call this the *optimal* (best) value. In this section we consider several such examples and use calculus to find the optimal value in each.

In all applications the first step is to translate a written description into a mathematical problem. In the problems we look at in this section there are *unknowns* that we are asked to find, there is an expression involving those unknowns that must be made as large or as small as possible—the **objective function**—and there may be **constraints**—equations or inequalities relating the variables.*

* If you have studied linear programming, you will notice a similarity here, but unlike the situation in linear programming, neither the objective function nor the constraints need be linear.

EXAMPLE 1   **Minimizing Average Cost**

Gymnast Clothing manufactures expensive hockey jerseys for sale to college bookstores in runs of up to 500. Its cost (in dollars) for a run of x hockey jerseys is

$$C(x) = 2{,}000 + 10x + 0.2x^2.$$

How many jerseys should Gymnast produce per run to minimize average cost?†

† Why don't we seek to minimize total cost? The answer would be uninteresting; to minimize total cost, we would make *no* jerseys at all. Minimizing the average cost is a more practical objective.

Solution Here is the procedure we will follow to solve problems like this:

1. ***Identify the unknown(s).*** There is one unknown: x, the number of hockey jerseys Gymnast should produce per run. (We know this because the question is "How many jerseys . . . ?")

2. ***Identify the objective function.*** The objective function is the quantity that must be made as small (in this case) as possible. In this example it is the average cost, which is given by

$$\overline{C}(x) = \frac{C(x)}{x} = \frac{2{,}000 + 10x + 0.2x^2}{x}$$

$$= \frac{2{,}000}{x} + 10 + 0.2x \text{ dollars per jersey.}$$

3. ***Identify the constraints (if any).*** At most 500 jerseys can be manufactured in a run. Also, $\overline{C}(0)$ is not defined. Thus, x is constrained by

$$0 < x \le 500.$$

Put another way, the domain of the objective function $\overline{C}(x)$ is $(0, 500]$.

4. *State and solve the resulting optimization problem.* Our optimization problem is:

$$\text{Minimize } \overline{C}(x) = \frac{2{,}000}{x} + 10 + 0.2x \qquad \text{Objective function}$$

$$\text{subject to } 0 < x \le 500. \qquad \text{Constraint}$$

We now solve this problem as in Section 12.1. We first calculate

$$\overline{C}'(x) = -\frac{2{,}000}{x^2} + 0.2.$$

We solve $\overline{C}'(x) = 0$ to find $x = \pm 100$. We reject $x = -100$ because -100 is not in the domain of $\overline{C}$ (and makes no sense), so we have one stationary point, at $x = 100$. There, the average cost is $\overline{C}(100) = \$50$ per jersey.

The only point at which the formula for $\overline{C}'$ is not defined is $x = 0$, but that is not in the domain of $\overline{C}$, so we have no singular points. We have one endpoint in the domain, at $x = 500$. There, the average cost is $\overline{C}(500) = \$114$.

To see the behavior of the function $\overline{C}$ at the interesting points we have found so far, we graph the function with $0 < x \le 500$ and $0 \le y \le 150$ (Figure 19). From the graph we can see that the stationary point at $x = 100$ gives the absolute minimum. We can therefore say that Gymnast Clothing should produce 100 jerseys per run, for a lowest possible average cost of \$50 per jersey.

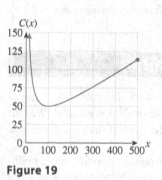

Figure 19

EXAMPLE 2 Maximizing Area

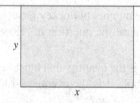

Slim wants to build a rectangular enclosure for his pet rabbit, Killer, against the side of his house, as shown in Figure 20. He has bought 100 feet of fencing. What are the dimensions of the largest area that he can enclose?

Figure 20

Solution

1. *Identify the unknown(s).* To identify the unknown(s), we look at the question: What are the *dimensions* of the largest area Slim can enclose? Thus, the unknowns are the dimensions of the fence. We call these x and y, as shown in Figure 21.

2. *Identify the objective function.* We look for what it is that we are trying to maximize (or minimize). The phrase "largest area" tells us that our object is to *maximize the area*, which is the product of length and width, so our objective function is

$$A = xy, \text{ where } A \text{ is the area of the enclosure.}$$

3. *Identify the constraints (if any).* What stops Slim from making the area as large as he wants? He has only 100 feet of fencing to work with. Looking again at Figure 21, we see that the sum of the lengths of the three sides must equal 100, so

$$x + 2y = 100.$$

One more point: Because x and y represent the lengths of the sides of the enclosure, neither can be a negative number.

4. *State and solve the resulting optimization problem.* Our mathematical problem is:

$$\text{Maximize } A = xy \qquad \text{Objective function}$$

$$\text{subject to } x + 2y = 100, x \ge 0, \text{ and } y \ge 0. \qquad \text{Constraints}$$

We know how to find maxima and minima of a function of one variable, but A appears to depend on two variables. We can remedy this by using a constraint to

Figure 21

express one variable in terms of the other. Let's take the constraint $x + 2y = 100$ and solve for x in terms of y:

$$x = 100 - 2y.$$

Substituting into the objective function gives

$$A = xy = (100 - 2y)y = 100y - 2y^2,$$

and we have eliminated x from the objective function. What about the inequalities? One says that $x \geq 0$, but we want to eliminate x from this as well. We substitute for x again, getting

$$100 - 2y \geq 0.$$

Solving this inequality for y gives $y \leq 50$. The second inequality says that $y \geq 0$. Now, we can restate our problem with x eliminated:

Maximize $A(y) = 100y - 2y^2$

subject to $0 \leq y \leq 50$.

We now proceed with our usual method of solving such problems. We calculate $A'(y) = 100 - 4y$. Solving $100 - 4y = 0$, we get one stationary point at $y = 25$. There, $A(25) = 1{,}250$. There are no points at which $A'(y)$ is not defined, so there are no singular points. We have two endpoints: at $y = 0$ and $y = 50$. The corresponding areas are $A(0) = 0$ and $A(50) = 0$. We record the three points we found in a table:

y	0	25	50
$A(y)$	0	1,250	0

It's clear now how A must behave: It increases from 0 at $y = 0$ to 1,250 at $y = 25$ and then decreases back to 0 at $y = 50$. Thus, the largest possible value of A is 1,250 square feet, which occurs when $y = 25$. To completely answer the question that was asked, we need to know the corresponding value of x. We have $x = 100 - 2y$, so $x = 50$ when $y = 25$. Thus, Slim should build his enclosure 50 feet across and 25 feet deep (the "missing" 50-foot side being formed by part of the house).

⇒ **Before we go on ...** Notice that the problem in Example 2 came down to finding the absolute maximum value of A on the closed and bounded interval $[0, 50]$. As we noted in Section 12.1, the table of values of A at its critical points and the endpoints of the interval gives us enough information to find the absolute maximum. ∎

Let's stop for a moment and summarize the steps we've taken in these two examples.

Solving an Optimization Problem

1. **Identify the unknown(s), possibly with the aid of a diagram.** These are usually the quantities asked for in the problem.

2. **Identify the objective function.** This is the quantity you are asked to maximize or minimize. You should name it explicitly, as in "Let S = surface area."

3. **Identify the constraint(s).** These can be equations relating variables or inequalities expressing limitations on the values of variables.

4. **State the optimization problem.** This will have the form "Maximize [minimize] the objective function subject to the constraint(s)."

5. **Eliminate extra variables.** If the objective function depends on several variables, solve the constraint equations to express all variables in terms of one particular variable. Substitute these expressions into the objective function to rewrite it as a function of a single variable. In short, if there is only one constraint equation:

   Solve the constraint for one of the unknowns, and substitute into the objective.

   Also substitute the expressions into any inequality constraints to help determine the domain of the objective function.

6. **Find the absolute maximum (or minimum) of the objective function.** Use the techniques of the preceding section.

Now for some further examples.

EXAMPLE 3 **Maximizing Revenue**

Cozy Carriage Company builds baby strollers. Using market research, the company estimates that if it sets the price of a stroller at p dollars, then it can sell $q = 300{,}000 - 10p^2$ strollers per year.* What price will bring in the greatest annual revenue?

*This equation is, of course, the demand equation for the baby strollers. However, coming up with a suitable demand equation in real life is hard, to say the least. In this regard, the very entertaining and also insightful article *Camels and Rubber Duckies* by Joel Spolsky at www.joelonsoftware.com/articles/ CamelsandRubberDuckies.html is a must-read.

Solution The question we are asked identifies our main unknown: the price p. However, there is another quantity that we do not know: q, the number of strollers the company will sell per year. The question also identifies the objective function, revenue, which is

$$R = pq.$$

Including the equality constraint given to us—that $q = 300{,}000 - 10p^2$—and the "reality" inequality constraints $p \geq 0$ and $q \geq 0$, we can write our problem as follows:

Maximize $R = pq$

subject to $q = 300{,}000 - 10p^2$, $p \geq 0$, and $q \geq 0$.

We are given q in terms of p, so let's substitute to eliminate q:

$$R = pq = p(300{,}000 - 10p^2) = 300{,}000p - 10p^3.$$

Substituting in the inequality $q \geq 0$, we get

$$300{,}000 - 10p^2 \geq 0.$$

Thus, $p^2 \leq 30{,}000$, which gives $-100\sqrt{3} \leq p \leq 100\sqrt{3}$. When we combine this with $p \geq 0$, we get the following restatement of our problem:

Maximize $R(p) = 300{,}000p - 10p^3$

subject to $0 \leq p \leq 100\sqrt{3}$.

We solve this problem in much the same way we did the preceding one. We calculate $R'(p) = 300{,}000 - 30p^2$. Setting $300{,}000 - 30p^2 = 0$, we find one stationary point at $p = 100$. There are no singular points, and we have the endpoints $p = 0$ and $p = 100\sqrt{3}$. Putting these points in a table and computing the corresponding values of R, we get the following:

p	0	100	$100\sqrt{3}$
$R(p)$	0	20,000,000	0

Thus, Cozy Carriage should price its strollers at $100 each, which will bring in the largest possible revenue of $20,000,000.

EXAMPLE 4   **Optimizing Resources**

The Metal Can Company has an order to make cylindrical cans with a volume of 250 cubic centimeters. What should be the dimensions of the cans in order to use the least amount of metal in their production?

Solution We are asked to find the dimensions of the cans. It is traditional to take as the dimensions of a cylinder the height h and the radius of the base r, as in Figure 22.
   We are also asked to minimize the amount of metal used in the can, which is the area of the surface of the cylinder. We can look up the formula or figure it out ourselves: Imagine removing the circular top and bottom and then cutting vertically and flattening out the hollow cylinder to get a rectangle, as shown in Figure 23.

Figure 22

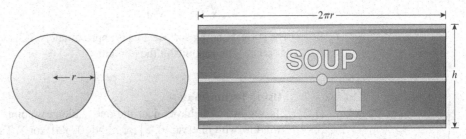

Figure 23

   Our objective function is the (total) surface area S of the can. The area of each disc is πr^2, while the area of the rectangular piece is $2\pi rh$. Thus, our objective function is

$$S = 2\pi r^2 + 2\pi rh.$$

As usual, there is a constraint: The volume must be exactly 250 cubic centimeters. The formula for the volume of a cylinder is $V = \pi r^2 h$, so

$$\pi r^2 h = 250.$$

It is easiest to solve this constraint for h in terms of r:

$$h = \frac{250}{\pi r^2}.$$

Substituting in the objective function, we get

$$S = 2\pi r^2 + 2\pi r \frac{250}{\pi r^2} = 2\pi r^2 + \frac{500}{r}.$$

Now, r cannot be negative or 0, but it can become very large (a very wide but very short can could have the right volume). We therefore take the domain of $S(r)$ to be $(0, +\infty)$, so our mathematical problem is as follows:

$$\text{Minimize } S(r) = 2\pi r^2 + \frac{500}{r}$$

subject to $r > 0$.

Now we calculate

$$S'(r) = 4\pi r - \frac{500}{r^2}.$$

To find stationary points, we set this equal to 0 and solve:

$$4\pi r - \frac{500}{r^2} = 0$$

$$4\pi r = \frac{500}{r^2}$$

$$4\pi r^3 = 500$$

$$r^3 = \frac{125}{\pi}.$$

So

$$r = \sqrt[3]{\frac{125}{\pi}} = \frac{5}{\sqrt[3]{\pi}} \approx 3.41.$$

The corresponding surface area is approximately $S(3.41) \approx 220$. There are no singular points or endpoints in the domain.

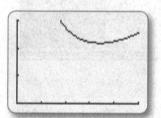

Figure 24

Using Technology

To see how S behaves near the one stationary point, let's graph it in a viewing window with interval $[0, 5]$ for r and $[0, 300]$ for S. The result is Figure 24.

From the graph we can clearly see that the smallest surface area occurs at the stationary point at $r \approx 3.41$. The height of the can will be

$$h = \frac{250}{\pi r^2} \approx 6.83.$$

Thus, the can that uses the least amount of metal has a height of approximately 6.83 centimeters and a radius of approximately 3.41 centimeters. Such a can will use approximately 220 square centimeters of metal.

 Before we go on ... We obtained the value of r in Example 4 by solving the equation

$$4\pi r = \frac{500}{r^2}.$$

This time, let us do things differently: Divide both sides by 4π to obtain

$$r = \frac{500}{4\pi r^2} = \frac{125}{\pi r^2}$$

and compare what we got with the expression for h:

$$h = \frac{250}{\pi r^2},$$

which we see is exactly twice the expression for r. Put another way, the height is exactly equal to the diameter, so the can looks square when viewed from the side. Have you ever seen cans with that shape? Why do you think most cans do not have this shape? ∎

EXAMPLE 5   **Allocation of Labor**

The Gym Sock Company manufactures cotton athletic socks. Production is partially automated through the use of robots. Daily operating costs amount to $50 per laborer and $30 per robot. The number of pairs of socks the company can manufacture in a day is given by a Cobb-Douglas* production formula

* Cobb-Douglas production formulas were discussed in Section 11.6.

$$q = 50n^{0.6}r^{0.4},$$

where q is the number of pairs of socks that can be manufactured by n laborers and r robots. Assuming that the company wishes to produce 1,000 pairs of socks per day at a minimum cost, how many laborers and how many robots should it use?

Solution The unknowns are the number of laborers n and the number of robots r. The objective is to minimize the daily cost:

$$C = 50n + 30r.$$

The constraints are given by the daily quota

$$1,000 = 50n^{0.6}r^{0.4}$$

and the fact that n and r are nonnegative. We solve the constraint equation for one of the variables; let's solve for n:

$$n^{0.6} = \frac{1,000}{50r^{0.4}} = \frac{20}{r^{0.4}}.$$

Taking the $1/0.6$ power of both sides gives

$$n = \left(\frac{20}{r^{0.4}}\right)^{1/0.6} = \frac{20^{1/0.6}}{r^{0.4/0.6}} = \frac{20^{5/3}}{r^{2/3}} \approx \frac{147.36}{r^{2/3}}.$$

Substituting in the objective equation gives us the cost as a function of r:

$$C(r) \approx 50\left(\frac{147.36}{r^{2/3}}\right) + 30r$$

$$= 7,368r^{-2/3} + 30r.$$

The only remaining constraint on r is that $r > 0$. To find the minimum value of $C(r)$, we first take the derivative:

$$C'(r) \approx -4,912r^{-5/3} + 30.$$

Setting this equal to zero, we solve for r:

$$r^{-5/3} \approx 0.006107$$

$$r \approx (0.006107)^{-3/5} \approx 21.3.$$

The corresponding cost is $C(21.3) \approx \$1,600$. There are no singular points or endpoints in the domain of C.

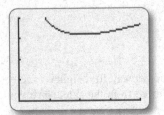

Figure 25

Using Technology

To see how C behaves near its stationary point, let's draw its graph in a viewing window with an interval of $[0, 40]$ for r and $[0, 2{,}000]$ for C. The result is Figure 25.

From the graph we can see that C does have its minimum at the stationary point. The corresponding value of n is

$$n \approx \frac{147.36}{r^{2/3}} \approx 19.2.$$

At this point, our solution appears to be this: Use (approximately) 19.2 laborers and (approximately) 21.3 robots to meet the manufacturing quota at a minimum cost. However, we are not interested in fractions of robots or people, so we need to find integer solutions for n and r. If we round these numbers, we get the solution $(n, r) = (19, 21)$. However, a quick calculation shows that

$$q = 50(19)^{0.6}(21)^{0.4} \approx 989 \text{ pairs of socks,}$$

which fails to meet the quota of 1,000. Thus, we need to round at least one of the quantities n and r *upward* to meet the quota. The three possibilities, with corresponding values of q and C, are as follows:

$$(n, r) = (20, 21), \text{ with } q \approx 1{,}020 \text{ and } C = \$1{,}630$$
$$(n, r) = (19, 22), \text{ with } q \approx 1{,}007 \text{ and } C = \$1{,}610$$
$$(n, r) = (20, 22), \text{ with } q \approx 1{,}039 \text{ and } C = \$1{,}660.$$

Of these, the solution that meets the quota at a minimum cost is $(n, r) = (19, 22)$. Thus, the Gym Sock Co. should use 19 laborers and 22 robots, at a cost of $50 \times 19 + 30 \times 22 = \$1{,}610$, to manufacture $50 \times 19^{0.6} \times 22^{0.4} \approx 1{,}007$ pairs of socks.

FAQs

Constraints and Objectives

Q : *How do I know whether or not there are constraints in an applied optimization problem?*

A : There are usually at least *inequality* constraints; the variables usually represent real quantities, such as length or number of items, and so cannot be negative, leading to constraints such as $x \geq 0$ (or $0 \leq x \leq 100$ in the event that there is an upper limit). *Equation* constraints usually arise when there is more than one unknown in the objective, and they dictate how one unknown is related to others as in, say, "the length is twice the width" or "the demand is 8 divided by the price" (a demand equation).

Q : *How do I know what to use as the objective and what to use as the constraint(s)?*

A : To identify the objective, look for a phrase such as "find the maximum (or minimum) value of." The amount you are trying to maximize or minimize is the objective. For example,

- ... *at the least cost* ... The objective function is the equation for cost, $C = \ldots$.
- ... *the greatest area* ... The objective function is the equation for area, $A = \ldots$.

To determine the constraint *inequalities*, ask yourself what limitations are placed on the unknown variables as above—are they nonnegative? are there upper limits? To identify the constraint *equations*, look for sentences that dictate restrictions in the form of relationships between the variables, as in the answer to the first question above.

12.2 EXERCISES

▼ more advanced   ◆ challenging

⊞ indicates exercises that should be solved using technology

In Exercises 1–8, solve the given optimization problems.
[HINT: See Example 2.]

1. Maximize $P = xy$ subject to $x + y = 10$.

2. Maximize $P = xy$ subject to $x + 2y = 40$.

3. Minimize $S = x + y$ subject to $xy = 9$ and both x and $y > 0$.

4. Minimize $S = x + 2y$ subject to $xy = 2$ and both x and $y > 0$.

5. Minimize $F = x^2 + y^2$ subject to $x + 2y = 10$.

6. Minimize $F = x^2 + y^2$ subject to $xy^2 = 16$.

7. ▼ Maximize $P = xyz$ subject to $x + y = 30$, $y + z = 30$, and $x, y, z \geq 0$.

8. ▼ Maximize $P = xyz$ subject to $x + z = 12$, $y + z = 12$, and $x, y, z \geq 0$.

9. For a rectangle with perimeter 20 to have the largest area, what dimensions should it have?

10. For a rectangle with area 100 to have the smallest perimeter, what dimensions should it have?

Applications

11. **Advertising Costs** The cost, in thousands of dollars, of airing x 30-second television commercials during a Super Bowl game can be approximated by[1]

$$C(x) = 20 + 4{,}000x + 0.05x^2.$$

How many 30-second television commercials should your company air to minimize average costs? What is the resulting average cost of a 30-second ad? [HINT: See Example 1.]

12. **Advertising Costs** The cost, in billions of dollars, of airing x five-second hologram commercials during a Galactic Chess game can be approximated by

$$C(x) = 490 + 320x + 0.001x^2.$$

How many hologram commercials should your company air to minimize average costs? What is the resulting average cost of a five-second ad? (Round your answer to the nearest billion dollars.) [HINT: See Example 1.]

13. **Average Cost: iPhones** Assume that it costs Apple approximately

$$C(x) = 400{,}000 + 160x + 0.001x^2$$

dollars to manufacture x 32GB iPhone 6's in an hour at the Foxconn Technology Group.[2] How many iPhone 6's should be manufactured each hour to minimize average cost? What is the resulting average cost of an iPhone? How does the average cost compare with the marginal cost at the optimal production level? (Give your answer to the nearest dollar.)

14. **Average Cost: PlayStation 4's** Assume that it costs Sony approximately

$$C(x) = 800{,}000 + 340x + 0.0005x^2$$

dollars to manufacture x PlayStation 4's in an hour.[3] How many PlayStations should be manufactured each hour to minimize average cost? What is the resulting average cost of a PlayStation 4? If fewer than the optimal number are manufactured per hour, will the marginal cost be larger, smaller, or equal to the average cost at that lower production level?

15. **Pollution Control** The cost of controlling emissions at a firm rises rapidly as the amount of emissions reduced increases. Here is a possible model:

$$C(q) = 4{,}000 + 100q^2,$$

where q is the reduction in emissions (in pounds of pollutant per day) and C is the daily cost to the firm (in dollars) of this reduction. What level of reduction corresponds to the lowest average cost per pound of pollutant, and what would be the resulting average cost to the nearest dollar?

16. **Pollution Control** Repeat Exercise 15 using the following cost function:

$$C(q) = 2{,}000 + 200q^2.$$

17. **Pollution Control** (Compare Exercise 15.) The cost of controlling emissions at a firm is given by

$$C(q) = 4{,}000 + 100q^2,$$

where q is the reduction in emissions (in pounds of pollutant per day) and C is the daily cost to the firm (in dollars) of this reduction. Government clean-air subsidies amount to $500 per pound of pollutant removed. How many pounds of pollutant should the firm remove each day to minimize *net* cost (cost minus subsidy)?

[1] The average cost of a 30-second ad during the 2014 Super Bowl game was an estimated $4 million. Source: "Who Bought What in Super Bowl XLVIII," *Advertising Age*, Feb. 3, 2014, http://adage.com.

[2] Not the actual cost equation; the authors do not know Apple's actual cost equation. The minimum average cost in the model given is in rough agreement with the actual cost for one of the 2014 models. Source for cost data: http://time.com.

[3] Not the actual cost equation; the authors do not know Sony's actual cost equation. The minimum average cost in the model given is in rough agreement with the actual cost to manufacture a PlayStation 4 in 2013. Source for estimate of marginal cost: VentureBeat (http://venturebeat.com).

18. Pollution Control (Compare Exercise 16.) Repeat Exercise 17 using the following cost function:

$$C(q) = 2,000 + 200q^2$$

with government subsidies amounting to $100 per pound of pollutant removed per day.

19. Fences I would like to create a rectangular vegetable patch. The fencing for the east and west sides costs $4 per foot, and the fencing for the north and south sides costs only $2 per foot. I have a budget of $80 for the project. What are the dimensions of the vegetable patch with the largest area I can enclose? [HINT: See Example 2.]

20. Fences I would like to create a rectangular orchid garden that abuts my house so that the house itself forms the northern boundary. The fencing for the southern boundary costs $4 per foot, and the fencing for the east and west sides costs $2 per foot. If I have a budget of $80 for the project, what are the dimensions of the garden with the largest area I can enclose? [HINT: See Example 2.]

21. Fences You are building a right-angled triangular flower garden along a stream as shown in the figure. (The borders can be in any direction as long as they are at right angles as shown.)

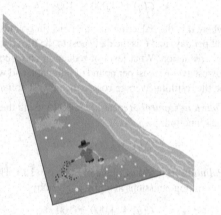

The fencing of the left border costs $5 per foot, while the fencing of the lower border costs $1 per foot. (No fencing is required along the river.) You want to spend $100 and enclose as much area as possible. What are the dimensions of your garden, and what area does it enclose? [HINT: The area of a right-triangle is given by $A = xy/2$.]

22. Fences Repeat Exercise 21, this time assuming that the fencing of the left border costs $8 per foot, while the fencing of the lower border costs $2 per foot, and that you can spend $400.

23. ▼ Fences (Compare Exercise 19.) For tax reasons I need to create a rectangular vegetable patch with an area of exactly 242 square feet. The fencing for the east and west sides costs $4 per foot, and the fencing for the north and south sides costs only $2 per foot. What are the dimensions of the vegetable patch with the least expensive fence? [HINT: Compare Exercise 3.]

24. ▼ Fences (Compare Exercise 20.) For reasons too complicated to explain, I need to create a rectangular orchid garden with an area of exactly 324 square feet abutting my house so that the house itself forms the northern boundary. The fencing for the southern boundary costs $4 per foot, and the fencing for the east and west sides costs $2 per foot. What are the dimensions of the orchid garden with the least expensive fence? [HINT: Compare Exercise 4.]

25. Revenue Hercules Films is deciding on the price of the video release of its film *Son of Frankenstein*. Its marketing people estimate that at a price of p dollars, it can sell a total of $q = 200,000 - 10,000p$ copies. What price will bring in the greatest revenue? [HINT: See Example 3.]

26. Profit Hercules Films is also deciding on the price of the video release of its film *Bride of the Son of Frankenstein*. Again, marketing estimates that at a price of p dollars, it can sell $q = 200,000 - 10,000p$ copies, but each copy costs $4 to make. What price will give the greatest *profit*?

27. Revenue: Smartphones Worldwide annual sales of smartphones in 2012–2013 were approximately $q = -6p + 3,030$ million phones at a selling price of p per phone.[4] What selling price would have resulted in the largest annual revenue? What, to the nearest $10 million, would have been the resulting annual revenue? (The actual selling price in 2013 was $335.)

28. Projected Revenue: Smartphones Worldwide annual sales of smartphones in 2013–2017 were projected to be approximately $q = -10p + 4,360$ million phones at a selling price of p per phone.[5] What selling price would have resulted in the largest projected annual revenue? What would have been the resulting projected annual revenue?

29. Revenue: Monorail Service The demand for monorail service in Las Vegas in 2005 can be approximated by $q = -4,500p + 41,500$ rides per day when the fare was p. What price should have been charged to maximize total daily revenue?[6]

30. Revenue: Mars Monorail The demand for monorail service in the three urbynes (or districts) of Utarek on Mars can be approximated by $q = -2p + 24$ million riders per day when the fare is Zp. What price should be charged to maximize total daily revenue?[7]

31. Revenue Assume that the demand for tuna in a small coastal town is given by

$$p = \frac{500,000}{q^{1.5}},$$

---

[4] Source for data: IDC Worldwide Quarterly Mobile Phone Tracker, Nov. 26, 2013, www.zdnet.com.

[5] Data based on historical 2013 data (source: *Ibid.*) and projected 2017 data.

[6] Source for ridership data: *New York Times*, February 10, 2007, p. A9.

[7] The zonar (Z) is the official currency in the city-state of Utarek, Mars (formerly www.Marsnext.com, a now extinct virtual society).

where q is the number of pounds of tuna that can be sold in a month at p dollars per pound. Assume that the town's fishery wishes to sell at least 5,000 pounds of tuna per month.

a. How much should the town's fishery charge for tuna to maximize monthly revenue? [HINT: See Example 3, and don't neglect endpoints.]

b. How much tuna will it sell per month at that price?

c. What will be its resulting revenue?

32. Revenue In the 1930s the economist Henry Schultz devised the following demand function for corn:

$$p = \frac{6{,}570{,}000}{q^{1.3}},$$

where q is the number of bushels of corn that could be sold at p dollars per bushel in one year.[8] Assume that at least 10,000 bushels of corn per year must be sold.

a. How much should farmers charge per bushel of corn to maximize annual revenue? [HINT: See Example 3, and don't neglect endpoints.]

b. How much corn can farmers sell per year at that price?

c. What will be the farmers' resulting revenue?

33. Revenue During the 1950s the wholesale price for chicken in the United States fell from 25¢ per pound to 14¢ per pound, while per capita chicken consumption rose from 22 pounds per year to 27.5 pounds per year.[9] Assuming that the demand for chicken depended linearly on the price, what wholesale price for chicken would have maximized revenues for poultry farmers, and what would that revenue have amounted to?

34. Revenue Your underground used-book business is booming. Your policy is to sell all used versions of *Calculus and You* at the same price (regardless of condition). When you set the price at $10, sales amounted to 120 volumes during the first week of classes. The following semester, you set the price at $30, and sales dropped to zero. Assuming that the demand for books depends linearly on the price, what price gives you the maximum revenue, and what does that revenue amount to?

35. Profit: Smartphones (Compare Exercise 27.) Worldwide annual sales of smartphones in 2012–2013 were approximately $q = -6p + 3{,}030$ million phones at a selling price of $\$p$ per phone.[10] Assuming a manufacturing cost of $80 per phone, what selling price would have resulted in the largest annual profit? What would have been the resulting annual profit? (The actual selling price in 2013 was $335.) [HINT: See Example 3, and recall that Profit = Revenue − Cost.]

36. Projected Profit: Smartphones (Compare Exercise 28.) Worldwide annual sales of smartphones in 2013–2017 were projected at approximately $q = -10p + 4{,}360$ million phones at a selling price of $\$p$ per phone.[11] Assuming a manufacturing cost of $100 per phone, what selling price would have resulted in the largest projected annual profit? What would have been the resulting annual profit? [HINT: See Example 3, and recall that Profit = Revenue − Cost.]

37. ▼ Profit The demand equation for your company's virtual reality video headsets is

$$p = \frac{1{,}000}{q^{0.3}},$$

where q is the total number of headsets that your company can sell in a week at a price of p dollars. The total manufacturing and shipping cost amounts to $100 per headset.

a. What is the greatest profit your company can make in a week, and how many headsets will your company sell at this level of profit? (Give answers to the nearest whole number.)

b. How much, to the nearest $1, should your company charge per headset for the maximum profit?

38. ▼ Profit Because of sales by a competing company, your company's sales of virtual reality video headsets have dropped, and your financial consultant revises the demand equation to

$$p = \frac{800}{q^{0.35}},$$

where q is the total number of headsets that your company can sell in a week at a price of p dollars. The total manufacturing and shipping cost still amounts to $100 per headset.

a. What is the greatest profit your company can make in a week, and how many headsets will your company sell at this level of profit? (Give answers to the nearest whole number.)

b. How much, to the nearest $1, should your company charge per headset for the maximum profit?

39. Paint Cans A company manufactures cylindrical paint cans with open tops with a volume of 27,000 cubic centimeters. What should be the dimensions of the cans in order to use the least amount of metal in their production? [HINT: See Example 4.]

40. Metal Drums A company manufactures cylindrical metal drums with open tops with a volume of 1 cubic meter. What should be the dimensions of the drums in order to use the least amount of metal in their production? [HINT: See Example 4.]

41. Tin Cans A company manufactures cylindrical tin cans with closed tops with a volume of 250 cubic centimeters. The metal used to manufacture the cans costs $0.01 per

---

[8] Based on data for the period 1915–1929. Source: Henry Schultz (1938), *The Theory and Measurement of Demand,* University of Chicago Press, Chicago.

[9] Data are provided for the years 1951–1958. Source: U.S. Department of Agriculture, *Agricultural Statistics.*

[10] See footnote for Exercise 27.

[11] See footnote for Exercise 28.

square centimeter for the sides and $0.02 per square centimeter for the (thicker) top and bottom. What should be the dimensions of the cans to minimize the cost of metal in their production? What is the ratio height/radius? [HINT: See Example 4.]

42. *Metal Drums* A company manufactures cylindrical metal drums with open tops with a volume of 2 cubic meters. The metal used to manufacture the drums costs $2 per square meter for the sides and $3 per square meter for the (thicker) bottom. What should be the dimensions of the drums to minimize the cost of metal in their production? What is the ratio height/radius? [HINT: See Example 4.]

43. ▼ ***Box Design*** *Chocolate Box Company* is going to make open-topped boxes out of 6 × 16-inch rectangles of cardboard by cutting squares out of the corners and folding up the sides. What is the largest volume box it can make this way?

44. ▼ ***Box Design*** *Vanilla Box Company* is going to make open-topped boxes out of 12 × 12-inch rectangles of cardboard by cutting squares out of the corners and folding up the sides. What is the largest volume box it can make this way?

45. ▼ ***Box Design*** A packaging company is going to make closed boxes, with square bases, that hold 125 cubic centimeters. What are the dimensions of the box that can be built with the least material?

46. ▼ ***Box Design*** A packaging company is going to make open-topped boxes, with square bases, that hold 108 cubic centimeters. What are the dimensions of the box that can be built with the least material?

47. ▼ ***Luggage Dimensions*** American Airlines requires that the total outside dimensions (length + width + height) of a checked bag not exceed 62 inches.[12] Suppose you want to check a bag whose height equals its width. What is the largest volume bag of this shape that you can check on an American flight?

48. ▼ ***Carry-on Dimensions*** American Airlines requires that the total outside dimensions (length + width + height) of a carry-on bag not exceed 45 inches.[13] Suppose you want to carry on a bag whose length is twice its height. What is the largest volume bag of this shape that you can carry on an American flight?

49. ▼ ***Luggage Dimensions*** *Fly-by-Night Airlines* has a peculiar rule about luggage: The length and width of a bag must add up to at most 45 inches, and the width and height must also add up to at most 45 inches. What are the dimensions of the bag with the largest volume that Fly-by-Night will accept?

50. ▼ ***Luggage Dimensions*** *Fair Weather Airlines* has a similar rule. It will accept only bags for which the sum of the length and width is at most 36 inches, while the sum of length, height, and twice the width is at most 72 inches. What are the dimensions of the bag with the largest volume that Fair Weather will accept?

51. ▼ ***Package Dimensions*** The U.S. Postal Service (USPS) will accept packages only if the length plus girth is no more than 108 inches.[14] (See the figure.)

Length

Girth

Assuming that the front face of the package (as shown in the figure) is square, what is the largest volume package that the USPS will accept?

52. ▼ ***Package Dimensions*** United Parcel Service (UPS) will accept only packages with a length of no more than 108 inches and length plus girth of no more than 165 inches.[15] (See the figure for Exercise 51.) Assuming that the front face of the package (as shown in the figure) is square, what is the largest volume package that UPS will accept?

53. ▼ ***Cellphone Revenues*** The number of cellphone subscribers in China in the years 2000–2005 was projected to follow the equation $N(t) = 39t + 68$ million subscribers in year t. ($t = 0$ represents January 2000.) The average annual revenue per cellphone user was $350 in 2000.[16] If we assume that because of competition the revenue per cellphone user decreases continuously at an annual rate of 30%, we can model the annual revenue as

$$R(t) = 350(39t + 68)e^{-0.3t} \text{ million dollars.}$$

Determine **(a)** when to the nearest 0.1 year the revenue was projected to peak and **(b)** the revenue, to the nearest $1 million, at that time.

54. ▼ ***Cellphone Revenues*** (Refer to Exercise 53.) If we assume instead that the revenue per cellphone user decreases continuously at an annual rate of 20%, we obtain the revenue model

$$R(t) = 350(39t + 68)e^{-0.2t} \text{ million dollars.}$$

Determine **(a)** when to the nearest 0.1 year the revenue was projected to peak and **(b)** the revenue, to the nearest $1 million, at that time.

---

[12] According to information on its website (www.aa.com).

[13] *Ibid.*

[14] The requirement for packages sent other than Retail Ground, as of September 2015 (www.usps.com).

[15] The requirement as of September 2015 (www.ups.com).

[16] Based on a regression of projected figures (coefficients are rounded). Source: Intrinsic Technology/*New York Times*, Nov. 24, 2000, p. C1.

55. ▼ *Research and Development* Spending on research and development by drug companies in the United States t years after 1970 can be modeled by

$$S(t) = 2.5e^{0.08t} \text{ billion dollars} \quad (0 \le t \le 31).$$

The number of new drugs approved by the Food and Drug Administration (FDA) over the same period can be modeled by

$$D(t) = 10 + t \text{ drugs per year}^{17} \quad (0 \le t \le 31).$$

When was the function $D(t)/S(t)$ at a maximum? What is the maximum value of $D(t)/S(t)$? What does the answer tell you about the cost of developing new drugs?

56. ▼ *Research and Development* (Refer to Exercise 55.) If the number of new drugs approved by the FDA had been $10 + 2t$ new drugs each year, when would the function $D(t)/S(t)$ have reached a maximum? What does the answer tell you about the cost of developing new drugs?

57. ▼ *Asset Appreciation* As the financial consultant to a classic auto dealership, you estimate that the total value (in dollars) of its collection of 1959 Chevrolets and Fords is given by the formula

$$v = 300,000 + 1,000t^2 \quad (t \ge 5),$$

where t is the number of years from now. You anticipate a continuous inflation rate of 5% per year, so that the discounted (present) value of an item that will be worth $\$v$ in t years' time is

$$p = ve^{-0.05t}.$$

When would you advise the dealership to sell the vehicles to maximize their discounted value?

58. ▼ *Plantation Management* The value of a fir tree in your plantation increases with the age of the tree according to the formula

$$v = \frac{20t}{1 + 0.05t},$$

where t is the age of the tree in years. Given a continuous inflation rate of 5% per year, the discounted (present) value of a newly planted seedling is

$$p = ve^{-0.05t}.$$

At what age (to the nearest year) should you harvest your trees to ensure the greatest possible discounted value?

59. ▼ *Marketing Strategy* *FeatureRich Software Company* has a dilemma. Its new program, Doors-X 10.27, is almost ready to go on the market. However, the longer the company works on it, the better it can make the program and the more it can charge for it. The company's marketing analysts estimate that if it delays t days, it can set the price at $100 + 2t$ dollars. On the other hand, the longer it delays, the more market share it will lose to its main competitor (see the next exercise), so if it delays t days it will be able to sell $400,000 - 2,500t$ copies of the program. How many days should FeatureRich delay the release to get the greatest revenue?

60. ▼ *Marketing Strategy* *FeatureRich Software's* main competitor (see Exercise 59) is *Moon Systems*, and Moon is in a similar predicament. Its product, Walls-Y 11.4, could be sold now for $200, but for each day Moon delays, it could increase the price by $4. On the other hand, it could sell 300,000 copies now, but each day it waits will cut sales by 1,500. How many days should Moon delay the release to get the greatest revenue?

61. ▼ *Average Profit* The *FeatureRich Software Company* sells its graphing program, Dogwood, with a volume discount. If a customer buys x copies, then he or she pays[18] $\$500\sqrt{x}$. It cost the company $10,000 to develop the program and $2 to manufacture each copy. If a single customer were to buy all the copies of Dogwood, how many copies would the customer have to buy for FeatureRich Software's average profit per copy to be maximized? How are average profit and marginal profit related at this number of copies?

62. ▼ *Average Profit* Repeat Exercise 61 with the charge to the customer $\$600\sqrt{x}$ and the cost to develop the program $9,000.

63. *Resource Allocation* Your company manufactures automobile alternators, and production is partially automated through the use of robots. Daily operating costs amount to $100 per laborer and $16 per robot. To meet production deadlines, the company calculates that the numbers of laborers and robots must satisfy the constraint

$$xy = 10,000,$$

where x is the number of laborers and y is the number of robots. Assuming that the company wishes to meet production deadlines at a minimum cost, how many laborers and how many robots should it use? [HINT: See Example 5.]

64. *Resource Allocation* Your company is the largest sock manufacturer in the solar system, and production is automated through the use of androids and robots. Daily operating costs amount to ₩200 per android and ₩8 per robot.[19] To meet

---

[17] The exponential model for R&D is based on the 1970 and 2001 spending in constant 2001 dollars, while the linear model for new drugs approved is based on the 6-year moving average from data from 1970 to 2000. Source for data: Pharmaceutical Research and Manufacturers of America, FDA/*New York Times*, April 19, 2002, p. C1.

[18] This is similar to the way site licenses have been structured for the program Maple.

[19] ₩ are Neptunian Standard Solar Units of currency.

production deadlines, the company calculates that the numbers of androids and robots must satisfy the constraint

$$xy = 1,000,000,$$

where x is the number of androids and y is the number of robots. Assuming that the company wishes to meet production deadlines at a minimum cost, how many androids and how many robots should it use? [HINT: See Example 5.]

65. ▼ *Resource Allocation* Your automobile assembly plant has a Cobb-Douglas production function given by

$$q = x^{0.4}y^{0.6},$$

where q is the number of automobiles it produces per year, x is the number of employees, and y is the daily operating budget (in dollars). Annual operating costs amount to an average of $20,000 per employee plus the operating budget of $365y. Assume that you wish to produce 1,000 automobiles per year at a minimum cost. How many employees should you hire? [HINT: See Example 5.]

66. ▼ *Resource Allocation* Repeat Exercise 65 using the production formula

$$q = x^{0.5}y^{0.5}.$$

[HINT: See Example 5.]

67. ▼ *Incarceration Rate* The incarceration rate (the number of persons in prison per 100,000 residents) in the United States can be approximated by

$$N(t) = 0.04t^3 - 2t^2 + 40t + 460 \quad (0 \le t \le 18).$$

(t is the year since 1990.)[20] When, to the nearest year, was the incarceration rate increasing most rapidly? When was it increasing least rapidly? [HINT: You are being asked to find the extreme values of the rate of change of the incarceration rate.]

68. ▼ *Prison Population* The prison population in the United States can be approximated by

$$N(t) = 0.02t^3 - 2t^2 + 100t + 1,100 \text{ thousand people}$$
$$(0 \le t \le 18).$$

(t is the year since 1990.)[21] When, to the nearest year, was the prison population increasing most rapidly? When was it increasing least rapidly? [HINT: You are being asked to find the extreme values of the rate of change of the prison population.]

69. ▼ *Embryo Development* The oxygen consumption of a bird embryo increases from the time the egg is laid through the time the chick hatches. In a typical galliform bird the oxygen consumption can be approximated by

$$c(t) = -0.065t^3 + 3.4t^2 - 22t + 3.6 \text{ milliliters per day}$$
$$(8 \le t \le 30),$$

where t is the time (in days) since the egg was laid.[22] (An egg will typically hatch at around $t = 28$.) When, to the nearest day, is $c'(t)$ a maximum? What does the answer tell you?

70. ▼ *Embryo Development* The oxygen consumption of a turkey embryo increases from the time the egg is laid through the time the chick hatches. In a brush turkey the oxygen consumption can be approximated by

$$c(t) = -0.028t^3 + 2.9t^2 - 44t + 95 \text{ milliliters per day}$$
$$(20 \le t \le 50),$$

where t is the time (in days) since the egg was laid.[23] (An egg will typically hatch at around $t = 50$.) When, to the nearest day, is $c'(t)$ a maximum? What does the answer tell you?

71. ▮▼ *Subprime Mortgages during the Housing Bubble* During the real estate run-up in 2000–2008 the percentage of mortgages issued in the United States that were subprime (normally classified as risky) could be approximated by

$$A(t) = \frac{15.0}{1 + 8.6(1.8)^{-t}} \text{ percent} \quad (0 \le t \le 8)$$

t years after the start of 2000.[24] Graph the *derivative* of $A(t)$, and determine the year during which this derivative had an absolute maximum and also its value at that point. What does the answer tell you?

72. ▮▼ *Subprime Mortgage Debt during the Housing Bubble* During the real estate run-up in 2000–2008 the value of subprime (normally classified as risky) mortgage debt outstanding in the United States was approximately

$$A(t) = \frac{1,350}{1 + 4.2(1.7)^{-t}} \text{ billion dollars} \quad (0 \le t \le 8)$$

t years after the start of 2000.[25] Graph the *derivative* of $A(t)$, and determine the year during which this derivative had an absolute maximum and also its value at that point. What does the answer tell you?

73. ▮▼ *Asset Appreciation* You manage a small antique company that owns a collection of Louis XVI jewelry boxes. Their value v is increasing according to the formula

$$v = \frac{10,000}{1 + 500e^{-0.5t}},$$

---

[20] Source for data: Sourcebook of Criminal Justice Statistics Online (www.albany.edu/sourcebook).
[21] *Ibid.*

[22] The model approximates graphical data published in the article "The Brush Turkey" by Roger S. Seymour, *Scientific American,* December 1991, pp. 108–114.
[23] *Ibid.*
[24] Sources: Mortgage Bankers Association, UBS.
[25] Source: www.data360.org/dataset.aspx?Data_Set_Id=9549.

where t is the number of years from now. You anticipate an inflation rate of 5% per year, so the present value of an item that will be worth $\$v$ in t years' time is given by

$$p = v \cdot (1.05)^{-t}.$$

When (to the nearest year) should you sell the jewelry boxes to maximize their present value? How much (to the nearest constant dollar) will they be worth at that time?

74. ▣ ▼ *Harvesting Forests* The following equation models the approximate volume in cubic feet of a typical Douglas fir tree of age t years.[26]

$$V = \frac{22,514}{1 + 22,514 t^{-2.55}}$$

The lumber will be sold at $10 per cubic foot, and you do not expect the price of lumber to appreciate in the foreseeable future. On the other hand, you anticipate a general inflation rate of 5% per year, so the present value of an item that will be worth $\$v$ in t years' time is given by

$$p = v \cdot (1.05)^{-t}.$$

At what age (to the nearest year) should you harvest a Douglas fir tree to maximize its present value? How much (to the nearest constant dollar) will a Douglas fir tree be worth at that time?

75. ◆ *Agriculture* The fruit yield per tree in an orchard containing 50 trees is 100 pounds per tree each year. Because of crowding, the yield decreases by 1 pound per season for every additional tree planted. How many additional trees should be planted for a maximum total annual yield?

76. ◆ *Agriculture* Two years ago, your orange orchard contained 50 trees, and the yield per tree was 75 bags of oranges. Last year, you removed 10 of the trees and noticed that the yield per tree increased to 80 bags. Assuming that the yield per tree depends linearly on the number of trees in the orchard, what should you do this year to maximize your total yield?

77. ◆ *Revenue* (*based on a question on the GRE Economics Test*)[27] If total revenue (TR) is specified by $TR = a + bQ - cQ^2$, where Q is quantity of output and a, b, and c are positive parameters, then TR is maximized for this firm when it produces Q equal to

(A) $b/2ac$.   (B) $b/4c$.
(C) $(a + b)/c$.   (D) $b/2c$.
(E) $c/2b$.

78. ◆ *Revenue* (*based on a question on the GRE Economics Test*) If total demand (Q) is specified by $Q = -aP + b$, where P is

unit price and a and b are positive parameters, then total revenue is maximized for this firm when it charges P equal to

(A) $b/2a$.   (B) $b/4a$.
(C) a/b.   (D) $a/2b$.
(E) $-b/2a$.

Communication and Reasoning Exercises

79. You are interested in knowing the height of the tallest condominium complex that meets the city zoning requirements that the height H should not exceed eight times the distance D from the road and that the complex must provide parking for at least 50 cars. The objective function of the associated optimization problem is then

(A) H.   (B) $H - 8D$.
(C) D.   (D) $D - 8H$.

One of the constraints is

(A) $8H = D$.   (B) $8D = H$.
(C) $H'(D) = 0$.   (D) $D'(H) = 0$.

80. You are interested in building a condominium complex with a height H of at least eight times the distance D from the road and parking area of at least 1,000 square feet at the cheapest cost C. The objective function of the associated optimization problem is then

(A) H.   (B) D.
(C) C.   (D) $H + D - C$.

One of the constraints is

(A) $H - 8D = 0$.   (B) $H + D - C = 0$.
(C) $C'(D) = 0$.   (D) $8H = D$.

81. Explain why the following problem is uninteresting: A packaging company wishes to make cardboard boxes with open tops by cutting square pieces from the corners of a square sheet of cardboard and folding up the sides. What is the box with the least surface area it can make this way?

82. Explain why finding the production level that minimizes a cost function is frequently uninteresting. What would a more interesting objective be?

83. Your friend Margo claims that all you have to do to find the absolute maxima and minima in applications is set the derivative equal to zero and solve. "All that other stuff about endpoints and so on is a waste of time just to make life hard for us," according to Margo. Explain why she is wrong, and find at least one exercise in this exercise set to illustrate your point.

84. You are having a hard time persuading your other friend Marco that maximizing revenue is not the same as maximizing profit. "How on earth can you expect to obtain the largest profit if you are not taking in the largest revenue?" Explain why he is wrong, and find at least one exercise in this exercise set to illustrate your point.

85. ▼ If demand q decreases as price p increases, what does the minimum value of dq/dp measure?

86. ▼ Explain how you would solve an optimization problem of the following form. Maximize $P = f(x, y, z)$ subject to $z = g(x, y)$ and $y = h(x)$.

---

[26] The model is the authors' and is based on data in *Environmental and Natural Resource Economics* by Tom Tietenberg, third edition (New York: HarperCollins, 1992), p. 282.

[27] Source: GRE Economics Test, by G. Gallagher, G. E. Pollock, W. J. Simeone, G. Yohe (Piscataway, NJ: Research and Education Association, 1989).

12.3 Higher Order Derivatives: Acceleration and Concavity

The Second Derivative and Acceleration

The **second derivative** is simply the derivative of the derivative function. To explain why we would be interested in such a thing, we start by discussing one of its interpretations. Suppose a car is traveling along a straight stretch of highway. We saw in Section 10.5 that if $s(t)$ represents the position at time t of any object moving in a straight line, then its velocity is given by the derivative: $v(t) = s'(t)$. But one rarely drives a car at a constant speed; the velocity itself may be changing. The rate at which the velocity is changing is the **acceleration**. Because the derivative measures the rate of change, acceleration is the derivative of velocity: $a(t) = v'(t)$. Because v is the derivative of s, we can express the acceleration in terms of s:

$$a(t) = v'(t) = (s')'(t) = s''(t).$$

That is, a is the derivative of the derivative of s; in other words, the second derivative of s, which we write as s''. (In this context you will often hear the derivative s' referred to as the **first derivative**.)

Second Derivative, Acceleration

If a function f has a derivative that is in turn differentiable, then its **second derivative** is the derivative of the derivative of f, written as f''. If $f''(a)$ exists, we say that f is **twice differentiable at** $x = a$.

Quick Examples

1. If $f(x) = x^3 - x$, then $f'(x) = 3x^2 - 1$, so $f''(x) = 6x$ and $f''(-2) = -12$.
2. If $f(x) = 3x + 1$, then $f'(x) = 3$, so $f''(x) = 0$.
3. If $f(x) = e^x$, then $f'(x) = e^x$, so $f''(x) = e^x$ as well.

The **acceleration** of a moving object is the derivative of its velocity—that is, the second derivative of the position function.

Quick Example

4. If t is time in hours and the position of a car at time t is $s(t) = t^3 + 2t^2$ miles, then the car's velocity is $v(t) = s'(t) = 3t^2 + 4t$ miles per hour, and its acceleration is $a(t) = s''(t) = v'(t) = 6t + 4$ miles per hour per hour.

Differential Notation for the Second Derivative

We have written the second derivative of $f(x)$ as $f''(x)$. We could also use differential notation:

$$f''(x) = \frac{d^2 f}{dx^2}.$$

This notation comes from writing the second derivative as the derivative of the derivative in differential notation:

$$f''(x) = \frac{d}{dx}\left[\frac{df}{dx}\right] = \frac{d^2f}{dx^2}.$$

Similarly, if $y = f(x)$, we write $f''(x)$ as $\frac{d}{dx}\left[\frac{dy}{dx}\right] = \frac{d^2y}{dx^2}$. For example, if $y = x^3$, then $\frac{d^2y}{dx^2} = 6x$.

An important example of acceleration is the acceleration due to gravity.

EXAMPLE 1   Acceleration Due to Gravity

According to the laws of physics, the height of an object near the surface of the Earth falling in a vacuum from an initial rest position s_0 feet above the ground under the influence of gravity is approximately

$$s(t) = s_0 - 16t^2 \text{ feet}$$

in t seconds.* Find its acceleration.

Solution The velocity of the object is

$$v(t) = s'(t) = -32t \text{ ft/sec.}$$ Differential notation: $v = \frac{ds}{dt} = -32t$ ft/sec

The reason for the negative sign is that the height of the object is decreasing with time, so its velocity is negative. Hence, the acceleration is

$$a(t) = s''(t) = -32 \text{ ft/sec}^2.$$ Differential notation: $a = \frac{d^2s}{dt^2} = -32$ ft/sec^2

(We write ft/sec^2 as an abbreviation for feet/second/second—that is, feet per second per second. It is often read "feet per second squared.") Thus, the *downward* velocity is increasing by 32 ft/sec every second. We say that 32 ft/sec^2 is the **acceleration due to gravity**. In the absence of air resistance, all falling bodies near the surface of the Earth, no matter what their weight, will fall with this acceleration.†

➡ **Before we go on ...** In very careful experiments using balls rolling down inclined planes, Galileo made one of his most important discoveries: that the acceleration due to gravity is constant and does not depend on the weight or composition of the object that is falling.§ A famous, though probably apocryphal, story has him dropping cannonballs of different weights off the Leaning Tower of Pisa to prove his point.‖ ∎

EXAMPLE 2   Acceleration of Sales

For the first 15 months after the introduction of a new video game, the accumulated sales can be modeled by the curve

$$S(t) = 20e^{0.4t} \text{ units sold,}$$

where t is the time in months since the game was introduced. After about 25 months, total sales follow more closely the curve

$$S(t) = 100,000 - 20e^{17-0.4t}.$$

How fast are accumulated sales accelerating after 10 months? How fast are they accelerating after 30 months? What do these numbers mean?

---

* If the object is initially moving upward with a velocity v_0, then the formula becomes

$$s(t) = s_0 + v_0 t - 16t^2.$$

We will see where this formula comes from in Section 13.1.

† On other planets the acceleration due to gravity is different. For example, on Jupiter it is about three times as large as on Earth.

§ An interesting aside: Galileo's experiments depended on getting extremely accurate timings. Because the timepieces of his day were very inaccurate, he used the most accurate time measurement he could: He sang and used the beat as his stopwatch.

‖ Here is a true story: The point was made again during the Apollo 15 mission to the moon (July 1971) when astronaut David R. Scott dropped a feather and a hammer from the same height. The moon has no atmosphere, so the two hit the surface of the moon simultaneously.

Solution By acceleration we mean the rate of change of the rate of change, which is the second derivative. During the first 15 months the first derivative of sales is

$$\frac{dS}{dt} = 8e^{0.4t},$$

so the second derivative is

$$\frac{d^2S}{dt^2} = 3.2e^{0.4t}.$$

Thus, after 10 months the acceleration of sales is

$$\left.\frac{d^2S}{dt^2}\right|_{t=10} = 3.2e^4 \approx 175 \text{ units/month/month, or units/month}^2.$$

We can also compute total sales

$$S(10) = 20e^4 \approx 1,092 \text{ units}$$

and the rate of change of sales

$$\left.\frac{dS}{dt}\right|_{t=10} = 8e^4 \approx 437 \text{ units/month.}$$

What do these numbers mean? By the end of the tenth month a total of 1,092 video games have been sold. At that time the game is selling at the rate of 437 units per month. This rate of sales is increasing by 175 units per month per month. More games will be sold each month than the month before.

Analysis of the sales after 30 months is done similarly, using the formula

$$S(t) = 100,000 - 20e^{17-0.4t}.$$

The derivative is

$$\frac{dS}{dt} = 8e^{17-0.4t},$$

and the second derivative is

$$\frac{d^2S}{dt^2} = -3.2e^{17-0.4t}.$$

After 30 months,

$$S(30) = 100,000 - 20e^{17-12} \approx 97,032 \text{ units}$$

$$\left.\frac{dS}{dt}\right|_{t=30} = 8e^{17-12} \approx 1,187 \text{ units/month}$$

$$\left.\frac{d^2S}{dt^2}\right|_{t=30} = -3.2e^{17-12} \approx -475 \text{ units/month}^2.$$

By the end of the thirtieth month, 97,032 video games have been sold, the game is selling at a rate of 1,187 units per month, and the rate of sales is *decreasing* by 475 units per month. Fewer games are sold each month than the month before.

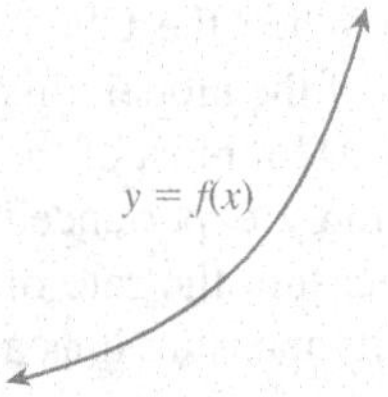

Geometric Interpretation of Second Derivative: Concavity

The first derivative of f tells us where the graph of f is rising [where $f'(x) > 0$] and where it is falling [where $f'(x) < 0$]. The second derivative tells in what direction the graph of f curves or *bends*. Consider the graphs in Figures 26 and 27. Think of a car driving from left to right along each of the roads shown in the two figures. A car driving along the graph of f in Figure 26 will turn to the left (upward); a car driving along the graph of g in Figure 27 will turn to the right (downward). We say that the graph of f is **concave up** and the graph of g is **concave down**. Now think about the derivatives of f and g. The derivative $f'(x)$ starts small but *increases* as the graph gets steeper. Because $f'(x)$ is increasing, its derivative $f''(x)$ must be positive. On the other hand, $g'(x)$ *decreases* as we go to the right. Because $g'(x)$ is decreasing, its derivative $g''(x)$ must be negative. Summarizing, we have the following.

$y = f(x)$

Figure 26

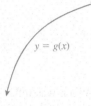

$y = g(x)$

Figure 27

> ### Concavity and the Second Derivative
>
> A curve is **concave up** if its slope is increasing, in which case the second derivative is positive. A curve is **concave down** if its slope is decreasing, in which case the second derivative is negative. A point in the domain of f where the graph of f changes concavity, from concave up to concave down or vice versa, is called a **point of inflection**. At a point of inflection the second derivative is either zero or undefined.
>
> **Locating Points of Inflection**
> To locate possible points of inflection, list points where $f''(x) = 0$ and also interior points where $f''(x)$ is not defined.

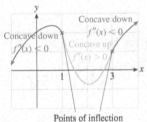

Figure 28

> ### Quick Examples
>
> **5.** The graph of the function f shown in Figure 28 is concave up when $1 < x < 3$, so $f''(x) > 0$ for $1 < x < 3$. It is concave down when $x < 1$ and $x > 3$, so $f''(x) < 0$ when $x < 1$ and $x > 3$. It has points of inflection at $x = 1$ and $x = 3$.
>
> **6.** Consider $f(x) = x^3 - 3x$, whose graph is shown in Figure 29. $f''(x) = 6x$ is negative when $x < 0$ and positive when $x > 0$. The graph of f is concave down when $x < 0$ and concave up when $x > 0$. f has a point of inflection at $x = 0$, where the second derivative is 0.

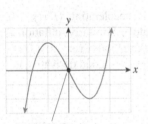

Point of inflection

Figure 29

The following example shows one of the reasons it's useful to look at concavity.

EXAMPLE 3   Inflation

Figure 30 shows the value of the U.S. Consumer Price Index (CPI) from September 2013 through August 2014.[28] The approximating curve shown on the figure is given by

$$I(t) = -0.0225t^3 + 0.390t^2 - 1.20t + 234 \quad (1 \le t \le 11),$$

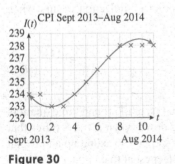

CPI Sept 2013–Aug 2014

Sept 2013   Aug 2014

Figure 30

---

[28] The CPI is compiled by the Bureau of Labor Statistics and is based upon a 1982 value of 100. For instance, a CPI of 200 means the CPI has doubled since 1982. Source: InflationData.com (www .inflationdata.com).

where t is time in months. ($t = 0$ represents September 2013.) When the CPI is increasing, the U.S. economy is **experiencing inflation**. In terms of the model, this means that the derivative is positive: $I'(t) > 0$. Notice that $I'(t) > 0$ for most of the period shown (the graph is sloping upward), so the U.S. economy experienced inflation for most of the associated period of time. We *could* measure the rate of inflation by the first derivative $I'(t)$ of the CPI, but we traditionally measure it as a ratio:

$$\text{Inflation rate} = \frac{I'(t)}{I(t)}, \qquad \text{Relative rate of change of the CPI}$$

expressed as a percentage per unit time (per month in this case).

a. Use the model to estimate the inflation rate in January 2014.

b. Was inflation slowing or speeding up in January 2014?

c. When was inflation slowing? When was inflation speeding up? When was inflation slowest?

Solution

a. We need to compute $I'(t)$:

$$I'(t) = -0.0675t^2 + 0.780t - 1.20.$$

Thus, the inflation rate in January 2014 ($t = 4$) was given by

$$\text{Inflation rate} = \frac{I'(4)}{I(4)} = \frac{-0.0675(4)^2 + 0.780(4) - 1.20}{-0.0225(4)^3 + 0.390(4)^2 - 1.20(4) + 234}$$

$$= \frac{0.84}{234} \approx 0.0036,$$

* The 0.36% monthly inflation rate corresponds to a $12 \times 0.36 = 4.32\%$ annual inflation rate. This result could be obtained directly by changing the units of the t-axis from months to years and then redoing the calculation.

or 0.36% per month.*

b. We say that inflation is "slowing" when the CPI is decelerating ($I''(t) < 0$; the index rises at a slower rate or falls at a faster rate†). Similarly, inflation is "speeding up" when the CPI is accelerating ($I''(t) > 0$; the index rises at a faster rate or falls at a slower rate). From the formula for $I'(t)$ the second derivative is

† When the CPI is falling, the inflation rate is negative, and we experience *deflation*.

$$I''(t) = -0.135t + 0.780$$
$$I''(4) = -0.135(4) + 0.780 = 0.24.$$

Since this quantity is positive, we conclude that inflation was speeding up in January 2014.

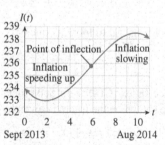

Figure 31

c. When inflation is speeding up, $I''(t)$ is positive, so the graph of the CPI is concave up. When inflation is slowing, it is concave down. At the point at which it switches, there is a point of inflection (Figure 31). The point of inflection occurs when $I''(t) = 0$; that is,

$$-0.135t + 0.780 = 0$$

$$t = \frac{0.780}{0.135} \approx 5.8.$$

Thus, inflation was speeding up when $t < 5.8$ (that is, until around three quarters of the way through February 2014) and slowing down when $t > 5.8$ (after that time). Inflation was "fastest" at the point when it stopped speeding up and began to slow down, $t \approx 5.8$. (Notice that the graph is steepest at that point.)

The Point of Diminishing Returns

After the introduction of a new video game, the accumulated worldwide sales are modeled by the curve

$$S(t) = \frac{1}{1 + 50e^{-0.2t}} \text{ million units sold,}$$

where t is the time in months since the game was introduced. (Compare Example 2.) The graphs of $S(t)$, $S'(t)$, and $S''(t)$ are shown in Figure 32. Where is the graph of S concave up, and where is it concave down? Where are any points of inflection? What does this all mean?

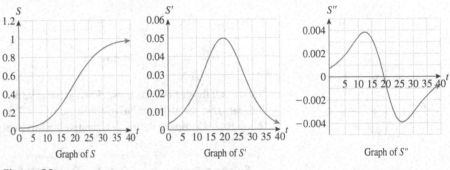

Graph of S Graph of S' Graph of S''

Figure 32

Solution Look at the graph of S. We see that the graph of S is concave up in the early months and then becomes concave down later. The point of inflection, where the concavity changes, is somewhere between 15 and 25 months.

Now look at the graph of S''. This graph crosses the t-axis very close to $t = 20$, is positive before that point, and negative after that point. Because positive values of S'' indicate that S is concave up and negative values indicate that it is concave down, we conclude that the graph of S is concave up for about the first 20 months, that is, for $0 < t < 20$, and concave down for $20 < t < 40$. The concavity switches at the point of inflection, which occurs at about $t = 20$ (when $S''(t) = 0$; a more accurate answer is $t \approx 19.56$).

What does this all mean? Look at the graph of S', which shows sales per unit time, or monthly sales. From this graph we see that monthly sales are increasing for $t < 20$: more units are being sold each month than the month before. Monthly sales reach a peak of 0.05 million $= 50,000$ games per month at the point of inflection $t = 20$ and then begin to drop off. Thus, the point of inflection occurs at the time when monthly sales stop increasing and start to fall off, that is, the time when monthly sales peak. The point of inflection is sometimes called the **point of diminishing returns**. Although the total sales figure continues to rise (see the graph of S: game units continue to be sold), the *rate* at which units are sold starts to drop. (See Figure 33.)

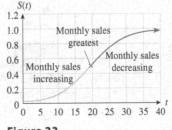

Figure 33

The Second Derivative Test for Relative Extrema

The second derivative often gives us a way of knowing whether or not a stationary point is a relative extremum. Figure 34 shows a graph with two stationary points: a relative maximum at $x = a$ and a relative minimum at $x = b$.

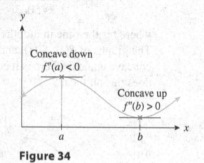

Figure 34

Notice that the curve is *concave down* at the relative maximum ($x = a$), so $f''(a) < 0$, and *concave up* at the relative minimum ($x = b$), so $f''(b) > 0$. This suggests the following. (Compare the first derivative test in Section 12.1.)

Second Derivative Test for Relative Extrema

Suppose that the function f has a stationary point at c and that $f''(c)$ exists. Determine the sign of $f''(c)$.

1. If $f''(c) > 0$, then f has a relative minimum at c.
2. If $f''(c) < 0$, then f has a relative maximum at c.

If $f''(c) = 0$, then the test is inconclusive, and you need to use one of the methods of Section 12.1 (such as the first derivative test) to determine whether or not f has a relative extremum at c.

Quick Examples

7. $f(x) = x^2 - 2x$ has $f'(x) = 2x - 2$ and hence a stationary point at $x = 1$. $f''(x) = 2$, and so $f''(1) = 2$, which is positive, so f has a relative minimum at 1.

8. Let $f(x) = x^3 - 3x^2 - 9x$. Then
$$f'(x) = 3x^2 - 6x - 9 = 3(x + 1)(x - 3)$$
Stationary points at $x = -1$, $x = 3$
$$f''(x) = 6x - 6$$
$f''(-1) = -12$, so there is a relative maximum at -1
$f''(3) = 12$, so there is a relative minimum at 3.

9. $f(x) = x^4$ has $f'(x) = 4x^3$ and hence a stationary point at $x = 0$. $f''(x) = 12x^2$, so $f''(0) = 0$, telling us that the second derivative test is inconclusive. However, we can see from the graph of f or the first derivative test that f has a minimum at $x = 0$.

Higher Order Derivatives

There is no reason to stop at the second derivative; we could once again take the derivative of the second derivative to obtain the **third derivative**, f''', and we could take the derivative once again to obtain the **fourth derivative**, written $f^{(4)}$, and then continue to obtain $f^{(5)}$, $f^{(6)}$, and so on (assuming that we get a differentiable function at each stage).

Higher Order Derivatives

We define

$$f'''(x) = \frac{d}{dx}[f''(x)]$$

$$f^{(4)}(x) = \frac{d}{dx}[f'''(x)]$$

$$f^{(5)}(x) = \frac{d}{dx}[f^{(4)}(x)],$$

and so on, assuming that all these derivatives exist.

Different Notations

$$f'(x), f''(x), f'''(x), f^{(4)}(x), \ldots, f^{(n)}(x), \ldots$$

$$\frac{df}{dx}, \frac{d^2f}{dx^2}, \frac{d^3f}{dx^3}, \frac{d^4f}{dx^4}, \ldots, \frac{d^nf}{dx^n}, \ldots$$

$$\frac{dy}{dx}, \frac{d^2y}{dx^2}, \frac{d^3y}{dx^3}, \frac{d^4y}{dx^4}, \ldots, \frac{d^ny}{dx^n}, \ldots \qquad \text{When } y = f(x)$$

$$y, y', y'', y''', y^{(4)}, \ldots, y^{(n)}, \ldots \qquad \text{When } y = f(x)$$

Quick Examples

10. If $f(x) = x^3 - x$, then $f'(x) = 3x^2 - 1$, $f''(x) = 6x$, $f'''(x) = 6$, $f^{(4)}(x) = f^{(5)}(x) = \cdots = 0$.

11. If $f(x) = e^x$, then $f'(x) = e^x$, $f''(x) = e^x$, $f'''(x) = e^x$, $f^{(4)}(x) = f^{(5)}(x) = \cdots = e^x$.

Q: We know that the second derivative can be interpreted as acceleration. How do we interpret the third derivative and the fourth, fifth, and so on?

A: Think of a car traveling down the road (with position $s(t)$ at time t) in such a way that its acceleration $\frac{d^2s}{dt^2}$ is changing with time (for instance, the driver may be slowly increasing pressure on the accelerator, causing the car to accelerate at a greater and greater rate). Then $\frac{d^3s}{dt^3}$ is the rate of change of acceleration.* $\frac{d^4s}{dt^4}$ would then be the *acceleration* of the acceleration, and so on.

* Sometimes called the "jerk."

Q: *How are these higher order derivatives reflected in the graph of a function f?*

A: Because the concavity is measured by f'', its derivative f''' tells us the rate of change of concavity. Similarly, $f^{(4)}$ would tell us the acceleration of concavity, and so on. These properties are very subtle and hard to discern by simply looking at the curve; the higher the order, the more subtle the property. There is a remarkable theorem by Taylor* that tells us that, for a large class of functions (including polynomial, exponential, logarithmic, and trigonometric functions) the values of all orders of derivative $f(a)$, $f'(a)$, $f''(a)$, $f'''(a)$, and so on at the single point $x = a$ are enough to describe the entire graph (even at points very far from $x = a$)! In other words, the smallest piece of a graph near any point *a* contains sufficient information to "clone" the entire graph!

* Brook Taylor (1685–1731) was an English mathematician.

FAQs

Interpreting Points of Inflection and Using the Second Derivative Test

Q: *It says in Example 4 that monthly sales reach a maximum at the point of inflection (second derivative is zero), but the second derivative test says that, for a maximum, the second derivative must be negative. What is going on here?*

A: What is a maximum in Example 4 is the *rate of change* of sales, which is measured in sales per unit time (monthly sales in the example). In other words, it is the *derivative* of the total sales function that is a maximum, so we located the maximum by setting its derivative (which is the *second* derivative of total sales) equal to zero. In general: To find relative (stationary) extrema of the *original* function, set $f'(x)$ equal to zero and solve for x as usual. The second derivative test can then be used to test the stationary point obtained. To find relative (stationary) extrema of the *rate of change of f*, set $f''(x) = 0$ and solve for x.

Q: *I used the second derivative test, and it was inconclusive. That means that there is neither a relative maximum nor a relative minimum at x = a, right?*

A: Wrong. If (as is often the case) the second derivative is zero at a stationary point, all it means is that the second derivative test itself cannot determine whether the given point is a relative maximum, minimum, or neither. For instance, $f(x) = x^4$ has a stationary minimum at $x = 0$, but the second derivative test is inconclusive. In such cases, one should use another test (such as the first derivative test) to decide if the point is a relative maximum, minimum, or neither.

12.3 EXERCISES

▼ more advanced   ◆ challenging
Ⓣ indicates exercises that should be solved using technology

In Exercises 1–10, calculate $\dfrac{d^2y}{dx^2}$. *[HINT: See Quick Examples 1–3.]*

1. $y = 3x^2 - 6$

2. $y = -x^2 + x$

3. $y = \dfrac{2}{x}$

4. $y = -\dfrac{2}{x^2}$

5. $y = 4x^{0.4} - x$

6. $y = 0.2x^{-0.1}$

7. $y = e^{-(x-1)} - x$

8. $y = e^{-x} + e^x$

9. $y = \dfrac{1}{x} - \ln x$

10. $y = x^{-2} + \ln x$

In Exercises 11–16 the position s of a point (in feet) is given as a function of time t (in seconds). Find (a) its acceleration as a function of t and (b) its acceleration at the specified time. [HINT: See Example 1.]

11. $s = 12 + 3t - 16t^2$; $t = 2$

12. $s = -12 + t - 16t^2$; $t = 2$

13. $s = \dfrac{1}{t} + \dfrac{1}{t^2}; t = 1$ **14.** $s = \dfrac{1}{t} - \dfrac{1}{t^2}; t = 2$

15. $s = \sqrt{t} + t^2; t = 4$ **16.** $s = 2\sqrt{t} + t^3; t = 1$

In Exercises 17–24 the graph of a function is given. Find the approximate coordinates of all points of inflection of each function (if any). [**HINT**: *See Quick Examples 5 and 6.*]

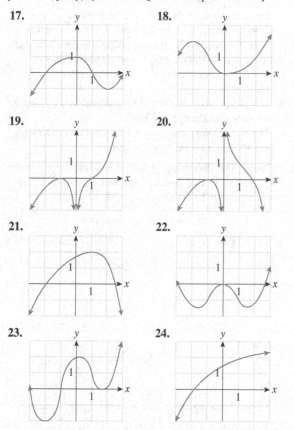

17.   **18.**

19.   **20.**

21.   **22.**

23.   **24.**

In Exercises 25–28 the graph of the derivative, $f'(x)$, *is given. Determine the x-coordinates of all points of inflection of* $f(x)$, *if any. (Assume that* $f(x)$ *is defined and continuous everywhere in* $[-3, 3]$.*)* [**HINT**: *See Quick Examples 5 and 6.*]

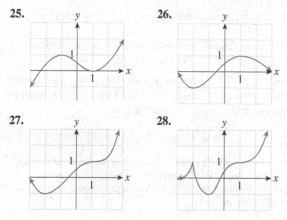

25.   **26.**

27.   **28.**

In Exercises 29–32 the graph of the second derivative, $f''(x)$, *is given. Determine the x-coordinates of all points of inflection of* $f(x)$, *if any. (Assume that* $f(x)$ *is defined and continuous everywhere in* $[-3, 3]$.*)* [**HINT**: *Remember that a point of inflection of f corresponds to a point at which* f'' *changes sign, from positive to negative or vice versa. This could be a point where its graph crosses the x-axis or a point where its graph is broken: positive on one side of the break and negative on the other.*]

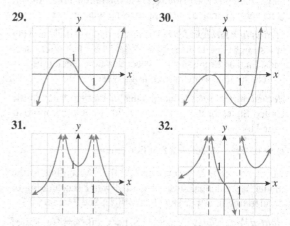

29.   **30.**

31.   **32.**

In Exercises 33–44, find the x-coordinates of all critical points of the given function. Determine whether each critical point is a relative maximum, a relative minimum, or neither, by first applying the second derivative test, and, if the test fails, by some other method. [**HINT**: *See Quick Examples 7–9.*]

33. $f(x) = x^2 - 4x + 1$ **34.** $f(x) = 2x^2 - 2x + 3$

35. $g(x) = x^3 - 12x$ **36.** $g(x) = 2x^3 - 6x + 3$

37. $f(t) = t^3 - t$ **38.** $f(t) = -2t^3 + 3t$

39. $f(x) = x^4 - 4x^3$ **40.** $f(x) = 3x^4 - 2x^3$

41. $f(x) = e^{-x^2}$ **42.** $f(x) = e^{2-x^2}$

43. $f(x) = xe^{1-x^2}$ **44.** $f(x) = xe^{-x^2}$

In Exercises 45–54, calculate the derivatives of all orders: $f'(x), f''(x), f'''(x), f^{(4)}(x), \ldots, f^{(n)}(x), \ldots$ [**HINT**: *See Quick Examples 10 and 11.*]

45. $f(x) = 4x^2 - x + 1$ **46.** $f(x) = -3x^3 + 4x$

47. $f(x) = -x^4 + 3x^2$ **48.** $f(x) = x^4 + x^3$

49. $f(x) = (2x + 1)^4$ **50.** $f(x) = (-2x + 1)^3$

51. $f(x) = e^{-x}$ **52.** $f(x) = e^{2x}$

53. $f(x) = e^{3x-1}$ **54.** $f(x) = 2e^{-x+3}$

Applications

55. *Acceleration on Mars* If a stone is dropped from a height of 40 meters above the Martian surface, its height in meters after t seconds is given by $s = 40 - 1.9t^2$. What is its acceleration? [**HINT**: See Example 1.]

56. **Acceleration on the Moon** If a stone is thrown up at 10 meters per second from a height of 100 meters above the surface of the Moon, its height in meters after t seconds is given by $s = 100 + 10t - 0.8t^2$. What is its acceleration? [HINT: See Example 1.]

57. **Motion in a Straight Line** The position of a particle moving in a straight line is given by $s = t^3 - t^2$ feet after t seconds. Find an expression for its acceleration after a time t. Is its velocity increasing or decreasing when $t = 1$?

58. **Motion in a Straight Line** The position of a particle moving in a straight line is given by $s = 3e^t - 8t^2$ feet after t seconds. Find an expression for its acceleration after a time t. Is its velocity increasing or decreasing when $t = 1$?

59. **Bottled Water Sales** Annual sales of bottled water in the United States in the period 2007–2014 could be approximated by

$$R(t) = 0.08t^2 - 0.26t + 8.8 \text{ billion gallons} \quad (0 \le t \le 7),$$

where t is time in years since 2007.[29] According to the model, were annual sales of bottled water accelerating or decelerating in 2011? How fast? [HINT: See Example 2.]

60. **Bottled Water Sales** Annual U.S. per capita sales of bottled water in the period 2007–2014 could be approximated by

$$R(t) = 0.25t^2 - t + 29 \text{ gallons} \quad (0 \le t \le 7),$$

where t is time in years since 2007.[30] According to the model, were annual U.S. per capita sales of bottled water accelerating or decelerating in 2009? How fast? [HINT: See Example 2.]

61. **Embryo Development** The daily oxygen consumption of a bird embryo increases from the time the egg is laid through the time the chick hatches. In a typical galliform bird the oxygen consumption can be approximated by

$$c(t) = -0.065t^3 + 3.4t^2 - 22t + 3.6 \text{ milliliters per day}$$
$$(8 \le t \le 30),$$

where t is the time (in days) since the egg was laid.[31] (An egg will typically hatch at around $t = 28$.) Use the model to estimate the following (give the units of measurement for each answer and round all answers to two significant digits):
a. The daily oxygen consumption 20 days after the egg was laid
b. The rate at which the oxygen consumption is changing 20 days after the egg was laid
c. The rate at which the oxygen consumption is accelerating 20 days after the egg was laid

62. **Embryo Development** The daily oxygen consumption of a turkey embryo increases from the time the egg is laid through the time the chick hatches. In a brush turkey the oxygen consumption can be approximated by

$$c(t) = -0.028t^3 + 2.9t^2 - 44t + 95 \text{ milliliters per day}$$
$$(20 \le t \le 50),$$

where t is the time (in days) since the egg was laid.[32] (An egg will typically hatch at around $t = 50$.) Use the model to estimate the following (give the units of measurement for each answer and round all answers to two significant digits):
a. The daily oxygen consumption 40 days after the egg was laid
b. The rate at which the oxygen consumption is changing 40 days after the egg was laid
c. The rate at which the oxygen consumption is accelerating 40 days after the egg was laid

63. **Inflation** The following graph shows the approximate value of the United States Consumer Price Index (CPI) from December 2006 through July 2007:[33]

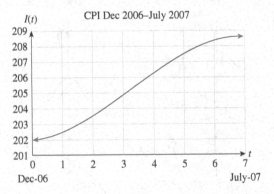

The approximating curve shown on the figure is given by

$$I(t) = -0.04t^3 + 0.4t^2 + 0.1t + 202 \quad (0 \le t \le 7),$$

where t is time in months since the start of December 2006.
a. Use the model to estimate the monthly inflation rate in February 2007 ($t = 2$). [Recall that the inflation *rate* is $I'(t)/I(t)$.]
b. Was inflation slowing or speeding up in February 2007?
c. When was inflation speeding up? When was inflation slowing? [HINT: See Example 3.]

64. **Inflation** The following graph shows the approximate value of the U.S. Consumer Price Index (CPI) from September 2004 through November 2005:[34]

---

[29] The 2014 figure is a projection. Source: Beverage Marketing Corporation (www.bottledwater.org).

[30] Ibid.

[31] The model approximates graphical data published in the article "The Brush Turkey" by Roger S. Seymour, *Scientific American*, December 1991, pp. 108–114.

[32] Ibid.

[33] The CPI is compiled by the Bureau of Labor Statistics and is based upon a 1982 value of 100. For instance, a CPI of 200 means that the CPI has doubled since 1982. Source: InflationData.com (www.inflationdata.com).

[34] Ibid.

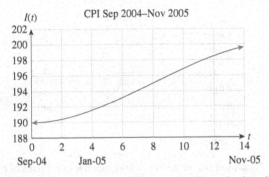

CPI Sep 2004–Nov 2005

The approximating curve shown on the figure is given by

$$I(t) = -0.005t^3 + 0.12t^2 - 0.01t + 190 \quad (0 \le t \le 14),$$

where t is time in months since the start of September 2004.

a. Use the model to estimate the monthly inflation rate in July 2005 ($t = 10$). [Recall that the inflation *rate* is $I'(t)/I(t)$.]

b. Was inflation slowing or speeding up in July 2005?

c. When was inflation speeding up? When was inflation slowing? [HINT: See Example 3.]

65. *Inflation* The following graph shows the approximate value of the U.S. Consumer Price Index (CPI) from July 2005 through March 2006:[35]

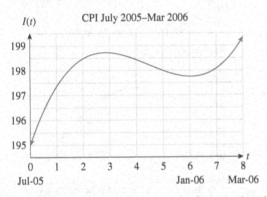

CPI July 2005–Mar 2006

The approximating curve shown on the figure is given by

$$I(t) = 0.06t^3 - 0.8t^2 + 3.1t + 195 \quad (0 \le t \le 8),$$

where t is time in months since the start of July 2005.

a. Use the model to estimate the monthly inflation rates in December 2005 and February 2006 ($t = 5$ and $t = 7$).

b. Was inflation slowing or speeding up in February 2006?

c. When was inflation speeding up? When was inflation slowing? [HINT: See Example 3.]

66. *Inflation* The following graph shows the approximate value of the U.S. Consumer Price Index (CPI) from March 2006 through May 2007.[36]

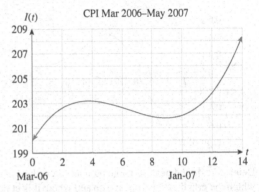

CPI Mar 2006–May 2007

The approximating curve shown on the figure is given by

$$I(t) = 0.02t^3 - 0.38t^2 + 2t + 200 \quad (0 \le t \le 14),$$

where t is time in months since the start of March 2006.

a. Use the model to estimate the monthly inflation rates in September 2006 and January 2007 ($t = 6$ and $t = 10$).

b. Was inflation slowing or speeding up in January 2007?

c. When was inflation speeding up? When was inflation slowing? [HINT: See Example 3.]

67. *Scientific Research: 1983–2003* The percentage of research articles in the prominent journal *Physical Review* that were written by researchers in the United States during 1983–2003 can be modeled by

$$P(t) = 25 + \frac{36}{1 + 0.06(0.7)^{-t}},$$

where t is time in years since 1983.[37] The graphs of P, P', and P'' are shown here:

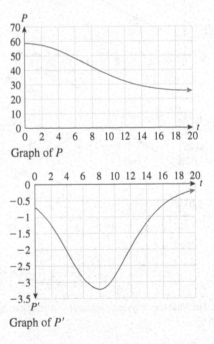

Graph of P

Graph of P'

[35] The CPI is compiled by the Bureau of Labor Statistics and is based upon a 1982 value of 100. For instance, a CPI of 200 means that the CPI has doubled since 1982. Source: InflationData.com (www.inflationdata.com).

[36] *Ibid.*

[37] Source: The American Physical Society/*New York Times*, May 3, 2003, p. A1.

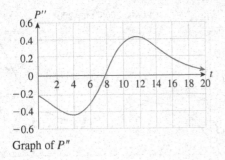

Graph of P''

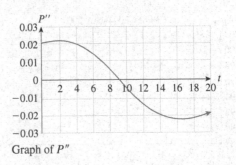

Graph of P''

Determine, to the nearest whole number, the values of t for which the graph of P is concave up and where it is concave down, and locate any points of inflection. What does the point of inflection tell you about science articles? [HINT: See Example 4.]

68. Scientific Research: 1983–2003 The number of research articles in the prominent journal *Physical Review* that were written by researchers in Europe during 1983–2003 can be modeled by

$$P(t) = \frac{7.0}{1 + 5.4(1.2)^{-t}},$$

where t is time in years since 1983.[38] The graphs of P, P', and P'' are shown here:

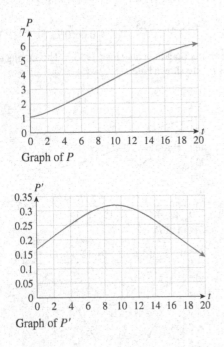

Graph of P

Graph of P'

---

[38] Source: The American Physical Society/*New York Times*, May 3, 2003, p. A1.

Determine, to the nearest whole number, the values of t for which the graph of P is concave up and where it is concave down, and locate any points of inflection. What does the point of inflection tell you about science articles? [HINT: See Example 4.]

69. Embryo Development Here are sketches of the graphs of c, c', and c'' from Exercise 61:

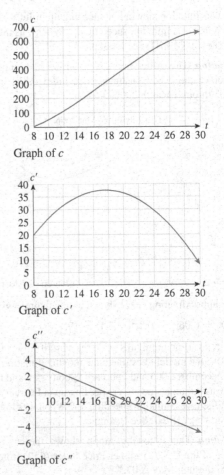

Graph of c

Graph of c'

Graph of c''

a. The graph of c'
   (A) has a point of inflection.
   (B) has no points of inflection.

b. At around 18 days after the egg is laid, daily oxygen consumption is
(**A**) at a maximum.
(**B**) increasing at a maximum rate.
(**C**) just beginning to decrease.

c. For $t > 18$ days the oxygen consumption is
(**A**) increasing at a decreasing rate.
(**B**) decreasing at an increasing rate.
(**C**) increasing at an increasing rate.

70. ***Embryo Development*** Here are sketches of the graphs of c, c', and c'' from Exercise 62:

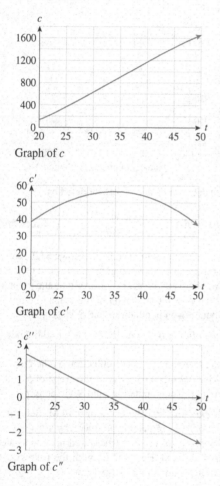

Graph of c

Graph of c'

Graph of c''

a. The graph of c
(**A**) has points of inflection.
(**B**) has no points of inflection.
(**C**) may or may not have a point of inflection, but the graphs do not provide enough information.

b. At around 35 days after the egg is laid, the rate of change of daily oxygen consumption is
(**A**) at a maximum.
(**B**) increasing at a maximum rate.
(**C**) just becoming negative.

c. For $t < 35$ days the oxygen consumption is
(**A**) increasing at an increasing rate.
(**B**) increasing at a decreasing rate.
(**C**) decreasing at an increasing rate.

71. ▊ ***Subprime Mortgages during the Housing Bubble*** During the real estate run-up in 2000–2008 the percentage of mortgages issued in the United States that were subprime (normally classified as risky) could be approximated by

$$A(t) = \frac{15.0}{1 + 8.6(1.8)^{-t}} \text{ percent} \quad (0 \le t \le 8)$$

t years after the start of 2000.[39] Graph the function as well as its first and second derivatives. Determine, to the nearest whole number, the values of t for which the graph of A is concave up and concave down and the t-coordinate of any points of inflection. What does the point of inflection tell you about subprime mortgages? [HINT: To graph the second derivative, see the margin note next to Example 4.]

72. ▊ ***Subprime Mortgage Debt during the Housing Bubble*** During the real estate run-up in 2000–2008 the value of subprime (normally classified as risky) mortgage debt outstanding in the United States was approximately

$$A(t) = \frac{1,350}{1 + 4.2(1.7)^{-t}} \text{ billion dollars} \quad (0 \le t \le 8)$$

t years after the start of 2000.[40] Graph the function as well as its first and second derivatives. Determine, to the nearest whole number, the values of t for which the graph of A is concave up and concave down and the t-coordinate of any points of inflection. What does the point of inflection tell you about subprime mortgages? [HINT: To graph the second derivative, see the margin note next to Example 4.]

73. ***Epidemics*** The following graph shows the total number n of people (in millions) infected in an epidemic as a function of time t (in years):

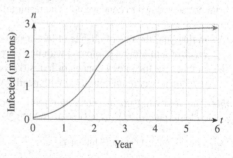

a. When, to the nearest year, was the rate of new infection largest?

b. When could the Centers for Disease Control and Prevention announce that the rate of new infection was beginning to drop? [HINT: See Example 4.]

[39] Sources: Mortgage Bankers Association, UBS.
[40] 2008 figure is an estimate. Source: www.data360.org.

74. *Sales* The following graph shows the total number of *Pomegranate Q4* computers sold since their release (*t* is in years):

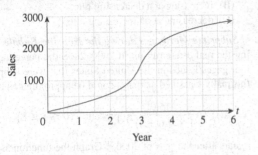

Year

a. When were the computers selling fastest?
b. Explain why this graph might look as it does. [HINT: See Example 4.]

75. *Industrial Output* The following graph shows the yearly industrial output (measured in billions of zonars) of the city-state of Utarek on Mars over a 7-year period:

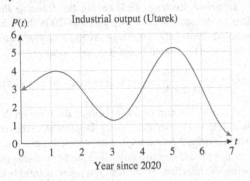

Industrial output (Utarek)

Year since 2020

a. When, to the nearest year, did the rate of change of yearly industrial output reach a maximum?
b. When, to the nearest year, did the rate of change of yearly industrial output reach a minimum?
c. When, to the nearest year, does the graph first change from concave down to concave up? The result tells you that
 (A) in that year the rate of change of industrial output reached a minimum compared with nearby years.
 (B) in that year the rate of change of industrial output reached a maximum compared with nearby years.

76. *Profits* The following graph shows the yearly profits of *Gigantic Conglomerate, Inc.* (GCI) from 2020 to 2035:

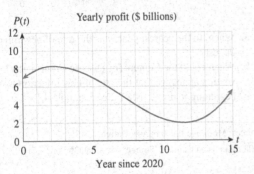

Yearly profit ($ billions)

Year since 2020

a. Approximately when were the profits rising most rapidly?
b. Approximately when were the profits falling most rapidly?
c. Approximately when could GCI's board of directors legitimately tell stockholders that they had "turned the company around"?

77. ▼ *Education and Crime* The following graph compares the total U.S. prison population and the average combined SAT score in the United States during the 1970s and 1980s:

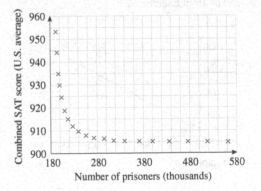

Number of prisoners (thousands)

These data can be accurately modeled by

$$S(n) = 904 + \frac{1{,}326}{(n - 180)^{1.325}} \quad (192 \le n \le 563).$$

Here, $S(n)$ is the combined U.S. average SAT score at a time when the total U.S. prison population was n thousand.[41]
a. Are there any points of inflection on the graph of S?
b. What does the concavity of the graph of S tell you about prison populations and SAT scores?

78. ▼ *Education and Crime* Refer back to the model in Exercise 77.
a. Are there any points of inflection on the graph of S'?
b. What does the concavity of the graph of S' tell you about prison populations and SAT scores?

79. ▼ *Patents* In 1965 the economist F. M. Scherer modeled the number, n, of patents produced by a firm as a function of the size, s, of the firm (measured in annual sales in millions of dollars). He came up with the following equation based on a study of 448 large firms:[42]

$$n = -3.79 + 144.42s - 23.86s^2 + 1.457s^3.$$

a. Find $\dfrac{d^2n}{ds^2}\Big|_{s=3}$. Is the rate at which patents are produced as the size of a firm goes up increasing or decreasing

---

[41] Based on data for the years 1967–1989. Sources: *Sourcebook of Criminal Justice Statistics*, 1990, p. 604/Educational Testing Service.

[42] Source: F. M. Scherer, "Firm Size, Market Structure, Opportunity, and the Output of Patented Inventions," *American Economic Review* 55 (December 1965): pp. 1097–1125.

with size when $s = 3$? Comment on Scherer's words, "... we find diminishing returns dominating."

b. Find $\left.\dfrac{d^2n}{ds^2}\right|_{s=7}$, and interpret the answer.

c. Find the s-coordinate of any points of inflection, and interpret the result.

80. ▽ *Returns on Investments* A company finds that the number of new products it develops per year depends on the size of its annual R&D budget, x (in thousands of dollars), according to the formula

$$n(x) = -1 + 8x + 2x^2 - 0.4x^3.$$

a. Find $n''(1)$ and $n''(3)$, and interpret the results.

b. Find the size of the budget that gives the largest rate of return as measured in new products per dollar (again, called the point of diminishing returns).

81. ▯▽ *Oil Imports from Mexico* Daily oil production in Mexico and daily U.S. oil imports from Mexico during 2009–2013 can be approximated by

$$P(t) = 3.1 - 0.014t \text{ million barrels} \quad (9 \le t \le 13)$$
$$I(t) = 1.7 - 0.063t \text{ million barrels} \quad (9 \le t \le 13),$$

where t is time in years since the start of 2000.[43]

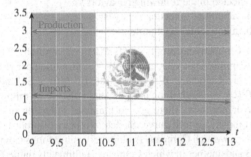

Graph the function $I(t)/P(t)$ and its derivative. Is the graph of $I(t)/P(t)$ concave up or concave down? The concavity of $I(t)/P(t)$ tells you that

(A) the percentage of oil produced in Mexico that was exported to the United States was decreasing.

(B) the percentage of oil produced in Mexico that was not exported to the United States was increasing.

(C) the percentage of oil produced in Mexico that was exported to the United States was decreasing at a slower rate.

(D) the percentage of oil produced in Mexico that was exported to the United States was decreasing at a faster rate.

82. ▯▽ *Oil Imports from Mexico* Repeat Exercise 81 using instead the models for 2000–2004 shown below:

$$P(t) = 3.0 + 0.13t \text{ million barrels} \quad (0 \le t \le 4)$$
$$I(t) = 1.4 + 0.06t \text{ million barrels} \quad (0 \le t \le 4).$$

(t is time in years since the start of 2000.)[44]

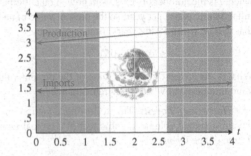

83. ◆ *Logistic Models* Let

$$f(x) = \frac{N}{1 + Ab^{-x}}$$

for constants N, A, and b (A and b positive and $b \ne 1$). Show that f has a single point of inflection at $x = \ln A / \ln b$.

84. ◆ *Logistic Models* Let

$$f(x) = \frac{N}{1 + Ae^{-kx}}$$

for constants N, A, and k (A and k positive). Show that f has a single point of inflection at $x = \ln A / k$.

85. ▯ *Population: Puerto Rico* The population of Puerto Rico in 1950–2025 can be approximated by

$$P(t) = \frac{4{,}500}{1 + 1.1466(1.0357)^{-t}} \text{ thousand people} \quad (0 \le t \le 75).$$

(t is the year since 1950.)[45] Use the result of Exercise 83 to find the location of the point of inflection in the graph of P. What does the result tell you about the population of Puerto Rico?

86. ▯ *Population: Virgin Islands* The population of the Virgin Islands in 1950–2025 can be approximated by

$$P(t) = \frac{110}{1 + 2.3596(1.0767)^{-t}} \text{ thousand people} \quad (0 \le t \le 75).$$

(t is the year since 1950.)[46] Use the result of Exercise 83 to find the location of the point of inflection in the graph of P. What does the result tell you about the population of the Virgin Islands?

---

[43] Source for data: Energy Information Administration (www.eia.doe.gov)/Pemex.

[44] *Ibid.*

[45] Figures from 2010 on are U.S. census projections. Source for data: The 2008 Statistical Abstract (www.census.gov).

[46] *Ibid.*

87. [T] ▼ *Asset Appreciation* You manage a small antique store that owns a collection of Louis XVI jewelry boxes. Their value v is increasing according to the formula

$$v = \frac{10,000}{1 + 500e^{-0.5t}},$$

where t is the number of years from now. You anticipate an inflation rate of 5% per year, so the present value of an item that will be worth $\$v$ in t years' time is given by

$$p = v \cdot (1.05)^{-t}.$$

What is the greatest rate of increase of the present value of your antiques, and when is this rate attained?

88. [T] ▼ *Harvesting Forests* The following equation models the approximate volume in cubic feet of a typical Douglas fir tree of age t years[47]:

$$V = \frac{22,514}{1 + 22,514t^{-2.55}}.$$

The lumber will be sold at $10 per cubic foot, and you do not expect the price of lumber to appreciate in the foreseeable future. On the other hand, you anticipate a general inflation rate of 5% per year, so the present value of an item that will be worth $\$v$ in t years' time is given by

$$p = v \cdot (1.05)^{-t}.$$

What is the largest rate of increase of the present value of a fir tree, and when is this rate attained?

89. [T] ▼ *Asset Appreciation* As the financial consultant to a classic auto dealership, you estimate that the total value of its collection of 1959 Chevrolets and Fords is given by the formula

$$v = 300,000 + 1,000t^2,$$

where t is the number of years from now. You anticipate a continuous inflation rate of 5% per year, so the discounted (present) value of an item that will be worth $\$v$ in t years' time is given by

$$p = ve^{-0.05t}.$$

When is the discounted value of the collection of classic cars increasing most rapidly? When is it decreasing most rapidly?

90. [T] ▼ *Plantation Management* The value of a fir tree in your plantation increases with the age of the tree according to the formula

$$v = \frac{20t}{1 + 0.05t},$$

where t is the age of the tree in years. Given a continuous inflation rate of 5% per year, the discounted (present) value of a newly planted seedling is

$$p = ve^{-0.05t}.$$

When is the discounted value of a tree increasing most rapidly? Decreasing most rapidly?

Communication and Reasoning Exercises

91. Complete the following: If the graph of a function is concave up on its entire domain, then its second derivative is _____ on the domain.

92. Complete the following: If the graph of a function is concave up on its entire domain, then its first derivative is _____ on the domain.

93. Daily sales of *Kent's Tents* reached a maximum in January 2002 and declined to a minimum in January 2003 before starting to climb again. The graph of daily sales shows a point of inflection at June 2002. What is the significance of the point of inflection?

94. The graph of daily sales of *Luddington's Wellington* boots is concave down, although sales continue to increase. What properties of the graph of daily sales versus time are reflected in the following behaviors?
a. a point of inflection next year
b. a horizontal asymptote

95. ▼ Company A's profits satisfy $P(0) = \$1$ million, $P'(0) = \$1$ million per year, and $P''(0) = -\$1$ million per year per year. Company B's profits satisfy $P(0) = \$1$ million, $P'(0) = -\$1$ million per year, and $P''(0) = \$1$ million per year per year. There are no points of inflection in either company's profit curve. Sketch two pairs of profit curves: one in which Company A ultimately outperforms Company B and another in which Company B ultimately outperforms Company A.

96. ▼ Company C's profits satisfy $P(0) = \$1$ million, $P'(0) = \$1$ million per year, and $P''(0) = -\$1$ million per year per year. Company D's profits satisfy $P(0) = \$0$ million, $P'(0) = \$0$ million per year, and $P''(0) = \$1$ million per year per year. There are no points of inflection in either company's profit curve. Sketch two pairs of profit curves: one in which Company C ultimately outperforms Company D and another in which Company D ultimately outperforms Company C.

97. ▼ Explain geometrically why the derivative of a function has a relative extremum at a point of inflection, if it is defined there. Which points of inflection give rise to relative maxima in the derivative?

98. ▼ If we regard position, s, as a function of time, t, what is the significance of the *third* derivative, $s'''(t)$? Describe an everyday scenario in which this arises.

---

[47] The model is the authors' and is based on data in *Environmental and Natural Resource Economics* by Tom Tietenberg, third edition (New York: HarperCollins, 1992), p. 282.

12.4 Analyzing Graphs

Mathematical curves are beautiful—their subtle form can be imitated by only the best of artists—and calculus gives us the tools we need to probe their secrets. While it is easy to use graphing technology to draw a graph, we must use calculus to understand what we are seeing. Following is a list of some of the most interesting features of the graph of a function.

Features of a Graph

1. ***The x- and y-intercepts:*** If $y = f(x)$, find the x-intercept(s) by setting $y = 0$ and solving for x; find the y-intercept by setting $x = 0$ and solving for y:

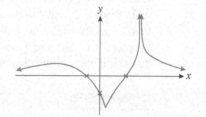

2. ***Extrema:*** Use the techniques of Section 12.1 to locate the maxima and minima:

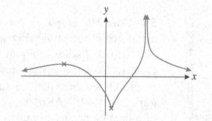

3. ***Points of inflection:*** Use the techniques of Section 12.2 to locate the points of inflection:

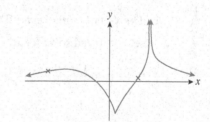

4. ***Behavior near singular points of f:*** If a is a singular point of f, consider $\lim_{x \to a^-} f(x)$ and $\lim_{x \to a^+} f(x)$ to see how the graph of f behaves as x approaches a:

* Recall from Section 10.2 that a is a singular point of f if $f(a)$ is not defined, but $f(x)$ is defined for (at least some) points arbitrarily close to and on both sides of a.

5. *Behavior at infinity:* Consider $\lim_{x \to -\infty} f(x)$ and $\lim_{x \to +\infty} f(x)$ if appropriate, to see how the graph of f behaves far to the left and right:

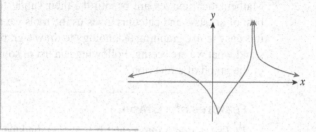

Note It is sometimes difficult or impossible to solve all of the equations that come up in Steps 1, 2, and 3 of the above analysis. As a consequence, we might not be able to say exactly where the x-intercept, extrema, or points of inflection are. When this happens, we will use graphing technology to assist us in determining accurate numerical approximations. ■

EXAMPLE 1   **Analyzing a Graph**

Analyze the graph of $f(x) = \dfrac{1}{x} - \dfrac{1}{x^2}$.

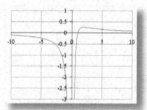
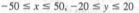

$-50 \le x \le 50, -20 \le y \le 20$

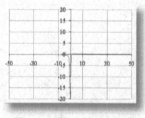
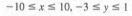

$-10 \le x \le 10, -3 \le y \le 1$

Figure 35

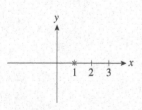

Figure 36

Solution The graph, as drawn using graphing technology, is shown in Figure 35, using two different viewing windows. (Note that $x = 0$ is not in the domain of f.) The second window in Figure 35 seems to show the features of the graph better than the first. Does the second viewing window include *all* the interesting features of the graph? Or are there perhaps some interesting features to the right of $x = 10$ or to the left of $x = -10$? Also, where exactly do features like maxima, minima, and points of inflection occur? In our five-step process of analyzing the interesting features of the graph, we will be able to sketch the curve by hand, and also answer these questions.

1. *The x- and y-intercepts:* We consider $y = \dfrac{1}{x} - \dfrac{1}{x^2}$. To find the x-intercept(s), we set $y = 0$ and solve for x:

$$0 = \frac{1}{x} - \frac{1}{x^2}$$

$$\frac{1}{x} = \frac{1}{x^2}.$$

Multiplying both sides by x^2 (we know that x cannot be zero, so we are not multiplying both sides by 0) gives

$$x = 1.$$

Thus, there is one x-intercept (which we can see in Figure 35): at $x = 1$.

For the y-intercept we would substitute $x = 0$ and solve for y. However, we cannot substitute $x = 0$; because $f(0)$ is not defined, the graph does not meet the y-axis.

We add features to our freehand sketch as we go. Figure 36 shows what we have so far.

2. **Relative extrema:** We calculate $f'(x) = -\dfrac{1}{x^2} + \dfrac{2}{x^3}$. To find any stationary points, we set the derivative equal to 0 and solve for x:

$$-\frac{1}{x^2} + \frac{2}{x^3} = 0$$

$$\frac{1}{x^2} = \frac{2}{x^3}$$

$$x = 2.$$

Thus, there is one stationary point: at $x = 2$. We can use a test point to the right to determine that this stationary point is a relative maximum:

x	1 (Intercept)	2	3 (Test point)
$y = \dfrac{1}{x} - \dfrac{1}{x^2}$	0	$\dfrac{1}{4}$	$\dfrac{2}{9}$

* Recall from Section 12.1 that a is a singular point of f' if a is an interior point of the domain of f where the derivative $f'(a)$ is not defined. (Note the distinction from a singular point of f above.)

The only possible singular point of f'* is at 0 because $f'(0)$ is not defined. However, $f(0)$ is not defined either, so there are no singular points. Figure 37 shows our graph so far.

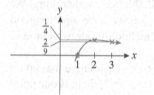

Figure 37

3. **Points of inflection:** We calculate $f''(x) = \dfrac{2}{x^3} - \dfrac{6}{x^4}$. To find points of inflection, we set the second derivative equal to 0 and solve for x:

$$\frac{2}{x^3} - \frac{6}{x^4} = 0$$

$$\frac{2}{x^3} = \frac{6}{x^4}$$

$$2x = 6$$

$$x = 3.$$

Figure 35 confirms that the graph of f changes from being concave down to being concave up at $x = 3$, so this is a point of inflection. $f''(x)$ is not defined at $x = 0$, but that is not in the domain, so there are no other points of inflection. In particular, the graph must be concave down in the whole region $(-\infty, 0)$, as we can see by calculating the second derivative at any one point in that interval: $f''(-1) = -8 < 0$. Figure 38 shows our graph so far. (We extended the curve near $x = 3$ to suggest a point of inflection at $x = 3$.)

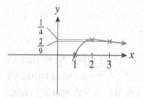

Figure 38

4. **Behavior near singular points of f:** The only singular point of f occurs at $x = 0$. From the graph, $f(x)$ appears to go to $-\infty$ as x approaches 0 from either side. To calculate these limits, we rewrite $f(x)$:

$$f(x) = \frac{1}{x} - \frac{1}{x^2} = \frac{x-1}{x^2}.$$

Now, if x is close to 0 (on either side), the numerator $x - 1$ is close to -1, and the denominator is a very small but positive number. The quotient is therefore a negative number of very large magnitude. Therefore,

$$\lim_{x \to 0^-} f(x) = -\infty$$

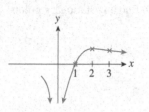

Figure 39

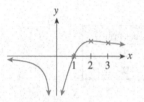

Figure 40

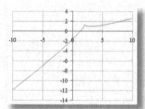

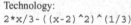

Technology:
2*x/3-((x-2)^2)^(1/3)

Figure 41

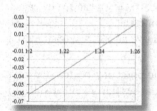

Figure 42

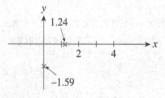

Figure 43

and

$$\lim_{x \to 0^+} f(x) = -\infty.$$

From these limits, we see the following:

(1) Immediately to the *left* of $x = 0$, the graph plunges down toward $-\infty$.

(2) Immediately to the *right* of $x = 0$, the graph also plunges down toward $-\infty$.

Figure 39 shows our graph with these features added. We say that f has a **vertical asymptote** at $x = 0$, meaning that the points on the graph of f get closer and closer to points on a vertical line (the y-axis in this case) farther and farther from the origin.

5. *Behavior at infinity:* Both $1/x$ and $1/x^2$ go to 0 as x goes to $-\infty$ or $+\infty$; that is,

$$\lim_{x \to -\infty} f(x) = 0$$

and

$$\lim_{x \to +\infty} f(x) = 0.$$

Thus, on the extreme left and right of our picture, the height of the curve levels off toward zero. Figure 40 shows the completed freehand sketch of the graph.

We say that f has a **horizontal asymptote** at $y = 0$. (Notice another thing: We haven't plotted a single point to the left of the y-axis, yet we have a pretty good idea of what the curve looks like there! Compare the technology-drawn curve in Figure 35.)

In summary, there is one x-intercept at $x = 1$; there is one relative maximum (which, we can now see, is also an absolute maximum) at $x = 2$; there is one point of inflection at $x = 3$, where the graph changes from being concave down to concave up. There is a vertical asymptote at $x = 0$, on both sides of which the graph goes down toward $-\infty$, and a horizontal asymptote at $y = 0$.

EXAMPLE 2 **Analyzing a Graph**

Analyze the graph of $f(x) = \dfrac{2x}{3} - (x - 2)^{2/3}$.

Solution Figure 41 shows a technology-generated version of the graph. Note that in the technology formulation, $(x - 2)^{2/3}$ is written as $[(x - 2)^2]^{1/3}$ to avoid problems with some graphing calculators and Excel. Let us now re-create this graph by hand and, in the process, identify the features we see in Figure 41.

1. *The x- and y-intercepts:* We consider $y = \dfrac{2x}{3} - (x - 2)^{2/3}$. For the y-intercept we set $x = 0$ and solve for y:

$$y = \frac{2(0)}{3} - (0 - 2)^{2/3} = -2^{2/3} \approx -1.59.$$

To find the x-intercept(s), we set $y = 0$ and solve for x. However, if we attempt this, we will find ourselves with a cubic equation that is hard to solve. (Try it!) Following the advice in the note preceding Example 1, we use graphing technology to locate the x-intercept we see in Figure 41 by zooming in (Figure 42). From Figure 42 we find $x \approx 1.24$. We shall see in the discussion to follow that there can be no other x-intercepts.

Figure 43 shows our freehand sketch so far.

2. **Relative extrema:** We calculate

$$f'(x) = \frac{2}{3} - \frac{2}{3}(x-2)^{-1/3}$$

$$= \frac{2}{3} - \frac{2}{3(x-2)^{1/3}}.$$

To find any stationary points, we set the derivative equal to 0 and solve for x:

$$\frac{2}{3} - \frac{2}{3(x-2)^{1/3}} = 0$$

$$(x-2)^{1/3} = 1$$

$$x - 2 = 1^3 = 1$$

$$x = 3.$$

To check for singular points, look for points where $f(x)$ is defined and $f'(x)$ is not defined. The only such point is $x = 2$: $f'(x)$ is not defined at $x = 2$, whereas $f(x)$ is defined there, so we have a singular point at $x = 2$.

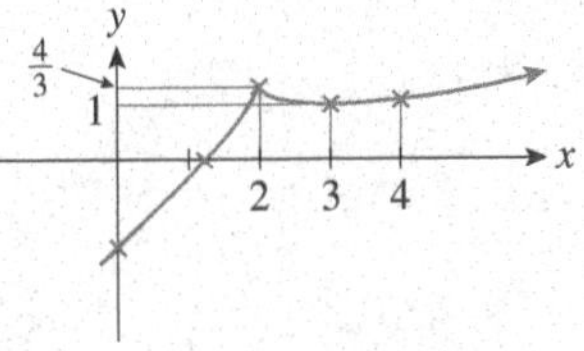

x	2 (Singular point)	3 (Stationary point)	4 (Test point)
$y = \dfrac{2x}{3} - (x-2)^{2/3}$	$\dfrac{4}{3}$	1	1.079

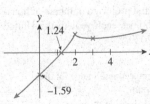

Figure 44

Figure 44 shows our graph so far.

We see that there is a singular relative maximum at $(2, 4/3)$ (we will confirm that the graph eventually gets higher on the right) and a stationary relative minimum at $x = 3$.

3. **Points of inflection:** We calculate

$$f''(x) = \frac{2}{9(x-2)^{4/3}}.$$

To find points of inflection, we set the second derivative equal to 0 and solve for x. But the equation

$$0 = \frac{2}{9(x-2)^{4/3}}$$

has no solution for x, so there are no points of inflection on the graph.

4. **Behavior near points where f is not defined:** Because $f(x)$ is defined everywhere, there are no such points to consider. In particular, there are no vertical asymptotes.

5. **Behavior at infinity:** We estimate the following limits numerically:

$$\lim_{x \to -\infty} \left[\frac{2x}{3} - (x-2)^{2/3} \right] = -\infty$$

and

$$\lim_{x \to +\infty} \left[\frac{2x}{3} - (x-2)^{2/3} \right] = +\infty.$$

Thus, on the extreme left the curve goes down toward $-\infty$, and on the extreme right the curve rises toward $+\infty$. In particular, there are no horizontal asymptotes. (There can also be no other x-intercepts.)

Figure 45 shows the completed graph.

Figure 45

12.4 EXERCISES

▼ more advanced ◆ challenging
▓ indicates exercises that should be solved using technology

In Exercises 1–26, sketch the graph of the given function, indicating (a) x- and y-intercepts, (b) extrema, (c) points of inflection, (d) behavior near singular points of f, and (e) behavior at infinity. Where indicated, technology should be used to approximate the intercepts, coordinates of extrema, and/or points of inflection to one decimal place. Check your sketch using technology. [HINT: See Example 1.]

1. $f(x) = x^2 + 2x + 1$

2. $f(x) = -x^2 - 2x - 1$

3. $g(x) = x^3 - 12x$, domain $[-4, 4]$

4. $g(x) = 2x^3 - 6x$, domain $[-4, 4]$

5. $h(x) = 2x^3 - 3x^2 - 36x$ [Use technology for x-intercepts.]

6. $h(x) = -2x^3 - 3x^2 + 36x$ [Use technology for x-intercepts.]

7. $f(x) = 2x^3 + 3x^2 - 12x + 1$ [Use technology for x-intercepts.]

8. $f(x) = 4x^3 + 3x^2 + 2$ [Use technology for x-intercepts.]

9. $k(x) = -3x^4 + 4x^3 + 36x^2 + 10$ [Use technology for x-intercepts.]

10. $k(x) = 3x^4 + 4x^3 - 36x^2 - 10$ [Use technology for x-intercepts.]

11. $g(t) = \dfrac{1}{4}t^4 - \dfrac{2}{3}t^3 + \dfrac{1}{2}t^2$

12. $g(t) = 3t^4 - 16t^3 + 24t^2 + 1$

13. $f(x) = x + \dfrac{1}{x}$

14. $f(x) = x^2 + \dfrac{1}{x^2}$

15. $g(x) = x^3/(x^2 + 3)$

16. $g(x) = x^3/(x^2 - 3)$

17. $f(t) = \dfrac{t^2 + 1}{t^2 - 1}$, domain $[-2, 2]$, $t \neq \pm 1$

18. $f(t) = \dfrac{t^2 - 1}{t^2 + 1}$, domain $[-2, 2]$

19. $k(x) = \dfrac{2x}{3} + (x + 1)^{2/3}$ [Use technology for x-intercepts.]

[HINT: See Example 2.]

20. $k(x) = \dfrac{2x}{5} - (x - 1)^{2/5}$ [Use technology for x-intercepts.]

[HINT: See Example 2.]

21. $f(x) = x - \ln x$, domain $(0, +\infty)$

22. $f(x) = x - \ln x^2$, domain $(0, +\infty)$

23. $f(x) = x^2 + \ln x^2$ [Use technology for x-intercepts.]

24. $f(x) = 2x^2 + \ln x$ [Use technology for x-intercepts.]

25. $g(t) = e^t - t$, domain $[-1, 1]$

26. $g(t) = e^{-t^2}$

▓ In Exercises 27–30, use technology to sketch the graph of the given function, labeling all relative and absolute extrema and points of inflection, and vertical and horizontal asymptotes. The coordinates of the extrema and points of inflection should be accurate to two decimal places. [HINT: To locate extrema accurately, plot the first derivative; to locate points of inflection accurately, plot the second derivative.]

27. ▼ $f(x) = x^4 - 2x^3 + x^2 - 2x + 1$

28. ▼ $f(x) = x^4 + x^3 + x^2 + x + 1$

29. ▼ $f(x) = e^x - x^3$

30. ▼ $f(x) = e^x - \dfrac{x^4}{4}$

Applications

31. **Home Prices** The following graph shows a rough approximation of historical and projected median home prices in the United States for the period 2000–2024:[48]

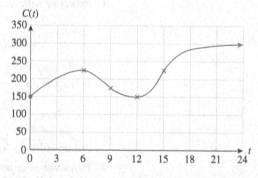

Here, t is time in years since the start of 2000, and $C(t)$ is the median home price in thousands of dollars. The locations of stationary points and points of inflection are indicated on the graph. Analyze the graph's important features, and interpret each feature in terms of the median home price.

32. **Housing Starts** The following graph shows a rough approximation of historical and projected numbers of housing starts of single-family homes each year in the United States for the period 2000–2020:[49]

---

[48] Values from 2015 on are authors' projections. Source for data through 2014: Zillow (www.zillow.com).
[49] Values from 2015 on are authors' projections. Source for data through 2014: U.S. Census Bureau (www.census.gov).

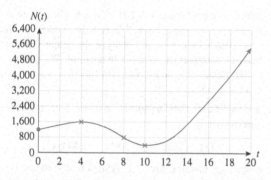

Here, t is time in years since 2000, and $N(t)$ is the number, in thousands, of housing starts per year. The locations of stationary points and points of inflection are indicated on the graph. Analyze the graph's important features, and interpret each feature in terms of the number of housing starts.

33. End of the Earth In 5 billion years the Sun will have run out of hydrogen fuel and will begin to expand into a red giant, eventually engulfing the Earth and causing it to spiral into the core of the Sun 7.5 billion years from now. The following graph shows the radius of the Earth's orbit around the Sun during its final five and a half million years. ($t = 6$ marks the end of the red giant expansion phase of the Sun.)[50]

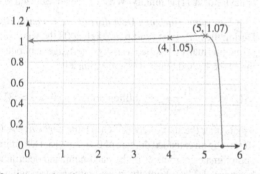

In the graph, r is in AU (astronomical units; 1 AU equals the current radius of the Earth's orbit, around 93 million miles), t is time in millions of years, and the locations of stationary points and points of inflection are indicated.
a. Analyze the graph's important features.
b. Select the correct answers: During the period $4 < t < 5$, the Earth's orbital radius will (increase/ decrease/increase and then decrease), and its rate of change will (increase/decrease/increase and then decrease).

34. Loss of Odyssia The following graph shows the radius of the planet Odyssia's orbit around the star Laertes during its first five and a half million years of existence, before it was flung out of orbit by a passing planetoid and doomed to wander the galaxy forever:[51]

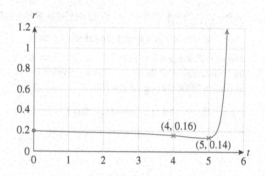

In the graph, r is in LU (Laertian units; 1 LU equals the current radius of the gas giant Pankratia, another planet orbiting Laertes, around 150 million miles), t is time in millions of years, and the locations of stationary points and points of inflection are indicated.
a. Analyze the graph's important features.
b. Select the correct answers: During the period $4 < t < 5$, Odyssia's orbital radius was (increasing/ decreasing/increasing and then decreasing), and its rate of change was (increasing/decreasing/increasing and then decreasing).

35. Consumer Price Index The following graph shows the approximate value of the U.S. Consumer Price Index (CPI) from July 2005 through March 2006:[52]

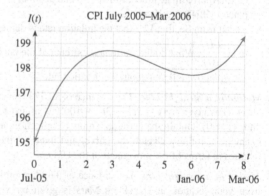

The approximating curve shown on the figure is given by

$$I(t) = 0.06t^3 - 0.8t^2 + 3.1t + 195 \quad (0 \le t \le 8),$$

where t is time in months. ($t = 0$ represents July 2005.)

---

[50] Based on estimates in "Distant future of the Sun and Earth revisited" by K-P Schröder and Robert Cannon Smith, *Monthly Notices of the Royal Astronomical Society* **386** (1): 155–163.

[51] Fictitious.

[52] The CPI is compiled by the Bureau of Labor Statistics and is based upon a 1982 value of 100. For instance, a CPI of 200 means the CPI has doubled since 1982. Source: InflationData.com (www.inflationdata.com).

a. Locate the intercepts, extrema, and points of inflection of the curve, and interpret each feature in terms of the CPI. (Approximate all coordinates to one decimal place.) [HINT: See Example 1.]

b. Recall from Section 12.2 that the inflation rate is defined to be $\dfrac{I'(t)}{I(t)}$. What do the stationary extrema of the curve shown above tell you about the inflation rate?

36. Consumer Price Index The following graph shows the approximate value of the U.S. Consumer Price Index (CPI) from March 2006 through May 2007:[53]

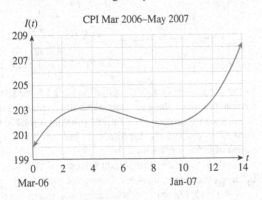

CPI Mar 2006–May 2007

The approximating curve shown on the figure is given by

$$I(t) = 0.02t^3 - 0.38t^2 + 2t + 200 \quad (0 \le t \le 14),$$

where t is time in months. ($t = 0$ represents March 2006.)

a. Locate the intercepts, extrema, and points of inflection of the curve, and interpret each feature in terms of the CPI. (Approximate all coordinates to one decimal place.) [HINT: See Example 1.]

b. Recall from Section 12.2 that the inflation rate is defined to be $\dfrac{I'(t)}{I(t)}$. What do the stationary extrema of the curve shown above tell you about the inflation rate?

37. Motion in a Straight Line The distance of a UFO from an observer is given by $s = 2t^3 - 3t^2 + 100$ feet after t seconds ($t \ge 0$). Obtain the extrema, points of inflection, and behavior at infinity. Sketch the curve, and interpret these features in terms of the movement of the UFO.

38. Motion in a Straight Line The distance of the Mars orbiter from your location in Utarek on Mars is given by $s = 2(t - 1)^3 - 3(t - 1)^2 + 100$ kilometers after t seconds ($t \ge 0$). Obtain the extrema, points of inflection, and behavior at infinity. Sketch the curve, and interpret these features in terms of the movement of the Mars orbiter.

39. Average Cost: iPhones Assume that it costs Apple approximately

$$C(x) = 400,000 + 160x + 0.001x^2$$

dollars to manufacture x 32GB iPhone 6's in an hour at the Foxconn Technology Group.[54] Obtain the average cost function, sketch its graph, and analyze the graph's important features. Interpret each feature in terms of iPhone 6's. [HINT: Recall that the average cost function is $\overline{C}(x) = C(x)/x$.]

40. Average Cost: PlayStation 4's Assume that it costs Sony approximately

$$C(x) = 800,000 + 340x + 0.0005x^2$$

dollars to manufacture x PlayStation 4's in an hour.[55] Obtain the average cost function, sketch its graph, and analyze the graph's important features. Interpret each feature in terms of PlayStation 4's. [HINT: Recall that the average cost function is $\overline{C}(x) = C(x)/x$.]

41. ⓘ▼ **Subprime Mortgages during the Housing Bubble** During the real estate run-up in 2000–2008 the percentage of mortgages issued in the United States that were subprime (normally classified as risky) could be approximated by

$$A(t) = \frac{15.0}{1 + 8.6(1.8)^{-t}} \text{ percent } \quad (0 \le t \le 8)$$

t years after the start of 2000.[56] Graph the *derivative* $A'(t)$ of $A(t)$ using an extended domain of $0 \le t \le 15$. Determine the approximate coordinates of the maximum, and determine the behavior of $A'(t)$ at infinity. What do the answers tell you?

42. ⓘ▼ **Subprime Mortgage Debt during the Housing Bubble** During the real estate run-up in 2000–2008 the value of subprime (normally classified as risky) mortgage debt outstanding in the United States was approximately

$$A(t) = \frac{1,350}{1 + 4.2(1.7)^{-t}} \text{ billion dollars } \quad (0 \le t \le 8)$$

t years after the start of 2000.[57] Graph the *derivative* $A'(t)$ of $A(t)$ using an extended domain of $0 \le t \le 15$. Determine the approximate coordinates of the maximum, and determine the behavior of $A'(t)$ at infinity. What do the answers tell you?

Communication and Reasoning Exercises

43. A function is *bounded* if its entire graph lies between two horizontal lines. Can a bounded function have vertical

---

[53] See footnote for Exercise 35.

[54] Not the actual cost equation; the authors do not know Apple's actual cost equation. The minimum average cost in the model given is in rough agreement with the actual for one of the 2014 models. Source for cost data: http://time.com.

[55] Not the actual cost equation; the authors do not know Sony's actual cost equation. The minimum average cost in the model given is in rough agreement with the actual cost to manufacture a PlayStation 4 in 2013. Source for estimate of marginal cost: VentureBeat (http://venturebeat.com).

[56] 2009 figure is an estimate. Sources: Mortgage Bankers Association, UBS.

[57] 2008–2009 figures are estimates. Source: www.data360.org.

43. asymptotes? Can a bounded function have horizontal asymptotes? Explain.

44. A function is *bounded above* if its entire graph lies below some horizontal line. Can a bounded above function have vertical asymptotes? Can a bounded above function have horizontal asymptotes? Explain.

45. If the graph of a function has a vertical asymptote at $x = a$ in such a way that y increases to $+\infty$ as $x \to a$, what can you say about the graph of its derivative? Explain.

46. If the graph of a function has a horizontal asymptote at $y = a$ in such a way that y decreases to a as $x \to +\infty$, what can you say about the graph of its derivative? Explain.

47. Your friend tells you that he has found a continuous function defined on $(-\infty, +\infty)$ with exactly two critical points, each of which is a relative maximum. Can he be right?

48. Your other friend tells you that she has found a continuous function with two critical points, one a relative minimum and one a relative maximum, and no point of inflection between them. Can she be right?

49. ▼ By thinking about extrema, show that, if $f(x)$ is a polynomial, then between every pair of zeros (x-intercepts) of $f(x)$ there is a zero of $f'(x)$.

50. ▼ If $f(x)$ is a polynomial of degree 2 or higher, show that between every pair of relative extrema of $f(x)$ there is a point of inflection of $f(x)$.

12.5 Related Rates

We start by recalling some basic facts about the rate of change of a quantity.

> **Rate of Change of Q**
>
> If Q is a quantity changing over time t, then the derivative dQ/dt is the rate at which Q changes over time.
>
> **Quick Examples**
>
> 1. If A is the area of an expanding circle, then dA/dt is the rate at which the area is increasing.
> 2. *Words:* The radius r of a sphere is currently 3 cm and increasing at a rate of 2 cm/sec.
>   *Symbols:* $r = 3$ cm and $dr/dt = 2$ cm/sec.

In this section we are concerned with what are called **related rates** problems. In such a problem we have two (sometimes more) related quantities, we know the rate at which one is changing, and we wish to find the rate at which another is changing. A typical example is the following.

EXAMPLE 1   The Expanding Circle

The radius of a circle is increasing at a rate of 10 cm/sec. How fast is the area increasing at the instant when the radius has reached 5 cm?

Solution We have two related quantities: the radius of the circle, r, and its area, A. The first sentence of the problem tells us that r is increasing at a certain rate. When we see a sentence referring to speed or change, it is very helpful to rephrase the sentence using the phrase "the rate of change of." Here, we can say

The rate of change of r is 10 cm/sec.

Because the rate of change is the derivative, we can rewrite this sentence as the equation

$$\frac{dr}{dt} = 10.$$

Similarly, the second sentence of the problem asks how fast A is changing. We can rewrite that question:

What is the rate of change of A when the radius is 5 cm?

Using mathematical notation, the question is

What is $\dfrac{dA}{dt}$ *when* $r = 5$?

Thus, knowing one rate of change, dr/dt, we wish to find a related rate of change, dA/dt. To find exactly how these derivatives are related, we need the equation relating the variables, which is

$$A = \pi r^2.$$

To find the relationship between the derivatives, we take the derivative of both sides of this equation *with respect to t.* On the left we get dA/dt. On the right we need to remember that r is a function of t and use the chain rule. We get

$$\frac{dA}{dt} = 2\pi r \frac{dr}{dt}.$$

Now we substitute the given values $r = 5$ and $dr/dt = 10$. This gives

$$\frac{dA}{dt}\bigg|_{r=5} = 2\pi(5)(10) = 100\pi \approx 314 \text{ cm}^2/\text{sec}.$$

Thus, the area is increasing at the rate of 314 cm²/sec when the radius is 5 cm.

We can organize our work as follows.

Solving a Related Rates Problem

A. The Problem

   1. List the related, changing quantities.

   2. Restate the problem in terms of rates of change. Rewrite the problem using mathematical notation for the changing quantities and their derivatives.

B. The Relationship

   1. Draw a diagram, if appropriate, showing the changing quantities.

   2. Find an equation or equations relating the changing quantities.

   3. Take the derivative with respect to time of the equation(s) relating the quantities to get the **derived equation(s)**, which relate the rates of change of the quantities.

C. The Solution

   1. Substitute into the derived equation(s) the given values of the quantities and their derivatives.

   2. Solve for the derivative required.

We can illustrate the procedure with the "ladder problem" that is found in almost every calculus textbook.

EXAMPLE 2   **The Falling Ladder**

Jane is at the top of a 5-foot ladder when it starts to slide down the wall at a rate of 3 feet per minute. Jack is standing on the ground behind her. How fast is the base of the ladder moving when it hits him if Jane is 4 feet from the ground at that instant?

Solution The first sentence talks about (the top of) the ladder sliding down the wall. Thus, one of the changing quantities is the height of the top of the ladder. The question asked refers to the motion of the base of the ladder, so another changing quantity is the distance of the base of the ladder from the wall. Let's record these variables and follow the outline above to obtain the solution.

A. The Problem

1. The changing quantities are

$$h = \text{height of the top of the ladder}$$
$$b = \text{distance of the base of the ladder from the wall.}$$

2. We rephrase the problem in words, using the phrase "rate of change":

The rate of change of the height of the top of the ladder is −3 feet per minute. What is the rate of change of the distance of the base from the wall when the top of the ladder is 4 feet from the ground?

We can now rewrite the problem mathematically:

$$\frac{dh}{dt} = -3. \text{ Find } \frac{db}{dt} \text{ when } h = 4.$$

B. The Relationship

Figure 46

1. Figure 46 shows the ladder and the variables h and b. Notice that we put in the figure the fixed length, 5, of the ladder, but any changing quantities, such as h and b, we leave as variables. We shall not use any specific values for h or b until the very end.

2. From the figure, we can see that h and b are related by the Pythagorean theorem:

$$h^2 + b^2 = 25.$$

3. Taking the derivative with respect to time of the equation above gives us the derived equation:

$$2h\frac{dh}{dt} + 2b\frac{db}{dt} = 0.$$

C. The Solution

1. We substitute the known values $dh/dt = -3$ and $h = 4$ into the derived equation:

$$2(4)(-3) + 2b\frac{db}{dt} = 0.$$

We would like to solve for db/dt, but first we need the value of b, which we can determine from the equation $h^2 + b^2 = 25$, using the value $h = 4$:

$$16 + b^2 = 25$$
$$b^2 = 9$$
$$b = 3. \quad \text{We reject the negative value because } b \text{ is a distance.}$$

Substituting into the derived equation, we get

$$-24 + 2(3)\frac{db}{dt} = 0.$$

2. Solving for db/dt gives

$$\frac{db}{dt} = \frac{24}{6} = 4.$$

Thus, the base of the ladder is sliding away from the wall at 4 feet per minute when it hits Jack.

EXAMPLE 3   Average Cost

The cost to manufacture x cellphones in a day is

$$C(x) = 10{,}000 + 20x + \frac{x^2}{10{,}000} \text{ dollars.}$$

The daily production level is currently $x = 5{,}000$ cellphones and is increasing at a rate of 100 units per day. How fast is the average cost changing?

Solution

A. The Problem

1. The changing quantities are the production level x and the average cost, $\overline{C}$.

2. We rephrase the problem as follows:

The daily production level is $x = 5{,}000$ units, and the rate of change of x is 100 units per day. What is the rate of change of the average cost, $\overline{C}$?

In mathematical notation,

$$x = 5{,}000 \text{ and } \frac{dx}{dt} = 100. \text{ Find } \frac{d\overline{C}}{dt}.$$

B. The Relationship

1. In this example the changing quantities cannot easily be depicted geometrically.

2. We are given a formula for the *total* cost. We get the *average* cost by dividing the total cost by x:

$$\overline{C} = \frac{C}{x}.$$

So

$$\overline{C} = \frac{10{,}000}{x} + 20 + \frac{x}{10{,}000}.$$

3. Taking derivatives with respect to t of both sides, we get the derived equation:

$$\frac{d\overline{C}}{dt} = \left(-\frac{10{,}000}{x^2} + \frac{1}{10{,}000}\right)\frac{dx}{dt}.$$

C. The Solution

Substituting the values from part A into the derived equation, we get

$$\frac{d\overline{C}}{dt} = \left(-\frac{10{,}000}{5{,}000^2} + \frac{1}{10{,}000}\right)100$$

$$= -0.03 \text{ dollars per day.}$$

Thus, the average cost is decreasing by 3¢ per day.

The scenario in the following example is similar to Example 5 in Section 12.2.

EXAMPLE 4 **Allocation of Labor**

The Gym Sock Company manufactures cotton athletic socks. Production is partially automated through the use of robots. The number of pairs of socks the company can manufacture in a day is given by a Cobb-Douglas production formula:

$$q = 50n^{0.6}r^{0.4},$$

where q is the number of pairs of socks that can be manufactured by n laborers and r robots. The company currently produces 1,000 pairs of socks each day and employs 20 laborers. It is bringing one new robot on line every month. At what rate are laborers being laid off, assuming that the number of socks produced remains constant?

Solution

A. The Problem

1. The changing quantities are the number of laborers n and the number of robots r.

2. $\dfrac{dr}{dt} = 1$. Find $\dfrac{dn}{dt}$ when $n = 20$.

B. The Relationship

1. No diagram is appropriate here.

2. The equation relating the changing quantities:

$$1,000 = 50n^{0.6}r^{0.4} \qquad \text{Productivity is constant at 1,000 pairs of socks each day.}$$

or

$$20 = n^{0.6}r^{0.4}.$$

3. The derived equation is

$$0 = 0.6n^{-0.4}\left(\frac{dn}{dt}\right)r^{0.4} + 0.4n^{0.6}r^{-0.6}\left(\frac{dr}{dt}\right)$$

$$= 0.6\left(\frac{r}{n}\right)^{0.4}\left(\frac{dn}{dt}\right) + 0.4\left(\frac{n}{r}\right)^{0.6}\left(\frac{dr}{dt}\right).$$

We solve this equation for dn/dt because we shall want to find dn/dt below and because the equation becomes simpler when we do this:

$$0.6\left(\frac{r}{n}\right)^{0.4}\left(\frac{dn}{dt}\right) = -0.4\left(\frac{n}{r}\right)^{0.6}\left(\frac{dr}{dt}\right)$$

$$\frac{dn}{dt} = -\frac{0.4}{0.6}\left(\frac{n}{r}\right)^{0.6}\left(\frac{n}{r}\right)^{0.4}\left(\frac{dr}{dt}\right)$$

$$= -\frac{2}{3}\left(\frac{n}{r}\right)\left(\frac{dr}{dt}\right).$$

C. The Solution

Substituting the numbers in part A into the last equation in part B, we get

$$\frac{dn}{dt} = -\frac{2}{3}\left(\frac{20}{r}\right)(1).$$

We need to compute r by substituting the known value of n in the original formula:

$$20 = n^{0.6} r^{0.4}$$
$$20 = 20^{0.6} r^{0.4}$$
$$r^{0.4} = \frac{20}{20^{0.6}} = 20^{0.4}$$
$$r = 20.$$

Thus,

$$\frac{dn}{dt} = -\frac{2}{3}\left(\frac{20}{20}\right)(1) = -\frac{2}{3} \text{ laborers per month.}$$

The company is laying off laborers at a rate of 2/3 per month, or two every three months.

We can interpret this result as saying that, at the current level of production and number of laborers, one robot is as productive as 2/3 of a laborer, or 3 robots are as productive as 2 laborers.

12.5　EXERCISES

▼ more advanced　　◆ challenging
ⅈ indicates exercises that should be solved using technology

Rewrite the statements and questions in Exercises 1–8 in mathematical notation. [HINT: See Quick Examples 1 and 2.]

1. The population P is currently 10,000 and growing at a rate of 1,000 per year.

2. There are currently 400 cases of Bangkok flu, and the number is growing by 30 new cases every month.

3. The annual revenue of your tie-dyed T-shirt operation is currently $7,000 but is decreasing by $700 each year. How fast are annual sales changing?

4. A ladder is sliding down a wall so that the distance between the top of the ladder and the floor is decreasing at a rate of 3 ft/sec. How fast is the base of the ladder receding from the wall?

5. The price of shoes is rising $5 per year. How fast is the demand changing?

6. Stock prices are rising $1,000 per year. How fast is the value of your portfolio increasing?

7. The average global temperature is 60°F and rising by 0.01°F per year. How fast are annual sales of Bermuda shorts increasing?

8. The country's population is now 260,000,000 and is increasing by 1,000,000 people per year. How fast is the annual demand for diapers increasing?

Applications

9. *Sunspots* The area of a circular sunspot is growing at a rate of 1,200 km²/sec.
   a. How fast is the radius growing at the instant when it equals 10,000 kilometers? [HINT: See Example 1.]
   b. How fast is the radius growing at the instant when the sunspot has an area of 640,000 square kilometers? [HINT: Use the area formula to determine the radius at that instant.]

10. *Puddles* The radius of a circular puddle is growing at a rate of 5 cm/sec.
    a. How fast is its area growing at the instant when the radius is 10 centimeters? [HINT: See Example 1.]
    b. How fast is the area growing at the instant when it equals 36 square centimeters? [HINT: Use the area formula to determine the radius at that instant.]

11. *Balloons* A spherical party balloon is being inflated with helium pumped in at a rate of 3 ft³/min. How fast is the radius growing at the instant when the radius has reached 1 foot? [HINT: See Example 1. (The volume of a sphere of radius r is $V = \frac{4}{3}\pi r^3$.)]

12. *More Balloons* A rather flimsy spherical balloon is designed to pop at the instant its radius has reached 10 centimeters. Assuming that the balloon is filled with helium at a rate of 10 cm³/sec, calculate how fast the radius is growing at the instant it pops. [HINT: See Example 1. (The volume of a sphere of radius r is $V = \frac{4}{3}\pi r^3$.)]

13. End of the Earth In 5 billion years the Sun will have run out of hydrogen fuel and begin to expand into a red giant, eventually engulfing the Earth and causing it to spiral into the core of the Sun 7.5 billion years from now. At that point, the Sun's radius will be around 93 million miles and increasing at a rate of around 0.003 mph.[58] How fast will its volume be increasing? (Round your answer to three significant digits.) [HINT: See the hint for Exercise 11.]

14. End of Venus (Refer to Exercise 13.) When the Sun engulfs Venus shortly before engulfing the Earth, the Sun's radius will be around 67 million miles and increasing at a rate of around 0.002 mph.[59] How fast will its volume be increasing? (Round your answer to three significant digits.) [HINT: See the hint for Exercise 11.]

15. Sliding Ladders The base of a 50-foot ladder is being pulled away from a wall at a rate of 10 ft/sec. How fast is the top of the ladder sliding down the wall at the instant when the base of the ladder is 30 feet from the wall? [HINT: See Example 2.]

16. Sliding Ladders The top of a 5-foot ladder is sliding down a wall at a rate of 10 ft/sec. How fast is the base of the ladder sliding away from the wall at the instant when the top of the ladder is 3 feet from the ground? [HINT: See Example 2.]

17. Rising Rocket You are situated 600 meters from the launch pad at the Jiuquan Satellite Launch Center and are watching the launch of China's latest manned lunar vehicle. At a certain instant the vehicle is 1,000 meters away from you and rising vertically at velocity of 100 m/sec. How fast is the vehicle moving away from you at that instant?

18. Descending Elevator You are situated 300 feet from the base of Tower Glitz Plaza watching an external elevator descend down the side of the building. At a certain instant the elevator is 500 feet away from you, and its distance from you is decreasing at a rate of 16 ft/sec. How fast is the elevator descending at that instant?

19. Average Cost The average cost function for the weekly manufacture of retro portable CD players is given by

$$\overline{C}(x) = 150{,}000x^{-1} + 20 + 0.0001x \text{ dollars per player,}$$

where x is the number of CD players manufactured that week. Weekly production is currently 3,000 players and is increasing at a rate of 100 players per week. What is happening to the average cost? [HINT: See Example 3.]

20. Average Cost Repeat Exercise 19, using the revised average cost function

$$\overline{C}(x) = 150{,}000x^{-1} + 20 + 0.01x \text{ dollars per player.}$$

[HINT: See Example 3.]

21. Demand Demand for your tie-dyed T-shirts is given by the formula

$$q = 500 - 100p^{0.5},$$

where q is the number of T-shirts you can sell each month at a price of p dollars. If you currently sell T-shirts for $15 each and you raise your price by $2 per month, how fast will the demand drop? (Round your answer to the nearest whole number.)

22. Supply The number of retro portable CD players you are prepared to supply to a retail outlet every week is given by the formula

$$q = 0.1p^2 + 3p,$$

where p is the price it offers you. The retail outlet is currently offering you $40 per CD player. If the price it offers decreases at a rate of $2 per week, how will this affect the number you supply?

23. Revenue You can now sell 50 cups of lemonade per week at 30¢ per cup, but demand is dropping at a rate of 5 cups per week each week. Assuming that raising the price does not affect demand, how fast do you have to raise your price if you want to keep your weekly revenue constant? [HINT: Revenue = Price × Quantity.]

24. Revenue You can now sell 40 cars per month at $20,000 per car, and demand is increasing at a rate of 3 cars per month each month. What is the fastest you could drop your price before your monthly revenue starts to drop? [HINT: Revenue = Price × Quantity.]

25. ▼ Oil Revenues Daily oil production by Pemex, Mexico's national oil company, can be approximated by

$$q(t) = 0.017t^2 - 0.4t + 5.23 \text{ million barrels} \quad (8 \leq t \leq 13)$$

where t is time in years since the start of 2000.[60] At the start of 2010 the price of oil was $86 per barrel and decreasing at a rate of $24 per year.[61] How fast was Pemex's (daily) oil revenue changing at that time?

26. ▼ Oil Expenditures Daily oil imports to the United States from Mexico can be approximated by

$$q(t) = -39t^2 + 800t - 3{,}000 \text{ thousand barrels} \quad (9 \leq t \leq 13),$$

where t is time in years since the start of 2000.[62] At the start of 2012 the price of oil was $105 per barrel and increasing at a rate of $70 per year.[63] How fast was (daily) oil expenditure for imports from Mexico changing at that time?

---

[58] Based on estimates in "Distant future of the Sun and Earth revisited" by K-P Schröder and Robert Cannon Smith, *Monthly Notices of the Royal Astronomical Society* **386** (1): 155–163.

[59] Ibid.

[60] Source for data: www.pemex.com.

[61] Based on January price and January–February change. Source for data: Energy Information Administration (http://tonto.eia.doe.gov).

[62] Source for data: www.pemex.com.

[63] Based on January price and January–February change. Source for data: Energy Information Administration (http://tonto.eia.doe.gov).

27. *Resource Allocation* Your company manufactures automobile alternators, and production is partially automated through the use of robots. To meet production deadlines, your company calculates that the numbers of laborers and robots must satisfy the constraint

$$xy = 10,000,$$

where x is the number of laborers and y is the number of robots. Your company currently uses 400 robots and is increasing robot deployment at a rate of 16 per month. How fast is it laying off laborers? [HINT: See Example 4.]

28. *Resource Allocation* Your company is the largest sock manufacturer in the solar system, and production is automated through the use of androids and robots. To meet production deadlines, your company calculates that the numbers of androids and robots must satisfy the constraint

$$xy = 1,000,000,$$

where x is the number of androids and y is the number of robots. Your company currently uses 5,000 androids and is increasing android deployment at a rate of 200 per month. How fast is it scrapping robots? [HINT: See Example 4.]

29. *Production* The automobile assembly plant you manage has a Cobb-Douglas production function given by

$$P = 10x^{0.3}y^{0.7},$$

where P is the number of automobiles it produces per year, x is the number of employees, and y is the daily operating budget (in dollars). You maintain a production level of 1,000 automobiles per year. If you currently employ 150 workers and are hiring new workers at a rate of 10 per year, how fast is your daily operating budget changing? [HINT: See Example 4.]

30. *Production* Refer back to the Cobb-Douglas production formula in Exercise 29. Assume that you maintain a constant workforce of 200 workers and wish to increase production in order to meet a demand that is increasing by 100 automobiles per year. The current demand is 1,000 automobiles per year. How fast should your daily operating budget be increasing? [HINT: See Example 4.]

31. *Demand* Assume that the demand equation for tuna in a small coastal town is

$$pq^{1.5} = 50,000,$$

where q is the number of pounds of tuna that can be sold in one month at the price of p dollars per pound. The town's fishery finds that the demand for tuna is currently 900 pounds per month and is increasing at a rate of 100 pounds per month each month. How fast is the price changing?

32. *Demand* The demand equation for rubies at *Royal Ruby Retailers* is

$$q + \frac{4}{3}p = 80,$$

where q is the number of rubies RRR can sell per week at p dollars per ruby. RRR finds that the demand for its rubies

is currently 20 rubies per week and is dropping at a rate of one ruby per week. How fast is the price changing?

33. ▼ *Ships Sailing Apart* The H.M.S. *Dreadnaught* is 40 miles south of Montauk and steaming due south at 20 mph, while the U.S.S. *Mona Lisa* is 50 miles east of Montauk and steaming due east at an even 30 mph. How fast is their distance apart increasing?

34. ▼ *Near Miss* My aunt and I were approaching the same intersection, she from the south and I from the west. She was traveling at a steady speed of 10 mph, while I was approaching the intersection at 60 mph. At a certain instant in time, I was one tenth of a mile from the intersection, while she was one twentieth of a mile from it. How fast were we approaching each other at that instant?

35. ▼ *Baseball* A baseball diamond is a square with side 90 feet.

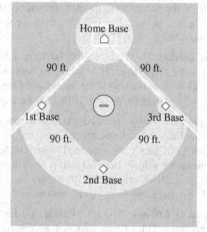

A batter at home base hits the ball and runs toward first base at a speed of 24 ft/sec. At what rate is his distance from third base increasing when he is halfway to first base?

36. ▼ *Baseball* Refer to Exercise 35. Another player is running from third base to home at 30 ft/sec. How fast is her distance from second base increasing when she is 60 feet from third base?

37. ▼ *Movement along a Graph* A point on the graph of $y = 1/x$ is moving along the curve in such a way that its x-coordinate is increasing at a rate of 4 units per second. What is happening to the y-coordinate at the instant the y-coordinate is equal to 2?

38. ▼ *Motion around a Circle* A point is moving along the circle $x^2 + (y - 1)^2 = 8$ in such a way that its x-coordinate is decreasing at a rate of 1 unit per second. What is happening to the y-coordinate at the instant when the point has reached $(-2, 3)$?

39. ▼ *Education* In 1991 the expected income of an individual depended on his or her educational level according to the following formula:

$$I(n) = 2.929n^3 - 115.9n^2 + 1,530n - 6,760$$
$$\text{thousand dollars} \quad (12 \le n \le 15).$$

Here, n is the number of school years completed, and $I(n)$ is the individual's expected income in thousands of dollars.[64] It is 1991, and you have completed 13 years of school and are currently a part-time student. Your schedule is such that you will complete the equivalent of one year of college every three years. Assuming that your salary is linked to the above model, how fast is your income going up? (Round your answer to the nearest $1.)

40. ▼ *Education* Refer back to the model in Exercise 39. Assume that you have completed 14 years of school and that your income is increasing by $5,000 per year. How much schooling per year is this rate of increase equivalent to?

41. ▼ *Employment* An employment research company estimates that the value of a recent MBA graduate to an accounting company is

$$V = 3e^2 + 5g^3,$$

where V is the value of the graduate, e is the number of years of prior business experience, and g is the graduate school grade-point average. A company that currently employs graduates with a 3.0 average wishes to maintain a constant employee value of $V = 200$ but finds that the grade-point average of its new employees is dropping at a rate of 0.2 per year. How fast must the experience of its new employees be growing to compensate for the decline in grade point average?

42. ▼ *Grades*[65] A production formula for a student's performance on a difficult English examination is given by

$$g = 4hx - 0.2h^2 - 10x^2,$$

where g is the grade the student can expect to obtain, h is the number of hours of study for the examination, and x is the student's grade point average. The instructor finds that students' grade point averages have remained constant at 3.0 over the years and that students currently spend an average of 15 hours studying for the examination. However, scores on the examination are dropping at a rate of 10 points per year. At what rate is the average study time decreasing?

43. ▼ *Cones* A right circular conical vessel is being filled with green industrial waste at a rate of 100 m³/sec. How fast is the level rising after 200π cubic meters have been poured in? The cone has a height of 50 meters and a radius of 30 meters at its brim. (The volume of a cone of height h and cross-sectional radius r at its brim is given by $V = \frac{1}{3}\pi r^2 h$.)

44. ▼ *More Cones* A circular conical vessel is being filled with ink at a rate of 10 cm³/sec. How fast is the level rising after 20 cubic centimeters have been poured in? The cone has height 50 centimeters and radius 20 centimeters at its brim. (The volume of a cone of height h and cross-sectional radius r at its brim is given by $V = \frac{1}{3}\pi r^2 h$.)

45. ▼ *Cylinders* The volume of paint in a right cylindrical can is given by $V = 4t^2 - t$, where t is time in seconds and V is the volume in cubic centimeters. How fast is the level rising when the height is 2 centimeters? The can has a height of 4 centimeters and a radius of 2 centimeters. [HINT: To get h as a function of t, first solve the volume $V = \pi r^2 h$ for h.]

46. ▼ *Cylinders* A cylindrical bucket is being filled with paint at a rate of 6 cm³/min. How fast is the level rising when the bucket starts to overflow? The bucket has a radius of 30 centimeters and a height of 60 centimeters.

47. ▼ *Computers vs. Income* In the 1990s the demand for personal computers in the home went up with household income. For a given community in the 1990s, the average number of computers in a home could be approximated by

$$q = 0.3454 \ln x - 3.047 \quad (10{,}000 \le x \le 125{,}000),$$

where x is mean household income.[66] A certain community had a mean income of $30,000, increasing at a rate of $2,000 per year. How many computers per household were there, and how fast was the number of computers in a home increasing? (Round your answer to four decimal places.)

48. ▼ *Computers vs. Income* Refer back to the model in Exercise 47. It is 1995, and the average number of computers per household in your town is 0.5 and is increasing at a rate of 0.02 computers per household per year. What is the average household income in your town, and how fast is it increasing? (Round your answers to the nearest $10.)

Education and Crime *The following graph compares the total U.S. prison population and the average combined SAT score in the United States during the 1970s and 1980s:*

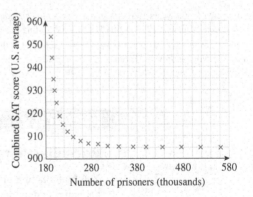

Exercises 49 and 50 are based on the following model for these data:

$$S(n) = 904 + \frac{1{,}326}{(n - 180)^{1.325}} \quad (192 \le n \le 563).$$

---

[64] The model is based on Table 358, U.S. Department of Education, *Digest of Education Statistics, 1991*, Washington, DC: Government Printing Office, 1991.

[65] Based on an exercise in *Introduction to Mathematical Economics* by A. L. Ostrosky Jr. and J. V. Koch (Waveland Press, Illinois, 1979).

[66] The model is a regression model. Source for data: Income distribution: Computer data: Forrester Research/*New York Times*, August 8, 1999, p. BU4.

Here, $S(n)$ is the combined average SAT score at a time when the total prison population is n thousand.[67]

49. ▼ In 1985 the U.S. prison population was 475,000 and increasing at a rate of 35,000 per year. What was the average SAT score, and how fast, and in what direction, was it changing? (Round your answers to two decimal places.)

50. ▼ In 1970 the U.S. combined SAT average was 940 and dropping by 10 points per year. What was the U.S. prison population, and how fast, and in what direction, was it changing? (Round your answers to the nearest 100.)

Divorce Rates *A study found that the divorce rate d (given as a percentage) appears to depend on the ratio r of available men to available women.*[68] *This function can be approximated by*

$$d(r) = \begin{cases} -40r + 74 & \text{if } r \le 1.3 \\ \dfrac{130r}{3} - \dfrac{103}{3} & \text{if } r > 1.3. \end{cases}$$

Exercises 51 and 52 are based on this model.

51. ◆ There are currently 1.1 available men per available woman in Littleville, and this ratio is increasing by 0.05 per year. What is happening to the divorce rate?

52. ◆ There are currently 1.5 available men per available woman in Largeville, and this ratio is decreasing by 0.03 per year. What is happening to the divorce rate?

Communication and Reasoning Exercises

53. Why is this section titled "Related Rates"?

54. If you know how fast one quantity is changing and need to compute how fast a second quantity is changing, what kind of information do you need?

---

[67] Based on data for the years 1967–1989. Sources: *Sourcebook of Criminal Justice Statistics*, 1990, p. 604/Educational Testing Service.

[68] The cited study, by Scott J. South and associates, appeared in the *American Sociological Review* (February 1995). Figures are rounded. Source: *New York Times*, February 19, 1995, p. 40.

55. In a related rates problem there is no limit to the number of changing quantities we can consider. Illustrate this by creating a related rates problem with four changing quantities.

56. If three quantities are related by a single equation, how would you go about computing how fast one of them is changing based on a knowledge of the other two?

57. ▼ The demand and unit price for your store's checkered T-shirts are changing with time. Show that the percentage rate of change of revenue equals the sum of the percentage rates of change of price and demand. (The percentage rate of change of a quantity Q is $Q'(t)/Q(t)$.)

58. ▼ The number N of employees and the total floor space S of your company are both changing with time. Show that the percentage rate of change of square footage per employee equals the percentage rate of change of S minus the percentage rate of change of N. (The percentage rate of change of a quantity Q is $Q'(t)/Q(t)$.)

59. ▼ In solving a related rates problem a key step is solving the derived equation for the unknown rate of change (once we have substituted the other values into the equation). Call the unknown rate of change X. The derived equation is what kind of equation in X?

60. ▼ On a recent exam you were given a related rates problem based on an algebraic equation relating two variables x and y. Your friend told you that the correct relationship between dx/dt and dy/dt was given by

$$\left(\frac{dx}{dt}\right) = \left(\frac{dy}{dt}\right)^2.$$

Could he be correct?

61. ▼ Transform the following into a mathematical statement about derivatives: If my grades are improving at twice the speed of yours, then your grades are improving at half the speed of mine.

62. ▼ If two quantities x and y are related by a linear equation, how are their rates of change related?

12.6 Elasticity

Price Elasticity of Demand

You manufacture an extremely popular brand of sneakers and want to know what will happen if you increase the selling price. Common sense tells you that demand will drop as you raise the price. But will the drop in demand be enough to cause your revenue to fall? Or will it be small enough that your revenue will rise because of the higher selling price? For example, if you raise the price by 1%, you might suffer only a 0.5% loss in sales. In this case the loss in sales will be more than offset by the increase in price, and your revenue will rise. In such a case we say that the demand is **inelastic**, because it is not very sensitive to the increase in price. On the other hand, if your 1% price increase results in a 2% drop in demand, then raising the price will cause a drop in revenues. We then say that the demand is **elastic** because it reacts strongly to a price change.

We can use calculus to measure the response of demand to price changes if we have a demand equation for the item we are selling.* We need to know the *percentage drop in demand per percentage increase in price*. This ratio is called the **elasticity of demand**, or **price elasticity of demand**, and is usually denoted by E. Let's derive a formula for E in terms of the demand equation.

Assume that we have a demand equation

$$q = f(p),$$

where q stands for the number of items we would sell (per week, per month, or what have you) if we set the price per item at p. Now suppose we increase the price p by a very small amount, Δp. Then our percentage increase in price is $(\Delta p/p) \times 100\%$. This increase in p will presumably result in a decrease in the demand q. Let's denote this corresponding decrease in q by $-\Delta q$. (We use the minus sign because, by convention, Δq stands for the *increase* in demand.) Thus, the percentage decrease in demand is $(-\Delta q/q) \times 100\%$.

Now E is the ratio

$$E = \frac{\text{Percentage decrease in demand}}{\text{Percentage increase in price}},$$

so

$$E = \frac{-\dfrac{\Delta q}{q} \times 100\%}{\dfrac{\Delta p}{p} \times 100\%}.$$

Canceling the 100%s and reorganizing, we get

$$E = -\frac{\Delta q}{\Delta p} \cdot \frac{p}{q}.$$

Q: *What small change in price will we use for* Δp?

A: It should probably be pretty small. If we increased the price of sneakers to, say, $1 million per pair, the sales would likely drop to zero. But knowing this tells us nothing about how the market would respond to a modest increase in price. In fact, we shall do the usual thing we do in calculus and let Δp approach 0.

In the expression for E, if we let Δp go to 0, then the ratio $\Delta q/\Delta p$ goes to the derivative dq/dp. This gives us our final and most useful definition of the elasticity.

Price Elasticity of Demand

The **price elasticity of demand** E is the percentage rate of decrease of demand per percentage increase in price. E is given by the formula

$$E = -\frac{dq}{dp} \cdot \frac{p}{q}.$$

We say that the demand is **elastic** if $E > 1$, is **inelastic** if $E < 1$, and has **unit elasticity** if $E = 1$.

* Coming up with a good demand equation is not always easy. We saw in Chapter 1 that it is possible to find a linear demand equation if we know the sales figures at two different prices. However, such an equation is only a first approximation. To come up with a more accurate demand equation, we might need to gather data corresponding to sales at several different prices and use curve-fitting techniques like regression. Another approach would be an analytic one, based on mathematical modeling techniques that an economist might use.

   That said, we refer you again to *Camels and Rubber Duckies* by Joel Spolsky at www.joelon software.com/articles/Camelsand RubberDuckies.html just in case you think there is nothing more to demand curves.

Quick Example

1. Suppose that the demand equation is $q = 20{,}000 - 2p$, where p is the price in dollars. Then

$$E = -(-2)\frac{p}{20{,}000 - 2p} = \frac{p}{10{,}000 - p}.$$

If $p = \$2{,}000$, then $E = 1/4$, and demand is inelastic at this price.

If $p = \$8{,}000$, then $E = 4$, and demand is elastic at this price.

If $p = \$5{,}000$, then $E = 1$, and the demand has unit elasticity at this price.

We are generally interested in the price that maximizes revenue, and in ordinary cases the price that maximizes revenue must give unit elasticity. One way of seeing this is as follows:* If the demand is inelastic (which ordinarily occurs at a low unit price), then raising the price by a small percentage—1%, say—results in a smaller percentage drop in demand. For example, in Quick Example 1, if $p = \$2{,}000$, then the demand would drop by only $\frac{1}{4}$% for every 1% increase in price. To see the effect on revenue, we use the fact[†] that, for small changes in price,

* For another—more rigorous— argument, see Exercise 37.

† See, for example, Exercise 57 in Section 12.5.

Percentage change in revenue $\approx$ Percentage change in price
$+$ Percentage change in demand

$$= 1 + \left(-\frac{1}{4}\right) = \frac{3}{4}\%.$$

Thus, the revenue will increase by about 3/4%. Put another way:

If the demand is inelastic, raising the price increases revenue.

On the other hand, if the price is elastic (which ordinarily occurs at a high unit price), then increasing the price slightly will lower the revenue, so:

If the demand is elastic, lowering the price increases revenue.

The price that results in the largest revenue must therefore be at unit elasticity.

EXAMPLE 1   **Price Elasticity of Demand: Dolls**

Suppose that the demand equation for *Bobby Dolls* is given by $q = 216 - p^2$, where p is the price per doll in dollars and q is the number of dolls sold per week.

a. Compute the price elasticity of demand when $p = \$5$ and $p = \$10$, and interpret the results.

b. Find the range of prices for which the demand is elastic and the range for which the demand is inelastic.

c. Find the price at which the weekly revenue is maximized. What is the maximum weekly revenue?

Solution

a. The price elasticity of demand is

$$E = -\frac{dq}{dp} \cdot \frac{p}{q}.$$

Taking the derivative and substituting for q gives

$$E = 2p \cdot \frac{p}{216 - p^2} = \frac{2p^2}{216 - p^2}.$$

When $p = \$5$,

$$E = \frac{2(5)^2}{216 - 5^2} = \frac{50}{191} \approx 0.26.$$

Thus, when the price is set at $5, the demand is dropping at a rate of 0.26% per 1% increase in the price. Because $E < 1$, the demand is inelastic at this price, so raising the price will increase revenue.

When $p = \$10$,

$$E = \frac{2(10)^2}{216 - 10^2} = \frac{200}{116} \approx 1.72.$$

Thus, when the price is set at $10, the demand is dropping at a rate of 1.72% per 1% increase in the price. Because $E > 1$, demand is elastic at this price, so raising the price will decrease revenue; lowering the price will increase revenue.

b. and **c.** We answer part (c) first. Setting $E = 1$, we get

$$\frac{2p^2}{216 - p^2} = 1$$

$$p^2 = 72.$$

Thus, we conclude that the maximum revenue occurs when $p = \sqrt{72} \approx \$8.49$. We can now answer part (b): The demand is elastic when $p > \$8.49$ (the price is too high), and the demand is inelastic when $p < \$8.49$ (the price is too low). Finally, we calculate the maximum weekly revenue, which equals the revenue corresponding to the price of $8.49:

$$R = qp = (216 - p^2)p = (216 - 72)\sqrt{72} = 144\sqrt{72} \approx \$1,222.$$

Using Technology
See the Technology Guides at the end of the chapter to find out how to automate computations like those in Example 1(a) using a graphing calculator or Excel. Here is an outline:

TI-83/84 Plus
$Y_1=216-X^2$
$Y_2=-nDeriv(Y_1,X,X)*X/Y_1$
2ND TABLE Enter $x = 5$
[More details in the Technology Guide.]

Spreadsheet
Enter values of p: 4.9, 4.91, ..., 5.0, 5.01, ..., 5.1 in A5–A25.
In B5, enter 216-A5^2 and copy down to B25.
In C5, enter = (A6-A5) /A5 and paste the formula in C5–D24.
In E5, enter =-D5/C5 and copy down to E24. This column contains the values of E for the values of p in column A.
[More details in the Technology Guide.]

Income Elasticity of Demand

The concept of elasticity can be applied in other situations. In the following example we consider *income* elasticity of demand—the percentage increase in demand for a particular item per percentage increase in personal income.

EXAMPLE 2   Income Elasticity of Demand: Porsches

You are the sales director at *Suburban Porsche* and have noticed that demand for Porsches depends on income according to

$$q = 0.005e^{-0.05x^2+x} \qquad (1 \le x \le 10).$$

Here, x is the income of a potential customer in hundreds of thousands of dollars and q is the probability that the person will actually purchase a Porsche.* The **income elasticity of demand** is

$$E = \frac{dq}{dx}\frac{x}{q}.$$

Compute and interpret E for $x = 2$ and 9.

* In other words, q is the fraction of visitors to your showroom having income x who actually purchase a Porsche.

Q: Why is there no negative sign in the formula?

A: Because we anticipate that the demand will increase as income increases, the ratio

$$\frac{\text{Percentage increase in demand}}{\text{Percentage increase in income}}$$

will be positive, so there is no need to introduce a negative sign.

Solution Turning to the calculation, since $q = 0.005e^{-0.05x^2+x}$,

$$\frac{dq}{dx} = 0.005e^{-0.05x^2+x}(-0.1x + 1),$$

so

$$E = \frac{dq}{dx}\frac{x}{q}$$

$$= 0.005e^{-0.05x^2+x}(-0.1x + 1)\frac{x}{0.005e^{-0.05x^2+x}}$$

$$= x(-0.1x + 1).$$

When $x = 2$, $E = 2[-0.1(2) + 1] = 1.6$. Thus, at an income level of $200,000 the probability that a customer will purchase a Porsche increases at a rate of 1.6% per 1% increase in income.

When $x = 9$, $E = 9[-0.1(9) + 1] = 0.9$. Thus, at an income level of $900,000 the probability that a customer will purchase a Porsche increases at a rate of 0.9% per 1% increase in income.

12.6 EXERCISES

▼ more advanced   ◆ challenging
Ⓣ indicates exercises that should be solved using technology

Applications

1. **Demand for Oranges** The weekly sales of *Honolulu Red Oranges* is given by $q = 1,000 - 20p$. Calculate the price elasticity of demand when the price is $30 per orange (yes, $30 per orange[69]). Interpret your answer. Also, calculate the price that gives a maximum weekly revenue, and find this maximum revenue. [**HINT**: See Example 1.]

2. **Demand for Oranges** Repeat Exercise 1 for weekly sales of $1,000 - 10p$. [**HINT**: See Example 1.]

3. **Demand for Smartphones** Worldwide annual sales of smartphones in 2012–2013 were approximately $q = -6p + 3,030$ million phones at a selling price of $p per phone.[70]
   a. Obtain a formula for the price elasticity of demand E.

b. In 2013 the actual selling price was $335 per phone. What was the corresponding price elasticity of demand? Interpret your answer.

c. Use your formula for E to determine the selling price that would have resulted in the largest annual revenue. What, to the nearest $10 million, would have been the resulting annual revenue?

4. **Projected Revenue: Smartphones** Worldwide annual sales of smartphones in 2013–2017 were projected to be approximately $q = -10p + 4,360$ million phones at a selling price of $p per phone.[71]
   a. Obtain a formula for the price elasticity of demand E.
   b. In 2014 the actual selling price was $297 per phone. What was the corresponding price elasticity of demand? Interpret your answer.
   c. Use your formula for E to determine the selling price that would have resulted in the largest annual revenue. What, to the nearest $10 million, would have been the resulting annual revenue?

---

[69] They are very hard to find, and their possession confers considerable social status.

[70] Source for data: IDC Worldwide Quarterly Mobile Phone Tracker, Nov. 26, 2013, www.zdnet.com.

[71] Data based on historical 2013 data (source: *Ibid.*) and projected 2017 data.

5. *College Tuition* An old study of about 1,800 U.S. colleges and universities resulted in the demand equation $q = 9{,}900 - 2.2p$, where q is the enrollment at a college or university and p is the average annual tuition (plus fees) it charges.[72]
   a. The study also found that the average tuition charged by universities and colleges was $2,900. What would the effect on the price elasticity of demand have been if the price had been lowered to $2,200? What does the answer suggest about the tuition price corresponding to maximum annual revenue?
   b. On the basis of the study, what would you have advised a college to charge its students to maximize total annual revenue, and what would the resulting enrollment and revenue have been?

6. *Monorail Services* The demand for monorail service in Las Vegas in 2005 could be approximated by $q = -4{,}500p + 41{,}500$ rides per day when the fare was $p.[73]
   a. In September 2005 the Las Vegas monorail increased the price from $3 per ride to $5 per ride. What was the effect on the price elasticity of demand? What does the answer suggest about the fare corresponding to maximum daily revenue?
   b. What would you have advised the Las Vegas Monorail Company to charge to maximize total daily revenue, and what would the resulting daily ridership and revenue have been?

7. *Tissues* The consumer demand equation for tissues is given by $q = (100 - p)^2$, where p is the price per case of tissues and q is the demand in weekly sales.
   a. Determine the price elasticity of demand E when the price is set at $30, and interpret your answer.
   b. At what price should tissues be sold to maximize the revenue?
   c. Approximately how many cases of tissues would be demanded at that price?

8. *Bodybuilding* The consumer demand curve for *Professor Stefan Schwarzenegger* dumbbells is given by $q = (100 - 2p)^2$, where p is the price per dumbbell and q is the demand in weekly sales. Find the price Professor Schwarzenegger should charge for his dumbbells to maximize revenue.

9. *T-Shirts* The Physics Club sells $E = mc^2$ T-shirts at the local flea market. Unfortunately, the club's previous administration has been losing money for years, so you decide to do an analysis of the sales. A quadratic regression based on old sales data reveals the following demand equation for the T-shirts:
   $$q = -2p^2 + 33p \quad (9 \le p \le 15).$$
   Here, p is the price the club charges per T-shirt and q is the number it can sell each day at the flea market.

   a. Obtain a formula for the price elasticity of demand for $E = mc^2$ T-shirts.
   b. Compute the elasticity of demand if the price is set at $10 per shirt. Interpret the result.
   c. How much should the Physics Club charge for the T-shirts to obtain the maximum daily revenue? What will this revenue be?

10. *Comics* The demand curve for original *Iguanawoman* comics is given by
    $$q = \frac{(400 - p)^2}{100} \quad (0 \le p \le 400),$$
    where q is the number of copies the publisher can sell per week if it sets the price at $p.
    a. Find the price elasticity of demand when the price is set at $40 per copy.
    b. Find the price at which the publisher should sell the comics to maximize weekly revenue.
    c. What, to the nearest $1, is the maximum weekly revenue the publisher can realize from sales of *Iguanawoman* comics?

11. *E-Readers* The demand for Amazon's Kindle e-reader can be approximated by
    $$q(p) = 21e^{-0.01p} \text{ million units per year} \quad (50 \le p \le 400),$$
    where p is the price charged by Amazon.[74] Obtain a formula for price elasticity of demand E, and calculate its value at the two endpoints of the given range of prices. Is the price that would maximize annual revenue within the range of prices shown? How would you know this without calculating that price?

12. *Monorail Service on Mars* The demand for monorail service on the Utarek monorail, which links the three urbynes (or districts) of Utarek on Mars, can be approximated by
    $$q(p) = 31e^{-0.7p} \text{ million rides per day} \quad (3 \le p \le 5),$$
    where p is the cost per ride in zonars (Z).[75] Obtain a formula for price elasticity of demand E, and calculate its value at the two endpoints of the given range of prices. Is the price that would maximize daily revenue within the range of prices shown? How would you know this without calculating that price?

13. *Corn* In the 1930s the economist Henry Schultz devised the following demand function for corn:
    $$p = \frac{6{,}570{,}000}{q^{1.3}},$$
    where q is the number of bushels of corn that could be sold at p dollars per bushel in one year.[76] Express q as a function of p, and find the price elasticity of demand if the price was set at $1.50 per bushel. Interpret the result.

---

[72] Based on a study by A. L. Ostrosky Jr. and J. V. Koch, as cited in their book *Introduction to Mathematical Economics* (Waveland Press, Illinois, 1979), p. 133.
[73] The model is the authors'. Source for data: The *New York Times*, February 10, 2007, p. A9.

[74] Model based on data from 2007 to 2013. Source: www.e-reader-info.com.
[75] The zonar (Z) is the official currency in the city-state of Utarek, Mars (formerly www.Marsnext.com, a now extinct virtual society).
[76] Based on data for the period 1915–1929. Source: Henry Schultz (1938), *The Theory and Measurement of Demand*, University of Chicago Press, Chicago.

14. **Demand for Fried Chicken** A fried chicken franchise finds that the demand equation for its new roast chicken product, "Roasted Rooster," is given by

$$p = \frac{40}{q^{1.5}},$$

where p is the price (in dollars) per quarter-chicken serving and q is the number of quarter-chicken servings that can be sold per hour at this price. Express q as a function of p, and find the price elasticity of demand when the price is set at $4 per serving. Interpret the result.

15. **Paint-By-Number** The estimated monthly sales of *Mona Lisa* paint-by-number sets is given by the formula $q = 100e^{-3p^2+p}$, where q is the demand in monthly sales and p is the retail price in hundreds of yen.
   a. Determine the price elasticity of demand E when the retail price is set at ¥300, and interpret your answer.
   b. At what price will revenue be a maximum?
   c. Approximately how many paint-by-number sets will be sold per month at the price in part (b)?

16. **Paint-By-Number** Repeat Exercise 15 using the demand equation $q = 100e^{p-3p^2/2}$.

17. ▼ **Linear Demand Functions** A general linear demand function has the form $q = mp + b$ (m and b constants, $m \neq 0$).
   a. Obtain a formula for the price elasticity of demand at a unit price of p.
   b. Obtain a formula for the price that maximizes revenue.

18. ▼ **Exponential Demand Functions** A general exponential demand function has the form $q = Ae^{-bp}$ (A and b nonzero constants).
   a. Obtain a formula for the price elasticity of demand at a unit price of p.
   b. Obtain a formula for the price that maximizes revenue.

19. ▼ **Hyperbolic Demand Functions** A general hyperbolic demand function has the form $q = \dfrac{k}{p^r}$ (r and k nonzero constants).
   a. Obtain a formula for the price elasticity of demand at unit price p.
   b. How does E vary with p?
   c. What does the answer to part (b) say about the model?

20. ▼ **Quadratic Demand Functions** A general quadratic demand function has the form $q = ap^2 + bp + c$ ($a, b,$ and c constants with $a \neq 0$).
   a. Obtain a formula for the price elasticity of demand at a unit price p.
   b. Obtain a formula for the price or prices that could maximize revenue.

21. ▼ **Modeling Linear Demand** You have been hired as a marketing consultant to *Johannesburg Burger Supply, Inc.*, and you wish to come up with a unit price for its hamburgers in order to maximize its weekly revenue. To make life as simple as possible, you assume that the demand equation for Johannesburg hamburgers has the linear form $q = mp + b$, where p is the price per hamburger, q is the demand in weekly sales, and m and b are certain constants you must determine.
   a. Your market studies reveal the following sales figures: When the price is set at $2.00 per hamburger, the sales amount to 3,000 per week, but when the price is set at $4.00 per hamburger, the sales drop to zero. Use these data to calculate the demand equation.
   b. Now estimate the unit price that maximizes weekly revenue, and predict what the weekly revenue will be at that price.

22. ▼ **Modeling Linear Demand** You have been hired as a marketing consultant by *Big Book Publishing, Inc.*, and you have been approached to determine the best-selling price for the hit calculus text by Whiner and Istanbul entitled *Fun with Derivatives*. You decide to make life easy and assume that the demand equation for *Fun with Derivatives* has the linear form $q = mp + b$, where p is the price per book, q is the demand in annual sales, and m and b are certain constants you must determine.
   a. Your market studies reveal the following sales figures: When the price is set at $50.00 per book, the sales amount to 10,000 per year; when the price is set at $80.00 per book, the sales drop to 1,000 per year. Use these data to calculate the demand equation.
   b. Now estimate the unit price that maximizes annual revenue and predict what Big Book Publishing, Inc.'s annual revenue will be at that price.

23. ▼ **Modeling Exponential Demand** As the new owner of a supermarket, you have inherited a large inventory of unsold imported Limburger cheese, and you would like to set the price so that your revenue from selling it is as large as possible. Previous sales figures of the cheese are shown in the following table:

Price per Pound, p	$3.00	$4.00	$5.00
Monthly Sales, q (pounds)	407	287	223

   a. Use the sales figures for the prices $3 and $5 per pound to construct a demand function of the form $q = Ae^{-bp}$, where A and b are constants you must determine. (Round A and b to two significant digits.)
   b. Use your demand function to find the price elasticity of demand at each of the prices listed.
   c. At what price should you sell the cheese to maximize monthly revenue?
   d. If your total inventory of cheese amounts to only 200 pounds and it will spoil 1 month from now, how should you price it to receive the greatest revenue? Is this the same answer you got in part (c)? If not, give a brief explanation.

24. ▼ **Modeling Exponential Demand** Repeat Exercise 23, but this time use the sales figures for $4 and $5 per pound to construct the demand function.

25. **Income Elasticity of Demand: Live Drama** The likelihood that a child will attend a live theatrical performance can be modeled by

$$q = 0.01(-0.0078x^2 + 1.5x + 4.1) \quad (15 \le x \le 100).$$

Here, q is the fraction of children with annual household income x thousand dollars who will attend a live dramatic performance at a theater during the year.[77] Compute the income elasticity of demand at an income level of $20,000 and interpret the result. (Round your answer to two significant digits.) [HINT: See Example 2.]

26. **Income Elasticity of Demand: Live Concerts** The likelihood that a child will attend a live musical performance can be modeled by

$$q = 0.01(0.0006x^2 + 0.38x + 35) \quad (15 \le x \le 100).$$

Here, q is the fraction of children with annual household income x thousand dollars who will attend a live musical performance during the year.[78] Compute the income elasticity of demand at an income level of $30,000, and interpret the result. (Round your answer to two significant digits.) [HINT: See Example 2.]

27. **Income Elasticity of Demand: Broadband in 2010** The following graph shows the percentage q of people in households with annual income x thousand dollars using broadband Internet access in 2010,[79] together with the exponential curve $q = -74e^{-0.021x} + 92$.

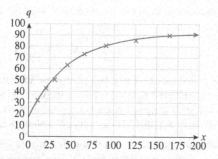

a. Find an equation for the income elasticity of demand for broadband usage, and use it to compute the elasticity for a household with annual income $100,000 to two decimal places. Interpret the result.

b. What does the model predict as the elasticity of demand for households with very large incomes?

28. **Income Elasticity of Demand: Broadband in 2007** The following graph shows the percentage q of people in households with annual income x thousand dollars using broadband

Internet access in 2007,[80] together with the exponential curve $q = -86e^{-0.013x} + 92$.

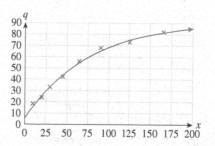

a. Find an equation for the income elasticity of demand for broadband usage, and use it to compute the elasticity for a household with annual income $60,000 to two decimal places. Interpret the result.

b. What does the model predict as the elasticity of demand for households with very large incomes?

29. **Income Elasticity of Demand: Computer Usage in the 1990s** The following graph shows the probability q that a household in the 1990s with annual income x dollars had a computer,[81] together with the logarithmic curve $q = 0.3454 \ln x - 3.047$.

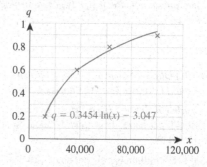

a. Compute the income elasticity of demand for computers, to two decimal places, for a household income of $60,000, and interpret the result.

b. As household income increases, how is income elasticity of demand affected?

c. How reliable is the given model of demand for incomes well above $120,000? Explain.

d. What can you say about E for incomes much larger than those shown?

30. **Income Elasticity of Demand: Internet Usage in the 1990s** The following graph shows the probability q that a person in the 1990s with household annual income x dollars used the Internet,[82] together with the logarithmic curve $q = 0.2802 \ln x - 2.505$.

---

[77] Based on a quadratic regression of data from a 2001 survey. Source for data: New York Foundation of the Arts (www.nyfa.org/culturalblueprint).

[78] *Ibid.*

[79] Source for data: *Digital Nation: Expanding Internet Usage,* National Telecommunications and Information Administration, U.S. Department of Commerce (http://search.ntia.doc.gov).

[80] *Ibid.*

[81] Source for data: Income distribution computer data: Forrester Research/*New York Times,* August 8, 1999, p. BU4.

[82] Sources: Luxembourg Income Study/*New York Times,* August 14, 1995, p. A9, Commerce Department, Deloitte & Touche Survey/*New York Times,* November 24, 1999, p. C1.

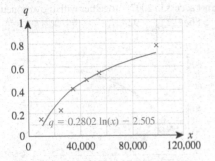

$q = 0.2802 \ln(x) - 2.505$

a. Compute the income elasticity of demand for Internet usage, to two decimal places, for a household income of $60,000 and interpret the result.
b. As household income increases, how is income elasticity of demand affected?
c. The logarithmic model shown above is not appropriate for incomes well above $100,000. Suggest a model that might be more appropriate.
d. In the model you propose, how would E behave for very large incomes?

Price Elasticity of Supply *Given a supply equation of the form* $q = f(p)$, *the associated* ***price elasticity of supply*** *is defined as the percentage rate of increase of supply per percentage increase in price:*

$$E = \frac{dq}{dp} \cdot \frac{p}{q}.$$

(Note that the formula is the same as for price elasticity of demand except for the sign.) Exercises 31 and 32 are based on this formula.

31. **Saudi Crude Oil Supply: High Prices** For crude oil prices of at least $20 per barrel the supply by Saudi Arabia can be approximated by

    $q = 0.035p + 6.5$ million barrels per day $(20 \le p \le 105)$,

    where p is the price per barrel.[83] Calculate the price elasticity of supply when the price of oil is $60 per barrel. What does the answer tell you about Saudi oil production?

32. **Saudi Crude Oil Supply: Low Prices** For crude oil prices of at most $20 per barrel the supply by Saudi Arabia can be approximated by

    $q = 0.34p + 1.2$ million barrels per day $(12 \le p \le 20)$,

    where p is the price per barrel.[84] Calculate the price elasticity of supply when the price of oil is $15 per barrel. What does the answer tell you about Saudi oil production?

33. ▼ **Income Elasticity of Demand** *(based on a question on the GRE Economics Test)* If $Q = aP^\alpha Y^\beta$ is the individual's demand function for a commodity, where P is the (fixed) price of the commodity, Y is the individual's income, and a,

α, and β are parameters, explain why β can be interpreted as the income elasticity of demand.

34. ▼ **College Tuition** *(from the GRE Economics Test)* A time-series study of the demand for higher education, using tuition charges as a price variable, yields the following result:

    $$\frac{dq}{dp} \cdot \frac{p}{q} = -0.4,$$

    where p is tuition and q is the quantity of higher education. Which of the following is suggested by the result?
    (A) As tuition rises, students want to buy a greater quantity of education.
    (B) As a determinant of the demand for higher education, income is more important than price.
    (C) If colleges lowered tuition slightly, their total tuition receipts would increase.
    (D) If colleges raised tuition slightly, their total tuition receipts would increase.
    (E) Colleges cannot increase enrollments by offering larger scholarships.

Communication and Reasoning Exercises

35. Complete the following: When demand is inelastic, revenue will decrease if _____ .

36. Complete the following: When demand has unit elasticity, revenue will decrease if _____ .

37. ▼ Given that the demand q is a differentiable function of the unit price p, show that the revenue $R = pq$ has a stationary point when

    $$q + p\frac{dq}{dp} = 0.$$

    Deduce that the stationary points of R are the same as the points of unit price elasticity of demand. (Ordinarily, there is only one such stationary point, corresponding to the absolute maximum of R.) [**HINT:** Differentiate R with respect to p.]

38. ▼ Given that the demand q is a differentiable function of income x, show that the quantity $R = q/x$ has a stationary point when

    $$q - x\frac{dq}{dx} = 0.$$

    Deduce that stationary points of R are the same as the points of unit income elasticity of demand. [**HINT:** Differentiate R with respect to x.]

39. ◆ Your calculus study group is discussing price elasticity of demand, and a member of the group asks the following question: "Since elasticity of demand measures the response of demand to change in unit price, what is the difference between elasticity of demand and the quantity $-dq/dp$?" How would you respond?

40. ◆ Another member of your study group claims that unit price elasticity of demand need not always correspond to maximum revenue. Is he correct? Explain your answer.

KEY CONCEPTS

www.WanerMath.com
Go to the Website to find a comprehensive and interactive Web-based summary of Chapter 12.

12.1 Maxima and Minima

Relative maximum, relative minimum [p. 905]

Absolute maximum, absolute minimum [p. 905]

Stationary points, singular points, endpoints [p. 907]

Finding and classifying maxima and minima [p. 908]

First derivative test for relative extrema [p. 910]

Extreme value theorem [p. 914]

Using technology to locate approximate extrema [p. 915]

12.2 Applications of Maxima and Minima

Minimizing average cost [p. 919]

Maximizing area [p. 920]

Steps in solving optimization problems [p. 921]

Maximizing revenue [p. 922]

Optimizing resources [p. 923]

Allocation of labor [p. 925]

12.3 Higher Order Derivatives: Acceleration and Concavity

The second derivative of a function f is the derivative of the derivative of f, written as f'' [p. 934]

The acceleration of a moving object is the second derivative of the position function [p. 934]

Acceleration due to gravity [p. 935]

Acceleration of sales [p. 935]

Concave up, concave down, point of inflection [p. 937]

Locating points of inflection [p. 937]

Application to inflation [p. 937]

Second derivative test for relative extrema [p. 940]

Higher order derivatives [p. 941]

12.4 Analyzing Graphs

Features of a graph: x- and y-intercepts, relative extrema, points of inflection, behavior near singular points, behavior at infinity [p. 951]

Analyzing a graph [p. 952]

12.5 Related Rates

If Q is a quantity changing over time t, then the derivative dQ/dt is the rate at which Q changes over time [p. 959]

The expanding circle [p. 959]

Steps in solving related rates problems [p. 960]

The falling ladder [p. 961]

Average cost [p. 962]

Allocation of labor [p. 963]

12.6 Elasticity

Price elasticity of demand
$$E = -\frac{dq}{dp} \cdot \frac{p}{q};$$ demand is elastic if $E > 1$, inelastic if $E < 1$, has unit elasticity if $E = 1$ [p. 969]

Computing and interpreting elasticity, and maximizing revenue [p. 970]

Income elasticity of demand [p. 971]

REVIEW EXERCISES

In Exercises 1–8, find all the relative and absolute extrema of the given function on the given domain (if supplied) or on the largest possible domain (if no domain is supplied).

1. $f(x) = 2x^3 - 6x + 1$ on $[-2, +\infty)$

2. $f(x) = x^3 - x^2 - x - 1$ on $(-\infty, \infty)$

3. $g(x) = x^4 - 4x$ on $[-1, 1]$

4. $f(x) = \dfrac{x+1}{(x-1)^2}$ for $-2 \le x \le 2, x \ne 1$

5. $g(x) = (x-1)^{2/3}$

6. $g(x) = x^2 + \ln x$ on $(0, +\infty)$

7. $h(x) = \dfrac{1}{x} + \dfrac{1}{x^2}$

8. $h(x) = e^{x^2} + 1$

In Exercises 9–12, find the approximate x-coordinates of all relative extrema and points of inflection of f, if any. (For Exercise 12 assume f is defined on $[-4, 4]$.)

9. Graph of f:

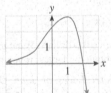

10. Graph of f:

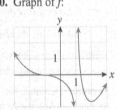

11. Graph of f':

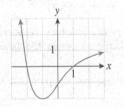

12. Graph of f':

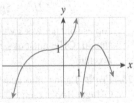

In Exercises 13 and 14, f is continuous on $[-3, 3]$, *and the graph of f″ is given. Find the approximate x-coordinates of all points of inflection of the original function f (if any).*

13. Graph of f'' **14.** Graph of f''

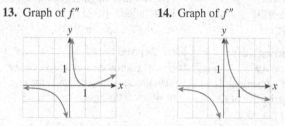

In Exercises 15 and 16 the position s of a point (in meters) is given as a function of time t (in seconds). Find (a) its acceleration as a function of t and (b) its acceleration at the specified time.

15. $s = \dfrac{2}{3t^2} - \dfrac{1}{t}; t = 1$ **16.** $s = \dfrac{4}{t^2} - \dfrac{3t}{4}; t = 2$

In Exercises 17–22, sketch the graph of the given function, indicating all relative and absolute extrema and points of inflection. Find the coordinates of these points exactly, where possible. Also indicate any horizontal and vertical asymptotes.

17. $f(x) = x^3 - 12x$ on $[-2, +\infty)$

18. $g(x) = x^4 - 4x$ on $[-1, 1]$

19. $f(x) = \dfrac{x^2 - 3}{x^3}$

20. $f(x) = (x - 1)^{2/3} + \dfrac{2x}{3}$

21. $g(x) = (x - 3)\sqrt{x}$

22. $g(x) = (x + 3)\sqrt{x}$

Applications: OHaganBooks.com
[Try the game at www.OHaganBooks.com]

23. *Revenue* Demand for the latest best-seller at OHaganBooks.com, *A River Burns through It*, is given by

$$q = -p^2 + 33p + 9 \quad (18 \le p \le 28)$$

copies sold per week when the price is p dollars. What price should the company charge to obtain the largest revenue?

24. *Revenue* Demand for *The Secret Loves of John O*, a romance novel by Margó Dufón that flopped after two weeks on the market, is given by

$$q = -2p^2 + 5p + 6 \quad (0 \le p \le 3.3)$$

copies sold per week when the price is p dollars. What price should OHaganBooks.com charge to obtain the largest revenue?

25. *Profit* Taking into account storage and shipping, it costs OHaganBooks.com

$$C = 9q + 100$$

dollars to sell q copies of *A River Burns through It* in a week (see Exercise 23).

a. If demand is as in Exercise 23, express the weekly profit earned by OHaganBooks.com from the sale of *A River Burns through It* as a function of unit price p.

b. What price should the company charge to get the largest weekly profit? What is the maximum possible weekly profit?

c. Compare your answer in part (b) with the price the company should charge to obtain the largest revenue (Exercise 23). Explain any difference.

26. *Profit* Taking into account storage and shipping, it costs OHaganBooks.com

$$C = 3q$$

dollars to sell q copies of Margó Dufón's *The Secret Loves of John O* in a week (see Exercise 24).

a. If demand is as in Exercise 24, express the weekly profit earned by OHaganBooks.com from the sale of *The Secret Loves of John O* as a function of unit price p.

b. What price should the company charge to get the largest weekly profit? What is the maximum possible weekly profit?

c. Compare your answer in part (b) with the price the company should charge to obtain the largest revenue (Exercise 24). Explain any difference.

27. *Office Space* Although still a sophomore at college, John O'Hagan's son Billy-Sean has already created several commercial video games and is currently working on his most ambitious project to date: a game called K that purports to be a "simulation of the world." John O'Hagan has decided to set aside some office space for Billy-Sean against the northern wall in the headquarters penthouse. The construction of the partition will cost $8 per foot for the south wall and $12 per foot for the east and west walls. What are the dimensions of the office space with the largest area that can be provided for Billy-Sean with a budget of $480, and what is its area?

28. *Recreation Space* As a result of complaints by the staff about noise, the coffee and recreation area for student interns at OHaganBooks.com will now be in a 384 square foot rectangular area in the headquarters basement against the southern wall. (The specified area was arrived at in complex negotiations between the student intern representative and management.) The construction of the partition will cost $12 per foot for the north wall and $4 per foot for the east and west walls. What are the dimensions of the cheapest recreation area that can be made, and how much will it cost?

29. *Box Design* The sales department at OHaganBooks.com, which has decided to send chocolate lobsters to each of its best customers, is trying to design a shipping box with a square base. It has a roll of cardboard 36 inches wide from which to make the boxes. Each box will be obtained by cutting out corners from a rectangle of cardboard as shown in the following diagram:

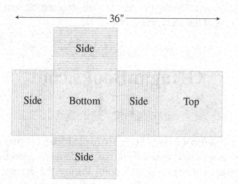

(Notice that the top and bottom of each box will be square, but the sides will not necessarily be square.) What are the dimensions of the boxes with the largest volume that can be made in this way? What is the maximum volume?

30. Box Redesign The sales department at OHaganBooks.com was not pleased with the result of the box design in Exercise 29; the resulting box was too large for the chocolate lobsters. Following a suggestion by a math major student intern, the department decided to redesign the boxes to meet the following specifications: As in Exercise 29, each box would be obtained by cutting out corners from a rectangle of cardboard, as shown in the following diagram:

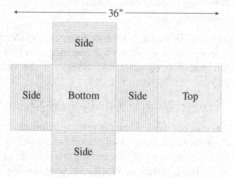

(Notice that the top and bottom of each box would be square, but not necessarily the sides.) The dimensions would be such that the total surface area of the sides plus the bottom of the box would be as large as possible. What are the dimensions of the boxes with the largest area that can be made in this way? How does this box compare with that obtained in Exercise 29?

31. Sales OHaganBooks.com modeled its weekly sales over a period of time with the function

$$s(t) = 6{,}053 + \frac{4{,}474}{1 + e^{-0.55(t-4.8)}},$$

where t is the time in weeks. Following are the graphs of s, s', and s'':

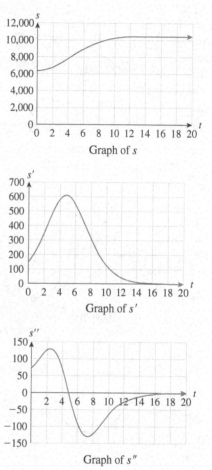

a. Estimate when, to the nearest week, the weekly sales were growing fastest.

b. To what features on the graphs of s, s', and s'' does your answer to part (a) correspond?

c. The graph of s has a horizontal asymptote. What is the approximate value (s-coordinate) of this asymptote, and what is its significance in terms of weekly sales at OHaganBooks.com?

d. The graph of s' has a horizontal asymptote. What is the value (s'-coordinate) of this asymptote, and what is its significance in terms of weekly sales at OHaganBooks.com?

32. Sales The quarterly sales of OHagan *oPods* (OHaganBooks.com's answer to the iPod; a portable audio book unit with an incidental music feature) from the fourth quarter of 2009 can be roughly approximated by the function

$$N(t) = \frac{1{,}100}{1 + 9(1.8)^{-t}} \text{ oPods} \quad (t \geq 0),$$

where t is time in quarters since the fourth quarter of 2009. Following are the graphs of N, N', and N'':

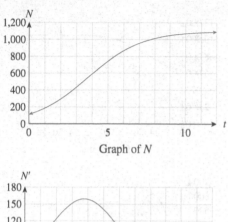

Graph of N

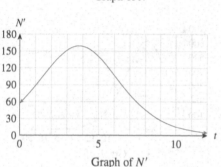

Graph of N'

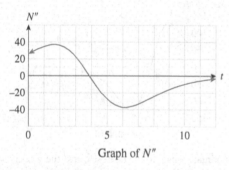

Graph of N''

a. Estimate when, to the nearest quarter, the quarterly sales were growing fastest.

b. To what features on the graphs of N, N', and N'' does your answer to part (a) correspond?

c. The graph of N has a horizontal asymptote. What is the approximate value (N-coordinate) of this asymptote, and what is its significance in terms of quarterly sales of *oPods*?

d. The graph of N' has a horizontal asymptote. What is the value (N'-coordinate) of this asymptote, and what is its significance in terms of quarterly sales of *oPods*?

33. **Chance Encounter** Marjory Duffin is walking north towards the corner entrance of OHaganBooks.com's company headquarters at 5 ft/sec, while John O'Hagan is walking west toward the same entrance, also at 5 ft/sec. How fast is their distance apart decreasing when

a. each of them is 2 feet from the corner?

b. each of them is 1 foot from the corner?

c. each of them is h feet from the corner?

d. they collide on the corner?

34. **Company Logos** OHaganBooks.com's website has an animated graphic with its name in a rectangle whose height and width change; on either side of the rectangle are semicircles, as in the figure, whose diameters are the same as the height of the rectangle.

For reasons too complicated to explain, the designer wanted the combined area of the rectangle and semicircles to remain constant. At one point during the animation the width of the rectangle is 1 inch, growing at a rate of 0.5 inches per second, while the height is 3 inches. How fast is the height changing?

35. **Elasticity of Demand** (Compare Exercise 23.) Demand for the latest best-seller at OHaganBooks.com, *A River Burns through It*, is given by

$$q = -p^2 + 33p + 9 \quad (18 \le p \le 28)$$

copies sold per week when the price is p dollars.

a. Find the price elasticity of demand as a function of p.

b. Find the elasticity of demand for this book at a price of $20 and at a price of $25. (Round your answers to two decimal places.) Interpret the answers.

c. What price should the company charge to obtain the largest revenue?

36. **Elasticity of Demand** (Compare Exercise 24.) Demand for *The Secret Loves of John O*, a romance novel by Margó Dufón that flopped after two weeks on the market, is given by

$$q = -2p^2 + 5p + 6 \quad (0 \le p \le 3.3)$$

copies sold per week when the price is p dollars.

a. Find the price elasticity of demand as a function of p.

b. Find the elasticity of demand for this book at a price of $2 and at a price of $3. (Round your answers to two decimal places.) Interpret the answers.

c. What price should the company charge to obtain the largest revenue?

37. **Elasticity of Demand** Last year OHaganBooks.com experimented with an online subscriber service, Red On Line (ROL), for its e-book service. The consumer demand for ROL was modeled by the equation

$$q = 1,000e^{-p^2+p},$$

where p was the monthly access charge and q is the number of subscribers.

a. Obtain a formula for the price elasticity of demand, E, for ROL services.

b. Compute the elasticity of demand if the monthly access charge is set at $2 per month. Interpret the result.

c. How much should the company have charged to obtain the maximum monthly revenue? What would this revenue have been?

38. *Elasticity of Demand* JungleBooks.com (one of OHaganBooks .com's main competitors) responded with its own online subscriber service, Better On Line (BOL), for its e-book service. The consumer demand for BOL was modeled by the equation

$$q = 2,000e^{-3p^2+2p},$$

where p was the monthly access charge and q is the number of subscribers.

a. Obtain a formula for the price elasticity of demand, E, for BOL services.

b. Compute the elasticity of demand if the monthly access charge is set at $2 per month. Interpret the result.

c. How much should the company have charged to obtain the maximum monthly revenue? What would this revenue have been?

CASE STUDY

Production Lot Size Management

Your publishing company, *Knockem Dead Paperbacks, Inc.,* is about to release its next best seller, *Henrietta's Heaving Heart* by Celestine A. Lafleur. The company expects to sell 100,000 books each month in the next year. You have been given the job of scheduling print runs to meet the anticipated demand and minimize total costs to the company. Each print run has a setup cost of $5,000, each book costs $1 to produce, and monthly storage costs for books awaiting shipment average 1¢ per book. What will you do?

If you decide to print all 1,200,000 books (the total demand for the year, 100,000 books per month for 12 months) in a single run at the start of the year and sales go as predicted, then the number of books in stock would begin at 1,200,000 and decrease to zero by the end of the year, as shown in Figure 47.

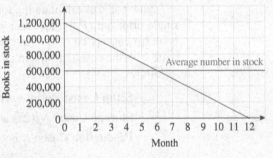

Figure 47

On average, you would be storing 600,000 books for 12 months at 1¢ per book, giving a total storage cost of $600,000 \times 12 \times 0.01 = \$72,000$. The setup cost for the single print run would be $5,000. When you add to these the total cost of producing 1,200,000 books at $1 per book, your total cost would be $1,277,000.

If, on the other hand, you decide to cut down on storage costs by printing the book in two runs of 600,000 each, you would get the picture shown in Figure 48.

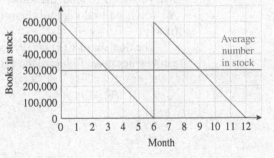

Figure 48

Now the storage cost would be cut in half because, on average, there would be only 300,000 books in stock. Thus, the total storage cost would be $36,000, and the setup cost would double to $10,000 (because there would now be two runs). The production costs would be the same: 1,200,000 books @ $1 per book. The total cost would therefore be reduced to $1,246,000, a savings of $31,000 compared to your first scenario.

"Aha!" you say to yourself, after doing these calculations. "Why not drastically cut costs by setting up a run every month?" You calculate that the setup costs alone would be $12 \times \$5,000 = \$60,000$, which is already more than the setup plus storage costs for two runs, so a run every month will cost too much. Perhaps, then, you should investigate three runs, four runs, and so on, until you find the lowest cost. This strikes you as too laborious a process, especially considering that you will have to do it all over again when planning for Lafleur's sequel, *Lorenzo's Lost Love*, due to be released next year. Realizing that this is an optimization problem, you decide to use some calculus to help you come up with a *formula* that you can use for all future plans. So you get to work.

Instead of working with the number 1,200,000, you use the letter N so that you can be as flexible as possible. (What if *Lorenzo's Lost Love* sells more copies?) Thus, you have a total of N books to be produced for the year. You now calculate the total cost of using x print runs per year. Because you are to produce a total of N books in x print runs, you will have to produce N/x books in each print run. N/x is called the **lot size**. As you can see from the diagrams above, the average number of books in storage will be half that amount, $N/(2x)$.

Now you can calculate the total cost for a year. Write P for the setup cost of a single print run ($P = \$5,000$ in your case) and c for the *annual* cost of storing a book (to convert all of the time measurements to years; $c = \$0.12$ here). Finally, write b for the cost of producing a single book ($b = \$1$ here). The costs break down as follows:

Setup Costs: x print runs @ P dollars per run: Px

Storage Costs: $N/(2x)$ books stored @ c dollars per year: $cN/(2x)$

Production Costs: N books @ b dollars per book: Nb

Total Cost: $Px + \dfrac{cN}{2x} + Nb$

Remember that P, N, c, and b are all constants and x is the only variable. Thus, your cost function is

$$C(x) = Px + \frac{cN}{2x} + Nb,$$

and you need to find the value of x that will minimize $C(x)$. But that's easy! All you need to do is find the relative extrema and select the absolute minimum (if any).

The domain of $C(x)$ is $(0, +\infty)$ because there is an x in the denominator and x can't be negative. To locate the extrema, you start by locating the critical points:

$$C'(x) = P - \frac{cN}{2x^2}.$$

The only singular point would be at $x = 0$, but 0 is not in the domain. To find stationary points, you set $C'(x) = 0$ and solve for x:

$$P - \frac{cN}{2x^2} = 0$$

$$2x^2 = \frac{cN}{P},$$

so

$$x = \sqrt{\frac{cN}{2P}}.$$

There is only one stationary point, and there are no singular points or endpoints. To graph the function, you will need to put in numbers for the various constants. Substituting $N = 1{,}200{,}000$, $P = 5{,}000$, $c = 0.12$, and $b = 1$, you get

$$C(x) = 5{,}000x + \frac{72{,}000}{x} + 1{,}200{,}000$$

with the stationary point at

$$x = \sqrt{\frac{(0.12)(1{,}200{,}000)}{2(5000)}} \approx 3.79.$$

The total cost at the stationary point is

$$C(3.79) \approx 1{,}237{,}900.$$

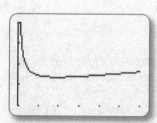

Figure 49

You now graph $C(x)$ in a window that includes the stationary point, say, $0 \le x \le 12$ and $1{,}100{,}000 \le C \le 1{,}500{,}000$, getting Figure 49.

From the graph you can see that the stationary point is an absolute minimum. In the graph it appears that the graph is always concave up, which also tells you that your stationary point is a minimum. You can check the concavity by computing the second derivative:

$$C''(x) = \frac{cN}{x^3} > 0.$$

The second derivative is always positive because c, N, and x are all positive numbers, so indeed the graph is always concave up. Now you also know that it works regardless of the particular values of the constants.

So now you are practically done! You know that the absolute minimum cost occurs when you have $x \approx 3.79$ print runs per year. Don't be disappointed that the answer is not a whole number; whole number solutions are rarely found in real scenarios. What the answer (and the graph) do indicate is that either three or four print runs per year will cost the least money. If you take $x = 3$, you get a total cost of

$$C(3) = \$1{,}239{,}000.$$

If you take $x = 4$, you get a total cost of

$$C(4) = \$1{,}238{,}000.$$

So four print runs per year will allow you to minimize your total costs.

EXERCISES

1. *Lorenzo's Lost Love* will sell 2,000,000 copies in a year. The remaining costs are the same. How many print runs should you use now?

2. In general, what happens to the number of runs that minimizes cost if both the setup cost and the total number of books are doubled?

3. In general, what happens to the number of runs that minimizes cost if the setup cost increases by a factor of 4?

4. Assuming that the total number of copies and storage costs are as originally stated, find the setup cost that would result in a single print run.

5. Assuming that the total number of copies and setup cost are as originally stated, find the storage cost that would result in a print run each month.

6. In Figure 48 we assumed that all the books in each run were manufactured in a very short time; otherwise, the figure might have looked more like the following graph, which shows the inventory, assuming a slower rate of production.

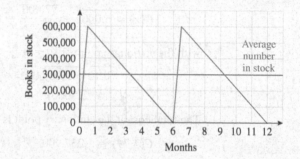

How would this affect the answer?

7. Referring to the general situation discussed in the text, find the cost as a function of the total number of books produced, assuming that the number of runs is chosen to minimize total cost. Also find the average cost per book.

8. Let $\overline{C}$ be the average cost function found in Exercise 7. Calculate $\lim_{N \to +\infty} \overline{C}(N)$, and interpret the result.

Section 12.6

Example 1(a) (page 970)   Suppose that the demand equation for *Bobby Dolls* is given by $q = 216 - p^2$, where p is the price per doll in dollars and q is the number of dolls sold per week. Compute the price elasticity of demand when $p = \$5$ and $p = \$10$, and interpret the results.

Solution

The TI-83/84 Plus function `nDeriv` can be used to compute approximations of the elasticity E at various prices.

1. Set

$Y_1=216-X^2$ Demand equation

$Y_2=-nDeriv(Y_1,X,X)*X/Y_1$ Formula for E

2. Use the table feature to list the values of elasticity for a range of prices. For part (a) we chose values of X close to 5:

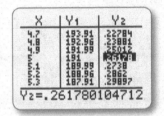

Section 12.6

Example 1(a) (page 970)   Suppose that the demand equation for *Bobby Dolls* is given by $q = 216 - p^2$, where p is the price per doll in dollars and q is the number of dolls sold per week. Compute the price elasticity of demand when $p = \$5$ and $p = \$10$, and interpret the results.

Solution

To approximate E in a spreadsheet, we can use the following approximation of E:

$$E \approx \frac{\text{Percentage decrease in demand}}{\text{Percentage increase in price}} \approx -\frac{\left(\dfrac{\Delta q}{q}\right)}{\left(\dfrac{\Delta p}{p}\right)}.$$

The smaller Δp is, the better the approximation. Let's use $\Delta p = 1\cent$, or 0.01 (which is small in comparison with the typical prices we consider—around $5 to $10).

1. We start by setting up our worksheet to list a range of prices, in increments of Δp, on either side of a price in which we are interested, such as $p_0 = \$5$:

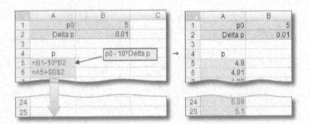

We start in cell A5 with the formula for $p_0 - 10\Delta p$ and then successively add Δp going down column A. You will find that the value $p_0 = 5$ appears midway down the list.

2. Next, we compute the corresponding values for the demand q in column B:

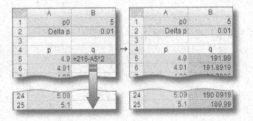

3. We add two new columns for the percentage changes in p and q. The formula shown in cell C5 is copied down columns C and D, to row 24. (Why not row 25?)

4. The elasticity can now be computed in column E as shown:

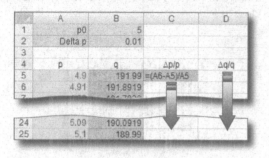

	A	B	C	D
1	p0	5		
2	Delta p	0.01		
3				
4	p	q	Δp/p	Δq/q
5	4.9	191.99	=(A6-A5)/A5	
6	4.91	191.8919		
7				
24	5.09	190.0919		
25	5.1	189.99		

	A	B	C	D	E
1	p0	5			
2	Delta p	0.01			
3					
4	p	q	Δp/p	Δq/q	E
5	4.9	191.99	0.00204082	-0.00051096	=-D5/C5
6	4.91	191.8919	0.00203666	-0.00051227	
7					
24	5.09	190.0919	0.00196464	-0.00053606	
25	5.1	189.99			

↓

	A	B	C	D	E
1	p0	5			
2	Delta p	0.01			
3					
4	p	q	Δp/p	Δq/q	E
5	4.9	191.99	0.00204082	-0.00051096	0.25037242
14	4.99	191.0999	0.00200401	-0.00052270	0.26085885
15	5	191	0.002	-0.00052408	0.26204188
16	5.01	190.8999	0.00199601	-0.00052541	0.26322853
17	5.02	190.7996	0.00199203	-0.00052673	0.26441879

13

THE INTEGRAL

CASE STUDY

Spending on Housing Construction

It is March 2007, and *Time* magazine, in its latest edition, is asking, "Will the Housing Bubble Burst in 2007?" You are a summer intern at *Schottie Construction Co.*, which is working with *Pack-Em-In Real Estate* on a major luxury condominium development to be called "Pack-Em-In/Schottie Towers." You have been asked to find formulas for monthly spending on housing construction in the United States and for the average spent per month starting 1 year ago. You have data about percentage spending changes.

How will you model the trend and estimate the total?

Rob Stothard/Stringer/Getty Images

 **www.WanerMath.com**

At the Website, in addition to the resources listed in the Preface, you will find:

- A numerical integration utility with Riemann sum grapher

The following extra topic:

- Numerical Integration

Introduction

Roughly speaking, calculus is divided into two parts: **differential calculus** (the calculus of derivatives) and **integral calculus**, which is the subject of this chapter and the next. Integral calculus is concerned with problems that are in some sense the reverse of the problems seen in differential calculus. For example, where differential calculus shows how to compute the rate of change of a quantity, integral calculus shows how to find the quantity if we know its rate of change. This idea is made precise in the **Fundamental Theorem of Calculus**. Integral calculus and the Fundamental Theorem of Calculus allow us to solve many problems in economics, physics, and geometry, including one of the oldest problems in mathematics: computing areas of regions with curved boundaries.

13.1 The Indefinite Integral

Antiderivatives and the Indefinite Integral

Suppose that we knew the marginal cost to manufacture an item and we wanted to reconstruct the cost function. We would have to *reverse* the process of differentiation to go from the derivative (the marginal cost function) back to the original function (the total cost). We'll first discuss how to do that and then look at some applications.

Here is an example: If the derivative of $F(x)$ is $4x^3$, what was $F(x)$? We recognize $4x^3$ as the derivative of x^4. So we might have $F(x) = x^4$. However, $F(x) = x^4 + 7$ works just as well. In fact, $F(x) = x^4 + C$ works for any number C. Thus, there are *infinitely many* possible answers to this question.

In fact, we will see shortly that the formula $F(x) = x^4 + C$ covers *all* possible answers to the question. Let's give a name to what we are doing.

Antiderivative

An **antiderivative** of a function f is a function F such that $F' = f$.

Quick Examples

1. An antiderivative of $4x^3$ is x^4.   Because the derivative of x^4 is $4x^3$
2. Another antiderivative of $4x^3$ is $x^4 + 7$.   Because the derivative of $x^4 + 7$ is $4x^3$
3. An antiderivative of $2x$ is $x^2 + 12$.   Because the derivative of $x^2 + 12$ is $2x$

Thus,

If the derivative of $A(x)$ is $B(x)$, then an antiderivative of $B(x)$ is $A(x)$.

We call the set of *all* antiderivatives of a function the **indefinite integral** of the function.

Indefinite Integral

$$\int f(x)\, dx$$

is read "the **indefinite integral** of $f(x)$ with respect to x" and stands for the set of all antiderivatives of f. Thus, $\int f(x)\, dx$ is a *collection of functions*; it is not a single function or a number. The function f that is being **integrated** is called the **integrand**, and the variable x is called the **variable of integration**.

> ### Quick Examples
>
> **4.** $\displaystyle \int 4x^3 \, dx = x^4 + C$ Every possible antiderivative of $4x^3$ has the form $x^4 + C$.
>
> **5.** $\displaystyle \int 2x \, dx = x^2 + C$ Every possible antiderivative of $2x$ has the form $x^2 + C$.

The **constant of integration** C reminds us that we can add any constant and get a different antiderivative.

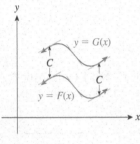

Figure 1

Q : *If $F(x)$ is one antiderivative of $f(x)$, why must all other antiderivatives have the form $F(x) + C$?*

A : Suppose $F(x)$ and $G(x)$ are both antiderivatives of $f(x)$, so that $F'(x) = G'(x)$. Consider what this means by looking at Figure 1. If $F'(x) = G'(x)$ for all x, then F and G have the *same slope* at each value of x. This means that their graphs must be *parallel* and hence remain exactly the same vertical distance apart. But that is the same as saying that the functions differ by a constant—that is, that $G(x) = F(x) + C$ for some constant C.*

---

* This argument can be turned into a more rigorous proof—that is, a proof that does not rely on geometric concepts such as parallel graphs. We should also say that the result (and our geometric argument as well!) requires that the domain of F and G be a single (possibly infinite) open interval.

EXAMPLE 1   Indefinite Integral

Check the following:

a. $\displaystyle \int x \, dx = \frac{x^2}{2} + C$ **b.** $\displaystyle \int x^2 \, dx = \frac{x^3}{3} + C$ **c.** $\displaystyle \int x^{-1} \, dx = \ln|x| + C$

Solution We check each equation by taking the derivative of its right-hand side and checking whether it equals the integrand on the left:

a. $\displaystyle \frac{d}{dx}\left(\frac{x^2}{2} + C\right) = \frac{2x}{2} + 0 = x$ ✔

b. $\displaystyle \frac{d}{dx}\left(\frac{x^3}{3} + C\right) = \frac{3x^2}{3} + 0 = x^2$ ✔

c. $\displaystyle \frac{d}{dx}(\ln|x| + C) = \frac{1}{x} + 0 = x^{-1}.$ ✔

Because the derivative of the right-hand side is the integrand in each case, we can conclude that the given statements are all valid.[†]

† We are glossing over a subtlety in part (c): The constant of integration C can be different for $x < 0$ and $x > 0$ because the graph breaks at $x = 0$. (See the comment at the end of the previous marginal note.) In general, our understanding will be that the constant of integration may be different on disconnected intervals of the domain.

➡ **Before we go on...** Example 1 gives us a very useful technique to check our answer every time we calculate an integral:

Take the derivative of the answer, and check that it equals the integrand. ∎

Calculating Indefinite Integrals

Now, we would like to make the process of finding indefinite integrals (antiderivatives) more mechanical. For example, it would be nice to have a power rule for indefinite integrals similar to the one we already have for derivatives. Example 1 already suggests such a rule for us.

Power Rule for the Indefinite Integral

$$\int x^n \, dx = \frac{x^{n+1}}{n+1} + C \qquad \text{This holds only if } n \neq -1.*$$

$$\int x^{-1} \, dx = \ln|x| + C \qquad \text{For the special case } n = -1^\dagger$$

Equivalent Form of Second Formula: $\int \frac{1}{x} \, dx = \ln|x| + C \quad \text{Because } x^{-1} = \frac{1}{x}$

In Words: For n other than -1, to find the integral of x^n, add 1 to the exponent, and then divide by the new exponent. When $n = -1$, the answer is the natural logarithm of the absolute value of x.

* Note that the right-hand side of the formula makes no sense if $n = -1$ because it has $n + 1$ in the denominator.

† If x is understood to be positive, then we can drop the absolute values and write

$$\int x^{-1} \, dx = \ln x + C.$$

Quick Examples

6. $\displaystyle \int x^{55} \, dx = \frac{x^{56}}{56} + C$

7. $\displaystyle \int \frac{1}{x^{55}} \, dx = \int x^{-55} \, dx \qquad$ Power form

$$= \frac{x^{-54}}{-54} + C \qquad \text{When we add 1 to } -55, \text{ we get } -54, \text{ not } -56.$$

$$= -\frac{1}{54x^{54}} + C$$

8. $\displaystyle \int 1 \, dx = x + C \qquad$ Because $1 = x^0$. This is an important special case.

9. $\displaystyle \int \sqrt{x} \, dx = \int x^{1/2} \, dx \qquad$ Power form

$$= \frac{x^{3/2}}{3/2} + C$$

$$= \frac{2x^{3/2}}{3} + C$$

Notes

1. The integral $\displaystyle \int 1 \, dx$ is commonly written as $\displaystyle \int dx$. Similarly, the integral $\displaystyle \int \frac{1}{x^{55}} \, dx$ may be written as $\displaystyle \int \frac{dx}{x^{55}}$.

2. We can easily check the power rule formula by taking the derivative of the right-hand side:

$$\frac{d}{dx}\left(\frac{x^{n+1}}{n+1} + C\right) = \frac{(n+1)x^n}{n+1} = x^n. \quad \checkmark$$

3. Because the derivative of $\ln x$ is also $1/x$, you might be tempted to write $\int x^{-1}\,dx = \ln x + C$. But $\ln x$, being defined only for positive x, does not have the same domain as $1/x$, whereas $\ln|x|$ does. So we must use $\ln|x| + C$ instead. ∎

Following are more indefinite integrals that come from formulas for differentiation we have encountered before.

Indefinite Integral of e^x, b^x, and $|x|$

$$\int e^x\,dx = e^x + C \qquad \text{Because } \frac{d}{dx}(e^x) = e^x$$

If b is any positive number other than 1, then

$$\int b^x\,dx = \frac{b^x}{\ln b} + C \qquad \text{Because } \frac{d}{dx}\left(\frac{b^x}{\ln b}\right) = \frac{b^x\ln b}{\ln b} = b^x$$

$$\int |x|\,dx = \frac{x|x|}{2} + C. \qquad \text{Because } \frac{d}{dx}\left(\frac{x|x|}{2}\right) = |x| \quad \text{(Check this yourself!)}$$

Quick Example

10. $\displaystyle\int 2^x\,dx = \frac{2^x}{\ln 2} + C$

For more complicated functions, such as $2x^3 + 6x^5 - 1$, we need the following rules for integrating sums, differences, and constant multiples.

Sums, Differences, and Constant Multiples

Sum and Difference Rules

$$\int [f(x) \pm g(x)]\,dx = \int f(x)\,dx \pm \int g(x)\,dx$$

In Words: The integral of a sum is the sum of the integrals, and the integral of a difference is the difference of the integrals.

Constant Multiple Rule

$$\int kf(x)\,dx = k\int f(x)\,dx \quad (k \text{ constant})$$

In Words: The integral of a constant times a function is the constant times the integral of the function. (In other words, the constant "goes along for the ride.")

Quick Examples

11. Sum Rule: $\displaystyle\int (x^3 + 1)\, dx = \int x^3\, dx + \int 1\, dx = \frac{x^4}{4} + x + C$

$f(x) = x^3;\ g(x) = 1$

12. Constant Multiple Rule: $\displaystyle\int 5x^3\, dx = 5 \int x^3\, dx = 5\frac{x^4}{4} + C$

$k = 5;\ f(x) = x^3$

13. Constant Multiple Rule: $\displaystyle\int 4\, dx = 4 \int 1\, dx = 4x + C$

$k = 4;\ f(x) = 1$

14. Constant Multiple Rule: $\displaystyle\int 4e^x\, dx = 4 \int e^x\, dx = 4e^x + C$

$k = 4;\ f(x) = e^x$

Proof of the Sum Rule

We saw above that if two functions have the same derivative, they differ by a (possibly zero) constant. Look at the rule for sums:

$$\int [f(x) + g(x)]\, dx = \int f(x)\, dx + \int g(x)\, dx.$$

If we take the derivative of the left-hand side with respect to x, we get the integrand, $f(x) + g(x)$. If we take the derivative of the right-hand side, we get

$$\frac{d}{dx}\left[\int f(x)\, dx + \int g(x)\, dx\right] = \frac{d}{dx}\left[\int f(x)\, dx\right] + \frac{d}{dx}\left[\int g(x)\, dx\right]$$

Derivative of a sum = Sum of derivatives.

$$= f(x) + g(x).$$

Because the left- and right-hand sides have the same derivative, they differ by a constant. But because both expressions are indefinite integrals, adding a constant does not affect their value, so they are the same as indefinite integrals.

Notice that a key step in the proof was the fact that the derivative of a sum is the sum of the derivatives.

A similar proof works for the difference and constant multiple rules.

EXAMPLE 2 **Using the Sum and Difference Rules**

Find the integrals:

a. $\displaystyle\int (x^3 + x^5 - 1)\, dx$ **b.** $\displaystyle\int \left(x^{2.1} + \frac{1}{x^{1.1}} + \frac{1}{x} + e^x \right) dx$ **c.** $\displaystyle\int (e^x + 3^x - |x|)\, dx$

Solution

a. $\displaystyle\int (x^3 + x^5 - 1)\, dx = \int x^3\, dx + \int x^5\, dx - \int 1\, dx$ Sum/difference rule

$$= \frac{x^4}{4} + \frac{x^6}{6} - x + C \qquad\qquad \text{Power rule}$$

b. $\int \left(x^{2.1} + \dfrac{1}{x^{1.1}} + \dfrac{1}{x} + e^x \right) dx$

$$= \int (x^{2.1} + x^{-1.1} + x^{-1} + e^x)\, dx \qquad \text{Power form}$$

$$= \int x^{2.1}\, dx + \int x^{-1.1}\, dx + \int x^{-1}\, dx + \int e^x\, dx \qquad \text{Sum rule}$$

$$= \frac{x^{3.1}}{3.1} + \frac{x^{-0.1}}{-0.1} + \ln|x| + e^x + C \qquad \text{Power rule and exponential rule}$$

$$= \frac{x^{3.1}}{3.1} - \frac{10}{x^{0.1}} + \ln|x| + e^x + C$$

c. $\int (e^x + 3^x - |x|)\, dx = \int e^x\, dx + \int 3^x\, dx - \int |x|\, dx \qquad \text{Sum/difference rule}$

$$= e^x + \frac{3^x}{\ln 3} - \frac{x|x|}{2} + C \qquad \text{Rules for powers, exponentials, and absolute value}$$

➡ **Before we go on ...** You should check each of the answers in Example 2 by differentiating.

Q : *Why is there only a single arbitrary constant C in each of the answers?*

A : We could have written the answer to part (a) as

$$\frac{x^4}{4} + D + \frac{x^6}{6} + E - x + F,$$

where D, E, and F are all arbitrary constants. Now suppose, for example, that we set $D = 1$, $E = -2$, and $F = 6$. Then the particular antiderivative we get is $x^4/4 + x^6/6 - x + 5$, which has the form $x^4/4 + x^6/6 - x + C$. Thus, we could have chosen the single constant C to be 5 and obtained the same answer. In other words, the answer $x^4/4 + x^6/6 - x + C$ is just as general as the answer $x^4/4 + D + x^6/6 + E - x + F$ but simpler.

In practice we do not explicitly write the integral of a sum as a sum of integrals but just "integrate term by term," much as we learned to differentiate term by term.

EXAMPLE 3   **Combining the Rules**

Find the integrals:

a. $\int (10x^4 + 2x^2 - 3e^x)\, dx$ **b.** $\int \left(\dfrac{2}{x^{0.1}} + \dfrac{x^{0.1}}{2} - \dfrac{3}{4x} \right) dx$

c. $\int (3e^x - 2(1.2^x) + 5|x|)\, dx$

Solution

a. We need to integrate separately each of the terms $10x^4$, $2x^2$, and $3e^x$. To integrate $10x^4$, we use the rules for constant multiples and powers:

$$\int 10x^4 \, dx = 10 \int x^4 \, dx = 10\frac{x^5}{5} + C = 2x^5 + C.$$

The other two terms are similar. We get

$$\int (10x^4 + 2x^2 - 3e^x) \, dx = 10\frac{x^5}{5} + 2\frac{x^3}{3} - 3e^x + C = 2x^5 + \frac{2}{3}x^3 - 3e^x + C.$$

b. We first convert to power form and then integrate term by term:

$$\int \left(\frac{2}{x^{0.1}} + \frac{x^{0.1}}{2} - \frac{3}{4x} \right) dx = \int \left(2x^{-0.1} + \frac{1}{2}x^{0.1} - \frac{3}{4}x^{-1} \right) dx \qquad \text{Power form}$$

$$= 2\frac{x^{0.9}}{0.9} + \frac{1}{2}\frac{x^{1.1}}{1.1} - \frac{3}{4}\ln|x| + C \qquad \text{Integrate term by term.}$$

$$= \frac{20x^{0.9}}{9} + \frac{x^{1.1}}{2.2} - \frac{3}{4}\ln|x| + C. \qquad \text{Back to positive exponent form}$$

c. $\displaystyle \int (3e^x - 2(1.2^x) + 5|x|) \, dx = 3e^x - 2\frac{1.2^x}{\ln 1.2} + 5\frac{x|x|}{2} + C$

EXAMPLE 4   Different Variable Name

Find $\displaystyle \int \left(\frac{1}{u} + \frac{1}{u^2} \right) du.$

Solution This integral may look a little strange because we are using the letter u instead of x, but there is really nothing special about x. Using u as the variable of integration, we get

$$\int \left(\frac{1}{u} + \frac{1}{u^2} \right) du = \int (u^{-1} + u^{-2}) \, du \qquad \text{Power form}$$

$$= \ln|u| + \frac{u^{-1}}{-1} + C \qquad \text{Integrate term by term.}$$

$$= \ln|u| - \frac{1}{u} + C. \qquad \text{Simplify the result.}$$

➡ **Before we go on...** When we compute an indefinite integral, we want the independent variable in the answer to be the same as the variable of integration. Thus, if the integral in Example 4 had been written in terms of x rather than u, we would have written

$$\int \left(\frac{1}{x} + \frac{1}{x^2} \right) dx = \ln|x| - \frac{1}{x} + C. \qquad ∎$$

Applications

EXAMPLE 5   Finding Cost from Marginal Cost

The marginal cost to produce baseball caps at a production level of x caps is $4 - 0.001x$ dollars per cap, and the cost of producing 100 caps is $500. Find the cost function.

Solution We are asked to find the cost function $C(x)$ given that the *marginal* cost function is $4 - 0.001x$. Recalling that the marginal cost function is the derivative of the cost function, we can write

$$C'(x) = 4 - 0.001x$$

and must find $C(x)$. Now $C(x)$ must be an antiderivative of $C'(x)$, so

$$C(x) = \int (4 - 0.001x)\, dx$$

$$= 4x - 0.001\frac{x^2}{2} + K \qquad K \text{ is the constant of integration.}*$$

$$= 4x - 0.0005x^2 + K.$$

> *We used K and not C for the constant of integration because we are using C for cost.

Now, unless we have a value for K, we don't really know what the cost function is. However, there is another piece of information we have ignored: The cost of producing 100 baseball caps is $500. In symbols,

$$C(100) = 500.$$

Substituting in our formula for $C(x)$, we have

$$C(100) = 4(100) - 0.0005(100)^2 + K$$
$$500 = 395 + K$$
$$K = 105.$$

Now that we know what K is, we can write down the cost function:

$$C(x) = 4x - 0.0005x^2 + 105.$$

➡ **Before we go on . . .** Let us consider the significance of the constant term 105 in Example 5. If we substitute $x = 0$ into the cost function, we get

$$C(0) = 4(0) - 0.0005(0)^2 + 105 = 105.$$

Thus, $105 is the cost of producing zero items; in other words, it is the **fixed cost**. ∎

EXAMPLE 6   Total Sales from Annual Sales

By the start of 2008, Apple had sold a total of about 3.5 million iPhones. From the start of 2008 through the end of 2014, sales of iPhones were approximately

$$s(t) = 1.5t^2 + 20t + 0.25 \text{ million iPhones per year} \qquad (0 \le t \le 6),$$

where t is time in years since the start of 2008.[1]

---

[1] Source for data: Apple quarterly press releases (www.apple.com/investor/).

a. Find an expression for the total sales of iPhones up to time t.

b. Use the answer to part (a) to estimate the total sales of iPhones by the end of 2014. (The actual figure was 472 million.)

Solution

a. Let $S(t)$ be the total sales of iPhones, in millions, up to time t, where t is measured in years since the start of 2008, so we know that $S(0) = 3.5$. We are also given an expression for the number of iPhones sold per year. This function is the *derivative* of $S(t)$:

$$S'(t) = 1.5t^2 + 20t + 0.25.$$

Thus, the desired total sales function must be an antiderivative of $S'(t)$:

$$S(t) = \int (1.5t^2 + 20t + 0.25)\, dt$$

$$= \frac{1.5t^3}{3} + 20\frac{t^2}{2} + 0.25t + C$$

$$= 0.5t^3 + 10t^2 + 0.25t + C.$$

To calculate the value of the constant C, we can, as in the preceding example, use the known value of S: $S(0) = 3.5$.

$$S(0) = 0.5(0)^3 + 10(0)^2 + 0.25(0) + C = 3.5,$$

so

$$C = 3.5.$$

We can now write down the total sales function:

$$S(t) = 0.5t^3 + 10t^2 + 0.25t + 3.5 \text{ million iPhones.}$$

b. Because the start of 2014 corresponds to $t = 6$, we calculate total sales as

$$S(3) = 0.5(6)^3 + 10(6)^2 + 0.25(6) + 3.5 = 473 \text{ million iPhones,}$$

remarkably close to the actual 472 million figure!

Motion in a Straight Line

An important application of the indefinite integral is to the study of motion. The application of calculus to problems about motion is an example of the intertwining of mathematics and physics. We begin by bringing together some facts, scattered through the last several chapters, that have to do with an object moving in a straight line. We then restate them in terms of antiderivatives.

Position, Velocity, and Acceleration: Derivative Form

If $s = s(t)$ is the **position** of an object at time t, then its **velocity** is given by the derivative

$$v = \frac{ds}{dt}.$$

In Words: Velocity is the derivative of position.

The **acceleration** of an object is given by the derivative

$$a = \frac{dv}{dt}.$$

In Words: Acceleration is the derivative of velocity.

Position, Velocity, and Acceleration: Integral Form

$$s(t) = \int v(t)\,dt \qquad \text{Because } v = \frac{ds}{dt}$$

$$v(t) = \int a(t)\,dt \qquad \text{Because } a = \frac{dv}{dt}$$

Quick Examples

15. If the velocity of a particle moving in a straight line is given by $v(t) = 4t + 1$, then its position after t seconds is given by $s(t) = \int v(t)\,dt = \int (4t + 1)\,dt = 2t^2 + t + C$.

16. If sales are accelerating at 2 golf balls per day per day, then the rate of change of sales ("velocity of sales") is $v(t) = \int a(t)\,dt = \int 2\,dt = 2t + C$ golf balls per day.

17. If the rate of change of sales is $v(t) = 2t + 5$ golf balls per day, then the total sales are $s(t) = \int v(t)\,dt = \int (2t + 5)\,dt = t^2 + 5t + C$ golf balls sold through time t.

EXAMPLE 7   Motion in a Straight Line

a. The velocity of a particle moving along a straight line is given by $v(t) = 4t + 1$ m/sec. Given that the particle is at position $s = 2$ meters at time $t = 1$, find an expression for s in terms of t.

b. For a freely falling body experiencing no air resistance and zero initial velocity, find an expression for the velocity v in terms of t. [Note: On Earth a freely falling body experiencing no air resistance accelerates downward at approximately 9.8 meters per second per second, or 9.8 m/sec² (or 32 ft/sec²).]

Solution

a. As we saw in Quick Example 15, the position of the particle after t seconds is given by

$$s(t) = \int v(t)\,dt$$

$$= \int (4t + 1)\,dt = 2t^2 + t + C.$$

But what is the value of C? Now, we are told that the particle is at position $s = 2$ at time $t = 1$. In other words, $s(1) = 2$. Substituting this into the expression for $s(t)$ gives

$$2 = 2(1)^2 + 1 + C$$

so

$$C = -1.$$

Hence the position after t seconds is given by

$$s(t) = 2t^2 + t - 1 \text{ meters.}$$

b. Let's measure heights above the ground as positive so that a rising object has positive velocity and the acceleration due to gravity is negative. (It causes the upward velocity to decrease in value.) Thus, the acceleration of the object is given by

$$a(t) = -9.8 \text{ m/sec}^2.$$

We wish to know the velocity, which is an antiderivative of acceleration, so we compute

$$v(t) = \int a(t)\, dt = \int (-9.8)\, dt = -9.8t + C.$$

To find the value of C, we use the given information that at time $t = 0$ the velocity is 0: $v(0) = 0$. Substituting this into the expression for $v(t)$ gives

$$0 = -9.8(0) + C$$

so

$$C = 0.$$

Hence, the velocity after t seconds is given by

$$v(t) = -9.8t \text{ m/sec.}$$

EXAMPLE 8 Vertical Motion under Gravity

You are standing on the edge of a cliff and toss a stone upward at a speed of $v_0 = 30$ ft/sec. (v_0 is called the *initial velocity*.)

a. Find the stone's velocity as a function of time. How fast and in what direction is it going after 5 seconds? (Neglect the effects of air resistance.)

b. Find the position of the stone as a function of time. Where will it be after 5 seconds?

c. When and where will the stone reach its zenith, its highest point?

Solution

a. This is similar to Example 7(b): Measuring height above the ground as positive, the acceleration of the stone is given by $a(t) = -32$ ft/sec^2, so

$$v(t) = \int (-32)\, dt = -32t + C.$$

To obtain C, we use the fact that you tossed the stone upward at 30 ft/sec; that is, when $t = 0$, $v = 30$, or $v(0) = 30$. Thus,

$$30 = v(0) = -32(0) + C,$$

so $C = 30$, and the formula for velocity is

$$v(t) = -32t + 30 \text{ ft/sec.} \qquad v(t) = -32t + v_0$$

In particular, after 5 seconds the velocity will be

$$v(5) = -32(5) + 30 = -130 \text{ ft/sec}.$$

After 5 seconds the stone is *falling* with a speed of 130 ft/sec.

b. We wish to know the position, but position is an antiderivative of velocity. Thus,

$$s(t) = \int v(t)\, dt = \int (-32t + 30)\, dt = -16t^2 + 30t + C.$$

Now to find C, we need to know the initial position $s(0)$. We are not told this, so let's measure heights so that the initial position is zero. Then

$$0 = s(0) = C,$$

and

$$s(t) = -16t^2 + 30t \text{ feet} \qquad \begin{aligned} s(t) &= -16t^2 + v_0 t + s_0 \\ s_0 &= \text{initial position} \end{aligned}$$

In particular, after 5 seconds the stone has a height of

$$s(5) = -16(5)^2 + 30(5) = -250 \text{ feet}.$$

In other words, the stone is now 250 feet *below* where it was when you first threw it, as shown in Figure 2.

c. The stone reaches its zenith when its height $s(t)$ is at its maximum value, which occurs when $v(t) = s'(t)$ is zero. So we solve

$$v(t) = -32t + 30 = 0$$

getting $t = 30/32 = 15/16 = 0.9375$ seconds. This is the time when the stone reaches its zenith. The height of the stone at that time is

$$s(15/16) = -16(15/16)^2 + 30(15/16) = 14.0625 \text{ feet}.$$

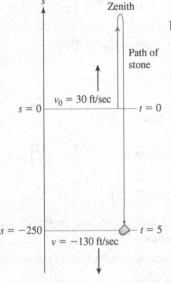

Figure 2

➡ **Before we go on...** Here again are the formulas we obtained in Example 8, together with their metric equivalents.

Vertical Motion under Gravity: Velocity and Position

If we ignore air resistance, the vertical velocity and position of an object moving under gravity are given by

British Units	**Metric Units**
Velocity: $v(t) = -32t + v_0$ ft/sec	$v(t) = -9.8t + v_0$ m/sec
Position: $s(t) = -16t^2 + v_0 t + s_0$ feet	$s(t) = -4.9t^2 + v_0 t + s_0$ meters

v_0 = initial velocity = velocity at time 0

s_0 = initial position = position at time 0

Quick Example

18. If a ball is thrown down at 2 ft/sec from a height of 200 feet, then its velocity and position after t seconds are $v(t) = -32t - 2$ ft/sec and $s(t) = -16t^2 - 2t + 200$ feet.

▼ more advanced   ◆ challenging
ℹ️ indicates exercises that should be solved using technology

In Exercises 1–42, evaluate the integral.
[**HINT**: for 1–6: See Quick Examples 6–9.]

1. $\int x^5 \, dx$ **2.** $\int x^7 \, dx$ **3.** $\int 6 \, dx$

4. $\int (-5) \, dx$ **5.** $\int x \, dx$ **6.** $\int (-x) \, dx$

[**HINT**: for 7–18: See Example 2.]

7. $\int (x^2 - x) \, dx$ **8.** $\int (x + x^3) \, dx$

9. $\int (1 + x) \, dx$ **10.** $\int (4 - x) \, dx$

11. $\int x^{-5} \, dx$ **12.** $\int x^{-7} \, dx$

13. $\int (x^{2.3} + x^{-1.3}) \, dx$ **14.** $\int (x^{-0.2} - x^{0.2}) \, dx$

15. $\int (u^2 - u^{-1}) \, du$ [**HINT**: See Example 4.]

16. $\int (v^{-2} + 2v^{-1}) \, dv$ [**HINT**: See Example 4.]

17. $\int \sqrt[4]{x} \, dx$ **18.** $\int \sqrt[3]{x} \, dx$

[**HINT**: for 19–42: See Example 3.]

19. $\int (3x^4 - 2x^{-2} + x^{-5} + 4) \, dx$

20. $\int (4x^7 - x^{-3} + 1) \, dx$

21. $\int \left(\frac{2}{u} + \frac{u}{4} \right) du$ **22.** $\int \left(\frac{2}{u^2} + \frac{u^2}{4} \right) du$

23. $\int \left(\frac{1}{x} + \frac{2}{x^2} - \frac{1}{x^3} \right) dx$ **24.** $\int \left(\frac{3}{x} - \frac{1}{x^5} + \frac{1}{x^7} \right) dx$

25. $\int (3x^{0.1} - x^{4.3} - 4.1) \, dx$ **26.** $\int \left(\frac{x^{2.1}}{2} - 2.3 \right) dx$

27. $\int \left(\frac{3}{x^{0.1}} - \frac{4}{x^{1.1}} \right) dx$ **28.** $\int \left(\frac{1}{x^{1.1}} - \frac{1}{x} \right) dx$

29. $\int \left(5.1t - \frac{1.2}{t} + \frac{3}{t^{1.2}} \right) dt$ **30.** $\int \left(3.2 + \frac{1}{t^{0.9}} + \frac{t^{1.2}}{3} \right) dt$

31. $\int (2e^x + 5|x| + 1/4) \, dx$

32. $\int (-4e^x + |x|/3 - 1/8) \, dx$

33. $\int \left(\frac{6.1}{x^{0.5}} + \frac{x^{0.5}}{6} - e^x \right) dx$ **34.** $\int \left(\frac{4.2}{x^{0.4}} + \frac{x^{0.4}}{3} - 2e^x \right) dx$

35. $\int (2^x - 3^x) \, dx$ **36.** $\int (1.1^x + 2^x) \, dx$

37. $\int \left(100(1.1^x) - \frac{2|x|}{3} \right) dx$

38. $\int \left(1,000(0.9^x) + \frac{4|x|}{5} \right) dx$

39. ▼ $\int x^{-2} \left(x^4 - \frac{3}{2x^4} \right) dx$ **40.** ▼ $\int 3x^4 \left(\frac{2}{x^4} + \frac{3}{5x^6} \right) dx$

41. ▼ $\int \frac{x+2}{x^3} \, dx$ **42.** ▼ $\int \frac{x^2 - 2}{x} \, dx$

43. Find $f(x)$ if $f(0) = 1$ and the tangent line at $(x, f(x))$ has slope x. [**HINT**: See Example 5.]

44. Find $f(x)$ if $f(1) = 1$ and the tangent line at $(x, f(x))$ has slope $\frac{1}{x}$. [**HINT**: See Example 5.]

45. Find $f(x)$ if $f(0) = 0$ and the tangent line at $(x, f(x))$ has slope $e^x - 1$.

46. Find $f(x)$ if $f(1) = -1$ and the tangent line at $(x, f(x))$ has slope $2e^x + 1$.

Applications

47. *Marginal Cost* The marginal cost of producing the xth box of light bulbs is $5 - \frac{x}{10,000}$, and the fixed cost is \$20,000. Find the cost function $C(x)$. [**HINT**: See Example 5.]

48. *Marginal Cost* The marginal cost of producing the xth box of DVDs is $10 + \frac{x^2}{100,000}$, and the fixed cost is \$100,000. Find the cost function $C(x)$. [**HINT**: See Example 5.]

49. *Marginal Cost* The marginal cost of producing the xth roll of film is $5 + 2x + \frac{1}{x}$. The total cost to produce one roll is \$1,000. Find the cost function $C(x)$.

50. *Marginal Cost* The marginal cost of producing the xth box of CDs is $10 + x + \frac{1}{x^2}$. The total cost to produce 100 boxes is \$10,000. Find the cost function $C(x)$.

51. *Facebook Membership* At the start of 2010, Facebook had 360 million members. Subsequently, new members joined at a rate of roughly

$$m(t) = -6.6t^2 + 18t + 220 \text{ million members per year}$$
$$(0 \le t \le 5),$$

where t is time in years since the start of 2010.[2]

a. Find an expression for total Facebook membership $M(t)$ at time t. [HINT: See Example 6.]

b. Use the answer to part (a) to estimate Facebook membership midway through 2014. (Round your answer to the nearest 1 million members. The actual figure was 1,317 million.)

52. _Uploads to YouTube_ Since YouTube first became available to the public in mid-2005, the rate at which video has been uploaded to the site can be approximated by

$$v(t) = 1.1t^2 - 2.6t + 2.3 \text{ million hours of video per year}$$
$$(0 \le t \le 9),$$

where t is time in years since June 2005.[3]

a. Find an expression for the total number of hours $V(t)$ of video at time t (starting from zero hours of video at $t = 0$). [HINT: See Example 6.]

b. Use the answer to part (a) to estimate the total number of hours of video uploaded by the start of 2014. (Round your answer to the nearest million hours of video.)

53. _Median Household Income_ From 2000 to 2007, median household income in the United States rose by an average of approximately \$1,200 per year.[4] Given that the median household income in 2000 was approximately \$42,000, use an indefinite integral to find a formula for the median household income I as a function of the year t ($t = 0$ represents 2000), and use your formula to estimate the median household income in 2005. (You can do this exercise without integration using the methods of Section 1.3, but here you should use an indefinite integral.)

54. _Mean Household Income_ From 2000 to 2007 the mean household income in the United States rose by an average of approximately \$1,500 per year.[5] Given that the mean household income in 2000 was approximately \$57,000, use an indefinite integral to find a formula for the mean household income I as a function of the year t ($t = 0$ represents 2000), and use your formula to estimate the mean household income in 2006. (You can do this exercise without integration using the methods of Section 1.3, but here you should use an indefinite integral.)

55. _Bottled Water Sales_ The rate of U.S. sales of bottled water for the period 2007–2014 can be approximated by

$$s(t) = 0.08t^2 - 0.26t + 8.8 \text{ billion gallons per year}$$
$$(0 \le t \le 7),$$

where t is time in years since the start of 2007.[6] Use an indefinite integral to approximate the total sales $S(t)$ of bottled water since the start of 2007. Approximately how much bottled water was sold from the start of 2007 to the start of 2014? [HINT: At the start of 2007, sales since that time are zero.]

56. _Bottled Water Sales_ The rate of U.S. per capita sales of bottled water for the period 2007–2014 can be approximated by

$$s(t) = 0.25t^2 - t + 29 \text{ gallons per year} \quad (0 \le t \le 7),$$

where t is time in years since the start of 2007.[7] Use an indefinite integral to approximate the total per capita sales $S(t)$ of bottled water since the start of 2007. Approximately how much bottled water was sold, per capita, from the start of 2007 to the end of 2012? [HINT: At the start of 2007, sales since that time are zero.]

57. ▽ **_Health-Care Spending in the 1990s_** Write $H(t)$ for the amount spent in the United States on health care in year t, where t is measured in years since 1990. The rate of increase of $H(t)$ was approximately \$65 billion per year in 1990 and rose to \$100 billion per year in 2000.[8]

a. Find a linear model for the rate of change $H'(t)$.

b. Given that \$700 billion was spent on health care in the United States in 1990, find the function $H(t)$.

58. ▽ **_Health-Care Spending in the 2000s_** Write $H(t)$ for the amount spent in the United States on health care in year t, where t is measured in years since 2000. The rate of increase of $H(t)$ was projected to rise from \$100 billion per year in 2000 to approximately \$190 billion per year in 2010.[9]

a. Find a linear model for the rate of change $H'(t)$.

b. Given that \$1,300 billion was spent on health care in the United States in 2000, find the function $H(t)$.

59. ▽ **_Subprime Mortgage during the Housing Bubble_** At the start of 2007 the percentage of U.S. mortgages that were subprime was about 13%, was increasing at a rate of 1 percentage point per year, but was decelerating at 0.4 percentage points per year per year.[10]

a. Find an expression for the rate of change (velocity) of this percentage at time t in years since the start of 2007.

b. Use the result of part (a) to find an expression for the percentage of mortgages that were subprime at time t, and use it to estimate the percentage at the start of 2008. [HINT: See Quick Examples 16 and 17.]

---

[2] Sources for data: www.facebook.com, www.statista.com.

[3] Sources for data: www.YouTube.com, www.statista.com.

[4] In current dollars, unadjusted for inflation. Source for data: U.S. Census Bureau (www.census.gov).

[5] _Ibid._

[6] Source for data: Beverage Marketing Corporation (www.bottledwater.org).

[7] _Ibid._

[8] Source: Centers for Medicare and Medicaid Services, "National Health Expenditures," 2002 version, released January 2004 (www.cms.hhs.gov/statistics/nhe/).

[9] Source: Centers for Medicare and Medicaid Services, "National Health Expenditures 1965–2013, History and Projections" (www.cms.hhs.gov/statistics/nhe/).

[10] Sources: Mortgage Bankers Association, UBS.

60. ▼ *Subprime Mortgage Debt during the Housing Bubble*
At the start of 2008 the value of subprime mortgage debt outstanding in the United States was about $1,300 billion, was increasing at a rate of 40 billion dollars per year, but was decelerating at 20 billion dollars per year per year.[11]
   a. Find an expression for the rate of change (velocity) of the value of subprime mortgage debt at time t in years since the start of 2008.
   b. Use the result of part (a) to find an expression for the value of subprime mortgage debt at time t, and use it to estimate the value at the start of 2009. [HINT: See Quick Examples 16 and 17.]

61. *Motion in a Straight Line* The velocity of a particle moving in a straight line is given by $v = t^2 + 1$.
   a. Find an expression for the position s after a time t.
   b. Given that $s = 1$ at time $t = 0$, find the constant of integration C, and hence find an expression for s in terms of t without any unknown constants. [HINT: See Example 7.]

62. *Motion in a Straight Line* The velocity of a particle moving in a straight line is given by $v = 3e^t + t$.
   a. Find an expression for the position s after a time t.
   b. Given that $s = 3$ at time $t = 0$, find the constant of integration C, and hence find an expression for s in terms of t without any unknown constants. [HINT: See Example 7.]

63. *Vertical Motion under Gravity* If a stone is dropped from a rest position above the ground, how fast (in feet per second) and in what direction will it be traveling after 10 seconds? (Neglect the effects of air resistance.) [HINT: See Example 8.]

64. *Vertical Motion under Gravity* If a stone is thrown upward at 10 feet per second, how fast (in feet per second) and in what direction will it be traveling after 10 seconds? (Neglect the effects of air resistance.) [HINT: See Example 8.]

65. *Vertical Motion under Gravity* Your name is Galileo Galilei, and you toss a weight upward at 16 ft/sec from the top of the Leaning Tower of Pisa (height 185 feet).
   a. Neglecting air resistance, find the weight's velocity as a function of time t in seconds.
   b. Find the height of the weight above the ground as a function of time. Where and when will it reach its zenith? [HINT: See Example 8 and the formulas that follow.]

66. *Vertical Motion under Gravity* Your name is Spaghettini Bologna (an assistant of Galileo Galilei), and, to impress your boss, you toss a weight upward at 24 ft/sec from the top of the Leaning Tower of Pisa (height 185 feet).
   a. Neglecting air resistance, find the weight's velocity as a function of time t in seconds.
   b. Find the height of the weight above the ground as a function of time. Where and when will it reach its zenith? [HINT: See Example 8 and the formulas that follow.]

67. ▼ *Tailwinds* The ground speed of an airliner is obtained by adding its air speed and the tailwind speed. On your recent trip from Mexico to the United States your plane was traveling at an air speed of 500 miles per hour and experienced tailwinds of $25 + 50t$ miles per hour, where t is the time in hours since takeoff.
   a. Obtain an expression for the distance traveled in terms of the time since takeoff. [HINT: Ground speed = Air speed + Tailwind speed.]
   b. Use the result of part (a) to estimate the time of your 1,800-mile trip.
   c. The equation solved in part (b) leads mathematically to two solutions. Explain the meaning of the solution you rejected.

68. ▼ *Headwinds* The ground speed of an airliner is obtained by subtracting its headwind speed from its air speed. On your recent trip to Mexico from the United States your plane was traveling at an air speed of 500 miles per hour and experienced headwinds of $25 + 50t$ miles per hour, where t is the time in hours since takeoff.
   a. Obtain an expression for the distance traveled in terms of the time since takeoff. [HINT: Ground speed = Air speed − Headwind speed.]
   b. Use the result of part (a) to estimate the time of your 1,500-mile trip.
   c. The equation solved in part (b) leads mathematically to two solutions. Explain the meaning of the solution you rejected.

69. ▼ *Vertical Motion* Show that if a projectile is thrown upward with a velocity of v_0 ft/sec, then (neglecting air resistance) it will reach its highest point after $v_0/32$ seconds. [HINT: See the formulas that follow Example 8.]

70. ▼ *Vertical Motion* Use the result of Exercise 69 to show that if a projectile is thrown upward with a velocity of v_0 ft/sec, its highest point will be $v_0^2/64$ feet above the starting point (if we neglect the effects of air resistance).

Exercises 71–76 use the results of Exercises 69 and 70.

71. ▼ I threw a ball up in the air to a height of 20 feet. How fast was the ball traveling when it left my hand?

72. ▼ I threw a ball up in the air to a height of 40 feet. How fast was the ball traveling when it left my hand?

73. ▼ A piece of chalk is tossed vertically upward by Prof. Schwarzenegger and hits the ceiling 100 feet above with a *BANG*.
   a. What is the minimum speed at which the piece of chalk must have been thrown to enable it to hit the ceiling?
   b. Assuming that Prof. Schwarzenegger in fact tossed the piece of chalk up at 100 ft/sec, how fast was it moving when it struck the ceiling?
   c. Assuming that Prof. Schwarzenegger tossed the chalk up at 100 ft/sec, and that it recoils from the ceiling with the same speed it had at the instant it hit, how long will it take the chalk to make the return journey and hit the ground?

---

[11] Source: www.data360.org/dataset.aspx?Data_Set_Id=9549.

74. ▼ A projectile is fired vertically upward from ground level at 16,000 ft/sec.
    a. How high does the projectile go?
    b. How long does it take to reach its zenith (highest point)?
    c. How fast is it traveling when it hits the ground?

75. ▼ **Strength** Prof. Strong can throw a 10-pound dumbbell twice as high as Prof. Weak can. How much faster can Prof. Strong throw it?

76. ▼ **Weakness** Prof. Weak can throw a book three times as high as Prof. Strong can. How much faster can Prof. Weak throw it?

Communication and Reasoning Exercises

77. Why is this section called "The *Indefinite* Integral"?

78. If the derivative of Julius is Augustus, then Augustus is _____ of Julius.

79. Linear functions are antiderivatives of what kind of function? Explain.

80. Constant functions are antiderivatives of what kind of function? Explain.

81. If we know the *derivative* of a function, do we know the function? Explain. If not, what further information will suffice?

82. If we know an *antiderivative* of a function, do we know the function? Explain. If not, what further information will suffice?

83. If $F(x)$ and $G(x)$ are both antiderivatives of $f(x)$, how are $F(x)$ and $G(x)$ related?

84. Your friend Marco claims that once you have one antiderivative of $f(x)$ you have all of them. Explain what he means.

85. Complete the following: The total cost function is a(n) _____ of the _____ cost function.

86. Complete the following: The distance covered is an antiderivative of the _____ function, and the velocity is an antiderivative of the _____ function.

87. If x represents the number of items manufactured and $f(x)$ represents dollars per item, what does $\int f(x)\,dx$ represent? In general, how are the units of $f(x)$ and the units of $\int f(x)\,dx$ related?

88. If t represents time in seconds since liftoff and $g(t)$ represents the volume of rocket fuel burned per second, what does $\int g(t)\,dt$ represent?

89. Why was the following marked wrong? What is the correct answer?

$$\int (3x + 1)\,dx = \frac{3x^2}{2} + 0 + C = \frac{3x^2}{2} + C \quad \text{✗ WRONG!}$$

90. Why was the following marked wrong? What is the correct answer?

$$\int (3x^2 - 11x)\,dx = x^3 - 11 + C \quad \text{✗ WRONG!}$$

91. Why was the following marked wrong? What is the correct answer?

$$\int (12x^5 - 4x)\,dx = \int 2x^6 - 2x^2 + C \quad \text{✗ WRONG!}$$

92. Why was the following marked wrong? What is the correct answer?

$$\int 5\,dt = 5x + C \quad \text{✗ WRONG!}$$

93. Why was the following marked wrong? What is the correct answer?

$$\int 4(e^x - 2x)\,dx = (4x)(e^x - x^2) + C \quad \text{✗ WRONG!}$$

94. Why was the following marked wrong? What is the correct answer?

$$\int (2^x - 1)\,dx = \frac{2^{x+1}}{x + 1} - x + C \quad \text{✗ WRONG!}$$

95. Why was the following marked wrong? How should it be corrected?

$$\frac{1}{x} = \ln|x| + C \quad \text{✗ WRONG!}$$

96. Why was the following marked wrong? What is the correct answer?

$$\int \frac{1}{x^3}\,dx = \ln|x^3| + C \quad \text{✗ WRONG!}$$

97. ▼ Give an argument for the rule that the integral of a sum is the sum of the integrals.

98. ▼ Give an argument for the rule that the integral of a constant multiple is the constant multiple of the integrals.

99. ▼ Give an example to show that the integral of a product is not, in general, the product of the integrals.

100. ▼ Give an example to show that the integral of a quotient is not the quotient of the integrals.

101. ▼ Complete the following: If you take the _____ of the _____ of $f(x)$, you obtain $f(x)$ back. On the other hand, if you take the _____ of the _____ of $f(x)$, you obtain $f(x) + C$.

102. ▼ If a Martian told you that the *Institute of Alien Mathematics*, after a long and difficult search, has announced the discovery of a new antiderivative of $x - 1$ called $M(x)$, completely different from $\frac{x^2}{2} - x + C$ [the formula for $M(x)$ is classified information and cannot be revealed here], how would you respond?

13.2 Substitution

The Technique of Substitution

The chain rule for derivatives gives us an extremely useful technique for finding antiderivatives. This technique is called **change of variables** or **substitution**.

Recall that to differentiate a function such as $(x^2 + 1)^6$, we first think of the function as $g(u)$, where $u = x^2 + 1$ and $g(u) = u^6$. We then compute the derivative, using the chain rule, as

$$\frac{d}{dx} g(u) = g'(u) \frac{du}{dx}.$$

Any rule for derivatives can be turned into a technique for finding antiderivatives by writing it in integral form. The integral form of the above formula is

$$\int g'(u) \frac{du}{dx} dx = g(u) + C.$$

But if we write $g(u) + C = \int g'(u) \, du$ we get the following interesting equation:

$$\int g'(u) \frac{du}{dx} dx = \int g'(u) \, du.$$

This equation is the one usually called the *change of variables formula*. We can turn it into a more useful integration technique as follows. Let $f = g'(u)(du/dx)$. We can rewrite the above change of variables formula using f:

$$\int f \, dx = \int \left(\frac{f}{du/dx} \right) du.$$

In essence, we are making the formal substitution

$$dx = \frac{1}{du/dx} du.$$

Here's the technique.

Substitution Rule

If u is a function of x, then we can use the following formula to evaluate an integral:

$$\int f \, dx = \int \left(\frac{f}{du/dx} \right) du.$$

Rather than using the formula directly, we use the following step-by-step procedure:

1. Write u as a function of x.
2. Take the derivative du/dx, and solve for the quantity dx in terms of du.
3. Use the expression you obtain in Step 2 to substitute for dx in the given integral and substitute u for its defining expression.

Now let's see how this procedure works in practice.

EXAMPLE 1   **Substitution**

Find $\int 4x(x^2 + 1)^6 \, dx$.

Solution To use substitution, we need to choose an expression to be u. There is no hard and fast rule, but here is one hint that often works:

Take u to be an expression that is being raised to a power.

In this case, let's set $u = x^2 + 1$. Continuing the procedure above, we place the calculations for Step 2 in a box.

$u = x^2 + 1$	Write u as a function of x.
$\dfrac{du}{dx} = 2x$	Take the derivative of u with respect to x.
$dx = \dfrac{1}{2x} \, du$	Solve for dx: $dx = \dfrac{1}{du/dx} \, du$.

Now we *substitute u for its defining expression and substitute for dx* in the original integral:

* This step is equivalent to using the formula stated in the Substitution Rule box. If it should bother you that the integral contains both x and u, note that x is now a function of u.

$$\int 4x(x^2 + 1)^6 \, dx = \int 4xu^6 \, \frac{1}{2x} \, du \qquad \text{Substitute* for } u \text{ and } dx.$$

$$= \int 2u^6 \, du. \qquad \text{Cancel the } xs \text{ and simplify.}$$

We have boiled the given integral down to the much simpler integral $\int 2u^6 \, du$, and we can now write down the solution:

$$2\frac{u^7}{7} + C = \frac{2(x^2 + 1)^7}{7} + C. \qquad \text{Substitute } (x^2 + 1) \text{ for } u \text{ in the answer.}$$

➡ **Before we go on . . .** There are two points to notice in Example 1. First, before we can actually integrate with respect to u, *we must eliminate all xs from the integrand*. If we cannot, we may have chosen the wrong expression for u. Second, after integrating, we must substitute back to obtain an expression involving x.

It is easy to check our answer. We differentiate:

$$\frac{d}{dx}\left[\frac{2(x^2 + 1)^7}{7} \right] = \frac{2(7)(x^2 + 1)^6(2x)}{7} = 4x(x^2 + 1)^6. \quad ✔$$

Notice how we used the chain rule to check the result obtained by substitution. ∎

When we use substitution, the first step is always to decide what to take as u. Again, there are no set rules, but we see some common cases in the examples.

EXAMPLE 2   More Substitution

Evaluate the following:

a. $\displaystyle\int x^2(x^3 + 1)^2\, dx$ **b.** $\displaystyle\int 3xe^{x^2}\, dx$ **c.** $\displaystyle\int \frac{1}{2x + 5}\, dx$ **d.** $\displaystyle\int \left(\frac{1}{2x + 5} + 4x^2 + 1\right) dx$

Solution

a. As we said in Example 1, it often works to take u to be an expression that is being raised to a power. We usually also want to see the derivative of u as a factor in the integrand so that we can cancel terms involving x. In this case, $x^3 + 1$ is being raised to a power, so let's set $u = x^3 + 1$. Its derivative is $3x^2$; in the integrand we see x^2, which is missing the factor 3, but missing or incorrect constant factors are not a problem.

$$u = x^3 + 1 \qquad \text{Write } u \text{ as a function of } x.$$

$$\frac{du}{dx} = 3x^2 \qquad \text{Take the derivative of } u \text{ with respect to } x.$$

$$dx = \frac{1}{3x^2}\, du \qquad \text{Solve for } dx\colon dx = \frac{1}{du/dx}\, du.$$

$$\int x^2(x^3 + 1)^2\, dx = \int x^2 u^2 \frac{1}{3x^2}\, du \qquad \text{Substitute for } u \text{ and } dx.$$

$$= \int \frac{1}{3} u^2\, du \qquad \text{Cancel the terms with } x.$$

$$= \frac{1}{9} u^3 + C \qquad \text{Take the antiderivative.}$$

$$= \frac{1}{9}(x^3 + 1)^3 + C \qquad \text{Substitute for } u \text{ in the answer.}$$

b. When we have an exponential with an expression in the exponent, it often works to substitute u for that expression. In this case, let's set $u = x^2$. (Notice again that we see a constant multiple of its derivative $2x$ as a factor in the integrand—a good sign.)

$$u = x^2$$

$$\frac{du}{dx} = 2x$$

$$dx = \frac{1}{2x}\, du$$

Substituting into the integral, we have

$$\int 3xe^{x^2}\, dx = \int 3xe^u \frac{1}{2x}\, du = \int \frac{3}{2} e^u\, du$$

$$= \frac{3}{2} e^u + C = \frac{3}{2} e^{x^2} + C.$$

c. We begin by rewriting the integrand as a power:

$$\int \frac{1}{2x + 5}\, dx = \int (2x + 5)^{-1}\, dx.$$

Now we take our earlier advice and set u equal to the expression that is being raised to a power:

$$
\begin{array}{l}
u = 2x + 5 \\[4pt]
\dfrac{du}{dx} = 2 \\[4pt]
dx = \dfrac{1}{2}\,du
\end{array}
$$

Substituting into the integral, we have

$$
\int \frac{1}{2x + 5}\,dx = \int \frac{1}{2}u^{-1}\,du = \frac{1}{2}\ln|u| + C
$$

$$
= \frac{1}{2}\ln|2x + 5| + C.
$$

d. Here, the substitution $u = 2x + 5$ works for the first part of the integrand, $1/(2x + 5)$ but not for the rest of it, so we break up the integral:

$$
\int\left(\frac{1}{2x + 5} + 4x^2 + 1\right)dx = \int \frac{1}{2x + 5}\,dx + \int (4x^2 + 1)\,dx.
$$

For the first integral we can use the substitution $u = 2x + 5$ (which we did in part (a)). For the second, no substitution is necessary:

$$
\int \frac{1}{2x + 5}\,dx + \int (4x^2 + 1)\,dx = \frac{1}{2}\ln|2x + 5| + \frac{4x^3}{3} + x + C.
$$

EXAMPLE 3   **Choosing u**

Evaluate $\displaystyle\int (x + 3)\sqrt{x^2 + 6x}\,dx$.

Solution There are two parenthetical expressions. Notice, however, that the derivative of the expression $(x^2 + 6x)$ is $2x + 6$, which is twice the term $(x + 3)$ in front of the radical. Recall that we would like the derivative of u to appear as a factor. Thus, let's take $u = x^2 + 6x$.

$$
\begin{array}{l}
u = x^2 + 6x \\[4pt]
\dfrac{du}{dx} = 2x + 6 = 2(x + 3) \\[4pt]
dx = \dfrac{1}{2(x + 3)}\,du
\end{array}
$$

Substituting into the integral, we have

$$
\int (x + 3)\sqrt{x^2 + 6x}\,dx
$$

$$
= \int (x + 3)\sqrt{u}\left(\frac{1}{2(x + 3)}\right)du
$$

$$
= \int \frac{1}{2}\sqrt{u}\,du = \frac{1}{2}\int u^{1/2}\,du
$$

$$
= \frac{1}{2}\frac{2}{3}u^{3/2} + C = \frac{1}{3}(x^2 + 6x)^{3/2} + C.
$$

Some cases require a little more work.

EXAMPLE 4   **When the x Terms Do Not Cancel**

Evaluate $\int \dfrac{2x}{(x-5)^2}\,dx$.

Solution We first rewrite

$$\int \frac{2x}{(x-5)^2}\,dx = \int 2x(x-5)^{-2}\,dx.$$

This suggests that we should set $u = x - 5$.

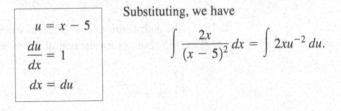

$$u = x - 5$$

$$\frac{du}{dx} = 1$$

$$dx = du$$

Substituting, we have

$$\int \frac{2x}{(x-5)^2}\,dx = \int 2xu^{-2}\,du.$$

Now, there is nothing in the integrand to cancel the x that appears. If, as here, there is still an x in the integrand after substituting, we go back to the expression for u, solve for x, and substitute the expression we obtain for x in the integrand. So we take $u = x - 5$ and solve for $x = u + 5$. Substituting, we get

$$\int 2xu^{-2}\,du = \int 2(u+5)u^{-2}\,du$$

$$= 2\int (u^{-1} + 5u^{-2})\,du$$

$$= 2\ln|u| - \frac{10}{u} + C$$

$$= 2\ln|x-5| - \frac{10}{x-5} + C.$$

Application

EXAMPLE 5   **Application: Bottled Water for Pets**

Annual sales of bottled spring water for pets can be modeled by the logistic function

$$s(t) = \frac{3{,}000e^{0.5t}}{3 + e^{0.5t}} \text{ million gallons per year} \qquad (0 \le t \le 12),$$

where t is time in years since the start of 2000.[12]

a. Find an expression for the total amount of bottled spring water for pets sold since the start of 2000.

b. How much bottled spring water for pets was sold from the start of 2005 to the start of 2008?

---

[12] Based on data through 2008 and the recovery in 2010 of the general bottled water market to pre-recession levels. Sources: "*Liquid Assets: America's Expensive Love Affair with Bottled Water*" Daniel Gross, April 26, 2011 (finance.yahoo.com), Beverage Marketing Corporation (www.beveragemarketing.com).

Solution

a. If we write the total amount of pet spring water sold since the start of 2000 as $S(t)$, then the information we are given says that

$$S'(t) = s(t) = \frac{3,000e^{0.5t}}{3 + e^{0.5t}}.$$

Thus,

$$S(t) = \int \frac{3,000e^{0.5t}}{3 + e^{0.5t}} \, dt$$

is the function we are after. To integrate the expression, take u to be the denominator of the integrand:

$$
\boxed{
\begin{aligned}
u &= 3 + e^{0.5t} \\[4pt]
\frac{du}{dt} &= 0.5e^{0.5t} \\[4pt]
dt &= \frac{1}{0.5e^{0.5t}} \, du
\end{aligned}
}
\qquad
\begin{aligned}
S(t) &= \int \frac{3,000e^{0.5t}}{3 + e^{0.5t}} \, dt \\[4pt]
&= \int \frac{3,000e^{0.5t}}{u} \cdot \frac{1}{0.5e^{0.5t}} \, du \\[4pt]
&= \frac{3,000}{0.5} \int \frac{1}{u} \, du
\end{aligned}
$$

$$= 6,000 \ln|u| + C = 6,000 \ln(3 + e^{0.5t}) + C.$$

(Why could we drop the absolute value in the last step?)

Now what is C? Because $S(t)$ represents the total amount of bottled spring water for pets sold *since time* $t = 0$, we have $S(0) = 0$ (because that is when we started counting). Thus,

$$0 = 6,000 \ln(3 + e^{0.5(0)}) + C$$
$$= 6,000 \ln 4 + C$$
$$C = -6,000 \ln 4 \approx -8,318.$$

Therefore, the total sales from the start of 2000 is approximately

$$S(t) = 6,000 \ln(3 + e^{0.5t}) - 8,318 \text{ million gallons.}$$

b. The period from the start of 2005 to the start of 2008 is represented by the interval $[5, 8]$. From part (a),

Sales through the start of $2005 = S(5)$
$$= 6,000 \ln(3 + e^{0.5(5)}) - 8,318 \approx 8,003 \text{ million gallons}$$

Sales through the start of $2008 = S(8)$
$$= 6,000 \ln(3 + e^{0.5(8)}) - 8,318 \approx 16,003 \text{ million gallons.}$$

Therefore, sales over the period were about $16,003 - 8,003 = 8,000$ million gallons.

➡ **Before we go on . . .** You might wonder why we are writing a logistic function in the form we used in Example 5 rather than in one of the standard forms $\dfrac{N}{1 + Ab^{-t}}$ or $\dfrac{N}{1 + Ae^{-kt}}$. Our only reason for doing this is to make the substitution work. To convert from the second standard form to the form we used in the example, multiply top and bottom by e^{kt}. (See Exercises 85 and 86 in Section 13.4 for further discussion.) ∎

Shortcuts

The following rule allows us to simply write down the antiderivative in cases where we would otherwise need the substitution $u = ax + b$, as in Example 2. (a and b are constants with $a \neq 0$.)

Shortcut Rule: Integrals of Expressions Involving $(ax + b)$

*The shortcut rule can be justified by making the substitution $u = ax + b$ in the general case as stated.

If $\int f(x)\, dx = F(x) + C$ and a and b are constants, with $a \neq 0$, then*

$$\int f(ax + b)\, dx = \frac{1}{a} F(ax + b) + C.$$

Quick Example

(Also see the examples in the table below.)

1. Because $\int x^4\, dx = \dfrac{x^5}{5} + C$, it follows that

$$\int (3x - 1)^4\, dx = \frac{1}{3} \frac{(3x - 1)^5}{5} + C = \frac{(3x - 1)^5}{15} + C.$$

Below are some instances of the shortcut rule with additional examples. (Their individual derivations using the substitution $u = ax + b$ will appear in the exercises.)

Shortcut Rule	Example
$\displaystyle\int (ax + b)^n\, dx = \frac{1}{a} \frac{(ax + b)^{n+1}}{n + 1} + C$ (if $n \neq -1$)	$\displaystyle\int (3x - 1)^2\, dx = \frac{(3x - 1)^3}{3(3)} + C$ $\displaystyle = \frac{(3x - 1)^3}{9} + C$
$\displaystyle\int (ax + b)^{-1}\, dx = \frac{1}{a} \ln\lvert ax + b\rvert + C$	$\displaystyle\int (3 - 2x)^{-1}\, dx = \frac{1}{(-2)} \ln\lvert 3 - 2x\rvert + C$ $\displaystyle = -\frac{1}{2} \ln\lvert 3 - 2x\rvert + C$
$\displaystyle\int e^{ax+b}\, dx = \frac{1}{a} e^{ax+b} + C$	$\displaystyle\int e^{-x+4}\, dx = \frac{1}{(-1)} e^{-x+4} + C$ $\displaystyle = -e^{-x+4} + C$
$\displaystyle\int c^{ax+b}\, dx = \frac{1}{a \ln c} c^{ax+b} + C$	$\displaystyle\int 2^{-3x+4}\, dx = \frac{1}{(-3 \ln 2)} 2^{-3x+4} + C$ $\displaystyle = -\frac{1}{3 \ln 2} 2^{-3x+4} + C$
$\displaystyle\int \lvert ax + b\rvert\, dx$ $\displaystyle = \frac{1}{2a} (ax + b)\lvert ax + b\rvert + C$	$\displaystyle\int \lvert 2x - 1\rvert\, dx = \frac{1}{4}(2x - 1)\lvert 2x - 1\rvert + C$

* Mike Fuschetto, who was a
Hofstra business calculus student
in spring 2010

The following more general version of the shortcut rule was suggested by a student.* We have marked it as optional so that you could skip it on a first reading, but we strongly suggest that you come back to it afterward, as the rule will allow you to easily write down the answers in most of the exercises, as well as in almost all the examples of this section.

(Optional) Mike's Shortcut Rule: Integrals of More General Expressions

If $\int f(x)\,dx = F(x) + C$ and g and u are any differentiable functions of x, then

$$\int g \cdot f(u)\,dx = \frac{g}{u'} \cdot F(u) + C \quad \text{provided that } \frac{g}{u'} \text{ is constant.}$$

Quick Example

(Also see the examples in the table below.)

2. $\int x^4\,dx = \dfrac{x^5}{5} + C,$ so

$$\int 5x^2(x^3 - 1)^4\,dx = \frac{5x^2}{3x^2} \cdot \frac{(x^3 - 1)^5}{5} + C$$

$$= \frac{5}{3} \cdot \frac{(x^3 - 1)^5}{5} + C = \frac{(x^3 - 1)^5}{3} + C.$$

Caution

If g/u' is not constant, then Mike's rule does not apply; for instance, the following calculation is *wrong*:

$$\int x(2x - 1)^2\,dx = \frac{x}{2} \cdot \frac{(2x - 1)^3}{3} + C. \qquad \text{✗ WRONG!}$$
$$\text{because } \tfrac{x}{2} \text{ is not constant.}$$

Here are some instances of Mike's rule with additional examples.

Shortcut Rule	Example
$\int g \cdot u^n\,dx = \dfrac{g}{u'}\dfrac{u^{n+1}}{n+1} + C$ (if $n \neq -1$)	$\int 3x(x^2 - 1)^3\,dx = \dfrac{3x}{2x}\dfrac{(x^2 - 1)^4}{4} + C$ $= \dfrac{3(x^2 - 1)^4}{8} + C$
$\int g \cdot u^{-1}\,dx = \dfrac{g}{u'}\ln|u| + C$	$\int e^x(3 - 2e^x)^{-1}\,dx = \dfrac{e^x}{-2e^x}\ln|3 - 2e^x| + C$ $= -\dfrac{1}{2}\ln|3 - 2e^x| + C$
$\int g \cdot e^u\,dx = \dfrac{g}{u'}e^u + C$	$\int x^2 e^{-x^3+4}\,dx = \dfrac{x^2}{-3x^2}e^{-x^3+4} + C$ $= -\dfrac{1}{3}e^{-x^3+4} + C$

(continued)

Shortcut Rule	Example
$\displaystyle\int g \cdot c^u \, dx = \frac{g}{u' \ln c} c^u + C$	$\displaystyle\int x^3 2^{x^4-1} \, dx = \frac{x^3}{4x^3 \ln 2} 2^{x^4-1} + C$ $\displaystyle = \frac{1}{4 \ln 2} 2^{x^4-1} + C$
$\displaystyle\int g \cdot |u| \, dx = \frac{g}{2u'} u \,|u| + C$	$\displaystyle\int x|x^2 - 1| \, dx = \frac{x}{4x}(x^2 - 1)|x^2 - 1| + C$ $\displaystyle = \frac{1}{4}(x^2 - 1)|x^2 - 1| + C$

FAQs

When to Use Substitution and What to Use for *u*

Q: *If I am asked to calculate an antiderivative, how do I know when to use a substitution and when not to use one?*

A: Do *not* use substitution when integrating sums, differences, and/or constant multiples of powers of x and exponential functions, such as $2x^3 - \dfrac{4}{x^2} + \dfrac{1}{2x} + 3^x + \dfrac{2^x}{3}$.

To recognize when you should try a substitution, pretend that you are *differentiating* the given expression instead of integrating it. If differentiating the expression would require use of the chain rule, then integrating that expression may well require a substitution, as in, say, $x(3x^2 - 4)^3$ or $(x + 1)e^{x^2+2x-1}$. (In the first we have a *quantity* cubed; in the second we have *e* raised to a *quantity*.)

Q: *If an integral seems to call for a substitution, what should I use for u?*

A: There are no set rules for deciding what to use for *u*, but the preceding examples show some common patterns:

- If you see a linear expression raised to a power, try setting *u* equal to that linear expression. For example, in $(3x - 2)^{-3}$, set $u = 3x - 2$. (Alternatively, try using the shortcuts above.)
- If you see a constant raised to a linear expression, try setting *u* equal to that linear expression. For example, in $3^{(2x+1)}$, set $u = 2x + 1$. (Alternatively, try a shortcut.)
- If you see an expression raised to a power multiplied by the derivative of that expression (or a constant multiple of the derivative), try setting *u* equal to that expression. For example, in $x^2(3x^3 - 4)^{-1}$, set $u = 3x^3 - 4$.
- If you see a constant raised to an expression, multiplied by the derivative of that expression (or a constant multiple of its derivative), try setting *u* equal to that expression. For example, in $5(x + 1)e^{x^2+2x-1}$, set $u = x^2 + 2x - 1$.
- If you see an expression in the denominator and its derivative (or a constant multiple of its derivative) in the numerator, try setting *u* equal to that expression. For example, in $\dfrac{2^{3x}}{3 - 2^{3x}}$, set $u = 3 - 2^{3x}$.

Persistence often pays off: If a certain substitution does not work, try another approach or a different substitution.

13.2 EXERCISES

▼ more advanced   ◆ challenging
⬛ indicates exercises that should be solved using technology

In Exercises 1–10, evaluate the given integral using the substitution (or method) indicated.

1. $\int (3x - 5)^3 \, dx; \ u = 3x - 5$

2. $\int (2x + 5)^{-2} \, dx; \ u = 2x + 5$

3. $\int (3x - 5)^3 \, dx;$ shortcut   **4.** $\int (2x + 5)^{-2} \, dx;$ shortcut

5. $\int e^{-x} \, dx; \ u = -x$ **6.** $\int e^{x/2} \, dx; \ u = x/2$

7. $\int e^{-x} \, dx;$ shortcut   **8.** $\int e^{x/2} \, dx;$ shortcut

9. $\int (x + 1) e^{(x+1)^2} \, dx; \ u = (x + 1)^2$

10. $\int (x - 1)^2 e^{(x-1)^3} \, dx; \ u = (x - 1)^3$

In Exercises 11–52, decide on what substitution to use, and then evaluate the given integral using a substitution. [**HINT:** See the FAQ at the end of the section for advice on deciding on u, and the examples for the mechanics of doing the substitution.]

11. $\int (3x + 1)^5 \, dx$ **12.** $\int (-x - 1)^7 \, dx$

13. $\int 7.2\sqrt{3x - 4} \, dx$ **14.** $\int 4.4 e^{(-3x+4)} \, dx$

15. $\int 1.2 e^{(0.6x+2)} \, dx$ **16.** $\int 8.1\sqrt{-3x + 4} \, dx$

17. $\int x(3x^2 + 3)^3 \, dx$ **18.** $\int x(-x^2 - 1)^3 \, dx$

19. $\int 2x\sqrt{3x^2 - 1} \, dx$ **20.** $\int 3x\sqrt{-x^2 + 1} \, dx$

21. $\int \dfrac{x}{(x^2 + 1)^{1.3}} \, dx$ **22.** $\int \dfrac{x^2}{(1 + x^3)^{1.4}} \, dx$

23. $\int x|4x^2 - 1| \, dx$ **24.** $\int x^2|4x^3 + 1| \, dx$

25. $\int (1 + 9.3 e^{3.1x-2}) \, dx$ **26.** $\int (3.2 - 4 e^{1.2x-3}) \, dx$

27. $\int x e^{-x^2+1} \, dx$ **28.** $\int x e^{2x^2-1} \, dx$

29. $\int (x + 1) e^{-(x^2+2x)} \, dx$ [**HINT:** See Example 2(b).]

30. $\int (2x - 1) e^{2x^2-2x} \, dx$ [**HINT:** See Example 2(b).]

31. $\int \dfrac{-2x - 1}{(x^2 + x + 1)^3} \, dx$ **32.** $\int \dfrac{x^3 - x^2}{3x^4 - 4x^3} \, dx$

33. $\int \dfrac{x^2 + x^5}{\sqrt{2x^3 + x^6 - 5}} \, dx$ [**HINT:** See Example 3.]

34. $\int \dfrac{2(x^3 - x^4)}{(5x^4 - 4x^5)^5} \, dx$ [**HINT:** See Example 3.]

35. $\int x(x - 2)^5 \, dx$ **36.** $\int x(x - 2)^{1/3} \, dx$
  [**HINT:** See Example 4.]   [**HINT:** See Example 4.]

37. $\int 2x\sqrt{x + 1} \, dx$ **38.** $\int \dfrac{x}{\sqrt{x + 1}} \, dx$

39. $\int \dfrac{e^{-0.05x}}{1 - e^{-0.05x}} \, dx$ **40.** $\int \dfrac{3e^{1.2x}}{2 + e^{1.2x}} \, dx$
  [**HINT:** See Example 5.]   [**HINT:** See Example 5.]

41. ▼ $\int \dfrac{3e^{-1/x}}{x^2} \, dx$ **42.** ▼ $\int \dfrac{2e^{2/x}}{x^2} \, dx$

43. ▼ $\int \dfrac{(4 + 1/x^2)^3}{x^3} \, dx$ **44.** ▼ $\int \dfrac{1}{x^2(2 - 1/x)} \, dx$

45. ▼ $\int \dfrac{e^x + e^{-x}}{2} \, dx$ [**HINT:** See Example 2(d).]

46. ▼ $\int (e^{x/2} + e^{-x/2}) \, dx$ [**HINT:** See Example 2(d).]

47. ▼ $\int \dfrac{e^x - e^{-x}}{e^x + e^{-x}} \, dx$ **48.** ▼ $\int \dfrac{e^{x/2} + e^{-x/2}}{e^{x/2} - e^{-x/2}} \, dx$

49. ▼ $\int e^{3x-1}|1 - e^{3x-1}| \, dx$ **50.** ▼ $\int |e^{-x-1} - 1|(e^{-x-1}) \, dx$

51. ▼ $\int \left((2x - 1)e^{2x^2-2x} + xe^{x^2}\right) dx$

52. ▼ $\int (xe^{-x^2+1} + e^{2x}) \, dx$

In Exercises 53–56, derive the given equation, where a and b are constants with $a \neq 0$.

53. $\int (ax + b)^n \, dx = \dfrac{(ax + b)^{n+1}}{a(n + 1)} + C$ (if $n \neq -1$)

54. $\int (ax + b)^{-1} \, dx = \dfrac{1}{a} \ln|ax + b| + C$

55. $\int |ax + b| \, dx = \dfrac{1}{2a}(ax + b)|ax + b| + C$

56. $\int e^{ax+b} \, dx = \dfrac{1}{a} e^{ax+b} + C$

In Exercises 57–72, use the shortcut formulas (see the shortcuts and Exercises 53–56) to calculate the given integral.

57. $\int e^{-x}\,dx$

58. $\int e^{x-1}\,dx$

59. $\int e^{2x-1}\,dx$

60. $\int e^{-3x}\,dx$

61. $\int (2x+4)^2\,dx$

62. $\int (3x-2)^4\,dx$

63. $\int \dfrac{1}{5x-1}\,dx$

64. $\int (x-1)^{-1}\,dx$

65. $\int (1.5x)^3\,dx$

66. $\int e^{2.1x}\,dx$

67. $\int 1.5^{3x}\,dx$

68. $\int 4^{-2x}\,dx$

69. $\int |2x+4|\,dx$

70. $\int |3x-2|\,dx$

71. $\int (2^{3x+4} + 2^{-3x+4})\,dx$

72. $\int (1.1^{-x+4} + 1.1^{x+4})\,dx$

73. Find $f(x)$ if $f(0) = 0$ and the tangent line at $(x, f(x))$ has slope $x(x^2+1)^3$.

74. Find $f(x)$ if $f(1) = 0$ and the tangent line at $(x, f(x))$ has slope $\dfrac{x}{x^2+1}$.

75. Find $f(x)$ if $f(1) = 1/2$ and the tangent line at $(x, f(x))$ has slope xe^{x^2-1}.

76. Find $f(x)$ if $f(2) = 1$ and the tangent line at x has slope $(x-1)e^{x^2-2x}$.

In Exercises 77–84, use Mike's shortcut method (see Mike's Shortcut Rule and the examples that follow) to calculate the given integral.

77. $\int x(5x^2-3)^6\,dx$

78. $\int \dfrac{x}{(5x^2-3)^6}\,dx$

79. $\int \dfrac{e^x}{\sqrt{3e^x-1}}\,dx$

80. $\int e^x\sqrt{1+2e^x}\,dx$

81. $\int x^3 e^{(x^4-8)}\,dx$

82. $\int \dfrac{x^3}{e^{(x^4-8)}}\,dx$

83. $\int \dfrac{e^{3x}}{1+2e^{3x}}\,dx$

84. $\int \dfrac{e^{-2x}}{e^{-2x}-3}\,dx$

Applications

85. *Cost* The marginal cost of producing the xth roll of film is given by $5 + 1/(x+1)^2$. The total cost to produce one roll is $1,000. Find the total cost function $C(x)$.

86. *Cost* The marginal cost of producing the xth box of CDs is given by $10 - x/(x^2+1)^2$. The total cost to produce two boxes is $1,000. Find the total cost function $C(x)$.

87. *Economic Growth* The Mexico GDP (total monetary value of all finished goods and services produced in Mexico) can be approximated by

$$g(t) = 2{,}000 - 480e^{-0.06t} \text{ billion pesos per year}$$
$$(0 \le t \le 5),$$

where t is time in years since January 2010.[13] Find an expression for the total GDP $G(t)$ of sold goods in Mexico from January 2010 to time t. Hence, estimate, to the nearest billion pesos, the total Mexico GDP from January 2010 through June 2014. (The actual value was 7,137 billion pesos.) [**HINT:** Use the shortcuts.]

88. *Housing Starts: The Great Recession* The Great Recession of 2007–2009 is largely attributed to the real estate crisis beginning in 2006, from which time the number of housing starts was approximately

$$n(t) = 2{,}400e^{-0.25t} - 200 \text{ thousand homes per year}$$
$$(0 \le t \le 4),$$

where t is time in years since January 2006.[14] Find an expression for the total number $N(t)$ of housing starts in the United States from January 2006 to time t. Hence estimate, to the nearest 0.1 million, the total number of housing starts from January 2006 through June 2009. (The actual number was around 4.9 million homes.) [**HINT:** Use the shortcuts.]

89. *Revenue: Pacific Sunwear* The annual revenue of Pacific Sunwear of California over the period January 2008–January 2015 can be approximated by

$$p(t) = (-0.075t + 0.97)^5 + 0.75 \text{ billion dollars per year}$$
$$(0 \le t \le 7),$$

where t is time in years since January 2008.[15] Find an expression for the total revenue $P(t)$ earned by Pacific Sunwear since the start of 2008, and hence estimate, to the nearest $0.1 billion, the total revenue earned from the start of 2008 to the start of 2015. (The actual revenue was about $7.1 billion.)

90. *Revenue: Google* The annual revenue of Google Inc. over the period January 2008–January 2015 can be approximated by

$$g(t) = (0.17t + 1.7)^4 + 10 \text{ billion dollars per year}$$
$$(0 \le t \le 7),$$

where t is time in years since January 2008.[16] Find an expression for the total revenue $G(t)$ earned by Google since the start of 2008, and hence estimate, to the nearest $ billion, the total revenue earned from the start of 2008 to the start of 2014. (The actual revenue was about $223 billion.)

---

[13] The GDP is in constant 2008 pesos. Source for data: Instituto Nacional de Estadística y Geografía (INEGI) (www.inegi.org.mx).

[14] Source for data: www.census.gov.

[15] Source for data: www.wikinvest.com.

[16] *Ibid.*

91. *Scientific Research: 1983–2003* The number of research articles in the prominent journal *Physical Review* written by researchers in Europe during 1983–2003 can be approximated by

$$E(t) = \frac{7e^{0.2t}}{5 + e^{0.2t}} \text{ thousand articles per year}$$

$$(0 \le t \le 20),$$

where t is time in years. ($t = 0$ represents 1983.)[17]

a. Find an (approximate) expression for the total number of articles written by researchers in Europe since 1983 ($t = 0$). [HINT: See Example 5.]

b. Roughly how many articles were written by researchers in Europe from 1983 to 2003? (Round your answer to the nearest 1,000 articles.)

92. *Scientific Research: 1983–2003* The number of research articles in the prominent journal *Physical Review* written by researchers in the United States during 1983–2003 can be approximated by

$$U(t) = \frac{4.6e^{0.6t}}{0.4 + e^{0.6t}} \text{ thousand articles per year,}$$

$$(0 \le t \le 20),$$

where t is time in years. ($t = 0$ represents 1983.)[18]

a. Find an (approximate) expression for the total number of articles written by researchers in the United States since 1983 ($t = 0$). [HINT: See Example 5.]

b. Roughly how many articles were written by researchers in the United States from 1983 to 2003?

93. *Sales* The rate of sales of your company's *Jackson Pollock Advanced Paint-by-Number* sets can be modeled by

$$s(t) = \frac{900e^{0.25t}}{3 + e^{0.25t}} \text{ sets per month}$$

t months after their introduction. Find an expression for the total number of paint-by-number sets $S(t)$ sold t months after their introduction, and use it to estimate the total sold in the first 12 months. [HINT: See Example 5.]

94. *Sales* The rate of sales of your company's *Jackson Pollock Beginners Paint-by-Number* sets can be modeled by

$$s(t) = \frac{1{,}800e^{0.75t}}{10 + e^{0.75t}} \text{ sets per month}$$

t months after their introduction. Find an expression for the total number of paint-by-number sets $S(t)$ sold t months after their introduction, and use it to estimate the total sold in the first 12 months. [HINT: See Example 5.]

95. *Motion in a Straight Line* The velocity of a particle moving in a straight line is given by $v = t(t^2 + 1)^4 + t$.

a. Find an expression for the position s after a time t. [HINT: See Example 2(d).]

b. Given that $s = 1$ at time $t = 0$, find the constant of integration C and hence an expression for s in terms of t without any unknown constants.

96. *Motion in a Straight Line* The velocity of a particle moving in a straight line is given by $v = 3te^{t^2} + t$.

a. Find an expression for the position s after a time t. [HINT: See Example 2(d).]

b. Given that $s = 3$ at time $t = 0$, find the constant of integration C and hence an expression for s in terms of t without any unknown constants.

97. *Bottled Water Sales* (Compare Exercise 55 in Section 13.1.) The rate of U.S. sales of bottled water for the period 2007–2014 could be approximated by

$$s(t) = 0.08(t - 2{,}007)^2 - 0.26(t - 2{,}007) + 8.8$$
$$\text{million gallons per year} \quad (2{,}007 \le t \le 2{,}014),$$

where t is the year.[19] Use an indefinite integral to approximate the total sales $S(t)$ of bottled water since 2010 ($t = 2{,}010$). Approximately how much bottled water was sold from 2010 to 2014?

98. *Bottled Water Sales* (Compare Exercise 56 in Section 13.1.) The rate of U.S. per capita sales of bottled water for the period 2007–2014 could be approximated by

$$s(t) = 0.25(t - 2{,}007)^2 - (t - 2{,}007) + 29$$
$$\text{gallons per year} \quad (2{,}007 \le t \le 2{,}014),$$

where t is the year.[20] Use an indefinite integral to approximate the total per capita sales $S(t)$ of bottled water since 2010 ($t = 2{,}010$). Approximately how much bottled water was sold, per capita, 2010 to 2013?

Communication and Reasoning Exercises

99. Are there any circumstances in which you should use the substitution $u = x$? Illustrate your answer by giving an example that shows the effect of this substitution.

100. You are asked to calculate $\displaystyle\int \frac{u}{u^2 + 1} \, du$. What is wrong with the substitution $u = u^2 + 1$?

101. If the xs do not cancel in a substitution, that means you chose the wrong expression for u, right?

102. At what stage of a calculation using a u substitution should you substitute back for u in terms of x: before or after taking the antiderivative?

---

[17] Source: The American Physical Society/*New York Times*, May 3, 2003, p. A1.

[18] *Ibid.*

[19] Source for data: Beverage Marketing Corporation/www.bottledwater.org.

[20] *Ibid.*

103. Consider $\int \left(\dfrac{x}{x^2 - 1} + \dfrac{3x}{x^2 + 1} \right) dx$. To compute it, you should use which of the following?

(A) $u = x^2 - 1$ (B) $u = x^2 + 1$
(C) Neither   (D) Both
Explain your answer.

104. If the substitution $u = x^2 - 1$ works in $\int \dfrac{x}{x^2 - 1}\, dx$, why does it not work nearly so easily in $\int \dfrac{x^2 - 1}{x}\, dx$? How would you do the second integral most simply?

105. Why was the following calculation marked wrong? What is the correct answer?

$$\boxed{\begin{array}{l} u = x^2 - 1 \\[4pt] \dfrac{du}{dx} = 2x \\[4pt] dx = \dfrac{1}{2x}\, du \end{array}} \quad \begin{array}{l} \displaystyle\int 3x(x^2 - 1) = \int 3xu \\[8pt] = 3x\dfrac{u^2}{2} + C = 3x\dfrac{(x^2 - 1)^2}{2} + C \\[8pt] \hspace{2cm} \text{✗ WRONG!} \end{array}$$

106. Why was the following calculation marked wrong? What is the correct answer?

$$\boxed{\begin{array}{l} u = x^3 - 1 \\[4pt] \dfrac{du}{dx} = 3x^2 \\[4pt] dx = \dfrac{1}{3x^2}\, du \end{array}} \quad \begin{array}{l} \displaystyle\int x^2(x^3 - 1)^2\, dx = \int x^2 u^2 \dfrac{1}{3x^2}\, du \\[8pt] = \dfrac{1}{3}u^2 + C = \dfrac{1}{3}(x^3 - 1)^2 + C \\[8pt] \hspace{2cm} \text{✗ WRONG!} \end{array}$$

107. Why was the following calculation marked wrong? What is the correct answer?

$$\boxed{\begin{array}{l} u = x^3 - 1 \\[4pt] \dfrac{du}{dx} = 3x^2 \\[4pt] dx = \dfrac{1}{3x^2}\, du \end{array}} \quad \begin{array}{l} \displaystyle\int x^2(x^3 - 1)\, dx = \int x^2 u \dfrac{1}{3x^2}\, du \\[8pt] = \int \dfrac{1}{3}u\, du = \int \dfrac{1}{3}(x^3 - 1)\, dx \\[8pt] = \dfrac{1}{3}\left(\dfrac{x^4}{4} - x \right) + C \quad \text{✗ WRONG!} \end{array}$$

108. Why was the following calculation marked wrong? What is the correct answer?

$$\boxed{\begin{array}{l} u = x^2 - 1 \\[4pt] \dfrac{du}{dx} = 2x \\[4pt] dx = \dfrac{1}{2x}\, du \end{array}} \quad \begin{array}{l} \displaystyle\int \dfrac{x}{x^2 - 1}\, dx = \int \dfrac{x}{u}\, du \\[8pt] = x\int \dfrac{1}{u}\, du = x \ln|u| + C \\[8pt] = x \ln|x^2 - 1| + C \quad \text{✗ WRONG!} \end{array}$$

109. ▼ Show that *none* of the following substitutions work for $\int e^{-x^2}\, dx$: $u = -x$, $u = x^2$, $u = -x^2$. (The antiderivative of e^{-x^2} involves the *error function* $\mathrm{erf}(x)$.)

110. ▼ Show that *none* of the following substitutions work for $\int \sqrt{1 - x^2}\, dx$: $u = 1 - x^2$, $u = x^2$, and $u = -x^2$. (The antiderivative of $\sqrt{1 - x^2}$ involves inverse trigonometric functions, discussion of which is beyond the scope of this book.)

13.3   The Definite Integral: Numerical and Graphical Viewpoints

Riemann Sums

In Sections 13.1 and 13.2 we discussed the indefinite integral. There is an older, related concept called the **definite integral**. Let's introduce this new idea with an example. (We'll drop hints now and then about how the two types of integral are related. In Section 13.4 we discuss the exact relationship, which is one of the most important results in calculus.)

In Section 13.1 we used antiderivatives to answer questions of the form "Given the marginal cost, compute the total cost." (See Example 5 in Section 13.1.) In this section we approach such questions more directly, and we will forget about antiderivatives for now.

EXAMPLE 1   Oil Spill

Your deep ocean oil rig has suffered a catastrophic failure, and oil is leaking from the ocean floor wellhead at a rate of

$$v(t) = 0.08t^2 - 4t + 60 \text{ thousand barrels per day} \qquad (0 \le t \le 20),$$

where t is time in days since the failure.[21] Use a numerical calculation to estimate the total volume of oil released during the first 20 days.

Solution The graph of $v(t)$ is shown in Figure 3.

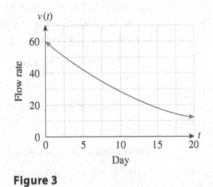

Figure 3

Let's start with a very crude estimate of the total volume of oil released, using the graph as a guide. The rate of change of this total volume at the beginning of the time period is $v(0) = 60$ thousand barrels per day. If this rate were to remain constant for the entire 20-day period, the total volume of oil released would be

$$\text{Total volume} = \text{Volume per day} \times \text{Number of days} = 60 \times 20$$
$$= 1{,}200 \text{ thousand barrels.}$$

Figure 4 shows how we can represent this calculation on the graph of $v(t)$.

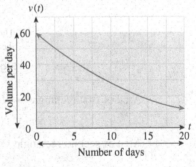

Figure 4

---

[21] The model is consistent with the order of magnitude of the BP Deepwater Horizon oil spill of April 20–June 15, 2010, when the rate of flow of oil was estimated by the Federal Emergency Management Agency's Flow Rate Technical Group to be between 35,000 and 60,000 barrels per day. (One barrel of oil is equivalent to about 0.16 cubic meters.) Source: www.doi.gov/deepwaterhorizon.

The volume per day based on $v(0) = 60$ is represented by the y-coordinate of the graph at its left edge, while the number of days is represented by the width of the interval $[0, 20]$ on the x-axis. Therefore, computing the area of the shaded rectangle in the figure gives the same calculation:

$$\text{Area of rectangle} = \text{Volume per day} \times \text{Number of days}$$
$$= 60 \times 20 = 1{,}200 = \text{Total volume.}$$

But as we see in the graph, the flow rate does not remain constant but goes down quite significantly over the course of the 20-day interval. We can obtain a somewhat more accurate estimate of the total volume by re-estimating the volume using 10-day periods—that is, by dividing the interval $[0, 20]$ into two equal intervals, or subdivisions. We estimate the volume over each 10-day period using the flow rate at the beginning of that period:

$$\text{Volume in first period} = \text{Volume per day} \times \text{Number of days}$$
$$= v(0) \times 10 = 60 \times 10 = 600 \text{ thousand barrels}$$

$$\text{Volume in second period} = \text{Volume per day} \times \text{Number of days}$$
$$= v(10) \times 10 = 28 \times 10 = 280 \text{ thousand barrels.}$$

Adding these volumes gives us the more accurate estimate

$$v(0) \times 10 + v(10) \times 10 = 880 \text{ thousand barrels.} \qquad \text{Calculation using two subdivisions}$$

In Figure 5 we see that we are computing the combined area of two rectangles, each of whose heights is determined by the height of the graph at its left edge.

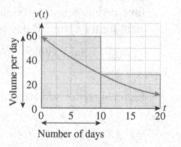

The areas of the rectangles are estimates of the volumes for successive 10-day periods.

Figure 5

$$\text{Area of first rectangle} = \text{Volume per day} \times \text{Number of days}$$
$$= v(0) \times 10 = 60 \times 10 = 600 = \text{Volume for first 10 days}$$

$$\text{Area of second rectangle} = \text{Volume per day} \times \text{Number of days} = v(10) \times 10$$
$$= 28 \times 10 = 280 = \text{Volume for second 10 days.}$$

We can get an even better estimate of the volume by using four divisions of $[0, 20]$ instead of two:

$$v(0) \times 5 + v(5) \times 5 + v(10) \times 5 + v(15) \times 5 \qquad \text{Calculation using four subdivisions}$$
$$= 300 + 210 + 140 + 90 = 740 \text{ thousand barrels.}$$

As we see in Figure 6, we have now computed the combined area of *four* rectangles, each of whose heights is again determined by the height of the graph at its left edge.

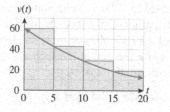

Estimated volume using four subdivisions. The areas of the rectangles are estimates of the volumes for successive 5-day periods.

Figure 6

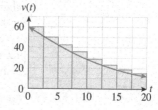

Estimated volume using eight subdivisions. The areas of the rectangles are estimates of the volumes for successive 2.5-day periods.

Figure 7

Notice how the volume seems to be decreasing as we use more subdivisions. More importantly, the total volume seems to be getting closer to the area under the graph. Figure 7 illustrates the calculation for eight equal subdivisions. The approximate total volume using eight subdivisions is the total area of the shaded region in Figure 7:

$$v(0) \times 2.5 + v(2.5) \times 2.5 + v(5) \times 2.5 + \cdots + v(17.5) \times 2.5$$
$$= 675 \text{ thousand barrels.} \qquad \text{Calculation using eight subdivisions}$$

Looking at Figure 7, we still get the impression that we are overestimating the volume. If we want to be *really* accurate in our estimation of the volume, we should really be calculating the volume *continuously* every few hours or, better yet, minute by minute, as illustrated in Figure 8.

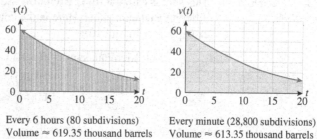

Every 6 hours (80 subdivisions)
Volume ≈ 619.35 thousand barrels

Every minute (28,800 subdivisions)
Volume ≈ 613.35 thousand barrels

Figure 8

Figure 8 strongly suggests that the more accurately we estimate the total volume, the closer the answer gets to the exact area under the portion of the graph of $v(t)$ with $0 \leq t \leq 20$ and leads us to the conclusion that the *exact* total volume is the exact area under the rate of change of volume curve for $0 \leq t \leq 20$. In other words, we have made the following remarkable discovery:

Total volume is the area under the rate of change of volume curve!

➡ **Before we go on . . .** The 80-subdivision calculation in Example 1 is tedious to do by hand, and no one in his or her right mind would even *attempt* to do the minute-by-minute calculation by hand! Below we discuss ways of doing these calculations with the aid of technology. ■

The type of calculation done in Example 1 is useful in many applications. Let's look at the general case and give the result a name.

In general, we have a function f (such as the function v in the example), and we consider an interval $[a, b]$ of possible values of the independent variable x. We subdivide the interval $[a, b]$ into some number of segments of equal length. Write n for the number of segments, or **subdivisions**.

Next, we label the endpoints of these subdivisions x_0 for a, x_1 for the end of the first subdivision, x_2 for the end of the second subdivision, and so on until we get to x_n, the end of the nth subdivision, so that $x_n = b$. Thus,

$$a = x_0 < x_1 < \cdots < x_n = b.$$

The first subdivision is the interval $[x_0, x_1]$, the second subdivision is $[x_1, x_2]$, and so on until we get to the last subdivision, which is $[x_{n-1}, x_n]$. We are dividing the interval $[a, b]$ into n subdivisions of equal length, so each segment has length $(b - a)/n$. We write Δx for $(b - a)/n$ (Figure 9).

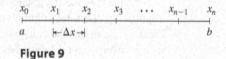

Figure 9

Having established this notation, we can write the calculation that we want to do as follows: For each subdivision $[x_{k-1}, x_k]$, compute $f(x_{k-1})$, the value of the function f at the left endpoint. Multiply this value by the length of the interval, which is Δx. Then add together all n of these products to get the number

$$f(x_0) \, \Delta x + f(x_1) \, \Delta x + \cdots + f(x_{n-1}) \, \Delta x.$$

*After Georg Friedrich Bernhard Riemann (1826–1866)

This sum is called a **(left) Riemann* sum** for f. In Example 1 we computed several different Riemann sums. Here is the computation for $n = 4$ we used in the oil spill example (see Figure 10):

$$\begin{aligned}
\text{Left Riemann sum} &= f(x_0) \, \Delta x + f(x_1) \, \Delta x + \cdots + f(x_{n-1}) \, \Delta x \\
&= f(0)(5) + f(5)(5) + f(10)(5) + f(15)(5) \\
&= 60(5) + 42(5) + 28(5) + 18(5) = 740.
\end{aligned}$$

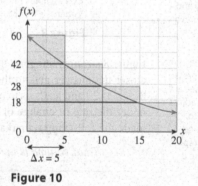

Figure 10

Because sums are often used in mathematics, mathematicians have developed a shorthand notation for them. We write

$$f(x_0) \, \Delta x + f(x_1) \, \Delta x + \cdots + f(x_{n-1}) \, \Delta x \quad \text{as} \quad \sum_{k=0}^{n-1} f(x_k) \, \Delta x.$$

The symbol $\sum$ is the Greek letter sigma and stands for **summation**. The letter k here is called the index of summation, and we can think of it as counting off the segments.

We read the notation as "the sum from $k = 0$ to $n - 1$ of the quantities $f(x_k)\,\Delta x$." Think of it as a set of instructions:

Set $k = 0$, and calculate $f(x_0)\,\Delta x$.　　　　$f(0)(5)$ in the above calculation

Set $k = 1$, and calculate $f(x_1)\,\Delta x$.　　　　$f(5)(5)$ in the above calculation

$\vdots$

Set $k = n - 1$, and calculate $f(x_{n-1})\,\Delta x$.　　$f(15)(5)$ in the above calculation

Then sum all the quantities so calculated.

Riemann Sum

If f is a continuous function, the **left Riemann sum** with n equal subdivisions for f over the interval $[a, b]$ is defined to be

$$\text{Left Riemann sum} = \sum_{k=0}^{n-1} f(x_k)\,\Delta x$$

$$= f(x_0)\,\Delta x + f(x_1)\,\Delta x + \cdots + f(x_{n-1})\,\Delta x$$

$$= [f(x_0) + f(x_1) + \cdots + f(x_{n-1})]\,\Delta x,$$

where $a = x_0 < x_1 < \cdots < x_n = b$ are the endpoints of the subdivisions, and $\Delta x = (b - a)/n$.

Interpretation of the Riemann Sum

If f is the rate of change of a quantity F (that is, $f = F'$), then the Riemann sum of f approximates the total change of F from $x = a$ to $x = b$. The approximation improves as the number of subdivisions increases toward infinity.

Quick Examples

1. If $f(t)$ is the rate of change in the number of bats in a belfry and $[a, b] = [2, 3]$, then the Riemann sum approximates the total change in the number of bats in the belfry from time $t = 2$ to time $t = 3$.

2. If $c(x)$ is the marginal cost of producing the xth item and $[a, b] = [10, 20]$, then the Riemann sum approximates the cost of producing items 11 through 20.

Visualizing a Left Riemann Sum (Nonnegative Function)

Graphically, we can represent a left Riemann sum of a nonnegative function as an approximation of the area under a curve:

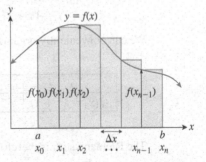

Riemann sum = Shaded area = Area of first rectangle + Area of second rectangle + $\cdots$ + Area of nth rectangle = $f(x_0)\,\Delta x + f(x_1)\,\Delta x + f(x_2)\,\Delta x + \cdots + f(x_{n-1})\,\Delta x$.

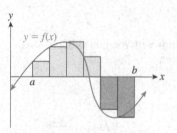

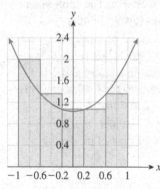

Riemann sum = Area above *x*-axis
− Area below *x*-axis

Figure 11

3. In Example 1 we computed several Riemann sums, including these:

$$n = 1: \quad \text{Riemann sum} = v(0)\,\Delta t = 60 \times 20 = 1{,}200$$
$$n = 2: \quad \text{Riemann sum} = \left[v(t_0) + v(t_1) \right] \Delta t$$
$$= \left[v(0) + v(10) \right](10) = 880$$
$$n = 4: \quad \text{Riemann sum} = \left[v(t_0) + v(t_1) + v(t_2) + v(t_3) \right] \Delta t$$
$$= \left[v(0) + v(5) + v(10) + v(15) \right](5) = 740$$
$$n = 8: \quad \text{Riemann sum} = \left[v(t_0) + v(t_1) + \cdots + v(t_7) \right] \Delta t$$
$$= \left[v(0) + v(2.5) + \cdots + v(17.5) \right](2.5) = 675.$$

Note To visualize the Riemann sum of a function that is negative, look again at the formula $f(x_0)\,\Delta x + f(x_1)\,\Delta x + f(x_2)\,\Delta x + \cdots + f(x_{n-1})\,\Delta x$ for the Riemann sum. Each term $f(x_k)\,\Delta x_k$ represents the area of one rectangle in the figure above. So the areas of the rectangles with negative values of $f(x_k)$ are automatically counted as negative. They appear as red rectangles in Figure 11. ∎

Calculating Riemann Sums

EXAMPLE 2 Calculating a Riemann Sum from a Formula

Compute the left Riemann sum for $f(x) = x^2 + 1$ over the interval $[-1, 1]$, using $n = 5$ subdivisions.

Solution Because the interval is $[a, b] = [-1, 1]$ and $n = 5$, we have

$$\Delta x = \frac{b - a}{n} = \frac{1 - (-1)}{5} = 0.4. \qquad \text{Width of subdivisions}$$

Figure 12

Thus, the subdivisions of $[-1, 1]$ are determined by

$$-1 < -0.6 < -0.2 < 0.2 < 0.6 < 1. \qquad \text{Start with } -1, \text{ and keep adding } \Delta x = 0.4.$$

Figure 12 shows the graph with a representation of the Riemann sum.
The Riemann sum we want is

$$\left[f(x_0) + f(x_1) + \cdots + f(x_4) \right] \Delta x$$
$$= \left[f(-1) + f(-0.6) + f(-0.2) + f(0.2) + f(0.6) \right] 0.4.$$

We can conveniently organize this calculation in a table as follows:

x	−1	−0.6	−0.2	0.2	0.6	**Total**
$f(x) = x^2 + 1$	2	1.36	1.04	1.04	1.36	6.8

The Riemann sum is therefore

$$6.8\,\Delta x = 6.8 \times 0.4 = 2.72.$$

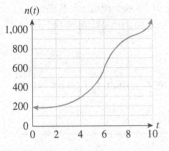

Figure 13

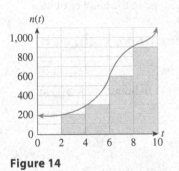

Figure 14

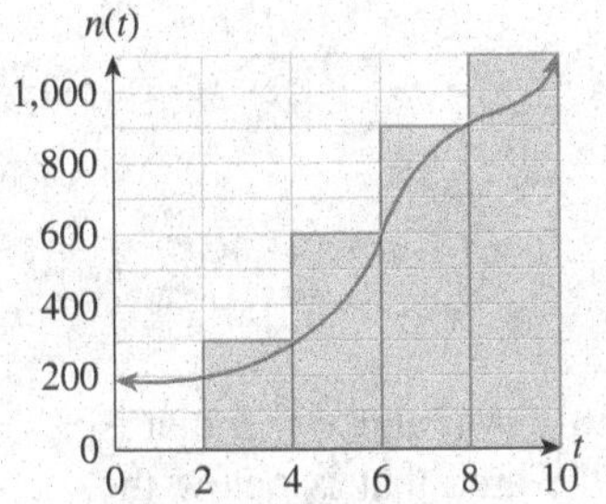

Right Riemann sum = (300)(2) +
(600)(2) + (900)(2) + (1,100)(2)
= 5,800
Height of each rectangle is determined
by height of graph at right edge.

Figure 15

＊This applies to some other functions as well, including "piecewise
continuous" functions discussed
in the next section.

EXAMPLE 3   **Computing a Riemann Sum from a Graph**

Figure 13 shows the approximate annual production $n(t)$ of engineering and technology PhD graduates in Mexico during the period 2000–2010.[22] Use a left Riemann sum with four subdivisions to estimate the total number of PhD graduates from 2002 to 2010.

Solution Let us represent the total number of (engineering and technology) PhD graduates up to time t (measured in years since 2000) by $N(t)$. The total number of PhD graduates from 2002 to 2010 is then the total change in $N(t)$ over the interval $[2, 10]$. In view of the above discussion we can approximate the total change in $N(t)$ using a Riemann sum of its rate of change $n(t)$. Because $n = 4$ subdivisions are specified, the width of each subdivision is

$$\Delta t = \frac{b - a}{n} = \frac{10 - 2}{4} = 2.$$

We can therefore represent the left Riemann sum by the shaded area shown in Figure 14.
  From the graph,

$$\text{Left sum} = n(2)\,\Delta t + n(4)\,\Delta t + n(6)\,\Delta t + n(8)\,\Delta t$$
$$= (200)(2) + (300)(2) + (600)(2) + (900)(2) = 4,000.$$

So we estimate that there was a total of about 4,000 engineering and technology PhD graduates during the given period.

➡ **Before we go on . . .** A glance at Figure 14 tells us that we have significantly underestimated the actual number of graduates, as the actual area under the curve is considerably larger. Figure 15 shows a **right Riemann sum** and gives us a much larger estimate. For continuous functions, the difference between these two types of Riemann sums approaches zero as the number of subdivisions approaches infinity (see below), so we will focus primarily on only one type: left Riemann sums. ■

The Definite Integral

As in Example 1, we're most interested in what happens to the Riemann sum when we let n get very large. When f is continuous,＊ its Riemann sums will always approach a limit as n goes to infinity. (This is not meant to be obvious. Proofs may be found in advanced calculus texts.) We give the limit a name.

The Definite Integral

If f is a continuous function, the **definite integral of f from a to b** is defined to be the limit of the Riemann sums as the number of subdivisions approaches infinity:

$$\int_a^b f(x)\,dx = \lim_{n \to \infty} \sum_{k=0}^{n-1} f(x_k)\,\Delta x.$$

In Words: The integral, from a to b, of $f(x)\,dx$ equals the limit, as $n \to \infty$, of the Riemann sum with a partition of n subdivisions.

[22] Source for data: Instituto Nacional de Estadística y Geografía (www.inegi.org.mx).

The function f is called the **integrand**, the numbers a and b are the **limits of integration**, and the variable x is the **variable of integration**. A Riemann sum with a large number of subdivisions may be used to approximate the definite integral.

Interpretation of the Definite Integral

If f is the rate of change of a quantity F (that is, $f = F'$), then $\int_a^b f(x)\, dx$ is the (exact) total change of F from $x = a$ to $x = b$.

Quick Examples

4. If $f(t)$ is the rate of change in the number of bats in a belfry and $[a, b] = [2, 3]$, then $\int_2^3 f(t)\, dt$ is the total change in the number of bats in the belfry from time $t = 2$ to time $t = 3$.

5. If, at time t hours, you are selling wall posters at a rate of $s(t)$ posters per hour, then

$$\text{Total number of posters sold from hour 3 to hour 5} = \int_3^5 s(t)\, dt.$$

Visualizing the Definite Integral

Nonnegative Functions: If $f(x) \geq 0$ for all x in $[a, b]$, then $\int_a^b f(x)\, dx$ is the area under the graph of f over the interval $[a, b]$, as shaded in the figure.

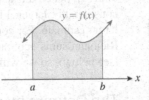

General Functions: $\int_a^b f(x)\, dx$ is the area between $x = a$ and $x = b$ that is above the x-axis and below the graph of f minus the area that is below the x-axis and above the graph of f:

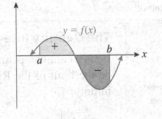

$$\int_a^b f(x)\, dx = \text{Area above } x\text{-axis} - \text{Area below } x\text{-axis}$$

Quick Examples

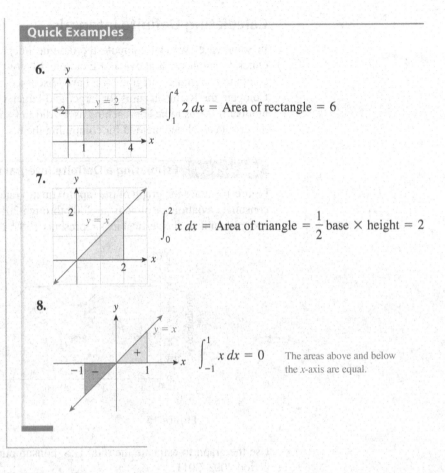

6. $\displaystyle\int_1^4 2\,dx = \text{Area of rectangle} = 6$

7. $\displaystyle\int_0^2 x\,dx = \text{Area of triangle} = \frac{1}{2}\,\text{base} \times \text{height} = 2$

8. $\displaystyle\int_{-1}^1 x\,dx = 0$ The areas above and below the x-axis are equal.

Notes

1. Remember that $\int_a^b f(x)\,dx$ stands for a number that depends on f, a, and b. The variable of integration x that appears is called a **dummy variable** because it has no effect on the answer. In other words,

$$\int_a^b f(x)\,dx = \int_a^b f(t)\,dt. \qquad x \text{ or } t \text{ is just a name we give the variable.}$$

2. The notation for the definite integral (due to Leibniz) comes from the notation for the Riemann sum. The integral sign $\int$ is an elongated S, the Roman equivalent of the Greek Σ. The d in dx is the lowercase Roman equivalent of the Greek Δ.

3. The definition above is adequate for continuous functions, but more complicated definitions are needed to handle other functions. For example, we broke the interval $[a, b]$ into n subdivisions of equal length, but other definitions allow a **partition** of the interval into subdivisions of possibly unequal lengths. We have evaluated f at the left endpoint of each subdivision, but we could equally well have used the right endpoint or any other point in the subdivision. All of these variations lead to the same answer when f is continuous.

4. The similarity between the notations for the definite integral and the indefinite integral is no mistake. We will discuss the exact connection in Section 13.4. ■

Calculating Definite Integrals

In some cases we can compute the definite integral directly from the graph. (See Quick Examples 6–8 above and Example 4 below.) In general, the only method of computing definite integrals we have discussed so far is numerical estimation: Compute the Riemann sums for larger and larger values of n, and then estimate the number it seems to be approaching as we did in Example 1. (In Section 13.4 we will discuss an algebraic method for computing them.)

> **EXAMPLE 4**   **Estimating a Definite Integral from a Graph**

Figure 16 shows the graph of the (approximate) rate $f'(t)$ at which the United States consumed aviation gasoline from 2000 through 2013. (t is time in years since 2000, and each unit on the vertical axis represents 100 million gallons per year.)[23]

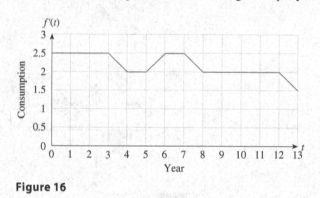

Figure 16

Use the graph to estimate the total U.S. consumption of aviation gasoline over the period 2002–2011.

Solution The derivative $f'(t)$ represents the rate of change of the total U.S. consumption of aviation gasoline, so the total U.S. consumption of aviation gasoline over the period 2002–2011 ($[2, 11]$ on the graph) is given by the definite integral

$$\text{Total U.S. consumption of aviation gasoline} = \text{Total change in } f(t) = \int_{2}^{11} f'(t)\, dt$$

and is given by the shaded area under the graph (Figure 17).

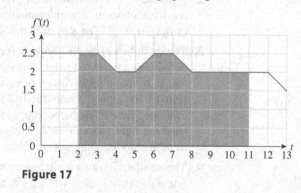

Figure 17

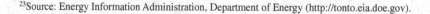

[23]Source: Energy Information Administration, Department of Energy (http://tonto.eia.doe.gov).

One way to determine the area is to count the number of filled rectangles as defined by the grid. Each rectangle has an area of $1 \times 0.5 = 0.5$ units (and the half-rectangles determined by diagonal portions of the graph have half that area). Counting rectangles, we find a total of 39.5 complete rectangles, so

Total area $= 19.75.$

Because $f'(t)$ is in 100 million gallons per year, we conclude that the total U.S. consumption of aviation gasoline over the given period was about 1,975 million gallons, or 1.975 billion gallons.

While counting rectangles might seem easy, it becomes awkward in cases involving large numbers of rectangles or partial rectangles whose area is not easy to determine. In a case like this, in which the graph consists of straight lines, rather than counting rectangles, we can get the area by averaging the left and right Riemann sums whose subdivisions are determined by the grid:

Left sum $= (2.5 + 2.5 + 2 + 2 + 2.5 + 2.5 + 2 + 2 + 2)(1) = 20$

Right sum $= (2.5 + 2 + 2 + 2.5 + 2.5 + 2 + 2 + 2 + 2)(1) = 19.5$

$$\text{Average} = \frac{20 + 19.5}{2} = 19.75.$$

To see why this works, look at the single interval $[3, 4]$. The left sum contributes $2.5 \times 1 = 2.5$, and the right sum contributes $2 \times 1 = 2$. The exact area is their average, 2.25 (Figure 18).

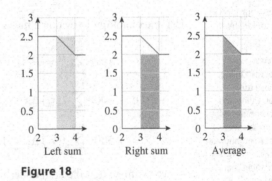

Left sum   Right sum   Average

Figure 18

The average of the left and right Riemann sums is frequently a better estimate of the definite integral than either is alone.

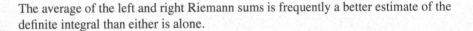

➡ **Before we go on ...** It is important to check that the units we are using in Example 4 match up correctly: t is given in *years*, and $f'(t)$ is given in 100 million gallons per *year*. The integral is then given in

$$\text{Years} \times \frac{100 \text{ million gallons}}{\text{Year}} = 100 \text{ million gallons.}$$

If we had specified $f'(t)$ in, say, 100 million gallons per *day* but t in years, then we would have needed to convert either t or $f'(t)$ so that the units of time match. ∎

The next example illustrates the use of technology in estimating definite integrals using Riemann sums.

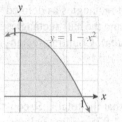

Figure 19

Using Technology

See the Technology Guides at the end of the chapter to find out how to compute these sums on a TI-83/84 Plus and a spreadsheet.

Website
www.WanerMath.com
At the Website, select the Online Utilities tab, and choose the Numerical Integration Utility and Grapher. This utility computes left and right Riemann sums as well as a good numerical approximation of the integral. There is also a downloadable Excel spreadsheet that computes and graphs Riemann sums (Riemann Sum Grapher).

EXAMPLE 5 ⊤ **Using Technology to Approximate the Definite Integral**

Use technology to estimate the area under the graph of $f(x) = 1 - x^2$ over the interval $[0, 1]$ using $n = 100$, $n = 200$, and $n = 500$ subdivisions.

Solution We need to estimate the area under the parabola shown in Figure 19. From the discussion above,

$$\text{Area} = \int_0^1 (1 - x^2)\, dx.$$

The Riemann sum with $n = 100$ has $\Delta x = (b - a)/n = (1 - 0)/100 = 0.01$ and is given by

$$\sum_{k=0}^{99} f(x_k)\, \Delta x = [f(0) + f(0.01) + \cdots + f(0.99)](0.01).$$

Similarly, the Riemann sum with $n = 200$ has $\Delta x = (b - a)/n = (1 - 0)/200 = 0.005$ and is given by

$$\sum_{k=0}^{199} f(x_k)\, \Delta x = [f(0) + f(0.005) + \cdots + f(0.995)](0.005).$$

For $n = 500$, $x = (b - a)/n = (1 - 0)/500 = 0.002$, and the Riemann sum is

$$\sum_{k=0}^{499} f(x_k)\, \Delta x = [f(0) + f(0.002) + \cdots + f(0.998)](0.002).$$

Using technology to evaluate these Riemann sums, we find

$$n = 100: \sum_{k=0}^{99} f(x_k)\, \Delta x = 0.67165$$

$$n = 200: \sum_{k=0}^{199} f(x_k)\, \Delta x = 0.6691625$$

$$n = 500: \sum_{k=0}^{499} f(x_k)\, \Delta x = 0.667666,$$

so we estimate that the area under the curve is about 0.67. (The exact answer is 2/3, as we will be able to verify using the techniques in Section 13.4.)

EXAMPLE 6 **Motion**

A fast car has velocity $v(t) = 6t^2 + 10t$ ft/sec after t seconds (as measured by a radar gun). Use several values of n to find the distance covered by the car from time $t = 3$ seconds to time $t = 4$ seconds.

Solution Because the velocity $v(t)$ is rate of change of position, the total change in position over the interval $[3, 4]$ is

$$\text{Distance covered} = \text{Total change in position} = \int_3^4 v(t)\, dt = \int_3^4 (6t^2 + 10t)\, dt.$$

As in Examples 1 and 5, we can subdivide the 1-second interval $[3, 4]$ into smaller and smaller pieces to get more and more accurate approximations of the integral. By computing Riemann sums for various values of n, we get the following results:

$$n = 10: \sum_{k=0}^{9} v(t_k)\,\Delta t = 106.41 \qquad n = 100: \sum_{k=0}^{99} v(t_k)\,\Delta t \approx 108.740$$

$$n = 1{,}000: \sum_{k=0}^{999} v(t_k)\,\Delta t \approx 108.974 \qquad n = 10{,}000: \sum_{k=0}^{9999} v(t_k)\,\Delta t \approx 108.997$$

These calculations suggest that the total distance covered by the car, the value of the definite integral, is approximately 109 feet.

Website
www.WanerMath.com
At the Website you will find
the following optional online
interactive section:

  Numerical Integration.

➡ **Before we go on...** Do Example 6 using antiderivatives instead of Riemann sums, as in Section 13.1. Do you notice a relationship between antiderivatives and definite integrals? This will be explored in Section 13.4. ∎

13.3 EXERCISES

▼ more advanced   ◆ challenging
🔲 indicates exercises that should be solved using technology

In Exercises 1–10, calculate the left Riemann sum for the given function over the given interval, using the given value of n. (When rounding, round answers to four decimal places. If using the tabular method, values of the function in the table should be accurate to at least five decimal places.) [HINT: See Example 2.]

1. $f(x) = 4x - 1$ over $[0, 2]$, $n = 4$

2. $f(x) = 1 - 3x$ over $[-1, 1]$, $n = 4$

3. $f(x) = x^2$ over $[-2, 2]$, $n = 4$

4. $f(x) = x^2$ over $[1, 5]$, $n = 4$

5. $f(x) = (x - 1)^3$ over $[-1, 4]$, $n = 5$

6. $f(x) = x^3$ over $[-2, 3]$, $n = 5$

7. $f(x) = \dfrac{1}{1 + x}$ over $[0, 1]$, $n = 5$

8. $f(x) = \dfrac{x}{1 + x^2}$ over $[0, 1]$, $n = 5$

9. $f(x) = e^{-x}$ over $[0, 10]$, $n = 5$

10. $f(x) = e^{-x}$ over $[-5, 5]$, $n = 5$

In Exercises 11–18, use the given graph to estimate the left Riemann sum for the given interval with the stated number of subdivisions. [HINT: See Example 3.]

11. $[0, 5]$, $n = 5$ 12. $[0, 8]$, $n = 4$

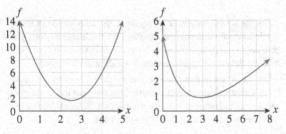

13. $[1, 9]$, $n = 4$ 14. $[0.5, 2.5]$, $n = 4$

15. $[1, 3.5]$, $n = 5$ 16. $[0.5, 3.5]$, $n = 3$

17. $[0, 3]$; $n = 3$ 18. $[0.5, 3]$; $n = 5$

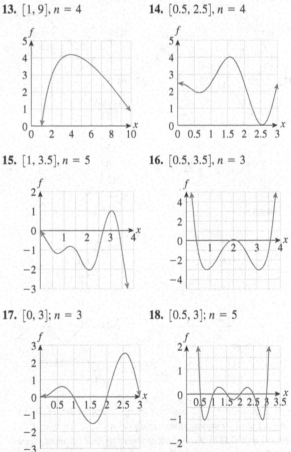

In Exercises 19–28, use geometry (not Riemann sums) to compute the integral. [HINT: See Quick Examples 6–8.]

19. $\displaystyle\int_{0}^{1} 1\,dx$ 20. $\displaystyle\int_{0}^{2} 5\,dx$

21. $\int_0^1 x\, dx$

22. $\int_1^2 x\, dx$

23. $\int_0^1 \dfrac{x}{2}\, dx$

24. $\int_1^2 \dfrac{x}{2}\, dx$

25. $\int_2^4 (x - 2)\, dx$

26. $\int_3^6 (x - 3)\, dx$

27. $\int_{-1}^1 x^3\, dx$

28. $\int_{-2}^2 \dfrac{x}{2}\, dx$

In Exercises 29–34, the graph of the derivative $f'(t)$ of $f(t)$ is shown. Compute the total change of $f(t)$ over the given interval. [**HINT:** See Example 4.]

29. $[1, 5]$

30. $[2, 6]$

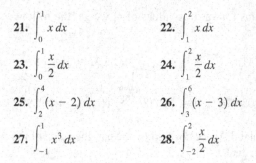

31. $[2, 6]$

32. $[0, 5]$

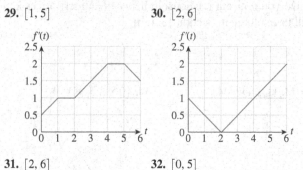

33. $[-1, 2]$

34. $[-1, 2]$

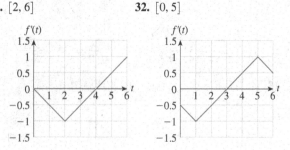

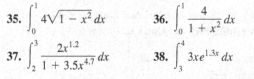 *In Exercises 35–38, use technology to approximate the given integral with Riemann sums, using (a) $n = 10$, (b) $n = 100$, and (c) $n = 1{,}000$. Round all answers to four decimal places.* [**HINT:** See Example 5.]

35. $\int_0^1 4\sqrt{1 - x^2}\, dx$

36. $\int_0^1 \dfrac{4}{1 + x^2}\, dx$

37. $\int_2^3 \dfrac{2x^{1.2}}{1 + 3.5x^{4.7}}\, dx$

38. $\int_3^4 3xe^{1.3x}\, dx$

Applications

39. *Pumps* A pump is delivering water into a tank at a rate of

$$r(t) = 3t^2 + 5 \text{ liters per minute,}$$

where t is time in minutes since the pump is turned on. Use a Riemann sum with $n = 5$ subdivisions to estimate the total volume of water pumped in during the first 2 minutes. [**HINT:** See Examples 1 and 2. This exercise is also discussed in the tutorial on the Website.]

40. *Pumps* A pump is delivering water into a tank at a rate of

$$r(t) = 6t^2 + 40 \text{ liters per minute,}$$

where t is time in minutes since the pump is turned on. Use a Riemann sum with $n = 6$ subdivisions to estimate the total volume of water pumped in during the first 3 minutes. [**HINT:** See Examples 1 and 2. A similar exercise is also discussed in the tutorial on the Website.]

41. *Cost* The marginal cost function for the manufacture of wireless headphones is given by

$$C'(x) = 20 - \dfrac{x}{200},$$

where x is the number of headphones manufactured. Use a Riemann sum with $n = 5$ to estimate the cost of producing the first 5 headphones. [**HINT:** See Examples 1 and 2 and Quick Example 2.]

42. *Cost* Repeat Exercise 41 using the marginal cost function

$$C'(x) = 25 - \dfrac{x}{50}.$$

[**HINT:** See Examples 1 and 2 and Quick Example 2.]

43. *Profit: iPhones* Assume that Apple's marginal cost function for the manufacture of x 32GB iPhone 6's per hour at the Foxconn Technology Group is[24]

$$c(x) = 160 - 0.002x,$$

and that Apple sells iPhone 6's for an average wholesale price of \$580. Use a Riemann sum with $n = 5$ subdivisions to estimate the total additional hourly profit corresponding to an increase in production and sales from 10,000 to 20,000 iPhone 6's per hour.

44. *Profit: PlayStation 4's* Assume that Sony's marginal cost function for the manufacture of x PlayStation 4's per hour is[25]

$$c(x) = 340 + 0.001x,$$

---

[24] Not the actual marginal cost equation; the authors do not know Apple's actual marginal cost equation, but the marginal costs given here are in rough agreement with the actual costs for one of the 2014 models. Sources: http://time.com, www.digitaltrends.com.

[25] Not the actual marginal cost equation; the authors do not know Sony's actual marginal cost equation, but the marginal costs given here are in rough agreement with the actual costs. Sources: VentureBeat (http://venturebeat.com), http://ps4daily.com.

and that Sony sells PlayStation 4's for an average whole-sale price of $400. Use a Riemann sum with $n = 5$ subdivisions to estimate the total additional hourly profit corresponding to an increase in production and sales from 50,000 to 60,000 PlayStation 4's per hour.

45. Bottled Water Sales The rate of U.S. sales of bottled water for the period 2007–2014 could be approximated by

$$s(t) = 0.08t^2 - 0.26t + 8.8 \text{ billion gallons per year}$$
$$(0 \le t \le 7),$$

where t is time in years since the start of 2007.[26] Use a Riemann sum with $n = 5$ to estimate the total U.S. sales of bottled water from the start of 2008 to the start of 2014. (Round your answer to the nearest billion gallons.) [**HINT:** See Example 2.]

46. Bottled Water Sales The rate of U.S. per capita sales of bottled water for the period 2007–2014 could be approximated by

$$s(t) = 0.25t^2 - t + 29 \text{ gallons per year} \quad (0 \le t \le 7),$$

where t is time in years since the start of 2007.[27] Use a Riemann sum with $n = 5$ to estimate the total U.S. per capita sales of bottled water from the start of 2008 to the start of 2012. (Round your answer to the nearest gallon.) [**HINT:** See Example 2.]

47. Online Payments The following graph shows the rate of change $p(t)$ of total payments through PayPal, in billions of dollars per quarter, from the first quarter of 2013 through the fourth quarter of 2014. (t is time in quarters; $t = 1$ represents the first quarter of 2013.)[28]

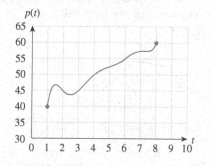

Use a left Riemann sum with three subdivisions to estimate the total value of payments through PayPal from the second quarter of 2013 to the fourth quarter of 2014 (the interval $[2, 8]$). [**HINT:** See Example 3.]

48. Online Auctions The following graph shows the rate of change $n(t)$ of the number of active eBay users, in millions of users per quarter, from the first quarter of 2008 through the first quarter of 2011. (t is time in quarters; $t = 1$ represents the first quarter of 2008.)[29]

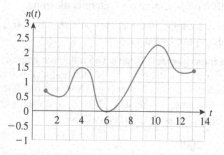

Use a left Riemann sum with four subdivisions to estimate the total change in the number of active users from the second quarter of 2008 to the second quarter of 2010 (the interval $[2, 10]$). [**HINT:** See Example 3.]

Scientific Research *Exercises 49 and 50 are based on the following figure, which shows the rate of publication of science research papers for researchers in the United States and the European Union in the years 1990–2010:*[30]

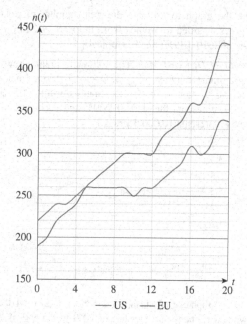

Here, t is time in years since 1990, and $n(t)$ is the publication rate in thousands of articles per year.

49. a. Use both left and right Riemann sums with five subdivisions to estimate the total number of science research papers by researchers in the United States during the 20-year period shown. [**HINT:** See Example 3.]

[26] Source for data: Beverage Marketing Corporation (www.bottledwater.org).

[27] *Ibid.*

[28] Source for data: Statista, www.statista.com.

[29] Source for data: eBay company reports (http://investor.ebay.com).

[30] Source for data: Jonathan Adams, David Pendlebury, Global Research Report November 2010, Thomson Reuters/www.sciencewatch.com.

b. Use the answers from part (a) to obtain an estimate of $\int_0^{20} n(t)\,dt$ for researchers in the United States. [HINT: See Example 4.] Interpret the result.

50. Repeat Exercise 49 for articles published by researchers in the European Union.

51. *Graduate Degrees: Women* The following graph shows the approximate number $f'(t)$ of doctoral degrees per year awarded to women in the United States during 2005–2013. ($t = 0$ represents the start of 2005, and each unit of the y-axis represents 10,000 degrees.)[31]

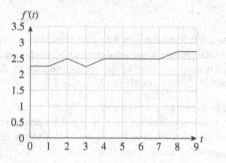

Use the graph to estimate the total number of doctoral degrees awarded to women from the start of 2005 to the start of 2010. [HINT: See Example 4.]

52. *Graduate Degrees: Men* The following graph shows the approximate number $m'(t)$ of doctoral degrees per year awarded to men in the United States during 2005–2013. ($t = 0$ represents the start of 2005, and each unit of the y-axis represents 10,000 degrees.)[32]

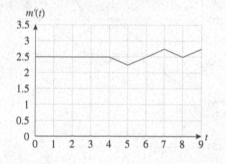

Use the graph to estimate the total number of doctoral degrees awarded to men from the start of 2009 to the end of 2013. [HINT: See Example 4.]

53. *Visiting Students in the Early 2000s* The aftermath of the September 11 attacks saw a decrease in the number of students visiting the United States. The following graph shows the approximate rate of change $c'(t)$ in the number of students from China who had taken the GRE exam

required for admission to U.S. universities. (t is time in years since the start of 2000.)[33]

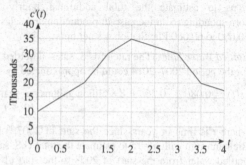

Use the graph to estimate, to the nearest 1,000, the total number of students from China who took the GRE exams from the start of 2002 to the start of 2004.

54. *Visiting Students in the Early 2000s* Repeat Exercise 53, using the following graph for students from India:[34]

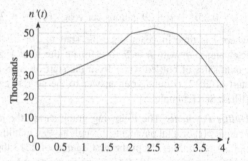

Net Income: Exercises 55 and 56 are based on the following graph, which shows General Electric's approximate net income in billions of dollars each year from 2005 to 2011:[35]

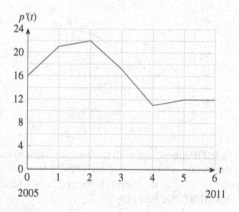

55. Compute the left and right Riemann sum estimates of $\int_0^4 p'(t)\,dt$ using $\Delta t = 1$. Which of these two sums gives

[31] Source for data and projections: National Center for Education Statistics (www.nces.ed.gov).

[32] *Ibid.*

[33] Source: Educational Testing Services/Shanghai and Jiao Tong University/*New York Times*, December 21, 2004, p. A25.

[34] *Ibid.*

[35] Source: Company reports (www.ge.com/investors).

the actual total net income earned by GE during the years 2005–2008? Explain.

56. Compute the left and right Riemann sum estimates of $\int_2^6 p'(t)\,dt$ using $\Delta t = 1$. Which of these two sums gives the actual total net income earned by GE during the years 2008–2011? Explain.

57. **Crude Oil Production: Mexico** The following table shows annual crude oil production in Mexico by Pemex for 2008–2014. ($t = 0$ represents 2008.)[36]

Year t (year since 2008)	0	1	2	3	4	5	6
Crude Oil Production p (billion barrels)	1.15	1.08	1.08	1.07	1.06	1.05	1.02

  a. Use the table to compute the left and right Riemann sums for $p(t)$ over the interval $[0, 5]$ using five subdivisions.

  b. What does the *right* Riemann sum in part (a) tell you about crude oil production by Pemex?

58. **Offshore Crude Oil Production: Mexico** The following table shows annual offshore crude oil production in Mexico by Pemex for 2008–2014. ($t = 0$ represents 2008.)[37]

Year t (year since 2008)	0	1	2	3	4	5	6
Offshore Crude Oil Production p (billion barrels)	0.82	0.73	0.71	0.69	0.69	0.69	0.68

  a. Use the table to compute the left and right Riemann sums for $p(t)$ over the interval $[1, 6]$ using five subdivisions.

  b. What does the *left* Riemann sum in part (a) tell you about offshore crude oil production by Pemex?

59. **Motion under Gravity** The velocity of a stone moving under gravity t seconds after being thrown up at 30 ft/sec is given by $v(t) = -32t + 30$ ft/sec. Use a Riemann sum with five subdivisions to estimate $\int_0^4 v(t)\,dt$. What does the answer represent? [HINT: See Example 6.]

60. **Motion under Gravity** The velocity of a stone moving under gravity t seconds after being thrown up at 4 m/sec is given by $v(t) = -9.8t + 4$ m/sec. Use a Riemann sum with five subdivisions to estimate $\int_0^1 v(t)\,dt$. What does the answer represent? [HINT: See Example 6.]

61. **Motion** A model rocket has upward velocity $v(t) = 40t^2$ ft/sec, t seconds after launch. Use a Riemann sum with $n = 10$ to estimate how high the rocket is 2 seconds after launch. (Use technology to compute the Riemann sum.)

62. **Motion** A race car has a velocity given by $v(t) = 600(1 - e^{-0.5t})$ ft/sec, t seconds after starting. Use a Riemann sum with $n = 10$ to estimate how far the car has traveled in the first 4 seconds. (Round your answer to the nearest whole number.) (Use technology to compute the Riemann sum.)

63. **Facebook Membership** From the start of 2007, new members joined Facebook at a rate of roughly

$$m(t) = 20t^2 + 60t + 12 \text{ million members per year}$$
$$(0 \le t \le 6),$$

where t is time in years since the start of 2007.[38] Estimate $\int_1^6 m(t)\,dt$ using a Riemann sum with $n = 150$. (Try the Numerical integration utility and grapher.) Round your answer to the nearest whole number, and interpret the answer. [HINT: See Example 5.]

64. **Uploads to YouTube** Since YouTube first became available to the public in mid-2005, the rate at which video has been uploaded to the site can be approximated by

$$v(t) = 1.1t^2 - 2.6t + 2.3 \text{ million hours of video per year}$$
$$(0 \le t \le 9),$$

where t is time in years since June 2005.[39] Estimate $\int_2^9 v(t)\,dt$ using a Riemann sum with $n = 150$. (Round your answer to the nearest whole number.) Interpret the answer. [HINT: See Example 5.]

65. **Big Brother** The total number of wiretaps authorized each year by U.S. state and federal courts from 1990 to 2015 can be approximated by

$$w(t) = 774e^{0.06t} \quad (0 \le t \le 25).$$

(t is time in years since the start of 1990.)[40] Estimate $\int_{10}^{25} w(t)\,dt$ using a (left) Riemann sum with $n = 100$. (Round your answer to the nearest 10.) Interpret the answer.

66. **Big Brother** The number of wiretaps authorized each year by U.S. state courts from 1990 to 2015 can be approximated by

$$w(t) = 412e^{0.071t} \quad (0 \le t \le 25).$$

(t is time in years since the start of 1990.)[41] Estimate $\int_5^{25} w(t)\,dt$ using a (left) Riemann sum with $n = 100$. (Round your answer to the nearest 10.) Interpret the answer.

---

[36] 2014 figure is a projection based on data through Nov. 2014. Source: www.pemex.com (January 2015).

[37] *Ibid.*

[38] Sources for data: www.facebook.com, www.insidefacebook.com.

[39] Sources for data: www.youtube.com, www.statista.com.

[40] Source for data: Wiretap Reports, Administrative Office of the United States Courts (www.uscourts.gov/Statistics/WiretapReports).

[41] *Ibid.*

67. ▼ *Surveying* My uncle intends to build a kidney-shaped swimming pool in his small yard, and the town zoning board will approve the project only if the total area of the pool does not exceed 500 square feet. The accompanying figure shows a diagram of the planned swimming pool, with measurements of its width at the indicated points. Will my uncle's plans be approved? Use a (left) Riemann sum to approximate the area.

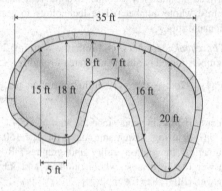

68. ▼ *Pollution* An aerial photograph of an ocean oil spill shows the pattern in the accompanying diagram. Assuming that the oil slick has a uniform depth of 0.01 meters, how many cubic meters of oil would you estimate to be in the spill? (Volume = Area × Thickness. Use a (left) Riemann sum to approximate the area.)

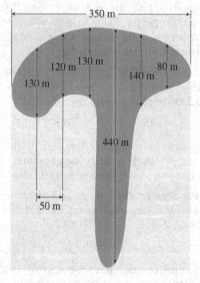

69. ☐▼ *Oil Consumption: United States* During the period 1980–2008 the United States was consuming oil at a rate of about

$$q(t) = 76t + 5{,}540 \text{ million barrels per year}$$
$$(0 \le t \le 28),$$

where t is time in years since the start of 1980.[42] During the same period, the price per barrel of crude oil in constant 2008 dollars was about

$$p(t) = 0.45t^2 - 12t + 105 \text{ dollars}[43] \quad (0 \le t \le 28).$$

a. Graph the function $r(t) = p(t)q(t)$ for $0 \le t \le 28$, indicating the area that represents $\int_{10}^{20} r(t)\,dt$. What does this area signify?

b. Estimate the area in part (a) using a Riemann sum with $n = 200$. (Round the answer to three significant digits.) Interpret the answer.

70. ☐▼ *Oil Consumption: China* Repeat Exercise 69 using instead the rate of consumption of oil in China:

$$q(t) = 82t + 221 \text{ million barrels per year}[44] \quad (0 \le t \le 28).$$

The Normal Curve The normal distribution curve, which models the distributions of data in a wide range of applications, is given by the function

$$p(x) = \frac{1}{\sqrt{2\pi}\sigma} e^{-(x-\mu)^2/(2\sigma^2)},$$

where $\pi = 3.14159265\ldots$ and σ and μ are constants called the **standard deviation** and the **mean**, respectively. The graph of the normal distribution (when $\sigma = 1$ and $\mu = 2$) is shown in the figure. Exercises 71 and 72 illustrate its use.

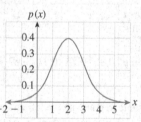

71. ☐▼ *Test Scores Enormous State University*'s Calculus I test scores are modeled by a normal distribution with $\mu = 72.6$ and $\sigma = 5.2$. The percentage of students who obtained scores between a and b on the test is given by

$$\int_a^b p(x)\,dx.$$

a. Use a Riemann sum with $n = 40$ to estimate the percentage of students who obtained between 60 and 100 on the test.

b. What percentage of students scored less than 30?

---

[42] Source for data: BP Statistical Review of World Energy (www.bp.com/statisticalreview).

[43] Source for data: www.inflationdata.com.

[44] Source for data: BP Statistical Review of World Energy (www.bp.com/statisticalreview).

72. ⬚ ▼ *Consumer Satisfaction* In a survey, consumers were asked to rate a new toothpaste on a scale of 1–10. The resulting data are modeled by a normal distribution with $\mu = 4.5$ and $\sigma = 1.0$. The percentage of consumers who rated the toothpaste with a score between a and b on the test is given by

$$\int_a^b p(x)\, dx.$$

a. Use a Riemann sum with $n = 10$ to estimate the percentage of customers who rated the toothpaste 5 or above. (Use the range 4.5 to 10.5.)

b. What percentage of customers rated the toothpaste 0 or 1? (Use the range -0.5 to 1.5.)

Communication and Reasoning Exercises

73. If $f(x) = 6$, then the left Riemann sum _____ (increases/decreases/stays the same) as n increases.

74. If $f(x) = -1$, then the left Riemann sum _____ (increases/decreases/stays the same) as n increases.

75. If f is an increasing function of x, then the left Riemann sum _____ (increases/decreases/stays the same) as n increases.

76. If f is a decreasing function of x, then the left Riemann sum _____ (increases/decreases/stays the same) as n increases.

77. If $\int_a^b f(x)\, dx = 0$, what can you say about the graph of f?

78. Sketch the graphs of two (different) functions f and g such that $\int_a^b f(x)\, dx = \int_a^b g(x)\, dx$.

79. ▼ The definite integral counts the area under the x-axis as negative. Give an example that shows how this can be useful in applications.

80. ▼ Sketch the graph of a nonconstant function whose Riemann sum with $n = 1$ gives the exact value of the definite integral.

81. ▼ Sketch the graph of a nonconstant function whose Riemann sums with $n = 1$, 5, and 10 are all zero.

82. ▼ Besides left and right Riemann sums, another approximation of the integral is the **midpoint** approximation, in which we compute the sum

$$\sum_{k=1}^{n} f(\bar{x}_k)\, \Delta x$$

where $\bar{x}_k = (x_{k-1} + x_k)/2$ is the point midway between the left and right endpoints of the interval $[x_{k-1}, x_k]$. Why is it true that the midpoint approximation is exact if f is linear? (Draw a picture.)

83. ▼ Your cellphone company charges you $c(t) = \dfrac{20}{t + 100}$ dollars for the tth minute. You make a 60-minute phone call. What kind of (left) Riemann sum represents the total cost of the call? Explain.

84. ▼ Your friend's cellphone company charges her $c(t) = \dfrac{20}{t + 100}$ dollars for the $(t + 1)$st minute. Your friend makes a 60-minute phone call. What kind of (left) Riemann sum represents the total cost of the call? Explain.

85. ▼ Give a formula for the **right Riemann sum** with n equal subdivisions $a = x_0 < x_1 < \cdots < x_n = b$ for f over the interval $[a, b]$.

86. ▼ Refer to Exercise 85. If f is continuous, what happens to the difference between the left and right Riemann sums as $n \to \infty$? Explain.

87. ▼ Sketch the graph of a nonzero function whose left Riemann sum with n subdivisions is zero for every *even* number n.

88. ▼ When approximating a definite integral by computing Riemann sums, how might you judge whether you have chosen n large enough to get your answer accurate to, say, three decimal places?

13.4 The Definite Integral: Algebraic Viewpoint and the Fundamental Theorem of Calculus

Connection Between Definite and Indefinite Integrals

In Section 13.3 we saw that the definite integral of the marginal cost function gives the total cost. However, in Section 13.1 we used antiderivatives to recover the cost function from the marginal cost function, so we can also use antiderivatives to compute total cost. The following example, based on Example 5 in Section 13.1, compares these two approaches.

EXAMPLE 1 **Finding Cost from Marginal Cost**

The marginal cost of producing baseball caps at a production level of x caps is $4 - 0.001x$ dollars per cap. Find the total change of cost if production is increased from 100 to 200 caps.

Solution

Method 1: Using an Antiderivative (based on Example 5 in Section 13.1): Let $C(x)$ be the cost function. Because the marginal cost function is the derivative of the cost function, we have $C'(x) = 4 - 0.001x$, so

$$C(x) = \int (4 - 0.001x)\, dx$$

$$= 4x - 0.001\frac{x^2}{2} + K \qquad \text{K is the constant of integration.}$$

$$= 4x - 0.0005x^2 + K.$$

Although we do not know what to use for the value of the constant K, we can say:

Cost at production level of 100 caps $= C(100)$

$$= 4(100) - 0.0005(100)^2 + K$$

$$= \$395 + K$$

Cost at production level of 200 caps $= C(200)$

$$= 4(200) - 0.0005(200)^2 + K$$

$$= \$780 + K.$$

Therefore,

Total change in cost $= C(200) - C(100)$

$$= (\$780 + K) - (\$395 + K) = \$385.$$

Notice how the constant of integration simply canceled out! So we could choose any value for K that we wanted (such as $K = 0$) and still come out with the correct total change. Put another way, we could use *any antiderivative* of $C'(x)$, such as

$$F(x) = 4x - 0.0005x^2 \qquad \text{$F(x)$ is any antiderivative of $C'(x)$,}$$
$$\text{whereas $C(x)$ is the actual cost function.}$$

or

$$F(x) = 4x - 0.0005x^2 + 4,$$

compute $F(200) - F(100)$, and obtain the total change, $385.

Summarizing this method: To compute the total change of $C(x)$ over the interval $[100, 200]$, use any antiderivative $F(x)$ of $C'(x)$, and compute $F(200) - F(100)$.

Method 2: Using a Definite Integral (based on the interpretation of the definite integral as total change discussed in Section 13.3): Because the marginal cost $C'(x)$ is the rate of change of the total cost function $C(x)$, the total change in $C(x)$ over the interval $[100, 200]$ is given by

Total change in cost $=$ Area under the marginal cost function curve

$$= \int_{100}^{200} C'(x)\, dx$$

$$= \int_{100}^{200} (4 - 0.001x)\, dx \qquad \text{See Figure 20.}$$

$$= \$385. \qquad \text{Using geometry or Riemann sums}$$

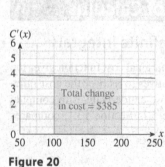

Figure 20

Putting these two methods together gives us the following surprising result:

$$\int_{100}^{200} C'(x)\, dx = F(200) - F(100),$$

where $F(x)$ is any antiderivative of $C'(x)$.

Now, there is nothing special in Example 1 about the specific function $C'(x)$ or the choice of endpoints of integration. So if we replace $C'(x)$ by a general continuous function $f(x)$, we can write

$$\int_{a}^{b} f(x)\, dx = F(b) - F(a),$$

where $F(x)$ is any antiderivative of $f(x)$. This result is known as the **Fundamental Theorem of Calculus**.

Statement of the Fundamental Theorem of Calculus

The Fundamental Theorem of Calculus (FTC)

Let f be a continuous function defined on the interval $[a, b]$, and let F be *any* antiderivative of f defined on $[a, b]$. Then

$$\int_{a}^{b} f(x)\, dx = F(b) - F(a).$$

Moreover, an antiderivative of f is guaranteed to exist.

In Words: Every continuous function has an antiderivative. To compute the definite integral of $f(x)$ over $[a, b]$, first find an antiderivative $F(x)$, then evaluate it at $x = b$, evaluate it at $x = a$, and subtract the two answers.

Q: *A technical point: What is meant by saying that F is an antiderivative of f when f is defined only on a closed interval $[a, b]$? (Remember that the derivative of F is not defined at endpoints of the domain.)*

A: *It means that F is a continuous function on $[a, b]$ such that $F'(x)$ exists and equals $f(x)$ for every x in the open interval (a, b).*

Quick Example

1. If $f(x) = 2x$, then an antiderivative of f is $F(x) = x^2$. Thus,

$$\int_{0}^{1} 2x\, dx = F(1) - F(0) = 1^2 - 0^2 = 1.$$

Note The Fundamental Theorem of Calculus actually applies to some other functions besides the continuous ones. The function f is **piecewise continuous** on $[a, b]$ if it is defined and continuous at all but finitely many points in the interval, and, at each point where the function is not defined or is discontinuous, the left and right limits of f exist and are finite. (See Figure 21 for some examples of piecewise continuous functions.)

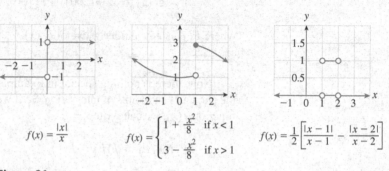

$$f(x) = \frac{|x|}{x}$$

$$f(x) = \begin{cases} 1 + \frac{x^2}{8} & \text{if } x < 1 \\ 3 - \frac{x^2}{8} & \text{if } x > 1 \end{cases}$$

$$f(x) = \frac{1}{2}\left[\frac{|x-1|}{x-1} - \frac{|x-2|}{x-2}\right]$$

Figure 21

The FTC also applies to any piecewise continuous function f, as long as we specify that the antiderivative F that we choose be continuous. To be precise, to say that F is an antiderivative of f means here that $F'(x) = f(x)$ except at the points at which f is discontinuous or not defined, where $F'(x)$ may not exist. For example, if f is the step function $f(x) = |x|/x$, shown on the left in Figure 21, then we can use $F(x) = |x|$. (Note that F is continuous, and $F'(x) = |x|/x$ except when $x = 0$.) ∎

EXAMPLE 2   **Using the FTC to Calculate a Definite Integral**

Calculate $\displaystyle\int_0^1 (1 - x^2)\, dx$.

Solution To use the FTC, we need to find an antiderivative of $1 - x^2$. But we know that

$$\int (1 - x^2)\, dx = x - \frac{x^3}{3} + C.$$

We need only one antiderivative, so let's take $F(x) = x - x^3/3$. The FTC tells us that

$$\int_0^1 (1 - x^2)\, dx = F(1) - F(0) = \left(1 - \frac{1}{3}\right) - (0) = \frac{2}{3}$$

which is the value we estimated in Section 13.3.

---

* There seem to be several notations in use, actually. Another common notation is $F(x)\Big|_a^b$.

➡ **Before we go on . . .** A useful piece of notation is often used here. We write*

$$[F(x)]_a^b = F(b) - F(a).$$

Thus, we can rewrite the computation in Example 2 more simply as follows:

$$\int_0^1 (1 - x^2)\, dx = \left[x - \frac{x^3}{3}\right]_0^1$$

Substitute $x = 1$.　　Substitute $x = 0$.

$$= \left(1 - \frac{1}{3}\right) - \left(0 - \frac{0}{3}\right)$$

$$= \left(1 - \frac{1}{3}\right) - (0) = \frac{2}{3}.$$

■

EXAMPLE 3   **More Use of the FTC**

Compute the following definite integrals:

a. $\int_0^1 (2x^3 + 10x + 1)\, dx$ **b.** $\int_1^5 \left(\frac{1}{x^2} + \frac{1}{x}\right) dx$

Solution

a. $\int_0^1 (2x^3 + 10x + 1)\, dx = \left[\frac{1}{2}x^4 + 5x^2 + x\right]_0^1$

$$\overset{\text{Substitute } x = 1.\qquad\qquad \text{Substitute } x = 0.}{= \left(\frac{1}{2} + 5 + 1\right) - \left(\frac{1}{2}(0) + 5(0) + 0\right)}$$

$$= \left(\frac{1}{2} + 5 + 1\right) - (0) = \frac{13}{2}$$

b. $\int_1^5 \left(\frac{1}{x^2} + \frac{1}{x}\right) dx = \int_1^5 (x^{-2} + x^{-1})\, dx$

$$= \left[-x^{-1} + \ln|x|\right]_1^5$$

$$\overset{\text{Substitute } x = 5.\qquad\qquad \text{Substitute } x = 1.}{= \left(-\frac{1}{5} + \ln 5\right) - (-1 + \ln 1)}$$

$$= \frac{4}{5} + \ln 5$$

When calculating a definite integral, we may have to use substitution to find the necessary antiderivative. We could substitute, evaluate the indefinite integral with respect to u, express the answer in terms of x, and then evaluate at the limits of integration. However, there is a shortcut, as we shall see in the next example.

EXAMPLE 4   **Using the FTC with Substitution**

Evaluate $\int_1^2 (2x - 1)e^{2x^2 - 2x}\, dx$.

Solution The shortcut we promised is to put *everything* in terms of u, including the limits of integration.

$u = 2x^2 - 2x$
$\dfrac{du}{dx} = 4x - 2$
$dx = \dfrac{1}{4x - 2}\, du$
When $x = 1$, $u = 0$.   Substitute $x = 1$ in the formula for u.
When $x = 2$, $u = 4$.   Substitute $x = 2$ in the formula for u.

We get the value $u = 0$, for example, by substituting $x = 1$ in the equation $u = 2x^2 - 2x$. We can now rewrite the integral:

$$\int_1^2 (2x - 1)e^{2x^2-2x}\, dx = \int_0^4 (2x - 1)e^u \frac{1}{4x - 2}\, du$$

$$= \int_0^4 \frac{1}{2}e^u\, du$$

$$= \left[\frac{1}{2}e^u\right]_0^4 = \frac{1}{2}e^4 - \frac{1}{2}.$$

➡ **Before we go on...** The alternative, longer calculation in Example 4 is first to calculate the indefinite integral:

$$\int (2x - 1)e^{2x^2-2x}\, dx = \int \frac{1}{2}e^u\, du$$

$$= \frac{1}{2}e^u + C = \frac{1}{2}e^{2x^2-2x} + C.$$

Then we can say that

$$\int_1^2 (2x - 1)e^{2x^2-2x}\, dx = \left[\frac{1}{2}e^{2x^2-2x}\right]_1^2 = \frac{1}{2}e^4 - \frac{1}{2}. \quad ■$$

Applications

Because, as we saw in Section 13.3, the definite integral allows us to calculate total change from the rate of change, or to calculate area between a graph and the x-axis, we can now use the Fundamental Theorem of Calculus to make such calculations simpler.

EXAMPLE 5   **Oil Spill**

In Section 13.3 we considered the following example: Your deep ocean oil rig has suffered a catastrophic failure, and oil is leaking from the ocean floor wellhead at a rate of

$$v(t) = 0.08t^2 - 4t + 60 \text{ thousand barrels per day} \quad (0 \le t \le 20),$$

where t is time in days since the failure. Compute the total volume of oil released during the first 20 days.

Solution We calculate

$$\text{Total volume} = \int_0^{20} (0.08t^2 - 4t + 60)\, dt = \left[0.08\frac{t^3}{3} - 2t^2 + 60t\right]_0^{20}$$

$$= \left[0.08\frac{20^3}{3} - 2(20)^2 + 60(20)\right] - [0.08(0) - 2(0) + 60(0)]$$

$$= \frac{640}{3} - 800 + 1{,}200 \approx 613.3 \text{ thousand barrels.}$$

Using Technology

TI-83/84 Plus
Home screen:
fnInt(0.08x^2-4x+60,x,0,20)
 (fnInt is MATH → 9)

Website
www.WanerMath.com
At the Website, select the Online Utilities tab, and choose the Numerical Integration Utility and Grapher. There, enter the formula

   0.08x^2-4x+60

for $f(x)$, enter 0 and 20 for the lower and upper limits, and press "Integral".

EXAMPLE 6   Computing Area

Find the total area of the region enclosed by the graph of $y = xe^{x^2}$, the x-axis, and the vertical lines $x = -1$ and $x = 1$.

Solution The region whose area we want is shown in Figure 22. Notice the symmetry of the graph. Also, half the region we are interested in is above the x-axis, while the other half is below. If we calculated the integral $\int_{-1}^{1} xe^{x^2}\, dx$, the result would be

$$\text{Area above } x\text{-axis} - \text{Area below } x\text{-axis} = 0,$$

which does not give us the total area. To prevent the area below the x-axis from being combined with the area above the axis, we do the calculation in two parts, as illustrated in Figure 23.

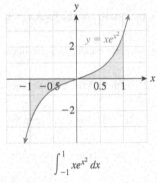

$$\int_{-1}^{1} xe^{x^2}\, dx$$

Figure 22

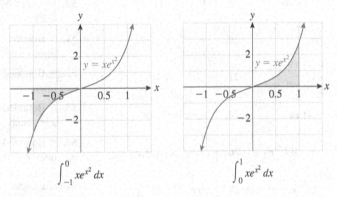

$$\int_{-1}^{0} xe^{x^2}\, dx \qquad \int_{0}^{1} xe^{x^2}\, dx$$

Figure 23

(In Figure 23 we broke the integral at $x = 0$ because that is where the graph crosses the x-axis.) These integrals can be calculated by using the substitution $u = x^2$:

$$\int_{-1}^{0} xe^{x^2}\, dx = \frac{1}{2}\left[e^{x^2} \right]_{-1}^{0} = \frac{1}{2}(1 - e) \approx -0.85914 \qquad \text{Why is it negative?}$$

$$\int_{0}^{1} xe^{x^2}\, dx = \frac{1}{2}\left[e^{x^2} \right]_{0}^{1} = \frac{1}{2}(e - 1) \approx 0.85914.$$

To obtain the total area, we should add the *absolute values* of these answers because we don't wish to count any area as negative. Thus,

$$\text{Total area} \approx 0.85914 + 0.85914 = 1.71828.$$

13.4 EXERCISES

▼ more advanced   ◆ challenging
☐ indicates exercises that should be solved using technology

In Exercises 1–44, evaluate the integral. [HINT: See Example 2.]

1. $\int_{-1}^{1} (x^2 + 2)\, dx$

2. $\int_{-2}^{1} (x - 2)\, dx$

3. $\int_{0}^{1} (12x^5 + 5x^4 - 6x^2 + 4)\, dx$

4. $\int_{0}^{1} (4x^3 - 3x^2 + 4x - 1)\, dx$

5. $\int_{-2}^{2} (x^3 - 2x)\, dx$

6. $\int_{-1}^{1} (2x^3 + x)\, dx$

7. $\int_1^3 \left(\frac{2}{x^2} + 3x\right) dx$

8. $\int_2^3 \left(x + \frac{1}{x}\right) dx$

9. $\int_0^1 (2.1x - 4.3x^{1.2}) \, dx$

10. $\int_{-1}^0 (4.3x^2 - 1) \, dx$

11. $\int_0^1 2e^x \, dx$

12. $\int_{-1}^0 3e^x \, dx$

13. $\int_0^1 \sqrt{x} \, dx$

14. $\int_{-1}^1 \sqrt[3]{x} \, dx$

15. $\int_0^1 2^x \, dx$

16. $\int_0^1 3^x \, dx$

[HINT: In Exercises 17–44, use a shortcut or see Example 4.]

17. $\int_0^1 18(3x + 1)^5 \, dx$

18. $\int_0^1 8(-x + 1)^7 \, dx$

19. $\int_{-1}^1 e^{2x-1} \, dx$

20. $\int_0^2 e^{-x+1} \, dx$

21. $\int_0^2 2^{-x+1} \, dx$

22. $\int_{-1}^1 3^{2x-1} \, dx$

23. $\int_0^4 |-3x + 4| \, dx$

24. $\int_{-4}^4 |-x - 2| \, dx$

25. $\int_0^1 5x(8x^2 + 1)^{-1/2} \, dx$

26. $\int_0^{\sqrt{2}} x\sqrt{2x^2 + 1} \, dx$

27. $\int_{-\sqrt{2}}^{\sqrt{2}} 3x\sqrt{2x^2 + 1} \, dx$

28. $\int_{-2}^2 xe^{-x^2+1} \, dx$

29. $\int_0^1 5xe^{x^2+2} \, dx$

30. $\int_0^2 \frac{3x}{x^2 + 2} \, dx$

31. $\int_2^3 \frac{x^2}{x^3 - 1} \, dx$

32. $\int_2^3 \frac{x}{2x^2 - 5} \, dx$

33. $\int_0^1 x(1.1)^{-x^2} \, dx$

34. $\int_0^1 x^2(2.1)^{x^3} \, dx$

35. $\int_1^2 \frac{e^{1/x}}{x^2} \, dx$

36. $\int_1^2 \frac{\sqrt{\ln x}}{x} \, dx$

37. $\int_0^2 \frac{e^{-2x}}{1 + 3e^{-2x}} \, dx$ (Round the answer to four decimal places.)

38. $\int_0^1 \frac{e^{2x}}{1 - 3e^{2x}} \, dx$ (Round the answer to four decimal places.)

39. ▼ $\int_0^2 \frac{x}{x + 1} \, dx$

40. ▼ $\int_{-1}^1 \frac{2x}{x + 2} \, dx$

41. ▼ $\int_1^2 x(x - 2)^5 \, dx$

42. ▼ $\int_1^2 x(x - 2)^{1/3} \, dx$

43. ▼ $\int_0^1 x\sqrt{2x + 1} \, dx$

44. ▼ $\int_{-1}^0 2x\sqrt{x + 1} \, dx$

In Exercises 45–54, calculate the total area of the region described. Do not count area beneath the x-axis as negative. [HINT: See Example 6.]

45. Bounded by the line $y = x$, the x-axis, and the lines $x = 0$ and $x = 1$

46. Bounded by the line $y = 2x$, the x-axis, and the lines $x = 1$ and $x = 2$

47. Bounded by the curve $y = \sqrt{x}$, the x-axis, and the lines $x = 0$ and $x = 4$

48. Bounded by the curve $y = 2\sqrt{x}$, the x-axis, and the lines $x = 0$ and $x = 16$

49. Bounded by the graph of $y = |2x - 3|$, the x-axis, and the lines $x = 0$ and $x = 3$

50. Bounded by the graph of $y = |3x - 2|$, the x-axis, and the lines $x = 0$ and $x = 3$

51. ▼ Bounded by the curve $y = x^2 - 1$, the x-axis, and the lines $x = 0$ and $x = 4$

52. ▼ Bounded by the curve $y = 1 - x^2$, the x-axis, and the lines $x = -1$ and $x = 2$

53. ▼ Bounded by the x-axis, the curve $y = xe^{x^2}$, and the lines $x = 0$ and $x = (\ln 2)^{1/2}$

54. ▼ Bounded by the x-axis, the curve $y = xe^{x^2-1}$, and the lines $x = 0$ and $x = 1$

Applications

A number of the following exercises are similar to ones you have already seen in Section 13.3, except that this time, rather than approximating the definite integrals by Riemann sums, you are asked to calculate them exactly using the FTC.

55. **Pumps** (Compare Exercise 39 in Section 13.3.) A pump is delivering water into a tank at a rate of

$$r(t) = 3t^2 + 5 \text{ liters per minute,}$$

where t is time in minutes since the pump is turned on. Determine the total volume of water pumped in during the first 2 minutes. [HINT: See Example 5.]

56. **Pumps** (Compare Exercise 40 in Section 13.3.) A pump is delivering water into a tank at a rate of

$$r(t) = 6t^2 + 40 \text{ liters per minute,}$$

where t is time in minutes since the pump is turned on. Determine the total volume of water pumped in during the first 3 minutes. [HINT: See Example 5.]

57. **Cost** The marginal cost of producing the xth box of light bulbs is $5 + \frac{x^2}{1,000}$ dollars. Determine how much is added to the total cost by a change in production from $x = 10$ to $x = 100$ boxes. [HINT: See Example 5.]

58. Revenue The marginal revenue of the xth box of flash cards sold is $100e^{-0.001x}$ dollars. Find the revenue generated by selling items 101 through 1,000. [HINT: See Example 5.]

59. Profit: iPhones (Compare Exercise 43 in Section 13.3.) Assume that Apple's marginal cost function for the manufacture of x 32GB iPhone 6's per hour at the Foxconn Technology Group is[45]

$$c(x) = 160 - 0.002x,$$

and that Apple sells iPhone 6's for an average wholesale price of $580. Determine the total additional hourly profit corresponding to an increase in production and sales from 10,000 to 20,000 iPhone 6's per hour.

60. Profit: PlayStation 4's (Compare Exercise 44 in Section 13.3.) Assume that Sony's marginal cost function for the manufacture of x PlayStation 4's per hour is[46]

$$c(x) = 340 + 0.001x,$$

and that Sony sells PlayStation 4's for an average wholesale price of $400. Determine the total additional hourly profit corresponding to an increase in production and sales from 50,000 to 60,000 PlayStation 4's per hour.

61. Motion A car traveling down a road has a velocity of $v(t) = 60 - e^{-t/10}$ mph at time t hours. Find the distance it has traveled from time $t = 1$ hour to time $t = 6$ hours. (Round your answer to the nearest mile.)

62. Motion A ball thrown in the air has a velocity of $v(t) = 100 - 32t$ ft/sec at time t seconds. Find the total displacement of the ball between times $t = 1$ second and $t = 7$ seconds, and interpret your answer.

63. Motion A car slows to a stop at a stop sign, then starts up again, in such a way that its speed at time t seconds after it starts to slow is $v(t) = |-10t + 40|$ ft/sec. How far does the car travel from time $t = 0$ to time $t = 10$ seconds?

64. Motion A truck slows, doesn't quite stop at a stop sign, and then speeds up again in such a way that its speed at time t seconds is $v(t) = 10 + |-5t + 30|$ ft/sec. How far does the truck travel from time $t = 0$ to time $t = 10$?

65. Fuel Consumption The way Professor Waner drives, he burns gas at the rate of $1 - e^{-t}$ gallons each hour, t hours after a fill-up. Find the number of gallons of gas he burns in the first 10 hours after a fill-up.

66. Fuel Consumption The way Professor Costenoble drives, he burns gas at the rate of $1/(t + 1)$ gallons each hour, t hours after a fill-up. Find the number of gallons of gas he burns in the first 10 hours after a fill-up.

67. Bottled Water Sales (Compare Exercise 45 in Section 13.3.) The rate of U.S. sales of bottled water for the period 2007–2014 can be approximated by

$$s(t) = 0.08t^2 - 0.26t + 8.8 \text{ billion gallons per year}$$
$$(0 \le t \le 7),$$

where t is time in years since the start of 2007.[47] Use a definite integral to estimate the total U.S. sales of bottled water from the start of 2008 to the start of 2014. (Round your answer to the nearest billion gallons.)

68. Bottled Water Sales (Compare Exercise 46 in Section 13.3.) The rate of U.S. per capita sales of bottled water for the period 2007–2014 can be approximated by

$$s(t) = 0.25t^2 - t + 29 \text{ gallons per year} \quad (0 \le t \le 7),$$

where t is time in years since the start of 2007.[48] Use a definite integral to estimate the total U.S. per capita sales of bottled water from the start of 2008 to the start of 2012. (Round your answer to the nearest gallon.)

69. Facebook Membership (Compare Exercise 63 in Section 13.3.) Starting in 2007, new members joined Facebook at a rate of roughly

$$m(t) = 20t^2 + 60t + 12 \text{ million members per year}$$
$$(0 \le t \le 6),$$

where t is time in years since the start of 2007.[49] Use a definite integral to estimate, to the nearest million, the total number of new Facebook members from the start of 2008 to the start of 2012.

70. Uploads to YouTube (Compare Exercise 64 in Section 13.3.) Since YouTube first became available to the public in mid-2005, the rate at which video has been uploaded to the site can be approximated by

$$v(t) = 1.1t^2 - 2.6t + 2.3 \text{ million hours of video per year}$$
$$(0 \le t \le 9),$$

where t is time in years since June 2005.[50] Use a definite integral to estimate, to the nearest million, the total number of hours of video uploaded from June 2010 to June 2014.

---

[45] Not the actual marginal cost equation; the authors do not know Apple's actual marginal cost equation, but the marginal costs given here are in rough agreement with the actual costs for one of the 2014 models. Sources: http://time.com, www.digitaltrends.com.

[46] Not the actual marginal cost equation; the authors do not know Sony's actual marginal cost equation, but the marginal costs given here are in rough agreement with the actual costs. Sources: VentureBeat (http://venturebeat.com), http://ps4daily.com.

---

[47] Source for data: Beverage Marketing Corporation.

[48] Ibid.

[49] Sources for data: www.facebook.com, www.insidefacebook.com.

[50] Sources for data: www.youtube.com, www.statista.com.

71. Big Brother (Compare Exercise 65 in Section 13.3.) The total number of wiretaps authorized each year by U.S. state and federal courts from 1990 to 2015 can be approximated by

$$w(t) = 774e^{0.06t} \quad (0 \le t \le 25).$$

(t is time in years since the start of 1990.)[51] Compute $\int_{10}^{25} w(t)\, dt$. (Round your answer to the nearest 10.) Interpret the answer.

72. Big Brother (Compare Exercise 66 in Section 13.3.) The number of wiretaps authorized each year by U.S. state courts from 1990 to 2015 can be approximated by

$$w(t) = 412e^{0.071t} \quad (0 \le t \le 25).$$

(t is time in years since the start of 1990.)[52] Compute $\int_{5}^{25} w(t)\, dt$. (Round your answer to the nearest 10.) Interpret the answer.

73. Economic Growth (Compare Exercise 87 in Section 13.2.) The Mexico GDP (total monetary value of all finished goods and services produced in Mexico) can be approximated by

$$g(t) = 2,000 - 480e^{-0.06t} \text{ billion pesos per year} \\ (0 \le t \le 5),$$

where t is time in years since January 2010.[53] Use the FTC to find an expression for the total GDP $G(T)$ of sold goods in Mexico from January 2010 to time T. Hence estimate, to the nearest billion pesos, the total Mexico GDP from January 2010 through June 2014. (The actual value was 7,137 billion pesos.)

74. Housing Starts: The Great Recession (Compare Exercise 88 in Section 13.2.) The Great Recession of 2007–2009 is largely attributed to the real estate crisis beginning in 2006, from which time the number of housing starts was approximately

$$n(t) = 2,400e^{-0.25t} - 200 \text{ thousand homes per year} \\ (0 \le t \le 4),$$

where t is time in years since January 2006.[54] Use the FTC to find an expression for the total number $N(T)$ of housing starts in the United States from January 2006 to time T. Hence estimate, to the nearest 0.1 million, the total number of housing starts from January 2006 through June 2009. (The actual number was around 4.9 million homes.) [HINT: Use the shortcuts.]

75. ▼ **Sales** Weekly sales of your *Lord of the Rings* T-shirts have been falling by 5% per week. Assuming that you are now selling 50 T-shirts per week, how many shirts will you sell during the coming year? (Round your answer to the nearest shirt.)

76. ▼ **Sales** Annual sales of fountain pens in Littleville are 4,000 per year and are increasing by 10% per year. How many fountain pens will be sold over the next 5 years?

77. ⊺ **Embryo Development** The oxygen consumption of a bird embryo increases from the time the egg is laid through the time the chick hatches. In a typical galliform bird the oxygen consumption can be approximated by

$$c(t) = -0.065t^3 + 3.4t^2 - 22t + 3.6 \text{ milliliters per day} \\ (8 \le t \le 30),$$

where t is the time (in days) since the egg was laid.[55] (An egg will typically hatch at around $t = 28$.) Use technology to estimate the total amount of oxygen consumed during the ninth and tenth days ($t = 8$ to $t = 10$). Round your answer to the nearest milliliter. [HINT: See the technology note in the margin next to Example 5.]

78. ⊺ **Embryo Development** The oxygen consumption of a turkey embryo increases from the time the egg is laid through the time the chick hatches. In a brush turkey the oxygen consumption can be approximated by

$$c(t) = -0.028t^3 + 2.9t^2 - 44t + 95 \text{ milliliters per day} \\ (20 \le t \le 50),$$

where t is the time (in days) since the egg was laid.[56] (An egg will typically hatch at around $t = 50$.) Use technology to estimate the total amount of oxygen consumed during the 21st and 22nd days ($t = 20$ to $t = 22$). Round your answer to the nearest 10 milliliters. [HINT: See the technology note in the margin next to Example 5.]

79. ⊺ **Online Payments** The rate of change of total payments through PayPal from the first quarter of 2013 through the fourth quarter of 2014 can be approximated by

$$p(t) = -0.1t^3 + 1.18t^2 - 0.89t + 41 \\ \text{billion dollars per quarter} \quad (1 \le t \le 8),$$

where t is time in quarters. ($t = 1$ represents the first quarter of 2013.)[57] Use technology to estimate $\int_{4}^{8} p(t)\, dt$. Interpret your answer.

---

[51] Source for data: Wiretap Reports, Administrative Office of the United States Courts (www.uscourts.gov/Statistics/WiretapReports).
[52] *Ibid.*
[53] The GDP is in constant 2008 pesos. Source for data: Instituto Nacional de Estadística y Geografía (INEGI) (www.inegi.org.mx).
[54] Source for data: www.census.gov.

[55] The model approximates graphical data published in the article "The Brush Turkey" by Roger S. Seymour, *Scientific American*, December 1991, pp. 108–114.
[56] *Ibid.*
[57] Source for data: Statista, www.statista.com.

80. ⬛ *Online Auctions* The rate of change $n(t)$ of the number of active eBay users could be approximated by

$$n(t) = -0.002t^4 + 0.06t^3 - 0.55t^2 + 1.9t - 1$$
$$\text{million users per quarter} \quad (1 \le t \le 13),$$

where t is time in quarters. ($t = 1$ represents the first quarter of 2008.)[58] Use technology to compute $\int_5^{13} n(t)\,dt$ correct to the nearest whole number. Interpret your answer.

81. ▼ *Cost* Use the Fundamental Theorem of Calculus to show that if $m(x)$ is the marginal cost at a production level of x items, then the cost function $C(x)$ is given by

$$C(x) = C(0) + \int_0^x m(t)\,dt.$$

What do we call $C(0)$?

82. ▼ *Cost* The total cost of producing x items is given by

$$C(x) = 246.76 + \int_0^x 5t\,dt.$$

Find the fixed cost and the marginal cost of producing the tenth item.

83. *Scientific Research: 1983–2003* (Compare Exercise 91 in Section 13.2.) The number of research articles in the prominent journal *Physical Review* written by researchers in Europe during 1983–2003 can be approximated by

$$E(t) = \frac{7e^{0.2t}}{5 + e^{0.2t}} \text{ thousand articles per year} \quad (0 \le t \le 20),$$

where t is time in years. ($t = 0$ represents 1983.)[59] Use a definite integral to estimate the number of articles written by researchers in Europe from 1983 to 2003. (Round your answer to the nearest 1,000 articles.) [HINT: See Example 5 in Section 13.2.]

84. *Scientific Research: 1983–2003* (Compare Exercise 92 in Section 13.2.) The number of research articles in the prominent journal *Physical Review* written by researchers in the United States during 1983–2003 can be approximated by

$$U(t) = \frac{4.6e^{0.6t}}{0.4 + e^{0.6t}} \text{ thousand articles per year} \quad (0 \le t \le 20),$$

where t is time in years. ($t = 0$ represents 1983.)[60] Use a definite integral to estimate the total number of articles written by researchers in the United States from 1983 to 2003. (Round your answer to the nearest 1,000 articles.) [HINT: See Example 5 in Section 13.2.]

85. ▼ *The Logistic Function and High School Graduates*

a. Show that the logistic function $f(x) = \dfrac{N}{1 + Ab^{-x}}$ can be written in the form

$$f(x) = \frac{Nb^x}{A + b^x}.$$

[HINT: See the note after Example 5 in Section 13.2.]

b. Use the result of part (a) and a suitable substitution to show that

$$\int \frac{N}{1 + Ab^{-x}}\,dx = \frac{N\ln(A + b^x)}{\ln b} + C.$$

c. The rate of graduation of private high school students in the United States for the period 1994–2008 was approximately

$$r(t) = 220 + \frac{110}{1 + 3.8(1.27)^{-t}} \text{ thousand students per year}$$
$$(0 \le t \le 14)$$

t years since 1994.[61] Use the result of part (b) to estimate the total number of private high school graduates over the period 2000–2008.

86. ▼ *The Logistic Function and Grant Spending*

a. Show that the logistic function $f(x) = \dfrac{N}{1 + Ae^{-kx}}$ can be written in the form

$$f(x) = \frac{Ne^{kx}}{A + e^{kx}}.$$

[HINT: See the note after Example 5 in Section 13.2.]

b. Use the result of part (a) and a suitable substitution to show that

$$\int \frac{N}{1 + Ae^{-kx}}\,dx = \frac{N\ln(A + e^{kx})}{k} + C.$$

c. The rate of spending on grants by U.S. foundations in the period 1993–2003 was approximately

$$s(t) = 11 + \frac{20}{1 + 1,800e^{-0.9t}} \text{ billion dollars per year}$$
$$(3 \le t \le 13),$$

where t is the number of years since 1990.[62] Use the result of part (b) to estimate, to the nearest $10 billion, the total spending on grants from 1998 to 2003.

---

[58] Source for data: eBay company reports (http://investor.ebay.com).

[59] Based on data from 1983 to 2003. Source: The American Physical Society/*New York Times*, May 3, 2003, p. A1.

[60] *Ibid.*

[61] Based on a logistic regression. Source for data: National Center for Educational Statistics (www.nces.ed.gov).

[62] Based on a logistic regression. Source for data: The Foundation Center, *Foundation Growth and Giving Estimates*, 2004, downloaded from the Center's website (www.fdncenter.org).

87. ◆ *Kinetic Energy* The work done in accelerating an object from velocity v_0 to velocity v_1 is given by

$$W = \int_{v_0}^{v_1} v \frac{dp}{dv} \, dv,$$

where p is its momentum, given by $p = mv \, (m = \text{mass})$. Assuming that m is a constant, show that

$$W = \frac{1}{2}mv_1^2 - \frac{1}{2}mv_0^2.$$

The quantity $\frac{1}{2}mv^2$ is referred to as the **kinetic energy** of the object, so the work required to accelerate an object is given by its change in kinetic energy.

88. ◆ *Einstein's Energy Equation* According to the special theory of relativity, the apparent mass of an object depends on its velocity according to the formula

$$m = \frac{m_0}{\sqrt{1 - \dfrac{v^2}{c^2}}},$$

where v is its velocity, m_0 is the "rest mass" of the object (that is, its mass when $v = 0$), and c is the velocity of light: approximately 3×10^8 m/sec.

a. Show that, if $p = mv$ is the momentum,

$$\frac{dp}{dv} = \frac{m_0}{\left(1 - \dfrac{v^2}{c^2}\right)^{3/2}}.$$

b. Use the integral formula for W in Exercise 87, together with the result in part (a), to show that the work required to accelerate an object from a velocity of v_0 to v_1 is given by

$$W = \frac{m_0 c^2}{\sqrt{1 - \dfrac{v_1^2}{c^2}}} - \frac{m_0 c^2}{\sqrt{1 - \dfrac{v_0^2}{c^2}}}.$$

We call the quantity $\dfrac{m_0 c^2}{\sqrt{1 - \frac{v^2}{c^2}}}$ the **total relativistic energy** of an object moving at velocity v. Thus, the work to accelerate an object from one velocity to another is given by the change in its total relativistic energy.

c. Deduce (as Albert Einstein did) that the total relativistic energy E of a body at rest with rest mass m is given by the famous equation

$$E = mc^2.$$

Communication and Reasoning Exercises

89. Explain how the indefinite integral and the definite integral are related.

90. What is "definite" about the definite integral?

91. The total change of a quantity from time a to time b can be obtained from its rate of change by doing what?

92. Complete the following: The total sales from time a to time b are obtained from the marginal sales by taking its _____ _____ from _____ to _____ .

93. What does the Fundamental Theorem of Calculus permit one to do?

94. If Felice and Philipe have different antiderivatives of f and each uses his or her own antiderivative to compute $\int_a^b f(x) \, dx$, they might get different answers—right?

95. ▼ Give an example of a nonzero velocity function that will produce a displacement of 0 from time $t = 0$ to time $t = 10$.

96. ▼ Give an example of a nonzero function whose definite integral over the interval $[4, 6]$ is zero.

97. ▼ Give an example of a decreasing function $f(x)$ with the property that $\int_a^b f(x) \, dx$ is positive for every choice of a and $b > a$.

98. ▼ Explain why, in computing the total change of a quantity from its rate of change, it is useful to have the definite integral subtract area below the x-axis.

99. ◆ If $f(x)$ is a continuous function defined for $x \geq a$, define a new function $F(x)$ by the formula

$$F(x) = \int_a^x f(t) \, dt.$$

Use the Fundamental Theorem of Calculus to deduce that $F'(x) = f(x)$. What, if anything, is interesting about this result?

100. ▣ ◆ Use the result of Exercise 99 and technology to compute a table of values for $x = 1, 2, 3$ for an antiderivative $A(x)$ of e^{-x^2} with the property that $A(0) = 0$. (Round answers to two decimal places.)

CHAPTER 13   REVIEW

KEY CONCEPTS

www.WanerMath.com
Go to the Website to find a comprehensive and interactive Web-based summary of Chapter 13.

13.1 The Indefinite Integral
An antiderivative of a function f is a function F such that $F' = f$. [p. 988]
Indefinite integral $\int f(x)\, dx$ [p. 988]
Power rule for the indefinite integral:

$$\int x^n\, dx = \frac{x^{n+1}}{n+1} + C$$
$$\text{(if } n \neq -1\text{)}$$

$$\int x^{-1}\, dx = \ln|x| + C \quad \text{[p. 990]}$$

Indefinite integral of e^x and b^x:

$$\int e^x\, dx = e^x + C$$

$$\int b^x\, dx = \frac{b^x}{\ln b} + C \quad \text{[p. 991]}$$

Indefinite integral of $|x|$:

$$\int |x|\, dx = \frac{x|x|}{2} + C \quad \text{[p. 991]}$$

Sums, differences, and constant multiples:

$$\int [f(x) \pm g(x)]\, dx$$
$$= \int f(x)\, dx \pm \int g(x)\, dx$$

$$\int kf(x)\, dx = k \int f(x)\, dx$$
$$\text{(}k \text{ constant) [p. 991]}$$

Combining the rules [p. 993]

Position, velocity, and acceleration:

$$v = \frac{ds}{dt} \qquad s(t) = \int v(t)\, dt$$

$$a = \frac{dv}{dt} \qquad v(t) = \int a(t)\, dt$$
[p. 996]

Motion in a straight line [p. 997]
Vertical motion under gravity [p. 999]

13.2 Substitution
Substitution rule:

$$\int f\, dx = \int \left(\frac{f}{du/dx}\right) du \quad \text{[p. 1004]}$$

Using the substitution rule [p. 1005]
Shortcuts: integrals of expressions involving $(ax + b)$:

$$\int (ax + b)^n\, dx = \frac{(ax + b)^{n+1}}{a(n + 1)} + C$$
$$\text{(if } n \neq -1\text{)}$$

$$\int (ax + b)^{-1}\, dx = \frac{1}{a}\ln|ax + b| + C$$

$$\int e^{ax+b}\, dx = \frac{1}{a}e^{ax+b} + C$$

$$\int c^{ax+b}\, dx = \frac{1}{a \ln c} c^{ax+b} + C$$

$$\int |ax + b|\, dx$$
$$= \frac{1}{2a}(ax + b)|ax + b| + C \quad \text{[p. 1010]}$$

Mike's shortcut rule:

If $\int f(x)\, dx = F(x) + C$ and g and u are differentiable functions of x, then

$$\int g \cdot f(u)\, dx = \frac{g}{u'} \cdot F(u) + C$$

provided that $\frac{g}{u'}$ is constant. [p. 1011]

13.3 The Definite Integral: Numerical and Graphical Viewpoints
Left Riemann sum:

$$\sum_{k=0}^{n-1} f(x_k)\, \Delta x$$
$$= [f(x_0) + f(x_1) + \cdots + f(x_{n-1})]\, \Delta x$$
[p. 1021]

Computing the Riemann sum from a formula [p. 1022]
Computing the Riemann sum from a graph [p. 1023]
Definite integral of f from a to b:

$$\int_a^b f(x)\, dx = \lim_{n \to \infty} \sum_{k=0}^{n-1} f(x_k)\, \Delta x$$
[p. 1023]

Estimating the definite integral from a graph [p. 1026]
Estimating the definite integral using technology [p. 1028]
Application to motion in a straight line [p. 1028]

13.4 The Definite Integral: Algebraic Viewpoint and the Fundamental Theorem of Calculus
Computing total cost from marginal cost [p. 1036]
The Fundamental Theorem of Calculus (FTC) [p. 1037]
Using the FTC to compute definite integrals [p. 1038]
Using the FTC with substitution [p. 1039]
Computing area [p. 1041]

REVIEW EXERCISES

In Exercises 1–18, evaluate the indefinite integral.

1. $\int (x^2 - 10x + 2)\, dx$

2. $\int (e^x + \sqrt{x})\, dx$

3. $\int \left(\frac{4x^2}{5} - \frac{4}{5x^2}\right) dx$

4. $\int \left(\frac{3x}{5} - \frac{3}{5x}\right) dx$

5. $\int (2x)^{-1}\, dx$

6. $\int (-2x + 2)^{-2}\, dx$

7. $\int e^{-2x+11}\, dx$

8. $\int \frac{dx}{(4x - 3)^2}$

9. $\int x(x^2 + 1)^{1.3}\, dx$

10. $\int x(x^2 + 4)^{10}\, dx$

11. $\int \frac{4x}{(x^2 - 7)}\, dx$

12. $\int \frac{x}{(3x^2 - 1)^{0.4}}\, dx$

13. $\int (x^3 - 1)\sqrt{x^4 - 4x + 1}\, dx$

14. $\int \dfrac{x^2 + 1}{(x^3 + 3x + 2)^2}\, dx$

15. $\int (-xe^{x^2/2})\, dx$ **16.** $\int xe^{-x^2/2}\, dx$

17. $\int \dfrac{x + 1}{x + 2}\, dx$ **18.** $\int x\sqrt{x - 1}\, dx$

In Exercises 19 and 20, use the given graph to estimate the left Riemann sum for the given interval with the stated number of subdivisions.

19. $[0, 3]$, $n = 6$ **20.** $[1, 3]$, $n = 4$

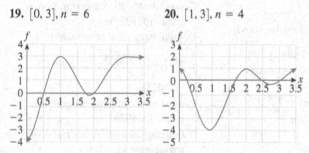

In Exercises 21–26, calculate the left Riemann sum for the given function over the given interval, using the given value of n. (When rounding, round answers to four decimal places.)

21. $f(x) = x^2 + 1$ over $[-1, 1]$, $n = 4$

22. $f(x) = (x - 1)(x - 2) - 2$ over $[0, 4]$, $n = 4$

23. $f(x) = x(x^2 - 1)$ over $[0, 1]$, $n = 5$

24. $f(x) = \dfrac{x - 1}{x - 2}$ over $[0, 1.5]$, $n = 3$

25. $f(x) = e^{-x^2}$ over $[0, 10]$, $n = 4$

26. $f(x) = e^{-x^2}$ over $[0, 100]$, $n = 4$

In Exercises 27 and 28, use technology to approximate the given definite integrals using left Riemann sums with n = 10, 100, and 1,000. (Round answers to four decimal places.)

27. $\displaystyle\int_0^1 e^{-x^2}\, dx$ **28.** $\displaystyle\int_1^3 x^{-x}\, dx$

In Exercises 29 and 30, the graph of the derivative $f'(x)$ of $f(x)$ is shown. Compute the total change of $f(x)$ over the given interval.

29. $[-1, 2]$ **30.** $[0, 2]$

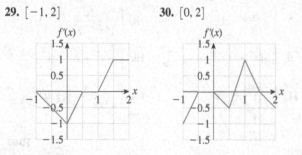

In Exercises 31–40, evaluate the definite integral using the Fundamental Theorem of Calculus.

31. $\displaystyle\int_{-1}^1 (x - x^3 + |x|)\, dx$ **32.** $\displaystyle\int_0^9 (x + \sqrt{x})\, dx$

33. $\displaystyle\int_{-1}^1 \dfrac{3}{(2x - 5)^2}\, dx$ **34.** $\displaystyle\int_0^9 \dfrac{1}{x + 1}\, dx$

35. $\displaystyle\int_0^{50} e^{-0.02x-1}\, dx$ **36.** $\displaystyle\int_{-20}^0 3e^{2.2x}\, dx$

37. $\displaystyle\int_0^2 x^2\sqrt{x^3 + 1}\, dx$ **38.** $\displaystyle\int_0^2 \dfrac{x^2}{\sqrt{x^3 + 1}}\, dx$

39. $\displaystyle\int_0^{\ln 2} \dfrac{e^{-2x}}{1 + 4e^{-2x}}\, dx$ **40.** $\displaystyle\int_0^{\ln 3} e^{2x}(1 - 3e^{2x})^2\, dx$

In Exercises 41–44, find the area of the specified region. (Do not count area below the x-axis as negative.)

41. The area bounded by $y = 4 - x^2$, the x-axis, and the lines $x = -2$ and $x = 2$

42. The area bounded by $y = 4 - x^2$, the x-axis, and the lines $x = 0$ and $x = 5$

43. The area bounded by $y = xe^{-x^2}$, the x-axis, and the lines $x = 0$ and $x = 5$

44. The area bounded by $y = |2x|$, the x-axis, and the lines $x = -1$ and $x = 1$

Applications: OHaganBooks.com
[Try the game at www.OHaganBooks.com]

45. *Sales* At OHaganBooks.com, the rate of net sales (sales minus returns) of *The Secret Loves of John O,* a romance novel by Margó Dufón, can be approximated by

$$n(t) = 196 + t^2 - 0.16t^5 \text{ copies per week}$$

t weeks since its release.
   a. Find the total net sales N as a function of time t.
   b. How many books are still held by customers after 6 weeks? (Round your answer to the nearest book.)

46. *Demand* If OHaganBooks.com were to give away its latest best seller, *A River Burns through It,* the demand q would be 100,000 books. The marginal demand (dq/dp) for the book is $-20p$ at a price of p dollars.
   a. What is the demand function for this book?
   b. At what price does demand drop to zero?

47. *Motion under Gravity* Billy-Sean O'Hagan's friend Juan says that he can throw a baseball vertically upward at 100 ft/sec. Assuming that Juan's claim is true,
   a. Where would the baseball be at time t seconds?
   b. How high would the ball go?
   c. When would the ball return to Juan's hand?

48. *Motion under Gravity* An overworked employee at OHaganBooks.com goes to the top of the company's 100-foot-tall headquarters building and flings a book up into the air at a speed of 60 ft/sec.

a. When will the book hit the ground 100 feet below? (Neglect air resistance.)

b. How fast will the book be traveling when it hits the ground?

c. How high will the book go?

49. **Projected Sales** Before OHaganBooks.com launched its online site, the sales consultant contracted by John O'Hagan had conservatively projected that online sales on the website would be

$$s(t) = 6.2e^{0.25t+3} \text{ thousand books per week}$$

t weeks after going online.

a. Calculate $\int s(t)\, dt$.

b. What is the projection of total online sales beginning at the launch to time t?

50. **Bandwidth** Billy-Sean O'Hagan has been using the company servers for his (classified) student intern work at *Brain Cybernetics*, and the bandwidth he is using has been growing exponentially, following the model

$$q(t) = 5.1e^{0.1t} + 3.3 \text{ terabytes per month},$$

where t is time in months since the beginning of the year.

a. Calculate $\int q(t)\, dt$.

b. What is the total bandwith consumed to time t given that Billy-Sean's internship started at the beginning of January?

51. **Sales** Sales at the OHaganBooks.com website of *Larry Potter and the Riemann Sum* fluctuated rather wildly in the first 5 months of last year, as the following graph shows:

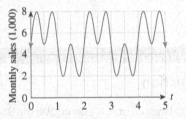

Puzzled by the graph, CEO John O'Hagan asks Jimmy Duffin[63] to estimate the total sales over the entire 5-month period shown. Jimmy decides to use a left Riemann sum with 10 partitions to estimate the total sales. What does he find?

52. **Sales** The following graph shows the approximate rate of change $s(t)$ of the total value, in thousands of dollars, of Spanish books sold online at OHaganBooks.com. (t is the number of months since January 1.)

---

[63] Marjory Duffin's nephew, currently at OHaganBooks.com on a summer internship.

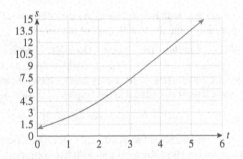

Use the graph to estimate the total value of Spanish books sold from March 1 through June 1. (Use a left Riemann sum with three subdivisions.)

53. **Promotions** Unlike sales of *Larry Potter and the Riemann Sum*, sales at OHaganBooks.com of the special leather-bound gift editions of *Calculus for Vampires* have been suffering lately, as shown in the following graph. (Negative sales indicate returns by dissatisfied customers; t is time in months since January 1 of this year.)

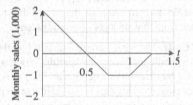

Use the graph to compute the total (net) sales over the period shown.

54. **Sales** Even worse than with the leather-bound *Calculus for Vampires*, sales of *Real Estate for Werewolves* have been dismal, as shown in the following graph. (Negative sales indicate returns by dissatisfied customers; t is time in months since January 1 of this year.)

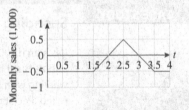

Use the graph to compute the total (net) sales over the period shown.

55. **Website Activity** The number of hits on the OHaganBooks.com website has been steadily increasing over the past month in response to recent publicity about a software glitch that caused the company to pay customers for buying books online. The activity can be modeled by

$$n(t) = 1,000t - 10t^2 + t^3 \text{ hits per day},$$

where t is time in days since news about the software glitch was first publicized on GrungeReport.com. Use a left

Riemann sum with five partitions to estimate the total number of hits during the first 10 days of the period.

56. Website Crashes The latest DoorsXL servers that OHaganBooks.com has been using for its website have been crashing with increasing frequency lately. One of the student summer interns has estimated the number of crashes to be

$$q(t) = 0.05t^2 + 0.4t + 9 \text{ crashes per week} \quad (0 \le t \le 10),$$

where t is the number of weeks since the DoorsXL system was first installed. Use a Riemann sum with five partitions to estimate the total number of crashes from the start of week 5 to the start of week 10. (Round your answer to the nearest crash.)

57. Student Intern Costs The marginal monthly cost of maintaining a group of summer student interns at OHaganBooks.com is calculated to be

$$c(x) = \frac{1,000(x + 3)^2}{(8 + (x + 3)^3)^{3/2}} \text{ thousand dollars per additional student.}$$

Compute, to the nearest $100, the total monthly cost if OHaganBooks.com increases the size of the student intern program from five students to seven students.

58. Legal Costs The legal team maintained by OHaganBooks.com to handle the numerous lawsuits brought against the company by disgruntled clients may have to be expanded. The marginal monthly cost to maintain a team of x lawyers is estimated (by a method too complicated to explain) to be

$$c(x) = (x - 2)^2[8 - (x - 2)^3]^{3/2} \text{ thousand dollars per additional lawyer.}$$

Compute, to the nearest $1,000, the total monthly cost if OHaganBooks.com goes ahead with a proposal to increase the size of the legal team from two to four.

59. Projected Sales When OHaganBooks.com was about to go online, it estimated that its weekly sales would begin at about 6,400 books per week, with sales increasing at such a rate that weekly sales would double about every 2 weeks. If these estimates had been correct, how many books would the company have sold in the first 5 weeks? (Round your answer to the nearest 1,000 books.)

60. Actual Sales Once OHaganBooks.com actually went online, its weekly sales began at about 7,500 books per week, with weekly sales doubling every 3 weeks. How many books did the company actually sell in the first 5 weeks? (Round your answer to the nearest 1,000 books.)

61. Revised Actual Sales OHaganBooks.com modeled its revised weekly sales over a period of time after it went online with the function

$$s(t) = 6,053 + \frac{4,474e^{0.55t}}{e^{0.55t} + 14.01},$$

where t is the time in weeks after it went online. According to this model, how many books, to the nearest 100, did it actually sell in the first 5 weeks?

62. Computer Usage A consultant recently hired by OHaganBooks.com estimates total weekly computer usage by company employees to be

$$w(t) = 620 + \frac{900e^{0.25t}}{3 + e^{0.25t}} \text{ hours} \quad (0 \le t \le 20),$$

where t is time in weeks since January 1 of this year. Use the model to estimate the total computer usage during the first 14 weeks of the year.

CASE STUDY

Spending on Housing Construction

It is March 2007, and *Time* magazine, in its latest edition, is asking, "Will the Housing Bubble Burst in 2007?"[64] You are a summer intern at *Schottie Construction Co.*, which is working with *Pack-Em-In Real Estate* on a major luxury condominium development to be called "Pack-Em-In/Schottie Towers."

Yesterday, you received the following memo from your supervisor:

DATE: March 15, 2007
TO: SW@EnormousStateU.edu
FROM: SC@Schottie.com (Junior VP Development)
CC: SGLombardoVP@Schottie.com (S. G. Lombardo, Senior VP Development)
SUBJECT: Residential Construction Trends. Urgent!

Help! There is a management meeting in two hours and Michelle Homestead, who, as you know, is spearheading the Pack-Em-In/Schottie Towers feasibility study, must report to

Rob Stothard/Stringer/Getty Images

---

[64] *Time*, February 2007 (www.time.com/time/business/article/0,8599,1592751,00.html).

Mr. Schottie by tomorrow and has asked me to immediately produce some mathematical formulas to (1) model the trend in residential construction spending since January 2006, when it was $618.7 billion, and (2) estimate the average spent per month on residential construction over a specified period of time. All I have on hand so far is data giving the month-over-month percentage changes (attached). Do you have any ideas?

ATTACHMENT*

Month	% Change	Month	% Change
1	1.16	16	−1.59
2	1.17	17	−1.62
3	1.33	18	−1.58
4	0.67	19	−1.67
5	0.42	20	−1.77
6	−0.04	21	−1.92
7	−0.24	22	−2.06
8	−0.44	23	−2.19
9	−0.70	24	−2.45
10	−0.94	25	−2.50
11	−1.31	26	−2.65
12	−1.34	27	−2.85
13	−1.49	28	−2.65
14	−1.75	29	−2.66
15	−1.74	30	−2.66

*Based on 12-month moving average; Source for data: U.S. Census Bureau: Manufacturing, Mining and Construction Statistics, Data 360 (www.data360.org/dataset.aspx? Data_Set_Id=3627).

Getting to work, you decide that the first thing to do is fit these data to a mathematical curve that you can use to project future changes in construction spending. You graph the data to get a sense of what mathematical models might be appropriate (Figure 24).

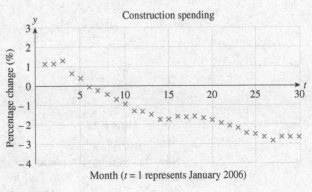

Month ($t = 1$ represents January 2006)

Figure 24

The graph suggests a decreasing trend, possibly concave up. You recall that there are a variety of curves that can behave this way, one of the simplest being

$$y = at^c + b \qquad (t > 0),$$

where a, b, and c are constants.

You convert all the percentages to decimals, giving the following table of data:

t	y	t	y
1	0.0116	16	−0.0159
2	0.0117	17	−0.0162
3	0.0133	18	−0.0158
4	0.0067	19	−0.0167
5	0.0042	20	−0.0177
6	−0.0004	21	−0.0192
7	−0.0024	22	−0.0206
8	−0.0044	23	−0.0219
9	−0.0070	24	−0.0245
10	−0.0094	25	−0.0250
11	−0.0131	26	−0.0265
12	−0.0134	27	−0.0285
13	−0.0149	28	−0.0265
14	−0.0175	29	−0.0266
15	−0.0174	30	−0.0266

You then find the values of a, b, and c that best fit the given data:*

$$a = -0.0200974, \ b = 0.0365316, \ c = 0.345051.$$

* To do this, you can use Excel's Solver or the Website function evaluator and grapher with model $1*x^$2+$3.

These values give you the following model for construction spending (with figures rounded to five significant digits):

$$y = -0.020097t^{0.34505} + 0.036532.$$

Figure 25 shows the graph of y superimposed on the data.

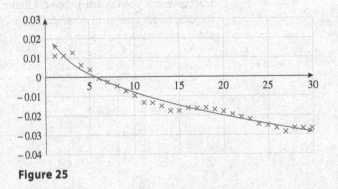

Figure 25

Now that you have a model for the month-over-month change in construction spending, you must use it to find the actual spending on construction. First, you realize that the model gives the *fractional rate of increase* of construction spending (because it is specified as a percentage, or fraction, of the total spending). In other words, if $p(t)$ represents the construction cost in month t, then

$$y = \frac{dp/dt}{p} = \frac{d}{dt}(\ln p). \qquad \text{By the chain rule for derivatives}$$

You find an equation for actual monthly construction cost at time t by solving for p:

$$\ln p = \int y \, dt$$

$$= \int (at^c + b) \, dt$$

$$= \frac{at^{c+1}}{c+1} + bt + K$$

$$= dt^{c+1} + bt + K,$$

where

$$d = \frac{a}{c+1} = \frac{-0.020097}{0.34505 + 1} \approx -0.014941,$$

b and c are as above, and K is the constant of integration. So

$$p(t) = e^{dt^{c+1}+bt+K}.$$

To compute K, you substitute the initial data from the memo: $p(1) = 618.7$. Thus,

$$618.7 = e^{d+b+K} = e^{-0.014941+0.036532+K} = e^{0.021591+K}.$$

Thus,

$$\ln(618.7) = 0.021591 + K,$$

which gives

$$K = \ln(618.7) - 0.021591 \approx 6.4060 \text{ (to five significant digits)}.$$

Now you can write down the following formula for the monthly spending on residential construction as a function of t, the number of months since the beginning of 2006:

$$p(t) = e^{dt^{c+1}+bt+K} = e^{-0.014941t^{0.34505+1}+0.036532t+6.4060}.$$

What remains is the calculation of the average spent per month over a specified period $[r, s]$. Since p is the rate of change of the total spent, the total spent on housing construction over this period is

$$P = \int_r^s p(t) \, dt,$$

so the average spent per month is

$$\overline{P} = \frac{1}{s-r} \int_r^s p(t) \, dt. \qquad \underset{\text{Number of months}}{\frac{1}{}} \times \text{Total spent}$$

Substituting the formula for $p(t)$ gives

$$\overline{P} = \frac{1}{s-r} \int_r^s e^{-0.014941t^{0.34505+1}+0.036532t+6.4060} \, dt.$$

You cannot find an explicit antiderivative for the integrand, so you decide that the only way to compute it is numerically. You send the following memo to SC.

DATE: March 15, 2007
TO: SC@Schottie.com (Junior VP Development)
FROM: SW@EnormousStateU.edu
CC: SGLombardoVP@Schottie.com (S. G. Lombardo, Senior VP Development)
SUBJECT: The formula you wanted

Spending in the U.S. on housing construction in the tth month of 2006 can be modeled by

$$p(t) = e^{-0.014941t^{0.34505+1} \div 0.036532t \div 6.4060} \text{ million dollars.}$$

Further, the average spent per month from month r to month s (since the start of January 2006) can be computed as

$$\overline{P} = \frac{1}{s-r} \int_r^s e^{-0.014941t^{0.34505+1} \div 0.036532t \div 6.4060} \, dt$$

To calculate it easily (and impress Mr. Schottie), I suggest you have a graphing calculator on hand and enter the following on your graphing calculator (watch the parentheses!):

```
Y₁=1/(S-R)*fnInt(e^(-0.014941T^(0.34505+1)+0.036532T+6.4060),T,R,S)
```

Then suppose, for example, you need to estimate the average for the period March 1, 2006 ($t = 3$) to February 1, 2007 ($t = 14$). All you do is enter

```
3→R
14→S
Y₁
```

and your calculator will give you the result: The average spending was $628 million per month.

Good luck with the meeting!

EXERCISES

1. Use the actual January 2006 spending figure of $618.7 million and the percentage changes in the table to compute the actual spending in February, March, and April of that year. Also use the model of monthly spending to estimate those figures, and compare the predicted values with the actual figures. Is it unacceptable that the April figures agree to only one significant digit? Explain.

2. Use the model developed above to estimate the average monthly spending on residential construction over the 12-month period beginning June 1, 2006. (Round your answer to the nearest $1 million.)

3. What (if any) advantages are there to using a model for residential construction spending when the actual residential construction spending figures are available?

4. The formulas for $p(t)$ and $\overline{P}$ were based on the January 2006 spending figure of $618.7 million. Change the models to allow for a possibly revised January 2006 spending figure of $\$p_0$ million.

5. If we had used quadratic regression to model the construction spending data, we would have obtained

$$y = 0.00005t^2 - 0.0028t + 0.0158.$$

(See the graph.)

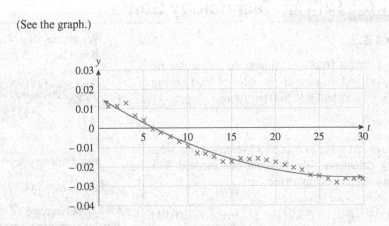

Use this formula and the given January 2006 spending figure to obtain corresponding models for $p(t)$ and $\overline{P}$.

6. Compare the model in the text with the quadratic model in Exercise 5 in terms of both short- and long-term predictions; in particular, when does the quadratic model predict construction spending will have reached its biggest monthly decrease? Are either of these models realistic in the near term? in the long term?

Section 13.3

Example 5 (page 1028) Estimate the area under the graph of $f(x) = 1 - x^2$ over the interval $[0, 1]$ using $n = 100$, $n = 200$, and $n = 500$ partitions.

Solution

There are several ways to compute Riemann sums with a graphing calculator. We illustrate one method. For $n = 100$ we need to compute the sum

$$\sum_{k=0}^{99} f(x_k) \Delta x = [f(0) + f(0.01) + \cdots + f(0.99)](0.01).$$

See discussion in Example 5.

Thus, we first need to calculate the numbers $f(0)$, $f(0.01)$, and so on and add them up. The TI-83/84 Plus has a built-in `sum` function (available in the LIST MATH menu), which, like the SUM function in a spreadsheet, sums the entries in a list.

1. To generate a list that contains the numbers we want to add together, use the `seq` function (available in the LIST OPS menu). If we enter

$$\texttt{seq(1-X\^{}2,X,0,0.99,0.01)}$$

seq: 2ND LIST OPS 5

the calculator will calculate a list by evaluating `1-X^2` for values of X from 0 to 0.99 in steps of 0.01.

2. To take the sum of all these numbers, we wrap the seq function in a call to `sum`:

$$\texttt{sum(seq(1-X\^{}2,X,0,0.99,0.01))}$$

sum: 2ND LIST MATH 5

This gives the sum

$$f(0) + f(0.01) + \cdots + f(0.99) = 67.165.$$

3. To obtain the Riemann sum, we need to multiply this sum by $\Delta x = 0.01$, and we obtain the estimate of $67.165 \times 0.01 = 0.67165$ for the Riemann sum:

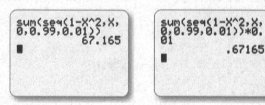

We obtain the other Riemann sums similarly, as shown here:

$n = 200$ $\qquad\qquad$ $n = 500$

One disadvantage of this method is that the TI-83/84 Plus can generate and sum a list of at most 999 entries. The LEFTSUM program below calculates left Riemann sums for any n. The TI-83/84 Plus also has a built-in function `fnInt`, which finds a very accurate approximation of a definite integral, using a more sophisticated technique than the one we are discussing here.

The LEFTSUM program for the TI-83/84 Plus

The following program calculates (left) Riemann sums for any n. The latest version of this program (and others) is available at the Website:

```
PROGRAM: LEFTSUM
:Input "LEFT ENDPOINT? ",A
```
Prompts for the left endpoint a
```
:Input "RIGHT ENDPOINT? ",B
```
Prompts for the right endpoint b
```
:Input "N? ",N
```
Prompts for the number of rectangles
```
:(B-A)/N→D
```
D is $\Delta x = (b - a)/n$.
```
:0→L
```
L will eventually be the left sum.
```
:A→X
```
X is the current x-coordinate.
```
:For(I,1,N)
```
Start of a loop—recall the sigma notation.
```
:L+Y₁→L
```
Add $f(x_{i-1})$ to L.
```
:A+I*D→X
```
Uses formula $x_i = a + i\Delta x$
```
:End
```
End of loop
```
:L*D→L
```
Multiply by Δx.
```
:Disp "LEFT SUM IS ",L
:Stop
```

Section 13.3

Example 5 (page 1028) Estimate the area under the graph of $f(x) = 1 - x^2$ over the interval $[0, 1]$ using $n = 100$, $n = 200$, and $n = 500$ partitions.

Solution

We need to compute various sums:

$$\sum_{k=0}^{99} f(x_k)\,\Delta x = [f(0) + f(0.01) + \cdots + f(0.99)](0.01)$$

See discussion in Example 5.

$$\sum_{k=0}^{199} f(x_k)\,\Delta x = [f(0) + f(0.005) + \cdots + f(0.995)](0.005)$$

$$\sum_{k=0}^{499} f(x_k)\,\Delta x = [f(0) + f(0.002) + \cdots + f(0.998)](0.002).$$

Here is how you can compute them all on the same spreadsheet.

1. Enter the values for the endpoints a and b, the number of subdivisions n, and the formula $\Delta x = (b - a)/n$:

	A	B	C	D
1	x	f(x)	a	0
2			b	1
3			n	100
4			Delta x	=(D2-D1)/D3

2. Next, we compute all the x-values we might need in column A. Because the largest value of n that we will be using is 500, we will need a total of 501 values of x. Note that the value in each cell below A3 is obtained from the one above by adding Δx.

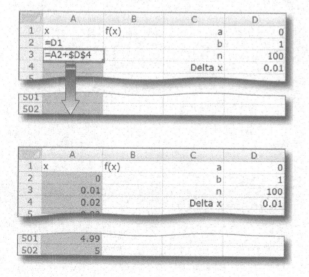

(The fact that the values of x currently go too far will be corrected in the next step.)

3. We need to calculate the numbers $f(0)$, $f(0.01)$, and so on, but only those for which the corresponding x-value is less than b. To do this, we use a logical formula like we did with piecewise-defined functions in Chapter 1:

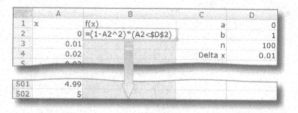

When the value of x is b or above, the function will evaluate to zero because we do not want to count it.

4. Finally, we compute the Riemann sum by adding up everything in column B and multiplying by Δx:

	A	B	C	D
1	x	f(x)	a	0
2		0	1	b	1
3	0.01	0.9999	n	100
4	0.02	0.9996	Delta x	0.01
5	0.03	0.9991	Left Sum	=SUM(B:B)*D4
6	0.04	0.9984		

	A	B	C	D
1	x	f(x)	a	0
2	0	1	b	1
3	0.01	0.9999	n	100
4	0.02	0.9996	Delta x	0.01
5	0.03	0.9991	Left Sum	0.67165
6	0.04	0.9984		

Now it is easy to obtain the sums for $n = 200$ and $n = 500$: Simply change the value of n in cell D3:

	A	B	C	D
1	x	f(x)	a	0
2	0	1	b	1
3	0.005	0.999975	n	200
4	0.01	0.9999	Delta x	0.005
5	0.015	0.999775	Left Sum	0.6691625
6	0.02	0.9996		

	A	B	C	D
1	x	f(x)	a	0
2	0	1	b	1
3	0.002	0.999996	n	500
4	0.004	0.999984	Delta x	0.002
5	0.006	0.999964	Left Sum	0.667666
6	0.008	0.999936		

1057

14

FURTHER INTEGRATION TECHNIQUES AND APPLICATIONS OF THE INTEGRAL

 www.WanerMath.com

At the Website, in addition to the resources listed in the Preface, you will find:

- A numerical integration utility
- Graphing calculator programs for numerical integration

as well as the following extra section:

- Linear Differitial Equations

CASE STUDY

Estimating Tax Revenues

You have just been hired by the incoming administration to coordinate national tax policy, and the so-called experts on your staff can't seem to agree on which of several tax proposals will result in the most revenue for the government. The data you have are the two income tax proposals (graphs of tax vs. income) and the distribution of incomes in the country.

How do you use this information to decide which tax policy will result in more revenue?

Dmitriy Shironosov/Shutterstock.com

Introduction

In Chapter 13 we learned how to compute many integrals and saw some of the applications of the integral. In this chapter we look at some further techniques for computing integrals and then at more applications of the integral. We also see how to extend the definition of the definite integral to include integrals over infinite intervals, and we show how such integrals can be used for long-term forecasting. Finally, we introduce the beautiful theory of differential equations and some of its numerous applications.

14.1 Integration by Parts

Integration-by-Parts Formula

Integration by parts is an integration technique that comes from the product rule for derivatives. The tabular method we present here has been around for some time and makes integration by parts quite simple, particularly in problems where it has to be used several times.*

* The version of the tabular method we use was developed and taught to us by Dan Rosen at Hofstra University.

We start with a little notation to simplify things while we introduce integration by parts. (We use this notation only in the next few pages.) If u is a function, denote its derivative by $D(u)$ and an antiderivative by $I(u)$. Thus, for example, if $u = 2x^2$, then

$$D(u) = 4x$$

and

$$I(u) = \frac{2x^3}{3}.$$

[If we wished, we could instead take $I(u) = \frac{2x^3}{3} + 46$, but we usually opt to take the simplest antiderivative.]

Integration by Parts

If u and v are continuous functions of x and u has a continuous derivative, then

$$\int u \cdot v \, dx = u \cdot I(v) - \int D(u)I(v) \, dx.$$

Quick Example

(Discussed more fully in Example 1 below)

1. $\displaystyle\int x \cdot e^x \, dx = xI(e^x) - \int D(x)I(e^x) \, dx$

$\qquad\qquad = xe^x - \displaystyle\int 1 \cdot e^x \, dx \qquad I(e^x) = e^x; D(x) = 1$

$\qquad\qquad = xe^x - e^x + C. \qquad \displaystyle\int e^x \, dx = e^x + C$

As Quick Example 1 shows, although we could not immediately integrate $u \cdot v = x \cdot e^x$, we could easily integrate $D(u)I(v) = 1 \cdot e^x = e^x$.

Derivation of Integration-by-Parts Formula

As we mentioned, the integration-by-parts formula comes from the product rule for derivatives. We apply the product rule to the function $uI(v)$:

$$D[u \cdot I(v)] = D(u)I(v) + uD(I(v))$$
$$= D(u)I(v) + uv$$

because $D(I(v))$ is the derivative of an antiderivative of v, which is v. Integrating both sides gives

$$u \cdot I(v) = \int D(u)I(v)\, dx + \int uv\, dx.$$

A simple rearrangement of the terms now gives us the integration-by-parts formula.

The Tabular Method

The integration-by-parts formula is easiest to use via the tabular method illustrated in the following example, where we repeat the calculation we did in Quick Example 1.

EXAMPLE 1   Integration by Parts: Tabular Method

Calculate $\int xe^x\, dx$.

Solution First, the reason we *need* to use integration by parts to evaluate this integral is that none of the other techniques of integration that we've talked about up to now will help us. Furthermore, we cannot simply find antiderivatives of x and e^x and multiply them together. [You should check that $(x^2/2)e^x$ is *not* an antiderivative of xe^x.] However, as we saw above, this integral can be found by integration by parts. We want to find the integral of the *product* of x and e^x. We must make a decision: Which function will play the role of u and which will play the role of v in the integration-by-parts formula? Because the derivative of x is just 1, differentiating makes it simpler, so we try letting x be u and letting e^x be v. We need to calculate $D(u)$ and $I(v)$, which we record in the following table:

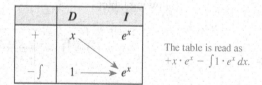

The table is read as
$+x \cdot e^x - \int 1 \cdot e^x\, dx.$

Below x in the D column, we put $D(x) = 1$; below e^x in the I column, we put $I(e^x) = e^x$. The arrow at an angle connecting x and $I(e^x)$ reminds us that the product $xI(e^x)$ will appear in the answer; the plus sign on the left of the table reminds us that it is $+x\,I(e^x)$ that appears. The integral sign and the horizontal arrow connecting $D(x)$ and $I(e^x)$ remind us that the *integral* of the product $D(x)I(e^x)$ also appears in the answer; the minus sign on the left reminds us that we need to subtract this integral. Combining these two contributions, we get

$$\int xe^x\, dx = xe^x - \int e^x\, dx.$$

The integral that appears on the right is much easier than the one we began with, so we can complete the problem:

$$\int xe^x\,dx = xe^x - \int e^x\,dx = xe^x - e^x + C.$$

➡ **Before we go on . . .** In Example 1, what if we had made the opposite decision and put e^x in the D column and x in the I column? Then we would have had the following table:

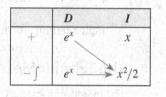

This gives

$$\int xe^x\,dx = \frac{x^2}{2}e^x - \int \frac{x^2}{2}e^x\,dx.$$

The integral on the right is harder than the one we started with, not easier! How do we know beforehand which way to go? We don't. We have to be willing to do a little trial and error: We try it one way, and if it doesn't make things simpler, we try it another way. *Remember, though, that the function we put in the I column must be one that we can integrate.* ∎

EXAMPLE 2   **Repeated Integration by Parts**

Calculate $\int x^2 e^{-x}\,dx$.

Solution Again, we have a product: The integrand is the product of x^2 and e^{-x}. Because differentiating x^2 makes it simpler, we put it in the D column and get the following table:

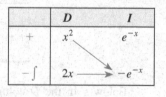

This table gives us

$$\int x^2 e^{-x}\,dx = x^2(-e^{-x}) - \int 2x(-e^{-x})\,dx.$$

The last integral is simpler than the one we started with, but it still involves a product. It's a good candidate for another integration by parts. The table we would use would start with $2x$ in the D column and $-e^{-x}$ in the I column, which is exactly what we see in the last row of the table we've already made. Therefore, we *continue the process*, elongating the table above:

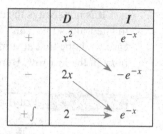

(Notice how the signs on the left alternate. Here's why: To compute $-\int 2x(-e^{-x})\,dx$, we use the negative of the following table:

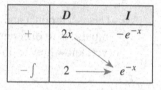

so we reverse all the signs.)

Now, we still have to compute an integral (the integral of the product of the functions in the bottom row) to complete the computation. But why stop here? Let's continue the process one more step:

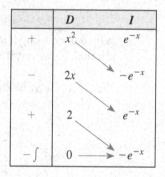

In the bottom line we see that all that is left to integrate is $0(-e^{-x}) = 0$. Because the indefinite integral of 0 is C, we can read the answer from the table as

$$\int x^2 e^{-x}\,dx = x^2(-e^{-x}) - 2x(e^{-x}) + 2(-e^{-x}) + C$$

$$= -x^2 e^{-x} - 2xe^{-x} - 2e^{-x} + C$$

$$= -e^{-x}(x^2 + 2x + 2) + C.$$

In Example 2 we saw a technique that we can summarize as follows.

Integrating a Polynomial Times a Function

If one of the factors in the integrand is a polynomial and the other factor is a function that can be integrated repeatedly, put the polynomial in the D column and keep differentiating until you get zero. Then complete the I column to the same depth, and read off the answer.

For practice, redo Example 1 using this technique.

It is not always the case that the integrand is a polynomial times something easy to integrate, so we can't always expect to end up with a zero in the D column. In that case we hope that at some point we will be able to integrate the product of the functions in the last row. Here are some examples.

EXAMPLE 3   **Polynomial Times a Logarithm**

Calculate: **a.** $\displaystyle\int x \ln x \, dx$ **b.** $\displaystyle\int (x^2 - x) \ln x \, dx$ **c.** $\displaystyle\int \ln x \, dx$

Solution

a. This is a product and therefore a good candidate for integration by parts. Our first impulse is to differentiate x, but that would mean integrating $\ln x$, and we do not (yet) know how to do that. So we try it the other way around and hope for the best.

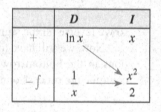

Why did we stop? If we continued the table, both columns would get more complicated. However, if we stop here, we get

$$\int x \ln x \, dx = (\ln x)\left(\frac{x^2}{2}\right) - \int \left(\frac{1}{x}\right)\left(\frac{x^2}{2}\right) dx$$

$$= \frac{x^2}{2}\ln x - \frac{1}{2}\int x \, dx$$

$$= \frac{x^2}{2}\ln x - \frac{x^2}{4} + C.$$

b. We can use the same technique we used in part (a) to integrate any polynomial times the logarithm of x:

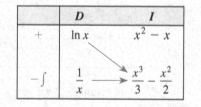

$$\int (x^2 - x)\ln x \, dx = (\ln x)\left(\frac{x^3}{3} - \frac{x^2}{2}\right) - \int \left(\frac{1}{x}\right)\left(\frac{x^3}{3} - \frac{x^2}{2}\right) dx$$

$$= \left(\frac{x^3}{3} - \frac{x^2}{2}\right)\ln x - \int \left(\frac{x^2}{3} - \frac{x}{2}\right) dx$$

$$= \left(\frac{x^3}{3} - \frac{x^2}{2}\right)\ln x - \frac{x^3}{9} + \frac{x^2}{4} + C$$

c. The integrand $\ln x$ is not a product. We can, however, *make* it into a product by thinking of it as $1 \cdot \ln x$. Because this is a polynomial times $\ln x$, we proceed as in parts (a) and (b):

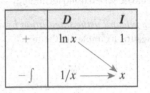

	D	I
+	$\ln x$	1
$-\int$	$1/x$	x

We notice that the product of $1/x$ and x is just 1, which we know how to integrate, so we can stop here:

$$\int \ln x \, dx = x \ln x - \int \left(\frac{1}{x}\right) x \, dx$$

$$= x \ln x - \int 1 \, dx$$

$$= x \ln x - x + C.$$

FAQs

Whether to Use Integration by Parts and What Goes in the D and I Columns

Q : *Will integration by parts always work to integrate a product?*

A : No. Although integration by parts often works for products in which one factor is a polynomial, it will almost *never* work in the examples of products we saw when discussing substitution in Section 13.2. For example, although integration by parts can be used to compute $\int (x^2 - x)e^{2x-1} \, dx$ (put $x^2 - x$ in the D column and e^{2x-1} in the I column), it *cannot* be used to compute $\int (2x - 1)e^{x^2-x} \, dx$ (put $u = x^2 - x$). Recognizing when to use integration by parts is best learned by experience.

Q : *When using integration by parts, which expression goes in the D column and which in the I column?*

A : Although there is no general rule, the following guidelines are useful:

- To integrate a product in which one factor is a polynomial and the other can be integrated several times, put the polynomial in the D column and the other factor in the I column. Then differentiate the polynomial until you get zero.
- If one of the factors is a polynomial but the other factor cannot be integrated easily, put the polynomial in the I column and the other factor in the D column. Stop when the product of the functions in the bottom row can be integrated.
- If neither factor is a polynomial, put the factor that seems easier to integrate in the I column and the other factor in the D column. Again, stop the table as soon as the product of the functions in the bottom row can be integrated.
- If your method doesn't work, try switching the functions in the D and I columns or try breaking the integrand into a product in a different way. If none of this works, maybe integration by parts isn't the technique to use on this problem.

▼ more advanced   ◆ challenging
⬛ indicates exercises that should be solved using technology

In Exercises 1–40, evaluate the integral using integration by parts where possible. [**HINT**: See the examples in the text.]

1. $\int 2xe^x \, dx$

2. $\int 3xe^{-x} \, dx$

3. $\int (3x - 1)e^{-x} \, dx$

4. $\int (1 - x)e^x \, dx$

5. $\int (x^2 - 1)e^{2x} \, dx$

6. $\int (x^2 + 1)e^{-2x} \, dx$

7. $\int (x^2 + 1)e^{-2x+4} \, dx$

8. $\int (x^2 + 1)e^{3x+1} \, dx$

9. $\int (2 - x)2^x \, dx$

10. $\int (3x - 2)4^x \, dx$

11. $\int (x^2 - 1)3^{-x} \, dx$

12. $\int (1 - x^2)2^{-x} \, dx$

13. ▼ $\int \dfrac{x^2 - x}{e^x} \, dx$

14. ▼ $\int \dfrac{2x + 1}{e^{3x}} \, dx$

15. $\int x(x + 2)^6 \, dx$ (See note.[1])

16. $\int x^2(x - 1)^6 \, dx$ (See note.[1])

17. ▼ $\int \dfrac{x}{(x - 2)^3} \, dx$

18. ▼ $\int \dfrac{x}{(x - 1)^2} \, dx$

19. $\int x^3 \ln x \, dx$

20. $\int x^2 \ln x \, dx$

21. $\int (t^2 + 1) \ln(2t) \, dt$

22. $\int (t^2 - 1) \ln(-t) \, dt$

23. $\int t^{1/3} \ln t \, dt$

24. $\int t^{-1/2} \ln t \, dt$

25. $\int \log_3 x \, dx$

26. $\int x \log_2 x \, dx$

27. ▼ $\int (xe^{2x} - 4e^{3x}) \, dx$

28. ▼ $\int (x^2e^{-x} + 2e^{-x+1}) \, dx$

29. ▼ $\int (x^2e^x - xe^{x^2}) \, dx$

30. ▼ $\int \left[(2x + 1)e^{x^2+x} - x^2e^{2x+1} \right] dx$

31. ▼ $\int (3x - 4)\sqrt{2x - 1} \, dx$ (See note.[1])

32. ▼ $\int \dfrac{2x + 1}{\sqrt{3x - 2}} \, dx$ (See note.[1])

33. $\int_0^1 (x + 1)e^x \, dx$

34. $\int_{-1}^1 (x^2 + x)e^{-x} \, dx$

35. $\int_0^1 x^2(x + 1)^{10} \, dx$

36. $\int_0^1 x^3(x + 1)^{10} \, dx$

37. $\int_1^2 x \ln(2x) \, dx$

38. $\int_1^2 x^2 \ln(3x) \, dx$

39. $\int_0^1 x \ln(x + 1) \, dx$

40. $\int_0^1 x^2 \ln(x + 1) \, dx$

41. Find the area bounded by the curve $y = xe^{-x}$, the x-axis, and the lines $x = 0$ and $x = 10$.

42. Find the area bounded by the curve $y = x \ln x$, the x-axis, and the lines $x = 1$ and $x = e$.

43. Find the area bounded by the curve $y = (x + 1) \ln x$, the x-axis, and the lines $x = 1$ and $x = 2$.

44. Find the area bounded by the curve $y = (x - 1)e^x$, the x-axis, and the lines $x = 0$ and $x = 2$.

Integrals of Functions Involving Absolute Values In Exercises 45–52, use integration by parts to evaluate the given integral using the following integral formulas where necessary. (You have seen some of these before; all can be checked by differentiating.)

Integral Formula	Shortcut Version
$\int \dfrac{\|x\|}{x} \, dx = \|x\| + C$ Because $\dfrac{d}{dx}\|x\| = \dfrac{\|x\|}{x}$	$\int \dfrac{\|ax + b\|}{ax + b} \, dx = \dfrac{1}{a}\|ax + b\| + C$
$\int \|x\| \, dx = \dfrac{1}{2}x\|x\| + C$	$\int \|ax + b\| \, dx$ $= \dfrac{1}{2a}(ax + b)\|ax + b\| + C$
$\int x\|x\| \, dx = \dfrac{1}{3}x^2\|x\| + C$	$\int (ax + b)\|ax + b\| \, dx$ $= \dfrac{1}{3a}(ax + b)^2\|ax + b\| + C$
$\int x^2\|x\| \, dx = \dfrac{1}{4}x^3\|x\| + C$	$\int (ax + b)^2\|ax + b\| \, dx$ $= \dfrac{1}{4a}(ax + b)^3\|ax + b\| + C$

45. $\int x\|x - 3\| \, dx$

46. $\int x\|x + 4\| \, dx$

47. $\int 2x\dfrac{\|x - 3\|}{x - 3} \, dx$

48. $\int 3x\dfrac{\|x + 4\|}{x + 4} \, dx$

49. ▼ $\int 2x^2|-x + 4|\ dx$ 50. ▼ $\int 3x^2|2x - 3|\ dx$

51. ▼ $\int (x^2 - 2x + 3)|x - 4|\ dx$

52. ▼ $\int (x^2 - x + 1)|2x - 4|\ dx$

Applications

53. **Displacement** A rocket rising from the ground has a velocity of $2{,}000te^{-t/120}$ ft/sec after t seconds. How far does it rise in the first 2 minutes?

54. **Sales** Weekly sales of graphing calculators can be modeled by the equation

$$s(t) = 10 - te^{-t/20},$$

where s is the number of calculators sold per week after t weeks. How many graphing calculators (to the nearest unit) will be sold in the first 20 weeks?

55. **Total Cost** The marginal cost of the xth box of light bulbs is $10 + [\ln(x + 1)]/(x + 1)^2$, and the fixed cost is \$5,000. Find the total cost to make x boxes of bulbs.

56. **Total Revenue** The marginal revenue for selling the xth box of light bulbs is $10 + 0.001x^2e^{-x/100}$. Find the total revenue generated by selling 200 boxes of bulbs.

57. **Spending on Gasoline** From the beginning of 2000 to the beginning of 2007 the United States consumed gasoline at a rate of about

$$q(t) = 2.0t + 131 \text{ billion gallons per year} \quad (0 \le t \le 7).$$

(t is the number of years since 2000.)[2] During the same period the price of gasoline was approximately

$$p(t) = 1.2e^{0.11t} \text{ dollars per gallon.}$$

Use an integral to estimate, to the nearest 10 billion dollars, the total spent on gasoline during the given period. [HINT: Rate of spending = $p(t)q(t)$.]

58. **Spending on Gasoline** From the beginning of 2007 to the beginning of 2014 the United States consumed gasoline at a rate of about

$$q(t) = -1.2t + 141 \text{ billion gallons per year} \quad (0 \le t \le 7).$$

(t is the number of years since 2007.)[3] During the same period the price of gasoline was approximately

$$p(t) = 3.5 - 2.38e^{-0.5t} \text{ dollars per gallon.}$$

Use an integral to estimate, to the nearest 10 billion dollars, the total spent on gasoline during the given period. [HINT: Rate of spending = $p(t)q(t)$.]

59. **Housing** The following graph shows the annual number of housing starts in the United States during 2000–2008 together with a quadratic approximating model:

$$s(t) = -30t^2 + 240t + 800 \text{ thousand homes per year}$$
$$(0 \le t \le 8).$$

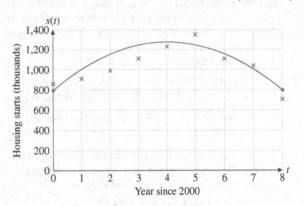

(t is the time in years since 2000.)[4] At the same time, the homes being built were getting larger: The average area per home was approximately

$$a(t) = 40t + 2{,}000 \text{ square feet.}$$

Use the given models to estimate the total housing area under construction over the given period. (Use integration by parts to evaluate the integral, and round your answer to the nearest billion square feet.) [HINT: Rate of change of area under construction = $s(t)a(t)$.]

60. **Housing for Sale** The following graph shows the number of housing starts for sale purposes in the United States during 2000–2008 together with a quadratic approximating model:

$$s(t) = -33t^2 + 240t + 700 \text{ thousand homes per year}$$
$$(0 \le t \le 8).$$

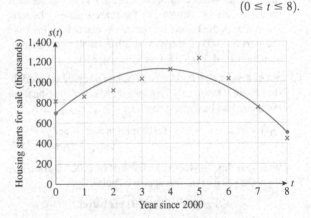

[2] Source for data: Energy Information Administration, Department of Energy (www.eia.gov).
[3] Ibid.
[4] Source for data: U.S. Census Bureau (www.census.gov).

(t is the time in years since 2000.)[5] At the same time, the homes being built were getting larger: The average area per home was approximately

$$a(t) = 40t + 2,000 \text{ square feet.}$$

Use the given models to estimate the total housing area under construction for sale purposes over the given period. (Use integration by parts to evaluate the integral, and round your answer to the nearest billion square feet.) [HINT: Rate of change of area under construction = $s(t)a(t)$.]

61. ▼ **Bottled Water Sales** The rate of U.S. sales of bottled water for the period 2000–2010 can be approximated by

$$s(t) = -45t^2 + 900t + 4,200 \text{ million gallons per year}$$
$$(0 \le t \le 10),$$

where t is time in years since the start of 2000.[6] After conducting a survey of sales in your town, you estimate that consumption in gyms accounts for a fraction

$$f(t) = \sqrt{0.1 + 0.02t}$$

of all bottled water sold in year t. Assuming that your model is correct, estimate, to the nearest hundred million gallons, the total amount of bottled water consumed in gyms from the start of 2005 to the start of 2010. [HINT: Rate of consumption = $s(t)f(t)$. Also see Exercise 31.]

62. Bottled Water Sales The rate of U.S. per capita sales of bottled water for the period 2000–2010 can be approximated by

$$s(t) = -0.18t^2 + 3t + 15 \text{ gallons per year} \quad (0 \le t \le 10),$$

where t is the time in years since the start of 2000.[7] After conducting a survey of sales in your state, you estimate that consumption in gyms accounts for a fraction

$$f(t) = \sqrt{0.2 + 0.04t}$$

of all bottled water consumed in year t. Assuming that your model is correct, estimate, to the nearest gallon, the total amount of bottled water consumed per capita in gyms from the start of 2005 to the start of 2010. [HINT: Rate of consumption = $s(t)f(t)$. Also see Exercise 31.]

63. ▼ **Oil Production in Mexico** The rate of crude oil production from 2008 to 2013 by Pemex, Mexico's national oil company, can be approximated by

$$q(t) = 6.2t^2 - 146t + 1,910 \text{ million barrels per year}$$
$$(8 \le t \le 13),$$

where t is time in years since the start of 2000.[8] During that time, the price of oil was approximately[9]

$$p(t) = 48e^{0.046t} \text{ dollars per barrel.}$$

Obtain an expression for Pemex's total oil revenue $R(x)$ from the start of 2008 to the start of year x as a function of x. (Do not simplify the answer; round all coefficients to three significant digits.) [HINT: Rate of revenue = $p(t)q(t)$.]

64. ▼ **Oil Imports from Mexico** The rate of crude oil imports to the United States from Mexico from 2009 to 2013 can be approximated by

$$r(t) = -14t^2 + 292t - 1,100 \text{ million barrels per year}$$
$$(9 \le t \le 13),$$

where t is time in years since the start of 2000.[10] During that time, the price of oil was approximately[11]

$$p(t) = 48e^{0.046t} \text{ dollars per barrel.}$$

Obtain an expression for the total oil revenue $R(x)$ Mexico earned from the United States from the start of 2009 to the start of year x as a function of x. (Do not simplify the answer; round all coefficients to three significant digits.) [HINT: Rate of revenue = $p(t)r(t)$.]

65. ▼ **Revenue** You have been raising the price of your *Lord of the Fields* T-shirts by 50¢ per week, and sales have been falling continuously at a rate of 2% per week. Assuming that you are now selling 50 T-shirts per week and charging $10 per T-shirt, how much revenue will you generate during the coming year? (Round your answer to the nearest dollar.) [HINT: Weekly revenue = Weekly sales × Price per T-shirt.]

66. ▼ **Revenue** Luckily, sales of your *Star Wars and Peace* T-shirts are now 50 T-shirts per week and increasing continuously at a rate of 5% per week. You are now charging $10 per T-shirt and are decreasing the price by 50¢ per week. How much revenue will you generate during the next 6 weeks?

Integrals of Piecewise-Linear Functions *Exercises 67 and 68 are based on the following formula that can be used to represent a piecewise-linear function as a closed-form function:*

$$\begin{cases} p(x) & \text{if } x < a \\ q(x) & \text{if } x > a \end{cases} = p(x) + \frac{1}{2}[q(x) - p(x)]\left[1 + \frac{|x-a|}{x-a}\right]$$

Such functions can then be integrated using the technique of Exercises 45–52.

67. ◆ **Population: Mexico** The rate of change of population in Mexico over 1990–2010 was approximately

$$r(t) = \begin{cases} -0.1t + 3 & \text{if } 0 \le t \le 10 \\ -0.05t + 2.5 & \text{if } 10 \le t \le 20 \end{cases}$$

million people per year, where t is time in years since 1990.

a. Use the formula given before the exercise to represent $r(t)$ as a closed-form function. [HINT: Use the formula with $a = 10$.]

---

[5] See footnote for Exercise 59.

[6] Source for data: Beverage Marketing Corporation (www.bottledwater.org).

[7] Ibid.

[8] Source for data: www.pemex.com.

[9] Source for data: www.inflationdata.com.

[10] Source for data: U.S. Energy Information Administration (www.eia.gov).

[11] Source for data: www.inflationdata.com.

b. Use the result of part (a) and a definite integral to estimate the total increase in population over the given 20-year period. [HINT: Break up the integral into two, and use the technique of Exercises 45–52 to evaluate one of them.]

68. ◆ *Population: Mexico* The rate of change of population in Mexico over 1950–1990 was approximately

$$r(t) = \begin{cases} 0.05t + 2.5 & \text{if } 0 \le t \le 20 \\ -0.075t + 5 & \text{if } 20 \le t \le 40 \end{cases}$$

million people per year, where t is time in years since 1950.
a. Use the formula given before the exercise to represent $r(t)$ as a closed-form function. [HINT: Use the formula with $a = 20$.]
b. Use the result of part (a) and a definite integral to estimate the total increase in population over the given 40-year period. [HINT: Break up the integral into two, and use the technique of Exercises 45–52 to evaluate one of them.]

Communication and Reasoning Exercises

69. Your friend Janice claims that integration by parts allows one to integrate any product of two functions. Prove her wrong by giving an example of a product of two functions that cannot be integrated using integration by parts.

70. Complete the following sentence in words: The integral of uv is the first times the integral of the second minus the integral of _____.

71. Give an example of an integral that can be computed in two ways: by substitution or integration by parts.

72. Give an example of an integral that can be computed by substitution but not by integration by parts. (You need not compute the integral.)

In Exercises 73–80, indicate whether the given integral calls for integration by parts or substitution.

73. $\int (6x - 1)e^{3x^2 - x} \, dx$

74. $\int \dfrac{x^2 - 3x + 1}{e^{2x - 3}} \, dx$

75. $\int (3x^2 - x)e^{6x - 1} \, dx$

76. $\int \dfrac{2x - 3}{e^{x^2 - 3x + 1}} \, dx$

77. $\int \dfrac{1}{(x + 1)\ln(x + 1)} \, dx$

78. $\int \dfrac{\ln(x + 1)}{x + 1} \, dx$

79. $\int \ln(x^2) \, dx$

80. $\int (x + 1)\ln(x + 1) \, dx$

81. ▼ If $P(x)$ is a polynomial of degree n and $f(x)$ is some function of x, how many times do we generally have to integrate $f(x)$ to compute $\int p(x)f(x) \, dx$?

82. ▼ Use integration by parts to show that $\int (\ln x)^2 \, dx = x(\ln x)^2 - 2x \ln x + 2x + C$.

83. ◆ *Hermite's Identity* If $f(x)$ is a polynomial of degree n, show that

$$\int_0^b f(x)e^{-x} \, dx = F(0) - F(b)e^{-b},$$

where $F(x) = f(x) + f'(x) + f''(x) + \cdots + f^{(n)}(x)$. (This is the sum of f and all of its derivatives.)

84. ◆ Write down a formula similar to Hermite's identity for $\int_0^b f(x)e^x \, dx$ when $f(x)$ is a polynomial of degree n.

14.2   Area between Two Curves and Applications

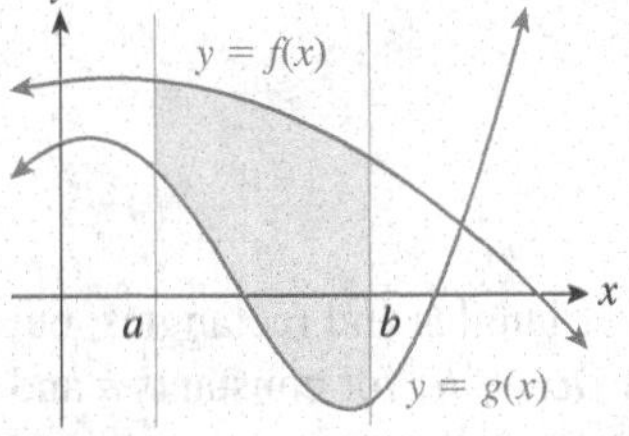

Figure 1

As we saw in Chapter 13, we can use the definite integral to calculate the area between the graph of a function and the x-axis. With only a little more work, we can use it to calculate the area between two graphs. Figure 1 shows the graphs of two functions, $f(x)$ and $g(x)$, with $f(x) \ge g(x)$ for every x in the interval $[a, b]$.

To find the shaded area between the graphs of the two functions, we use the following formula.

Area between Two Graphs

If $f(x) \ge g(x)$ for all x in $[a, b]$ (so that the graph of f does not move below that of g), then the area of the region between the graphs of f and g and between $x = a$ and $x = b$ is given by

$$A = \int_a^b [f(x) - g(x)] \, dx. \qquad \text{Integral of (Top − Bottom)}$$

Caution

If the graphs of f and g cross in the interval, the above formula does not hold. For instance, if $f(x) = x$ and $g(x) = -x$, then the total area shown in the figure is 2 square units, whereas $\int_{-1}^{1} [f(x) - g(x)] \, dx = 0$.

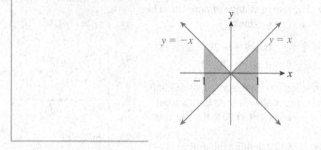

Let's look at an example and then discuss why the formula works.

EXAMPLE 1 **The Area between Two Curves**

Find the areas of the following regions:

a. Between $f(x) = -x^2 - 3x + 4$ and $g(x) = x^2 - 3x - 4$ and between $x = -1$ and $x = 1$

b. Between $f(x) = |x|$ and $g(x) = -|x - 1|$ over $[-1, 2]$

Solution

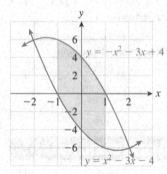

Figure 2

a. The area in question is shown in Figure 2. Because the graph of f lies above the graph of g in the interval $[-1, 1]$, we have $f(x) \geq g(x)$ for all x in $[-1, 1]$. Therefore, we can use the formula given above and calculate the area as follows:

$$A = \int_{-1}^{1} [f(x) - g(x)] \, dx$$

$$= \int_{-1}^{1} [(-x^2 - 3x + 4) - (x^2 - 3x - 4)] \, dx$$

$$= \int_{-1}^{1} (8 - 2x^2) \, dx$$

$$= \left[8x - \frac{2}{3}x^3 \right]_{-1}^{1}$$

$$= \frac{44}{3}.$$

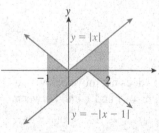

Figure 3

b. The given area (see Figure 3) can be broken up into triangles and rectangles, but we already know a formula for the antiderivative of $|ax + b|$ for constants a and b, so we can use calculus instead:

$$A = \int_{-1}^{2} [f(x) - g(x)] \, dx$$

$$= \int_{-1}^{2} [|x| - (-|x - 1|)] \, dx$$

$$= \int_{-1}^{2} [|x| + |x - 1|] \, dx$$

$$= \frac{1}{2}[x|x| + (x-1)|x-1|]_{-1}^{2} \qquad \int |ax+b| \, dx = \frac{1}{2a}(ax+b)|ax+b| + C$$

$$= \frac{1}{2}[(4+1) - (-1-4)]$$

$$= \frac{1}{2}(10) = 5.$$

Q : *Why does the formula for the area between two curves work?*

A : Let's go back once again to the general case illustrated in Figure 1, where we were given two functions f and g with $f(x) \geq g(x)$ for every x in the interval $[a, b]$. To avoid complicating the argument by the fact that the graph of g, or f, or both may dip below the x-axis in the interval $[a, b]$ (as occurs in Figure 1 and also in Example 1), we shift both graphs vertically upward by adding a big enough constant M to lift them both above the x-axis in the interval $[a, b]$, as shown in Figure 4.

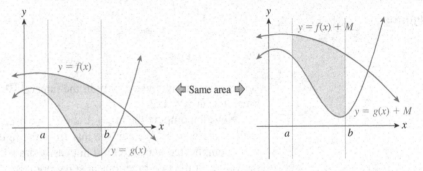

Figure 4

As the figure illustrates, the area of the region between the graphs is not affected, so we will calculate the area of the region shown on the right of Figure 4. That calculation is shown in Figure 5.

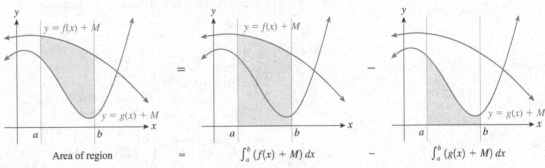

Figure 5

From the figure, the area we want is

$$\int_{a}^{b}(f(x) + M)\,dx - \int_{a}^{b}(g(x) + M)\,dx = \int_{a}^{b}[(f(x) + M) - (g(x) + M)]\,dx$$

$$= \int_{a}^{b}[f(x) - g(x)]\,dx,$$

which is the formula we gave originally.

So far, we've been assuming that $f(x) \geq g(x)$, so the graph of f never dips below the graph of g and so the graphs cannot cross (although they can touch). Example 2 shows how we compute the area between graphs that *do* cross.

EXAMPLE 2   **Regions Enclosed by Crossing Curves**

Find the area of the region between $y = 3x^2$ and $y = 1 - x^2$ and between $x = 0$ and $x = 1$.

Solution The area we wish to calculate is shown in Figure 6. From the figure, we can see that neither graph lies above the other over the whole interval. To get around this, we break the area into the two pieces on either side of the point at which the graphs cross and then compute each area separately. To do this, we need to know exactly where that crossing point is. The crossing point is where $3x^2 = 1 - x^2$, so we solve for x:

$$3x^2 = 1 - x^2$$
$$4x^2 = 1$$
$$x^2 = \frac{1}{4}$$
$$x = \pm\frac{1}{2}.$$

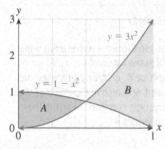

Figure 6

Because we are interested only in the interval $[0, 1]$, the crossing point we're interested in is at $x = 1/2$.

Now, to compute the areas A and B, we need to know which graph is on top in each of these areas. We can see that from the figure, but what if the functions were more complicated and we could not easily draw the graphs? To be sure, we can test the values of the two functions at some point in each region. But we really need not worry. If we make the wrong choice for the top function, the integral will yield the negative of the area (why?), so we can simply take the absolute value of the integral to get the area of the region in question. For this example we have

$$A = \int_0^{1/2} [(1 - x^2) - 3x^2]\, dx = \int_0^{1/2} (1 - 4x^2)\, dx$$

$$= \left[x - \frac{4x^3}{3} \right]_0^{1/2}$$

$$= \left(\frac{1}{2} - \frac{1}{6} \right) - (0 - 0) = \frac{1}{3}$$

and

$$B = \int_{1/2}^1 [3x^2 - (1 - x^2)]\, dx = \int_{1/2}^1 (4x^2 - 1)\, dx$$

$$= \left[\frac{4x^3}{3} - x \right]_{1/2}^1$$

$$= \left(\frac{4}{3} - 1 \right) - \left(\frac{1}{6} - \frac{1}{2} \right) = \frac{2}{3}.$$

This gives a total area of $A + B = \frac{1}{3} + \frac{2}{3} = 1$.

➡ **Before we go on . . .** What would have happened in Example 2 if we had not broken the area into two pieces but had just calculated the integral of the difference of the two functions? We would have calculated

$$\int_0^1 [(1 - x^2) - 3x^2]\, dx = \int_0^1 [1 - 4x^2]\, dx = \left[x - \frac{4x^3}{3} \right]_0^1 = -\frac{1}{3},$$

which is not even close to the right answer. What this integral calculated was actually $A - B$ rather than $A + B$. Why? ∎

<table>
<tr><td>**EXAMPLE 3**</td><td>**The Area Enclosed by Two Curves**</td></tr>
</table>

Find the area enclosed by $y = x^2$ and $y = x^3$.

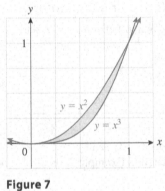

Figure 7

Solution This example has a new wrinkle: We are not told what interval to use for x. However, if we look at the graph in Figure 7, we see that the question can have only one meaning. We are being asked to find the area of the shaded sliver, which is the only region that is actually *enclosed* by the two graphs. This sliver is bounded on either side by the two points where the graphs cross, so our first task is to find those points. They are the points where $x^2 = x^3$, so we solve for x:

$$x^2 = x^3$$
$$x^3 - x^2 = 0$$
$$x^2(x - 1) = 0$$
$$x = 0 \quad \text{or} \quad x = 1.$$

Thus, we must integrate over the interval $[0, 1]$. Although we see from the diagram (or by substituting $x = 1/2$) that the graph of $y = x^2$ is above that of $y = x^3$, if we didn't notice that, we might calculate

$$\int_0^1 (x^3 - x^2)\, dx = \left[\frac{x^4}{4} - \frac{x^3}{3} \right]_0^1 = -\frac{1}{12}.$$

This tells us that the required area is $1/12$ square units and also that we had our integral reversed. Had we calculated $\int_0^1 (x^2 - x^3)\, dx$ instead, we would have found the correct answer: $1/12$.

We can summarize the procedure we used in Examples 2 and 3.

> **Finding the Area between the Graphs of $f(x)$ and $g(x)$**
>
> **1.** Find all points of intersection by solving $f(x) = g(x)$ for x. This either determines the interval over which you will integrate or breaks up a given interval into regions between the intersection points.
>
> **2.** Determine the area of each region you found by integrating the difference of the larger and the smaller function. (If you accidentally take the smaller minus the larger, the integral will give the negative of the area, so just take the absolute value.)
>
> **3.** Add together the areas you found in Step 2 to get the total area.

Q: *Is there any quick and easy method to find the area between two graphs without having to find all points of intersection? What if it is hard or impossible to find out where the curves intersect?*

A: We can use technology to give the approximate area between two graphs. First recall that, if $f(x) \geq g(x)$ for all x in $[a, b]$, then the area between their graphs over $[a, b]$ is given by $\int_a^b [f(x) - g(x)]\, dx$, whereas if $g(x) \geq f(x)$, the area is given by $\int_a^b [g(x) - f(x)]\, dx$. Notice that both expressions are equal to

$$\int_a^b |f(x) - g(x)|\, dx,$$

telling us that we can use this same formula in both cases.

Area between Two Graphs: Approximation Using Technology

The area of the region between the graphs of f and g and between $x = a$ and $x = b$ is given by

$$A = \int_a^b |f(x) - g(x)|\, dx.$$

Quick Example

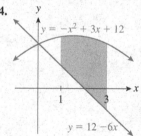

1. To approximate the area of the region between $y = 3x^2$ and $y = 1 - x^2$ and between $x = 0$ and $x = 1$ that we calculated in Example 2, use technology to compute

$$\int_0^1 |3x^2 - (1 - x^2)|\, dx = 1.$$

TI-83/84 Plus: Enter `fnInt(abs(3x^2-(1-x^2)),X,0,1)`

Website: Online Utilities → Numerical Integration Utility and Grapher Enter `abs(3x^2-(1-x^2))` for $f(x)$ and 0 and 1 for the lower and upper limits, and press "Integral". (See Figure 8.)

Figure 8

14.2 EXERCISES

▼ more advanced   ◆ challenging

▢ indicates exercises that should be solved using technology

In Exercises 1–8, find the area of the shaded region. (We suggest that you use technology to check your answers.)

1.
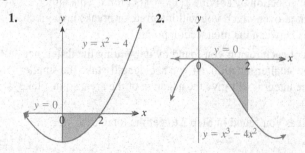

2.

3.
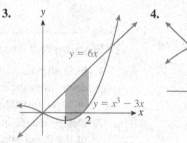

4.
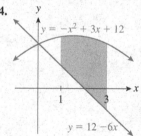

5.

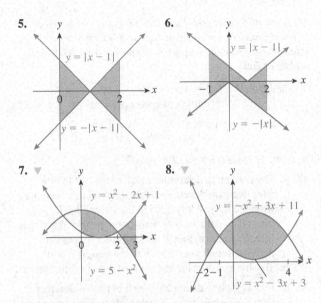

6.

7. ▼

8. ▼

In Exercises 9–42, find the area of the indicated region. We suggest that you graph the curves to check whether one is above the other or whether they cross, and that you use technology to check your answers.

9. Between $y = x^2$ and $y = -1$ for x in $[-1, 1]$
[HINT: See Example 1.]

10. Between $y = x^3$ and $y = -1$ for x in $[-1, 1]$
[HINT: See Example 1.]

11. Between $y = -x$ and $y = x$ for x in $[0, 2]$

12. Between $y = -x$ and $y = x/2$ for x in $[0, 2]$

13. Between $y = |x|$ and $y = x^2$ for x in $[-1, 1]$

14. Between $y = -|x|$ and $y = x^2 - 2$ for x in $[-1, 1]$

15. Between $y = x$ and $y = x^2$ for x in $[-1, 1]$
[HINT: See Example 2.]

16. Between $y = x$ and $y = x^3$ for x in $[-1, 1]$
[HINT: See Example 2.]

17. Between $y = x^2 - 2x$ and $y = -x^2 + 4x - 4$ for x in $[0, 2]$

18. Between $y = x^2 - 4x + 2$ and $y = -x^2 + 4x - 4$ for x in $[0, 3]$

19. Between $y = 2x^2 + 10x - 5$ and $y = -x^2 + 4x + 4$ for x in $[-3, 2]$

20. Between $y = 2x^2 + 7x - 2$ and $y = -x^2 + 4x + 4$ for x in $[-2, 2]$

21. Between $y = e^x$ and $y = x$ for x in $[0, 1]$

22. Between $y = e^{-x}$ and $y = -x$ for x in $[0, 1]$

23. Between $y = (x - 1)^2$ and $y = -(x - 1)^2$ for x in $[0, 1]$

24. Between $y = x^2(x^3 + 1)^{10}$ and $y = -x(x^2 + 1)^{10}$ for x in $[0, 1]$

25. Enclosed by $y = x$ and $y = x^4$ [HINT: See Example 3.]

26. Enclosed by $y = x$ and $y = -x^4$ [HINT: See Example 3.]

27. Enclosed by $y = x^3$ and $y = x^4$

28. Enclosed by $y = x$ and $y = x^3$

29. Enclosed by $y = x^2$ and $y = x^4$

30. Enclosed by $y = x^4 - x^2$ and $y = x^2 - x^4$

31. Enclosed by $y = x^2 - 2x$ and $y = -x^2 + 4x - 4$

32. Enclosed by $y = x^2 - 4x + 2$ and $y = -x^2 + 4x - 4$

33. Enclosed by $y = 2x^2 + 10x - 5$ and $y = -x^2 + 4x + 4$

34. Enclosed by $y = 2x^2 + 7x - 2$ and $y = -x^2 + 4x + 4$

35. Enclosed by $y = e^x$, $y = 2$, and the y-axis

36. Enclosed by $y = e^{-x}$, $y = 3$, and the y-axis

37. Enclosed by $y = \ln x$, $y = 2 - \ln x$, and $x = 4$

38. Enclosed by $y = \ln x$, $y = 1 - \ln x$, and $x = 4$

39. ▓ Enclosed by $y = e^x$, $y = 2x + 1$, $x = -1$, and $x = 1$ (Round answer to four significant digits.) [HINT: See Quick Example 1.]

40. ▓ Enclosed by $y = 2^x$, $y = x + 2$, $x = -2$, and $x = 2$ (Round answer to four significant digits.) [HINT: See Quick Example 1.]

41. ▓ Enclosed by $y = \ln x$ and $y = \dfrac{x}{2} - \dfrac{1}{2}$ (Round answer to four significant digits.) (First use technology to determine approximately where the graphs cross.)

42. ▓ Enclosed by $y = \ln x$, and $y = x - 2$ (Round answer to four significant digits.) (First use technology to determine approximately where the graphs cross.)

Applications

43. *Revenue and Cost* Suppose your daily revenue from selling used DVDs is

$$R(t) = 100 + 10t \quad (0 \le t \le 5)$$

dollars per day, where t represents days from the beginning of the week, while your daily costs are

$$C(t) = 90 + 5t \quad (0 \le t \le 5)$$

dollars per day. Find the area between the graphs of $R(t)$ and $C(t)$ for $0 \le t \le 5$. What does your answer represent?

44. *Income and Expenses* Suppose your annual income is

$$I(t) = 50,000 + 2,000t \quad (0 \le t \le 3)$$

dollars per year, where t represents the number of years since you began your job, while your annual expenses are

$$E(t) = 45,000 + 1,500t \quad (0 \le t \le 3)$$

dollars per year. Find the area between the graphs of $I(t)$ and $E(t)$ for $0 \le t \le 3$. What does your answer represent?

45. Housing The total number of housing starts in the United States during 2000–2008 was approximately

$$h(t) = -30t^2 + 240t + 800 \text{ thousand homes per year}$$
$$(0 \le t \le 8),$$

where t is time in years since the start of 2000.[12] During that time, the number of housing starts for sale purposes in the United States was approximately

$$s(t) = -33t^2 + 240t + 700 \text{ thousand homes per year}$$
$$(0 \le t \le 8).$$

Compute the area shown in the graph, and interpret the answer.

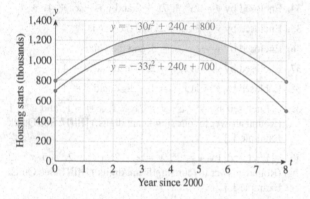

Year since 2000

46. Oil Production in Mexico: Pemex The rate of crude oil production from 2009 to 2013 by Pemex, Mexico's national oil company, can be approximated by

$$q(t) = 6.2t^2 - 146t + 1,910 \text{ million barrels per year}$$
$$(9 \le t \le 13),$$

where t is time in years since the start of 2000.[13] During that time, Mexico exported crude oil to the United States at a rate of[14]

$$r(t) = -14t^2 + 292t - 1,100 \text{ million barrels per year}$$
$$(9 \le t \le 13).$$

Compute the area shown in the graph, and interpret the answer.

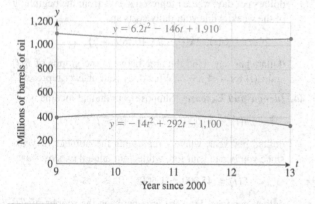

Year since 2000

MySpace and Facebook *Exercises 47 and 48 are based on the following models, which show the rate at which new members joined Facebook and MySpace in the period from 2005 to the middle of 2008:*

Facebook:[15] $f(t) = 12t^2 - 20t + 10$
      million members per year $(0 \le t \le 3.5)$

MySpace:[16] $m(t) = 10.5t^2 + 25t + 18.5$
      million members per year $(0 \le t \le 3.5).$

(t is time in years since the start of 2005.)

47. a. Use a graph to determine which of the two Internet sites was experiencing a larger influx of new members from the start of July 2005 to the start of 2007. Use an integral to estimate how many more people joined that Internet site than joined its competitor during that period. (Round your answer to the nearest million.)
   b. To what area does the integral used in part (a) correspond?

48. a. Use a graph to determine which of the two Internet sites was experiencing a larger influx of new members from the start of 2007 through June 2008. Use an integral to estimate how many more people joined that Internet site than joined its competitor during that period. (Round your answer to the nearest million.)
   b. To what area does the integral used in part (a) correspond?

Big Brother *Exercises 49 and 50 are based on the following models, which show the total number of wiretaps authorized per year by all state and federal courts in the United States and the number authorized by state courts:*

State and federal courts: $a(t) = 770e^{0.060t}$ $(0 \le t \le 23)$
      State courts: $s(t) = 410e^{0.071t}$ $(0 \le t \le 23).$

(t is time in years since the start of 1990.)[17]

49. ▼ Estimate the area between the graphs of the two functions over the interval $[0, t]$. Interpret your answer.

50. ▼ Estimate the area between the graphs of the two functions over the interval $[t, 23]$. Interpret your answer.

Communication and Reasoning Exercises

51. If f and g are continuous functions with $\int_a^b [f(x) - g(x)] \, dx = 0$, it follows that the area between the graphs of f and g is zero—right?

52. You know that f and g are continuous and their graphs do not cross on the interval $[a, b]$, so you calculate $\int_a^b [f(x) - g(x)] \, dx$ and find that the answer is -40. Why is it negative, and what is the area between the curves?

[15] Sources for data: www.facebook.com, www.insidehighered.com. (Some data are interpolated.)

[16] Source for data: www.swivel.com/data_sets.

[17] Source for data: Wiretap Reports, Administrative Office of the United States Courts (www.uscourts.gov/Statistics/WiretapReports/wiretap-report-2013.aspx).

[12] Source for data: U.S. Census Bureau (www.census.gov).

[13] Source for data: www.pemex.com.

[14] Source for data: U.S. Energy Information Administration (www.eia.gov).

53. The following graph shows annual U.S. exports and imports for the period 1960–2007:[18]

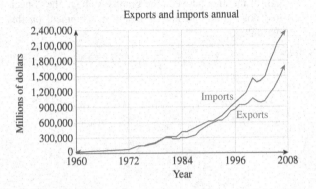

Exports and imports annual

What does the area between the export and import curves represent?

54. The following graph shows a fictitious country's monthly exports and imports for the period 1997–2001:

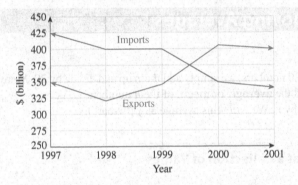

What does the total area enclosed by the export and import curves represent, and what does the definite integral of the difference, Exports − Imports, represent?

55. ▼ The following graph shows the daily revenue and cost in your *Adopt-a-Chia* operation t days from its inception:

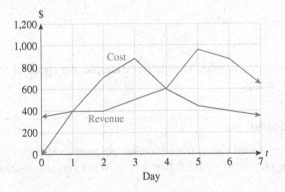

Multiple choice: The area between the cost and revenue curves represents:

(A) the accumulated loss through day 4 plus the accumulated profit for days 5 through 7.
(B) the accumulated profit for the week.
(C) the accumulated loss for the week.
(D) the accumulated cost through day 4 plus the accumulated revenue for days 5 through 7.

56. ▼ The following graph shows daily orders and inventory (stock on hand) for your *Jackson Pollock Paint-by-Number* sets t days into last week:

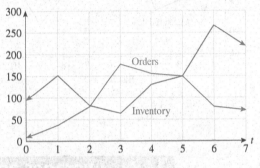

a. Multiple choice: Which is greatest?

(A) $\int_0^7 (\text{Orders} - \text{Inventory})\, dt$

(B) $\int_0^7 (\text{Inventory} - \text{Orders})\, dt$

(C) The area between the Orders and Inventory curves

b. Multiple choice: The answer to part (a) measures

(A) the accumulated gap between orders and inventory.
(B) the accumulated surplus through day 3 minus the accumulated shortage for days 3 through 5 plus the accumulated surplus through days 5 through 7.
(C) the total net surplus.
(D) the total net loss.

57. ▼ What is wrong with the following claim? "I purchased Novartis AG shares for $50 at the beginning of March 2008. My total profit per share from this investment from March through August is represented by the area between the stock price curve and the purchase price curve as shown on the following graph, where t is time in months since March 1, 2008."[19]

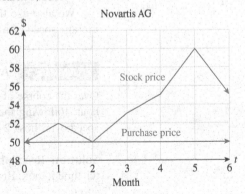

Novartis AG

[18] Source: Data 360 (www.data360.org).

[19] Source: www.finance.google.com.

58. ▼ Your pharmaceutical company monitors the amount of medication in successive batches of 100-mg tetracycline capsules and obtains the following graph:

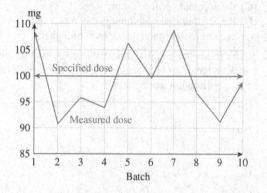

Your production manager claims that the batches of tetracycline conform to the exact dosage requirement because half of the area between the graphs is above the "Specified dose" line and half is below it. Comment on this reasoning.

14.3 Averages and Moving Averages

Averages

To find the average of, say, 20 numbers, we simply add them up and divide by 20. More generally, if we want to find the **average**, or **mean**, of the n numbers $y_1, y_2, y_3, \ldots y_n$, we add them up and divide by n. We write this average as $\bar{y}$ ("y-bar").

Average, or Mean, of a Collection of Values

$$\bar{y} = \frac{y_1 + y_2 + \cdots + y_n}{n}$$

Quick Example

1. The average of $\{0, 2, -1, 5\}$ is $\bar{y} = \dfrac{0 + 2 - 1 + 5}{4} = \dfrac{6}{4} = 1.5$.

We also use the word *average* in other senses. For example, we speak of the average speed of a car during a trip.

EXAMPLE 1 Average Speed

Over the course of 2 hours, my speed varied from 50 miles per hour to 60 miles per hour, following the function $v(t) = 50 + 2.5t^2$, $0 \le t \le 2$. What was my average speed over those 2 hours?

Solution Recall that average speed is simply the total distance traveled divided by the time it took. Recall, also, that we can find the distance traveled by integrating the speed:

$$\text{Distance traveled} = \int_0^2 v(t) \, dt$$

$$= \int_0^2 (50 + 2.5t^2) \, dt$$

$$= \left[50t + \frac{2.5}{3}t^3 \right]_0^2$$

$$= 100 + \frac{20}{3}$$

$$\approx 106.67 \text{ miles.}$$

It took 2 hours to travel this distance, so the average speed was

$$\text{Average speed} \approx \frac{106.67}{2} \approx 53.3 \text{ mph.}$$

In general, if we travel with velocity $v(t)$ from time $t = a$ to time $t = b$, we will travel a distance of $\int_a^b v(t) \, dt$ in time $b - a$, which gives an average velocity of

$$\text{Average velocity} = \frac{1}{b - a} \int_a^b v(t) \, dt.$$

Thinking of this calculation as finding the average value of the velocity function, we generalize and make the following definition.

Average Value of a Function

The **average**, or **mean**, of a function $f(x)$ on an interval $[a, b]$ is

$$\bar{f} = \frac{1}{b - a} \int_a^b f(x) \, dx.$$

Quick Example

2. The average of $f(x) = x$ on $[1, 5]$ is

$$\bar{f} = \frac{1}{b - a} \int_a^b f(x) \, dx$$

$$= \frac{1}{5 - 1} \int_1^5 x \, dx$$

$$= \frac{1}{4} \left[\frac{x^2}{2} \right]_1^5 = \frac{1}{4}\left(\frac{25}{2} - \frac{1}{2} \right) = 3.$$

Interpreting the Average of a Function Geometrically

The average of a function has a geometric interpretation. Referring to Quick Example 2, we can compare the graph of $y = f(x)$ with the graph of $y = 3$, both over the interval $[1, 5]$ (Figure 9). We can find the area under the graph of $f(x) = x$ by geometry or by calculus; it is 12. The area in the rectangle under $y = 3$ is also 12.

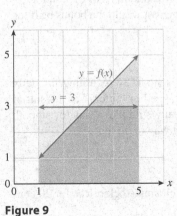

Figure 9

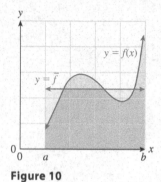

Figure 10

In general, the average $\bar{f}$ of a positive function over the interval $[a, b]$ gives the height of the rectangle over the interval $[a, b]$ that has the same area as the area under the graph of $f(x)$ as illustrated in Figure 10. The equality of these areas follows from the equation

$$(b - a)\bar{f} = \int_a^b f(x)\, dx,$$

because the left-hand side is the area of the rectangle, while the right-hand side is the area under the graph.

EXAMPLE 2   Average Balance

A savings account at the *People's Credit Union* pays 3% interest, compounded continuously, and at the end of the year you get a bonus of 1% of the average balance in the account during the year. If you deposit $10,000 at the beginning of the year, how much interest and how large a bonus will you get?

Solution We can use the continuous compound interest formula to calculate the amount of money you have in the account at time t:

$$A(t) = 10,000e^{0.03t},$$

where t is measured in years. At the end of 1 year the account will have

$$A(1) = \$10,304.55,$$

so you will have earned $304.55 interest. To compute the bonus, we need to find the average amount in the account, which is the average of $A(t)$ over the interval $[0, 1]$. Thus,

$$\bar{A} = \frac{1}{b - a} \int_a^b A(t)\, dt$$

$$= \frac{1}{1 - 0} \int_0^1 10,000e^{0.03t}\, dt = \frac{10,000}{0.03}[e^{0.03t}]_0^1$$

$$\approx \$10,151.51.$$

The bonus is 1% of this, or $101.52.

➡ **Before we go on ...** The 1% bonus in Example 2 was one third of the total interest. Why did this happen? What fraction of the total interest would the bonus be if the interest rate was 4%, 5%, or 10%? ∎

Moving Averages

Suppose you follow the performance of a company's stock by recording the daily closing prices. The graph of these prices may seem jagged or "jittery" as a result of random day-to-day fluctuations. To see any trends, you would like a way to "smooth out" these data. The **moving average** is one common way to do that.

EXAMPLE 3   Stock Prices

The following table shows *Colossal Conglomerate*'s closing stock prices for 20 consecutive trading days:

Day	1	2	3	4	5	6	7	8	9	10
Price	20	22	21	24	24	23	25	26	20	24
Day	11	12	13	14	15	16	17	18	19	20
Price	26	26	25	27	28	27	29	27	25	24

Plot these prices and the 5-day moving average.

Solution The 5-day moving average is the average of each day's price together with the prices of the preceding 4 days. We can compute the 5-day moving averages starting on the fifth day. We get these numbers:

Day	1	2	3	4	5	6	7	8	9	10
Moving Average					22.2	22.8	23.4	24.4	23.6	23.6
Day	11	12	13	14	15	16	17	18	19	20
Moving Average	24.2	24.4	24.2	25.6	26.4	26.6	27.2	27.6	27.2	26.4

Using Technology

See the Technology Guides at the end of the chapter to find out how to tabulate and graph moving averages using a graphing calculator or a spreadsheet. Outline:

TI-83/84 Plus
STAT EDIT; days in L_1, prices in L_2.
Home screen:
seq((L₂(X)+L₂(X-1)
+L₂(X-2)+L₂(X-3)
+L₂(X-4))/5,X,5,20)
→L₃
[More details in the Technology Guide.]

Spreadsheet
Day data in A2–A21
Price data in B2–B21
Enter =AVERAGE(B2:B6) in C6, copy down to C21.
Graph the data in columns A–C.
[More details in the Technology Guide.]

The closing stock prices and moving averages are plotted in Figure 11.

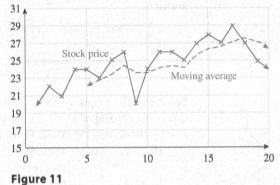

Figure 11

As you can see, the moving average is less volatile than the closing price. Because the moving average incorporates the stock's performance over 5 days at a time, a single day's fluctuation is smoothed out. Look at day 9 in particular. The moving average also tends to lag behind the actual performance because it takes past performance into account. Look at the downturns at days 6 and 18 in particular.

The period of 5 days for a moving average, as used in Example 3, is arbitrary. Using a longer period of time would smooth the data more but increase the lag. For data used as economic indicators, such as housing prices or retail sales, it is common to compute the four-quarter moving average to smooth out seasonal variations.

It is also sometimes useful to compute moving averages of continuous functions. We may want to do this if we use a mathematical model of a large collection of data. Also, some physical systems have the effect of converting an input function (an electrical signal, for example) into its moving average. By an **n-unit moving average** of a function $f(x)$, we mean the function $\bar{f}$ for which $\bar{f}(x)$ is the average of the value of $f(x)$ on $[x - n, x]$. Using the formula for the average of a function, we get the following formula.

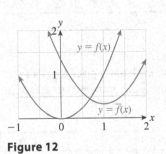

Figure 12

n-Unit Moving Average of a Function

The *n*-unit moving average of a function *f* is

$$\bar{f}(x) = \frac{1}{n} \int_{x-n}^{x} f(t)\, dt.$$

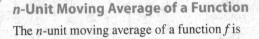

Quick Example

3. The 2-unit moving average of $f(x) = x^2$ is

$$\bar{f}(x) = \frac{1}{2} \int_{x-2}^{x} t^2\, dt = \frac{1}{6}[t^3]_{x-2}^{x} = x^2 - 2x + \frac{4}{3}.$$

The graphs of $f(x)$ and $\bar{f}(x)$ are shown in Figure 12.

EXAMPLE 4   Moving Averages: Sawtooth and Step Functions

Graph the following functions, and then compute and graph their 1-unit moving averages:

$$f(x) = |x| - |x - 1| + |x - 2| \qquad \text{Sawtooth}$$

$$g(x) = \frac{1}{2}\left[1 + \frac{|x-1|}{x-1}\right]. \qquad \text{Unit step at } x = 1$$

Solution The graphs of *f* and *g* are shown in Figure 13. (Notice that the step function is not defined at $x = 1$. Some graphers will show the step function as an actual step by connecting the points $(1, 0)$ and $(1, 1)$ with a vertical line.)

The 1-step moving averages are

$$\bar{f}(x) = \int_{x-1}^{x} f(t)\, dt = \int_{x-1}^{x} [\,|t| - |t - 1| + |t - 2|\,]\, dt$$

$$= \frac{1}{2}[t|t| - (t - 1)|t - 1| + (t - 2)|t - 2|]_{x-1}^{x}$$

$$= \frac{1}{2}([x|x| - (x - 1)|x - 1| + (x - 2)|x - 2|]$$

$$\qquad - [(x - 1)|x - 1| - (x - 2)|x - 2| + (x - 3)|x - 3|])$$

$$= \frac{1}{2}[x|x| - 2(x - 1)|x - 1| + 2(x - 2)|x - 2| - (x - 3)|x - 3|]$$

$$\bar{g}(x) = \int_{x-1}^{x} g(t)\, dt = \int_{x-1}^{x} \frac{1}{2}\left[1 + \frac{|t-1|}{t - 1}\right] dt$$

$$= \frac{1}{2}[t + |t - 1|]_{x-1}^{x}$$

$$= \frac{1}{2}[(x + |x - 1|) - (x - 1 + |x - 2|)]$$

$$= \frac{1}{2}[1 + |x - 1| - |x - 2|].$$

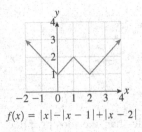

$f(x) = |x| - |x - 1| + |x - 2|$

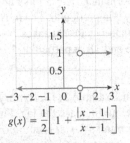

$g(x) = \dfrac{1}{2}\left[1 + \dfrac{|x-1|}{x-1}\right]$

Figure 13

The graphs of $\bar{f}$ and $\bar{g}$ are shown in Figure 14.

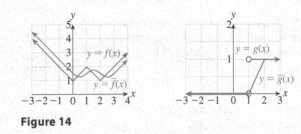

Figure 14

Notice how the graph of $\bar{f}$ smooths out the zigzags of the sawtooth function.

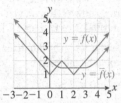

Figure 15

➡ **Before we go on . . .** Figure 15 shows the 2-unit moving average of f in Example 4,

$$\bar{f}(x) = \frac{1}{2} \int_{x-2}^{x} f(t)\, dt$$

$$= \frac{1}{4}(x|x| - (x-1)|x-1| + (x-3)|x-3| - (x-4)|x-4|).$$

Notice how the 2-point moving average has completely eliminated the zigzags, illustrating how moving averages can be used to remove seasonal fluctuations in real-life situations. ∎

14.3 EXERCISES

▼ more advanced   ◆ challenging

🖥 indicates exercises that should be solved using technology

In Exercises 1–8, find the average of the function over the given interval. Plot each function and its average on the same graph (as in Figure 10). [**HINT**: See Quick Example 2.]

1. $f(x) = x^3$ over $[0, 2]$ **2.** $f(x) = x^3$ over $[-1, 1]$

3. $f(x) = x^3 - x$ over $[0, 2]$ **4.** $f(x) = x^3 - x$ over $[0, 1]$

5. $f(x) = e^{-x}$ over $[0, 2]$ **6.** $f(x) = e^x$ over $[-1, 1]$

7. $f(x) = |2x - 5|$ over $[0, 4]$

8. $f(x) = |-x + 2|$ over $[-1, 3]$

In Exercises 9 and 10, complete the given table with the values of the 3-unit moving average of the given function. [**HINT**: See Example 3.]

9.

x	0	1	2	3	4	5	6	7
$r(x)$	3	5	10	3	2	5	6	7
$\bar{r}(x)$								

10.

x	0	1	2	3	4	5	6	7
$s(x)$	2	9	7	3	2	5	7	1
$\bar{s}(x)$								

In Exercises 11 and 12, some values of a function and its 3-unit moving average are given. Supply the missing information.

11.

x	0	1	2	3	4	5	6	7
$r(x)$	1	2			11		10	2
$\bar{r}(x)$			3	5		11		

12.

x	0	1	2	3	4	5	6	7
$s(x)$	1	5		1				
$\bar{s}(x)$			5			5	2	3	2

In Exercises 13–24, calculate the 5-unit moving average of the given function. Plot the function and its moving average on the same graph, as in Example 4. (You may use graphing technology for these plots, but you should compute the moving averages analytically.) [**HINT**: See Quick Example 3 and Example 4.]

13. $f(x) = x^3$ **14.** $f(x) = x^3 - x$

15. $f(x) = x^{2/3}$ **16.** $f(x) = x^{2/3} + x$

17. $f(x) = e^{0.5x}$ **18.** $f(x) = e^{-0.02x}$

19. $f(x) = \sqrt{x}$ **20.** $f(x) = x^{1/3}$

21. $f(x) = 1 - \dfrac{|2x - 1|}{2x - 1}$ **22.** $f(x) = 2 + \dfrac{|3x + 1|}{3x + 1}$

23. ▼ $f(x) = 2 - |x + 1| + |x|$ [Do not simplify the answer.]

24. ▼ $f(x) = |2x + 1| - |2x| - 2$ [Do not simplify the answer.]

🔲 In Exercises 25–34, use graphing technology to plot the given function together with its 3-unit moving averages. [HINT: See the technology note for Example 4.]

25. $f(x) = \dfrac{10x}{1 + 5|x|}$ 　　　26. $f(x) = \dfrac{1}{1 + e^x}$

27. $f(x) = \ln(1 + x^2)$ 　　　28. $f(x) = e^{1-x^2}$

29. $f(x) = |x| - |x - 1| + |x - 2| - |x - 3| + |x - 4|$

30. $f(x) = |x| - 2|x - 1| + 2|x - 2| - 2|x - 3| + |x - 4|$

31. $f(x) = \dfrac{|x|}{x} - \dfrac{|x - 1|}{x - 1} + \dfrac{|x - 2|}{x - 2} - \dfrac{|x - 3|}{x - 3}$

32. $f(x) = \dfrac{|x|}{x} - 2\dfrac{|x - 1|}{x - 1} + 2\dfrac{|x - 2|}{x - 2} - \dfrac{|x - 3|}{x - 3}$

33. $f(x) = \dfrac{|x|}{x} + \dfrac{|x - 1|}{x - 1} + \dfrac{|x - 2|}{x - 2} + \dfrac{|x - 3|}{x - 3}$

34. $f(x) = 4 - \dfrac{|x|}{x} - \dfrac{|x - 1|}{x - 1} - \dfrac{|x - 2|}{x - 2} - \dfrac{|x - 3|}{x - 3}$

Applications

35. **Television Advertising** The cost, in millions of dollars, of a 30-second television ad during the Super Bowl in the years 2000–2010 can be approximated by

    $C(t) = 0.14t + 1.1$ million dollars $(0 \le t \le 10)$.

    ($t = 0$ represents 2000.)[20] What was the average cost of a Super Bowl ad during the given period? [HINT: See Example 1.]

36. **Television Advertising** The cost, in millions of dollars, of a 30-second television ad during the Super Bowl in the years 1980–2000 can be approximated by

    $C(t) = 0.044t + 0.222$ million dollars $(0 \le t \le 20)$.

    ($t = 0$ represents 1980.)[21] What was the average cost of a Super Bowl ad during the given period? [HINT: See Example 1.]

37. **Membership: Facebook** The number of new members joining Facebook each year in the period from 2005 to the middle of 2008 can be modeled by

    $m(t) = 12t^2 - 20t + 10$ million members per year
    $(0 \le t \le 3.5)$,

    where t is time in years since the start of 2005.[22] What was the average number of new members joining Facebook each year from the start of 2005 to the start of 2008?

38. **Membership: MySpace** The number of new members joining MySpace each year in the period from 2004 to the middle of 2007 can be modeled by

    $m(t) = 10.5t^2 + 14t - 6$ million members per year
    $(0 \le t \le 3.5)$,

    where t is time in years since the start of 2004.[23] What was the average number of new members joining MySpace each year from the start of 2004 to the start of 2007?

39. **Freon Production** Annual production of ozone-layer-damaging Freon 22 (chlorodifluoromethane) in developing countries from 2000 to 2010 can be modeled by

    $F(t) = 97.2(1.20)^t$ million tons $(0 \le t \le 10)$.

    (t is the number of years since 2000.)[24] What was the average annual production over the period shown? (Round your answer to the nearest million tons.) [HINT: See Example 2.]

40. **Health Expenditures** Annual expenditures on health in the United States from 1980 to 2010 could be modeled by

    $F(t) = 296(1.08)^t$ billion dollars $(0 \le t \le 30)$.

    ($t = 0$ represents 1980.)[25] What was the average annual expenditure over the period shown? (Round your answer to the nearest billion dollars.) [HINT: See Example 2.]

41. **Investments** If you invest $10,000 at 8% interest compounded continuously, what is the average amount in your account over 1 year?

42. **Investments** If you invest $10,000 at 12% interest compounded continuously, what is the average amount in your account over 1 year?

43. ▼ **Average Balance** Suppose you have an account (paying no interest) into which you deposit $3,000 at the beginning of each month. You withdraw money continuously so that the amount in the account decreases linearly to 0 by the end of the month. Find the average amount in the account over a period of several months. (Assume that the account starts at $0 at $t = 0$ months.)

44. ▼ **Average Balance** Suppose you have an account (paying no interest) into which you deposit $4,000 at the beginning of each month. You withdraw $3,000 during the course of each month in such a way that the amount decreases linearly. Find the average amount in the account in the first 2 months. (Assume that the account starts at $0 at $t = 0$ months.)

---

[20] Source for data: en.wikipedia.org/wiki/Super_Bowl_advertising.

[21] Ibid.

[22] Sources for data: www.facebook.com, insidehighered.com. (Some data are interpolated.)

[23] Source for data: www.swivel.com/data_sets.

[24] Figures are approximate. Source: Lampert Kuijpers (Panel of the Montreal Protocol), National Bureau of Statistics in China, via CEIC Data/*New York Times*, February 23, 2007, p. C1.

[25] Source for data: U.S. Department of Health & Human Services/ Centers for Medicare & Medicaid Services, National Health Expenditure Data, downloaded April 2011 from www.cms.gov.

45. ▧ *Online Payments* The value of payments made through PayPal from the first quarter of 2013 through the fourth quarter of 2014 can be approximated by

$$p(t) = -0.1t^3 + 1.18t^2 - 0.89t + 41$$
$$\text{billion dollars per quarter} \quad (1 \le t \le 8),$$

where t is time in quarters. ($t = 1$ represents the first quarter of 2013.)[26] Use technology to estimate the average value of payments made each quarter through PayPal during the given period. (Round your answer to the nearest billion dollars.)

46. ▧ *Online Auctions* The net number of new active eBay users each quarter from the first quarter of 2008 through the last quarter of 2010 could be approximated by

$$n(t) = -0.002x^4 + 0.06x^3 - 0.55x^2 + 1.9x - 1$$
$$\text{million users per quarter} \quad (1 \le t \le 13)$$

where t is time in quarters. ($t = 1$ represents the first quarter of 2008.)[27] Use technology to estimate the average number of new active eBay users each quarter during the given period. (Round your answer to the nearest hundred thousand users.)

47. *Stock Prices: Exxon Mobil* The following table shows the approximate price of Exxon Mobil stock in December of each year from 2005 through 2014, as well as the 4-year moving averages for 2005 through 2007.[28] Complete the table by computing the remaining 4-year moving averages. Round each average to the nearest dollar.

Year t	2005	2006	2007	2008	2009	2010	2011	2012	2013	2014
Stock Price	56	77	94	80	68	73	85	87	101	92
Moving Average (rounded)	46	56	70							

The stock price spiked in 2007, dropped steeply to 2009, then recovered. What happened to the corresponding moving average? [HINT: See Example 3.]

48. *Stock Prices: Nokia* The following table shows the approximate price of Nokia stock in December of each year from 2005 through 2014, as well as the 4-year moving averages for 2005 through 2007.[29] Complete the table by computing the remaining 4-year moving averages. (Note the peak in 2007 and the drop in subsequent years.) Round each average to the nearest dollar.

Year t	2005	2006	2007	2008	2009	2010	2011	2012	2013	2014
Stock Price	18	20	38	16	13	10	5	4	8	8
Moving Average (rounded)	17	18	23							

How does the average size of the year-by-year change in the moving average compare with the average year-by-year change in the stock price? [HINT: See Example 3.]

49. ▽ *Cancun* The *Playa Loca Hotel* in Cancun has an advertising brochure with the following chart, showing the year-round temperature:[30]

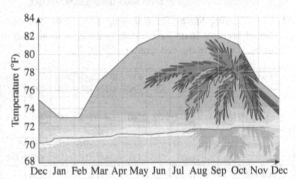

a. Estimate and plot the year-round 6-month moving average. (Use graphing technology, if available, to check your graph.)

b. What can you say about the 12-month moving average?

50. ▽ *Reykjavik* Repeat Exercise 49, using the following data from the brochure of the *Tough Traveler Lodge* in Reykjavik:[31]

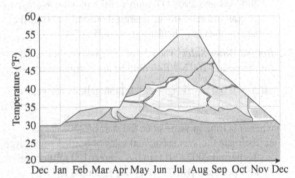

51. ▧ ▽ *Sales: Apple* The following table shows approximate quarterly sales of Apple iPods in millions of units, starting in the first quarter of 2006:[32]

Quarter	2006 Q1	2006 Q2	2006 Q3	2006 Q4	2007 Q1	2007 Q2	2007 Q3	2007 Q4	2008 Q1	2008 Q2
Sales (millions)	8.5	8.1	8.7	21.1	10.5	9.8	10.2	22.1	10.6	11.0

Quarter	2008 Q3	2008 Q4	2009 Q1	2009 Q2	2009 Q3	2009 Q4	2010 Q1	2010 Q2	2010 Q3	2010 Q4
Sales (millions)	11.1	22.7	11.0	10.2	10.2	21.0	10.9	9.4	9.1	19.5

---

[26] Source for data: Statista, www.statista.com.

[27] Source for data: eBay company reports http://investor.ebay.com.

[28] Source: finance.yahoo.com.

[29] *Ibid.*

[30] Source: www.holiday-weather.com. (Temperatures are rounded.)

[31] *Ibid.*

[32] Source: Apple quarterly press releases, www.apple.com/investor.

a. Use technology to compute and plot the four-quarter moving average of these data.

b. The graph of the moving average for the last eight quarters will appear almost linear during 2009 and 2010. Use the 2009 Q1 and 2010 Q4 figures of the moving average to give an estimate (to the nearest 0.1 million units) of the rate of change of iPod sales during 2009–2010.

52. ▼ *Housing Starts* The following table shows the number of housing starts for one-family units, in thousands of units, starting in the first quarter of 2006:[33]

Quarter	2006 Q1	2006 Q2	2006 Q3	2006 Q4	2007 Q1	2007 Q2	2007 Q3	2007 Q4	2008 Q1	2008 Q2
Housing Starts (thousands)	382	433	372	278	260	333	265	188	162	194

Quarter	2008 Q3	2008 Q4	2009 Q1	2009 Q2	2009 Q3	2009 Q4	2010 Q1	2010 Q2	2010 Q3	2010 Q4
Housing Starts (thousands)	163	103	78	124	138	105	114	142	119	96

a. Use technology to compute and plot the four-quarter moving average of these data.

b. The graph of the moving average for the eight quarters in 2007 and 2008 will appear almost linear. Use the 2007 Q1 and 2008 Q4 figures of the moving average to give an estimate (to the nearest thousand units) of the rate of change of housing starts during 2007–2008.

53. *Bottled Water Sales* The rate of U.S. sales of bottled water for the period 2007–2014 could be approximated by

$$s(t) = 0.08t^2 - 0.26t + 8.8 \text{ billion gallons per year}$$
$$(0 \le t \le 7),$$

where t is time in years since the start of 2007.[34]

a. Estimate the average annual sales of bottled water over the period 2007–2014, to the nearest 100 million gallons per year. [HINT: See Quick Example 2.]

b. Compute the 2-year moving average of s. (You need not simplify the answer.) [HINT: See Quick Example 3.]

c. Without simplifying the answer in part (b), say what kind of function the moving average is.

54. *Bottled Water Sales* The rate of U.S. per capita sales of bottled water for the period 2007–2014 coud be approximated by

$$s(t) = 0.25t^2 - t + 29 \text{ billion gallons per year}$$
$$(0 \le t \le 7),$$

where t is the time in years since the start of 2007.[35] Repeat Exercise 53 as applied to per capita sales. (Give your answer to part (a) to the nearest gallon per year.)

55. *Medicare Spending* Annual spending on Medicare was projected to increase from $526 billion in 2010 to around $977 billion in 2021.[36]

a. Use this information to express s, the annual spending on Medicare (in billions of dollars) as a linear function of t, the number of years since 2010.

b. Find the 4-year moving average of your model.

c. What can you say about the slope of the moving average?

56. *Pasta Imports in the 1990s* In 1990 the United States imported 290 million pounds of pasta. From 1990 to 2000, imports increased by an average of 40 million pounds per year.[37]

a. Use these data to express q, the annual U.S. imports of pasta (in millions of pounds) as a linear function of t, the number of years since 1990.

b. Find the 4-year moving average of your model.

c. What can you say about the slope of the moving average?

57. ▼ *Moving Average of a Linear Function* Find a formula for the a-unit moving average of a general linear function $f(x) = mx + b$.

58. ▼ *Moving Average of an Exponential Function* Find a formula for the a-unit moving average of a general exponential function $f(x) = Ae^{kx}$.

Communication and Reasoning Exercises

59. Explain why it is sometimes more useful to consider the moving average of a stock price rather than the stock price itself.

60. Sales this month were sharply lower than they were last month, but the 12-unit moving average this month was higher than it was last month. How can that be?

61. Your company's 6-month moving average of sales is constant. What does that say about the sales figures?

62. Your monthly salary has been increasing steadily for the past year, and your average monthly salary over the past year was x dollars. Would you have earned more money if you had been paid x dollars per month? Explain your answer.

63. ▼ What property does the graph of a (nonconstant) function have if its average value over an interval is zero? Give an example of such a function.

64. ▼ Can the average value of a function f on an interval be greater than its value at every point in that interval? Explain.

65. ▼ Criticize the following claim: The average value of a function on an interval is midway between its highest and lowest value.

---

[33] Source: U.S. Census Bureau, www.census.gov/const/www/newresconstindex.html.

[34] Source for data: Beverage Marketing Corporation (www.bottledwater.org).

[35] *Ibid.*

[36] Source: Congressional Budget Office, *March 2011 Medicare Baseline* (www.cbo.gov).

[37] Data are rounded. Sources: Department of Commerce/*New York Times*, September 5, 1995, p. D4; International Trade Administration (www.ita.doc.gov), March 31, 2002.

66. ▼ Your manager tells you that 12-month moving averages give at least as much information as shorter-term moving averages and very often more. How would you argue that he is wrong?

67. ▼ Which of the following most closely approximates the original function: (A) its 10-unit moving average, (B) its 1-unit moving average, or (C) its 0.8-unit moving average? Explain your answer.

68. ▼ Is an increasing function larger or smaller than its 1-unit moving average? Explain.

14.4   Applications to Business and Economics: Consumers' and Producers' Surplus and Continuous Income Streams

Consumers' Surplus

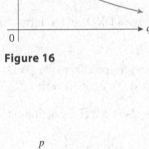

Figure 16

Consider a general demand curve presented, as is traditional in economics, as $p = D(q)$, where p is unit price and q is demand measured, say, in annual sales (Figure 16). Thus, $D(q)$ is the price at which the demand will be q units per year. The price p_0 shown on the graph is the highest price that customers are willing to pay.

Suppose, for example, that the graph in Figure 16 is the demand curve for a particular new model of computer. When the computer first comes out and supplies are low (q is small), "early adopters" will be willing to pay a high price. This is the part of the graph on the left, near the p-axis. As supplies increase and the price drops, more consumers will be willing to pay and more computers will be sold. Pick any particular number of units, $\bar{q}$. We can ask the following question: How much are consumers willing to spend for the first $\bar{q}$ units?

Consumers' Willingness to Spend

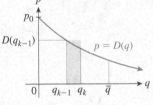

Figure 17

We can approximate consumers' willingness to spend on the first $\bar{q}$ units as follows. We partition the interval $[0, \bar{q}]$ into n subintervals of equal length, as we did when discussing Riemann sums. Figure 17 shows a typical subinterval, $[q_{k-1}, q_k]$.

The price consumers are willing to pay for each of units q_{k-1} through q_k is approximately $D(q_{k-1})$, so the total that consumers are willing to spend for these units is approximately $D(q_{k-1})(q_k - q_{k-1}) = D(q_{k-1}) \Delta q$, the area of the shaded region in Figure 17. Thus, the total amount that consumers are willing to spend for items 0 through $\bar{q}$ is

$$W \approx D(q_0) \Delta q + D(q_1) \Delta q + \cdots + D(q_{n-1}) \Delta q = \sum_{k=0}^{n-1} D(q_k) \Delta q,$$

which is a Riemann sum. The approximation becomes better the larger n becomes, and in the limit, the Riemann sums converge to the integral

$$W = \int_0^{\bar{q}} D(q) \, dq.$$

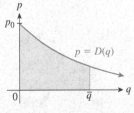

Figure 18

This quantity, the area shaded in Figure 18, is the total consumers' willingness to spend to buy the first $\bar{q}$ units.

Consumers' Expenditure

Now suppose that the manufacturer simply sets the price at some value $\bar{p}$, with a corresponding demand of $\bar{q}$, so $D(\bar{q}) = \bar{p}$. Then the amount that consumers will actually spend to buy these $\bar{q}$ units is $\bar{p} \, \bar{q}$, the product of the unit price and the quantity sold.

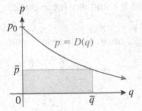

Figure 19

* Multiletter variables such as *CS* used here may be unusual in a math textbook but are traditional in the math of finance. In particular, the notations *PV* and *FV* used later in this section are almost universally used in finance textbooks, calculators (such as the TI-83/84 Plus), and such places as study guides for the finance portion of the Society of Actuaries exams.

This is the area of the rectangle shown in Figure 19. Notice that we can write $\bar{p}\bar{q} = \int_0^{\bar{q}} \bar{p}\, dq$, as suggested by the figure.

The difference between what consumers are willing to pay and what they actually pay is money in their pockets and is called the **consumers' surplus**.

Consumers' Surplus

If demand for an item is given by $p = D(q)$, the selling price is $\bar{p}$, and $\bar{q}$ is the corresponding demand [so that $D(\bar{q}) = \bar{p}$], then the **consumers' surplus** is the difference between willingness to spend and actual expenditure:*

$$CS = \int_0^{\bar{q}} D(q)\, dq - \bar{p}\bar{q} = \int_0^{\bar{q}} (D(q) - \bar{p})\, dq.$$

Graphically, it is the area between the graphs of $p = D(q)$ and $p = \bar{p}$, as shown in the figure.

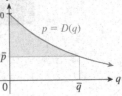

EXAMPLE 1 Consumers' Surplus

Your video store has an exponential demand equation for used DVDs of the form

$$p = 15e^{-0.01q},$$

where q represents daily sales of used DVDs and p is the price you charge per DVD. Calculate the daily consumers' surplus if you sell your used DVDs at $5 each.

Solution We are given $D(q) = 15e^{-0.01q}$ and $\bar{p} = 5$. We also need $\bar{q}$. By definition,

$$D(\bar{q}) = \bar{p}$$

or $15e^{-0.01\bar{q}} = 5$,

which we must solve for $\bar{q}$:

$$e^{-0.01\bar{q}} = \frac{1}{3}$$

$$-0.01\bar{q} = \ln\left(\frac{1}{3}\right) = -\ln 3$$

$$\bar{q} = \frac{\ln 3}{0.01} \approx 109.8612.$$

We now have

$$CS = \int_0^{\bar{q}} (D(q) - \bar{p})\, dq$$

$$= \int_0^{109.8612} (15e^{-0.01q} - 5)\, dq$$

$$= \left[\frac{15}{-0.01} e^{-0.01q} - 5q\right]_0^{109.8612}$$

$$\approx (-500 - 549.31) - (-1{,}500 - 0)$$

$$= \$450.69 \text{ per day.}$$

Producers' Surplus

We can also calculate extra income earned by producers. Consider a supply equation of the form $p = S(q)$, where $S(q)$ is the price at which a supplier is willing to supply q items (per time period). Because a producer is generally willing to supply more units at a higher price per unit, a supply curve usually has a positive slope, as shown in Figure 20. The price p_0 is the lowest price that a producer is willing to charge.

Arguing as before, we see that the minimum amount of money producers are willing to receive in exchange for $\bar{q}$ items is $\int_0^{\bar{q}} S(q)\, dq$. On the other hand, if the producers charge $\bar{p}$ per item for $\bar{q}$ items, their actual revenue is $\bar{p}\,\bar{q} = \int_0^{\bar{q}} \bar{p}\, dq$.

The difference between the producers' actual revenue and the minimum they would have been willing to receive is the **producers' surplus**.

Figure 20

Producers' Surplus

The **producers' surplus** is the extra amount earned by producers who were willing to charge less than the selling price of $\bar{p}$ per unit and is given by

$$PS = \int_0^{\bar{q}} (\bar{p} - S(q))\, dq,$$

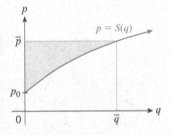

where $S(\bar{q}) = \bar{p}$. Graphically, it is the area of the region between the graphs of $p = \bar{p}$ and $p = S(q)$ for $0 \le q \le \bar{q}$, as in the figure.

EXAMPLE 2   **Producers' Surplus**

My tie-dyed T-shirt enterprise has grown to the extent that I am now able to produce T-shirts in bulk, and several campus groups have begun placing orders. I have informed one group that I am prepared to supply $20\sqrt{p-4}$ T-shirts at a price of p dollars per shirt. What is my total surplus if I sell T-shirts to the group at $8 each?

Solution We need to calculate the producers' surplus when $\bar{p} = 8$. The supply equation is

$$q = 20\sqrt{p-4},$$

but to use the formula for producers' surplus, we need to express p as a function of q. First, we square both sides to remove the radical sign:

$$q^2 = 400(p-4),$$

so

$$p - 4 = \frac{q^2}{400},$$

giving

$$p = S(q) = \frac{q^2}{400} + 4.$$

We now need the value of $\bar{q}$ corresponding to $\bar{p} = 8$. Substituting $p = 8$ in the original equation gives

$$\bar{q} = 20\sqrt{8-4} = 20\sqrt{4} = 40.$$

Thus,

$$PS = \int_0^{\bar{q}} (\bar{p} - S(q))\, dq$$

$$= \int_0^{40} \left[8 - \left(\frac{q^2}{400} + 4 \right) \right] dq$$

$$= \int_0^{40} \left(4 - \frac{q^2}{400} \right) dq$$

$$= \left[4q - \frac{q^3}{1{,}200} \right]_0^{40} \approx \$106.67.$$

Thus, I earn a surplus of $106.67 if I sell T-shirts to the group at $8 each.

EXAMPLE 3   **Equilibrium**

To continue the preceding example: A representative informs me that the campus group is prepared to order only $\sqrt{200(16 - p)}$ T-shirts at p dollars each. I would like to produce as many T-shirts for them as possible but avoid being left with unsold T-shirts. Given the supply curve from the preceding example, what price should I charge per T-shirt, and what are the consumers' and producers' surpluses at that price?

Solution The price that guarantees neither a shortage nor a surplus of T-shirts is the **equilibrium price**, the price where supply equals demand. We have

Supply: $q = 20\sqrt{p - 4}.$

Demand: $q = \sqrt{200(16 - p)}.$

Equating these gives

$$20\sqrt{p - 4} = \sqrt{200(16 - p)}$$
$$400(p - 4) = 200(16 - p)$$
$$400p - 1{,}600 = 3{,}200 - 200p$$
$$600p = 4{,}800$$
$$p = \$8 \text{ per T-shirt.}$$

We therefore take $\bar{p} = 8$ (which happens to be the price we used in Example 2). We get the corresponding value for q by substituting $p = 8$ into either the demand or supply equation:

$$\bar{q} = 20\sqrt{8 - 4} = 40.$$

Thus, $\bar{p} = 8$ and $\bar{q} = 40$.

We must now calculate the consumers' surplus and the producers' surplus. We calculated the producers' surplus for $\bar{p} = 8$ in the preceding example:

$$PS = \$106.67.$$

For the consumers' surplus we must first express p as a function of q for the demand equation. Thus, we solve the demand equation for p as we did for the supply equation, and we obtain

Demand: $D(q) = 16 - \dfrac{q^2}{200}.$

Therefore,

$$CS = \int_0^{\bar{q}} (D(q) - \bar{p})\, dq$$

$$= \int_0^{40} \left[\left(16 - \frac{q^2}{200} \right) - 8 \right] dq$$

$$= \int_0^{40} \left(8 - \frac{q^2}{200} \right) dq$$

$$= \left[8q - \frac{q^3}{600} \right]_0^{40} \approx \$213.33.$$

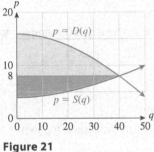

Figure 21

➡ **Before we go on . . .** Figure 21 shows both the consumers' surplus (top portion) and the producers' surplus (bottom portion) from Example 3. Because extra money in people's pockets is a good thing, the total of the consumers' and the producers' surpluses is called the **total social gain**. In this case it is

Social gain = $CS + PS = 213.33 + 106.67 = \$320.00.$

As you can see from the figure, the total social gain is also the area between two curves and equals

$$\int_0^{40} (D(q) - S(q))\, dq. \quad \blacksquare$$

Continuous Income Streams

For purposes of calculation it is often convenient to assume that a company with a high sales volume receives money continuously. In such a case we have a function $R(t)$ that represents the rate at which money is being received by the company at time t.

EXAMPLE 4   Continuous Income

An ice cream store's business peaks in late summer. The store's summer revenue is approximated by

$$R(t) = 300 + 4.5t - 0.05t^2 \text{ dollars per day} \qquad (0 \le t \le 92),$$

where t is measured in days after June 1. What is its total revenue for the months of June, July, and August?

Solution Let's approximate the total revenue by breaking up the interval $[0, 92]$ representing the 3 months into n subintervals $[t_{k-1}, t_k]$, each with length Δt. In the interval $[t_{k-1}, t_k]$ the store receives money at a rate of approximately $R(t_{k-1})$ dollars per day for Δt days, so it will receive a total of $R(t_{k-1})\, \Delta t$ dollars. Over the whole summer, then, the store will receive approximately

$$R(t_0)\, \Delta t + R(t_1)\, \Delta t + \cdots + R(t_{n-1})\, \Delta t \text{ dollars.}$$

As we let n become large to better approximate the total revenue, this Riemann sum approaches the integral

$$\text{Total revenue} = \int_0^{92} R(t)\, dt.$$

Substituting the function we were given, we get

$$\text{Total revenue} = \int_0^{92} (300 + 4.5t - 0.05t^2) \, dt$$

$$= \left[300t + 2.25t^2 - \frac{0.05}{3}t^3 \right]_0^{92}$$

$$\approx \$33,666.$$

➡ **Before we go on ...** We could approach the calculation in Example 4 another way: $R(t) = S'(t)$, where $S(t)$ is the total revenue earned up to day t. By the Fundamental Theorem of Calculus,

$$\text{Total revenue} = S(92) - S(0) = \int_0^{92} R(t) \, dt.$$

We did the calculation using Riemann sums mainly as practice for the next example. ∎

Generalizing Example 4, we can say the following.

Total Value of a Continuous Income Stream

If the rate of receipt of income is $R(t)$ dollars per unit of time, then the total income received from time $t = a$ to $t = b$ is

$$\text{Total value} = TV = \int_a^b R(t) \, dt.$$

EXAMPLE 5 **Future Value**

Suppose the ice cream store in Example 4 deposits its receipts in an account paying 5% interest per year compounded continuously. How much money will it have in its account at the end of August?

Solution Now we have to take into account not only the revenue but also the interest it earns in the account. Again, we break the interval $[0, 92]$ into n subintervals. During the interval $[t_{k-1}, t_k]$, approximately $R(t_{k-1}) \, \Delta t$ dollars are deposited in the account. That money will earn interest until the end of August, a period of $92 - t_{k-1}$ days, or $(92 - t_{k-1})/365$ years. The formula for continuous compounding tells us that by the end of August, those $R(t_{k-1}) \, \Delta t$ dollars will have turned into

$$R(t_{k-1}) \, \Delta t e^{0.05(92-t_{k-1})/365} = R(t_{k-1}) e^{0.05(92-t_{k-1})/365} \, \Delta t \text{ dollars.}$$

(Recall that 5% is the *annual* interest rate.) Adding up the contributions from each subinterval, we see that the total in the account at the end of August will be approximately

$$R(t_0) e^{0.05(92-t_0)/365} \, \Delta t + R(t_1) e^{0.05(92-t_1)/365} \, \Delta t + \cdots + R(t_{n-1}) e^{0.05(92-t_{n-1})/365} \, \Delta t.$$

This is a Riemann sum; as n gets large, the sum approaches the integral

$$\text{Future value} = FV = \int_0^{92} R(t) e^{0.05(92-t)/365} \, dt.$$

Substituting $R(t) = 300 + 4.5t - 0.05t^2$, we obtain

$$FV = \int_0^{92} (300 + 4.5t - 0.05t^2)e^{0.05(92-t)/365} \, dt$$

$$\approx \$33{,}880. \qquad \qquad \text{Using technology or integration by parts}$$

➡ **Before we go on ...** The interest earned in the account in Example 5 was fairly small. (Compare this answer to that in Example 4.) Not only was the money in the account for only 3 months, but much of it was put in the account toward the end of that period, so it had very little time to earn interest. ∎

Generalizing again, we have the following.

Future Value of a Continuous Income Stream

If the rate of receipt of income from time $t = a$ to $t = b$ is $R(t)$ dollars per unit of time and the income is deposited as it is received in an account paying interest at rate r per unit of time, compounded continuously, then the amount of money in the account at time $t = b$ is

$$\text{Future value} = FV = \int_a^b R(t)e^{r(b-t)} \, dt.$$

EXAMPLE 5 **Present Value**

You are thinking of buying the ice cream store discussed in Examples 4 and 5. What is its income stream worth to you on June 1? Assume that you have access to the same account paying 5% per year compounded continuously.

Solution The value of the income stream on June 1 is the amount of money that, if deposited June 1, would give you the same future value as the income stream will. If we let PV denote this "present value," its value after 92 days will be

$$PVe^{0.05 \times 92/365}.$$

We equate this with the future value of the income stream to get

$$PVe^{0.05 \times 92/365} = \int_0^{92} R(t)e^{0.05(92-t)/365} \, dt,$$

so

$$PV = \int_0^{92} R(t)e^{-0.05t/365} \, dt.$$

Substituting the formula for $R(t)$ and integrating using technology or integration by parts, we get

$$PV \approx \$33{,}455.$$

The general formula is the following.

Present Value of a Continuous Income Stream

If the rate of receipt of income from time $t = a$ to $t = b$ is $R(t)$ dollars per unit of time and the income is deposited as it is received in an account paying interest at rate r per unit of time, compounded continuously, then the value of the income stream at time $t = a$ is

$$\text{Present value} = PV = \int_a^b R(t)e^{r(a-t)}\, dt.$$

We can derive this formula from the relation

$$FV = PVe^{r(b-a)}$$

because the present value is the amount that would have to be deposited at time $t = a$ to give a future value of FV at time $t = b$.

Note These formulas are more general than we've said. They still work when $R(t) < 0$ if we interpret negative values as money flowing *out* rather than in. That is, we can use these formulas for income we receive, for payments that we make, or for situations in which we sometimes receive money and sometimes pay it out. These formulas can also be used for flows of quantities other than money. For example, if we use an exponential model for population growth and we let $R(t)$ represent the rate of immigration $[R(t) > 0]$ or emigration $[R(t) < 0]$, then the future value formula gives the future population. ■

14.4 EXERCISES

▼ more advanced   ◆ challenging
⊤ indicates exercises that should be solved using technology

In Exercises 1–12, calculate the consumers' surplus at the indicated unit price $\bar{p}$ for the given demand equations.
[HINT: See Example 1.]

1. $p = 10 - 2q; \bar{p} = 5$

2. $p = 100 - q; \bar{p} = 20$

3. $p = 100 - 3\sqrt{q}; \bar{p} = 76$

4. $p = 10 - 2q^{1/3}; \bar{p} = 6$

5. $p = 500e^{-2q}; \bar{p} = 100$

6. $p = 100 - e^{0.1q}; \bar{p} = 50$

7. $q = 100 - 2p; \bar{p} = 20$

8. $q = 50 - 3p; \bar{p} = 10$

9. $q = 100 - 0.25p^2; \bar{p} = 10$

10. $q = 20 - 0.05p^2; \bar{p} = 5$

11. $q = 500e^{-0.5p} - 50; \bar{p} = 1$

12. $q = 100 - e^{0.1p}; \bar{p} = 20$

In Exercises 13–24, calculate the producers' surplus for the given supply equations at the indicated unit price $\bar{p}$.
[HINT: See Example 2.]

13. $p = 10 + 2q; \bar{p} = 20$

14. $p = 100 + q; \bar{p} = 200$

15. $p = 10 + 2q^{1/3}; \bar{p} = 12$

16. $p = 100 + 3\sqrt{q}; \bar{p} = 124$

17. $p = 500e^{0.5q}; \bar{p} = 1{,}000$

18. $p = 100 + e^{0.01q}; \bar{p} = 120$

19. $q = 2p - 50; \bar{p} = 40$

20. $q = 4p - 1{,}000; \bar{p} = 1{,}000$

21. $q = 0.25p^2 - 10; \bar{p} = 10$

22. $q = 0.05p^2 - 20; \bar{p} = 50$

23. $q = 500e^{0.05p} - 50; \bar{p} = 10$

24. $q = 10(e^{0.1p} - 1); \bar{p} = 5$

In Exercises 25–30, find the total value of the given income stream and also find its future value (at the end of the given interval) using the given interest rate. [**HINT**: See Examples 4 and 5.]

25. $R(t) = 30,000, 0 \le t \le 10$, at 7%

26. $R(t) = 40,000, 0 \le t \le 5$, at 10%

27. $R(t) = 30,000 + 1,000t, 0 \le t \le 10$, at 7%

28. $R(t) = 40,000 + 2,000t, 0 \le t \le 5$, at 10%

29. $R(t) = 30,000e^{0.05t}, 0 \le t \le 10$, at 7%

30. $R(t) = 40,000e^{0.04t}, 0 \le t \le 5$, at 10%

In Exercises 31–36, find the total value of the given income stream and also find its present value (at the beginning of the given interval) using the given interest rate. [**HINT**: See Examples 4 and 6.]

31. $R(t) = 20,000, 0 \le t \le 5$, at 8%

32. $R(t) = 50,000, 0 \le t \le 10$, at 5%

33. $R(t) = 20,000 + 1,000t, 0 \le t \le 5$, at 8%

34. $R(t) = 50,000 + 2,000t, 0 \le t \le 10$, at 5%

35. $R(t) = 20,000e^{0.03t}, 0 \le t \le 5$, at 8%

36. $R(t) = 50,000e^{0.06t}, 0 \le t \le 10$, at 5%

Applications

37. *College Tuition* A study of U.S. colleges and universities resulted in the demand equation $q = 20,000 - 2p$, where q is the enrollment at a public college or university and p is the average annual tuition (plus fees) it charges.[38] Officials at *Enormous State University* have developed a policy whereby the number of students it will accept per year at a tuition level of p dollars is given by $q = 7,500 + 0.5p$. Find the equilibrium tuition price $\bar{p}$ and the consumers' and producers' surpluses at this tuition level. What is the total social gain at the equilibrium price? [**HINT**: See Example 3.]

38. *Fast Food* A fast-food outlet finds that the demand equation for its new side dish, "Sweetdough Tidbit," is given by

$$p = \frac{128}{(q + 1)^2},$$

where p is the price (in cents) per serving and q is the number of servings that can be sold per hour at this price. At the same time, the franchise is prepared to sell $q = 0.5p - 1$ servings per hour at a price of p cents. Find the equilibrium price $\bar{p}$ and the consumers' and producers' surpluses at this price level. What is the total social gain at the equilibrium price? [**HINT**: See Example 3.]

39. *Revenue: Nokia* The annual net sales (revenue) earned by Nokia in the years January 2004 to January 2010 can be approximated by

$$R(t) = -1.75t^2 + 12.5t + 30 \text{ billion euros per year}$$
$$(0 \le t \le 6),$$

where t is time in years. ($t = 0$ represents January 2004.)[39] Estimate, to the nearest €10 billion, Nokia's total revenue from January 2006 to January 2010. [**HINT**: See Example 4.]

40. *Revenue: Nintendo* The annual net sales (revenue) earned by Nintendo in the fiscal years 2000–2014, can be approximated by

$$R(t) = -3.75t^3 + 65.8t^2 - 206t + 578 \text{ billion yen per year}$$
$$(0 \le t \le 14),$$

where t is time in years. ($t = 0$ represents the start of fiscal year 2000.)[40] Estimate, to the nearest ¥100 billion, Nintendo's total revenue from the start of fiscal year 2006 to the start of fiscal year 2014. [**HINT**: See Example 4.]

41. *Revenue: Walmart* The annual revenue earned by Walmart in the years from January 2000 to January 2014 can be approximated by

$$R(t) = 176e^{0.079t} \text{ billion dollars per year} \quad (0 \le t \le 14),$$

where t is time in years. ($t = 0$ represents January 2000.)[41] Estimate, to the nearest $10 billion, Walmart's total revenue from January 2004 to January 2014.

42. *Revenue: Target* The annual revenue earned by Target for fiscal years 2004 through 2010 can be approximated by

$$R(t) = 41e^{0.094t} \text{ billion dollars per year} \quad (0 \le t \le 7),$$

where t is time in years. ($t = 0$ represents the beginning of fiscal year 2004.)[42] Estimate, to the nearest $10 billion, Target's total revenue from the beginning of fiscal year 2006 to the beginning of fiscal year 2010.

43. ▼ *Revenue* Refer back to Exercise 39. Suppose that, from January 2004 on, Nokia invested its revenue in an investment yielding 4% compounded continuously. What, to the nearest €10 billion, would the total value of Nokia's revenue from January 2006 to January 2010 have been in January 2010? [**HINT**: See Example 5.]

44. ▼ *Revenue* Refer back to Exercise 40. Suppose that, from the beginning of fiscal year 2006 on, Nintendo invested its revenue in an investment yielding 5% compounded continuously. What, to the nearest ¥100 billion, would the total value of Nintendo's revenue from the start of fiscal year

---

[38] Idea based on a study by A. L. Ostrosky, Jr. and J. V. Koch, as cited in their book *Introduction to Mathematical Economics* (Waveland Press, Illinois, 1979, p. 133). The data used here are fictitious, however.

[39] Source for data: Nokia financial statements (www.investors.nokia.com).

[40] Source for data: Nintendo annual reports (www.nintendo.com/corp).

[41] Source for data: Walmart annual reports (www.Walmartstores.com/Investors).

[42] Source for data: Target annual reports (investors.target.com).

2006 to the start of fiscal year 2014 have been at the start of fiscal year 2014? [HINT: See Example 5.]

45. ▼ *Revenue* Refer back to Exercise 41. Suppose that, from January 2004 on, Walmart invested its revenue in an investment that depreciated continuously at a rate of 5% per year. What, to the nearest $10 billion, would the total value of Walmart's revenues from January 2004 to January 2014 have been in January 2014?

46. ▼ *Revenue* Refer back to Exercise 42. Suppose that, from the start of fiscal year 2004 on, Target invested its revenue in an investment that depreciated continuously at a rate of 3% per year. What, to the nearest $10 billion, would the total value of Target's revenue from the beginning of fiscal year 2006 to the beginning of fiscal year 2010 have been at the beginning of fiscal year 2010?

47. ▼ *Saving for Retirement* You are saving for your retirement by investing $700 per month in an annuity with a guaranteed interest rate of 6% per year. With a continuous stream of investment and continuous compounding, how much will you have accumulated in the annuity by the time you retire in 45 years?

48. ▼ *Saving for College* When your first child is born, you begin to save for college by depositing $400 per month in an account paying 12% interest per year. With a continuous stream of investment and continuous compounding, how much will you have accumulated in the account by the time your child enters college 18 years later?

49. ▼ *Saving for Retirement* You begin saving for your retirement by investing $700 per month in an annuity with a guaranteed interest rate of 6% per year. You increase the amount you invest at the rate of 3% per year. With continuous investment and compounding, how much will you have accumulated in the annuity by the time you retire in 45 years?

50. ▼ *Saving for College* When your first child is born, you begin to save for college by depositing $400 per month in an account paying 12% interest per year. You increase the amount you save by 2% per year. With continuous investment and compounding, how much will have accumulated in the account by the time your child enters college 18 years later?

51. ▼ *Bonds* The U.S. Treasury issued a 30-year bond on October 15, 2014, paying 3.125% interest.[43] Thus, if you bought $100,000 worth of these bonds, you would receive $3,125 per year in interest for 30 years. An investor wishes to buy the rights to receive the interest on $100,000 worth of these bonds. The amount the investor is willing to pay is the present value of the interest payments, assuming a 4% rate of return. Assuming (incorrectly but approximately) that the interest payments are made continuously, what will the investor pay? [HINT: See Example 6.]

52. ▼ *Bonds* The Megabucks Corporation is issuing a 20-year bond paying 7% interest. (See Exercise 51.) An investor wishes to buy the rights to receive the interest on $50,000 worth of these bonds and seeks a 6% rate of return. Assuming that the interest payments are made continuously, what will the investor pay? [HINT: See Example 6.]

53. ▼ *Valuing Future Income* Inga was injured and can no longer work. As a result of a lawsuit, she is to be awarded the present value of the income she would have received over the next 20 years. Her income at the time she was injured was $100,000 per year, increasing by $5,000 per year. What will be the amount of her award, assuming continuous income and a 5% interest rate?

54. ▼ *Valuing Future Income* Max was injured and can no longer work. As a result of a lawsuit, he is to be awarded the present value of the income he would have received over the next 30 years. His income at the time he was injured was $30,000 per year, increasing by $1,500 per year. What will be the amount of his award, assuming continuous income and a 6% interest rate?

Communication and Reasoning Exercises

55. Complete the following: The future value of a continuous income stream earning 0% interest is the same as the _____ value.

56. Complete the following: The present value of a continuous income stream earning 0% interest is the same as the _____ value.

57. ▼ *Linear Demand* Given a linear demand equation $q = -mp + b$ $(m > 0)$, find a formula for the consumers' surplus at a price level of $\bar{p}$ per unit.

58. ▼ *Linear Supply* Given a linear supply equation of the form $q = mp + b$ $(m > 0)$, find a formula for the producers' surplus at a price level of $\bar{p}$ per unit.

59. ▼ Your study group friend says that the future value of a continuous stream of income is always greater than the total value, assuming a positive rate of return. Is she correct? Why?

60. ▼ Your other study group friend says that the present value of a continuous stream of income can sometimes be greater than the total value, depending on the (positive) interest rate. Is he correct? Explain.

61. ▼ Arrange from smallest to largest: total value, future value, and present value of a continuous stream of income (assuming a positive income and positive rate of return).

62. ▼ **a.** Arrange the following functions from smallest to largest $R(t)$, $R(t)e^{r(b-t)}$, $R(t)e^{r(a-t)}$, where $a \le t \le b$, and r and $R(t)$ are positive.
    b. Use the result from part (a) to justify your answers in Exercises 59–61.

---

[43] Source: The Bureau of the Public Debt (www.publicdebt.treas.gov).

14.5 Improper Integrals and Applications

All the definite integrals we have seen so far have had the form $\int_a^b f(x)\,dx$ with a and b finite and $f(x)$ piecewise continuous on the closed interval $[a, b]$. If we relax one or both of these requirements somewhat, we obtain what are called **improper integrals**. There are various types of improper integrals.

Integrals in Which a Limit of Integration is Infinite

Integrals in which one or more limits of integration are infinite can be written as

$$\int_a^{+\infty} f(x)\,dx, \quad \int_{-\infty}^b f(x)\,dx, \quad \text{or} \quad \int_{-\infty}^{+\infty} f(x)\,dx.$$

Let's concentrate for a moment on the first form, $\int_a^{+\infty} f(x)\,dx$. What does the $+\infty$ mean here? As it often does, it means that we are to take a limit as something gets large. Specifically, it means the limit as the upper bound of integration gets large.

Improper Integral with an Infinite Limit of Integration

We define

$$\int_a^{+\infty} f(x)\,dx = \lim_{M \to +\infty} \int_a^M f(x)\,dx,$$

provided that the limit exists. If the limit exists, we say that $\int_a^{+\infty} f(x)\,dx$ **converges**. Otherwise, we say that $\int_a^{+\infty} f(x)\,dx$ **diverges**. Similarly, we define

$$\int_{-\infty}^b f(x)\,dx = \lim_{M \to -\infty} \int_M^b f(x)\,dx,$$

provided that the limit exists. Finally, we define

$$\int_{-\infty}^{+\infty} f(x)\,dx = \int_{-\infty}^a f(x)\,dx + \int_a^{+\infty} f(x)\,dx$$

for some convenient a, provided that *both* integrals on the right converge.

Quick Examples

1. $\displaystyle\int_1^{+\infty} \frac{dx}{x^2} = \lim_{M \to +\infty} \int_1^M \frac{dx}{x^2} = \lim_{M \to +\infty} \left[-\frac{1}{x}\right]_1^M = \lim_{M \to +\infty} \left(-\frac{1}{M} + 1\right) = 1$

   Converges

2. $\displaystyle\int_1^{+\infty} \frac{dx}{x} = \lim_{M \to +\infty} \int_1^M \frac{dx}{x} = \lim_{M \to +\infty} \left[\ln|x|\right]_1^M = \lim_{M \to +\infty} (\ln M - \ln 1) = +\infty$

   Diverges

3. $\displaystyle\int_{-\infty}^{-1} \frac{dx}{x^2} = \lim_{M \to -\infty} \int_M^{-1} \frac{dx}{x^2} = \lim_{M \to -\infty} \left[-\frac{1}{x}\right]_M^{-1} = \lim_{M \to -\infty} \left(1 + \frac{1}{M}\right) = 1$

   Converges

4. $\displaystyle\int_{-\infty}^{+\infty} e^{-x}\, dx = \int_{-\infty}^{0} e^{-x}\, dx + \int_{0}^{+\infty} e^{-x}\, dx$

$$= \lim_{M \to -\infty} \int_{M}^{0} e^{-x}\, dx + \lim_{M \to +\infty} \int_{0}^{M} e^{-x}\, dx$$

$$= \lim_{M \to -\infty} \left[-e^{-x}\right]_{M}^{0} + \lim_{M \to +\infty} \left[-e^{-x}\right]_{0}^{M}$$

$$= \lim_{M \to -\infty} \left(e^{-M} - 1\right) + \lim_{M \to +\infty} \left(1 - e^{-M}\right)$$

$$= +\infty + 1 \qquad\qquad\qquad\qquad \text{Diverges}$$

5. $\displaystyle\int_{-\infty}^{+\infty} xe^{-x^2}\, dx = \int_{-\infty}^{0} xe^{-x^2}\, dx + \int_{0}^{+\infty} xe^{-x^2}\, dx$

$$= \lim_{M \to -\infty} \int_{M}^{0} xe^{-x^2}\, dx + \lim_{M \to +\infty} \int_{0}^{M} xe^{-x^2}\, dx$$

$$= \lim_{M \to -\infty} \left[-\frac{1}{2}e^{-x^2}\right]_{M}^{0} + \lim_{M \to +\infty} \left[-\frac{1}{2}e^{-x^2}\right]_{0}^{M}$$

$$= \lim_{M \to -\infty} \left(-\frac{1}{2} + \frac{1}{2}e^{-M^2}\right) + \lim_{M \to +\infty} \left(-\frac{1}{2}e^{-M^2} + \frac{1}{2}\right)$$

$$= -\frac{1}{2} + \frac{1}{2} = 0 \qquad\qquad\qquad \text{Converges}$$

Q: *We learned that the integral can be interpreted as the area under the curve. Is this still true for improper integrals?*

A: Yes. Figure 22 illustrates how we can represent an improper integral as the area of an infinite region.

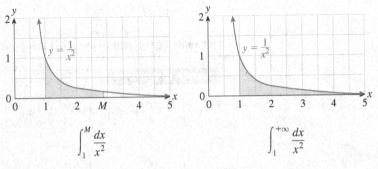

$$\int_{1}^{M} \frac{dx}{x^2} \qquad\qquad\qquad \int_{1}^{+\infty} \frac{dx}{x^2}$$

Figure 22

On the left we see the area represented by $\int_{1}^{M} dx/x^2$. As M gets larger, the integral approaches $\int_{1}^{+\infty} dx/x^2$. In the picture, think of M being moved farther and farther along the x-axis in the direction of increasing x, resulting in the region shown on the right.

Q : *Wait! We calculated $\int_1^{+\infty} dx/x^2 = 1$. Does this mean that the infinitely long area in Figure 22 has an area of only 1 square unit?*

A : That is exactly what it means. If you had enough paint to cover 1 square unit, you would never run out of paint while painting the region in Figure 22. This is one of the places where mathematics seems to contradict common sense. But common sense is notoriously unreliable when dealing with infinities.

Using Technology

You can estimate the integral in Example 1 with technology by computing $\int_0^M 290(0.77)^t \, dt$ for $M = 10, 100, 1{,}000, \ldots$. You will find that the resulting values appear to converge to about 1,110. (Stop when the effect of further increases of M has no effect at this level of accuracy.)

TI-83/84 Plus
$Y_1 = 290*0.77\^X$
Home screen:
$\text{fnInt}(Y_1, X, 0, 10)$
$\text{fnInt}(Y_1, X, 0, 100)$
$\text{fnInt}(Y_1, X, 0, 1000)$

W Website
www.WanerMath.com
Online Utilities
→ Numerical Integration
   Utility and Grapher
Enter
$290*0.77\^x$
for $f(x)$. Enter 0 and 10 for the lower and upper limits, and press "Integral" for the most accurate estimate of the integral. Repeat with the upper limit set to 100, 1,000, and higher.

EXAMPLE 1   **Future Sales of CDs**

By 2009, music downloads were making serious inroads into the sales of physical CDs. Approximately 290 million CD albums were sold in 2009, and sales declined by about 23% per year the following year.[44] Suppose that this rate of decrease were to continue indefinitely and continuously. How many CD albums, total, would be sold from 2009 on?

Solution Recall that the total sales between two dates can be computed as the definite integral of the rate of sales. So if we wanted to estimate the sales between 2009 and a time far in the future, we would compute $\int_0^M s(t) \, dt$ with a large M, where $s(t)$ is the annual sales t years after 2009. Because we want to know the *total* number of CD albums sold from 2009 on, we let $M \to +\infty$; that is, we compute $\int_0^{+\infty} s(t) \, dt$.

Because sales of CD albums are decreasing by 23% per year, we can model $s(t)$ by

$$s(t) = 290(0.77)^t \text{ million CD albums per year,}$$

where t is the number of years since 2009:

$$\text{Total sales from 2009 on} = \int_0^{+\infty} 290(0.77)^t \, dt$$

$$= \lim_{M \to +\infty} \int_0^M 290(0.77)^t \, dt$$

$$= \frac{290}{\ln 0.77} \lim_{M \to +\infty} \left[(0.77)^t \right]_0^M$$

$$= \frac{290}{\ln 0.77} \lim_{M \to +\infty} (0.77^M - 0.77^0)$$

$$= \frac{290}{\ln 0.77} (-1)$$

$$\approx 1{,}110 \text{ million CD albums.}$$

Integrals in Which the Integrand Becomes Infinite

We can sometimes compute integrals $\int_a^b f(x) \, dx$ in which $f(x)$ becomes infinite. As we'll see in Example 4, the Fundamental Theorem of Calculus does not work for such integrals. The first case to consider is when $f(x)$ approaches $\pm\infty$ at either a or b.

---

[44] Source: *2010 Year-End Shipment Statistics*, Recording Industry Association of America (www.riaa.com).

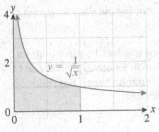

Figure 23

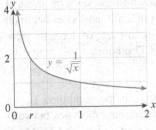

Figure 24

EXAMPLE 2   **Integrand Infinite at One Endpoint**

Calculate $\int_0^1 \frac{1}{\sqrt{x}} \, dx$.

Solution Notice that the integrand approaches $+\infty$ as x approaches 0 from the right and is not defined at 0. This makes the integral an improper integral. Figure 23 shows the region whose area we are trying to calculate; it extends infinitely vertically rather than horizontally.

Now, if $0 < r < 1$, the integral $\int_r^1 (1/\sqrt{x}) \, dx$ is a proper integral because we avoid the bad behavior at 0. This integral gives the area shown in Figure 24. If we let r approach 0 from the right, the area in Figure 24 will approach the area in Figure 23. So we calculate

$$\int_0^1 \frac{1}{\sqrt{x}} \, dx = \lim_{r \to 0^+} \int_r^1 \frac{1}{\sqrt{x}} \, dx$$

$$= \lim_{r \to 0^+} \left[2\sqrt{x} \right]_r^1$$

$$= \lim_{r \to 0^+} (2 - 2\sqrt{r})$$

$$= 2.$$

Thus, we again have an infinitely long region with finite area.

Generalizing, we make the following definition.

Improper Integral in Which the Integrand Becomes Infinite

If $f(x)$ is defined for all x with $a < x \le b$ but approaches $\pm\infty$ as x approaches a, we define

$$\int_a^b f(x) \, dx = \lim_{r \to a^+} \int_r^b f(x) \, dx$$

provided that the limit exists. Similarly, if $f(x)$ is defined for all x with $a \le x < b$ but approaches $\pm\infty$ as x approaches b, we define

$$\int_a^b f(x) \, dx = \lim_{r \to b^-} \int_a^r f(x) \, dx$$

provided that the limit exists. In either case, if the limit exists, we say that $\int_a^b f(x) \, dx$ **converges**. Otherwise, we say that $\int_a^b f(x) \, dx$ **diverges**.

Note We saw in Chapter 13 that the Fundamental Theorem of Calculus applies to piecewise continuous functions as well as continuous ones. Examples are $f(x) = |x|/x$ and $(x^2 - 1)/(x - 1)$. The integrals of such functions are not improper, and we can use the Fundamental Theorem of Calculus to evaluate such integrals in the usual way. ■

EXAMPLE 3 **Testing for Convergence**

Does $\int_{-1}^{3} \dfrac{x}{x^2 - 9}\, dx$ converge? If so, to what?

Solution We first check to see where, if anywhere, the integrand approaches $\pm\infty$. That will happen where the denominator becomes 0, so we solve $x^2 - 9 = 0$:

$$x^2 - 9 = 0$$
$$x^2 = 9$$
$$x = \pm 3.$$

The solution $x = -3$ is outside of the range of integration, so we ignore it. However, the solution $x = 3$ is the right endpoint of the range of integration, so the integral is improper. We need to investigate the following limit:

$$\int_{-1}^{3} \frac{x}{x^2 - 9}\, dx = \lim_{r \to 3^-} \int_{-1}^{r} \frac{x}{x^2 - 9}\, dx.$$

Now, to calculate the integral we use a substitution:

$$u = x^2 - 9$$
$$\frac{du}{dx} = 2x$$
$$dx = \frac{1}{2x}\, du$$

when $x = r$, $u = r^2 - 9$
when $x = -1$, $u = (-1)^2 - 9 = -8$

Thus,

$$\int_{-1}^{r} \frac{x}{x^2 - 9}\, dx = \int_{-8}^{r^2-9} \frac{1}{2u}\, du$$

$$= \frac{1}{2}[\ln|u|]_{-8}^{r^2-9}$$

$$= \frac{1}{2}(\ln|r^2 - 9| - \ln 8).$$

Now we take the limit:

$$\int_{-1}^{3} \frac{x}{x^2 - 9}\, dx = \lim_{r \to 3^-} \int_{-1}^{r} \frac{x}{x^2 - 9}\, dx$$

$$= \lim_{r \to 3^-} \frac{1}{2}(\ln|r^2 - 9| - \ln 8)$$

$$= -\infty$$

because, as $r \to 3$, $r^2 - 9 \to 0$, so $\ln|r^2 - 9| \to -\infty$. Thus, this integral diverges.

> **EXAMPLE 4** **Integrand Infinite between the Endpoints**

Does $\displaystyle\int_{-2}^{3} \frac{1}{x^2}\, dx$ converge? If so, to what?

Solution Again we check to see whether there are any points at which the integrand approaches $\pm\infty$. There is such a point, at $x = 0$. This is between the endpoints of the range of integration. To deal with this, we break the integral into two integrals:

$$\int_{-2}^{3} \frac{1}{x^2}\, dx = \int_{-2}^{0} \frac{1}{x^2}\, dx + \int_{0}^{3} \frac{1}{x^2}\, dx.$$

Each integral on the right is an improper integral with the integrand approaching $\pm\infty$ at an endpoint. If both of the integrals on the right converge, we take the sum as the value of the integral on the left. So now we compute

$$\int_{-2}^{0} \frac{1}{x^2}\, dx = \lim_{r \to 0^-} \int_{-2}^{r} \frac{1}{x^2}\, dx$$

$$= \lim_{r \to 0^-} \left[-\frac{1}{x} \right]_{-2}^{r}$$

$$= \lim_{r \to 0^-} \left(-\frac{1}{r} - \frac{1}{2} \right),$$

which diverges to $+\infty$. There is no need now to check $\int_{0}^{3} (1/x^2)\, dx$; because one of the two pieces of the integral diverges, we simply say that $\int_{-2}^{3} (1/x^2)\, dx$ diverges.

➡ **Before we go on...** What if we had been sloppy in Example 4 and had not checked first whether the integrand approached $\pm\infty$ somewhere? Then we probably would have applied the Fundamental Theorem of Calculus and done the following:

$$\int_{-2}^{3} \frac{1}{x^2}\, dx = \left[-\frac{1}{x} \right]_{-2}^{3} = \left(-\frac{1}{3} - \frac{1}{2} \right) = -\frac{5}{6}. \quad \times \; \text{WRONG!}$$

Notice that the answer this "calculation" gives is patently ridiculous. Because $1/x^2 > 0$ for all x for which it is defined, the definite integral of $1/x^2$ over any interval cannot be negative. *Moral:* Always check to see whether the integrand blows up anywhere in the range of integration. If it does, the FTC does not apply, and we must use the methods of this example. ■

We end with an example of what to do if an integral is improper for more than one reason.

> **EXAMPLE 5** **An Integral Improper in Two Ways**

Does $\displaystyle\int_{0}^{+\infty} \frac{1}{\sqrt{x}}\, dx$ converge? If so, to what?

Solution This integral is improper for two reasons. First, the range of integration is infinite. Second, the integrand blows up at the endpoint 0. To separate these two problems, we break up the integral at some convenient point:

$$\int_{0}^{+\infty} \frac{1}{\sqrt{x}}\, dx = \int_{0}^{1} \frac{1}{\sqrt{x}}\, dx + \int_{1}^{+\infty} \frac{1}{\sqrt{x}}\, dx.$$

We chose to break the integral at 1. Any positive number would have sufficed, but 1 is generally easier to use in calculations.

The first piece, $\int_0^1 (1/\sqrt{x})\, dx$, we discussed in Example 2; it converges to 2. For the second piece we have

$$\int_1^{+\infty} \frac{1}{\sqrt{x}}\, dx = \lim_{M \to +\infty} \int_1^M \frac{1}{\sqrt{x}}\, dx$$

$$= \lim_{M \to +\infty} \left[2\sqrt{x} \right]_1^M$$

$$= \lim_{M \to +\infty} (2\sqrt{M} - 2),$$

which diverges to $+\infty$. Because the second piece of the integral diverges, we conclude that $\int_0^{+\infty} (1/\sqrt{x})\, dx$ diverges.

14.5 EXERCISES

▼ more advanced   ◆ challenging

⊺ indicates exercises that should be solved using technology

Note: For some of the exercises in this section you need to assume the fact that $\lim_{M \to +\infty} M^n e^{-M} = 0$ *for all* $n \geq 0$. *(See Exercises 73 and 74 in Section 10.1 and Exercise 111 in Section 10.3.)*

In Exercises 1–26, decide whether or not the given integral converges. If the integral converges, compute its value. [HINT: See Quick Examples 1–5.]

1. $\int_1^{+\infty} x\, dx$

2. $\int_0^{+\infty} e^{-x}\, dx$

3. $\int_{-2}^{+\infty} e^{-0.5x}\, dx$

4. $\int_1^{+\infty} \frac{1}{x^{1.5}}\, dx$

5. $\int_{-\infty}^2 e^x\, dx$

6. $\int_{-\infty}^{-1} \frac{1}{x^{1/3}}\, dx$

7. $\int_{-\infty}^{-2} \frac{1}{x^2}\, dx$

8. $\int_{-\infty}^0 e^{-x}\, dx$

9. $\int_0^{+\infty} x^2 e^{-6x}\, dx$

10. $\int_0^{+\infty} (2x - 4)e^{-x}\, dx$

11. $\int_0^5 \frac{2}{x^{1/3}}\, dx$ [HINT: See Example 2.]

12. $\int_0^2 \frac{1}{x^2}\, dx$

13. $\int_{-1}^2 \frac{3}{(x + 1)^2}\, dx$ [HINT: See Example 3.]

14. $\int_{-1}^2 \frac{3}{(x + 1)^{1/2}}\, dx$

15. $\int_{-1}^2 \frac{3x}{x^2 - 1}\, dx$ [HINT: See Example 4.]

16. $\int_{-1}^2 \frac{3}{x^{1/3}}\, dx$

17. $\int_{-2}^2 \frac{1}{(x + 1)^{1/5}}\, dx$

18. $\int_{-2}^2 \frac{2x}{\sqrt{4 - x^2}}\, dx$

19. $\int_{-1}^1 \frac{2x}{x^2 - 1}\, dx$

20. $\int_{-1}^2 \frac{2x}{x^2 - 1}\, dx$

21. $\int_{-\infty}^{+\infty} xe^{-x^2}\, dx$

22. $\int_{-\infty}^{\infty} xe^{1-x^2}\, dx$

23. $\int_0^{+\infty} \frac{1}{x \ln x}\, dx$ [HINT: See Example 5.]

24. $\int_0^{+\infty} \ln x\, dx$

25. ▼ $\int_0^{+\infty} \frac{2x}{x^2 - 1}\, dx$

26. ▼ $\int_{-\infty}^0 \frac{2x}{x^2 - 1}\, dx$

⊺ *In Exercises 27–34, use technology to approximate the given integrals with* $M = 10, 100, 1,000, \ldots$. *Then decide whether the associated improper integral converges, and estimate its value to four significant digits if it does.* [HINT: See the technology note for Example 1.]

27. $\int_1^M \frac{1}{x^2}\, dx$

28. $\int_0^M e^{-x^2}\, dx$

29. $\int_0^M \frac{x}{1 + x}\, dx$

30. $\int_{1/M}^1 \frac{1}{\sqrt{x}}\, dx$

31. $\int_{1+1/M}^2 \frac{1}{\sqrt{x - 1}}\, dx$

32. $\int_1^M \frac{1}{x}\, dx$

33. $\int_0^{1-1/M} \frac{1}{(1 - x)^2}\, dx$

34. $\int_0^{2-1/M} \frac{1}{(2 - x)^3}\, dx$

Applications

35. New Home Sales Sales of new homes in the United States decreased dramatically from 2005 to 2010 as shown in the model

$$n(t) = 1.33e^{-0.299t} \text{ million homes per year} \quad (0 \le t \le 5),$$

where t is the year since 2005.[45] If this trend were to have continued into the indefinite future, estimate the total number of new homes that would have been sold in the United States from 2005 on. [HINT: See Example 1.]

36. Revenue from New Home Sales Revenue from the sale of new homes in the United States decreased dramatically from 2005 to 2010 as shown in the model

$$r(t) = 412e^{-0.323t} \text{ billion dollars per year} \quad (0 \le t \le 5),$$

where t is the year since 2005.[46] If this trend were to have continued into the indefinite future, estimate the total revenue from the sale of new homes in the United States from 2005 on. [HINT: See Example 1.]

37. Cigarette Sales According to data published by the Federal Trade Commission, the number of cigarettes sold domestically has been decreasing by about 4% per year from the 2000 total of about 415 billion.[47] Use an exponential model to forecast the total number of cigarettes sold from 2000 on. (Round your answer to the nearest 100 billion cigarettes.) [HINT: Use a model of the form Ab^t.]

38. Sales Sales of the text *Calculus and You* have been declining continuously at a rate of 5% per year. Assuming that *Calculus and You* currently sells 5,000 copies per year and that sales will continue this pattern of decline, calculate total future sales of the text. [HINT: Use a model of the form Ae^{rt}.]

39. ▼ Sales My financial adviser has predicted that annual sales of Frodo T-shirts will continue to decline by 10% each year. At the moment, I have 3,200 of the shirts in stock and am selling them at a rate of 200 per year. Will I ever sell them all?

40. ▼ Revenue Alarmed about the sales prospects for my Frodo T-shirts (see Exercise 39), I will try to make up lost revenues by increasing the price by $1 each year. I now charge $10 per shirt. What is the total amount of revenue I can expect to earn from sales of my T-shirts, assuming the sales levels described in the previous exercise? (Round your answer to the nearest $1,000.)

41. ▼ Education Let $N(t)$ be the number of high school students who graduated in the United States in year t. This number has been changing at a rate of about

$$N'(t) = 0.30t^{-0.87} \text{ million graduates per year} \quad (5 \le t \le 13),$$

where t is time in years since 2000.[48] In 2005 about 2.8 million high school students graduated. By extrapolating the model, what can you say about the number of high school students who will graduate in a year far in the future?

42. ▼ Education: Martian Let $M(t)$ be the number of high school students who graduated in the Republic of Mars in year t. This number is projected to change at a rate of about

$$M'(t) = 0.321t^{-1.10} \text{ thousand graduates per year} \quad (1 \le t \le 50),$$

where t is time in years since 2150. In 2151 about 1,300 high school students graduated. By extrapolating the model, what can you say about the number of high school students who will graduate in a year far in the future?

43. ▼ Cellphone Revenues The number of cellphone subscribers in China in the early 2000s was projected to follow the equation[49]

$$N(t) = 39t + 68 \text{ million subscribers}$$

in year t. ($t = 0$ represents 2000.) The average annual revenue per cellphone user was $350 in 2000.

a. Assuming that, because of competition, the revenue per cellphone user decreases continuously at an annual rate of 10%, give a formula for the annual revenue in year t.

b. Using the model you obtained in part (a) as an estimate of the rate of change of total revenue, estimate the total revenue from 2000 into the indefinite future.

44. ▼ Vidphone Revenues The number of vidphone subscribers in the Republic of Mars for the period 2200–2300 was projected to follow the equation

$$N(t) = 18t - 10 \text{ thousand subscribers}$$

in year t. ($t = 0$ represents 2200.) The average annual revenue per vidphone user was $Z40$ in 2200.[50]

a. Assuming that, because of competition, the revenue per vidphone user decreases continuously at an annual rate of 20%, give a formula for the annual revenue in year t.

b. Using the model you obtained in part (a) as an estimate of the rate of change of total revenue, estimate the total revenue from 2200 into the indefinite future.

45. ⓘ Development Assistance According to data published by the Organisation for Economic Co-operation and Development (OECD), development assistance to developing countries from 2005 through 2013 was approximately

$$q(t) = 0.13t^2 + 4.1t + 110 \text{ billion dollars per year,}$$

---

[45] Based on new home sales data from the U.S. Census Bureau (www.census.gov/const/www/newressalesindex.html).

[46] Ibid.

[47] Source for data: Federal Trade Commission Cigarette Report for 2011, issued May 2013 (www.ftc.gov).

[48] Based on a regression model. Source for Data: U.S. Department of Education, National Center for Education Statistics, *Digest of Education Statistics: 2013* (nces.ed.gov).

[49] Based on a regression of projected figures (coefficients are rounded). Source: Intrinsic Technology/*New York Times*, Nov. 24, 2000, p. C1.

[50] The zonar (Z) is the official currency in the city-state of Utarek, Mars. Source: www.Marsnext.com, a now extinct virtual society.

where t is time in years since 2005.[51] Assuming a worldwide inflation rate of 3% per year and that the above model remains accurate into the indefinite future, find the value of all development assistance to developing countries from 2005 on in constant dollars. (The constant dollar value of $q(t)$ dollars t years from now is given by $q(t)e^{-rt}$, where r is the fractional rate of inflation. Give your answer to the nearest $100 billion.) [HINT: See the technology note for Example 1.]

46. **Humanitarian Aid** Repeat Exercise 45, using the following model for humanitarian aid:[52]

$$q(t) = 0.051t^2 + 0.34t + 9.1 \text{ billion dollars per year.}$$

47. ▼ **Hair Mousse Sales** The amount of extremely popular hair mousse sold online at your website can be approximated by

$$N(t) = \frac{80(7)^t}{20 + 7^t} \text{ million gallons per year.}$$

($t = 0$ represents the current year.) Investigate the integrals $\int_0^{+\infty} N(t)\,dt$ and $\int_{-\infty}^0 N(t)\,dt$, and interpret your answers.

48. ▼ **Chocolate Mousse Sales** The weekly demand for your company's *Lo-Cal Chocolate Mousse* is modeled by the equation

$$q(t) = \frac{50e^{2t-1}}{1 + e^{2t-1}} \text{ gallons per week,}$$

where t is time from now in weeks. Investigate the integrals $\int_0^{+\infty} q(t)\,dt$ and $\int_{-\infty}^0 q(t)\,dt$, and interpret your answers.

The Normal Curve *Exercises 49–52 require the use of a graphing calculator or computer programmed to do numerical integration. The normal distribution curve, which models the distributions of data in a wide range of applications, is given by the function*

$$p(x) = \frac{1}{\sqrt{2\pi}\sigma}e^{-(x-\mu)^2/(2\sigma^2)},$$

where $\pi = 3.14159265\ldots$ and σ and μ are constants called the standard deviation and the mean, respectively. Its graph (for $\sigma = 1$ and $\mu = 2$) is shown in the figure.

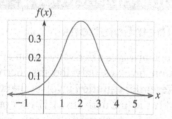

49. ▼ With $\sigma = 4$ and $\mu = 1$, approximate $\int_{-\infty}^{+\infty} p(x)\,dx$. [HINT: See Example 5 and the technology note for Example 1.]

50. ▼ With $\sigma = 1$ and $\mu = 0$, approximate $\int_0^{+\infty} p(x)\,dx$.

51. ▼ With $\sigma = 1$ and $\mu = 0$, approximate $\int_1^{+\infty} p(x)\,dx$.

52. ▼ With $\sigma = 1$ and $\mu = 0$, approximate $\int_{-\infty}^1 p(x)\,dx$.

53. ◆ **Variable Sales** The value of your *Chateau Petit Mont Blanc* 1963 vintage burgundy is increasing continuously at an annual rate of 40%, and you have a supply of 1,000 bottles worth $85 each at today's prices. To ensure a steady income, you have decided to sell your wine at a diminishing rate, starting at 500 bottles per year and then decreasing this figure continuously at a fractional rate of 100% per year. How much income (to the nearest dollar) can you expect to generate by this scheme? [HINT: Use the formula for continuously compounded interest.]

54. ◆ **Panic Sales** Unfortunately, your large supply of *Chateau Petit Mont Blanc* is continuously turning to vinegar at a fractional rate of 60% per year! You have thus decided to sell off your Petit Mont Blanc at $50 per bottle, but the market is a little thin, and you can sell only 400 bottles per year. Because you have no way of knowing which bottles now contain vinegar until they are opened, you shall have to give refunds for all the bottles of vinegar. What will your net income be before all the wine turns to vinegar?

55. ◆ **Meteor Impacts** The frequency of meteor impacts on the Earth can be modeled by

$$n(k) = \frac{1}{5.6997k^{1.081}},$$

where $n(k) = N'(k)$, and $N(k)$ is the average number of meteors of energy less than or equal to k megatons that will hit the Earth in 1 year.[53] (A small nuclear bomb releases on the order of 1 megaton of energy.)

a. How many meteors of energy at least $k = 0.2$ hit the Earth each year?

b. Investigate and interpret the integral $\int_0^1 n(k)\,dk$.

56. ◆ **Meteor Impacts** (continuing Exercise 55)

a. Explain why the integral

$$\int_a^b kn(k)\,dk$$

computes the total energy released each year by meteors with energies between a and b megatons.

b. Compute and interpret

$$\int_0^1 kn(k)\,dk.$$

c. Compute and interpret

$$\int_1^{+\infty} kn(k)\,dk.$$

---

[51] The authors' approximation, based on data from OECD, obtained from www.oecd.org.
[52] *Ibid.*

[53] The authors' model, based on data published by NASA International Near-Earth-Object Detection Workshop (*The New York Times*, Jan. 25, 1994, p. C1).

57. ◆ *The Gamma Function* The gamma function is defined by the formula

$$\Gamma(x) = \int_0^{+\infty} t^{x-1} e^{-t}\, dt.$$

a. Find $\Gamma(1)$ and $\Gamma(2)$.
b. Use integration by parts to show that for every positive integer n, $\Gamma(n + 1) = n\Gamma(n)$.
c. Deduce that $\Gamma(n) = (n - 1)!\,[=(n - 1)(n - 2)\cdots 2 \cdot 1]$ for every positive integer n.

58. ◆ *Laplace Transforms* The Laplace transform $F(x)$ of a function $f(t)$ is given by the formula

$$F(x) = \int_0^{+\infty} f(t)e^{-xt}\, dt \quad (x > 0).$$

a. Find $F(x)$ for $f(t) = 1$ and for $f(t) = t$.
b. Find a formula for $F(x)$ if $f(t) = t^n$ $(n = 1, 2, 3, \ldots)$.
c. Find a formula for $F(x)$ if $f(t) = e^{at}$ (a constant).

Communication and Reasoning Exercises

59. Why can't the Fundamental Theorem of Calculus be used to evaluate $\int_{-1}^{1} \dfrac{1}{x}\, dx$?

60. Why can't the Fundamental Theorem of Calculus be used to evaluate $\int_{1}^{+\infty} \dfrac{1}{x^2}\, dx$?

61. It sometimes happens that the Fundamental Theorem of Calculus gives the correct answer for an improper integral. Does the FTC give the correct answer for improper integrals of the form

$$\int_{-a}^{a} \frac{1}{x^{1/r}}\, dx$$

if $r = 3, 5, 7, \ldots$?

62. Does the FTC give the correct answer for improper integrals of the form

$$\int_{-a}^{a} \frac{1}{x^r}\, dx$$

if $r = 3, 5, 7, \ldots$?

63. Which of the following integrals are improper, and why? (Do not evaluate any of them.)

a. $\displaystyle\int_{-1}^{1} \frac{|x|}{x}\, dx$
b. $\displaystyle\int_{-1}^{1} x^{-1/3}\, dx$

c. $\displaystyle\int_{0}^{2} \frac{x - 2}{x^2 - 4x + 4}\, dx$

64. Which of the following integrals are improper, and why? (Do not evaluate any of them.)

a. $\displaystyle\int_{-1}^{1} \frac{|x - 1|}{x - 1}\, dx$
b. $\displaystyle\int_{0}^{1} \frac{1}{x^{2/3}}\, dx$

c. $\displaystyle\int_{0}^{2} \frac{x^2 - 4x + 4}{x - 2}\, dx$

65. ▯▼ How could you use technology to approximate improper integrals? (Your discussion should refer to each type of improper integral.)

66. ▯▼ Use technology to approximate the integrals $\int_0^{M} e^{-(x-10)^2}\, dx$ for larger and larger values of M, using Riemann sums with 500 subdivisions. What do you find? Comment on the answer.

67. ▼ Make up an interesting application whose solution is $\int_{10}^{+\infty} 100te^{-0.2t}\, dt = \$1,015.01$.

68. ▼ Make up an interesting application whose solution is $\int_{100}^{+\infty} \frac{1}{r^2}\, dr = 0.01$.

14.6 Differential Equations and Applications

Differential Equations and Their Solutions

A **differential equation** is an equation that involves a derivative of an unknown function. A **first-order differential equation** involves only the first derivative of the unknown function. A **second-order differential equation** involves the second derivative of the unknown function (and possibly the first derivative). Higher order differential equations are defined similarly. In this book we will deal only with first-order differential equations.

To **solve** a differential equation means to find the unknown function. Many of the laws of science and other fields describe how things change. When expressed mathematically, these laws take the form of equations involving derivatives—that is, differential equations. The field of differential equations is a large and very active area of study in mathematics, and we shall see only a small part of it in this section.

EXAMPLE 1   **Motion**

A dragster accelerates from a stop so that its speed t seconds after starting is $40t$ ft/sec. How far will the car go in 8 seconds?*

Solution   We wish to find the car's position function $s(t)$. We are told about its speed, which is ds/dt. Precisely, we are told that

$$\frac{ds}{dt} = 40t.$$

This is the differential equation we have to solve to find $s(t)$. But we already know how to solve this kind of differential equation; we integrate:

$$s(t) = \int 40t \, dt = 20t^2 + C.$$

We now have the **general solution** to the differential equation. By letting C take on different values, we get all the possible solutions. We can specify the one **particular solution** that gives the answer to our problem by imposing the **initial condition** that $s(0) = 0$. Substituting into $s(t) = 20t^2 + C$, we get

$$0 = s(0) = 20(0)^2 + C = C,$$

so $C = 0$ and $s(t) = 20t^2$. To answer the question, the car travels $20(8)^2 = 1,280$ feet in 8 seconds.

* Notice that we can answer this question by integrating the speed from 0 to 8. However, we pretend here that we didn't notice this fact and instead approach it from the point of view of differential equations.

Simple Differential Equations

We did not have to work hard to solve the differential equation in Example 1. In fact, any differential equation of the form $dy/dx = f(x)$ can (in theory) be solved by integrating. (Whether we can actually carry out the integration is another matter!)

Simple Differential Equations

A **simple** differential equation has the form

$$\frac{dy}{dx} = f(x).$$

Its general solution is

$$y = \int f(x) \, dx.$$

Quick Example

1. The differential equation

$$\frac{dy}{dx} = 2x^2 - 4x^3$$

is simple and has general solution

$$y = \int f(x) \, dx = \frac{2x^3}{3} - x^4 + C.$$

Separable Differential Equations

Not all differential equations are simple, as the next example shows.

EXAMPLE 2   **Separable Differential Equation**

Consider the differential equation $\dfrac{dy}{dx} = \dfrac{x}{y^2}$.

a. Find the general solution.

b. Find the particular solution that satisfies the initial condition $y(0) = 2$.

Solution

a. This is not a simple differential equation because the right-hand side is a function of both x and y. We cannot solve this equation by just integrating; the solution to this problem is to "separate" the variables.

Step 1: *Separate the variables algebraically.* We rewrite the equation as

$$y^2\, dy = x\, dx.$$

Step 2: *Integrate both sides.*

$$\int y^2\, dy = \int x\, dx,$$

giving

$$\frac{y^3}{3} = \frac{x^2}{2} + C.$$

Step 3: *Solve for the dependent variable.* We solve for y:

$$y^3 = \frac{3}{2}x^2 + 3C = \frac{3}{2}x^2 + D$$

(rewriting $3C$ as D, an equally arbitrary constant), so

$$y = \left(\frac{3}{2}x^2 + D\right)^{1/3}.$$

This is the general solution of the differential equation.

b. We now need to find the value for D that will give us the solution satisfying the condition $y(0) = 2$. Substituting 0 for x and 2 for y in the general solution, we get

$$2 = \left(\frac{3}{2}(0)^2 + D\right)^{1/3} = D^{1/3},$$

so

$$D = 2^3 = 8.$$

Thus, the particular solution we are looking for is

$$y = \left(\frac{3}{2}x^2 + 8\right)^{1/3}.$$

➡ **Before we go on ...** We can check the general solution in Example 2 by calculating both sides of the differential equation and comparing:

$$\frac{dy}{dx} = \frac{d}{dx}\left(\frac{3}{2}x^2 + D\right)^{1/3} = x\left(\frac{3}{2}x^2 + D\right)^{-2/3}$$

$$\frac{x}{y^2} = \frac{x}{\left(\frac{3}{2}x^2 + D\right)^{2/3}} = x\left(\frac{3}{2}x^2 + D\right)^{-2/3}. \quad ✔$$

∎

Q : *In Example 2 we wrote $y^2\,dy$ and $x\,dx$. What do they mean?*

A : Although it is possible to give meaning to these symbols, for us they are just a notational convenience. We could have done the following instead:

$$y^2\frac{dy}{dx} = x.$$

Now we integrate both sides with respect to x:

$$\int y^2\frac{dy}{dx}\,dx = \int x\,dx.$$

We can use substitution to rewrite the left-hand side:

$$\int y^2\frac{dy}{dx}\,dx = \int y^2\,dy,$$

which brings us back to the equation

$$\int y^2\,dy = \int x\,dx.$$

We were able to separate the variables in the preceding example because the right-hand side, x/y^2, was a *product* of a function of x and a function of y—namely,

$$\frac{x}{y^2} = x\left(\frac{1}{y^2}\right).$$

In general, we can say the following.

Separable Differential Equation

A **separable** differential equation has the form

$$\frac{dy}{dx} = f(x)g(y).$$

We solve a separable differential equation by separating the xs and the ys algebraically, writing

$$\frac{1}{g(y)}\,dy = f(x)\,dx,$$

and then integrating:

$$\int \frac{1}{g(y)}\,dy = \int f(x)\,dx.$$

Quick Examples

2. $\dfrac{dy}{dx} = x^2 y^2$ is separable. To solve it, we write $\dfrac{dy}{y^2} = x^2 \, dx$ and integrate:

$$\int y^{-2} \, dy = \int x^2 \, dx$$

$$-y^{-1} = \frac{1}{3}x^3 + C$$

$$y = \frac{-1}{\frac{1}{3}x^3 + C} = \frac{-3}{x^3 + D}.$$

3. $\dfrac{dy}{dx} = x + y$ is not separable.

EXAMPLE 3 **Rising Medical Costs**

Spending on Medicare from 2010 to 2021 was projected to rise continuously at an instantaneous rate of 5.6% per year.[54] Find a formula for Medicare spending y as a function of time t in years since 2010.

Solution When we say that Medicare spending y was going up continuously at an instantaneous rate of 5.6% per year, we mean that

the instantaneous rate of increase of y was 5.6% of its value

or

$$\frac{dy}{dt} = 0.056y.$$

This is a separable differential equation. Separating the variables gives

$$\frac{1}{y} \, dy = 0.056 \, dt.$$

Integrating both sides, we get

$$\int \frac{1}{y} \, dy = \int 0.056 \, dt,$$

so

$$\ln y = 0.056t + C.$$

(We should write $\ln|y|$, but we know that the medical costs are positive.) We now solve for y:

$$y = e^{0.056t + C} = e^C e^{0.056t} = A e^{0.056t},$$

where A is a positive constant. This is the formula we used before for continuous percentage growth.

---

[54] Spending is in constant 2010 dollars. Source for projected data: Congressional Budget Office, *March 2011 Medicare Baseline* (www.cbo.gov).

➡ **Before we go on . . .** To determine A in Example 3, we need to know, for example, Medicare spending at time $t = 0$ (the initial condition). The source cited gives Medicare spending as \$525.6 billion in 2010. Substituting $t = 0$ in the equation above gives

$$525.6 = Ae^0 = A.$$

Thus, projected Medicare spending is

$$y = 525.6e^{0.056t} \text{ billion dollars}$$

t years after 2010. ∎

EXAMPLE 4   **Newton's Law of Cooling**

Newton's Law of Cooling states that a hot object cools at a rate proportional to the difference between its temperature and the temperature of the surrounding environment (the **ambient temperature**). If a hot cup of coffee, initially at 170°F, is left to sit in a room at 70°F, how will the temperature of the coffee change over time?

Solution We let $H(t)$ denote the temperature of the coffee at time t. Newton's Law of Cooling tells us that $H(t)$ *decreases* at a rate proportional to the difference between $H(t)$ and 70°F, the ambient temperature. In other words,

$$\frac{dH}{dt} = -k(H - 70),$$

* When we say that a quantity Q is *proportional* to a quantity R, we mean that $Q = kR$ for some constant k. The constant k is referred to as the **constant of proportionality**.

where k is some positive constant.* Note that $H \geq 70$: The coffee will never cool to less than the ambient temperature.

The variables here are H and t, which we can separate as follows:

$$\frac{dH}{H - 70} = -k \, dt.$$

Integrating, we get

$$\int \frac{dH}{H - 70} = \int (-k) \, dt,$$

so

$$\ln(H - 70) = -kt + C.$$

(Note that $H - 70$ is positive, so we don't need absolute values.) We now solve for H:

$$
\begin{aligned}
H - 70 &= e^{-kt + C} \\
&= e^C e^{-kt} \\
&= Ae^{-kt},
\end{aligned}
$$

so

$$H(t) = 70 + Ae^{-kt},$$

where A is some positive constant. We can determine the constant A using the initial condition $H(0) = 170$:

$$170 = 70 + Ae^0 = 70 + A,$$

so

$$A = 100.$$

Therefore,

$$H(t) = 70 + 100e^{-kt}.$$

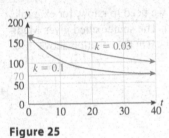

Figure 25

$\boxed{Q}$: *But what is k?*

$\boxed{A}$: The constant k determines the rate of cooling. Its value depends on the units of time we are using, on the substance cooling—in this case the coffee—and on its container. Because k depends so heavily on the particular circumstances, it's usually easiest to determine it experimentally. Figure 25 shows two possible graphs, one with $k = 0.1$ and the other with $k = 0.03$. ($k \approx 0.03$ would be reasonable for a cup of coffee in a polystyrene container with t measured in minutes.)

In any case we can see from the graph or the formula for $H(t)$ that the temperature of the coffee will approach the ambient temperature exponentially.

➡ **Before we go on . . .** Notice that the calculation in Example 4 shows that the temperature of an object cooling according to Newton's Law is given in general by

$$H(t) = T_a + (T_0 - T_a)e^{-kt},$$

where T_a is the ambient temperature (70° in the example) and T_0 is the initial temperature (170° in the example). The formula also holds if the ambient temperature is higher than the initial temperature ("Newton's Law of Heating"). ∎

14.6 EXERCISES

▼ more advanced   ◆ challenging
🔲 indicates exercises that should be solved using technology

In Exercises 1–10, find the general solution of the given differential equation. Where possible, solve for y as a function of x.

1. $\dfrac{dy}{dx} = x^2 + \sqrt{x}$

[HINT: See Quick Example 1.]

2. $\dfrac{dy}{dx} = \dfrac{1}{x} + 3$

[HINT: See Quick Example 1.]

3. $\dfrac{dy}{dx} = \dfrac{x}{y}$

[HINT: See Example 2(a).]

4. $\dfrac{dy}{dx} = \dfrac{y}{x}$

[HINT: See Example 2(a).]

5. $\dfrac{dy}{dx} = xy$

6. $\dfrac{dy}{dx} = x^2 y$

7. $\dfrac{dy}{dx} = (x + 1)y^2$

8. $\dfrac{dy}{dx} = \dfrac{1}{(x + 1)y^2}$

9. $x\dfrac{dy}{dx} = \dfrac{1}{y}\ln x$

10. $\dfrac{1}{x}\dfrac{dy}{dx} = \dfrac{1}{y}\ln x$

In Exercises 11–20, find the indicated particular solution of the given differential equation. [HINT: See Example 2(b).]

11. $\dfrac{dy}{dx} = x^3 - 2x$; $y = 1$ when $x = 0$

12. $\dfrac{dy}{dx} = 2 - e^{-x}$; $y = 0$ when $x = 0$

13. $\dfrac{dy}{dx} = \dfrac{x^2}{y^2}$; $y = 2$ when $x = 0$

14. $\dfrac{dy}{dx} = \dfrac{y^2}{x^2}$; $y = \dfrac{1}{2}$ when $x = 1$

15. $x\dfrac{dy}{dx} = y$; $y(1) = 2$

16. $x^2\dfrac{dy}{dx} = y$; $y(1) = 1$

17. $\dfrac{dy}{dx} = x(y + 1)$; $y(0) = 0$

18. $\dfrac{dy}{dx} = \dfrac{y + 1}{x}$; $y(1) = 2$

19. $\dfrac{dy}{dx} = \dfrac{xy^2}{x^2 + 1}$; $y(0) = -1$

20. $\dfrac{dy}{dx} = \dfrac{xy}{(x^2 + 1)^2}$; $y(0) = 1$

Applications

21. *Sales* Your monthly sales of green tea ice cream are falling at an instantaneous rate of 5% per month. If you currently sell 1,000 quarts per month, find the differential equation that describes your change in sales and then solve it to predict your monthly sales. [HINT: See Example 3.]

22. *Profit* Your monthly profit on sales of avocado ice cream is rising at an instantaneous rate of 10% per month. If you currently make a profit of $15,000 per month, find the differential equation describing your change in profit, and solve it to predict your monthly profits. [HINT: See Example 3.]

23. *Newton's Law of Cooling* For coffee in a ceramic cup, suppose $k \approx 0.05$ with time measured in minutes. **(a)** Use Newton's Law of Cooling to predict the temperature of the coffee, initially at a temperature of 200°F, that is left to sit in a room at 75°F. **(b)** When will the coffee have cooled to 80°F? [HINT: See Example 4.]

24. *Newton's Law of Cooling* For coffee in a paper cup, suppose $k \approx 0.08$ with time measured in minutes. **(a)** Use Newton's Law of Cooling to predict the temperature of the coffee, initially at a temperature of 210°F, that is left to sit in a room at 60°F. **(b)** When will the coffee have cooled to 70°F? [**HINT:** See Example 4.]

25. *Cooling* A bowl of clam chowder at 190°F is placed in a room whose air temperature is 75°F. After 10 minutes the soup has cooled to 150°F. Find the value of k in Newton's Law of Cooling, and hence find the temperature of the chowder as a function of time.

26. *Heating* Suppose that a pie at 20°F is put in an oven at 350°F. After 15 minutes, its temperature has risen to 80°F. Find the value of k in Newton's Law of Heating (see the note after Example 4), and hence find the temperature of the pie as a function of time.

27. *Market Saturation* You have just introduced a new 3D monitor to the market. You predict that you will eventually sell 100,000 monitors and that your monthly rate of sales will be 10% of the difference between the saturation value of 100,000 and the total number you have sold up to that point. Find a differential equation for your total sales (as a function of the month), and solve. (What are your total sales at the moment when you first introduce the monitor?)

28. *Market Saturation* Repeat Exercise 27, assuming that monthly sales will be 5% of the difference between the saturation value (of 100,000 monitors) and the total sales to that point, and assuming that you sell 5,000 monitors to corporate customers before placing the monitor on the open market.

29. *Determining Demand* *Nancy's Chocolates* estimates that the elasticity of demand for its dark chocolate truffles is $E = 0.05p - 1.5$, where p is the price per pound. Nancy's sells 20 pounds of truffles per week when the price is $20 per pound. Find the formula expressing the demand q as a function of p. Recall that the elasticity of demand is given by

$$E = -\frac{dq}{dp} \times \frac{p}{q}.$$

30. *Determining Demand* *Nancy's Chocolates* estimates that the elasticity of demand for its chocolate strawberries is $E = 0.02p - 0.5$, where p is the price per pound. It sells 30 pounds of chocolate strawberries per week when the price is $30 per pound. Find the formula expressing the demand q as a function of p. Recall that the elasticity of demand is given by

$$E = -\frac{dq}{dp} \times \frac{p}{q}.$$

Linear Differential Equations *Exercises 31–36 are based on* *first-order linear differential equations with constant coefficients. These have the form*

$$\frac{dy}{dt} + py = f(t) \quad (p \text{ constant})$$

and the general solution is

$$y = e^{-pt} \int f(t)e^{pt}\, dt.$$

(Check this by substituting!)

31. Solve the linear differential equation

$$\frac{dy}{dt} + y = e^{-t}; \quad y = 1 \text{ when } t = 0.$$

32. Solve the linear differential equation

$$\frac{dy}{dt} - y = e^{2t}; \quad y = 2 \text{ when } t = 0.$$

33. Solve the linear differential equation

$$2\frac{dy}{dt} - y = 2t; \quad y = 1 \text{ when } t = 0.$$

[**HINT:** First rewrite the differential equation in the form $\frac{dy}{dt} + py = f(t)$.]

34. Solve the linear differential equation

$$2\frac{dy}{dt} + y = -t; \quad y = 1 \text{ when } t = 0$$

[**HINT:** First rewrite the differential equation in the form $\frac{dy}{dt} + py = f(t)$.]

35. ▼ *Electric Circuits* The flow of current $i(t)$ in an electric circuit without capacitance satisfies the linear differential equation

$$L\frac{di}{dt} + Ri = V(t),$$

where L and R are constants (the *inductance* and *resistance*, respectively) and $V(t)$ is the applied voltage. (See figure.)

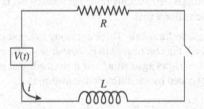

If the voltage is supplied by a 10-volt battery and the switch is turned on at time $t = 1$, then the voltage V is a step function that jumps from 0 to 10 at $t = 1$: $V(t) = 5\left[1 + \dfrac{|t - 1|}{t - 1}\right]$. Find the current as a function of time for $L = R = 1$. Use a grapher to plot the resulting current as a function of time. (Assume that there is no current flowing at time $t = 0$.) [**HINT:** Use the following integral formula:

$$\int \left[1 + \frac{|t - 1|}{t - 1}\right]e^t\, dt = \left[1 + \frac{|t - 1|}{t - 1}\right](e^t - e) + C.]$$

36. ▼ *Electric Circuits* Repeat Exercise 35 for $L = 1$, $R = 5$, and $V(t) = 5\left[1 + \dfrac{|t - 2|}{t - 2}\right]$. (The switch flipped on at time $t = 2$.) [**HINT:** Use the following integral formula:

$$\int \left[1 + \frac{|t - 2|}{t - 2}\right]e^{5t}\, dt = \left[1 + \frac{|t - 2|}{t - 2}\right]\left(\frac{e^{5t} - e^{10}}{5}\right) + C.]$$

37. ▼ *Approach to Equilibrium* The *Extrasoft Toy Co.* has just released its latest creation, a plush platypus named "Eggbert." The demand function for Eggbert dolls is $D(p) = 50,000 - 500p$ dolls per month when the price is p dollars. The supply function is $S(p) = 30,000 + 500p$ dolls per month when the price is p dollars. This makes the equilibrium price $20. The **Evans price adjustment model** assumes that if the price is set at a value other than the equilibrium price, it will change over time in such a way that its rate of change is proportional to the shortage $D(p) - S(p)$.
  a. Write the differential equation given by the Evans price adjustment model for the price p as a function of time.
  b. Find the general solution of the differential equation you wrote in part (a). (You will have two unknown constants, one being the constant of proportionality.)
  c. Find the particular solution in which Eggbert dolls are initially priced at $10 and the price rises to $12 after one month.

38. ▼ *Approach to Equilibrium* Spacely Sprockets has just released its latest model, the Dominator. The demand function is $D(p) = 10,000 - 1,000p$ sprockets per year when the price is p dollars. The supply function is $S(p) = 8,000 + 1,000p$ sprockets per year when the price is p dollars.
  a. Using the Evans price adjustment model described in Exercise 37, write the differential equation for the price $p(t)$ as a function of time.
  b. Find the general solution of the differential equation you wrote in part (a).
  c. Find the particular solution in which Dominator sprockets are initially priced at $5 each but fall to $3 each after 1 year.

39. ▼ *Logistic Equation* There are many examples of growth in which the rate of growth is slow at first, becomes faster, and then slows again as a limit is reached. This pattern can be described by the differential equation

$$\frac{dy}{dt} = ay(L - y),$$

where a is a constant and L is the limit of y. Show by substitution that

$$y = \frac{CL}{e^{-aLt} + C}$$

is a solution of this equation, where C is an arbitrary constant.

40. ▼ *Logistic Equation* Using separation of variables and integration with a table of integrals or a symbolic algebra program, solve the differential equation in Exercise 39 to derive the solution given there.

▯ *Exercises 41–44 require the use of technology.*

41. ▼ *Market Saturation* You have just introduced a new model of Blu-ray disc player. You predict that the market

will saturate at 2,000,000 Blu-ray disc players and that your total sales will be governed by the equation

$$\frac{dS}{dt} = \frac{1}{4}S(2 - S),$$

where S is the total sales in millions of Blu-ray disc players and t is measured in months. If you give away 1,000 Blu-ray disc players when you first introduce them, what will S be? Sketch the graph of S as a function of t. About how long will it take to saturate the market? (See Exercise 39.)

42. ▼ *Epidemics* A certain epidemic of influenza is predicted to follow the function defined by

$$\frac{dA}{dt} = \frac{1}{10}A(20 - A),$$

where A is the number of people infected in millions and t is the number of months after the epidemic starts. If 20,000 cases are reported initially, find $A(t)$ and sketch its graph. When is A growing fastest? How many people will eventually be affected? (See Exercise 39.)

43. ▼ *Growth of Tumors* The growth of tumors in animals can be modeled by the Gompertz equation:

$$\frac{dy}{dt} = -ay \ln\left(\frac{y}{b}\right),$$

where y is the size of a tumor, t is time, and a and b are constants that depend on the type of tumor and the units of measurement.
  a. Solve for y as a function of t.
  b. If $a = 1$, $b = 10$, and $y(0) = 5$ cubic centimeters (with t measured in days), find the specific solution and graph it.

44. ▼ *Growth of Tumors* Refer back to Exercise 43. Suppose that $a = 1$, $b = 10$, and $y(0) = 15$ cubic centimeters. Find the specific solution and graph it. Comparing its graph to the one obtained in Exercise 43, what can you say about tumor growth in these instances?

Communication and Reasoning Exercises

45. What is the difference between a particular solution and the general solution of a differential equation? How do we get a particular solution from the general solution?

46. Why is there always an arbitrary constant in the general solution of a differential equation? Why are there not two or more arbitrary constants in a first-order differential equation?

47. ▼ Show by example that a second-order differential equation (one involving the second derivative y'') usually has two arbitrary constants in its general solution.

48. ▼ Find a differential equation that is not separable.

49. ▼ Find a differential equation whose general solution is $y = 4e^{-x} + 3x + C$.

50. ▼ Explain how, knowing the elasticity of demand as a function of either price or demand, you may find the demand equation. (See Exercise 29.)

CHAPTER 14 REVIEW

KEY CONCEPTS

www.WanerMath.com
Go to the Website to find a comprehensive and interactive Web-based summary of Chapter 14.

14.1 Integration by Parts
Integration-by-parts formula:

$$\int u \cdot v \, dx = u \cdot I(v) - \int D(u)I(v) \, dx$$

[p. 1060]
Tabular method for integration by parts [p. 1061]
Integrating a polynomial times a logarithm [p. 1064]

14.2 Area between Two Curves and Applications
If $f(x) \geq g(x)$ for all x in $[a, b]$, then the area of the region between the graphs of f and g and between $x = a$ and $x = b$ is given by

$$A = \int_a^b [f(x) - g(x)] \, dx. \quad [p. 1069]$$

Regions enclosed by crossing curves [p. 1072]
Area enclosed by two curves [p. 1073]
General instructions for finding the area between the graphs of $f(x)$ and $g(x)$ [p. 1073]
Approximating the area between two curves using technology:

$$A = \int_a^b |f(x) - g(x)| \, dx \quad [p. 1074]$$

14.3 Averages and Moving Averages
Average, or mean, of a collection of values:

$$\bar{y} = \frac{y_1 + y_2 + \cdots + y_n}{n} \quad [p. 1078]$$

The *average*, or *mean*, of a function $f(x)$ on an interval $[a, b]$:

$$\bar{f} = \frac{1}{b-a} \int_a^b f(x) \, dx. \quad [p. 1079]$$

Average balance [p. 1080]
Computing the moving average of a set of data [p. 1080]
n-Unit moving average of a function:

$$\bar{f}(x) = \frac{1}{n} \int_{x-n}^x f(t) \, dt \quad [p. 1082]$$

Computing moving averages of sawtooth and step functions [p. 1082]

14.4 Applications to Business and Economics: Consumers' and Producers' Surplus and Continuous Income Streams
Consumers' surplus:

$$CS = \int_0^{\bar{q}} (D(q) - \bar{p}) \, dq \quad [p. 1088]$$

Producers' surplus:

$$PS = \int_0^{\bar{q}} (\bar{p} - S(q)) \, dq \quad [p. 1089]$$

Equilibrium price [p. 1090]
Social gain $= CS + PS$ [p. 1091]
Total value of a continuous income stream: $TV = \int_a^b R(t) \, dt$ [p. 1092]

Future value of a continuous income stream: $FV = \int_a^b R(t)e^{r(b-t)} \, dt$

[p. 1093]
Present value of a continuous income stream: $PV = \int_a^b R(t)e^{r(a-t)} \, dt$

[p. 1094]

14.5 Improper Integrals and Applications
Improper integral with an infinite limit of integration:

$$\int_a^{+\infty} f(x) \, dx, \quad \int_{-\infty}^b f(x) \, dx,$$

$$\int_{-\infty}^{+\infty} f(x) \, dx \quad [p. 1097]$$

Improper integral in which the integrand becomes infinite [p. 1100]
Testing for convergence [p. 1101]
Integrand infinite between the endpoints [p. 1102]
Integral improper in two ways [p. 1102]

14.6 Differential Equations and Applications
Simple differential equations:

$$\frac{dy}{dx} = f(x) \quad [p. 1107]$$

Separable differential equations:

$$\frac{dy}{dx} = f(x)g(y) \quad [p. 1109]$$

Newton's Law of Cooling [p. 1111]

REVIEW EXERCISES

In Exercises 1–10, evaluate the given integral.

1. $\int (x^2 + 2)e^x \, dx$

2. $\int (x^2 - x)e^{-3x+1} \, dx$

3. $\int x^2 \ln(2x) \, dx$

4. $\int \log_5 x \, dx$

5. $\int 2x|2x + 1| \, dx$

6. $\int 3x|-x + 5| \, dx$

7. $\int 5x \frac{|-x + 3|}{-x + 3} \, dx$

8. $\int 2x \frac{|3x + 1|}{3x + 1} \, dx$

9. $\int_{-2}^2 (x^3 + 1)e^{-x} \, dx$

10. $\int_1^e x^2 \ln x \, dx$

In Exercises 11–14, find the area of the given region.

11. Between $y = x^3$ and $y = 1 - x^3$ for x in $[0, 1]$
12. Between $y = e^x$ and $y = e^{-x}$ for x in $[0, 2]$
13. Enclosed by $y = 1 - x^2$ and $y = x^2$
14. Between $y = x$ and $y = xe^{-x}$ for x in $[0, 2]$

In Exercises 15–18, find the average value of the given function over the indicated interval.

15. $f(x) = x^3 - 1$ over $[-2, 2]$

16. $f(x) = \frac{x}{x^2 + 1}$ over $[0, 1]$

17. $f(x) = x^2 e^x$ over $[0, 1]$

18. $f(x) = (x + 1) \ln x$ over $[1, 2e]$

In Exercises 19–22, find the 2-unit moving averages of the given function.

19. $f(x) = 3x + 1$

20. $f(x) = 6x^2 + 12$

21. $f(x) = x^{4/3}$

22. $f(x) = \ln x$

In Exercises 23 and 24, calculate the consumers' surplus at the indicated unit price $\bar{p}$ for the given demand equation.

23. $p = 50 - \dfrac{1}{2}q; \bar{p} = 10$

24. $p = 10 - q^{1/2}; \bar{p} = 4$

In Exercises 25 and 26, calculate the producers' surplus at the indicated unit price $\bar{p}$ for the given supply equation.

25. $p = 50 + \dfrac{1}{2}q; \bar{p} = 100$

26. $p = 10 + q^{1/2}; \bar{p} = 40$

In Exercises 27–32, decide whether the given integral converges. If the integral converges, compute its value.

27. $\displaystyle\int_1^\infty \dfrac{1}{x^5}\, dx$

28. $\displaystyle\int_0^1 \dfrac{1}{x^5}\, dx$

29. $\displaystyle\int_{-1}^1 \dfrac{x}{(x^2 - 1)^{5/3}}\, dx$

30. $\displaystyle\int_0^2 \dfrac{x}{(x^2 - 1)^{1/3}}\, dx$

31. $\displaystyle\int_0^{+\infty} 2xe^{-x^2}\, dx$

32. $\displaystyle\int_0^{+\infty} x^2 e^{-6x^3}\, dx$

In Exercises 33–36, solve the given differential equation.

33. $\dfrac{dy}{dx} = x^2 y^2$

34. $\dfrac{dy}{dx} = xy + 2x$

35. $xy\dfrac{dy}{dx} = 1; y(1) = 1$

36. $y(x^2 + 1)\dfrac{dy}{dx} = xy^2; y(0) = 2$

Applications: OHaganBooks.com
[Try the game at www.OHaganBooks.com]

37. *Spending on Stationery* Alarmed by the volume of pointless memos and reports being copied and circulated by management at OHaganBooks.com, John O'Hagan ordered a 5-month audit of paper usage at the company. He found that management consumed paper at a rate of

$q(t) = 45t + 200$ thousand sheets per month $(0 \le t \le 5)$.

(t is the time in months since the audit began.) During the same period the price of paper was escalating; the company was charged approximately

$p(t) = 9e^{0.09t}$ dollars per thousand sheets.

Use an integral to estimate, to the nearest hundred dollars, the total spent on paper for management during the given period.

38. *Spending on Shipping* During the past 10 months, OHaganBooks.com shipped orders at a rate of about

$q(t) = 25t + 3,200$ packages per month $(0 \le t \le 10)$.

(t is the time in months since the beginning of the year.) During the same period the cost of shipping a package averaged approximately

$p(t) = 4e^{0.04t}$ dollars per package.

Use an integral to estimate, to the nearest thousand dollars, the total spent on shipping orders during the given period.

39. *Education Costs* Billy-Sean O'Hagan, having graduated *summa cum laude* from college, has been accepted by the doctoral program in biophysics at Oxford. John O'Hagan estimates that the total cost (minus scholarships) he will need to pay is \$2,000 per month but that this cost will escalate at a continuous compounding rate of 1% per month.
a. What, to the nearest dollar, will be the average monthly cost over the course of 2 years?
b. Find the 4-month moving average of the monthly cost.

40. *Investments* OHaganBooks.com keeps its cash reserves in a hedge fund paying 6% compounded continuously. It starts a year with \$1 million in reserves and does not withdraw or deposit any money.
a. What is the average amount it will have in the fund over the course of 2 years?
b. Find the 1-month moving average of the amount it has in the fund.

41. *Consumers' and Producers' Surplus* Currently, the hottest-selling item at OHaganBooks.com is *Mensa for Dummies,*[55] with a demand curve of $q = 20,000(28 - p)^{1/3}$ books per week and a supply curve of $q = 40,000(p - 19)^{1/3}$ books per week.
a. Find the equilibrium price and demand.
b. Find the consumers' and producers' surpluses at the equilibrium price.

42. *Consumers' and Producers' Surplus* OHaganBooks.com is about to start selling a new coffee table book, *Computer Designs of the Late Twentieth Century.* It estimates the demand curve to be $q = 1,000\sqrt{200 - 2p}$, and its willingness to order books from the publisher is given by the supply curve $q = 1,000\sqrt{10p - 400}$.
a. Find the equilibrium price and demand.
b. Find the consumers' and producers' surpluses at the equilibrium price.

43. *Revenue* Sales of the bestseller *A River Burns through It* are dropping at OHaganBooks.com. To try to bolster sales, the company is decreasing the price of the book, now \$40, at a rate of \$2 per week. As a result, this week OHaganBooks.com will sell 5,000 copies, and it estimates that sales will

---

[55] The actual title is: *Let Us Just Have A Ball! Mensa for Dummies,* by Wendu Mekbib, Silhouette Publishing Corporation.

fall continuously at a rate of 10% per week. How much revenue will it earn on sales of this book over the next 8 weeks?

44. *Foreign Investments* Panicked by the performance of the U.S. stock market, Marjory Duffin is investing her 401(k) money in a Russian hedge fund at a rate of approximately

$$q(t) = 1.7t^2 - 0.5t + 8 \text{ thousand shares per month,}$$

where t is time in months since the stock market began to plummet. At the time she started making the investments, the hedge fund was selling for $1 per share, but it subsequently declined in value at a continuous rate of 5% per month. What was the total amount of money Marjory Duffin invested after 1 year? (Answer to the nearest $1,000.)

45. *Investments* OHaganBooks.com CEO John O'Hagan has started a gift account for the *Marjory Duffin Foundation*. The account pays 6% compounded continuously and is initially empty. OHaganBooks.com deposits money continuously into it, starting at the rate of $100,000 per month and increasing by $10,000 per month.
  a. How much money will the company have in the account at the end of 2 years?
  b. How much of the amount you found in part (a) was principal deposited and how much was interest earned? (Round answers to the nearest $1,000.)

46. *Savings* John O'Hagan had been saving money for Billy-Sean's education since Billy-Sean was a wee lad. O'Hagan began depositing money at the rate of $1,000 per month and increased his deposits by $50 per month. If the account earned 5% compounded continuously and O'Hagan continued these deposits for 15 years,
  a. How much money did he accumulate?

  b. How much was money deposited and how much was interest?

47. *Acquisitions* The *Megabucks Corporation* is considering buying OHaganBooks.com. It estimates OHaganBooks.com's revenue stream at $50 million per year, growing continuously at a 10% rate. Assuming an interest rate of 6%, how much is OHaganBooks.com's revenue for the next year worth now?

48. *More Acquisitions* OHaganBooks.com is thinking of buying *JungleBooks* and would like to recoup its investment after 3 years. The estimated net profit for JungleBooks is $40 million per year, growing linearly by $5 million per year. Assuming an interest rate of 4%, how much should OHaganBooks.com pay for JungleBooks?

49. *Incompetence* OHaganBooks.com is shopping around for a new bank. A junior executive at one bank offers it the following interesting deal: The bank will pay OHaganBooks.com interest continuously at a rate numerically equal to 0.01% of the square of the amount of money it has in the account at any time. By considering what would happen if $10,000 was deposited in such an account, explain why the junior executive was fired shortly after this offer was made.

50. *Shrewd Bankers* The new junior officer at the bank (who replaced the one fired in Exercise 49) offers OHaganBooks.com the following deal for the $800,000 they plan to deposit: While the amount in the account is less than $1 million, the bank will pay interest continuously at a rate equal to 10% of the difference between $1 million and the amount of money in the account. When it rises over $1 million, the bank will pay interest of 20%. Why should OHaganBooks.com not take this offer?

Estimating Tax Revenues

You have just been hired by the incoming administration of your country as chief consultant for national tax policy, and you have been getting conflicting advice from the finance experts on your staff. Several of them have come up with plausible suggestions for new tax structures, and your job is to choose the plan that results in the most revenue for the government.

* To simplify our discussion, we are assuming (1) that all tax revenues are based on earned income and (2) that everyone in the population we consider earns some income.

Before you can evaluate their plans, you realize that it is essential to know your country's income distribution—that is, how many people earn how much money per year.* You might think that the most useful way of specifying income distribution would be to use a function that gives the exact number $f(x)$ of people who earn a given salary x. This would necessarily be a discrete function—it makes sense only if x happens to be a whole number of cents. There is, after all, no one earning a salary of exactly $22,000.142567! Furthermore, this function would behave rather erratically because there are, for example, probably many more people making a salary of exactly $30,000 than exactly $30,000.01. Given these problems, it is far more convenient to start with the function defined by

$$N(x) = \text{Total number of people earning between 0 and } x \text{ dollars.}$$

Actually, you would want a "smoothed" version of this function. The graph of $N(x)$ might look like the one shown in Figure 26.

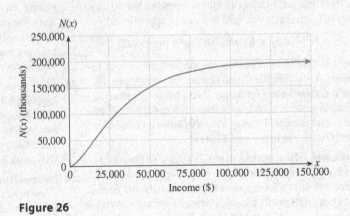

Figure 26

If we take the *derivative* of $N(x)$, we get an income distribution function. Its graph might look like the one shown in Figure 27.

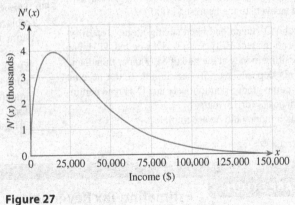

Figure 27

Because the derivative measures the rate of change, its value at x is the additional number of taxpayers per \$1 increase in salary. Thus, the fact that $N'(25,000) \approx 3,500$ tells us that approximately 3,500 people are earning a salary of between \$25,000 and \$25,001. In other words, N' shows the distribution of incomes among the population—hence, the name "distribution function."*

* A very similar idea is used in probability. See the optional chapter "Calculus Applied to Probability and Statistics" on the Website.

† Gamma distributions are often good models for income distributions. The one used in the text is the authors' approximation of the income distribution in the United States in 2013. Source for data: U.S. Census Bureau, Current Population Survey, 2014 Annual Social and Economic Supplement (www.census.gov).

You therefore send a memo to your experts requesting the income distribution function for the nation. After much collection of data, they tell you that the income distribution function is

$$N'(x) = 12x^{0.676}e^{-x/21,500}.$$

This is in fact the function whose graph is shown in Figure 27 and is an example of a **gamma distribution**.† (You might find it odd that you weren't given the original function N, but it will turn out that you don't need it. How would you compute it?)

Given this income distribution, your financial experts have come up with the two possible tax policies illustrated in Figures 28 and 29.

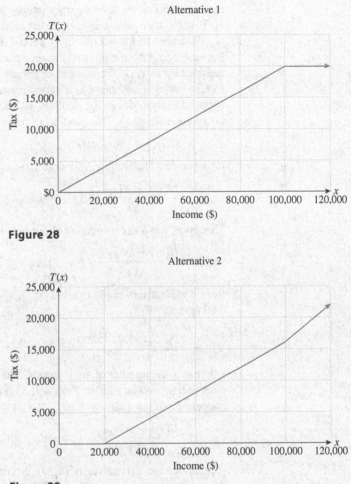

Figure 28

Figure 29

In the first alternative, all taxpayers pay 20% of their income in taxes, except that no one pays more than $20,000 in taxes. In the second alternative, there are three tax brackets, described by the following table:

Income	Marginal Tax Rate
$0–20,000	0%
$20,000–100,000	20%
Above $100,000	30%

Now you must determine which alternative will generate more tax revenue.

Each of Figures 28 and 29 is the graph of a function, T. Rather than using the formulas for these particular functions, you begin by working with the general situation. You have an income distribution function N' and a tax function T, both functions of annual income. You need to find a formula for total tax revenues. First you decide to use a cutoff so that you need to work only with incomes in some finite interval $[0, M]$; you might use, for example, $M = \$10$ million. (Later you will let M approach $+\infty$.) Next, you subdivide the interval $[0, M]$ into a large number of intervals of small width, Δx. If $[x_{k-1}, x_k]$ is a typical such interval, you wish to calculate the approximate tax revenue from people whose total incomes lie between x_{k-1} and x_k. You will then sum over k to get the total revenue.

You need to know how many people are making incomes between x_{k-1} and x_k. Because $N(x_k)$ people are making incomes *up to* x_k and $N(x_{k-1})$ people are making incomes up to x_{k-1}, the number of people making incomes between x_{k-1} and x_k is $N(x_k) - N(x_{k-1})$. Because x_k is very close to x_{k-1}, the incomes of these people are all approximately equal to x_{k-1} dollars, so each of these taxpayers is paying an annual tax of about $T(x_{k-1})$. This gives a tax revenue of

$$[N(x_k) - N(x_{k-1})]T(x_{k-1}).$$

Now you do a clever thing. You write $x_k - x_{k-1} = \Delta x$ and replace $N(x_k) - N(x_{k-1})$ by

$$\frac{N(x_k) - N(x_{k-1})}{\Delta x}\Delta x.$$

This gives you a tax revenue of about

$$\frac{N(x_k) - N(x_{k-1})}{\Delta x} T(x_{k-1}) \Delta x$$

from wage-earners in the bracket $[x_{k-1}, x_k]$. Summing over k gives an approximate total revenue of

$$\sum_{k=1}^{n} \frac{N(x_k) - N(x_{k-1})}{\Delta x} T(x_{k-1}) \Delta x,$$

where n is the number of subintervals. The larger n is, the more accurate your estimate will be, so you take the limit of the sum as $n \to \infty$. When you do this, two things happen. First, the quantity

$$\frac{N(x_k) - N(x_{k-1})}{\Delta x}$$

approaches the derivative, $N'(x_{k-1})$. Second, the sum, which you recognize as a Riemann sum, approaches the integral

$$\int_0^M N'(x)T(x)\, dx.$$

You now take the limit as $M \to +\infty$ to get

$$\text{Total tax revenue} = \int_0^{+\infty} N'(x)T(x)\, dx.$$

This improper integral is fine in theory, but the actual calculation will have to be done numerically, so you stick with the upper limit of $10 million for now. You will have to check that it is reasonable at the end. (Notice that, by the graph of N', it appears that extremely few, if any, people earn that much.) Now you already have a formula for $N'(x)$, but you still need to write formulas for the tax functions $T(x)$ for both alternatives.

Alternative 1 The graph in Figure 28 rises linearly from 0 to 20,000 as x ranges from 0 to 100,000 and then stays constant at 20,000. The slope of the first part is $20,000/100,000 = 0.2$. The taxation function is therefore

$$T_1(x) = \begin{cases} 0.2x & \text{if } 0 \le x < 100{,}000 \\ 20{,}000 & \text{if } x \ge 100{,}000. \end{cases}$$

For use of technology, it's convenient to express this in closed form using absolute values:*

* To see how to obtain the formula, consult the introduction to Exercises 67–68 in Section 14.1.

$$T_1(x) = 0.2x + \frac{1}{2}\left(1 + \frac{|x - 100,000|}{x - 100,000}\right)(20,000 - 0.2x).$$

The total revenue generated by this tax scheme is, therefore,

$$R_1 = \int_0^{10,000,000} (12x^{0.676}e^{-x/21,500})$$

$$\times \left[0.2x + \frac{1}{2}\left(1 + \frac{|x - 100,000|}{x - 100,000}\right)(20,000 - 0.2x)\right] dx.$$

You decide not to attempt this by hand! You use numerical integration software to obtain a grand total of $R_1 = \$1,394,730,000,000$, or $\$1.39473$ trillion (rounded to six significant digits).†

† **Note** If you use the Numerical Integration utility on the Website,

Online Utilities

→ Numerical Integration Utility and Grapher

Enter

12x^(0.676)*exp(-x/21500)*
(0.2x+0.5*(20000-0.2x)*
(1+abs(x-100000)/(x-100000)))
for f(x), and 0 and 10000000 for a and b respectively, and press "Integral".

Alternative 2 The graph in Figure 29 rises with a slope of 0.2 from 0 to 16,000 as x ranges from 20,000 to 100,000, then rises from that point on with a slope of 0.3. (This is why we say that the *marginal* tax rates are 20% and 30%, respectively.) The taxation function is therefore

$$T_2(x) = \begin{cases} 0 & \text{if } 0 \le x < 20,000 \\ 0.2(x - 20,000) & \text{if } 20,000 \le x < 100,000 \\ 16,000 + 0.3(x - 100,000) & \text{if } x \ge 100,000. \end{cases}$$

Again, you express this in closed form using absolute values:

$$T_2(x) = [0.2(x - 20,000)]\frac{1}{2}\left(\frac{|x - 20,000|}{x - 20,000} - \frac{|x - 100,000|}{x - 100,000}\right)$$

$$+ [16,000 + 0.3(x - 100,000)]\frac{1}{2}\left(1 + \frac{|x - 100,000|}{x - 100,000}\right)$$

$$= 0.1(x - 20,000)\left(\frac{|x - 20,000|}{x - 20,000} - \frac{|x - 100,000|}{x - 100,000}\right)$$

$$+ [8,000 + 0.15(x - 100,000)]\left(1 + \frac{|x - 100,000|}{x - 100,000}\right).$$

Values of x between 0 and 20,000 do not contribute to the integral, so

$$R_2 = \int_{20,000}^{10,000,000} 12x^{0.676}e^{-x/21,500} T_2(x)\, dx$$

with $T_2(x)$ as above. Numerical integration software gives $R_2 = \$0.766843$ trillion— considerably less than Alternative 1. Thus, even though Alternative 2 taxes the wealthy more heavily, it yields less total revenue.

Now, what about the cutoff at $10 million annual income? If you try either integral again with an upper limit of $100 million, you will see no change in either result to six significant digits. There simply are not enough taxpayers earning an income above $10,000,000 to make a difference. You conclude that your answers are sufficiently accurate and that the first alternative provides more tax revenue.

EXERCISES

In Exercises 1–4, calculate the total tax revenue for a country with the given income distribution and tax policies (all currency in dollars).

1. $N'(x) = 100x^{0.466}e^{-x/23,000}$; 25% tax on all income

2. $N'(x) = 100x^{0.4}e^{-x/30,000}$; 45% tax on all income

3. $N'(x) = 100x^{0.466}e^{-x/23,000}$; tax brackets as in the following tax table:

Income	Marginal Tax Rate
$0–30,000	0%
$30,000–250,000	10%
Above $250,000	80%

4. $N'(x) = 100x^{0.4}e^{-x/30,000}$; no tax on any income below $250,000, 100% marginal tax rate on any income above $250,000

5. Let $N'(x)$ be an income distribution function.
   a. If $0 \le a < b$, what does $\int_a^b N'(x)\,dx$ represent? [**HINT**: Use the Fundamental Theorem of Calculus.]
   b. What does $\int_0^{+\infty} N'(x)\,dx$ represent?

6. Let $N'(x)$ be an income distribution function. What does $\int_0^{+\infty} xN'(x)\,dx$ represent? [**HINT**: Argue as in the text.]

7. Let $P(x)$ be the number of people earning more than x dollars.
   a. What is $N(x) + P(x)$?
   b. Show that $P'(x) = -N'(x)$.
   c. Use integration by parts to show that, if $T(0) = 0$, then the total tax revenue is

   $$\int_0^{+\infty} P(x)T'(x)\,dx.$$

   [Note: You may assume that $T'(x)$ is continuous, but the result is still true if we assume only that $T(x)$ is continuous and piecewise continuously differentiable.]

8. Income tax functions T are most often described, as in the text, by tax brackets and marginal tax rates.
   a. If one tax bracket is $a < x \le b$, show that $\int_a^b P(x)\,dx$ is the total income earned in the country that falls into that bracket (P as in Exercise 7).
   b. Use part (a) to explain directly why $\int_0^{+\infty} P(x)T'(x)\,dx$ gives the total tax revenue in the case in which T is described by tax brackets and constant marginal tax rates in each bracket.

Section 14.3

Example 3 (page 1080) The following table shows *Colossal Conglomerate*'s closing stock prices for 20 consecutive trading days:

Day	1	2	3	4	5	6	7	8	9	10
Price	20	22	21	24	24	23	25	26	20	24
Day	11	12	13	14	15	16	17	18	19	20
Price	26	26	25	27	28	27	29	27	25	24

Plot these prices and the 5-day moving average.

Solution

Here is how to automate this calculation on a TI-83/84 Plus.

1. Use

   $$\text{seq}(X,X,1,20)\to L_1$$
   $$\boxed{2\text{ND}}\ \boxed{\text{STAT}} \to \text{OPS} \to 5$$
   $$\boxed{\text{STO}}\ \boxed{2\text{ND}}\ \boxed{\text{STAT}} \to L_1$$

   to enter the sequence of numbers 1 through 20 into the list L_1, representing the trading days.

2. Using the list editor accessible through the $\boxed{\text{STAT}}$ menu, enter the daily stock prices in list L_2.

3. Calculate the list of 5-day moving averages by using the following command:

   $$\text{seq}((L_2(X)+L_2(X-1)+L_2(X-2)+L_2(X-3)$$
   $$+L_2(X-4))/5,X,5,20)\to L_3$$

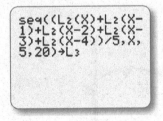

   This has the effect of putting the moving averages into elements 1 through 16 of list L_3.

4. If you wish to plot the moving average on the same graph as the daily prices, you will want the averages in L_3 to match up with the prices in L_2. One way to do this is to put four more entries at the beginning of L_3—say, copies of the first four entries of L_2. The following command accomplishes this:

   $$\text{augment}(\text{seq}(L_2(X),X,1,4),L_3)\to L_3$$
   $$\boxed{2\text{ND}}\ \boxed{\text{STAT}} \to \text{OPS} \to 9$$

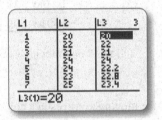

5. You can now graph the prices and moving averages by creating an xyLine scatter plot through the $\boxed{\text{STAT PLOT}}$ menu, with L_1 being the Xlist and L_2 being the Ylist for Plot1 and L_1 being the Xlist and L_3 the Ylist for Plot2:

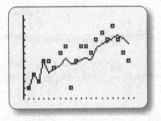

Section 14.3

Example 3 (page 1080) The following table shows *Colossal Conglomerate*'s closing stock prices for 20 consecutive trading days:

Day	1	2	3	4	5	6	7	8	9	10
Price	20	22	21	24	24	23	25	26	20	24
Day	11	12	13	14	15	16	17	18	19	20
Price	26	26	25	27	28	27	29	27	25	24

Plot these prices and the 5-day moving average.

Solution

1. Compute the moving averages in a column next to the daily prices, as shown here:

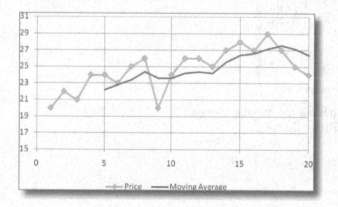

2. You can then graph the price and moving average using a scatter plot:

15

FUNCTIONS OF SEVERAL VARIABLES

W www.WanerMath.com

At the Website, in addition to the resources listed in the Preface, you will find:

- A surface grapher
- An Excel surface grapher
- A multiple linear regression utility

The following optional extra sections:

- Maxima and Minima: Boundaries and the Extreme Value Theorem
- The Chain Rule for Functions of Several Variables

CASE STUDY

Modeling College Population

College Malls, Inc. is planning to build a national chain of shopping malls in college neighborhoods. The company is planning to lease only to stores that target the specific age demographics of the national college student population. To decide which age brackets to target, the company has asked you, a paid consultant, for an analysis of the college population by student age and of its trends over time.

How can you analyze the relevant data?

david pearson/Alamy Stock Photo

Introduction

We have studied functions of a single variable extensively. But not every useful function is a function of only one variable. In fact, most are not. For example, if you operate an online bookstore in competition with Amazon.com, BN.com, and BooksAMillion.com, your sales may depend on those of your competitors. Your company's daily revenue might be modeled by a function such as

$$R(x, y, z) = 10,000 - 0.01x - 0.02y - 0.01z + 0.00001yz,$$

where x, y, and z are the online daily revenues of Amazon.com, BN.com, and BooksAMillion.com, respectively. Here, R is a function of three variables because it *depends on x, y, and z*. As we shall see, the techniques of calculus extend readily to such functions. Among the applications we shall look at is optimization: finding, where possible, the maximum or minimum of a function of two or more variables.

15.1   Functions of Several Variables from the Numerical, Algebraic, and Graphical Viewpoints

Numerical and Algebraic Viewpoints

Recall that a function of one variable is a rule for manufacturing a new number $f(x)$ from a single independent variable x. A function of two or more variables is similar, but the new number now depends on more than one independent variable.

Function of Several Variables

A **real-valued function**, f, **of** $x, y, z, \ldots$ is a rule for manufacturing a new number, written $f(x, y, z, \ldots)$, from the values of a sequence of independent variables $(x, y, z, \ldots)$. The function f is called a **real-valued function of two variables** if there are two independent variables, a **real-valued function of three variables** if there are three independent variables, and so on.

Quick Examples

1. $f(x, y) = x - y$ Function of two variables

   $f(1, 2) = 1 - 2 = -1$ Substitute 1 for x and 2 for y.

   $f(2, -1) = 2 - (-1) = 3$ Substitute 2 for x and -1 for y.

   $f(y, x) = y - x$ Substitute y for x and x for y.

2. $g(x, y) = x^2 + y^2$ Function of two variables

   $g(-1, 3) = (-1)^2 + 3^2 = 10$ Substitute -1 for x and 3 for y.

3. $h(x, y, z) = x + y + xz$ Function of three variables

   $h(2, 2, -2) = 2 + 2 + 2(-2) = 0$ Substitute 2 for x, 2 for y, and -2 for z.

Note It is often convenient to use $x_1, x_2, x_3, \ldots$ for the independent variables, so, for instance, the third example above would be $h(x_1, x_2, x_3) = x_1 + x_2 + x_1 x_3$. ∎

Figure 1 illustrates the concept of a function of two variables: In goes a pair of numbers, and out comes a single number.

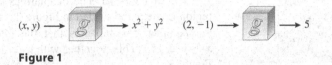

$$(x, y) \longrightarrow \boxed{g} \longrightarrow x^2 + y^2 \qquad (2, -1) \longrightarrow \boxed{g} \longrightarrow 5$$

Figure 1

As with functions of one variable, functions of several variables can be represented numerically (using a table of values), algebraically (using a formula as in the above examples), and sometimes graphically (using a graph).

Let's now look at a number of examples of interesting functions of several variables.

Roy Mehta/The Image Bank/Getty Images

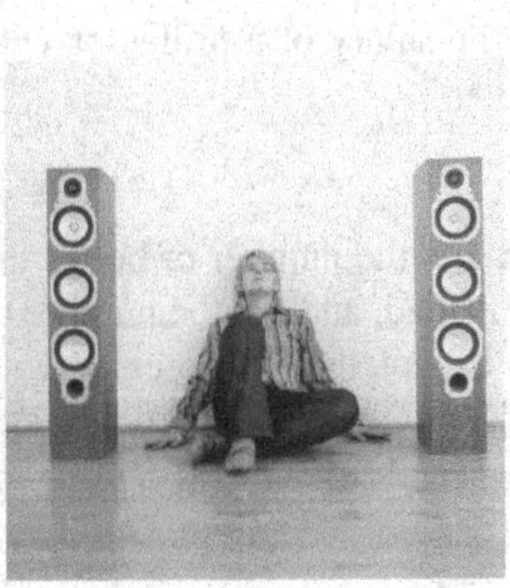

EXAMPLE 1   Cost Function

You own a company that makes two models of speakers: the Ultra Mini and the Big Stack. Your total monthly cost (in dollars) to make x Ultra Minis and y Big Stacks is given by

$$C(x, y) = 10{,}000 + 20x + 40y.$$

What is the significance of each term in this formula?

Solution The terms have meanings similar to those we saw for linear cost functions of a single variable. Let us look at the terms one at a time.

Constant Term Consider the monthly cost of making no speakers at all ($x = y = 0$). We find

$$C(0, 0) = 10{,}000. \qquad \text{Cost of making no speakers is \$10,000.}$$

Thus, the constant term 10,000 is the **fixed cost**, the amount you have to pay each month even if you make no speakers.

Coefficients of x and y Suppose you make a certain number of Ultra Minis and Big Stacks one month and the next month you increase production by one Ultra Mini. The costs are

$$\begin{aligned} C(x, y) &= 10{,}000 + 20x + 40y & \text{First month} \\ C(x + 1, y) &= 10{,}000 + 20(x + 1) + 40y & \text{Second month} \\ &= 10{,}000 + 20x + 20 + 40y \\ &= C(x, y) + 20 \end{aligned}$$

Thus, each Ultra Mini adds $20 to the total cost. We say that $20 is the **marginal cost** of each Ultra Mini. Similarly, because of the term $40y$, each Big Stack adds $40 to the total cost. The marginal cost of each Big Stack is $40.

This cost function is an example of a *linear function of two variables*. The coefficients of x and y play roles similar to that of the slope of a line. In particular, they give the rates of change of the function as each variable increases while the other stays constant. (Think about it.) We shall say more about linear functions below.

➡ **Before we go on . . .** In Example 1, which values of x and y may we substitute into $C(x, y)$? Certainly, we must have $x \geq 0$ and $y \geq 0$ because it makes no sense to speak of manufacturing a negative number of speakers. Also, there is certainly some

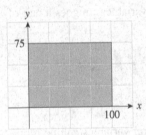

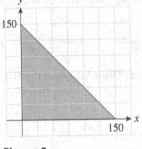

Figure 2

Figure 3

upper bound to the number of speakers that can be made in a month. The bound might take one of several forms. The number of each model may be bounded—say $x \leq 100$ and $y \leq 75$. The inequalities $0 \leq x \leq 100$ and $0 \leq y \leq 75$ describe the region in the plane shaded in Figure 2.

Another possibility is that the *total* number of speakers is bounded—say, $x + y \leq 150$. This, together with $x \geq 0$ and $y \geq 0$, describes the region shaded in Figure 3.

In either case the region shown represents the pairs (x, y) for which $C(x, y)$ is defined. Just as with a function of one variable, we call this region the **domain** of the function. As before, when the domain is not given explicitly, we agree to take the largest domain possible. ■

EXAMPLE 2 **Faculty Salaries**

David Katz came up with the following function for the salary of a professor with 10 years of teaching experience in a large university:

$$S(x, y, z) = 13{,}005 + 230x + 18y + 102z.$$

Here, S is the salary in 1969–1970 in dollars per year, x is the number of books the professor has published, y is the number of articles published, and z is the number of "excellent" articles published.[1] What salary do you expect that a professor with 10 years' experience earned in 1969–1970 if she published 2 books, 20 articles, and 3 "excellent" articles?

Solution All we need to do is calculate

$$S(2, 20, 3) = 13{,}005 + 230(2) + 18(20) + 102(3)$$
$$= \$14{,}131.$$

➡ **Before we go on...** In Example 1 we gave a linear function of two variables. In Example 2 we have a linear function of three variables. Katz came up with his model by surveying a large number of faculty members and then finding the linear function that "best" fit the data. Such models are called **multiple linear regression** models. In the Case Study at the end of this chapter we shall see a spreadsheet method of finding the coefficients of a multiple regression model from a set of observed data.

What does this model say about the value of a single book or a single article? If a book takes 15 times as long to write as an article, how would you recommend that a professor spend her writing time? ■

Here are two simple kinds of functions of several variables.

Linear Function

A function f of n variables is **linear** if f has the property that

$$f(x_1, x_2, \ldots, x_n) = a_0 + a_1 x_1 + \cdots + a_n x_n \qquad (a_0, a_1, a_2, \ldots, a_n \text{ constants}).$$

---

[1] David A. Katz, "Faculty Salaries, Promotions and Productivity at a Large University," *American Economic Review*, June 1973, pp. 469–477. Prof. Katz's equation actually included other variables, such as the number of dissertations supervised; our equation assumes that all of these are zero.

Quick Examples

4. $f(x, y) = 3x - 5y$ — Linear function of x and y
5. $C(x, y) = 10,000 + 20x + 40y$ — Example 1
6. $S(x_1, x_2, x_3) = 13,005 + 230x_1 + 18x_2 + 102x_3$ — Example 2

Interaction Function

If we add to a linear function one or more terms of the form $bx_i x_j$ (where b is a nonzero constant and $i \neq j$), we get a **second-order interaction function**.

Quick Examples

7. $C(x, y) = 10,000 + 20x + 40y + 0.1xy$
8. $R(x_1, x_2, x_3) = 10,000 - 0.01x_1 - 0.02x_2 - 0.01x_3 + 0.00001x_2 x_3$

So far, we have been specifying functions of several variables **algebraically**—by using algebraic formulas. If you have ever studied statistics, you are probably familiar with statistical tables. These tables may also be viewed as representing functions **numerically**, as the next example shows.

EXAMPLE 3 **Function Represented Numerically: Body Mass Index**

The following table lists some values of the body mass index, which gives a measure of the massiveness of your body, taking height into account.* The variable w represents your weight in pounds, and h represents your height in inches. An individual with a body mass index of 25 or above is generally considered overweight.

* It is interesting that weight-lifting competitions are usually based on weight rather than body mass index. As a consequence, taller people are at a significant disadvantage in these competitions because they must compete with shorter, stockier people of the same weight. (An extremely thin, very tall person can weigh as much as a muscular short person, although the tall person's body mass index would be significantly lower.)

$w \rightarrow$

$h \downarrow$	130	140	150	160	170	180	190	200	210
60	25.2	27.1	29.1	31.0	32.9	34.9	36.8	38.8	40.7
61	24.4	26.2	28.1	30.0	31.9	33.7	35.6	37.5	39.4
62	23.6	25.4	27.2	29.0	30.8	32.7	34.5	36.3	38.1
63	22.8	24.6	26.4	28.1	29.9	31.6	33.4	35.1	36.9
64	22.1	23.8	25.5	27.2	28.9	30.7	32.4	34.1	35.8
65	21.5	23.1	24.8	26.4	28.1	29.7	31.4	33.0	34.7
66	20.8	22.4	24.0	25.6	27.2	28.8	30.4	32.0	33.6
67	20.2	21.8	23.3	24.9	26.4	28.0	29.5	31.1	32.6
68	19.6	21.1	22.6	24.1	25.6	27.2	28.7	30.2	31.7
69	19.0	20.5	22.0	23.4	24.9	26.4	27.8	29.3	30.8
70	18.5	19.9	21.4	22.8	24.2	25.6	27.0	28.5	29.9
71	18.0	19.4	20.8	22.1	23.5	24.9	26.3	27.7	29.1
72	17.5	18.8	20.2	21.5	22.9	24.2	25.6	26.9	28.3
73	17.0	18.3	19.6	20.9	22.3	23.6	24.9	26.2	27.5
74	16.6	17.8	19.1	20.4	21.7	22.9	24.2	25.5	26.7
75	16.1	17.4	18.6	19.8	21.1	22.3	23.6	24.8	26.0
76	15.7	16.9	18.1	19.3	20.5	21.7	22.9	24.2	25.4

As the table shows, the value of the body mass index depends on two quantities: w and h. Let us write $M(w, h)$ for the body mass index function. What are $M(140, 62)$ and $M(210, 63)$?

Solution We can read the answers from the table:

$$M(140, 62) = 25.4 \qquad w = 140 \text{ lb}, h = 62 \text{ in}$$

and

$$M(210, 63) = 36.9. \qquad w = 210 \text{ lb}, h = 63 \text{ in}$$

The function $M(w, h)$ is actually given by the formula

$$M(w, h) = \frac{0.45w}{(0.0254h)^2}.$$

[The factor 0.45 converts the weight to kilograms, and 0.0254 converts the height to meters. If w is in kilograms and h is in meters, the formula is simpler: $M(w, h) = w/h^2$.]

Using Technology
See the Technology Guides at the end of the chapter to see how to use a spreadsheet to create the table in Example 3. Here is an outline:

Spreadsheet
w-values 130 to 210 in B1–J1
h-values 60 to 76 in A2–A18
=0.45*B$1/
(0.0254*$A2)^2
in B2; copy down and across through J18. [More details in the Technology Guide.]

Geometric Viewpoint: Three-Dimensional Space and the Graph of a Function of Two Variables

Just as functions of a single variable have graphs, so do functions of two or more variables. Recall that the graph of $f(x)$ consists of all points $(x, f(x))$ in the xy-plane. By analogy we would like to say that the graph of a function of *two* variables, $f(x, y)$, consists of all points of the form $(x, y, f(x, y))$. Thus, we need three axes: the x-, y-, and z-axes. In other words, our graph will live in **three-dimensional space**, or **3-space**.*

Just as we had two mutually perpendicular axes in two-dimensional space (the xy-plane; see Figure 4(a)), so we have three mutually perpendicular axes in three-dimensional space (Figure 4(b)).

* If we were dealing instead with a function of *three* variables, then we would need to go to *four-dimensional* space. Here, we run into visualization problems (to say the least!), so we won't discuss the graphs of functions of three or more variables in this text.

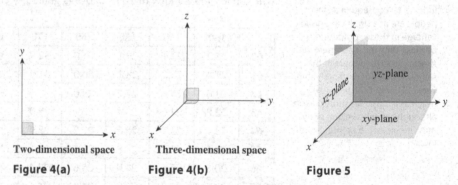

Two-dimensional space	Three-dimensional space	
Figure 4(a)	**Figure 4(b)**	**Figure 5**

In both 2-space and 3-space the axis labeled with the last letter goes up. Thus, the z-direction is the "up" direction in 3-space rather than the y-direction.

Three important planes are associated with these axes: the xy-plane, the yz-plane, and the xz-plane. These planes are shown in Figure 5. Any two of these planes intersect in one of the axes (for example, the xy- and xz-planes intersect in the x-axis), and all three meet at the origin. Notice that the xy-plane consists of all points with z-coordinate zero, the xz-plane consists of all points with $y = 0$, and the yz-plane consists of all points with $x = 0$.

In 3-space, each point has *three* coordinates, as you might expect: the x-coordinate, the y-coordinate, and the z-coordinate. To see how this works, look at the following examples.

The z-coordinate of a point is its height above the xy-plane.

EXAMPLE 4 **Plotting Points in Three Dimensions**

Locate the points $P(1, 2, 3)$, $Q(-1, 2, 3)$, $R(1, -1, 0)$, and $S(1, 2, -2)$ in 3-space.

Solution To locate P, the procedure is similar to the one we used in 2-space: Start at the origin, proceed 1 unit in the x-direction, then proceed 2 units in the y-direction, and finally, proceed 3 units in the z-direction. We wind up at the point P shown in Figures 6(a) and 6(b).

Here is another, extremely useful way of thinking about the location of P: First, look at the x- and y-coordinates, obtaining the point $(1, 2)$ in the xy-plane. The point we want is then 3 units vertically above the point $(1, 2)$ because the z-coordinate of a point is just its height above the xy-plane. This strategy is shown in Figure 6(c).

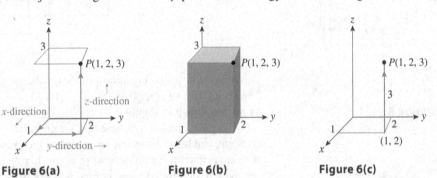

Figure 6(a)   **Figure 6(b)**   **Figure 6(c)**

Plotting the points Q, R, and S is similar, using the convention that negative coordinates correspond to moves back, left, or down. (See Figure 7.)

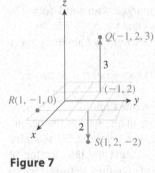

Figure 7

Our next task is to describe the graph of a function $f(x, y)$ of two variables.

Graph of a Function of Two Variables

The **graph of the function f of two variables** is the set of all points $(x, y, f(x, y))$ in three-dimensional space, where we restrict the values of (x, y) to lie in the domain of f. In other words, the graph is the set of all the points (x, y, z) with $z = f(x, y)$.

Note For *every* point (x, y) in the domain of f, the z-coordinate of the corresponding point on the graph is given by evaluating the function at (x, y). Thus, there will be a point of the graph on the vertical line through *every* point in the domain of f, so the graph is usually a *surface* of some sort (see the figure). ∎

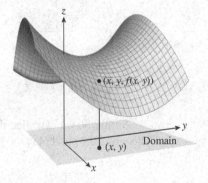

EXAMPLE 5 Graph of a Function of Two Variables

Describe the graph of $f(x, y) = x^2 + y^2$.

Solution Your first thought might be to make a table of values. You could choose some values for x and y and then, for each such pair, calculate $z = x^2 + y^2$. For example, you might get the following table:

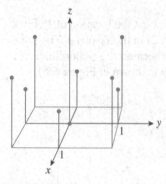

z

	$x \to$		
$y \downarrow$	**−1**	**0**	**1**
−1	2	1	2
0	1	0	1
1	2	1	2

$f(x, y) = x^2 + y^2$

Figure 8

This gives the following nine points on the graph of f: $(-1, -1, 2)$, $(-1, 0, 1)$, $(-1, 1, 2)$, $(0, -1, 1)$, $(0, 0, 0)$, $(0, 1, 1)$, $(1, -1, 2)$, $(1, 0, 1)$, and $(1, 1, 2)$. These points are shown in Figure 8.

The points on the xy-plane that we chose for our table are the grid points in the xy-plane, and the corresponding points on the graph are marked with solid dots. The problem is that this small number of points hardly tells us what the surface looks like, and even if we plotted more points, it is not clear that we would get anything more than a mass of dots on the page.

What can we do? There are several alternatives. One place to start is to use technology to draw the graph. (See the technology note on the next page.) We then obtain something like Figure 9. This particular surface is called a **paraboloid**.

If we slice vertically through this surface along the yz-plane, we get the picture in Figure 10. The shape of the front edge, where we cut, is a parabola. To see why, note that the yz-plane is the set of points where $x = 0$. To get the intersection of $x = 0$ and $z = x^2 + y^2$, we substitute $x = 0$ in the second equation, getting $z = y^2$. This is the equation of a parabola in the yz-plane.

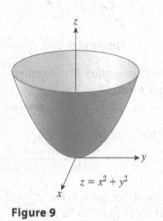

$z = x^2 + y^2$

Figure 9

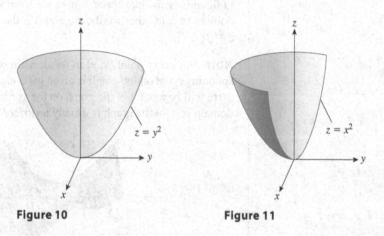

Figure 10   **Figure 11**

Similarly, we can slice through the surface with the xz-plane by setting $y = 0$. This gives the parabola $z = x^2$ in the xz-plane (Figure 11).

We can also look at horizontal slices through the surface, that is, slices by planes parallel to the xy-plane. These are given by setting $z = c$ for various numbers c. For example, if we set $z = 1$, we will see only the points with height 1. Substituting in the equation $z = x^2 + y^2$ gives the equation

$$1 = x^2 + y^2,$$

* See Section 0.7 for a discussion of equations of circles.

which is the equation of a circle of radius 1.* If we set $z = 4$, we get the equation of a circle of radius 2:

$$4 = x^2 + y^2.$$

In general, if we slice through the surface at height $z = c$, we get a circle (of radius $\sqrt{c}$). Figure 12 shows several of these circles.

Using Technology

We can use technology to obtain the graph of the function in Example 5:

Spreadsheet
Table of values:
x-values -3 to 3 in B1–H1
y-values -3 to 3 in A2–A8
=B1^2+A2^2
in B2; copy down and across through H8.
Graph: Highlight A1 through H8 and insert a surface chart. [More details in the Technology Guide.]

Website
www.WanerMath.com
 Online Utilities
 → Surface Graphing Utility
Enter x^2+y^2 for $f(x, y)$
Set xMin = -3, xMax = 3,
yMin = -3, yMax = 3
Press "Graph".

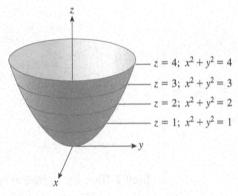

Figure 12

Looking at these circular slices, we see that this surface is the one we get by taking the parabola $z = x^2$ and spinning it around the z-axis. This is an example of what is known as a **surface of revolution**.

➡ **Before we go on...** The graph of any function of the form $f(x, y) = Ax^2 + By^2 + Cxy + Dx + Ey + F$ ($A, B, \ldots, F$ constants), with $4AB - C^2$ positive, can be shown to be a paraboloid of the same general shape as that in Example 5 if A and B are positive or upside-down if A and B are negative. If $A \neq B$, the horizontal slices will be ellipses rather than circles.

Notice that each horizontal slice through the surface in Example 5 was obtained by putting $z = constant$. This gave us an equation in x and y that described a curve. These curves are called the **level curves** of the surface $z = f(x, y)$ (see the discussion on the next page). In Example 5 the equations are of the form $x^2 + y^2 = c$ (c constant), so the level curves are circles. Figure 13 shows the level curves for $c = 0, 1, 2, 3,$ and 4.

The level curves give a contour map or topographical map of the surface. Each curve shows all of the points on the surface at a particular height c. You can use this contour map to visualize the shape of the surface. Imagine moving the contour at $c = 1$ to a height of 1 unit above the xy-plane, the contour at $c = 2$ to a height of 2 units above the xy-plane, and so on. You will end up with something like Figure 12. ■

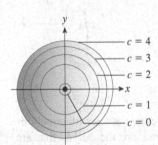

Level curves of the paraboloid
$z = x^2 + y^2$

Figure 13

The following summary includes the techniques we have just used plus some additional ones.

Analyzing the Graph of a Function of Two Variables

If possible, use technology to render the graph $z = f(x, y)$ of a given function f of two variables. You can analyze its graph as follows:

Step 1 Obtain the **x-, y-, and z-intercepts** (the places where the surface crosses the coordinate axes).

x-Intercept(s): Set $y = 0$ and $z = 0$, and solve for x.

y-Intercept(s): Set $x = 0$ and $z = 0$, and solve for y.

z-Intercept: Set $x = 0$ and $y = 0$, and compute z.

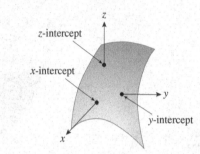

Step 2 Slice the surface along planes parallel to the xy-, yz-, and xz-planes.

z = constant: Set $z = constant$, and analyze the resulting curves.
These are the curves resulting from horizontal slices; they are called the **level curves** (see below).

x = constant: Set $x = constant$, and analyze the resulting curves.
These are the curves resulting from slices parallel to the yz-plane.

y = constant: Set $y = constant$, and analyze the resulting curves.
These are the curves resulting from slices parallel to the xz-plane.

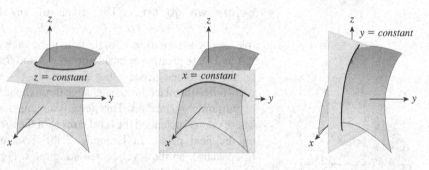

Level Curves

The **level curves** of a function f of two variables are the curves with equations of the form $f(x, y) = c$, where c is constant. These are the curves that are obtained from the graph of f by slicing it horizontally as above.

Quick Examples

9. Figure 13 shows some level curves of $f(x, y) = x^2 + y^2$. The ones shown have equations $f(x, y) = 0, 1, 2, 3,$ and 4.

10. Let $f(x, y) = y - x^2 + 4$. Its level curves have the form $y - x^2 + 4 = c$ (where c is constant). If we solve this equation for y, we see that $y = x^2 + c - 4$, the equation of a parabola with its vertex on the y-axis at the point $c - 4$. The following figure shows a portion of the graph of f and some of its level curves.

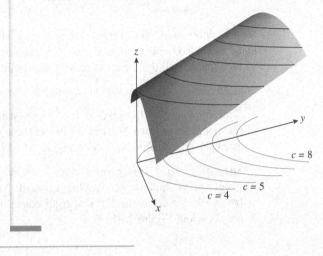

Spreadsheets often have built-in features to render surfaces such as the paraboloid in Example 5. In the following example we use Excel to graph another surface and then analyze it as above.

EXAMPLE 6 T **Analyzing a Surface**

Describe the graph of $f(x, y) = x^2 - y^2$.

Solution First, we obtain a picture of the graph using technology. Figure 14 shows two graphs obtained using resources at the Website.

Chapter 15 → Math Tools for Chapter 15   Chapter 15 → Math Tools for Chapter 15
    → Surface Graphing Utility   → Excel Surface Graphing Utility

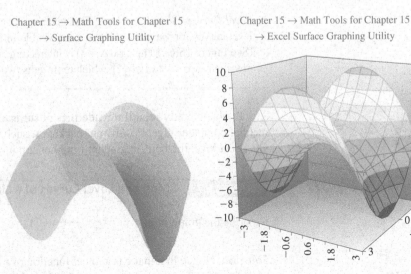

Figure 14

See the Technology Guides at the end of the chapter to find out how to obtain a similar graph from scratch using a spreadsheet.

The graph shows an example of a "saddle point" at the origin. (We return to this idea in Section 15.3.) To analyze the graph for the features shown in the box above, replace $f(x, y)$ by z to obtain

$$z = x^2 - y^2.$$

Step 1: *Intercepts* Setting any two of the variables x, y, and z equal to zero results in the third also being zero, so the x-, y-, and z-intercepts are all 0. In other words, the surface touches all three axes in exactly one point: the origin.

Step 2: *Slices* Slices in various directions show more interesting features.

Slice by $x = c$ This gives $z = c^2 - y^2$, which is the equation of a parabola that opens downward. You can see two of these slices ($c = -3$, $c = 3$) as the front and back edges of the surface in Figure 14. (More are shown in Figure 15(a).)

Slice by $y = c$ This gives $z = x^2 - c^2$, which is the equation of a parabola once again—this time, opening upward. You can see two of these slices ($c = -3$, $c = 3$) as the left and right edges of the surface in Figure 14. (More are shown in Figure 15(b).)

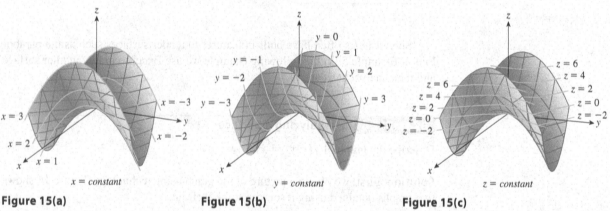

Figure 15(a)   **Figure 15(b)**   **Figure 15(c)**

Level Curves: Slice by $z = c$ This gives $x^2 - y^2 = c$, which is a hyperbola. The level curves for various values of c are visible in Figure 14 as the horizontal slices. (See Figure 15(c).) The case $c = 0$ is interesting: The equation $x^2 - y^2 = 0$ can be rewritten as $x = \pm y$ (why?), which represents two lines at right angles to each other.

To obtain really beautiful renderings of surfaces, you could use one of the commercial computer algebra software packages, such as Mathematica or Maple, or, if you use a Mac, the built-in grapher (grapher.app located in the Utilities folder).

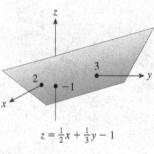

$z = \frac{1}{2}x + \frac{1}{3}y - 1$

Figure 16

EXAMPLE 7 **Graph and Level Curves of a Linear Function**

Describe the graph of $g(x, y) = \frac{1}{2}x + \frac{1}{3}y - 1$.

Solution Notice first that g is a linear function of x and y. Figure 16 shows a portion of the graph, which is a plane.

We can get a good idea of what plane this is by looking at the *x*-, *y*-, and *z*-intercepts:

x-intercept: Set $y = z = 0$, which gives $x = 2$.

y-intercept: Set $x = z = 0$, which gives $y = 3$.

z-intercept: Set $x = y = 0$, which gives $z = -1$.

Three points are enough to define a plane, so we can say that the plane is the one passing through the three points $(2, 0, 0)$, $(0, 3, 0)$, and $(0, 0, -1)$. It can be shown that the graph of every linear function of two variables is a plane.

Level curves: Set $g(x, y) = c$ to obtain $\frac{1}{2}x + \frac{1}{3}y - 1 = c$, or $\frac{1}{2}x + \frac{1}{3}y = c + 1$. We can rewrite this equation as $3x + 2y = 6(c + 1)$, which is the equation of a straight line. Choosing different values of *c* gives us a family of parallel lines as shown in Figure 17. (For example, the line corresponding to $c = 1$ has equation $3x + 2y = 6(1 + 1) = 12$.) In general, the set of level curves of every nonconstant linear function is a set of parallel straight lines.*

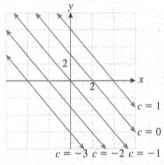

Level curves: $3x + 2y = 12$

Figure 17

*Think about what happens when the function is constant.

EXAMPLE 8   Using Level Curves

A certain function *f* of two variables has level curves $f(x, y) = c$ for $c = -2, -1, 0, 1$, and 2, as shown in Figure 18. (Each grid square is 1×1.)

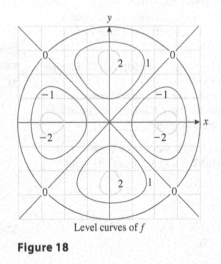

Level curves of *f*

Figure 18

Estimate the following: $f(1, 1)$, $f(1.5, -2)$, $f(1.5, 0)$ and $f(1, 2)$.

Solution The point $(1, 1)$ appears to lie exactly on the red level curve $c = 0$, so $f(1, 1) \approx 0$. Similarly, the point $(1.5, -2)$ appears to lie exactly on the blue level curve $c = 1$, so $f(1.5, -2) \approx 1$. The point $(1.5, 0)$ appears to lie midway between the level curves $c = -1$ and $c = -2$, so we estimate $f(1.5, 0) \approx -1.5$. Finally, the point $(1, 2)$ lies between the level curves $c = 1$ and $c = 2$ but closer to $c = 1$, so we can estimate $f(1, 2)$ at around 1.3.

15.1 EXERCISES

▼ more advanced   ◆ challenging
🅣 indicates exercises that should be solved using technology

For each function in Exercises 1–4, evaluate (a) $f(0, 0)$;
(b) $f(1, 0)$; (c) $f(0, -1)$; (d) $f(a, 2)$; (e) $f(y, x)$; and
(f) $f(x + h, y + k)$. [HINT: See Quick Examples 1–3.]

1. $f(x, y) = x^2 + y^2 - x + 1$

2. $f(x, y) = x^2 - y - xy + 1$

3. $f(x, y) = 0.2x + 0.1y - 0.01xy$

4. $f(x, y) = 0.4x - 0.5y - 0.05xy$

For each function in Exercises 5–8, evaluate (a) $g(0, 0, 0)$;
(b) $g(1, 0, 0)$; (c) $g(0, 1, 0)$; (d) $g(z, x, y)$; and
(e) $g(x + h, y + k, z + l)$, provided that such a value exists.

5. $g(x, y, z) = e^{x+y+z}$

6. $g(x, y, z) = \ln(x + y + z)$

7. $g(x, y, z) = \dfrac{xyz}{x^2 + y^2 + z^2}$

8. $g(x, y, z) = \dfrac{e^{xyz}}{x + y + z}$

9. Let $f(x, y, z) = 1.5 + 2.3x - 1.4y - 2.5z$. Complete the following sentences. [HINT: See Example 1.]
   a. f ___ by ___ units for every 1 unit of increase in x.
   b. f ___ by ___ units for every 1 unit of increase in y.
   c. _____ by 2.5 units for every _____.

10. Let $g(x, y, z) = 0.01x + 0.02y - 0.03z - 0.05$. Complete the following sentences.
    a. g ___ by ___ units for every 1 unit of increase in z.
    b. g ___ by ___ units for every 1 unit of increase in x.
    c. _____ by 0.02 units for every _____.

In Exercises 11–18, classify each function as linear, interaction, or neither. [HINT: See Quick Examples 4–8.]

11. $L(x, y) = 3x - 2y + 6xy - 4y^2$

12. $L(x, y, z) = 3x - 2y + 6xz$

13. $P(x_1, x_2, x_3) = 0.4 + 2x_1 - x_3$

14. $Q(x_1, x_2) = 4x_2 - 0.5x_1 - x_1^2$

15. $f(x, y, z) = \dfrac{x + y - z}{3}$

16. $g(x, y, z) = \dfrac{xz - 3yz + z^2}{4z}$ $(z \neq 0)$

17. $g(x, y, z) = \dfrac{xz - 3yz + z^2y}{4z}$ $(z \neq 0)$

18. $f(x, y) = x + y + xy + x^2y$

In Exercises 19 and 20, use the given tabular representation of the function f to compute the quantities asked for. [HINT: See Example 3.]

19.

$x \rightarrow$	10	20	30	40
y ↓ 10	−1	107	162	−3
20	−6	194	294	−14
30	−11	281	426	−25
40	−16	368	558	−36

a. $f(20, 10)$
b. $f(40, 20)$
c. $f(10, 20) - f(20, 10)$

20.

$x \rightarrow$	10	20	30	40
y ↓ 10	162	107	−5	−7
20	294	194	−22	−30
30	426	281	−39	−53
40	558	368	−56	−76

a. $f(10, 30)$
b. $f(20, 10)$
c. $f(10, 40) + f(10, 20)$

🅣 *In Exercises 21 and 22, use a spreadsheet or some other method to complete the given tables.*

21. $P(x, y) = x - 0.3y + 0.45xy$

$x \rightarrow$	10	20	30	40
y ↓ 10				
20				
30				
40				

22. $Q(x, y) = 0.4x + 0.1y - 0.06xy$

$x \rightarrow$	10	20	30	40
y ↓ 10				
20				
30				
40				

23. ▢ ▼ The following statistical table lists some values of the "inverse F distribution" ($\alpha = 0.5$):

$n \rightarrow$

	1	**2**	**3**	**4**	**5**	**6**	**7**	**8**	**9**	**10**
1	161.4	199.5	215.7	224.6	230.2	234.0	236.8	238.9	240.5	241.9
2	18.51	19.00	19.16	19.25	19.30	19.33	19.35	19.37	19.38	19.40
3	10.13	9.552	9.277	9.117	9.013	8.941	8.887	8.845	8.812	8.786
4	7.709	6.944	6.591	6.388	6.256	6.163	6.094	6.041	5.999	5.964
5	6.608	5.786	5.409	5.192	5.050	4.950	4.876	4.818	4.772	4.735
6	5.987	5.143	4.757	4.534	4.387	4.284	4.207	4.147	4.099	4.060
7	5.591	4.737	4.347	4.120	3.972	3.866	3.787	3.726	3.677	3.637
8	5.318	4.459	4.066	3.838	3.687	3.581	3.500	3.438	3.388	3.347
9	5.117	4.256	3.863	3.633	3.482	3.374	3.293	3.230	3.179	3.137
10	4.965	4.103	3.708	3.478	3.326	3.217	3.135	3.072	3.020	2.978

$d \downarrow$

In a spreadsheet you can compute the value of this function at (n, d) by the formula

`=FINV(0.05, n, d)`   The 0.05 is the value of alpha (α).

Use a spreadsheet to re-create this table.

24. ▢ ▼ The formula for body mass index $M(w, h)$, if w is given in kilograms and h is given in meters, is

$$M(w, h) = \frac{w}{h^2}.$$ See Example 3.

Use this formula to complete the following table in a spreadsheet:

$w \rightarrow$

	70	**80**	**90**	**100**	**110**	**120**	**130**
1.8							
1.85							
1.9							
1.95							
2							
2.05							
2.1							
2.15							
2.2							
2.25							
2.3							

$h \downarrow$

▢ *In Exercises 25–28, use either a graphing calculator or a spreadsheet to complete each table. Express all your answers as decimals rounded to four decimal places.*

25.

x	y	$f(x, y) = x^2\sqrt{1 + xy}$
3	1	
1	15	
0.3	0.5	
56	4	

26.

x	y	$f(x, y) = x^2 e^y$
0	2	
−1	5	
1.4	2.5	
11	9	

27.

x	y	$f(x, y) = x \ln(x^2 + y^2)$
3	1	
1.4	−1	
e	0	
0	e	

28.

x	y	$f(x, y) = \dfrac{x}{x^2 - y^2}$
−1	2	
0	0.2	
0.4	2.5	
10	0	

29. ▼ Brand Z's annual sales are affected by the sales of related products X and Y as follows: Each \$1 million increase in sales of brand X causes a \$2.1 million decline in sales of brand Z, whereas each \$1 million increase in sales of brand Y results in an increase of \$0.4 million in sales of brand Z. Currently, brands X, Y, and Z are each selling \$6 million per year. Model the sales of brand Z using a linear function.

30. ▼ Brand Z's annual sales are affected by the sales of related products X and Y as follows: Each \$1 million increase in sales of brand X causes a \$2.5 million decline in sales of brand Z, whereas each \$2 million increase in sales of brand Y results in an increase of \$23 million in sales of brand Z. Currently, brands X and Y are each selling \$2 million per year, and brand Z is selling \$62 million per year. Model the sales of brand Z using a linear function.

31. Sketch the cube with vertices $(0, 0, 0)$, $(1, 0, 0)$, $(0, 1, 0)$, $(0, 0, 1)$, $(1, 1, 0)$, $(1, 0, 1)$, $(0, 1, 1)$, and $(1, 1, 1)$. [**HINT:** See Example 4.]

32. Sketch the cube with vertices $(-1, -1, -1)$, $(1, -1, -1)$, $(-1, 1, -1)$, $(-1, -1, 1)$, $(1, 1, -1)$, $(1, -1, 1)$, $(-1, 1, 1)$, and $(1, 1, 1)$. [HINT: See Example 4.]

33. Sketch the pyramid with vertices $(1, 1, 0)$, $(1, -1, 0)$, $(-1, 1, 0)$, $(-1, -1, 0)$, and $(0, 0, 2)$.

34. Sketch the solid with vertices $(1, 1, 0)$, $(1, -1, 0)$, $(-1, 1, 0)$, $(-1, -1, 0)$, $(0, 0, -1)$, and $(0, 0, 1)$.

In Exercises 35–40, sketch the given plane.

35. $z = -2$ **36.** $z = 4$

37. $y = 2$ **38.** $y = -3$

39. $x = -3$ **40.** $x = 2$

In Exercises 41–48, match the given equation with one of the graphs below. (If necessary, use technology to render the surfaces.) [HINT: See Examples 5, 6, and 7.]

41. $f(x, y) = 1 - 3x + 2y$ **42.** $f(x, y) = 1 - \sqrt{x^2 + y^2}$

43. $f(x, y) = 1 - (x^2 + y^2)$ **44.** $f(x, y) = y^2 - x^2$

45. $f(x, y) = -\sqrt{1 - (x^2 + y^2)}$

46. $f(x, y) = 1 + (x^2 + y^2)$

47. $f(x, y) = \dfrac{1}{x^2 + y^2}$ **48.** $f(x, y) = 3x - 2y + 1$

(A) **(B)**

(C) **(D)**

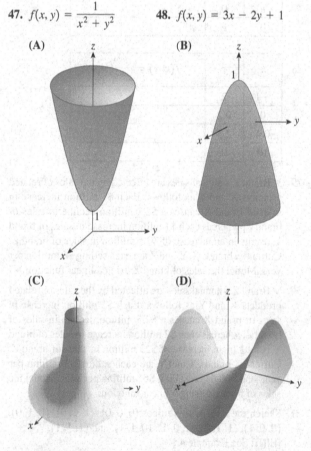

(E) **(F)**

(G) **(H)**

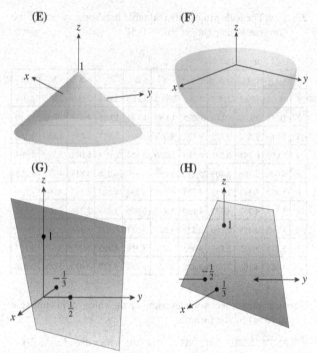

In Exercises 49–54, sketch the level curves $f(x, y) = c$ for the given function and values of c. [HINT: See Example 5.]

49. $f(x, y) = 2x^2 + 2y^2$; $c = 0, 2, 18$

50. $f(x, y) = 3x^2 + 3y^2$; $c = 0, 3, 27$

51. $f(x, y) = y + 2x^2$; $c = -2, 0, 2$

52. $f(x, y) = 2y - x^2$; $c = -2, 0, 2$

53. $f(x, y) = 2xy - 1$; $c = -1, 0, 1$

54. $f(x, y) = 2 + xy$; $c = -2, 0, 2$

Exercises 55–58 refer to the following plot of some level curves of $f(x, y) = c$ for $c = -2, 0, 2, 4,$ and 6. (Each grid square is 1 unit $\times$ 1 unit.) [HINT: See Example 8.]

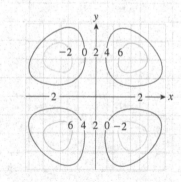

55. Estimate: **a.** $f(1, 1)$ **b.** $f(-2, -1)$ **c.** $f(3, -2.5)$

56. Estimate: **a.** $f(0, 1)$ **b.** $f(-1, -0.5)$ **c.** $f(-2, 1)$

57. At approximately which point or points does f appear to attain a maximum value?

58. At approximately which point or points does f appear to attain a minimum value?

In Exercises 59–74, sketch the graph of the function.
[HINT: See Example 7.]

59. $f(x, y) = 1 - x - y$ **60.** $f(x, y) = x + y - 2$

61. $g(x, y) = 2x + y - 2$ **62.** $g(x, y) = 3 - x + 2y$

63. $h(x, y) = x + 2$ **64.** $h(x, y) = 3 - y$

▮ *For Exercises 65–74, we suggest the use of technology.*
[HINT: See Example 6.]

65. $s(x, y) = 2x^2 + 2y^2$. Show cross sections at $z = 1$ and $z = 2$.

66. $s(x, y) = -(x^2 + y^2)$. Show cross sections at $z = -1$ and $z = -2$.

67. $f(x, y) = 2 + \sqrt{x^2 + y^2}$. Show cross sections at $z = 3$ and $y = 0$.

68. $f(x, y) = 2 - \sqrt{x^2 + y^2}$. Show cross sections at $z = 0$ and $y = 0$.

69. $f(x, y) = y^2$ **70.** $g(x, y) = x^2$

71. $h(x, y) = \dfrac{1}{y}$ **72.** $k(x, y) = e^y$

73. $f(x, y) = e^{-(x^2+y^2)}$ **74.** $g(x, y) = \dfrac{1}{\sqrt{x^2 + y^2}}$

Applications

75. *Cost* Your weekly cost (in dollars) to manufacture x cars and y trucks is

$$C(x, y) = 240{,}000 + 6{,}000x + 4{,}000y.$$

a. What is the marginal cost of a car? of a truck?
[HINT: See Example 1.]
b. Describe the graph of the cost function C.
[HINT: See Example 7.]
c. Describe the slice $x = 10$. What cost function does this slice describe?
d. Describe the level curve $z = 480{,}000$. What does this curve tell you about costs?

76. *Cost* Your weekly cost (in dollars) to manufacture x bicycles and y tricycles is

$$C(x, y) = 24{,}000 + 60x + 20y.$$

a. What is the marginal cost of a bicycle? of a tricycle?
[HINT: See Example 1.]
b. Describe the graph of the cost function C.
[HINT: See Example 7.]
c. Describe the slice by $y = 100$. What cost function does this slice describe?
d. Describe the level curve $z = 72{,}000$. What does this curve tell you about costs?

77. *Cost* Your sales of online video and audio clips are booming. Your Internet provider, Moneydrain.com, wants to get in on the action and has offered you unlimited technical assistance and consulting if you agree to pay Moneydrain 3¢ for every video clip and 4¢ for every audio clip you sell on the site. Further, Moneydrain agrees to charge you only $10 per month to host your site. Set up a (monthly) cost function for the scenario, and describe each variable.

78. *Cost* Your Cabaret nightspot "Jazz on Jupiter" has become an expensive proposition: You are paying monthly costs of $50,000 just to keep the place running. On top of that, your regular cabaret artist is charging you $3,000 per performance, and your jazz ensemble is charging $1,000 per hour. Set up a (monthly) cost function for the scenario, and describe each variable.

79. *Scientific Research* In each year from 1983 to 2003 the percentage y of research articles in *Physical Review* written by researchers in the United States can be approximated by

$$y = 82 - 0.78t - 1.02x \text{ percentage points} \quad (0 \le t \le 20),$$

where t is the year since 1983 and x is the percentage of articles written by researchers in Europe.[2]
a. In 2003, researchers in Europe wrote 38% of the articles published by the journal that year. What percentage was written by researchers in the United States?
b. In 1983, researchers in the United States wrote 61% of the articles published that year. What percentage was written by researchers in Europe?
c. What are the units of measurement of the coefficient of t?

80. *Scientific Research* The number z of research articles in *Physical Review* that were written by researchers in the United States from 1993 through 2003 can be approximated by

$$z = 5{,}960 - 0.71x + 0.50y \quad (3{,}000 \le x, y \le 6{,}000)$$

articles each year, where x is the number of articles written by researchers in Europe and y is the number written by researchers in other countries (excluding Europe and the United States).[3]
a. In 2000, approximately 5,500 articles were written by researchers in Europe, and 4,500 were written by researchers in other countries. How many (to the nearest 100) were written by researchers in the United States?
b. According to the model, if 5,000 articles were written in Europe and an equal number were written by researchers in the United States and other countries, what would that number be?
c. What is the significance of the fact that the coefficient of x is negative?

---

[2] Based on a linear regression. Source for data: The American Physical Society/*New York Times*, May 3, 2003, p. A1.
[3] Ibid.

81. *Market Share in the 1990s: Chrysler, Ford, General Motors* In the late 1990s the relationship between the domestic market shares of three major U.S. manufacturers of cars and light trucks could be modeled by

$$x_3 = 0.66 - 2.2x_1 - 0.02x_2,$$

where x_1, x_2, and x_3 are the fractions of the market held by Chrysler, Ford, and General Motors, respectively.[4] Thinking of General Motors' market share as a function of the shares of the other two manufacturers, describe the graph of the resulting function. How are the different slices by $x_1 =$ *constant* related to one another? What does this say about market share?

82. *Market Share in the 1990s: Kellogg, General Mills, General Foods* In the late 1990s the relationship among the domestic market shares of three major manufacturers of breakfast cereal was

$$x_1 = -0.4 + 1.2x_2 + 2x_3,$$

where x_1, x_2, and x_3 are the fractions of the market held by Kellogg, General Mills, and General Foods, respectively.[5] Thinking of Kellogg's market share as a function of the shares of the other two manufacturers, describe the graph of the resulting function. How are the different slices by $x_2 =$ *constant* related to one another? What does this say about market share?

83. *Prison Population* The number of prisoners in federal prisons in the United States can be approximated by

$$N(x, y) = 134 - 0.11x - 0.26y + 0.0004xy \text{ thousand inmates,}$$

where x is the number, in thousands, in state prisons and y is the number, in thousands, in local jails.[6]
   a. In 2011 there were approximately 1.29 million prisoners in state prisons and 736 thousand in local jails. Estimate, to the nearest thousand, the number of prisoners in federal prisons that year.
   b. Obtain N as a function of x for $y = 300$ and again for $y = 500$. Interpret the slopes of the resulting linear functions.

84. *Prison Population* The number of prisoners in state prisons in the United States can be approximated by

$$N(x, y) = -540 + 7.5x + 2.5y - 0.01xy \text{ thousand inmates,}$$

where x is the number, in thousands, in federal prisons and y is the number, in thousands, in local jails.[7]

[4] Based on a linear regression. Source of data: Ward's AutoInfoBank/ *New York Times*, July 29, 1998, p. D6.

[5] Based on a linear regression. Source of data: Bloomberg Financial Markets/*New York Times*, November 28, 1998, p. C1.

[6] Source for data: Sourcebook of Criminal Justice Statistics Online (www.albany.edu/sourcebook/pdf/t6132011.pdf).

[7] *Ibid.*

   a. In 2010 there were approximately 198 thousand prisoners in federal prisons and 749 thousand in local jails. Estimate, to the nearest 0.1 million, the number of prisoners in state prisons that year.
   b. Obtain N as a function of y for $x = 80$ and again for $x = 100$. Interpret the slopes of the resulting linear functions.

85. *Marginal Cost (Interaction Model)* Your weekly cost (in dollars) to manufacture x cars and y trucks is

$$C(x, y) = 240{,}000 + 6{,}000x + 4{,}000y - 20xy.$$

(Compare with Exercise 75.)
   a. Describe the slices $x =$ *constant* and $y =$ *constant*.
   b. Is the graph of the cost function a plane? How does your answer relate to part (a)?
   c. What are the slopes of the slices $x = 10$ and $x = 20$? What does this say about cost?

86. *Marginal Cost (Interaction Model)* Repeat Exercise 85 using the weekly cost to manufacture x bicycles and y tricycles given by

$$C(x, y) = 24{,}000 + 60x + 20y + 0.3xy.$$

(Compare with Exercise 76.)

87. ▼ *Online Revenue* Your major online bookstore is in direct competition with Amazon.com, BN.com, and BooksAMillion .com. Your company's daily revenue in dollars is given by

$$R(x, y, z) = 10{,}000 - 0.01x - 0.02y - 0.01z + 0.00001yz,$$

where x, y, and z are the online daily revenues of Amazon .com, BN.com, and BooksAMillion.com, respectively.
   a. If, on a certain day, Amazon.com shows revenue of $12,000, while BN.com and BooksAMillion.com each show $5,000, what does the model predict for your company's revenue that day?
   b. If Amazon.com and BN.com each show daily revenue of $5,000, give an equation showing how your daily revenue depends on that of BooksAMillion.com.

88. ▼ *Online Revenue* Repeat Exercise 87 using the revised revenue function

$$R(x, y, z) = 20{,}000 - 0.02x - 0.04y - 0.01z + 0.00001yz.$$

89. ▼ *Sales: Walmart, Target* The following table shows the approximate net earnings, in billions of dollars, of Walmart and Target in 2008, 2010, and 2014:[8]

	2008	**2010**	**2014**
Walmart	370	420	470
Target	62	68	73

Model Walmart's net earnings as a function of Target's net earnings and time, using a linear function of the form

$$f(x, t) = Ax + Bt + C \quad (A, B, C \text{ constants}),$$

where f is Walmart's net earnings (in billions of dollars), x is Target's net earnings (in billions of dollars), and t is time in years since 2008. In 2012, Target's net earnings were about $72 billion. What, to the nearest billion dollars, does your model estimate as Walmart's net earnings that year?

90. ▼ **Sales: Nintendo, Nokia** The following table shows the approximate net sales of Nintendo (in billions of yen) and Nokia (in billions of euro) in 2004, 2008, and 2010:[9]

	2004	2008	2010
Nintendo	510	1,700	1,010
Nokia	30	52	42

Model Nintendo's net earnings as a function of Nokia's net earnings and time, using a linear function of the form

$$f(x, t) = Ax + Bt + C \quad (A, B, C \text{ constants}),$$

where f is Nintendo's net earnings (in billions of yen), x is Nokia's net earnings (in billions of euro), and t is time in years since 2004. In 2007, Nokia's net earnings were about €50 billion. What, to the nearest billion yen, does your model estimate as Nintendo's net earnings that year?

91. ▼ **Utility** Suppose your newspaper is trying to decide between two competing desktop publishing software packages: Macro Publish and Turbo Publish. You estimate that if you purchase x copies of Macro Publish and y copies of Turbo Publish, your company's daily productivity will be

$$U(x, y) = 6x^{0.8}y^{0.2} + x,$$

where $U(x, y)$ is measured in pages per day. (U is called a *utility function*.) If $x = y = 10$, calculate the effect of increasing x by 1 unit, and interpret the result.

92. ▼ **Housing Costs**[10] The cost C (in dollars) of building a house is related to the number k of carpenters used and the number e of electricians used by

$$C(k, e) = 15,000 + 50k^2 + 60e^2.$$

If $k = e = 10$, compare the effects of increasing k by 1 unit and of increasing e by 1 unit. Interpret the result.

[9] Sources: www.nintendo.com/corp, http://investors.nokia.com, www.wikinvest.com.

[10] Based on an exercise in *Introduction to Mathematical Economics* by A. L. Ostrosky Jr. and J. V. Koch (Waveland Press, Illinois, 1979).

93. ▼ **Volume** The volume of an ellipsoid with cross-sectional radii a, b, and c is $V(a, b, c) = \frac{4}{3}\pi abc$.

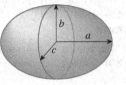

a. Find at least two sets of values for a, b, and c such that $V(a, b, c) = 1$.
b. Find the value of a such that $V(a, a, a) = 1$, and describe the resulting ellipsoid.

94. ▼ **Volume** The volume of a right elliptical cone with height h and radii a and b of its base is $V(a, b, h) = \frac{1}{3}\pi abh$.

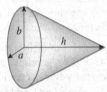

a. Find at least two sets of values for a, b, and h such that $V(a, b, h) = 1$.
b. Find the value of a such that $V(a, a, a) = 1$, and describe the resulting cone.

Exercises 95–98 involve Cobb-Douglas productivity functions. These functions have the form

$$P(x, y) = Kx^a y^{1-a},$$

where P stands for the number of items produced per year, x is the number of employees, and y is the annual operating budget. (The numbers K and a are constants that depend on the situation we are looking at, with $0 \leq a \leq 1$.)

95. **Productivity** How many items will be produced per year by a company with 100 employees and an annual operating budget of $500,000 if $K = 1,000$ and $a = 0.5$? (Round your answer to one significant digit.)

96. **Productivity** How many items will be produced per year by a company with 50 employees and an annual operating budget of $1,000,000 if $K = 1,000$ and $a = 0.5$? (Round your answer to one significant digit.)

97. ▼ **Modeling Production with Cobb-Douglas** Two years ago, my piano manufacturing plant employed 1,000 workers, had an operating budget of $1 million, and turned out 100 pianos. Last year, I slashed the operating budget to $10,000, and production dropped to 10 pianos.

a. Use the data for each of the two years and the Cobb-Douglas formula to obtain two equations in K and a.
b. Take logs of both sides in each equation, and obtain two linear equations in a and $\log K$.
c. Solve these equations to obtain values for a and K.
d. Use these values in the Cobb-Douglas formula to predict production if I increase the operating budget back to $1 million but lay off half the workforce.

98. ▼ *Modeling Production with Cobb-Douglas* Repeat Exercise 97 using the following data: Two years ago—1,000 employees, $1 million operating budget, 100 pianos; last year—1,000 employees, $100,000 operating budget, 10 pianos.

99. ▼ *Pollution* The burden of human-made aerosol sulfate in the Earth's atmosphere, in grams per square meter, is

$$B(x, n) = \frac{xn}{A},$$

where x is the total weight of aerosol sulfate emitted into the atmosphere per year and n is the number of years it remains in the atmosphere. A is the surface area of the Earth, approximately 5.1×10^{14} square meters.[11]
   a. Calculate the burden, given the 1995 estimated values of $x = 1.5 \times 10^{14}$ grams per year and $n = 5$ days.
   b. What does the function $W(x, n) = xn$ measure?

100. ▼ *Pollution* The amount of aerosol sulfate (in grams) was approximately 45×10^{12} grams in 1940 and has been increasing exponentially ever since, with a doubling time of approximately 20 years.[12] Use the model from Exercise 99 to give a formula for the atmospheric burden of aerosol sulfate as a function of the time t in years since 1940 and the number of years n it remains in the atmosphere.

101. ▼ *Alien Intelligence* Frank Drake, an astronomer at the University of California at Santa Cruz, devised the following equation to estimate the number of planet-based civilizations in our Milky Way galaxy that are willing and able to communicate with Earth:[13]

$$N(R, f_p, n_e, f_l, f_i, f_c, L) = R f_p n_e f_l f_i f_c L$$

   R = the number of new stars formed in our galaxy each year
   f_p = the fraction of those stars that have planetary systems
   n_e = the average number of planets in each such system that can support life
   f_l = the fraction of such planets on which life actually evolves
   f_i = the fraction of life-sustaining planets on which intelligent life evolves
   f_c = the fraction of intelligent-life-bearing planets on which the intelligent beings develop the means and the will to communicate over interstellar distances
   L = the average lifetime of such technological civilizations (in years).

   a. What would be the effect on N if any one of the variables were doubled?

   b. How would you modify the formula if you were interested only in the number of intelligent-life-bearing planets in the galaxy?
   c. How could one convert this function into a linear function?
   d. (For discussion) Try to come up with an estimate of N.

102. ▼ *More Alien Intelligence* The formula given in Exercise 101 restricts attention to planet-based civilizations in our galaxy. Give a formula that includes intelligent planet-based aliens from the galaxy Andromeda. (Assume that all the variables used in the formula for the Milky Way have the same values for Andromeda.)

Communication and Reasoning Exercises

103. Let $f(x, y) = \frac{x}{y}$. How are $f(x, y)$ and $f(y, x)$ related?

104. Let $f(x, y) = x^2 y^3$. How are $f(x, y)$ and $f(-x, -y)$ related?

105. Give an example of a function of the two variables x and y with the property that interchanging x and y has no effect.

106. Give an example of a function f of the two variables x and y with the property that $f(x, y) = -f(y, x)$.

107. Give an example of a function f of the three variables x, y, and z with the property that $f(x, y, z) = f(y, x, z)$ and $f(-x, -y, -z) = -f(x, y, z)$.

108. Give an example of a function f of the three variables x, y, and z with the property that $f(x, y, z) = f(y, x, z)$ and $f(-x, -y, -z) = f(x, y, z)$.

109. Illustrate by means of an example how a real-valued function of the two variables x and y gives different real-valued functions of one variable when we restrict y to be different constants.

110. Illustrate by means of an example how a real-valued function of one variable x gives different real-valued functions of the two variables y and z when we substitute for x suitable functions of y and z.

111. ▼ If f is a linear function of x and y, show that if we restrict y to be a fixed constant, then the resulting function of x is linear. Does the slope of this linear function depend on the choice of y?

112. ▼ If f is an interaction function of x and y, show that if we restrict y to be a fixed constant, then the resulting function of x is linear. Does the slope of this linear function depend on the choice of y?

113. ▼ Suppose that $C(x, y)$ represents the cost of x CDs and y cassettes. If $C(x, y + 1) < C(x + 1, y)$ for every $x \geq 0$ and $y \geq 0$, what does this tell you about the cost of CDs and cassettes?

114. ▼ Suppose that $C(x, y)$ represents the cost of renting x DVDs and y video games. If $C(x + 2, y) < C(x, y + 1)$ for every $x \geq 0$ and $y \geq 0$, what does this tell you about the cost of renting DVDs and video games?

---

[11] Source: Robert J. Charlson and Tom M. L. Wigley, "Sulfate Aerosol and Climatic Change," *Scientific American*, February, 1994, pp. 48–57.

[12] *Ibid.*

[13] Source: "First Contact" (Plume Books/Penguin Group)/*New York Times*, October 6, 1992, p. C1.

115. Complete the following: The graph of a linear function of two variables is a _____ .

116. Complete the following: The level curves of a linear function of two variables are ___ .

117. ▼ *Heat-Seeking Missiles* The following diagram shows some level curves of the temperature, in degrees Fahrenheit, of a region in space, as well as the location, on the 100-degree curve, of a heat-seeking missile moving through the region. (These level curves are called **isotherms**.) In which of the three directions shown should the missile be traveling so as to experience the fastest rate of increase in temperature at the given point? Explain your answer.

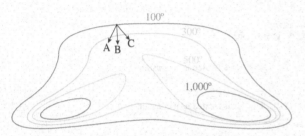

118. ▼ *Hiking* The following diagram shows some level curves of the altitude of a mountain valley, as well as the location, on the 2,000-ft curve, of a hiker. The hiker is currently moving at the greatest possible rate of descent. In which of the three directions shown is he moving? Explain your answer.

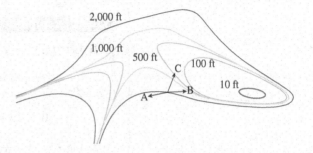

119. Your study partner Slim claims that because the surface $z = f(x, y)$ you have been studying is a plane, it follows that all the slices $x = constant$ and $y = constant$ are straight lines. Do you agree or disagree? Explain.

120. Your other study partner Shady just told you that the surface $z = xy$ you have been trying to graph must be a plane because you've already found that the slices $x = constant$ and $y = constant$ are all straight lines. Do you agree or disagree? Explain.

121. Why do we not sketch the graphs of functions of three or more variables?

122. The surface of a mountain can be thought of as the graph of what function?

123. Why is *three*-dimensional space used to represent the graph of a function of *two* variables?

124. Why is it that we can sketch the graphs of functions of two variables on the two-dimensional flat surfaces of these pages?

15.2 Partial Derivatives

Calculating and Interpreting Partial Derivatives

Recall that if f is a function of x, then the derivative df/dx measures how fast f changes as x increases. If f is a function of two or more variables, we can ask how fast f changes as each variable increases while the others remain fixed. These rates of change are called the "partial derivatives of f," and they measure how each variable contributes to the change in f. Here is a more precise definition.

Partial Derivatives

The **partial derivative of f with respect to x** is the derivative of f with respect to x, when all other variables are treated as constant. Similarly, the **partial derivative of f with respect to y** is the derivative of f with respect to y, with all other variables treated as constant, and so on for other variables. The partial derivatives are written as $\dfrac{\partial f}{\partial x}$, $\dfrac{\partial f}{\partial y}$, and so on. The symbol ∂ is used (instead of d) to remind us that there is more than one variable and that we are holding the other variables fixed.

Quick Examples

1. Let $f(x, y) = x^2 + y^2$.

$$\frac{\partial f}{\partial x} = 2x + 0 = 2x \qquad \text{Because } y^2 \text{ is treated as a constant}$$

$$\frac{\partial f}{\partial y} = 0 + 2y = 2y \qquad \text{Because } x^2 \text{ is treated as a constant}$$

2. Let $z = x^2 + xy$.

$$\frac{\partial z}{\partial x} = 2x + y \qquad \frac{\partial}{\partial x}(xy) = \frac{\partial}{\partial x}(x \cdot \text{constant}) = \text{constant} = y$$

$$\frac{\partial z}{\partial y} = 0 + x \qquad \frac{\partial}{\partial y}(xy) = \frac{\partial}{\partial y}(\text{constant} \cdot y) = \text{constant} = x$$

3. Let $f(x, y) = x^2y + y^2x - xy + y$.

$$\frac{\partial f}{\partial x} = 2xy + y^2 - y \qquad y \text{ is treated as a constant.}$$

$$\frac{\partial f}{\partial y} = x^2 + 2xy - x + 1 \qquad x \text{ is treated as a constant.}$$

Interpretation

$\dfrac{\partial f}{\partial x}$ is the rate at which f changes as x changes, for a fixed (constant) y.

$\dfrac{\partial f}{\partial y}$ is the rate at which f changes as y changes, for a fixed (constant) x.

EXAMPLE 1   Marginal Cost: Linear Model

We return to Example 1 from Section 15.1. Suppose that you own a company that makes two models of speakers: the Ultra Mini and the Big Stack. Your total monthly cost (in dollars) to make x Ultra Minis and y Big Stacks is given by

$$C(x, y) = 10{,}000 + 20x + 40y.$$

What is the significance of $\dfrac{\partial C}{\partial x}$ and of $\dfrac{\partial C}{\partial y}$?

Solution First, we compute these partial derivatives:

$$\frac{\partial C}{\partial x} = 20$$

$$\frac{\partial C}{\partial y} = 40.$$

We interpret the results as follows: $\dfrac{\partial C}{\partial x} = 20$ means that the cost is increasing at a rate of \$20 per additional Ultra Mini (if production of Big Stacks is held constant), and $\dfrac{\partial C}{\partial y} = 40$ means that the cost is increasing at a rate of \$40 per additional Big Stack (if production of Ultra Minis is held constant). In other words, these are the **marginal costs** of each model of speaker.

➡ **Before we go on . . .** How much does the cost rise if you increase x by Δx and y by Δy? In Example 1 the change in cost is given by

$$\Delta C = 20\,\Delta x + 40\,\Delta y = \frac{\partial C}{\partial x}\,\Delta x + \frac{\partial C}{\partial y}\,\Delta y.$$

This suggests the **chain rule for several variables**. Part of this rule says that if x and y are both functions of t, then C is a function of t through them, and the rate of change of C with respect to t can be calculated as

$$\frac{dC}{dt} = \frac{\partial C}{\partial x} \cdot \frac{dx}{dt} + \frac{\partial C}{\partial y} \cdot \frac{dy}{dt}.$$

See the optional section on the chain rule for several variables for further discussion and applications of this interesting result. ■

EXAMPLE 2   **Marginal Cost: Interaction Model**

Another possibility for the cost function in Example 1 is an interaction model:

$$C(x, y) = 10{,}000 + 20x + 40y + 0.1xy.$$

a. *Now* what are the marginal costs of the two models of speakers?

b. What is the marginal cost of manufacturing Big Stacks at a production level of 100 Ultra Minis and 50 Big Stacks per month?

Solution

a. We compute the partial derivatives:

$$\frac{\partial C}{\partial x} = 20 + 0.1y$$

$$\frac{\partial C}{\partial y} = 40 + 0.1x.$$

Thus, the marginal cost of manufacturing Ultra Minis increases by \$0.1, or 10¢, for each Big Stack that is manufactured. Similarly, the marginal cost of manufacturing Big Stacks increases by 10¢ for each Ultra Mini that is manufactured.

b. From part (a) the marginal cost of manufacturing Big Stacks is

$$\frac{\partial C}{\partial y} = 40 + 0.1x.$$

At a production level of 100 Ultra Minis and 50 Big Stacks per month, we have $x = 100$ and $y = 50$. Thus, the marginal cost of manufacturing Big Stacks at these production levels is

$$\frac{\partial C}{\partial y}\bigg|_{(100,50)} = 40 + 0.1(100) = \$50 \text{ per Big Stack.}$$

Partial derivatives of functions of three variables are obtained in the same way as those for functions of two variables, as the following example shows.

EXAMPLE 3   **Function of Three Variables**

Calculate $\dfrac{\partial f}{\partial x}$, $\dfrac{\partial f}{\partial y}$, and $\dfrac{\partial f}{\partial z}$ if $f(x, y, z) = xy^2z^3 - xy$.

Solution Although we now have three variables, the calculation remains the same: $\partial f/\partial x$ is the derivative of f with respect to x, with *both* other variables, y and z, held constant:

$$\frac{\partial f}{\partial x} = y^2z^3 - y.$$

Similarly, $\partial f/\partial y$ is the derivative of f with respect to y, with both x and z held constant:

$$\frac{\partial f}{\partial y} = 2xyz^3 - x.$$

Finally, to find $\partial f/\partial z$, we hold both x and y constant and take the derivative with respect to z.

$$\frac{\partial f}{\partial z} = 3xy^2z^2.$$

Note The procedure for finding a partial derivative is the same for any number of variables: To get the partial derivative with respect to any one variable, we treat all the others as constants. ■

Geometric Interpretation of Partial Derivatives

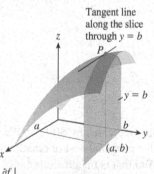

Tangent line along the slice through $y = b$

$\dfrac{\partial f}{\partial x}\Big|_{(a,b)}$ is the slope of the tangent line at the point $P(a, b, f(a, b))$ along the slice through $y = b$.

Figure 19

Recall that if f is a function of one variable x, then the derivative df/dx gives the slopes of the tangent lines to its graph. Now, suppose that f is a function of x and y. By definition, $\partial f/\partial x$ is the derivative of the function of x that we get by holding y fixed. If we evaluate this derivative at the point (a, b), we are holding y fixed at the value b, taking the ordinary derivative of the resulting function of x, and evaluating this at $x = a$. Now, holding y fixed at b amounts to slicing through the graph of f along the plane $y = b$, resulting in a curve. Thus, the partial derivative is the slope of the tangent line to this curve at the point where $x = a$ and $y = b$, along the plane $y = b$ (Figure 19). This fits with our interpretation of $\partial f/\partial x$ as the rate of increase of f with increasing x when y is held fixed at b.

The other partial derivative, $\partial f/\partial y\big|_{(a,b)}$, is, similarly, the slope of the tangent line at the same point $P(a, b, f(a, b))$ but along the slice by the plane $x = a$. You should draw the corresponding picture for this on your own.

EXAMPLE 4   **Marginal Cost**

Referring to the interactive cost function $C(x, y) = 10{,}000 + 20x + 40y + 0.1xy$ in Example 2, we can identify the marginal costs $\partial C/\partial x$ and $\partial C/\partial y$ of manufacturing Ultra Minis and Big Stacks at a production level of 100 Ultra Minis and 50 Big Stacks per month as the slopes of the tangent lines to the two slices by $y = 50$ and $x = 100$ at the point on the graph where $(x, y) = (100, 50)$ as seen in Figure 20.

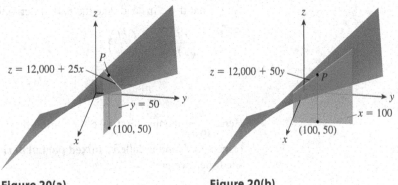

Figure 20(a)   **Figure 20(b)**

Figure 20(a) shows the slice at $y = 50$ through the point $P = (100, 50, C(100, 50)) = (100, 50, 14,500)$. The equation of that slice is given by substituting $y = 50$ in the cost equation:

$$C(x, 50) = 10,000 + 20x + 40(50) + 0.1x(50) = 12,000 + 25x. \qquad \text{A line of slope 25}$$

Because the slice is already a line, it coincides with the tangent line through P as depicted in Figure 19. This slope is equal to $\partial C/\partial x|_{(100,50)}$:

$$\frac{\partial C}{\partial x} = 20 + 0.1y \qquad\qquad \text{See Example 2.}$$

so

$$\left.\frac{\partial C}{\partial x}\right|_{(100,50)} = 20 + 0.1(50) = 25.$$

Similarly, Figure 20(b) shows the slice at $x = 100$ through the same point P. The equation of that slice is given by substituting $x = 100$ in the cost equation:

$$C(100, y) = 10,000 + 20(100) + 40y + 0.1(100)y = 12,000 + 50y. \qquad \text{A line of slope 50}$$

This slope is equal to $\partial C/\partial y|_{(100,50)} = 50$ as we calculated in Example 2.

Second-Order Partial Derivatives

Just as for functions of a single variable, we can calculate second derivatives. Suppose, for example, that we have a function of x and y, say, $f(x, y) = x^2 - x^2y^2$. We know that

$$\frac{\partial f}{\partial x} = 2x - 2xy^2.$$

If we take the partial derivative with respect to x once again, we obtain

$$\frac{\partial}{\partial x}\left(\frac{\partial f}{\partial x}\right) = 2 - 2y^2. \qquad \text{Take } \frac{\partial}{\partial x} \text{ of } \frac{\partial f}{\partial x}.$$

(The symbol $\partial/\partial x$ means "the partial derivative with respect to x," just as d/dx stands for "the derivative with respect to x.") This is called the **second-order partial derivative** and is written $\dfrac{\partial^2 f}{\partial x^2}$. We get the following derivatives similarly:

$$\frac{\partial f}{\partial y} = -2x^2y$$

$$\frac{\partial^2 f}{\partial y^2} = -2x^2. \qquad\qquad \text{Take } \frac{\partial}{\partial y} \text{ of } \frac{\partial f}{\partial y}.$$

Now what if we instead take the partial derivative with respect to y of $\partial f/\partial x$?

$$\frac{\partial^2 f}{\partial y \partial x} = \frac{\partial}{\partial y}\left(\frac{\partial f}{\partial x}\right) \qquad \text{Take } \frac{\partial}{\partial y} \text{ of } \frac{\partial f}{\partial x}.$$

$$= \frac{\partial}{\partial y}[2x - 2xy^2] = -4xy.$$

Here, $\dfrac{\partial^2 f}{\partial y \partial x}$ means "first take the partial derivative with respect to x and then with respect to y" and is called a **mixed partial derivative**. If we differentiate in the opposite order, we get

$$\frac{\partial^2 f}{\partial x \partial y} = \frac{\partial}{\partial x}\left(\frac{\partial f}{\partial y}\right) = \frac{\partial}{\partial x}[-2x^2 y] = -4xy,$$

the same expression as $\dfrac{\partial^2 f}{\partial y \partial x}$. This is no coincidence: The mixed partial derivatives $\dfrac{\partial^2 f}{\partial x \partial y}$ and $\dfrac{\partial^2 f}{\partial y \partial x}$ are always the same as long as the first partial derivatives are both differentiable functions of x and y and the mixed partial derivatives are continuous. Because all the functions we shall use are of this type, we can take the derivatives in any order we like when calculating mixed derivatives.

Here is another notation for partial derivatives that is especially convenient for second-order partial derivatives:

$$f_x \text{ means } \frac{\partial f}{\partial x}$$

$$f_y \text{ means } \frac{\partial f}{\partial y}$$

$$f_{xy} \text{ means } (f_x)_y = \frac{\partial^2 f}{\partial y \partial x} \qquad \text{(Note the order in which the derivatives are taken.)}$$

$$f_{yx} \text{ means } (f_y)_x = \frac{\partial^2 f}{\partial x \partial y}.$$

15.2 EXERCISES

▼ more advanced   ◆ challenging
⧉ indicates exercises that should be solved using technology

In Exercises 1–18, calculate $\dfrac{\partial f}{\partial x}, \dfrac{\partial f}{\partial y}, \left.\dfrac{\partial f}{\partial x}\right|_{(1,-1)}$, and $\left.\dfrac{\partial f}{\partial y}\right|_{(1,-1)}$ when defined. [HINT: See Quick Examples 1–3.]

1. $f(x, y) = 10{,}000 - 40x + 20y$

2. $f(x, y) = 1{,}000 + 5x - 4y$

3. $f(x, y) = 3x^2 - y^3 + x - 1$

4. $f(x, y) = x^{1/2} - 2y^4 + y + 6$

5. $f(x, y) = 10{,}000 - 40x + 20y + 10xy$

6. $f(x, y) = 1{,}000 + 5x - 4y - 3xy$

7. $f(x, y) = 3x^2 y$ 8. $f(x, y) = x^4 y^2 - x$

9. $f(x, y) = x^2 y^3 - x^3 y^2 - xy$

10. $f(x, y) = x^{-1} y^2 + xy^2 + xy$

11. $f(x, y) = (2xy + 1)^3$ 12. $f(x, y) = \dfrac{1}{(xy + 1)^2}$

13. ▼ $f(x, y) = e^{x+y}$ 14. ▼ $f(x, y) = e^{2x+y}$

15. ▼ $f(x, y) = 5x^{0.6} y^{0.4}$ 16. ▼ $f(x, y) = -2x^{0.1} y^{0.9}$

17. ▼ $f(x, y) = e^{0.2xy}$ 18. ▼ $f(x, y) = xe^{xy}$

In Exercises 19–28, find $\dfrac{\partial^2 f}{\partial x^2}, \dfrac{\partial^2 f}{\partial y^2}, \dfrac{\partial^2 f}{\partial x \partial y}$, and $\dfrac{\partial^2 f}{\partial y \partial x}$, and evaluate them all at $(1, -1)$ if possible. [HINT: See the discussion of second-order partial derivatives.]

19. $f(x, y) = 10{,}000 - 40x + 20y$

20. $f(x, y) = 1{,}000 + 5x - 4y$

21. $f(x, y) = 10{,}000 - 40x + 20y + 10xy$

22. $f(x, y) = 1,000 + 5x - 4y - 3xy$

23. $f(x, y) = 3x^2y$ **24.** $f(x, y) = x^4y^2 - x$

25. ▼ $f(x, y) = e^{x+y}$ **26.** ▼ $f(x, y) = e^{2x+y}$

27. ▼ $f(x, y) = 5x^{0.6}y^{0.4}$ **28.** ▼ $f(x, y) = -2x^{0.1}y^{0.9}$

In Exercises 29–40, find $\dfrac{\partial f}{\partial x}, \dfrac{\partial f}{\partial y}, \dfrac{\partial f}{\partial z}$, and their values at $(0, -1, 1)$ if possible. [HINT: See Example 3.]

29. $f(x, y, z) = xyz$ **30.** $f(x, y, z) = xy + xz - yz$

31. ▼ $f(x, y, z) = -\dfrac{4}{x + y + z^2}$

32. ▼ $f(x, y, z) = \dfrac{6}{x^2 + y^2 + z^2}$

33. ▼ $f(x, y, z) = xe^{yz} + ye^{xz}$

34. ▼ $f(x, y, z) = xye^z + xe^{yz} + e^{xyz}$

35. ▼ $f(x, y, z) = x^{0.1}y^{0.4}z^{0.5}$

36. ▼ $f(x, y, z) = 2x^{0.2}y^{0.8} + z^2$

37. ▼ $f(x, y, z) = e^{xyz}$

38. ▼ $f(x, y, z) = \ln(x + y + z)$

39. ▼ $f(x, y, z) = \dfrac{2,000z}{1 + y^{0.3}}$

40. ▼ $f(x, y, z) = \dfrac{e^{0.2x}}{1 + e^{-0.1y}}$

Applications

41. Marginal Cost (Linear Model) Your weekly cost (in dollars) to manufacture x cars and y trucks is

$$C(x, y) = 240,000 + 6,000x + 4,000y.$$

Calculate and interpret $\dfrac{\partial C}{\partial x}$ and $\dfrac{\partial C}{\partial y}$. [HINT: See Example 1.]

42. Marginal Cost (Linear Model) Your weekly cost (in dollars) to manufacture x bicycles and y tricycles is

$$C(x, y) = 24,000 + 60x + 20y.$$

Calculate and interpret $\dfrac{\partial C}{\partial x}$ and $\dfrac{\partial C}{\partial y}$. [HINT: See Example 1.]

43. Scientific Research In each year from 1983 to 2003 the percentage y of research articles in *Physical Review* written by researchers in the United States can be approximated by

$$y = 82 - 0.78t - 1.02x \text{ percentage points} \quad (0 \le t \le 20),$$

where t is the year since 1983 and x is the percentage of articles written by researchers in Europe.[14] Calculate and interpret $\dfrac{\partial y}{\partial t}$ and $\dfrac{\partial y}{\partial x}$.

44. Scientific Research The number z of research articles in *Physical Review* that were written by researchers in the United States from 1993 through 2003 can be approximated by

$$z = 5,960 - 0.71x + 0.50y \quad (3,000 \le x, y \le 6,000)$$

articles each year, where x is the number of articles written by researchers in Europe and y is the number written by researchers in other countries (excluding Europe and the United States).[15] Calculate and interpret $\dfrac{\partial z}{\partial x}$ and $\dfrac{\partial z}{\partial y}$.

45. Marginal Cost (Interaction Model) Your weekly cost (in dollars) to manufacture x cars and y trucks is

$$C(x, y) = 240,000 + 6,000x + 4,000y - 20xy.$$

(Compare with Exercise 41.) Compute the marginal cost of manufacturing cars at a production level of 10 cars and 20 trucks. [HINT: See Example 2.]

46. Marginal Cost (Interaction Model) Your weekly cost (in dollars) to manufacture x bicycles and y tricycles is

$$C(x, y) = 24,000 + 60x + 20y + 0.3xy.$$

(Compare with Exercise 42.) Compute the marginal cost of manufacturing tricycles at a production level of 10 bicycles and 20 tricycles. [HINT: See Example 2.]

47. Brand Loyalty The fraction of Mazda car owners who chose another new Mazda can be modeled by the following function:[16]

$$M(c, f, g, h, t) = 1.1 - 3.8c + 2.2f + 1.9g - 1.7h - 1.3t.$$

Here, c is the fraction of Chrysler car owners who remained loyal to Chrysler, f is the fraction of Ford car owners remaining loyal to Ford, g the corresponding figure for General Motors, h the corresponding figure for Honda, and t for Toyota.

a. Calculate $\dfrac{\partial M}{\partial c}$ and $\dfrac{\partial M}{\partial f}$, and interpret the answers.

b. One year it was observed that $c = 0.56$, $f = 0.56$, $g = 0.72$, $h = 0.50$, and $t = 0.43$. According to the model, what percentage of Mazda owners remained loyal to Mazda? (Round your answer to the nearest percentage point.)

48. Brand Loyalty The fraction of Mazda car owners who chose another new Mazda can be modeled by the following function:[17]

$$M(c, f) = 9.4 + 7.8c + 3.6c^2 - 38f - 22cf + 43f^2,$$

---

[14] Based on a linear regression. Source for data: The American Physical Society/*New York Times*, May 3, 2003, p. A1.

[15] *Ibid.*

[16] The model is an approximation of a linear regression based on data from the period 1988–1995. Source for data: Chrysler, Maritz Market Research, Consumer Attitude Research, and Strategic Vision/*New York Times*, November 3, 1995, p. D2.

[17] The model is an approximation of a second-order regression based on data from the period 1988–1995. Source for data: Chrysler, Maritz Market Research, Consumer Attitude Research, and Strategic Vision/*New York Times*, November 3, 1995, p. D2.

where c is the fraction of Chrysler car owners who remained loyal to Chrysler and f is the fraction of Ford car owners remaining loyal to Ford.

a. Calculate $\dfrac{\partial M}{\partial c}$ and $\dfrac{\partial M}{\partial f}$ evaluated at the point $(0.7, 0.7)$, and interpret the answers.

b. One year it was observed that $c = 0.56$, and $f = 0.56$. According to the model, what percentage of Mazda owners remained loyal to Mazda? (Round your answer to the nearest percentage point.)

49. *Marginal Cost* Your weekly cost (in dollars) to manufacture x cars and y trucks is

$$C(x, y) = 200{,}000 + 6{,}000x + 4{,}000y - 100{,}000e^{-0.01(x+y)}.$$

What is the marginal cost of a car? of a truck? How do these marginal costs behave as total production increases?

50. *Marginal Cost* Your weekly cost (in dollars) to manufacture x bicycles and y tricycles is

$$C(x, y) = 20{,}000 + 60x + 20y + 50\sqrt{xy}.$$

What is the marginal cost of a bicycle? of a tricycle? How do these marginal costs behave as x and y increase?

51. ▼ *Income Gap* The following model is based on data on the median incomes of Hispanic and white households in the United States for the period 2000–2013:[18]

$$z(t, x) = 44{,}200 - 330t + 17{,}500x + 40xt,$$

where

$z(t, x) = $ median household income

$t = $ year ($t = 0$ represents 2000)

$x = \begin{cases} 0 & \text{if the income was for a Hispanic household} \\ 1 & \text{if the income was for a white household.} \end{cases}$

a. Use the model to estimate the median income of a Hispanic household and that of a white household in 2010.

b. According to the model, how fast was the median income for a Hispanic household increasing in 2010? How fast was the median income for a white household increasing in 2010?

c. Do the answers in part (b) suggest that the income gap between white and Hispanic households was widening or narrowing during the given period?

d. What does the coefficient of xt in the formula for $z(t, x)$ represent in terms of the income gap?

52. ▼ *Income Gap* The following model is based on data on the median incomes of black and white households in the United States for the period 2000–2013:[19]

$$z(t, x) = 39{,}300 - 430t + 22{,}400x + 140xt,$$

[18] Incomes are in 2013 dollars. Source for data: U.S. Census Bureau (www.census.gov).
[19] Ibid.

where

$z(t, x) = $ median family income

$t = $ year ($t = 0$ represents 2000)

$x = \begin{cases} 0 & \text{if the income was for a black household} \\ 1 & \text{if the income was for a white household.} \end{cases}$

a. Use the model to estimate the median income of a black household and that of a white household in 2010.

b. According to the model, how fast was the median income for a black household increasing in 2010? How fast was the median income for a white household increasing in 2010?

c. Do the answers in part (b) suggest that the income gap between white and black households was widening or narrowing during the given period?

d. What does the coefficient of xt in the formula for $z(t, x)$ represent in terms of the income gap?

53. ▼ *Average Cost* If you average your costs over your total production, you get the **average cost**, written $\bar{C}$:

$$\bar{C}(x, y) = \frac{C(x, y)}{x + y}.$$

Find the average cost for the cost function in Exercise 49. Then find the marginal average cost of a car and the marginal average cost of a truck at a production level of 50 cars and 50 trucks. Interpret your answers.

54. ▼ *Average Cost* Find the average cost for the cost function in Exercise 50. (See Exercise 53.) Then find the marginal average cost of a bicycle and the marginal average cost of a tricycle at a production level of five bicycles and five tricycles. Interpret your answers.

55. ▼ *Marginal Revenue* As manager of an auto dealership, you offer a car rental company the following deal: You will charge $15,000 per car and $10,000 per truck, but you will then give the company a discount of $5,000 times the square root of the total number of vehicles it buys from you. Looking at your marginal revenue, is this a good deal for the rental company? Why or why not?

56. ▼ *Marginal Revenue* As marketing director for a bicycle manufacturer, you come up with the following scheme: You will offer to sell a dealer x bicycles and y tricycles for

$$R(x, y) = 3{,}500 - 3{,}500e^{-0.02x-0.01y} \text{ dollars.}$$

Find your marginal revenue for bicycles and for tricycles. Are you likely to be fired for your suggestion? Why or why not?

57. ▼ *Research Productivity* Here we apply a variant of the Cobb-Douglas function to the modeling of research productivity. A mathematical model of research productivity at a particular physics laboratory is

$$P = 0.04x^{0.4}y^{0.2}z^{0.4},$$

where P is the annual number of groundbreaking research papers produced by the staff, x is the number of physicists on the research team, y is the laboratory's annual research budget, and z is the annual National Science Foundation subsidy to the laboratory. Find the rate of increase of research papers per government-subsidy dollar at a subsidy level of $1,000,000 per year and a staff level of 10 physicists if the annual budget is $100,000.

58. ▼ **Research Productivity** A major drug company estimates that the annual number P of patents for new drugs developed by its research team is best modeled by the formula

$$P = 0.3x^{0.3}y^{0.4}z^{0.3},$$

where x is the number of research biochemists on the payroll, y is the annual research budget, and z is the size of the bonus awarded to discoverers of new drugs. Assuming that the company has 12 biochemists on the staff, has an annual research budget of $500,000, and pays $40,000 bonuses to developers of new drugs, calculate the rate of growth in the annual number of patents per new research staff member.

59. ▼ **Utility** Your newspaper is trying to decide between two competing desktop publishing software packages: Macro Publish and Turbo Publish. You estimate that if you purchase x copies of Macro Publish and y copies of Turbo Publish, your company's daily productivity will be

$$U(x, y) = 6x^{0.8}y^{0.2} + x \text{ pages per day.}$$

   a. Calculate $U_x(10, 5)$ and $U_y(10, 5)$ to two decimal places, and interpret the results.
   b. What does the ratio $\dfrac{U_x(10, 5)}{U_y(10, 5)}$ tell about the usefulness of these products?

60. ▼ **Grades**[20] A production formula for a student's performance on a difficult English examination is given by

$$g(t, x) = 4tx - 0.2t^2 - x^2,$$

where g is the grade the student can expect to get, t is the number of hours of study for the examination, and x is the student's grade-point average.
   a. Calculate $g_t(10, 3)$ and $g_x(10, 3)$, and interpret the results.
   b. What does the ratio $\dfrac{g_t(10, 3)}{g_x(10, 3)}$ tell about the relative merits of study and grade-point average?

61. ▼ **Electrostatic Repulsion** If positive electric charges of Q and q coulombs are situated at positions (a, b, c) and (x, y, z), respectively, then the force of repulsion they experience is given by

$$F = K\frac{Qq}{(x - a)^2 + (y - b)^2 + (z - c)^2},$$

where $K \approx 9 \times 10^9$, F is given in newtons, and all positions are measured in meters. Assume that a charge of

10 coulombs is situated at the origin and that a second charge of 5 coulombs is situated at $(2, 3, 3)$ and moving in the y-direction at 1 m/sec. How fast is the electrostatic force it experiences decreasing? (Round the answer to one significant digit.)

62. ▼ **Electrostatic Repulsion** Repeat Exercise 61, assuming that a charge of 10 coulombs is situated at the origin and that a second charge of 5 coulombs is situated at $(2, 3, 3)$ and moving in the negative z-direction at 1 m/sec. (Round the answer to one significant digit.)

63. ▼ **Investments** Recall that the compound interest formula for annual compounding is

$$A(P, r, t) = P(1 + r)^t,$$

where A is the future value of an investment of P dollars after t years at an interest rate of r.
   a. Calculate $\dfrac{\partial A}{\partial P}, \dfrac{\partial A}{\partial r}$, and $\dfrac{\partial A}{\partial t}$, all evaluated at $(100, 0.10, 10)$. (Round your answers to two decimal places.) Interpret your answers.
   b. What does the function $\dfrac{\partial A}{\partial P}\Big|_{(100, 0.10, t)}$ of t tell about your investment?

64. ▼ **Investments** Repeat Exercise 63, using the formula for continuous compounding:

$$A(P, r, t) = Pe^{rt}.$$

65. ▼ **Modeling with the Cobb-Douglas Production Formula** Assume that you are given a production formula of the form

$$P(x, y) = Kx^ay^b \quad (a + b = 1).$$

   a. Obtain formulas for $\dfrac{\partial P}{\partial x}$ and $\dfrac{\partial P}{\partial y}$, and show that $\dfrac{\partial P}{\partial x} = \dfrac{\partial P}{\partial y}$ precisely when $x/y = a/b$.
   b. Let x be the number of workers a firm employs, and let y be its monthly operating budget in thousands of dollars. Assume that the firm currently employs 100 workers and has a monthly operating budget of $200,000. If each additional worker contributes as much to productivity as each additional $1,000 per month, find values of a and b that model the firm's productivity.

66. ▼ **Housing Costs**[21] The cost C of building a house is related to the number k of carpenters used and the number e of electricians used by

$$C(k, e) = 15,000 + 50k^2 + 60e^2.$$

If three electricians are currently employed in building your new house and the marginal cost per additional electrician is the same as the marginal cost per additional carpenter, how many carpenters are being used? (Round your answer to the nearest carpenter.)

---

[20] Based on an exercise in *Introduction to Mathematical Economics* by A. L. Ostrosky Jr. and J. V. Koch (Waveland Press, Illinois, 1979).

[21] *Ibid.*

67. ▼ *Nutrient Diffusion* Suppose that 1 cubic centimeter of nutrient is placed at the center of a circular petri dish filled with water. We might wonder how the nutrient is distributed after a time of t seconds. According to the classical theory of diffusion, the concentration of nutrient (in parts of nutrient per part of water) after a time t is given by

$$u(r, t) = \frac{1}{4\pi Dt} e^{-r^2/(4Dt)}.$$

Here, D is the *diffusivity*, which we will take to be 1, and r is the distance from the center in centimeters. How fast is the concentration increasing at a distance of 1 centimeter from the center 3 seconds after the nutrient is introduced?

68. ▼ *Nutrient Diffusion* Refer to Exercise 67. How fast is the concentration increasing at a distance of 4 centimeters from the center 4 seconds after the nutrient is introduced?

Communication and Reasoning Exercises

69. Given that $f(a, b) = r$, $f_x(a, b) = s$, and $f_y(a, b) = t$, complete the following: _____ is increasing at a rate of _____ units per unit of x, _____ is increasing at a rate of _____ units per unit of y, and the value of _____ is _____ when $x =$ _____ and $y =$ _____.

70. A firm's productivity depends on two variables, x and y. Currently, $x = a$ and $y = b$, and the firm's productivity is 4,000 units. Productivity is increasing at a rate of 400 units per unit *decrease* in x and is decreasing at a rate of 300 units per unit increase in y. What does all of this information tell you about the firm's productivity function $g(x, y)$?

71. Complete the following: Let $f(x, y, z)$ be the cost to build a development of x cypods (one-bedroom units) in the city-state of Utarek on Mars, y argaats (two-bedroom units), and z orbici (singular: orbicus; three-bedroom units) in $\overline{Z}$ (zonars, the designated currency in Utarek). Then $\dfrac{\partial f}{\partial z}$ measures _____ and has units _____ .

72. Complete the following: Let $f(t, x, y)$ be the projected number of citizens of the Principality State of Voodice, Luna, in year t since its founding, assuming the presence of x lunar vehicle factories and y domed settlements. Then $\dfrac{\partial f}{\partial x}$ measures _____ and has units _____ .

73. Give an example of a function $f(x, y)$ with $f_x(1, 1) = -2$ and $f_y(1, 1) = 3$.

74. Give an example of a function $f(x, y, z)$ that has all of its partial derivatives equal to nonzero constants.

75. ▼ The graph of $z = b + mx + ny$ (where b, m, and n are constants) is a plane.
   a. Explain the geometric significance of the numbers b, m, and n.
   b. Show that the equation of the plane passing through (h, k, l) with slope m in the x direction (in the sense of $\partial/\partial x$) and slope n in the y direction is

$$z = l + m(x - h) + n(y - k).$$

76. ▼ The **tangent plane** to the graph of $f(x, y)$ at $P(a, b, f(a, b))$ is the plane containing the lines tangent to the slice through the graph by $y = b$ (as in Figure 19) and the slice through the graph by $x = a$. Use the result of Exercise 75 to show that the equation of the tangent plane is

$$z = f(a, b) + f_x(a, b)(x - a) + f_y(a, b)(y - b).$$

15.3   Maxima and Minima

Relative and Absolute Maxima and Minima

In Chapter 12, on applications of the derivative, we saw how to locate relative extrema of a function of a single variable. In this section we extend our methods to functions of two variables. Similar techniques work for functions of three or more variables.

Figure 21 shows a portion of the graph of the function

$$f(x, y) = 2(x^2 + y^2) - (x^4 + y^4) + 1.$$

The graph in Figure 21 resembles a "flying carpet," and several interesting points, marked a, b, c, and d, are shown.

1. The point a has coordinates $(0, 0, f(0, 0))$, is directly above the origin $(0, 0)$, and is the lowest point in its vicinity; water would puddle there. We say that f has a **relative minimum** at $(0, 0)$ because $f(0, 0)$ is smaller than $f(x, y)$ for any (x, y) near $(0, 0)$.

2. Similarly, the point b is higher than any point in its vicinity. Thus, we say that f has a **relative maximum** at $(1, 1)$.

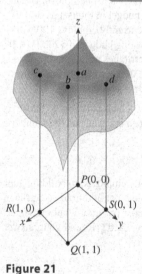

Figure 21

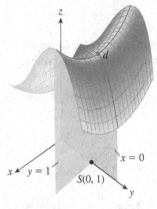

Figure 22

3. The points c and d represent a new phenomenon and are called **saddle points**. They are neither relative maxima nor relative minima but seem to be a little of both.

To see more clearly what features a saddle point has, look at Figure 22, which shows a portion of the graph near the point d.

If we slice through the graph along $y = 1$, we get a curve on which d is the *lowest* point. Thus, d looks like a relative minimum along this slice. On the other hand, if we slice through the graph along $x = 0$, we get another curve, on which d is the *highest* point, so d looks like a relative maximum along this slice. This kind of behavior characterizes a saddle point: f has a **saddle point** at (r, s) if f has a relative minimum at (r, s) along some slice through that point and a relative maximum along another slice through that point. If you look at the other saddle point, c, in Figure 21, you see the same characteristics.

While numerical information can help us to locate the approximate positions of relative extrema and saddle points, calculus permits us to locate these points accurately, as we did for functions of a single variable. Look once again at Figure 21, and notice the following:

- The points P, Q, R, and S are all in the **interior** of the domain of f; that is, none lie on the boundary of the domain. Said another way, we can move some distance in any direction from any of these points without leaving the domain of f.

- The tangent lines along the slices through these points parallel to the x- and y-axes are *horizontal*. Thus, the partial derivatives $\partial f/\partial x$ and $\partial f/\partial y$ are zero when evaluated at any of the points P, Q, R, and S. This gives us a way of locating candidates for relative extrema and saddle points.

The following summary generalizes and also expands on some of what we have just said.

Relative and Absolute Maxima and Minima

The function f of n variables has a **relative maximum** at $(r_1, r_2, \ldots, r_n)$ if $f(r_1, r_2, \ldots, r_n) \geq f(x_1, x_2, \ldots, x_n)$ for every point $(x_1, x_2, \ldots, x_n)$ near* $(r_1, r_2, \ldots, r_n)$ in the domain of f. We say that f has an **absolute maximum** at $(r_1, r_2, \ldots, r_n)$ if $f(r_1, r_2, \ldots, r_n) \geq f(x_1, x_2, \ldots, x_n)$ for every point $(x_1, x_2, \ldots, x_n)$ in the domain of f. The terms **relative minimum** and **absolute minimum** are defined in a similar way. Note that, as with functions of a single variable, absolute extrema are special kinds of relative extrema.

Locating Candidates for Extrema and Saddle Points in the Interior of the Domain of f

- Set $\dfrac{\partial f}{\partial x_1} = 0, \dfrac{\partial f}{\partial x_2} = 0, \ldots, \dfrac{\partial f}{\partial x_n} = 0$ simultaneously, and solve for $x_1, x_2, \ldots, x_n$.
- Check that the resulting points $(x_1, x_2, \ldots, x_n)$ are in the interior of the domain of f.

Points at which all the partial derivatives of f are zero are called **critical points**. The critical points are the only candidates for extrema and saddle points in the interior of the domain of f, assuming that its partial derivatives are defined at every point.[†]

* For $(x_1, x_2, \ldots, x_n)$ to be near $(r_1, r_2, \ldots, r_n)$, we mean that x_1 is in some open interval centered at r_1, x_2 is in some open interval centered at r_2, and so on.

† One can use the techniques of Section 15.4 to find extrema on the *boundary* of the domain of a function; for a complete discussion, see the optional extra section: *Maxima and Minima: Boundaries and the Extreme Value Theorem.* (We shall not consider the analogs of the singular points.)

Quick Examples

In each of the following Quick Examples the domain is the whole Cartesian plane, and the partial derivatives are defined at every point, so the critical points give us the only candidates for extrema and saddle points:

1. Let $f(x, y) = x^3 + (y - 1)^2$. Then $\dfrac{\partial f}{\partial x} = 3x^2$ and $\dfrac{\partial f}{\partial y} = 2(y - 1)$. Thus, we solve the system

$$3x^2 = 0 \quad \text{and} \quad 2(y - 1) = 0.$$

The first equation gives $x = 0$, and the second gives $y = 1$. Thus, the only critical point is $(0, 1)$.

2. Let $f(x, y) = x^2 - 4xy + 8y$. Then $\dfrac{\partial f}{\partial x} = 2x - 4y$ and $\dfrac{\partial f}{\partial y} = -4x + 8$. Thus, we solve

$$2x - 4y = 0 \quad \text{and} \quad -4x + 8 = 0.$$

The second equation gives $x = 2$, and the first then gives $y = 1$. Thus, the only critical point is $(2, 1)$.

3. Let $f(x, y) = e^{-(x^2+y^2)}$. Taking partial derivatives and setting them equal to zero, we get

$$-2xe^{-(x^2+y^2)} = 0 \qquad \text{We set } \frac{\partial f}{\partial x} = 0.$$

$$-2ye^{-(x^2+y^2)} = 0. \qquad \text{We set } \frac{\partial f}{\partial y} = 0.$$

The first equation implies that $x = 0$,* and the second implies that $y = 0$. Thus, the only critical point is $(0, 0)$.

* Recall that if a product of two numbers is zero, then one or the other must be zero. In this case the number $e^{-(x^2+y^2)}$ can't be zero (because e^u is never zero), which gives the result claimed.

In the remainder of this section we will be interested in locating all critical points of a given function and then classifying each one as a relative maximum, relative minimum, saddle point, or none of these. Whether or not any relative extrema we find are in fact absolute is a subject that we discuss in Section 15.4.†

† In some of the applications in the exercises you will, however, need to consider whether the extrema you find are absolute.

EXAMPLE 1 Locating and Classifying Critical Points

Locate all critical points of $f(x, y) = x^2y - x^2 - 2y^2$. Graph the function to classify the critical points as relative maxima, relative minima, saddle points, or none of these.

Solution The partial derivatives are

$$f_x = 2xy - 2x = 2x(y - 1)$$
$$f_y = x^2 - 4y.$$

Setting these equal to zero gives

$$x = 0 \text{ or } y = 1$$
$$x^2 = 4y.$$

We get a solution by choosing either $x = 0$ or $y = 1$ and substituting into $x^2 = 4y$.

Case 1: $x = 0$ Substituting into $x^2 = 4y$ gives $0 = 4y$ and hence $y = 0$. Thus, the critical point for this case is $(x, y) = (0, 0)$.

Case 2: y = 1   Substituting into $x^2 = 4y$ gives $x^2 = 4$ and hence $x = \pm 2$. Thus, we get two critical points for this case: $(2, 1)$ and $(-2, 1)$.

We now have three critical points altogether: $(0, 0)$, $(2, 1)$, and $(-2, 1)$. Because the domain of f is the whole Cartesian plane and the partial derivatives are defined at every point, these critical points are the only candidates for relative extrema and saddle points. We get the corresponding points on the graph by substituting for x and y in the equation for f to get the z-coordinates. The points are $(0, 0, 0)$, $(2, 1, -2)$, and $(-2, 1, -2)$.

 Classifying the Critical Points Graphically   To classify the critical points graphically, we look at the graph of f shown in Figure 23.

Examining the graph carefully, we see that the point $(0, 0, 0)$ is a relative maximum. As for the other two critical points, are they saddle points or are they relative maxima? They are relative maxima along the y-direction, but they are relative minima along the lines $y = \pm x$ (see the top edge of the picture, which shows a dip at $(-2, 1, -2)$), so they are saddle points. If you don't believe this, we will get more evidence following and in a later example.

 Classifying the Critical Points Numerically   We can use a tabular representation of the function to classify the critical points numerically. The following tabular representation of the function can be obtained by using a spreadsheet. (See the Spreadsheet Technology Guide discussion of Example 3 of Section 15.1 at the end of the chapter for information on using a spreadsheet to generate such a table.)

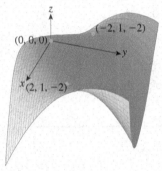

(0, 0, 0)

(−2, 1, −2)

(2, 1, −2)

Figure 23

		$x \rightarrow$						
		−3	**−2**	**−1**	**0**	**1**	**2**	**3**
y	**−3**	−54	−34	−22	−18	−22	−34	−54
$\downarrow$	**−2**	−35	−20	−11	−8	−11	−20	−35
	−1	−20	−10	−4	−2	−4	−10	−20
	0	−9	−4	−1	0	−1	−4	−9
	1	−2	−2	−2	−2	−2	−2	−2
	2	1	−4	−7	−8	−7	−4	1
	3	0	−10	−16	−18	−16	−10	0

The shaded and colored cells show rectangular neighborhoods of the three critical points $(0, 0)$, $(2, 1)$, and $(-2, 1)$. (Notice that they overlap.) The values of f at the critical points are at the centers of these rectangles. Looking at the gray neighborhood of $(x, y) = (0, 0)$, we see that $f(0, 0) = 0$ is the largest value of f in the shaded cells, suggesting that f has a maximum at $(0, 0)$. The shaded neighborhood of $(2, 1)$ on the right shows $f(2, 1) = -2$ as the maximum along some slices (e.g., the vertical slice) and a minimum along the diagonal slice from top left to bottom right. This is what results in a saddle point on the graph. The point $(-2, 1)$ is similar; thus, f also has a saddle point at $(-2, 1)$.

Second Derivative Test

Q: *Is there an algebraic way of deciding whether a given point is a relative maximum, relative minimum, or saddle point?*

A: There is a second derivative test for functions of two variables, stated as follows.

Second Derivative Test for Functions of Two Variables

Suppose (a, b) is a critical point in the interior of the domain of the function f of two variables. Let H be the quantity

$$H = f_{xx}(a, b)f_{yy}(a, b) - [f_{xy}(a, b)]^2. \quad \text{\textit{H} is called the \textit{Hessian}.}$$

Then, if H is *positive*,

- f has a relative minimum at (a, b) if $f_{xx}(a, b) > 0$;
- f has a relative maximum at (a, b) if $f_{xx}(a, b) < 0$.

If H is *negative*,

- f has a saddle point at (a, b).

If $H = 0$ the test tells us nothing, so we need to look at the graph or a numerical table to see what is going on.

Quick Examples

4. Let $f(x, y) = x^2 - y^2$. Then

$$f_x = 2x \quad \text{and} \quad f_y = -2y,$$

which gives $(0, 0)$ as the only critical point. Also,

$$f_{xx} = 2, \quad f_{xy} = 0, \quad \text{and} \quad f_{yy} = -2, \quad \text{Note that these are constant.}$$

which gives $H = (2)(-2) - 0^2 = -4$. Because H is negative, we have a saddle point at $(0, 0)$.

5. Let $f(x, y) = x^2 + 2y^2 + 2xy + 4x$. Then

$$f_x = 2x + 2y + 4 \quad \text{and} \quad f_y = 2x + 4y.$$

Setting these equal to zero gives a system of two linear equations in two unknowns:

$$x + y = -2$$
$$x + 2y = 0.$$

This system has solution $(-4, 2)$, so this is our only critical point. The second partial derivatives are $f_{xx} = 2, f_{xy} = 2$, and $f_{yy} = 4$, so $H = (2)(4) - 2^2 = 4$. Because $H > 0$ and $f_{xx} > 0$, we have a relative minimum at $(-4, 2)$.

Note There is a second derivative test for functions of three or more variables, but it is considerably more complicated. We stick with functions of two variables for the most part in this book. The justification of the second derivative test is beyond the scope of this book. ∎

EXAMPLE 2   Using the Second Derivative Test

Use the second derivative test to analyze the function $f(x, y) = x^2y - x^2 - 2y^2$ discussed in Example 1, and confirm the results we got there.

Solution We saw in Example 1 that the first-order derivatives are

$$f_x = 2xy - 2x = 2x(y - 1)$$
$$f_y = x^2 - 4y$$

and the critical points are $(0, 0)$, $(2, 1)$, and $(-2, 1)$. We also need the second derivatives:

$$f_{xx} = 2y - 2$$
$$f_{xy} = 2x$$
$$f_{yy} = -4.$$

The point $(0, 0)$: $f_{xx}(0, 0) = -2$, $f_{xy}(0, 0) = 0$, and $f_{yy}(0, 0) = -4$, so $H = 8$. Because $H > 0$ and $f_{xx}(0, 0) < 0$, the second derivative test tells us that f has a relative maximum at $(0, 0)$.

The point $(2, 1)$: $f_{xx}(2, 1) = 0$, $f_{xy}(2, 1) = 4$, and $f_{yy}(2, 1) = -4$, so $H = -16$. Because $H < 0$, we know that f has a saddle point at $(2, 1)$.

The point $(-2, 1)$: $f_{xx}(-2, 1) = 0$, $f_{xy}(-2, 1) = -4$, and $f_{yy}(-2, 1) = -4$, so once again $H = -16$, and f has a saddle point at $(-2, 1)$.

Application: Deriving the Formulas for Linear Regression

In Section 1.4 we presented the following set of formulas for the **regression** or **best-fit** line associated with a given set of data points (x_1, y_1), (x_2, y_2), . . . , (x_n, y_n).

Regression Line

The line that best fits the n data points (x_1, y_1), (x_2, y_2), . . . , (x_n, y_n) has the form

$$y = mx + b,$$

where

$$m = \frac{n(\Sigma xy) - (\Sigma x)(\Sigma y)}{n(\Sigma x^2) - (\Sigma x)^2}$$

$$b = \frac{\Sigma y - m(\Sigma x)}{n}$$

n = number of data points.

Derivation of the Regression Line Formulas

Recall that the regression line is defined to be the line that minimizes the sum of the squares of the **residuals**, measured by the vertical distances shown in Figure 24, which shows a regression line associated with $n = 5$ data points. In the figure, the points $P_1, \ldots, P_n$ on the regression line have coordinates $(x_1, mx_1 + b)$, $(x_2, mx_2 + b)$, . . . , $(x_n, mx_n + b)$. The residuals are the quantities $y_{\text{Observed}} - y_{\text{Predicted}}$:

$$y_1 - (mx_1 + b), y_2 - (mx_2 + b), \ldots, y_n - (mx_n + b).$$

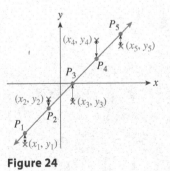

Figure 24

The sum of the squares of the residuals is therefore

$$S(m, b) = [y_1 - (mx_1 + b)]^2 + [y_2 - (mx_2 + b)]^2 + \cdots + [y_n - (mx_n + b)]^2,$$

and this is the quantity we must minimize by choosing m and b. Because we reason that there is a line that minimizes this quantity, there must be a relative minimum at that point. We shall see in a moment that the function S has at most one critical point, which must therefore be the desired absolute minimum. To obtain the critical points of S, we set the partial derivatives equal to zero and solve:

$$S_m = 0: \quad -2x_1[y_1 - (mx_1 + b)] - \cdots - 2x_n[y_n - (mx_n + b)] = 0$$
$$S_b = 0: \quad -2[y_1 - (mx_1 + b)] - \cdots - 2[y_n - (mx_n + b)] = 0.$$

Dividing by -2 and gathering terms allows us to rewrite the equations as

$$m(x_1^2 + \cdots + x_n^2) + b(x_1 + \cdots + x_n) = x_1y_1 + \cdots + x_ny_n$$
$$m(x_1 + \cdots + x_n) + nb \qquad\qquad = y_1 + \cdots + y_n.$$

We can rewrite these equations more neatly using Σ-notation:

$$m(\Sigma x^2) + b(\Sigma x) = \Sigma xy$$
$$m(\Sigma x) + nb = \Sigma y.$$

This is a system of two linear equations in the two unknowns m and b. It may or may not have a unique solution. When there is a unique solution, we can conclude that the best-fit line is given by solving these two equations for m and b. Alternatively, there is a general formula for the solution of any system of two equations in two unknowns, and if we apply this formula to our two equations, we get the regression formulas above.

15.3 EXERCISES

▼ more advanced   ◆ challenging
🔲 indicates exercises that should be solved using technology

In Exercises 1–4, classify each labeled point on the graph as one of the following:

Relative maximum
Relative minimum
Saddle point
Critical point but neither a relative extremum nor a saddle point
None of the above [HINT: See Example 1.]

1.

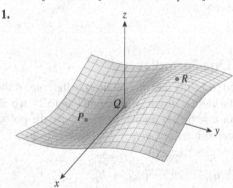

2.

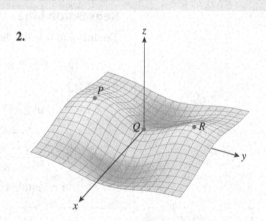

3.

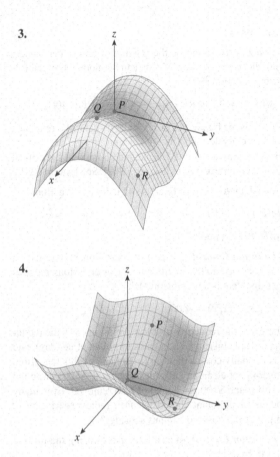

4.

In Exercises 5–10, classify the shaded value in each table as one of the following:

Relative maximum
Relative minimum
Saddle point
Neither a relative extremum nor a saddle point

Assume that the shaded value represents a critical point.

5.

	$x \rightarrow$					
$y \downarrow$		**-3**	**-2**	**-1**	**0**	**1**	**2**
	-3	10	5	2	1	2	5
	-2	9	4	1	0	1	4
	-1	10	5	2	1	2	5
	0	13	8	5	4	5	8
	1	18	13	10	9	10	13
	2	25	20	17	16	17	20
	3	34	29	26	25	26	29

6.

	$x \rightarrow$					
$y \downarrow$		**-3**	**-2**	**-1**	**0**	**1**	**2**
	-3	5	0	-3	-4	-3	0
	-2	8	3	0	-1	0	3
	-1	9	4	1	0	1	4
	0	8	3	0	-1	0	3
	1	5	0	-3	-4	-3	0
	2	0	-5	-8	-9	-8	-5
	3	-7	-12	-15	-16	-15	-12

7.

	$x \rightarrow$					
$y \downarrow$		**-3**	**-2**	**-1**	**0**	**1**	**2**
	-3	5	0	-3	-4	-3	0
	-2	8	3	0	-1	0	3
	-1	9	4	1	0	1	4
	0	8	3	0	-1	0	3
	1	5	0	-3	-4	-3	0
	2	0	-5	-8	-9	-8	-5
	3	-7	-12	-15	-16	-15	-12

8.

	$x \rightarrow$					
$y \downarrow$		**-3**	**-2**	**-1**	**0**	**1**	**2**
	-3	2	3	2	-1	-6	-13
	-2	3	4	3	0	-5	-12
	-1	2	3	2	-1	-6	-13
	0	-1	0	-1	-4	-9	-16
	1	-6	-5	-6	-9	-14	-21
	2	-13	-12	-13	-16	-21	-28
	3	-22	-21	-22	-25	-30	-37

9.

	$x \rightarrow$					
$y \downarrow$		**-3**	**-2**	**-1**	**0**	**1**	**2**
	-3	4	5	4	1	-4	-11
	-2	3	4	3	0	-5	-12
	-1	4	5	4	1	-4	-11
	0	7	8	7	4	-1	-8
	1	12	13	12	9	4	-3
	2	19	20	19	16	11	4
	3	28	29	28	25	20	13

10.

		$x \to$				
		−3	**−2**	**−1**	**0**	**1**	**2**
y	**−3**	100	101	100	97	92	85
↓	**−2**	99	100	99	96	91	84
	−1	98	99	98	95	90	83
	0	91	92	91	88	83	76
	1	72	73	72	69	64	57
	2	35	36	35	32	27	20
	3	−26	−25	−26	−29	−34	−41

In Exercises 11–36, locate and classify all the critical points of the given function. [**HINT:** See Example 2.]

11. $f(x, y) = x^2 + y^2 + 1$ **12.** $f(x, y) = 4 - (x^2 + y^2)$

13. $g(x, y) = 1 - x^2 - x - y^2 + y$

14. $g(x, y) = x^2 + x + y^2 - y - 1$

15. $k(x, y) = x^2 - 3xy + y^2$ **16.** $k(x, y) = x^2 - xy + 2y^2$

17. $f(x, y) = x^2 + 2xy + 2y^2 - 2x + 4y$

18. $f(x, y) = x^2 + xy - y^2 + 3x - y$

19. $g(x, y) = -x^2 - 2xy - 3y^2 - 3x - 2y$

20. $g(x, y) = -x^2 - 2xy + y^2 + x - 4y$

21. $h(x, y) = x^2y - 2x^2 - 4y^2$

22. $h(x, y) = x^2 + y^2 - y^2x - 4$

23. $f(x, y) = x^2 + 2xy^2 + 2y^2$

24. $f(x, y) = x^2 + x^2y + y^2$

25. $s(x, y) = e^{x^2+y^2}$ **26.** $s(x, y) = e^{-(x^2+y^2)}$

27. $t(x, y) = x^4 + 8xy^2 + 2y^4$

28. $t(x, y) = x^3 - 3xy + y^3$

29. $f(x, y) = x^2 + y - e^y$ **30.** $f(x, y) = xe^y$

31. $f(x, y) = e^{-(x^2+y^2+2x)}$ **32.** $f(x, y) = e^{-(x^2+y^2-2x)}$

33. ▼ $f(x, y) = xy + \dfrac{2}{x} + \dfrac{2}{y}$ **34.** ▼ $f(x, y) = xy + \dfrac{4}{x} + \dfrac{2}{y}$

35. ▼ $g(x, y) = x^2 + y^2 + \dfrac{2}{xy}$

36. ▼ $g(x, y) = x^3 + y^3 + \dfrac{3}{xy}$

37. ▼ Refer back to Exercise 11. Which (if any) of the critical points of $f(x, y) = x^2 + y^2 + 1$ are absolute extrema?

38. ▼ Refer back to Exercise 12. Which (if any) of the critical points of $f(x, y) = 4 - (x^2 + y^2)$ are absolute extrema?

39. ▮▼ Refer back to Exercise 21. Which (if any) of the critical points of $h(x, y) = x^2y - 2x^2 - 4y^2$ are absolute extrema?

40. ▮▼ Refer back to Exercise 22. Which (if any) of the critical points of $h(x, y) = x^2 + y^2 - y^2x - 4$ are absolute extrema?

Applications

41. *Brand Loyalty* Suppose the fraction of Mazda car owners who chose another new Mazda can be modeled by the following function:[22]

$$M(c, f) = 11 + 8c + 4c^2 - 40f - 20cf + 40f^2,$$

where c is the fraction of Chrysler car owners who remained loyal to Chrysler and f is the fraction of Ford car owners remaining loyal to Ford. Locate and classify all the critical points and interpret your answer. [**HINT:** See Example 2.]

42. *Brand Loyalty* Repeat Exercise 41 using the function

$$M(c, f) = -10 - 8f - 4f^2 + 40c + 20fc - 40c^2.$$

[**HINT:** See Example 2.]

43. ▼ *Pollution Control* The cost of controlling emissions at a firm goes up rapidly as the amount of emissions reduced goes up. Here is a possible model:

$$C(x, y) = 4{,}000 + 100x^2 + 50y^2,$$

where x is the reduction in sulfur emissions, y is the reduction in lead emissions (in pounds of pollutant per day), and C is the daily cost to the firm (in dollars) of this reduction. Government clean-air subsidies amount to $500 per pound of sulfur and $100 per pound of lead removed. How many pounds of pollutant should the firm remove each day to minimize *net* cost (cost minus subsidy)?

44. ▼ *Pollution Control* Repeat Exercise 43 using the following information:

$$C(x, y) = 2{,}000 + 200x^2 + 100y^2$$

with government subsidies amounting to $100 per pound of sulfur and $500 per pound of lead removed per day.

45. ▼ *Revenue* Your company manufactures two models of speakers, the Ultra Mini and the Big Stack. Demand for each depends partly on the price of the other. If one is expensive, then more people will buy the other. If p_1 is the price of the Ultra Mini and p_2 is the price of the Big Stack, demand for the Ultra Mini is given by

$$q_1(p_1, p_2) = 100{,}000 - 100p_1 + 10p_2,$$

where q_1 represents the number of Ultra Minis that will be sold in a year. The demand for the Big Stack is given by

$$q_2(p_1, p_2) = 150{,}000 + 10p_1 - 100p_2.$$

Find the prices for the Ultra Mini and the Big Stack that will maximize your total revenue.

---

[22] This model is not accurate, although it was inspired by an approximation of a second-order regression based on data from the period 1988–1995. Source for original data: Chrysler, Maritz Market Research, Consumer Attitude Research, and Strategic Vision/*New York Times*, November 3, 1995, p. D2.

46. ▼ *Revenue* Repeat Exercise 45, using the following demand functions:

$$q_1(p_1, p_2) = 100{,}000 - 100p_1 + p_2$$
$$q_2(p_1, p_2) = 150{,}000 + p_1 - 100p_2.$$

47. ▼ *Luggage Dimensions: American Airlines* American Airlines requires that the total outside dimensions (length + + width + height) of a checked bag not exceed 62 inches.[23] What are the dimensions of the largest-volume bag that you can check on an American flight?

48. ▼ *Carry-on Bag Dimensions: American Airlines* American Airlines requires that the total outside dimensions (length + width + height) of a carry-on bag not exceed 45 inches.[24] What are the dimensions of the largest-volume bag that you can carry on an American flight?

49. ▼ *Package Dimensions: USPS* The U.S. Postal Service (USPS) will accept only packages with a length plus girth no more than 108 inches.[25] (See the figure.)

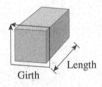

Girth · Length

What are the dimensions of the largest-volume package that the USPS will accept? What is its volume?

50. ▼ *Package Dimensions: UPS* United Parcel Service (UPS) will accept only packages with length no more than 108 inches and length plus girth no more than 165 inches.[26] (See figure for Exercise 49.) What are the dimensions of the largest-volume package that UPS will accept? What is its volume?

---

[23] According to information on its website (www.aa.com).

[24] *Ibid.*

[25] The requirement for packages sent other than Retail Ground, as of September 2015 (www.usps.com).

[26] The requirement as of September 2015 (www.ups.com).

Communication and Reasoning Exercises

51. Sketch the graph of a function that has one extremum and no saddle points.

52. Sketch the graph of a function that has one saddle point and one extremum.

53. ▼ Sketch the graph of a function that has one relative extremum, no absolute extrema, and no saddle points.

54. ▼ Sketch the graph of a function that has infinitely many absolute maxima.

55. Let $H = f_{xx}(a, b)f_{yy}(a, b) - f_{xy}(a, b)^2$. What condition on H guarantees that f has a relative extremum at the point (a, b)?

56. Let H be as in Exercise 55. Give an example to show that it is possible to have $H = 0$ and a relative minimum at (a, b).

57. ▼ Suppose that when the graph of $f(x, y)$ is sliced by a vertical plane through (a, b) parallel to either the xz-plane or the yz-plane, the resulting curve has a relative maximum at (a, b). Does this mean that f has a relative maximum at (a, b)? Explain your answer.

58. ▼ Suppose that f has a relative maximum at (a, b). Does it follow that, if the graph of f is sliced by a vertical plane parallel to either the xz-plane or the yz-plane, the resulting curve has a relative maximum at (a, b)? Explain your answer.

59. ▼ *Average Cost* Let $C(x, y)$ be any cost function, where x and y represent the numbers of two different items manufactured. Show that when the average cost is minimized, the marginal costs C_x and C_y both equal the average cost. Explain why this is reasonable.

60. ▼ *Average Profit* Let $P(x, y)$ be any profit function, where x and y represent the numbers of two different items manufactured and sold. Show that when the average profit is maximized, the marginal profits P_x and P_y both equal the average profit. Explain why this is reasonable.

61. ◆ The tangent plane to a graph was introduced in Exercise 76 in Section 15.2. Use the equation of the tangent plane given there to explain why the tangent plane is parallel to the xy-plane at a relative maximum or minimum of $f(x, y)$.

62. ◆ Use the equation of the tangent plane given in Exercise 76 in Section 15.2 to explain why the tangent plane is parallel to the xy-plane at a saddle point of $f(x, y)$.

15.4 Constrained Maxima and Minima and Applications

So far, we have looked only at the relative extrema of functions with no constraints. However, in Section 12.2 we saw examples in which we needed to find the maximum or minimum of an objective function subject to one or more constraints on the independent variables. For instance, consider the following problem:

Minimize $S = xy + 2xz + 2yz$ subject to $xyz = 4$ with $x > 0, y > 0, z > 0$.

One strategy for solving such problems is essentially the same as the strategy we used earlier: Solve the constraint equation for one of the variables, substitute into the objective function, and then optimize the resulting function using the methods of Section 15.3. We will call this the *substitution method*.* An alternative method, called the *method of Lagrange multipliers*, is useful when it is difficult or impossible to solve the constraint equation for one of the variables, and even when it is possible to do so.

* Although often the method of choice, the substitution method is not infallible (see Exercises 19 and 20).

Substitution Method

EXAMPLE 1 Using Substitution

Minimize $S = xy + 2xz + 2yz$ subject to $xyz = 4$ with $x > 0$, $y > 0$, $z > 0$.

Solution As suggested in the above discussion, we proceed as follows:

Solve the constraint equation for one of the variables, and then substitute in the objective function. The constraint equation is $xyz = 4$. Solving for z gives

$$z = \frac{4}{xy}.$$

The objective function is $S = xy + 2xz + 2yz$, so substituting $z = 4/xy$ gives

$$S = xy + 2x\frac{4}{xy} + 2y\frac{4}{xy}$$

$$= xy + \frac{8}{y} + \frac{8}{x}.$$

Minimize the resulting function of two variables. We use the method in Section 15.3 to find the minimum of $S = xy + \frac{8}{y} + \frac{8}{x}$ for $x > 0$ and $y > 0$. We look for critical points:

$$S_x = y - \frac{8}{x^2}, \quad S_y = x - \frac{8}{y^2}$$

$$S_{xx} = \frac{16}{x^3}, \quad S_{xy} = 1, \quad S_{yy} = \frac{16}{y^3}.$$

We now equate the first partial derivatives to zero:

$$y = \frac{8}{x^2} \quad \text{and} \quad x = \frac{8}{y^2}.$$

To solve for x and y, we substitute the first of these equations in the second, getting

$$x = \frac{x^4}{8}$$

$$x^4 - 8x = 0$$

$$x(x^3 - 8) = 0.$$

The two solutions are $x = 0$, which we reject because x cannot be zero, and $x = 2$. Substituting $x = 2$ in $y = 8/x^2$ gives $y = 2$ also. Thus, the only critical point is $(2, 2)$. To apply the second derivative test, we compute

$$S_{xx}(2, 2) = 2, \quad S_{xy}(2, 2) = 1, \quad S_{yy}(2, 2) = 2$$

and find that $H = 3 > 0$ and $S_{xx}(2, 2) > 0$, so we have a relative minimum at $(2, 2)$.

The corresponding value of z is given by the constraint equation:

$$z = \frac{4}{xy} = \frac{4}{4} = 1.$$

The corresponding value of the objective function is

$$S = xy + \frac{8}{y} + \frac{8}{x} = 4 + \frac{8}{2} + \frac{8}{2} = 12.$$

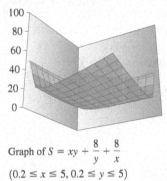

Graph of $S = xy + \dfrac{8}{y} + \dfrac{8}{x}$

$(0.2 \le x \le 5, 0.2 \le y \le 5)$

Figure 25

Figure 25 shows a portion of the graph of $S = xy + \dfrac{8}{y} + \dfrac{8}{x}$ for positive x and y (drawn by using the Excel Surface Grapher in the Chapter 15 utilities at the Website) and suggests that there is a single absolute minimum, which must be at our only candidate point: $(2, 2)$.

We conclude that the minimum of S is 12 and occurs at $(2, 2, 1)$.

The Method of Lagrange Multipliers

As we mentioned above, the method of Lagrange multipliers has the advantage that it can be used in constrained optimization problems when it is difficult or impossible to solve a constraint equation for one of the variables. We restrict attention to the case of a single constraint equation, although the method also generalizes to any number of constraint equations.

Locating Relative Extrema Using the Method of Lagrange Multipliers

To locate the candidates for relative extrema of a function $f(x, y, \ldots)$ subject to the constraint $g(x, y, \ldots) = 0$:

1. Construct the **Lagrangian function**

$$L(x, y, \ldots) = f(x, y, \ldots) - \lambda g(x, y, \ldots),$$

where λ is a new unknown called a **Lagrange multiplier**.

2. The candidates for the relative extrema occur at the critical points of $L(x, y, \ldots)$. To find them, set all the partial derivatives of $L(x, y, \ldots)$ equal to zero, and solve the resulting system, together with the constraint equation $g(x, y, \ldots) = 0$, for the unknowns $x, y, \ldots$ and λ.

The points $(x, y, \ldots)$ that occur in solutions are then the candidates for the relative extrema of f subject to $g = 0$.

Although the justification for the method of Lagrange multipliers is beyond the scope of this text (a derivation can be found in many vector calculus textbooks), we will demonstrate by example how it is used.

EXAMPLE 2   Using Lagrange Multipliers

Use the method of Lagrange multipliers to find the maximum value of $f(x, y) = 2xy$ subject to $x^2 + 4y^2 = 32$.

Solution We start by rewriting the problem with the constraint in the form $g(x, y) = 0$:

$$\text{Maximize } f(x, y) = 2xy \text{ subject to } x^2 + 4y^2 - 32 = 0.$$

Here, $g(x, y) = x^2 + 4y^2 - 32$, and the Lagrangian function is

$$L(x, y) = f(x, y) - \lambda g(x, y)$$
$$= 2xy - \lambda(x^2 + 4y^2 - 32).$$

The system of equations we need to solve is thus

$$L_x = 0: \quad 2y - 2\lambda x = 0$$
$$L_y = 0: \quad 2x - 8\lambda y = 0$$
$$g = 0: \quad x^2 + 4y^2 - 32 = 0.$$

It is often convenient to solve such a system by first solving one of the equations for λ and then substituting in the remaining equations. Thus, we start by solving the first equation to obtain

$$\lambda = \frac{y}{x}.$$

(A word of caution: Because we divided by x, we made the implicit assumption that $x \neq 0$, so before continuing we should check what happens if $x = 0$. But if $x = 0$, then the first equation, $2y = 2\lambda x$, tells us that $y = 0$ as well, and this contradicts the third equation: $x^2 + 4y^2 - 32 = 0$. Thus, we can rule out the possibility that $x = 0$.) Substituting the value of λ in the second equation gives

$$2x - 8\left(\frac{y}{x}\right)y = 0 \quad \text{or} \quad x^2 = 4y^2.$$

We can now substitute $x^2 = 4y^2$ in the constraint equation, obtaining

$$4y^2 + 4y^2 - 32 = 0$$
$$8y^2 = 32$$
$$y = \pm 2.$$

We now substitute back to obtain

$$x^2 = 4y^2 = 16,$$

or $x = \pm 4.$

We don't need the value of λ, so we won't solve for it. Thus, the candidates for relative extrema are given by $x = \pm 4$ and $y = \pm 2$; that is, the four points $(-4, -2)$, $(-4, 2)$, $(4, -2)$, and $(4, 2)$. Recall that we are seeking the maximum value of $f(x, y) = 2xy$. Because we now have only four points to choose from, we compare the values of f at these four points and conclude that the maximum value of f occurs when $(x, y) = (-4, -2)$ or $(4, 2)$ and equals $f(-4, -2) = 2(-4)(-2) = 16$.

Something is suspicious in Example 2. We didn't check to see whether these candidates were relative extrema to begin with, let alone absolute extrema! How do we justify this omission? One of the difficulties with using the method of Lagrange multipliers is that it does not provide us with a test analogous to the second derivative test for functions of several variables. However, if you grant that the function in question does have an absolute maximum, then we require no test, because one of the candidates must give this maximum.

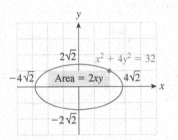

Figure 26

Q : *But how do we know that the given function has an absolute maximum?*

A : The best way to see this is by giving a geometric interpretation. The constraint $x^2 + 4y^2 = 32$ tells us that the point (x, y) must lie on the ellipse shown in Figure 26. The function $f(x, y) = 2xy$ gives the area of the rectangle shaded in the figure. There must be a *largest* such rectangle, because the area varies continuously from 0 when (x, y) is on the x-axis, to positive when (x, y) is in the first quadrant, to 0 again when (x, y) is on the y-axis, so f must have an absolute maximum for at least one pair of coordinates (x, y).

We now show how to use Lagrange multipliers to solve the minimization problem in Example 1.

EXAMPLE 3   **Using Lagrange Multipliers: Function of Three Variables**

Use the method of Lagrange multipliers to find the minimum value of $S = xy + 2xz + 2yz$ subject to $xyz = 4$ with $x > 0, y > 0, z > 0$.

Solution We start by rewriting the problem in standard form:

Maximize $f(x, y, z) = xy + 2xz + 2yz$
subject to $xyz - 4 = 0$ (with $x > 0, y > 0, z > 0$).

Here, $g(x, y, z) = xyz - 4$, and the Lagrangian function is

$$L(x, y, z) = f(x, y, z) - \lambda g(x, y, z)$$
$$= xy + 2xz + 2yz - \lambda(xyz - 4).$$

The system of equations we need to solve is thus

$$L_x = 0: \quad y + 2z - \lambda yz = 0$$
$$L_y = 0: \quad x + 2z - \lambda xz = 0$$
$$L_z = 0: \quad 2x + 2y - \lambda xy = 0$$
$$g = 0: \quad xyz - 4 = 0.$$

As in Example 2, we solve one of the equations for λ and substitute in the others. The first equation gives

$$\lambda = \frac{1}{z} + \frac{2}{y}.$$

Substituting this into the second equation gives

$$x + 2z = x + \frac{2xz}{y}$$

or $\qquad 2 = \frac{2x}{y}$, $\qquad$ Subtract x from both sides and then divide by z.

giving $\qquad y = x$.

Substituting the expression for λ into the third equation gives

$$2x + 2y = \frac{xy}{z} + 2x$$

or $\qquad 2 = \frac{x}{z}$, $\qquad$ Subtract $2x$ from both sides and then divide by y.

giving $\qquad z = \frac{x}{2}$.

Now we have both y and z in terms of x. We substitute these values in the last (constraint) equation:

$$x(x)\left(\frac{x}{2}\right) - 4 = 0$$
$$x^3 = 8$$
$$x = 2.$$

Thus, $y = x = 2$, and $z = \dfrac{x}{2} = 1$. Therefore, the only critical point occurs at $(2, 2, 1)$, as we found in Example 1, and the corresponding value of S is

$$S = xy + 2xz + 2yz = (2)(2) + 2(2)(1) + 2(2)(1) = 12.$$

➡ **Before we go on ...** Again, the method of Lagrange multipliers does not tell us whether the critical point in Example 3 is a maximum, a minimum, or neither. However, if you grant that the function in question does have an absolute minimum, then the values we found must give this minimum value. ∎

Applications

EXAMPLE 4 **Minimizing Area**

Find the dimensions of an open-topped rectangular box that has a volume of 4 cubic feet and the smallest possible surface area.

Solution Our first task is to rephrase this request as a mathematical optimization problem. Figure 27 shows a picture of the box with dimensions x, y, and z. We want to minimize the total surface area, which is given by

$$S = xy + 2xz + 2yz. \qquad \text{Base + Sides + Front and back}$$

This is our objective function. We can't simply choose x, y, and z to all be zero, however, because the enclosed volume must be 4 cubic feet. So

$$xyz = 4. \qquad \text{Constraint}$$

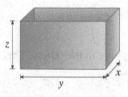

Figure 27

This is our constraint equation. Other unstated constraints are $x > 0$, $y > 0$, and $z > 0$, because the dimensions of the box must be positive. We now restate the problem as follows:

Minimize $S = xy + 2xz + 2yz$ subject to $xyz = 4$, $x > 0$, $y > 0$, $z > 0$.

But this is exactly the problem in Examples 1 and 3, and it has a solution $x = 2$, $y = 2$, $z = 1$, $S = 12$. Thus, the required dimensions of the box are

$$x = 2 \text{ feet}, \quad y = 2 \text{ feet}, \quad z = 1 \text{ foot},$$

requiring a total surface area of 12 square feet.

Q : *In Example 1 we checked that we had a relative minimum at $(x, y) = (2, 2)$, and we were persuaded graphically that this was probably an absolute minimum. Can we be sure that this relative minimum is an absolute minimum?*

A : Yes. There must be a least surface area among all boxes that hold 4 cubic feet. (Why?) Because this would give a relative minimum of S and because the only possible relative minimum of S occurs at (2, 2), this is the absolute minimum.

| EXAMPLE 5 | **Maximizing Productivity** |

An electric motor manufacturer uses workers and robots on its assembly line and has a Cobb-Douglas productivity function* of the form

*Cobb-Douglas production formulas were discussed in Section 11.6.

$$P(x, y) = 10x^{0.2}y^{0.8} \text{ motors manufactured per day,}$$

where x is the number of assembly-line workers and y is the number of robots. Daily operating costs amount to $100 per worker and $16 per robot. How many workers and robots should be used to maximize productivity if the manufacturer has a daily budget of $4,000?

Solution Our objective function is the productivity $P(x, y)$, and the constraint is

$$100x + 16y = 4,000.$$

So the optimization problem is

Maximize $P(x, y) = 10x^{0.2}y^{0.8}$ subject to $100x + 16y = 4,000$ ($x \geq 0$, $y \geq 0$).

Here, $g(x, y) = 100x + 16y - 4,000$, and the Lagrangian function is

$$L(x, y) = P(x, y) - \lambda g(x, y)$$
$$= 10x^{0.2}y^{0.8} - \lambda(100x + 16y - 4,000).$$

The system of equations we need to solve is thus

$$L_x = 0: \quad 2x^{-0.8}y^{0.8} - 100\lambda = 0$$
$$L_y = 0: \quad 8x^{0.2}y^{-0.2} - 16\lambda = 0$$
$$g = 0: \quad 100x + 16y = 4,000.$$

We can rewrite the first two equations as

$$2\left(\frac{y}{x}\right)^{0.8} = 100\lambda \quad \text{and} \quad 8\left(\frac{x}{y}\right)^{0.2} = 16\lambda.$$

Dividing the first by the second to eliminate λ gives

$$\frac{1}{4}\left(\frac{y}{x}\right)^{0.8}\left(\frac{y}{x}\right)^{0.2} = \frac{100}{16}$$

that is,

$$\frac{1}{4}\frac{y}{x} = \frac{25}{4},$$

giving

$$y = 25x.$$

Substituting this result into the constraint equation gives

$$100x + 16(25x) = 4{,}000$$
$$500x = 4{,}000$$

so $x = 8$ workers   and $y = 25x = 200$ robots

for a productivity of

$$P(8, 200) = 10(8)^{0.2}(200)^{0.8} \approx 1{,}051 \text{ motors manufactured per day.}$$

FAQs

When to Use Lagrange Multipliers

Q: *When can I use the method of Lagrange multipliers? When should I use it?*

A: We have discussed the method only when there is a single equality constraint. There is a generalization, which we have not discussed, that works when there are more equality constraints. (We need to introduce one multiplier for each constraint.) So if you have a problem with more than one equality constraint or with any inequality constraints, you must use the substitution method. On the other hand, if you have one equality constraint and it would be difficult to solve it for one of the variables, then you should use Lagrange multipliers.

15.4 EXERCISES

▼ more advanced   ◆ challenging
Ⓣ indicates exercises that should be solved using technology

In Exercises 1–6, solve the given optimization problem by using substitution. [**HINT**: See Example 1.]

1. Find the maximum value of $f(x, y, z) = 1 - x^2 - y^2 - z^2$ subject to $z = 2y$. Also find the corresponding point(s) (x, y, z).

2. Find the minimum value of $f(x, y, z) = x^2 + y^2 + z^2 - 2$ subject to $x = y$. Also find the corresponding point(s) (x, y, z).

3. Find the maximum value of $f(x, y, z) = 1 - x^2 - x - y^2 + y - z^2 + z$ subject to $3x = y$. Also find the corresponding point(s) (x, y, z).

4. Find the maximum value of $f(x, y, z) = 2x^2 + 2x + y^2 - y + z^2 - z - 1$ subject to $z = 2y$. Also find the corresponding point(s) (x, y, z).

5. Minimize $S = xy + 4xz + 2yz$ subject to $xyz = 1$ with $x > 0, y > 0, z > 0$.

6. Minimize $S = xy + xz + yz$ subject to $xyz = 2$ with $x > 0, y > 0, z > 0$.

In Exercises 7–18, use Lagrange multipliers to solve the given optimization problem. [**HINT**: See Example 2.]

7. Find the maximum value of $f(x, y) = xy$ subject to $x + 2y = 40$. Also find the corresponding point(s) (x, y).

8. Find the maximum value of $f(x, y) = xy$ subject to $3x + y = 60$. Also find the corresponding point(s) (x, y).

9. Find the maximum value of $f(x, y) = 4xy$ subject to $x^2 + y^2 = 8$. Also find the corresponding point(s) (x, y).

10. Find the maximum value of $f(x, y) = xy$ subject to $y = 3 - x^2$. Also find the corresponding point(s) (x, y).

11. Find the minimum value of $f(x, y) = x^2 + y^2$ subject to $x + 2y = 10$. Also find the corresponding point(s) (x, y).

12. Find the minimum value of $f(x, y) = x^2 + y^2$ subject to $xy^2 = 16$. Also find the corresponding point(s) (x, y).

13. The problem in Exercise 1. [**HINT:** See Example 3.]

14. The problem in Exercise 2. [**HINT:** See Example 3.]

15. The problem in Exercise 3.

16. The problem in Exercise 4.

17. The problem in Exercise 5.

18. The problem in Exercise 6.

19. ◆ Consider the following constrained optimization problem:

Minimize $f(x, y, z) = (x - 3)^2 + y^2 + z^2$
subject to $x^2 + y^2 - z = 0$.

a. Explain why this minimization problem must have a solution, and solve it using the method of Lagrange multipliers.

b. Solve it again using the substitution method by solving the constraint equation for z.

c. Now try to solve it using the substitution method by solving the constraint equation for y.

d. Explain what goes wrong in part (c).

20. ◆ Consider the following constrained optimization problem:

Minimize $f(x, y, z) = x^2 + (y + 3)^2 + (z - 4)^2$
subject to $4 - x^2 - y^2 - z = 0$.

a. Explain why this minimization problem must have a solution, and solve it using the method of Lagrange multipliers.

b. Solve it again using the substitution method by solving the constraint equation for z.

c. Now try to solve it using the substitution method by solving the constraint equation for x.

d. Explain what goes wrong in part (c).

Applications

Exercises 21–24 were solved in Section 12.2. This time, use the method of Lagrange multipliers to solve them.

21. *Fences* I want to fence in a rectangular vegetable patch. The fencing for the east and west sides costs $4 per foot, and the fencing for the north and south sides costs only $2 per foot. I have a budget of $80 for the project. What is the largest area I can enclose?

22. *Fences* My orchid garden abuts my house so that the house itself forms the northern boundary. The fencing for the southern boundary costs $4 per foot, and the fencing for the east and west sides costs $2 per foot. If I have a budget of $80 for the project, what is the largest area I can enclose?

23. *Revenue* Hercules Films is deciding on the price of the video release of its film *Son of Frankenstein*. Its marketing people estimate that at a price of p dollars, it can sell a total of $q = 200{,}000 - 10{,}000p$ copies. What price will bring in the greatest revenue?

24. *Profit* Hercules Films is also deciding on the price of the video release of its film *Bride of the Son of Frankenstein*. Again, marketing estimates that at a price of p dollars it can sell $q = 200{,}000 - 10{,}000p$ copies, but each copy costs $4 to make. What price will give the greatest *profit*?

25. *Geometry* At what points on the sphere $x^2 + y^2 + z^2 = 1$ is the product xyz a maximum? (The method of Lagrange multipliers can be used.)

26. *Geometry* At what point on the surface $z = (x^2 + x + y^2 + 4)^{1/2}$ is the quantity $x^2 + y^2 + z^2$ a minimum? (The method of Lagrange multipliers can be used.)

27. ▼ *Geometry* What point on the surface $z = x^2 + y - 1$ is closest to the origin? [**HINT:** Minimize the square of the distance from (x, y, z) to the origin.]

28. ▼ *Geometry* What point on the surface $z = x + y^2 - 3$ is closest to the origin? [**HINT:** Minimize the square of the distance from (x, y, z) to the origin.]

29. ▼ *Geometry* Find the point on the plane $-2x + 2y + z - 5 = 0$ closest to $(-1, 1, 3)$. [**HINT:** Minimize the square of the distance from the given point to a general point on the plane.]

30. ▼ *Geometry* Find the point on the plane $2x - 2y - z + 1 = 0$ closest to $(1, 1, 0)$. [**HINT:** Minimize the square of the distance from the given point to a general point on the plane.]

31. *Construction Cost* A closed rectangular box is made with two kinds of materials. The top and bottom are made with heavy-duty cardboard costing 20¢ per square foot, and the sides are made with lightweight cardboard costing 10¢ per square foot. Given that the box is to have a capacity of 2 cubic feet, what should its dimensions be if the cost is to be minimized? [**HINT:** See Example 4.]

32. *Construction Cost* Repeat Exercise 31 assuming that the heavy-duty cardboard costs 30¢ per square foot, the lightweight cardboard costs 5¢ per square foot, and the box is to have a capacity of 6 cubic feet. [**HINT:** See Example 4.]

33. *Package Dimensions: USPS* The U.S. Postal Service (USPS) will accept only packages with a length plus girth no more than 108 inches.[27] (See the figure.)

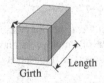

Length

Girth

What are the dimensions of the largest-volume package that the USPS will accept? What is its volume? (This exercise is the same as Exercise 49 in Section 15.3. This time, solve it using Lagrange multipliers.)

---

[27] The requirement for packages sent other than Retail Ground, as of September 2015 (www.usps.com).

34. *Package Dimensions: UPS* United Parcel Service (UPS) will accept only packages with length no more than 108 inches and length plus girth no more than 165 inches.[28] (See figure for Exercise 33.) What are the dimensions of the largest-volume package that UPS will accept? What is its volume? (This exercise is the same as Exercise 50 in Section 15.3. This time, solve it using Lagrange multipliers.)

35. ▼ *Construction Cost* My company wishes to manufacture boxes similar to those described in Exercise 31 as cheaply as possible. Unfortunately, the company that manufactures the cardboard is unable to give me price quotes for the heavy-duty and lightweight cardboard. Find formulas for the dimensions of the box in terms of the price per square foot of heavy-duty and lightweight cardboard.

36. ▼ *Construction Cost* Repeat Exercise 35, assuming that only the bottoms of the boxes are to be made with heavy-duty cardboard.

37. ▼ *Geometry* Find the dimensions of the rectangular box with largest volume that can be inscribed above the xy-plane and under the paraboloid $z = 1 - (x^2 + y^2)$.

38. ▼ *Geometry* Find the dimensions of the rectangular box with largest volume that can be inscribed above the xy-plane and under the paraboloid $z = 2 - (2x^2 + y^2)$.

39. *Productivity* The *Gym Shirt Company* manufactures cotton socks. Production is partially automated through the use of robots. Daily operating costs amount to $150 per laborer and $60 per robot. The number of pairs of socks the company can manufacture in a day is given by a Cobb-Douglas production formula

$$q = 50n^{0.6}r^{0.4},$$

where q is the number of pairs of socks that can be manufactured by n laborers and r robots. Assuming that the company has a daily operating budget of $1,500 and wishes to maximize productivity, how many laborers and how many robots should it use? What is the productivity at these levels? [HINT: See Example 5.]

40. *Productivity* Your automobile assembly plant has a Cobb-Douglas production function given by

$$q = 100x^{0.3}y^{0.7},$$

where q is the number of automobiles it produces per year, x is the number of employees, and y is the monthly assembly-line budget (in thousands of dollars). Annual operating costs amount to an average of $60 thousand per employee plus the operating budget of $12y$ thousand. Your annual budget is $1,200,000. How many employees should you hire and what should your assembly-line budget be to maximize productivity? What is the productivity at these levels? [HINT: See Example 5.]

Communication and Reasoning Exercises

41. Outline two methods of solution of the problem "*Maximize* $f(x, y, z)$ *subject to* $g(x, y, z) = 0$," and give an advantage and disadvantage of each.

42. Suppose we know that $f(x, y)$ has both partial derivatives in its domain $D: x > 0, y > 0$, and that (a, b) is the only point in D such that $f_x(a, b) = f_y(a, b) = 0$. Must it be the case that, if f has an absolute maximum, it occurs at (a, b)? Explain.

43. Under what circumstances would it be necessary to use the method of Lagrange multipliers?

44. Under what circumstances would the method of Lagrange multipliers not apply?

45. Restate the following problem as a maximization problem of the form "*Maximize* $f(x, y)$ *subject to* $g(x, y) = 0$":

Find the maximum value of $h(x) = 1 - 2x^2$.

46. Restate the following problem as a maximization problem of the form "*Maximize* $f(x, y, z)$ *subject to* $g(x, y, z) = 0$":

Find the maximum value of $h(x, y) = 1 - 2(x^2 + y^2)$.

47. ▼ If the partial derivatives of a function of several variables are always defined and never 0, is it possible for the function to have relative extrema when restricted to some domain? Explain your answer.

48. ▼ Give an example of a function f of three variables with an absolute maximum at $(0, 0, 0)$ but where the partial derivatives of f are never zero wherever they are defined.

49. ◆ A **linear programming problem in two variables** is a problem of the form: *Maximize (or minimize)* $f(x, y)$ *subject to constraints of the form* $C(x, y) \geq 0$ *or* $C(x, y) \leq 0$. Here, the objective function f and the constraints C are linear functions. There may be several linear constraints in one problem. Explain why the solution cannot occur in the interior of the domain of f.

50. ◆ Refer back to Exercise 49. Explain why the solution will actually be at a corner of the domain of f (where two or more of the line segments that make up the boundary meet). This result—or rather a slight generalization of it—is known as the Fundamental Theorem of Linear Programming.

---

[28] The requirement as of September 2015 (www.ups.com).

15.5 Double Integrals and Applications

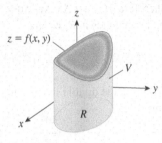

Figure 28

When discussing functions of one variable, we computed the area under a graph by integration. The analog for the graph of a function of two variables is the *volume V* under the graph, as in Figure 28. Think of the region R in the *xy*-plane as the "shadow" under the portion of the surface $z = f(x, y)$ shown.

By analogy with the definite integral of a function of one variable, we make the following definition.

Geometric Definition of the Double Integral

The **double integral of $f(x, y)$ over the region R in the *xy*-plane** is defined as

(Volume *above* the region R and under the graph of f)

$-$(Volume *below* the region R and above the graph of f).

We denote the double integral of $f(x, y)$ over the region R by $\iint_R f(x, y)\, dx\, dy$.

Quick Example

1. Take $f(x, y) = 2$ and take R to be the rectangle $0 \le x \le 1, 0 \le y \le 1$. Then the graph of f is a flat horizontal surface $z = 2$, and

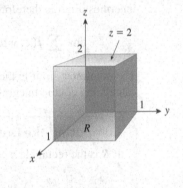

$$\iint_R f(x, y)\, dx\, dy = \text{Volume of box}$$
$$= \text{Width} \times \text{Length} \times \text{Height} = 1 \times 1 \times 2 = 2.$$

---

* The *Banach-Tarski paradox* is an example of the trouble we can get into if we try to rely on our intuition about volume. There are many descriptions of the paradox available on the web.

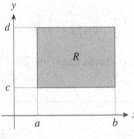

Figure 29

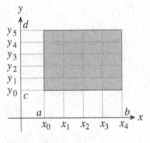

Figure 30

As we saw in the case of the definite integral of a function of one variable, we also desire *numerical* and *algebraic* definitions for two reasons: (1) to make the mathematical definition more precise, so as not to rely on any intuitive notion of "volume,"* and (2) for direct computation of the integral using technology or analytical tools.

We start with the simplest case: when the region R is a rectangle $a \le x \le b$ and $c \le y \le d$. (See Figure 29.) To compute the volume over R, we mimic what we did to find the area under the graph of a function of one variable. We break up the interval $[a, b]$ into m intervals all of width $\Delta x = (b - a)/m$, and we break up $[c, d]$ into n intervals all of width $\Delta y = (d - c)/n$. Figure 30 shows an example with $m = 4$ and $n = 5$.

This gives us mn rectangles defined by $x_{i-1} \le x \le x_i$ and $y_{j-1} \le y \le y_j$. Over one of these rectangles, f is approximately equal to its value at one corner—say,

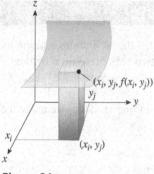

Figure 31

$f(x_i, y_j)$. The volume under f over this small rectangle is then approximately the volume of the rectangular brick (size exaggerated) shown in Figure 31. This brick has height $f(x_i, y_j)$, and its base is Δx by Δy. Its volume is therefore $f(x_i, y_j) \Delta x \Delta y$. Adding together the volumes of all of the bricks over the small rectangles in R, we get

$$\iint_R f(x, y)\, dx\, dy \approx \sum_{j=1}^{n} \sum_{i=1}^{m} f(x_i, y_j) \Delta x \Delta y.$$

This double sum is called a **double Riemann sum**. We define the double integral to be the limit of the Riemann sums as m and n go to infinity.

Algebraic Definition of the Double Integral

$$\iint_R f(x, y)\, dx\, dy = \lim_{n \to \infty} \lim_{m \to \infty} \sum_{j=1}^{n} \sum_{i=1}^{m} f(x_i, y_j) \Delta x \Delta y$$

Note This definition is adequate (the limit exists) when f is continuous. More elaborate definitions are needed for general functions. ∎

This definition also gives us a clue about how to compute a double integral. The innermost sum is $\sum_{i=1}^{m} f(x_i, y_j) \Delta x$, which is a Riemann sum for $\int_a^b f(x, y_j)\, dx$. The innermost limit is therefore

$$\lim_{m \to \infty} \sum_{i=1}^{m} f(x_i, y_j) \Delta x = \int_a^b f(x, y_j)\, dx.$$

The outermost limit is then also a Riemann sum, and we get the following way of calculating double integrals.

Computing the Double Integral over a Rectangle

If R is the rectangle $a \leq x \leq b$ and $c \leq y \leq d$, then

$$\iint_R f(x, y)\, dx\, dy = \int_c^d \left(\int_a^b f(x, y)\, dx \right) dy = \int_a^b \left(\int_c^d f(x, y)\, dy \right) dx.$$

The second formula comes from switching the order of summation in the double sum.

Quick Example

2. If R is the rectangle $1 \leq x \leq 2$ and $1 \leq y \leq 3$, then

$$\iint_R 1\, dx\, dy = \int_1^3 \left(\int_1^2 1\, dx \right) dy$$

$$= \int_1^3 [x]_{x=1}^2\, dy \qquad \text{Evaluate the inner integral.}$$

$$= \int_1^3 1\, dy \qquad\qquad [x]_{x=1}^2 = 2 - 1 = 1.$$

$$= [y]_{y=1}^3 = 3 - 1 = 2.$$

Quick Example 2 used a constant function for the integrand. Here is an example in which the integrand is not constant.

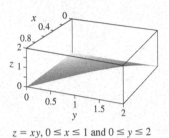

$z = xy, 0 \le x \le 1$ and $0 \le y \le 2$

Figure 32

EXAMPLE 1   **Double Integral over a Rectangle**

Let R be the rectangle $0 \le x \le 1$ and $0 \le y \le 2$. Compute $\iint_R xy \, dx \, dy$. This integral gives the volume of the part of the boxed region under the surface $z = xy$ shown in Figure 32.

Solution

$$\iint_R xy \, dx \, dy = \int_0^2 \int_0^1 xy \, dx \, dy$$

(We usually drop the parentheses around the inner integral as we did here.) As in Quick Example 2, we compute this **iterated integral** from the inside out. First, we compute

$$\int_0^1 xy \, dx.$$

To do this computation, we do as we did when finding partial derivatives: We treat y as a constant. This gives

$$\int_0^1 xy \, dx = \left[\frac{x^2}{2} \cdot y \right]_{x=0}^1 = \frac{1}{2}y - 0 = \frac{y}{2}.$$

We can now calculate the outer integral:

$$\int_0^2 \int_0^1 xy \, dx \, dy = \int_0^2 \frac{y}{2} \, dy = \left[\frac{y^2}{4} \right]_0^2 = 1.$$

 Before we go on . . . We could also reverse the order of integration in Example 1:

$$\int_0^1 \int_0^2 xy \, dy \, dx = \int_0^1 \left[x \cdot \frac{y^2}{2} \right]_{y=0}^2 dx = \int_0^1 2x \, dx = [x^2]_0^1 = 1. \qquad \blacksquare$$

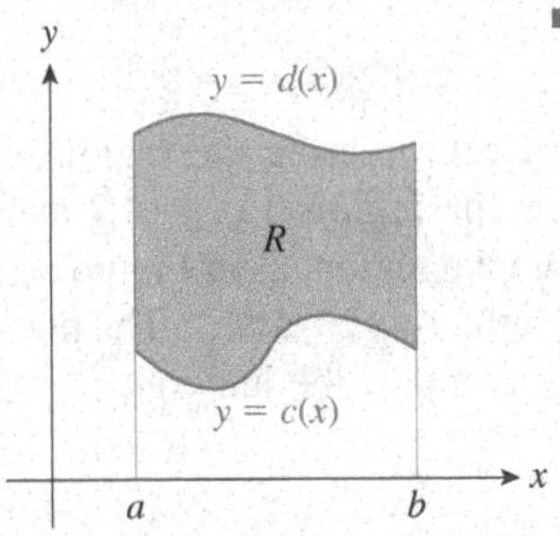

Often, we need to integrate over regions R that are not rectangular. There are two cases that come up. The first is a region like the one shown in Figure 33. In this region the bottom and top sides are defined by functions $y = c(x)$ and $y = d(x)$, respectively, so that the whole region can be described by the inequalities $a \le x \le b$ and $c(x) \le y \le d(x)$. To evaluate a double integral over such a region, we have the following formula.

Figure 33

Computing the Double Integral over a Nonrectangular Region

If R is the region $a \le x \le b$ and $c(x) \le y \le d(x)$ (Figure 33), then we integrate over R according to the following equation:

$$\iint_R f(x, y) \, dx \, dy = \int_a^b \int_{c(x)}^{d(x)} f(x, y) \, dy \, dx.$$

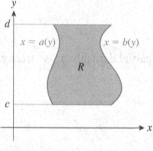

Figure 34

EXAMPLE 2   Double Integral over a Nonrectangular Region

R is the triangle shown in Figure 34. Compute $\iint_R x\, dx\, dy$.

Solution R is the region described by $0 \le x \le 2, 0 \le y \le x$. We have

$$\iint_R x\, dx\, dy = \int_0^2 \int_0^x x\, dy\, dx$$

$$= \int_0^2 [xy]_{y=0}^x\, dx$$

$$= \int_0^2 x^2\, dx$$

$$= \left[\frac{x^3}{3}\right]_0^2 = \frac{8}{3}.$$

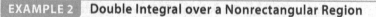

Figure 35

The second type of region is shown in Figure 35. This is the region described by $c \le y \le d$ and $a(y) \le x \le b(y)$. To evaluate a double integral over such a region, we have the following formula.

> **Double Integral over a Nonrectangular Region (continued)**
>
> If R is the region $c \le y \le d$ and $a(y) \le x \le b(y)$ (Figure 35), then we integrate over R according to the following equation:
>
> $$\iint_R f(x, y)\, dx\, dy = \int_c^d \int_{a(y)}^{b(y)} f(x, y)\, dx\, dy.$$

EXAMPLE 3   Double Integral over a Nonrectangular Region

Redo Example 2, integrating in the opposite order.

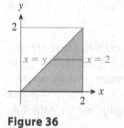

Figure 36

Solution We can integrate in the opposite order if we can describe the region in Figure 34 in the way shown in Figure 35. In fact, it is the region $0 \le y \le 2$ and $y \le x \le 2$. To see this, we draw a horizontal line through the region, as in Figure 36. The line extends from $x = y$ on the left to $x = 2$ on the right, so $y \le x \le 2$. The possible heights for such a line are $0 \le y \le 2$. We can now compute the integral:

$$\iint_R x\, dx\, dy = \int_0^2 \int_y^2 x\, dx\, dy$$

$$= \int_0^2 \left[\frac{x^2}{2}\right]_{x=y}^2\, dy$$

$$= \int_0^2 \left(2 - \frac{y^2}{2}\right) dy$$

$$= \left[2y - \frac{y^3}{6}\right]_0^2 = \frac{8}{3}.$$

Note Many regions can be described in two different ways, as we saw in Examples 2 and 3. Sometimes one description will be much easier to work with than the other, so it pays to consider both. ∎

Applications

There are many applications of double integrals besides finding volumes. For example, we can use them to find *averages*. Remember that the average of $f(x)$ on $[a, b]$ is given by $\int_a^b f(x)\, dx$ divided by $(b - a)$, the length of the interval.

Average of a Function of Two Variables

The average of $f(x, y)$ on the region R is

$$\bar{f} = \frac{1}{A} \iint_R f(x, y)\, dx\, dy.$$

Here, A is the area of R. We can compute the area A geometrically, by using the techniques from Section 14.2, or by computing

$$A = \iint_R 1\, dx\, dy.$$

Quick Example

3. The average value of $f(x, y) = xy$ on the rectangle given by $0 \leq x \leq 1$ and $0 \leq y \leq 2$ is

$$\bar{f} = \frac{1}{2} \iint_R xy\, dx\, dy \qquad \text{The area of the rectangle is 2.}$$

$$= \frac{1}{2} \int_0^2 \int_0^1 xy\, dx\, dy$$

$$= \frac{1}{2} \cdot 1 = \frac{1}{2}. \qquad \text{We calculated the integral in Example 1.}$$

EXAMPLE 4   Average Revenue

Your company is planning to price its new line of subcompact cars at between $10,000 and $15,000. The marketing department reports that if the company prices the cars at p dollars per car, the demand will be between $q = 20,000 - p$ and $q = 25,000 - p$ cars sold in the first year. What is the average of all the possible revenues your company could expect in the first year?

Solution Revenue is given by $R = pq$ as usual, and we are told that

$$10,000 \leq p \leq 15,000$$

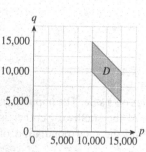

Figure 37

and $20,000 - p \leq q \leq 25,000 - p.$

This domain D of prices and demands is shown in Figure 37.

To average the revenue R over the domain D, we need to compute the area A of D. Using either calculus or geometry, we get $A = 25,000,000$. We then need to integrate R over D:

$$\iint_D pq \, dp \, dq = \int_{10,000}^{15,000} \int_{20,000-p}^{25,000-p} pq \, dq \, dp$$

$$= \int_{10,000}^{15,000} \left[\frac{pq^2}{2} \right]_{q=20,000-p}^{25,000-p} dp$$

$$= \frac{1}{2} \int_{10,000}^{15,000} \left[p(25,000 - p)^2 - p(20,000 - p)^2 \right] dp$$

$$= \frac{1}{2} \int_{10,000}^{15,000} \left[225,000,000p - 10,000p^2 \right] dp$$

$$\approx 3,072,900,000,000,000.$$

The average of all the possible revenues your company could expect in the first year is therefore

$$\overline{R} = \frac{3,072,900,000,000,000}{25,000,000} \approx \$122,900,000.$$

➡ **Before we go on . . .** To check that the answer obtained in Example 4 is reasonable, notice that the revenues at the corners of the domain are $100,000,000 per year, $150,000,000 per year (at two corners), and $75,000,000 per year. Some of these are smaller than the average and some are larger, as we would expect. ■

Another useful application of the double integral comes about when we consider density. For example, suppose that $P(x, y)$ represents the population density (in people per square mile, say) in the city of Houston, shown in Figure 38.

If we break the city up into small rectangles (for example, city blocks), then the population in the small rectangle $x_{i-1} \le x \le x_i$ and $y_{j-1} \le y \le y_j$ is approximately $P(x_i, y_j) \, \Delta x \, \Delta y$. Adding up all of these population estimates, we get

$$\text{Total population} \approx \sum_{j=1}^{n} \sum_{i=1}^{m} P(x_i, y_j) \, \Delta x \, \Delta y.$$

Because this is a double Riemann sum, when we take the limit as m and n go to infinity, we get the following calculation of the population of the city:

$$\text{Total population} = \iint_{\text{City}} P(x, y) \, dx \, dy.$$

Darker regions have higher population density

Figure 38

EXAMPLE 5   Population

Squaresville is a city in the shape of a square that is 5 miles on a side. The population density at a distance of x miles east and y miles north of the southwest corner is $P(x, y) = x^2 + y^2$ thousand people per square mile. Find the total population of Squaresville.

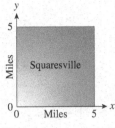

Figure 39

Solution Squaresville is pictured in Figure 39, in which we put the origin in the southwest corner of the city.

To compute the total population, we integrate the population density over the city.

$$\text{Total population} = \iint_{\text{Squaresville}} P(x, y) \, dx \, dy$$

$$= \int_0^5 \int_0^5 (x^2 + y^2) \, dx \, dy$$

$$= \int_0^5 \left[\frac{x^3}{3} + xy^2 \right]_{x=0}^5 \, dy$$

$$= \int_0^5 \left[\frac{125}{3} + 5y^2 \right] \, dy$$

$$= \frac{1{,}250}{3} \approx 417 \text{ thousand people.}$$

➡ **Before we go on ...** Note that the average population density is the total population divided by the area of the city, which is about 17,000 people per square mile in Example 5. This is the same as the calculation of the average of $P(x, y)$ over the city. (Compare to Example 4.) ∎

15.5 EXERCISES

▼ more advanced   ◆ challenging
🔲 indicates exercises that should be solved using technology

In Exercises 1–16, compute the given integral.
[**HINT**: See Example 1.]

1. $\int_0^1 \int_0^1 (x - 2y) \, dx \, dy$

2. $\int_{-1}^1 \int_0^2 (2x + 3y) \, dx \, dy$

3. $\int_0^1 \int_0^2 (ye^x - x - y) \, dx \, dy$

4. $\int_1^2 \int_2^3 \left(\frac{1}{x} + \frac{1}{y} \right) dx \, dy$

5. $\int_0^2 \int_0^3 e^{x+y} \, dx \, dy$

6. $\int_0^1 \int_0^1 e^{x-y} \, dx \, dy$

7. $\int_0^1 \int_0^{2-y} x \, dx \, dy$

8. $\int_0^1 \int_0^{2-y} y \, dx \, dy$

9. $\int_{-1}^1 \int_{y-1}^{y+1} e^{x+y} \, dx \, dy$
[**HINT**: See Example 2.]

10. $\int_0^1 \int_y^{y+2} \frac{1}{\sqrt{x+y}} \, dx \, dy$
[**HINT**: See Example 2.]

11. $\int_0^1 \int_{-x^2}^{x^2} x \, dy \, dx$

12. $\int_1^4 \int_{-\sqrt{x}}^{\sqrt{x}} \frac{1}{x} \, dy \, dx$

13. $\int_0^1 \int_0^x e^{x^2} \, dy \, dx$

14. $\int_0^1 \int_0^{x^2} e^{x^3+1} \, dy \, dx$

15. $\int_0^2 \int_{1-x}^{8-x} (x + y)^{1/3} \, dy \, dx$

16. $\int_1^2 \int_{1-2x}^{x^2} \frac{x+1}{(2x+y)^3} \, dy \, dx$

In Exercises 17–24, find $\iint_R f(x, y) \, dx \, dy$, where R is the indicated domain. (Remember that you often have a choice as to the order of integration.) [**HINT**: See Example 2.]

17. $f(x, y) = 2$

18. $f(x, y) = x$

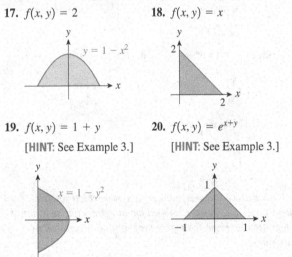

19. $f(x, y) = 1 + y$
[**HINT**: See Example 3.]

20. $f(x, y) = e^{x+y}$
[**HINT**: See Example 3.]

21. $f(x, y) = xy^2$

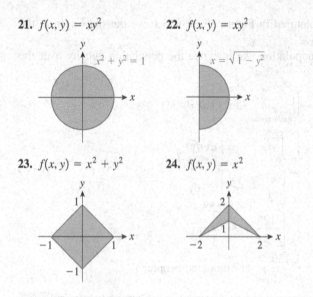

22. $f(x, y) = xy^2$

23. $f(x, y) = x^2 + y^2$

24. $f(x, y) = x^2$

In Exercises 25–30, find the average value of the given function over the indicated domain. [**HINT:** See Quick Example 3.]

25. $f(x, y) = y$

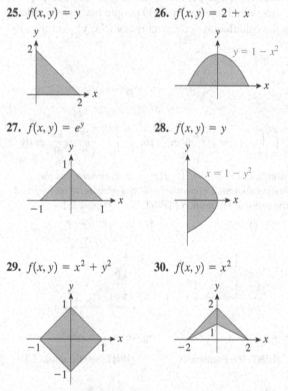

26. $f(x, y) = 2 + x$

27. $f(x, y) = e^y$

28. $f(x, y) = y$

29. $f(x, y) = x^2 + y^2$

30. $f(x, y) = x^2$

In Exercises 31–36, sketch the region over which you are integrating, and then write down the integral with the order of integration reversed (changing the limits of integration as necessary).

31. ▼ $\displaystyle\int_0^1 \int_0^{1-y} f(x, y) \, dx \, dy$

32. ▼ $\displaystyle\int_{-1}^1 \int_0^{1+y} f(x, y) \, dx \, dy$

33. ▼ $\displaystyle\int_{-1}^1 \int_0^{\sqrt{1+y}} f(x, y) \, dx \, dy$

34. ▼ $\displaystyle\int_{-1}^1 \int_0^{\sqrt{1-y}} f(x, y) \, dx \, dy$

35. ▼ $\displaystyle\int_1^2 \int_1^{4/x^2} f(x, y) \, dy \, dx$

36. ▼ $\displaystyle\int_1^{e^2} \int_0^{\ln x} f(x, y) \, dy \, dx$

37. Find the volume under the graph of $z = 1 - x^2$ over the region $0 \le x \le 1$ and $0 \le y \le 2$.

38. Find the volume under the graph of $z = 1 - x^2$ over the triangle $0 \le x \le 1$ and $0 \le y \le 1 - x$.

39. ▼ Find the volume of the tetrahedron shown in the figure. Its corners are $(0, 0, 0)$, $(1, 0, 0)$, $(0, 1, 0)$, and $(0, 0, 1)$.

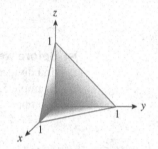

40. ▼ Find the volume of the tetrahedron with corners at $(0, 0, 0)$, $(a, 0, 0)$, $(0, b, 0)$, and $(0, 0, c)$.

Applications

41. **Productivity** A productivity model at the *Handy Gadget Company* is

$$P = 10{,}000x^{0.3} y^{0.7},$$

where P is the number of gadgets the company turns out per month, x is the number of employees at the company, and y is the monthly operating budget in thousands of dollars. Because the company hires part-time workers, it uses anywhere between 45 and 55 workers each month, and its operating budget varies from \$8,000 to \$12,000 per month. What is the average of the possible numbers of gadgets the company can turn out per month? (Round the answer to the nearest 1,000 gadgets.) [**HINT:** See Quick Example 3.]

42. **Productivity** Repeat Exercise 41 using the productivity model

$$P = 10{,}000x^{0.7} y^{0.3}.$$

43. **Revenue** Your latest game app is expected to sell between $q = 8{,}000 - p^2$ and $q = 10{,}000 - p^2$ copies if priced at p dollars. You plan to set the price between \$40 and \$50. What is the average of all the possible revenues you can make? [**HINT:** See Example 4.]

44. *Revenue* Your latest solid-state drive is expected to sell between $q = 180,000 - p^2$ and $q = 200,000 - p^2$ units if priced at p dollars. You plan to set the price between \$300 and \$400. What is the average of all the possible revenues you can make? [HINT: See Example 4.]

45. *Revenue* Your self-published novel has demand curves between $p = 15,000/q$ and $p = 20,000/q$. You expect to sell between 500 and 1,000 copies. What is the average of all the possible revenues you can make?

46. *Revenue* Your self-published book of poetry has demand curves between $p = 80,000/q^2$ and $p = 100,000/q^2$. You expect to sell between 50 and 100 copies. What is the average of all the possible revenues you can make?

47. *Population Density* The town of West Podunk is shaped like a rectangle that is 20 miles from west to east and 30 miles from north to south. (See the figure.) It has a population density of $P(x, y) = e^{-0.1(x+y)}$ hundred people per square mile x miles east and y miles north of the southwest corner of town. What is the total population of the town? [HINT: See Example 5.]

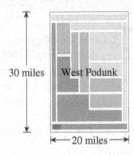

48. *Population Density* The town of East Podunk is shaped like a triangle with an east-west base of 20 miles and a north-south height of 30 miles. (See the figure.) It has a population density of $P(x, y) = e^{-0.1(x+y)}$ hundred people per square mile x miles east and y miles north of the southwest corner of town. What is the total population of the town? [HINT: See Example 5.]

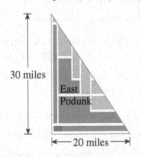

49. *Temperature* The temperature at the point (x, y) on the square with vertices $(0, 0), (0, 1), (1, 0)$, and $(1, 1)$ is given by $T(x, y) = x^2 + 2y^2$ degrees Celsius. Find the average temperature on the square.

50. *Temperature* The temperature at the point (x, y) on the square with vertices $(0, 0), (0, 1), (1, 0)$, and $(1, 1)$ is given by $T(x, y) = x^2 + 2y^2 - x$ degrees Celsius. Find the average temperature on the square.

Communication and Reasoning Exercises

51. Explain how double integrals can be used to compute the area between two curves in the xy plane.

52. Explain how double integrals can be used to compute the volume of solids in 3-space.

53. Complete the following: The first step in calculating an integral of the form

$$\int_a^b \int_{r(x)}^{s(x)} f(x, y) \, dy \, dx$$

is to evaluate the integral ____, obtained by holding ____ constant and integrating with respect to ____ .

54. If the units of $f(x, y)$ are zonars per square meter and x and y are given in meters, what are the units of $\int_a^b \int_{r(x)}^{s(x)} f(x, y) \, dy \, dx$?

55. If the units of $\int_a^b \int_{r(x)}^{s(x)} f(x, y) \, dy \, dx$ are paintings, the units of x are picassos, and the units of y are dalis, what are the units of $f(x, y)$?

56. Complete the following: If the region R is bounded on the left and right by vertical lines and on the top and bottom by the graphs of functions of x, then we integrate over R by first integrating with respect to ____ and then with respect to ____ .

57. ▼ Show that if a, b, c, and d are constant, then

$$\int_a^b \int_c^d f(x)g(y) \, dx \, dy = \int_c^d f(x) \, dx \int_a^b g(y) \, dy.$$

Test this result on the integral $\int_0^1 \int_1^2 ye^x \, dx \, dy$.

58. ▼ Refer to Exercise 57. If a, b, c, and d are constants, can

$$\int_a^b \int_c^d \frac{f(x)}{g(y)} \, dx \, dy$$

be expressed as a product of two integrals? Explain.

CHAPTER 15 REVIEW

KEY CONCEPTS

W www.WanerMath.com
Go to the Website to find a comprehensive and interactive Web-based summary of Chapter 15.

15.1 Functions of Several Variables from the Numerical, Algebraic, and Graphical Viewpoints
A real-valued function, f, of $x, y, z, \ldots$ [p. 1126]
Cost functions [p. 1127]
A linear function of the variables $x_1, x_2, \ldots, x_n$ is a function of the form
$f(x_1, x_2, \ldots, x_n) = a_0 + a_1 x_1 + \cdots + a_n x_n$ ($a_0, a_1, \ldots, a_n$ constants)
[p. 1128]
Representing functions of two variables numerically [p. 1129]
Using a spreadsheet to represent a function of two variables [p. 1130]
Plotting points in three dimensions [p. 1131]
Graph of a function of two variables [p. 1131]
Analyzing the graph of a function of two variables [p. 1134]
Graph of a linear function [p. 1136]

15.2 Partial Derivatives
Definition of partial derivatives [p. 1145]

Application to marginal cost: linear cost function [p. 1146]
Application to marginal cost: interaction cost function [p. 1147]
Geometric interpretation of partial derivatives [p. 1148]
Second-order partial derivatives [p. 1149]

15.3 Maxima and Minima
Definition of relative maximum and minimum [p. 1155]
Locating candidates for relative maxima and minima [p. 1155]
Classifying critical points graphically [p. 1157]
Classifying critical points numerically [p. 1157]
Second derivative test for a function of two variables [p. 1158]
Using the second derivative test [p. 1158]
Formulas for linear regression:

$$m = \frac{n(\Sigma xy) - (\Sigma x)(\Sigma y)}{n(\Sigma x^2) - (\Sigma x)^2}$$

$$b = \frac{\Sigma y - m(\Sigma x)}{n}$$

n = number of data points [p. 1159]

15.4 Constrained Maxima and Minima and Applications
Constrained maximum and minimum problem [p. 1163]
Solving constrained maxima and minima problems using substitution [p. 1164]
The method of Lagrange multipliers [p. 1165]
Using Lagrange multipliers [p. 1166]

15.5 Double Integrals and Applications
Geometric definition of the double integral [p. 1173]
Algebraic definition of the double integral:

$$\iint_R f(x, y) \, dx \, dy =$$

$$\lim_{n \to \infty} \lim_{m \to \infty} \sum_{j=1}^{n} \sum_{i=1}^{m} f(x_i, y_j) \, \Delta x \, \Delta y$$

[p. 1174]
Computing the double integral over a rectangle [p. 1174]
Computing the double integral over nonrectangular regions [p. 1175]
Average of $f(x, y)$ on the region R:

$$\bar{f} = \frac{1}{A} \iint_R f(x, y) \, dx \, dy \quad \text{[p. 1177]}$$

REVIEW EXERCISES

1. Let $f(x, y, z) = \dfrac{x}{y + xz} + x^2 y$. Evaluate $f(0, 1, 1), f(2, 1, 1),$
   $f(-1, 1, -1), f(z, z, z),$ and $f(x + h, y + k, z + l).$

2. Let $g(x, y, z) = xy(x + y - z) + x^2$. Evaluate $g(0, 0, 0),$
   $g(1, 0, 0), g(0, 1, 0), g(x, x, x),$ and $g(x, y + k, z).$

3. Let $f(x, y, z) = 2.72 - 0.32x - 3.21y + 12.5z$. Complete the following: f ___ by ___ units for every 1 unit of increase in x and ___ by ___ units for every unit of increase in z.

4. Let $g(x, y, z) = 2.16x + 11y - 1.53z + 31.4$. Complete the following: g ___ by ___ units for every 1 unit of increase in y and ___ by ___ units for every unit of increase in z.

In Exercises 5 and 6, complete the given table for values for
$h(x, y) = 2x^2 + xy - x.$

5.

	$x \rightarrow$		
$y \downarrow$		-1	0	1
	-1			
	0			
	1			

6.

	$x \rightarrow$		
$y \downarrow$		-2	2	3
	-2			
	2			
	3			

7. Give a formula for a (single) function f with the property that $f(x, y) = -f(y, x)$ and $f(1, -1) = 3$.

8. Let $f(x, y) = x^2 + (y + 1)^2$. Show that $f(y, x) = f(x + 1, y - 1)$.

In Exercises 9–14, sketch the graph of the given function.

9. $r(x, y) = x + y$ 10. $r(x, y) = x - y$

11. $t(x, y) = x^2 + 2y^2$. Show cross sections at $x = 0$ and $z = 1$.

12. $t(x, y) = \dfrac{1}{2}x^2 + y^2$. Show cross sections at $x = 0$ and $z = 1$.

13. $f(x, y) = -2\sqrt{x^2 + y^2}$. Show cross sections at $z = -4$ and $y = 1$.

14. $f(x, y) = 2 + 2\sqrt{x^2 + y^2}$. Show cross sections at $z = 4$ and $y = 1$.

In Exercises 15–20, compute the partial derivatives shown for the given function.

15. $f(x, y) = x^2 + xy$; find f_x, f_y, and f_{yy}.

16. $f(x, y) = \dfrac{6}{xy} + \dfrac{xy}{6}$; find f_x, f_y, and f_{yy}.

17. $f(x, y) = 4x + 5y - 6xy$; find $f_{xx}(1, 0) - f_{xx}(3, 2)$.

18. $f(x, y) = e^{xy} + e^{3x^2 - y^2}$; find $\dfrac{\partial f}{\partial x}$ and $\dfrac{\partial^2 f}{\partial x \partial y}$.

19. $f(x, y, z) = \dfrac{x}{x^2 + y^2 + z^2}$; find $\dfrac{\partial f}{\partial x}, \dfrac{\partial f}{\partial y}, \dfrac{\partial f}{\partial z}$, and $\dfrac{\partial f}{\partial x}\Big|_{(0, 1, 0)}$.

20. $f(x, y, z) = x^2 + y^2 + z^2 + xyz$; find $f_{xx} + f_{yy} + f_{zz}$.

In Exercises 21–26, locate and classify all critical points.

21. $f(x, y) = (x - 1)^2 + (2y - 3)^2$

22. $g(x, y) = (x - 1)^2 - 3y^2 + 9$

23. $k(x, y) = x^2 y - x^2 - y^2$ **24.** $j(x, y) = xy + x^2$

25. $h(x, y) = e^{xy}$

26. $f(x, y) = \ln(x^2 + y^2) - (x^2 + y^2)$

In Exercises 27–30, solve the given constrained optimization problem by using substitution to eliminate a variable. (Do not use Lagrange multipliers.)

27. Find the largest value of xyz subject to $x + y + z = 1$ with $x > 0, y > 0, z > 0$. Also find the corresponding point(s) (x, y, z).

28. Find the minimum value of $f(x, y, z) = x^2 + y^2 + z^2 - 1$ subject to $x = y + z$. Also find the corresponding point(s) (x, y, z).

29. Find the point on the surface $z = \sqrt{x^2 + 2(y - 3)^2}$ closest to the origin.

30. Minimize $S = xy + x^2 z^2 + 4yz$ subject to $xyz = 1$ with $x > 0, y > 0, z > 0$.

In Exercises 31–34, use Lagrange multipliers to solve the given optimization problem.

31. Find the minimum value of $f(x, y) = x^2 + y^2$ subject to $xy = 2$. Also find the corresponding point(s) (x, y).

32. The problem in Exercise 28.

33. The problem in Exercise 29.

34. The problem in Exercise 30.

In Exercises 35–40, compute the given quantities.

35. $\displaystyle\int_0^1 \int_0^2 2xy \, dx \, dy$

36. $\displaystyle\int_1^2 \int_0^1 xye^{x+y} \, dx \, dy$

37. $\displaystyle\int_0^2 \int_0^{2x} \dfrac{1}{x^2 + 1} \, dy \, dx$

38. The average value of xye^{x+y} over the rectangle $0 \le x \le 1$, $1 \le y \le 2$.

39. $\iint_R (x^2 - y^2) \, dx \, dy$, where R is the region shown in the figure

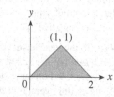

40. The volume under the graph of $z = 1 - y$ over the region in the xy-plane between the parabola $y = 1 - x^2$ and the x-axis

Applications: OHaganBooks.com
[Try the game at www.OHaganBooks.com]

41. *Website Traffic* OHaganBooks.com has two principal competitors: *JungleBooks.com* and *FarmerBooks.com*. Current website traffic at OHaganBooks.com is estimated at 5,000 hits per day. This number is predicted to decrease by 0.8 for every new customer of JungleBooks.com and by 0.6 for every new customer of FarmerBooks.com.

a. Use this information to model the daily website traffic at OHaganBooks.com as a linear function of the new customers of its two competitors.

b. According to the model, if Junglebooks.com gets 100 new customers and OHaganBooks.com traffic drops to 4,770 hits per day, how many new customers has FarmerBooks.com obtained?

c. The model in part (a) did not take into account the growth of the total online consumer base. OHaganBooks.com expects to get approximately one additional hit per day for every 10,000 new Internet shoppers. Modify your model in part (a) to include this information using a new independent variable.

d. How many new Internet shoppers would it take to offset the effects on traffic at OHaganBooks.com of 100 new customers at each of its competitor sites?

42. *Productivity* Billy-Sean O'Hagan is writing his PhD thesis in biophysics but finds that his productivity is affected by the temperature and the number of text messages he receives per hour. On a brisk winter's day when the temperature is 0°C and there are no text messages, Billy-Sean can produce 15 pages of his thesis. His productivity goes down by 0.3 pages per degree Celsius increase in the temperature and by 1.2 pages for each additional text message per hour.

a. Use this information to model Billy-Sean's productivity p as a function of the temperature and the hourly rate of text messages.

b. The other day the temperature was 20°C, and Billy-Sean managed to produce only three pages of his thesis. What was the hourly rate of incoming text messages?

c. Billy-Sean finds that each cup of coffee he drinks per hour can counter the effect on his productivity of two text messages per hour. Modify the model in part (a) to take consumption of coffee into account.

d. What would the domain of your function look like to ensure that p is never negative?

43. **Internet Advertising** To increase business at OHaganBooks.com, you have purchased banner ads at well-known Internet portals and have advertised on television. The following interaction model shows the average number h of hits per day as a function of monthly expenditures x on banner ads and y on television advertising (x and y are in dollars):

$$h(x, y) = 1,800 + 0.05x + 0.08y + 0.00003xy.$$

a. Based on your model, how much traffic can you anticipate if you spend $2,000 per month for banner ads and $3,000 per month on television advertising?

b. Evaluate $\dfrac{\partial h}{\partial y}$, specify its units of measurement, and indicate whether it increases or decreases with increasing x.

c. How much should the company spend on banner ads to obtain 1 hit per day for each $5 spent per month on television advertising?

44. **Company Retreats** Their companies having recently been bailed out by the government at taxpayer expense, Marjory Duffin and John O'Hagan are planning a joint winter business retreat in Cancun, but they are not sure how many sales reps to take along. The following interaction model shows the estimated cost C to their companies (in dollars) as a function of the number of sales reps x and the length of time t in days:

$$C(x, t) = 20,000 - 100x + 600t + 300xt.$$

a. Based on the model, how much would it cost to take five sales reps along for a 10-day retreat?

b. Evaluate $\dfrac{\partial C}{\partial t}$, specify its units of measurement, and indicate whether it increases or decreases with increasing x.

c. How many reps should they take along if they wish to limit the rate of increase of cost with respect to time to $1,200 per day?

45. **Internet Advertising** Refer to the model in Exercise 43. One or more of the following statements is correct. Identify which one(s).
   (A) If nothing is spent on television advertising, one more dollar spent per month in banner ads will buy approximately 0.05 hits per day at OHaganBooks.com.
   (B) If nothing is spent on television advertising, one more hit per day at OHaganBooks.com will cost the company about 5¢ per month in banner ads.
   (C) If nothing is spent on banner ads, one more hit per day at OHaganBooks.com will cost the company about 5¢ per month in banner ads.

(D) If nothing is spent on banner ads, one more dollar spent per month in banner ads will buy approximately 0.05 hits per day at OHaganBooks.com.
   (E) Hits at OHaganBooks.com cost approximately 5¢ per month spent on banner ads, and this cost increases at a rate of 0.003¢ per month, per hit.

46. **Company Retreats** Refer to the model in Exercise 44. One or more of the following statements is correct. Identify which one(s).
   (A) If the retreat lasts for 10 days, the daily cost per sales rep is $400.
   (B) If the retreat lasts for 10 days, each additional day will cost the company $2,900.
   (C) If the retreat lasts for 10 days, each additional sales rep will cost the company $800.
   (D) If the retreat lasts for 10 days, the daily cost per sales rep is $2,900.
   (E) If the retreat lasts for 10 days, each additional sales rep will cost the company $2,900.

47. **Productivity** The holiday season is now at its peak, and OHaganBooks.com has been understaffed and swamped with orders. The current backlog (orders unshipped for two or more days) has grown to a staggering 50,000, and new orders are coming in at a rate of 5,000 per day. Research based on productivity data at OHaganBooks.com results in the following model:

$$P(x, y) = 1,000x^{0.9}y^{0.1} \text{ additional orders filled per day,}$$

where x is the number of additional personnel hired and y is the daily budget (excluding salaries) allocated to eliminating the backlog.

a. How many additional orders will be filled per day if the company hires 10 additional employees and budgets an additional $1,000 per day? (Round the answer to the nearest 100.)

b. In addition to the daily budget, extra staffing costs the company $150 per day for every new staff member hired. To fill at least 15,000 additional orders per day at a minimum total daily cost, how many new staff members should the company hire? (Use the method of Lagrange multipliers.)

48. **Productivity** The holiday season has now ended, and orders at OHaganBooks.com have plummeted, leaving staff members in the shipping department with little to do besides spend their time on Facebook, so the company is considering laying off a number of personnel and slashing the shipping budget. Research based on productivity data at OHaganBooks.com results in the following model:

$$C(x, y) = 1,000x^{0.8}y^{0.2} \text{ fewer orders filled per day,}$$

where x is the number of personnel laid off and y is the cut in the shipping budget (excluding salaries).

a. How many fewer orders will be filled per day if the company lays off 15 additional employees and cuts the budget by an additional $2,000 per day? (Round the answer to the nearest 100.)

b. In addition to the cut in the shipping budget, the layoffs will save the company $200 per day for every new staff member laid off. The company needs to meet a target of 20,000 fewer orders per day, but, for tax reasons, it must minimize the total resulting savings. How many new staff members should the company lay off? (Use the method of Lagrange multipliers.)

49. *Profit* If OHaganBooks.com sells x paperback books and y hardcover books per week, it will make an average weekly profit of

$$P(x, y) = 3x + 10y \text{ dollars.}$$

If it sells between 1,200 and 1,500 paperback books and between 1,800 and 2,000 hardcover books per week, what is the average of all its possible weekly profits?

50. *Cost* It costs *Duffin House*

$$C(x, y) = x^2 + 2y \text{ dollars}$$

to produce x coffee table art books and y paperback books per week. If it produces between 100 and 120 art books and between 800 and 1,000 paperbacks per week, what is the average of all its possible weekly costs?

Modeling College Population

College Malls, Inc. is planning to build a national chain of shopping malls in college neighborhoods. However, malls in general have been experiencing large numbers of store closings due to, among other things, misjudgments of the shopper demographics. As a result, the company is planning to lease only to stores that target the specific age demographics of the national college student population.

As a marketing consultant to College Malls, you will be providing the company with a report that addresses the following specific issues:

- A quick way of estimating the number of students of any specified age and in any particular year and the effect of increasing age on the college population
- The ages that correspond to relatively high and low college populations
- How fast the 20-year-old and 25-year-old student populations are increasing
- Some near-term projections of the student population trend

You decide that a good place to start would be with a visit to the Census Bureau's website at www.census.gov. After some time battling with search engines, all you can find is some data on college enrollment for three age brackets for the period 1980–2009, as shown in the following table:[29]

College Enrollment (thousands)

Year	1980	1985	1990	1995	2000	2001	2002	2003	2004	2005	2006	2007	2008	2009
18–24	7,229	7,537	7,964	8,541	9,451	9,629	10,033	10,365	10,611	10,834	10,587	11,161	11,466	12,072
25–34	2,703	3,063	3,161	3,349	3,207	3,422	3,401	3,494	3,690	3,600	3,658	3,838	4,013	6,141
35–44	700	963	1,344	1,548	1,454	1,557	1,678	1,526	1,615	1,657	1,548	1,520	1,672	1,848

The data are inadequate for several reasons: The data are given only for certain years and in age brackets rather than year by year and for each individual age; nor is it obvious how you would project the figures. However, you notice that the table is actually a numerical representation of a function of two variables: year and age. Since the age brackets are of different sizes, you normalize the data by dividing each figure by the number of years represented in the corresponding age bracket; for

[29] Source: Census Bureau (www.census.gov/population/www/socdemo/school.html).

instance, you divide the 1980 figure for the first age group by 7 to obtain the average enrollment for each year of age in that group. You then rewrite the resulting table representing the years by values of t and each age bracket by the (rounded) age x at its center (enrollment values are rounded):

$t \rightarrow$	0	5	10	15	20	21	22	23	24	25	26	27	28	29
x ↓ 21	1,033	1,077	1,138	1,220	1,350	1,376	1,433	1,481	1,516	1,548	1,512	1,594	1,638	1,725
30	270	306	316	335	321	342	340	349	369	360	366	384	401	614
40	70	96	134	155	145	156	168	153	162	166	155	152	167	185

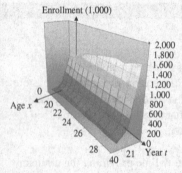

Figure 40

To see a visual representation of what the data are saying, you use Excel to graph the data as a surface (Figure 40). It is important to notice that Excel does not scale the t-axis as you would expect: It uses one subdivision for each year shown in the chart, and the result is an uneven scaling of the t-axis. Despite this drawback, you do see two trends after looking at views of the graph from various angles. First, enrollment of 21-year olds (the back edge of the graph) seems to be increasing faster than enrollment of other age groups. Second, the enrollments for all ages seem to be increasing approximately linearly with time, though at different rates for different age groups; for instance, the front and rear edges rise more or less linearly but do not seem to be parallel.

At this point you realize that a mathematical model of these data would be useful; not only would it "smooth out the bumps," but it would give you a way to estimate enrollment N at each specific age, project the enrollments, and thereby complete the project for College Malls. Although technology can give you a regression model for data such as these, it is up to you to decide on the form of the model. It is in choosing an appropriate model that your analysis of the graph comes in handy. Because N should vary linearly with time t for each value of x, you would like

$$N = mt + k$$

for each value of x. Also, because there are three values of x for every value of time, you try a quadratic model for N as a function of x:

$$N = a + bx + cx^2.$$

Putting these together, you get the following candidate model:

$$N(t, x) = a_1 + a_2t + a_3x + a_4x^2,$$

where a_1, a_2, a_3, and a_4 are constants. However, for each specific age $x = k$, you get

$$N(t, k) = a_1 + a_2t + a_3k + a_4k^2 = \text{Constant} + a_2t$$

with the same slope a_2 for every choice of the age k, contrary to your observation that enrollment for different age groups is rising at different rates, so you will need a more elaborate model. You recall from your applied calculus course that interaction functions give a way to model the effect of one variable on the rate of change of another, so, as an experiment, you try adding interaction terms to your model:

Model 1: $N(t, x) = a_1 + a_2t + a_3x + a_4x^2 + a_5xt$ Second-order model

Model 2: $N(t, x) = a_1 + a_2t + a_3x + a_4x^2 + a_5xt + a_6x^2t.$ Third-order model

(Model 1 is referred to as a second-order model because it contains no products of more than two independent variables, whereas Model 2 contains the third-order term $x^2t = x \cdot x \cdot t$.) If you study these two models for specific values k of x you get

Model 1: $N = \text{Constant} + (a_2 + a_5 k)t$.   Slope depends linearly on age.

Model 2: $N = \text{Constant} + (a_2 + a_5 k + a_6 k^2)t$.   Slope depends quadratically on age.

This is encouraging: Both models show different slopes for different ages. Model 1 would predict that the slope either increases with increasing age (a_5 positive) or decreases with increasing age (a_5 negative). However, the graph suggests that the slope is larger for both younger and older students but smaller for students of intermediate age, contrary to what Model 1 predicts, so you decide to go with the more flexible Model 2, which permits the slope to decrease and then increase with increasing age, which is exactly what you observe on the graph.

You decide to use Excel to generate your model. However, the data as shown in the table are not in a form that Excel can use for regression; the data need to be organized into columns: Column A for the dependent variable N and Columns B–C for the independent variables, as shown in Figure 41.

You then add columns for the higher order terms x^2, xt, and x^2t as shown below:

◇	A	B	C
1	N	t	x
2	1033	0	21
3	1077	5	21
4	1138	10	21
5	1220	15	21
6	1350	20	21
7	1376	21	21
8	1433	22	21
9	1481	23	21
10	1516	24	21
11	1548	25	21
12	1512	26	21
13	1594	27	21
14	1638	28	21
15	1725	29	21
16	270	0	30
17	306	5	30
18	316	10	30
19	335	15	30
20	321	20	30
21	342	21	30
22	340	22	30
23	349	23	30
24	369	24	30
25	360	25	30
26	366	26	30
27	384	27	30
28	401	28	30
29	614	29	30
30	70	0	40
31	96	5	40
32	134	10	40
33	155	15	40
34	145	20	40
35	156	21	40
36	168	22	40
37	153	23	40
38	162	24	40
39	166	25	40
40	155	26	40
41	152	27	40
42	167	28	40
43	185	29	40

Figure 41

◇	A	B	C	D	E	F
1	N	t	x	x^2	x*t	x^2*t
2	1033	0	21	=C2^2	=C2*B2	=C2^2*B2
3	1077	5	21			
4	1138	10	21			
5	1220	15	21			
6	1350	20	21			
7	1376	21	21			
8	1433	22	21			
9	1481	23	21			

◇	A	B	C	D	E	F
1	N	t	x	x^2	x*t	x^2*t
2	1033	0	21	441	0	0
3	1077	5	21	441	105	2205
4	1138	10	21	441	210	4410
5	1220	15	21	441	315	6615
6	1350	20	21	441	420	8820
7	1376	21	21	441	441	9261
8	1433	22	21	441	462	9702
9	1481	23	21	441	483	10143

Next, highlight a vacant 5×6 block (the block A46:F50, say), type the formula =LINEST(A2:A43,B2:F43,TRUE,TRUE), and press Ctrl+Shift+Enter (not just Enter!). You will see a table of statistics like the following:

42						
43	185	29	40	1600	1160	46400
44						
45						
46	=LINEST(A2:A43,B2:F43,,TRUE)					
47						
48						
49						
50						

42					
43	185	29	40	1600	1160	46400
44					
45					
46	0.088570354	-6.46546922	3.21423521	-241.273271	120.009278	4594.62978
47	0.02096866	1.28767845	0.44955302	27.6069027	18.6958148	400.824866
48	0.99337478	49.506512	#N/A	#N/A	#N/A	#N/A
49	1079.5571	36	#N/A	#N/A	#N/A	#N/A
50	13229404.1	88232.2104	#N/A	#N/A	#N/A	#N/A

The desired constants $a_1, a_2, a_3, a_4, a_5, a_6$ appear in the first row of the data but in *reverse order*. Thus, if we round to five significant digits, we have

$$a_1 = 4{,}594.6 \quad a_2 = 120.01 \quad a_3 = -241.27$$
$$a_4 = 3.2142 \quad a_5 = -6.4655 \quad a_6 = 0.088570,$$

which gives our regression model:

$$N(t, x) = 4{,}594.6 + 120.01t - 241.27x + 3.2142x^2 - 6.4655xt + 0.088570x^2t.$$

Fine, you say to yourself, now you have the model, but how good a fit is it to the data? That is where the rest of the data shown in the output comes in: In the second row are the standard errors corresponding to the corresponding coefficients. Notice that each of the standard errors is small in comparison with the magnitude of the coefficient above it; for instance, 0.021 is only around 1/4 of the magnitude of $a_6 \approx 0.088$ and indicates that the dependence of N on x^2t is statistically significant. (What we do not want to see are standard errors of magnitudes comparable to the coefficients, as those could indicate the wrong choice of independent variables.) The third figure in the left column, 0.99337478, is R^2, where R generalizes the coefficient of correlation discussed in the section on regression in Chapter 1: The closer R is to 1, the better the fit. We can interpret R^2 as indicating that approximately 99.3% of the variation in college enrollment is explained by the regression model, indicating an excellent fit. The figure 1,079.5571 beneath R^2 is called the "F-statistic." The higher the F-statistic (typically, anything above 4 or so would be considered "high"), the more confident we can be that N does depend on the independent variables we are using.*

* We are being deliberately vague about the exact meaning of these statistics, which are discussed fully in many applied statistics texts.

As comforting as these statistics are, nothing can be quite as persuasive as a graph. You turn to the graphing software of your choice and notice that the graph of the model appears to be a faithful representation of the data. (See Figure 42.)

Now you get to work, using the model to address the questions posed by College Malls.

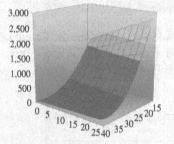

Figure 42

1. *A quick way of estimating the number of students of any specified age and in any particular year, and the effect of increasing age on the college population.* You already have a quantitative relationship in the form of the regression model. As for the second part of the question, the rate of change of college enrollment with respect to age is given by the partial derivative

$$\frac{\partial N}{\partial x} = -241.27 + 6.4284x - 6.4655t + 0.17714xt \text{ thousand students per additional year of age.}$$

Thus, for example, with $x = 20$ in 2004 ($t = 24$) we have

$$\frac{\partial N}{\partial x} = -241.27 + 6.4284(20) - 6.4655(24) + 0.17714(20)(24)$$

$$\approx -183 \text{ thousand students per additional year of age,}$$

so there were about 183,000 fewer students of age 21 than age 20 in 2004.

On the other hand, when $x = 38$ in the same year, we have

$$\frac{\partial N}{\partial x} = -241.27 + 6.4284(38) - 6.4655(24) + 0.17714(38)(24)$$

$$\approx 9.4 \text{ thousand students per additional year of age,}$$

so there were about 9,400 more students of age 39 than age 38 that year.

2. *The ages that correspond to relatively high and low college populations.* Although a glance at the graph shows you that there are no relative maxima, holding t constant (that is, on any given year) gives a parabola along the corresponding slice and hence a minimum somewhere along the slice.

$$\frac{\partial N}{\partial x} = 0$$

when $\qquad -241.27 + 6.4284x - 6.4655t + 0.17714xt = 0,$

which gives $x = \dfrac{241.27 + 6.4655t}{6.4284 + 0.17714t}$ years of age.

For instance, in 2010 ($t = 30$; we are extrapolating the model slightly) the age at which there were fewest students (in the given range) is 37 years of age. The relative maxima for each slice occur at the front and back edges of the surface, meaning that there are relatively more students of the lowest and highest ages represented. The absolute maximum for each slice occurs, as expected, at the lowest age. In short, a mall catering to college students in 2010 should have focused mostly on freshman-age students, least on 37-year-olds, and somewhat more on people around age 40.

3. *How fast the 20-year-old and 25-year-old student populations are increasing.* The rate of change of student population with respect to time is

$$\frac{\partial N}{\partial t} = 120.01 - 6.4655x + 0.088570x^2 \text{ thousand students per year}$$

For the two age groups in question, we obtain

$$x = 20: \quad 120.01 - 6.4655(20) + 0.088570(20)^2 \approx 26.1 \text{ thousand} \\ \text{students per year}$$

$$x = 25: \quad 120.01 - 6.4655(25) + 0.088570(25)^2 \approx 13.7 \text{ thousand} \\ \text{students per year.}$$

(Note that these rates of change are independent of time, as we chose a model that is linear in time.)

4. *Some near-term projections of the student population trend.* As we have seen throughout the book, extrapolation can be a risky venture; however, near-term extrapolation from a good model can be reasonable. You enter the model in an Excel spreadsheet to obtain the following predicted college enrollments (in thousands) for the years 2010–2015:

		$t \rightarrow$				
		30	31	32	33	34	35
x	21	1,644	1,668	1,691	1,714	1,737	1,761
$\downarrow$	30	422	428	434	439	445	451
	40	180	183	186	189	192	195

EXERCISES

1. Use a spreadsheet to obtain Model 1:

$$N(t, x) = a_1 + a_2 t + a_3 x + a_4 x^2 + a_5 xt.$$

   Compare the fit of this model with that of the quadratic model above. Comment on the result.

2. Obtain Model 2 using only the data through 2005, and also obtain the projections for 2010–2015 using the resulting model. Compare the projections with those based on the more complete set of data in the text.

3. Compute and interpret $\left.\dfrac{\partial N}{\partial t}\right|_{(10,\ 18)}$ and $\left.\dfrac{\partial^2 N}{\partial t \partial x}\right|_{(10,\ 18)}$ for the model in the text. What are their units of measurement?

4. Notice that the derivatives in Exercise 3 do not depend on time. What additional polynomial term(s) would make both $\partial N/\partial t$ and $\partial^2 N/\partial t \partial x$ depend on time? (Write down the entire model.) Of what order is your model?

5. Test the model you constructed in Exercise 4 by inspecting the standard errors associated with the additional coefficients.

Section 15.1

Example 1 (page 1127) You own a company that makes two models of speakers: the Ultra Mini and the Big Stack. Your total monthly cost (in dollars) to make x Ultra Minis and y Big Stacks is given by

$$C(x, y) = 10{,}000 + 20x + 40y.$$

Compute several values of this function.

Solution

You can have a TI-83/84 Plus compute $C(x, y)$ numerically as follows:

1. In the "Y=" screen, enter

$$Y_1 = 10000 + 20X + 40Y$$

2. To evaluate, say, $C(10, 30)$ (the cost to make 10 Ultra Minis and 30 Big Stacks), enter

$$10 \rightarrow X$$
$$30 \rightarrow Y$$
$$Y_1$$

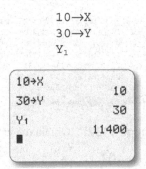

and the calculator will evaluate the function and give the answer $C(10, 30) = 11{,}400$.

This procedure is too laborious if you want to calculate $f(x, y)$ for a large number of different values of x and y.

Section 15.1

Example 1 (page 1127) You own a company that makes two models of speakers: the Ultra Mini and the Big Stack. Your total monthly cost (in dollars) to make x Ultra Minis and y Big Stacks is given by

$$C(x, y) = 10{,}000 + 20x + 40y$$

Compute several values of this function.

Solution

Spreadsheets handle functions of several variables easily. The following setup shows how a table of values of C can be created, using values of x and y you enter:

	A	B	C
1	x	y	C(x, y)
2	10	30	=10000+20*A2+40*B2
3	20	30	
4	15	0	
5	0	30	
6	30	30	

↓

	A	B	C
1	x	y	C(x, y)
2	10	30	11400
3	20	30	11600
4	15	0	10300
5	0	30	11200
6	30	30	11800

A disadvantage of this layout is that it's not easy to enter values of x and y systematically in two columns. Can you find a way to remedy this? (See Example 3 for one method.)

Example 3 (page 1129) Use technology to create a table of values of the body mass index

$$M(w, h) = \frac{0.45w}{(0.0254h)^2}.$$

Solution

We can use this formula to recreate a table in a spreadsheet, as follows:

	A	B	C	D
1		130	140	150
2	60	=0.45*B$1/(0.0254*$A2)^2		
3	61			
4	62			
5	63			
6	64			
7	65			
8	66			
9	67			

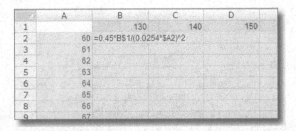

In the formula in cell B2 we have used B$1 instead of B1 for the w-coordinate because we want all references to w to use the same row (1). Similarly, we want all references to h to refer to the same column (A), so we used $A2 instead of A2.

We copy the formula in cell B2 to all of the red shaded area to obtain the desired table:

	A	B	C	D	
1		130	140	150	
2	60	25.18755038	27.12505425	29.06255813	3
3	61	24.36849808	26.24299793	28.11749778	29.9
4	62	23.58875685	25.40327661	27.21779637	29.0
5	63	22.84585068	24.60322381	26.36059694	28.1
6	64	22.13749545	23.84037971	25.54326398	27.2
7	65	21.46158138	23.11247226	24.76336314	26.4
8	66	20.81615733	22.41740021	24.01864308	25.6
9	67	20.19941665	21.75321793	23.30701921	24.8

Example 5 (page 1132)   Obtain the graph of

$$f(x, y) = x^2 + y^2.$$

Solution

1. Set up a table showing a range of values of x and y and the corresponding values of the function (see Example 3):

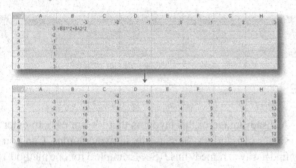

2. Select the cells with the values (B2: H8) and insert a chart, with the "Surface" option selected and "Series in Columns" selected as the data option, to obtain a graph like the following:

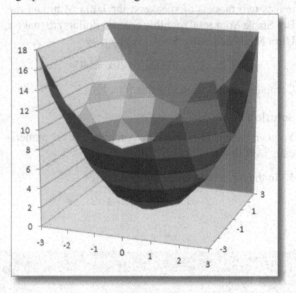

APPENDIX A — LOGIC

Website

www.WanerMath.com

For a much more extensive interactive treatment of logic, including discussion of proofs, rules of inference, and an introduction to the predicate calculus, go online and follow:

Everything

→ Chapter L: Introduction to Logic

Introduction

Logic is the underpinning of all reasoned argument. The ancient Greeks recognized its role in mathematics and philosophy, and studied it extensively. Aristotle, in his *Organon*, wrote the first systematic treatise on logic. His work had a heavy influence on philosophy, science, and religion through the Middle Ages.

But Aristotle's logic was expressed in ordinary language and so was subject to the ambiguities of ordinary language. Philosophers came to want to express logic more formally and symbolically, more like the way that mathematics is written. (Leibniz, in the 17th century, was probably the first to envision and call for such a formalism.) It was with the publication in 1847 of G. Boole's *The Mathematical Analysis of Logic* and A. DeMorgan's *Formal Logic* that **symbolic logic** came into being, and logic became recognized as part of mathematics. Since Boole and DeMorgan, logic and mathematics have been inextricably intertwined. Logic is part of mathematics, but at the same time it is the language of mathematics.

The study of symbolic logic is usually broken into several parts. The first and most fundamental is the **propositional logic**. Built on top of this is the **predicate logic**, which is the language of mathematics. In this appendix we give an introduction to propositional logic.

A.1 Statements and Logical Operators

Propositional logic is the study of *propositions*. A **statement**, or **proposition**, is any declarative sentence which is either true (T) or false (F). We refer to T or F as the **truth value** of the statement.

EXAMPLE 1   Statements

a. "$2 + 2 = 4$" is a statement because it can be either true or false.* Because it happens to be a true statement, its truth value is T.

b. "$1 = 0$" is also a statement, but its truth value is F.

c. "It will rain tomorrow" is a statement. To determine its truth value, we shall have to wait for tomorrow.

d. "Solve the following equation for x" is not a statement, because it cannot be assigned any truth value whatsoever. It is an imperative, or command, rather than a declarative sentence.

e. "The number 5" is not a statement, because it is not even a complete sentence.

f. "This statement is false" gets us into a bind: If it were true, then, because it is declaring itself to be false, it must be false. On the other hand, if it were false, then its declaring itself false is a lie, so it is true! In other words, if it is true, then it is

*Is "$2 + 2 = 4$" a sentence? Read it aloud: "Two plus two equals four" is a perfectly respectable English sentence.

false, and if it is false, then it is true, and we go around in circles. We get out of this bind by saying that because the sentence cannot be either true or false, we refuse to call it a statement. An equivalent pseudo-statement is: "I am lying," so this sentence is known as **the liar's paradox**.

Note Sentences that refer to themselves, or *self-referential sentences*, as illustrated in Example 1(f), are not permitted to be statements. This eliminates the liar's paradox and several similar problems. ∎

We shall use letters like p, q, r, and so on to stand for statements. Thus, for example, we might decide that p should stand for the statement "The moon is round." We write

p: "The moon is round" p is the statement that the moon is round.

to express this.

We can form new statements from old ones in several different ways. For example, starting with p: "I am an Anchovian," we can form the **negation** of p: "It is not the case that I am an Anchovian" or simply "I am not an Anchovian."

Negation of a Statement

If p is a statement, then its **negation** is the statement "not p" and is denoted by $\sim p$. We mean by this that, if p is true, then $\sim p$ is false, and vice versa.

Quick Examples

1. If p: "$2 + 2 = 4$," then $\sim p$: "It is not the case that $2 + 2 = 4$," or, more simply, $\sim p$: "$2 + 2 \neq 4$."

2. If q: "$1 = 0$," then $\sim q$: "$1 \neq 0$."

3. If r: "Diamonds are a pearl's best friend," then $\sim r$: "Diamonds are not a pearl's best friend."

4. If s: "All politicians are crooks," then $\sim s$: "Not all politicians are crooks."

5. **Double Negation:** If p is any statement, then the negation of $\sim p$ is $\sim(\sim p)$: "not (not p)," or, in other words, p. Thus, $\sim(\sim p)$ has the same meaning as p.

Notes

1. Notice in Quick Example 1 that $\sim p$ is false, because p is true. However, in Quick Example 2, $\sim q$ is true, because q is false. A statement of the form $\sim q$ can very well be true; it is a common mistake to think that it must be false.

2. Saying that not all politicians are crooks is not the same as saying that no politicians are crooks but is the same as saying that some (meaning one or more) politicians are not crooks.

3. The symbol $\sim$ is our first example of a **logical operator**.

4. When we say in Quick Example 5 that $\sim(\sim p)$ has the same meaning as p, we mean that they are *logically equivalent*—a notion we will make precise below. ∎

Here is another way we can form a new statement from old ones. Starting with p: "I am wise," and q: "I am strong," we can form the statement "I am wise and I am strong." We denote this new statement by $p \wedge q$, read "p and q." In order for $p \wedge q$ to be true, *both p and q* must be true. Thus, for example, if I am wise but not strong, then $p \wedge q$ is false. The symbol $\wedge$ is another logical operator. The statement $p \wedge q$ is called the **conjunction** of p and q.

Conjunction

The **conjunction** of p and q is the statement $p \wedge q$, which we read "p and q." It can also be said in a number of different ways, such as "p even though q." The statement $p \wedge q$ is true when both p and q are true, and $p \wedge q$ is false otherwise.

Quick Examples

6. If p: "This galaxy will ultimately disappear into a black hole" and q: "$2 + 2 = 4$," then $p \wedge q$ is the statement "Not only will this galaxy ultimately disappear into a black hole, but $2 + 2 = 4$!"

7. If p: "$2 + 2 = 4$" and q: "$1 = 0$," then $p \wedge q$: "$2 + 2 = 4$ and $1 = 0$." Its truth value is F because q is F.

8. With p and q as in Quick Example 6, the statement $p \wedge (\sim q)$ says: "This galaxy will ultimately disappear into a black hole and $2 + 2 \neq 4$," or, more colorfully, as "Contrary to your hopes, this galaxy is doomed to disappear into a black hole; moreover, two plus two is decidedly *not* equal to four!"

Notes

1. We sometimes use the word "but" as an emphatic form of "and." For instance, if p: "It is hot," and q: "It is not humid," then we can read $p \wedge q$ as "It is hot but not humid." There are always many ways of saying essentially the same thing in a natural language; one of the purposes of symbolic logic is to strip away the verbiage and record the underlying logical structure of a statement.

2. A **compound statement** is a statement formed from simpler statements via the use of logical operators. Examples are $\sim p$, $(\sim p) \wedge (q \wedge r)$, and $p \wedge (\sim p)$. A statement that cannot be expressed as a compound statement is called an **atomic statement**.* For example, "I am clever" is an atomic statement. In a compound statement such as $(\sim p) \wedge (q \wedge r)$, we refer to p, q, and r as the **variables** of the statement. Thus, for example, $\sim p$ is a compound statement in the single variable p. ∎

*"Atomic" comes from the Greek for "not divisible." Atoms were originally thought to be the indivisible components of matter. Although the march of science proved that wrong, the name stuck.

Before discussing other logical operators, we pause for a moment to talk about **truth tables**, which give a convenient way to analyze compound statements.

Truth Table

The **truth table** for a compound statement shows, for each combination of possible truth values of its variables, the corresponding truth value of the statement.

Quick Examples

9. The truth table for negation, that is, for $\sim p$, is as follows:

p	$\sim p$
T	F
F	T

Each row shows a possible truth value for p and the corresponding value of $\sim p$.

10. The truth table for conjunction, that is, for $p \wedge q$, is as follows:

p	q	$p \wedge q$
T	T	T
T	F	F
F	T	F
F	F	F

Each row shows a possible combination of truth values of p and q and the corresponding value of $p \wedge q$.

EXAMPLE 2 Construction of Truth Tables

Construct truth tables for the following compound statements:

a. $\sim(p \wedge q)$ **b.** $(\sim p) \wedge q$

Solution

a. Whenever we encounter a complex statement, we work from the inside out, just as we might do if we had to evaluate an algebraic expression such as $-(a + b)$. Thus, we start with the p and q columns, then construct the $p \wedge q$ column, and finally, construct the $\sim(p \wedge q)$ column.

p	q	$p \wedge q$	$\sim(p \wedge q)$
T	T	T	F
T	F	F	T
F	T	F	T
F	F	F	T

Notice how we get the $\sim(p \wedge q)$ column from the $p \wedge q$ column: We reverse all the truth values.

b. Because there are two variables, p and q, we again start with the p and q columns. We then evaluate $\sim p$ and finally take the conjunction of the result with q.

p	q	$\sim p$	$(\sim p) \wedge q$
T	T	F	F
T	F	F	F
F	T	T	T
F	F	T	F

Because we are "and-ing" $\sim p$ with q, we look at the values in the $\sim p$ and q columns and combine these according to the instructions for "and." Thus, for example, in the first row we have $F \wedge T = F$, and in the third row we have $T \wedge T = T$.

Here is a third logical operator. Starting with p: "You are over 18" and q: "You are accompanied by an adult," we can form the statement "You are over 18 or are accompanied by an adult," which we write symbolically as $p \vee q$, read "p or q." Now in English the word "or" has several possible meanings, so we have to agree on which one we want here. Mathematicians have settled on the **inclusive or:** $p \vee q$ means p is true or q is true *or both are true.** With p and q as above, $p \vee q$ stands for "You are over 18 or are accompanied by an adult, or both." We shall sometimes include the phrase "or both" for emphasis, but even if we leave it off, we still interpret "or" as inclusive.

* There is also the **exclusive or:** "*p or q but not both.*" This can be expressed as $(p \vee q) \wedge \sim(p \wedge q)$. Do you see why?

Disjunction

The **disjunction** of p and q is the statement $p \vee q$, which we read "p or q." Its truth value is defined by the following truth table:

p	q	$p \vee q$
T	T	T
T	F	T
F	T	T
F	F	F

This is the **inclusive or**, so $p \vee q$ is true when p is true or q is true *or both* are true.

Quick Examples

11. Let p: "The butler did it," and let q: "The cook did it." Then $p \vee q$: "Either the butler or the cook did it."

12. Let p: "The butler did it," and let q: "The cook did it," and let r: "The lawyer did it." Then $(p \vee q) \wedge (\sim r)$: "Either the butler or the cook did it, but not the lawyer."

Note The only way for $p \vee q$ to be false is for *both* p and q to be false. For this reason we can say that $p \vee q$ also means "p and q are not both false." ∎

To introduce our next logical operator, we ask you to consider the following statement: "If you earn an A in logic, then I'll buy you a new car." It seems to be made up out of two simpler statements:

p: "You earn an A in logic," and
q: "I will buy you a new car."

The original statement says: *If p is true, then q is true*, or, more simply, *if p*, **then** q. We can also phrase this as p **implies** q, and we write the statement symbolically as $p \rightarrow q$.

Now let us suppose for the sake of argument that the original statement: "If you earn an A in logic, then I'll buy you a new car," is true. This does *not* mean that you *will* earn an A in logic. All it says is that *if* you do so, then I will buy you that car. If we think of this as a promise, the only way that it can be broken is if you *do* earn an A and I do *not* buy you a new car. With this in mind, we define the logical statement $p \rightarrow q$ as follows.

Conditional

The **conditional** $p \rightarrow q$, which we read "if p, then q" or "p implies q," is defined by the following truth table:

p	q	$p \rightarrow q$
T	T	T
T	F	F
F	T	T
F	F	T

The arrow "$\rightarrow$" is the **conditional** operator, and in $p \rightarrow q$ the statement p is called the **antecedent** or **hypothesis**, and q is called the **consequent**, or **conclusion**. A statement of the form $p \rightarrow q$ is also called an **implication**.

Quick Examples

13. "If $1 + 1 = 2$ then the sun rises in the east" has the form $p \rightarrow q$ where p: "$1 + 1 = 2$" is true and q: "the sun rises in the east" is also true. Therefore, the statement is true.

14. "If the moon is made of green cheese, then I am Arnold Schwarzenegger" has the form $p \rightarrow q$ where p is false. From the truth table, we see that $p \rightarrow q$ is therefore true, regardless of whether or not I am Arnold Schwarzenegger.

15. "If $1 + 1 = 2$ then $0 = 1$" has the form $p \rightarrow q$ where this time p is true but q is false. Therefore, by the truth table, the given statement is false.

Notes

1. The only way that $p \rightarrow q$ can be false is if p is true and q is false. This is the case of the "broken promise" in the car example above.

2. If you look at the last two rows of the truth table, you see that we say that "$p \rightarrow q$" is true when p is false, *no matter what the truth value of q*. Think again about the promise: If you don't get that A, then whether or not I buy you a new car, I have not broken my promise. It may seem strange at first to say that F $\rightarrow$ T is T and F $\rightarrow$ F is also T, but, as they did in choosing to say that "or" is always inclusive, mathematicians agreed that the truth table above gives the most useful definition of the conditional. ■

It is usually misleading to think of $p \rightarrow q$ as meaning that one of them causes the other. For instance, take p: "no one likes algebra," and q: "there are seven days in a week." Then $p \rightarrow q$ is true whereas neither causes the other. Here is a list of some English phrases that *do* have the same meaning as $p \rightarrow q$.

Some Phrasings of the Conditional

We interpret each of the following as equivalent to the conditional $p \to q$.

If p, then q.	p implies q.
q follows from p.	Not p unless q.
q if p.	p only if q.
Whenever p, q.	q whenever p.
p is sufficient for q.	q is necessary for p.
p is a sufficient condition for q.	q is a necessary condition for p.

Quick Example

16. "If it's Tuesday, this must be Belgium" can be rephrased in several ways as follows:

    "Its being Tuesday implies that this is Belgium."
    "This is Belgium if it's Tuesday."
    "It's Tuesday only if this is Belgium."
    "It can't be Tuesday unless this is Belgium."
    "Its being Tuesday is sufficient for this to be Belgium."
    "That this is Belgium is a necessary condition for its being Tuesday."

Notice the difference between "if" and "only if." We say that "p only if q" means $p \to q$ because, assuming that $p \to q$ is true, p can be true only if q is also. In other words, the only line of the truth table that has $p \to q$ true and p true also has q true. The phrasing "p is a sufficient condition for q" says that it suffices to know that p is true to be able to conclude that q is true. For example, it is sufficient that you get an A in logic for me to buy you a new car. Other things might induce me to buy you the car, but an A in logic would suffice. The phrasing "q is necessary for p" says that for p to be true, q must be true (just as we said for "p only if q").

Q : *Does the commutative law hold for the conditional? In other words, is $p \to q$ the same as $q \to p$?*

A : *No, as we can see in the following truth table:*

p	q	$p \to q$	$q \to p$
T	T	T	T
T	F	F	T
F	T	T	F
F	F	T	T

Not the same

Converse and Contrapositive

The statement $q \to p$ is called the **converse** of the statement $p \to q$. A conditional and its converse are *not* the same.

The statement $\sim q \to \sim p$ is the **contrapositive** of the statement $p \to q$. A conditional and its contrapositive are logically equivalent in the sense we define below: They have the same truth value for all possible values of p and q.

EXAMPLE 3 **Converse and Contrapositive**

Give the converse and contrapositive of the statement "If you earn an A in logic, then I'll buy you a new car."

Solution This statement has the form $p \rightarrow q$, where p: "you earn an A" and q: "I'll buy you a new car." The converse is $q \rightarrow p$. In words, this is "If I buy you a new car then you earned an A in logic."

The contrapositive is $(\sim q) \rightarrow (\sim p)$. In words, this is "If I don't buy you a new car, then you didn't earn an A in logic."

Assuming that the original statement is true, notice that the converse is not necessarily true. There is nothing in the original promise that prevents me from buying you a new car if you do not earn the A. On the other hand, the contrapositive is true. If I don't buy you a new car, it must be that you didn't earn an A; otherwise I would be breaking my promise.

It sometimes happens that we do want both a conditional and its converse to be true. The conjunction of a conditional and its converse is called a **biconditional**.

Biconditional

The **biconditional**, written $p \leftrightarrow q$, is defined to be the statement $(p \rightarrow q) \wedge (q \rightarrow p)$. Its truth table is the following:

p	q	$p \leftrightarrow q$
T	T	T
T	F	F
F	T	F
F	F	T

Phrasings of the Biconditional

We interpret each of the following as equivalent to $p \leftrightarrow q$:

p if and only if q.
p is necessary and sufficient for q.
p is equivalent to q.

Quick Example

17. "I teach math if and only if I am paid a large sum of money" can be rephrased in several ways as follows:

"I am paid a large sum of money if and only if I teach math."
"My teaching math is necessary and sufficient for me to be paid a large sum of money."
"For me to teach math, it is necessary and sufficient that I be paid a large sum of money."

A.2 Logical Equivalence

We mentioned above that we say that two statements are **logically equivalent** if, for all possible truth values of the variables involved, the two statements always have the same truth values. If s and t are equivalent, we write $s \equiv t$. This is *not* another logical statement. It is simply the claim that the two statements s and t are logically equivalent. Here are some examples.

EXAMPLE 4 Logical Equivalence

Use truth tables to show the following:

a. $p \equiv \sim(\sim p)$. This is called **double negation**.

b. $\sim(p \wedge q) \equiv (\sim p) \vee (\sim q)$. This is one of **DeMorgan's laws**.

Solution

a. To demonstrate the logical equivalence of these two statements, we construct a truth table with columns for both p and $\sim(\sim p)$:

Same

p	$\sim p$	$\sim(\sim p)$
T	F	T
F	T	F

Because the p and $\sim(\sim p)$ columns contain the same truth values in all rows, the two statements are logically equivalent.

b. We construct a truth table showing both $\sim(p \wedge q)$ and $(\sim p) \vee (\sim q)$:

Same

p	q	$p \wedge q$	$\sim(p \wedge q)$	$\sim p$	$\sim q$	$(\sim p) \vee (\sim q)$
T	T	T	F	F	F	F
T	F	F	T	F	T	T
F	T	F	T	T	F	T
F	F	F	T	T	T	T

Because the $\sim(p \wedge q)$ column and $(\sim p) \vee (\sim q)$ column agree, the two statements are equivalent.

➡ **Before we go on . . .** The statement $\sim(p \wedge q)$ can be read as "It is not the case that both p and q are true" or "p and q are not both true." We have just shown that this is equivalent to "Either p is false or q is false." ∎

Here are the two equivalences known as DeMorgan's laws.

DeMorgan's Laws

If p and q are statements, then

$$\sim(p \wedge q) \equiv (\sim p) \vee (\sim q)$$
$$\sim(p \vee q) \equiv (\sim p) \wedge (\sim q)$$

Quick Example

18. Let p: "The President is a Democrat," and let q: "The President is a Republican." Then the following two statements say the same thing:

$\sim(p \wedge q)$: "The President is not both a Democrat and a Republican."

$(\sim p) \vee (\sim q)$: "Either the President is not a Democrat, or is not a Republican (or is neither)."

Here is a list of some important logical equivalences, some of which we have already encountered. All of them can be verified by using truth tables as in Example 4. (The verifications of some of these are in the exercise set.)

Important Logical Equivalences

$\sim(\sim p) \equiv p$	The double negative law
$p \wedge q \equiv q \wedge p$	The commutative law for conjunction
$p \vee q \equiv q \vee p$	The commutative law for disjunction
$(p \wedge q) \wedge r \equiv p \wedge (q \wedge r)$	The associative law for conjunction
$(p \vee q) \vee r \equiv p \vee (q \vee r)$	The associative law for disjunction
$\sim(p \vee q) \equiv (\sim p) \wedge (\sim q)$	DeMorgan's laws
$\sim(p \wedge q) \equiv (\sim p) \vee (\sim q)$	
$p \wedge (q \vee r) \equiv (p \wedge q) \vee (p \wedge r)$	The distributive laws
$p \vee (q \wedge r) \equiv (p \vee q) \wedge (p \vee r)$	
$p \wedge p \equiv p$	The absorption laws
$p \vee p \equiv p$	
$p \rightarrow q \equiv (\sim q) \rightarrow (\sim p)$	The contrapositive law

Note that these logical equivalences apply to *any* statement. The ps, qs, and rs can stand for atomic statements or compound statements, as we see in the next example.

EXAMPLE 5   Applying Logical Equivalences

a. Apply DeMorgan's law (once) to the statement $\sim([p \wedge (\sim q)] \wedge r)$.

b. Apply the distributive law to the statement $(\sim p) \wedge [q \vee (\sim r)]$.

c. Consider: "You will get an A if either you are clever and the sun shines or you are clever and it rains." Rephrase the condition more simply using the distributive law.

Solution

a. We can analyze the given statement from the outside in. It is first of all a negation, but further, it is the negation $\sim(A \wedge B)$, where A is the compound statement $[p \wedge (\sim q)]$ and B is r:

$$\sim(\overbrace{[p \wedge (\sim q)]}^{A} \wedge \quad r)$$

Now one of DeMorgan's laws is

$$\sim(A \land B) \equiv (\sim A) \lor (\sim B).$$

Applying this equivalence gives

$$\sim([p \land (\sim q)] \land r) \equiv (\sim[p \land (\sim q)]) \lor (\sim r).$$

b. The given statement has the form $A \land [B \lor C]$, where $A = (\sim p)$, $B = q$, and $C = (\sim r)$. So we apply the distributive law $A \land [B \lor C] \equiv [A \land B] \lor [A \land C]$:

$$(\sim p) \land [q \lor (\sim r)] \equiv [(\sim p) \land q] \lor [(\sim p) \land (\sim r)].$$

(We need not stop here: The second expression on the right is just begging for an application of DeMorgan's law . . .)

c. The condition is "either you are clever and the sun shines or you are clever and it rains." Let's analyze this symbolically: Let p: "You are clever," q: "The sun shines," and r: "It rains." The condition is then $(p \land q) \lor (p \land r)$. We can "factor out" the p using one of the distributive laws in reverse, getting

$$(p \land q) \lor (p \land r) \equiv p \land (q \lor r).$$

We are taking advantage of the fact that the logical equivalences we listed can be read from right to left as well as from left to right. Putting $p \land (q \lor r)$ back into English, we can rephrase the sentence as "You will get an A if you are clever and either the sun shines or it rains."

➡ **Before we go on . . .** In Example 5(a) we could, if we wanted, apply DeMorgan's law again, this time to the statement $\sim[p \land (\sim q)]$ that is part of the answer. Doing so gives

$$\sim[p \land (\sim q)] \equiv (\sim p) \lor \sim(\sim q) \equiv (\sim p) \lor q.$$

Notice that we've also used the double negative law. Therefore, the original expression can be simplified as follows:

$$\sim([p \land (\sim q)] \land r) \equiv (\sim[p \land (\sim q)]) \lor (\sim r) \equiv ((\sim p) \lor q) \lor (\sim r),$$

which we can write as

$$(\sim p) \lor q \lor (\sim r)$$

because the associative law tells us that it does not matter which two expressions we "or" first. ∎

A.3 Tautologies, Contradictions, and Arguments

Tautologies and Contradictions

A compound statement is a **tautology** if its truth value is always T, regardless of the truth values of its variables. It is a **contradiction** if its truth value is always F, regardless of the truth values of its variables.

Quick Examples

19. $p \vee (\sim p)$ has truth table

p	$\sim p$	$p \vee (\sim p)$
T	F	T
F	T	T

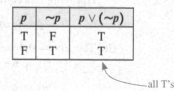

all T's

and is therefore a tautology.

20. $p \wedge (\sim p)$ has truth table

p	$\sim p$	$p \wedge (\sim p)$
T	F	F
F	T	F

and is therefore a contradiction.

When a statement is a tautology, we also say that the statement is **tautological**. In common usage this sometimes means simply that the statement is self-evident. In logic it means something stronger: that the statement is always true under all circumstances. In contrast, a contradiction, or **contradictory** statement, is *never* true under any circumstances.

Some of the most important tautologies are the **tautological implications**, tautologies that have the form of implications. We look at two of them: direct reasoning and indirect reasoning.

Modus Ponens or Direct Reasoning

The following tautology is called *modus ponens* or **direct reasoning**:

$$[(p \rightarrow q) \wedge p] \rightarrow q.$$

In Words

If an implication and its antecedent (p) are both true, then so is its consequent (q).

Quick Example

21. *If my loving math implies that I will pass this course, and if I do love math, then I will pass this course.*

Note You can check that the statement $[(p \rightarrow q) \wedge p] \rightarrow q$ is a tautology by constructing its truth table. ∎

Tautological implications are useful mainly because they allow us to check the validity of **arguments**.

Argument

An **argument** is a list of statements called **premises** followed by a statement called the **conclusion**. If the premises are $P_1, P_2, \ldots, P_n$ and the conclusion is C, then we say that the argument is **valid** if the statement $(P_1 \wedge P_2 \wedge \ldots \wedge P_n) \to C$ is a tautology. In other words, an argument is valid if the truth of all its premises logically implies the truth of its conclusion.

Quick Examples

22. The following is a valid argument:

$$p \to q$$
$$\underline{p}$$
$$\therefore \quad q$$

(This is the traditional way of writing an argument: We list the premises above a line and then put the conclusion below; the symbol "$\therefore$" stands for the word "therefore.") This argument is valid because the statement $[(p \to q) \wedge p] \to q$ is a tautology, namely, *modus ponens*.

23. The following is an invalid argument:

$$p \to q$$
$$\underline{q}$$
$$\therefore \quad p$$

The argument is invalid because the statement $[(p \to q) \wedge q] \to p$ is not a tautology. In fact, if p is F and q is T, then the whole statement is F.

The argument in Quick Example 23 is known as the *fallacy of affirming the consequent*. It is a common invalid argument and not always obviously flawed at first sight, so it is often exploited by advertisers. For example, consider the following claim: All Olympic athletes drink Boors, so you should too. The suggestion is that, if you drink Boors, you will be an Olympic athlete:

If you are an Olympic Athlete you drink Boors.	Premise (Let's pretend this is true.)
You drink Boors.	Premise (True)
$\therefore$ You are an Olympic Athlete.	Conclusion (May be false!)

This is an error that Boors hopes you will make!

There is, however, a correct argument in which we *deny* the consequent.

Modus Tollens or Indirect Reasoning

The following tautology is called *modus tollens* or **indirect reasoning**:

$$[(p \to q) \wedge (\sim q)] \to (\sim p)$$

In Words

If an implication is true but its consequent (q) is false, then its antecedent (p) is false.

In Argument Form

$$p \to q$$
$$\sim q$$
$$\therefore \sim p$$

Quick Example

24. *If my loving math implies that I will pass this course, and if I do not pass the course, then it must be the case that I do not love math.*
    In argument form:

    > If I love math, then I will pass this course.
    >
    > I will not pass the course.
    > _____
    > Therefore, I do not love math.

Note This argument is not as direct as *modus ponens*; it contains a little twist: "If I loved math, I would pass this course. However, I will not pass this course. Therefore, it must be that I don't love math (else I *would* pass this course)." Hence the name "indirect reasoning."

Note that, again, there is a similar but fallacious argument to avoid, for instance: "If I were an Olympic athlete then I would drink Boors ($p \to q$). However, I am not an Olympic athlete ($\sim p$). Therefore, I won't drink Boors ($\sim q$)." This is a mistake Boors certainly hopes you do *not* make! ∎

There are other interesting tautologies that we can use to justify arguments. We mention one more and refer the interested reader to the Website for more examples and further study.

Website
www.WanerMath.com
For an extensive list of tautologies go online and follow:
Chapter L Logic
→ List of Tautologies and Tautological Implications

Disjunctive Syllogism or "One or the Other"

The following tautologies are both known as the **disjunctive syllogism** or **one-or-the-other:**

$$[(p \lor q) \land (\sim p)] \to q \qquad\qquad [(p \lor q) \land (\sim q)] \to p$$

In Words
If one or the other of two statements is true, but one is known to be false, then the other must be true.

In Argument Form

$$p \lor q \qquad\qquad p \lor q$$
$$\sim p \qquad\qquad\quad \sim q$$
$$\therefore \ q \qquad\qquad\quad \therefore \ p$$

> **Quick Example**
>
> **25.** *The butler or the cook did it. The butler didn't do it. Therefore, the cook did it.*
> In argument form:
>
> The butler or the cook did it.
>
> The butler did not do it.
>
> Therefore, the cook did it.

A   EXERCISES

Which of Exercises 1–10 are statements? Comment on the truth values of all the statements you encounter. If a sentence fails to be a statement, explain why. [**HINT**: See Example 1.]

1. All swans are white. **2.** The fat cat sat on the mat.

3. Look in thy glass and tell whose face thou viewest.[1]

4. My glass shall not persuade me I am old.[2]

5. There is no largest number.

6. 1,000,000,000 is the largest number.

7. Intelligent life abounds in the universe.

8. There may or may not be a largest number.

9. This is exercise number 9. **10.** This sentence no verb.[3]

Let p: "Our mayor is trustworthy," q: "Our mayor is a good speller," and r = "Our mayor is a patriot." Express each of the statements in Exercises 11–16 in logical form: [**HINT**: See Quick Examples 1–8, 11, and 12.]

11. Although our mayor is not trustworthy he is a good speller.

12. Either our mayor is trustworthy or he is a good speller.

13. Our mayor is a trustworthy patriot who spells well.

14. While our mayor is both trustworthy and patriotic, he is not a good speller.

15. It may or may not be the case that our mayor is trustworthy.

16. Our mayor is either not trustworthy or not a patriot, yet he is an excellent speller.

Let p: "Willis is a good teacher," q: "Carla is a good teacher," r: "Willis' students hate math," and s: "Carla's students hate math." Express the statements in Exercises 17–24 in words.

17. $p \land (\sim r)$ **18.** $(\sim p) \land (\sim q)$

19. $q \lor (\sim q)$ **20.** $((\sim p) \land (\sim s)) \lor q$

21. $r \land (\sim r)$ **22.** $(\sim s) \lor (\sim r)$

23. $\sim(q \lor s)$ **24.** $\sim(p \land r)$

Assume that it is true that "Polly sings well," it is false that "Quentin writes well," and it is true that "Rita is good at math." Determine the truth of each of the statements in Exercises 25–32.

25. Polly sings well and Quentin writes well.

26. Polly sings well or Quentin writes well.

27. Polly sings poorly and Quentin writes well.

28. Polly sings poorly or Quentin writes poorly.

29. Either Polly sings well and Quentin writes poorly, or Rita is good at math.

30. Either Polly sings well and Quentin writes poorly, or Rita is not good at math.

31. Either Polly sings well or Quentin writes well, or Rita is good at math.

32. Either Polly sings well and Quentin writes well, or Rita is bad at math.

Find the truth value of each of the statements in Exercises 33–48. [**HINT**: See Quick Examples 13–15.]

33. "If 1 = 1, then 2 = 2." **34.** "If 1 = 1, then 2 = 3."

35. "If 1 ≠ 0, then 2 ≠ 2." **36.** "If 1 = 0, then 1 = 1."

37. "A sufficient condition for 1 to equal 2 is 1 = 3."

38. "1 = 1 is a sufficient condition for 1 to equal 0."

39. "1 = 0 is a necessary condition for 1 to equal 1."

40. "1 = 1 is a necessary condition for 1 to equal 2."

41. "If I pay homage to the great Den, then the sun will rise in the east."

42. "If I fail to pay homage to the great Den, then the sun will still rise in the east."

---

[1] William Shakespeare, Sonnet 3.

[2] *Ibid.*, Sonnet 22.

[3] From *Metamagical Themas: Questing for the Essence of Mind and Pattern* by Douglas R. Hofstadter (Bantam Books, New York 1986).

43. "In order for the sun to rise in the east, it is necessary that it sets in the west."

44. "In order for the sun to rise in the east, it is sufficient that it sets in the west."

45. "The sun rises in the west only if it sets in the west."

46. "The sun rises in the east only if it sets in the east."

47. "In order for the sun to rise in the east, it is necessary and sufficient that it sets in the west."

48. "In order for the sun to rise in the west, it is necessary and sufficient that it sets in the east."

Construct the truth tables for the statements in Exercises 49–62. [HINT: See Example 2.]

49. $p \wedge (\sim q)$

50. $p \vee (\sim q)$

51. $\sim(\sim p) \vee p$

52. $p \wedge (\sim p)$

53. $(\sim p) \wedge (\sim q)$

54. $(\sim p) \vee (\sim q)$

55. $(p \wedge q) \wedge r$

56. $p \wedge (q \wedge r)$

57. $p \wedge (q \vee r)$

58. $(p \wedge q) \vee (p \wedge r)$

59. $p \rightarrow (q \vee p)$

60. $(p \vee q) \rightarrow \sim p$

61. $p \leftrightarrow (p \vee q)$

62. $(p \wedge q) \leftrightarrow \sim p$

Use truth tables to verify the logical equivalences given in Exercises 63–72.

63. $p \wedge p \equiv p$

64. $p \vee p \equiv p$

65. $p \vee q \equiv q \vee p$
(Commutative law for disjunction)

66. $p \wedge q \equiv q \wedge p$
(Commutative law for conjunction)

67. $\sim(p \vee q) \equiv (\sim p) \wedge (\sim q)$

68. $\sim(p \wedge (\sim q)) \equiv (\sim p) \vee q$

69. $(p \wedge q) \wedge r \equiv p \wedge (q \wedge r)$
(Associative law for conjunction)

70. $(p \vee q) \vee r \equiv p \vee (q \vee r)$
(Associative law for disjunction)

71. $p \rightarrow q \equiv (\sim q) \rightarrow (\sim p)$ **72.** $\sim(p \rightarrow q) \equiv p \wedge (\sim q)$

In Exercises 73–78, use truth tables to check whether the given statement is a tautology, a contradiction, or neither. [HINT: See Quick Examples 19 and 20.]

73. $p \wedge (\sim p)$

74. $p \wedge p$

75. $p \wedge \sim(p \vee q)$

76. $p \vee \sim(p \vee q)$

77. $p \vee \sim(p \wedge q)$

78. $q \vee \sim(p \wedge (\sim p))$

Apply the stated logical equivalence to the given statement in Exercises 79–84. [HINT: See Example 5(a), (b).]

79. $p \vee (\sim p)$; the commutative law

80. $p \wedge (\sim q)$; the commutative law

81. $\sim(p \wedge (\sim q))$; DeMorgan's law

82. $\sim(q \vee (\sim q))$; DeMorgan's law

83. $p \vee ((\sim p) \wedge q)$; the distributive law

84. $(\sim q) \wedge ((\sim p) \vee q)$; the distributive law

In Exercises 85–88, use the given logical equivalence to rewrite the given sentence. [HINT: See Example 5(c).]

85. It is not true that both I am Julius Caesar and you are a fool. DeMorgan's law.

86. It is not true that either I am Julius Caesar or you are a fool. DeMorgan's law.

87. Either it is raining and I have forgotten my umbrella, or it is raining and I have forgotten my hat. The distributive law.

88. I forgot my hat or my umbrella, and I forgot my hat or my glasses. The distributive law.

Give the contrapositive and converse of each of the statements in Exercises 89 and 90, phrasing your answers in words.

89. "If I think, then I am."

90. "If these birds are of a feather, then they flock together."

Exercises 91 and 92 are multiple choice. Indicate which statement is equivalent to the given statement, and say why that statement is equivalent to the given one.

91. "In order for you to worship Den, it is necessary for you to sacrifice beasts of burden."
   (A) "If you are not sacrificing beasts of burden, then you are not worshiping Den."
   (B) "If you are sacrificing beasts of burden, then you are worshiping Den."
   (C) "If you are not worshiping Den, then you are not sacrificing beasts of burden."

92. "In order to read the Tarot, it is necessary for you to consult the Oracle."
   (A) "In order to consult the Oracle, it is necessary to read the Tarot."
   (B) "In order not to consult the Oracle, it is necessary not to read the Tarot."
   (C) "In order not to read the Tarot, it is necessary not to read the Oracle."

In Exercises 93–102, write the given argument in symbolic form (use the underlined letters to represent the statements containing them), then decide whether it is valid or not. If it is valid, name the validating tautology. [HINT: See Quick Examples 19–25.]

93. If I am <u>h</u>ungry I am also <u>t</u>hirsty. I am hungry. Therefore, I am thirsty.

94. If I am not <u>h</u>ungry, then I certainly am not <u>t</u>hirsty either. I am not thirsty, and so I cannot be hungry.

95. For me to bring my umbrella, it's sufficient that it rain. It is not raining. Therefore, I will not bring my umbrella.

96. For me to bring my umbrella, it's necessary that it rain. But it is not raining. Therefore, I will not bring my umbrella.

97. For me to pass math, it is sufficient that I have a good teacher. I will not pass math. Therefore, I have a bad teacher.

98. For me to pass math, it is necessary that I have a good teacher. I will pass math. Therefore, I have a good teacher.

99. I will either pass math or I have a bad teacher. I have a good teacher. Therefore, I will pass math.

100. Either roses are not red or violets are not blue. But roses are red. Therefore, violets are not blue.

101. I am either smart or athletic, and I am athletic. So I must not be smart.

102. The president is either wise or strong. She is strong. Therefore, she is not wise.

In Exercises 103–108, use the stated tautology to complete the argument.

103. If John is a swan, it is necessary that he is green. John is indeed a swan. Therefore, _____. (*Modus ponens.*)

104. If Jill had been born in Texas, then she would be able to ride horses. But Jill cannot ride horses. Therefore, _____. (*Modus tollens.*)

105. If John is a swan, it is necessary that he is green. But John is not green. Therefore, _____. (*Modus tollens.*)

106. If Jill had been born in Texas, then she would be able to ride horses. Jill was born in Texas. Therefore, _____ (*Modus ponens.*)

107. Peter is either a scholar or a gentleman. He is not, however, a scholar. Therefore, _____. (Disjunctive syllogism.)

108. Pam is either a plumber or an electrician. She is not, however, an electrician. Therefore, _____ (Disjunctive syllogism.)

Communication and Reasoning Exercises

109. If two statements are logically equivalent, what can be said about their truth tables?

110. If a proposition is neither a tautology nor a contradiction, what can be said about its truth table?

111. If A and B are two compound statements such that $A \vee B$ is a contradiction, what can you say about A and B?

112. If A and B are two compound statements such that $A \wedge B$ is a tautology, what can you say about A and B?

113. Give an example of an instance where $p \to q$ means that q causes p.

114. Complete the following. If $p \to q$, then its converse, _____ , is the statement that _____ and (is/is not) logically equivalent to $p \to q$.

115. Give an instance of a true biconditional $p \leftrightarrow q$ where neither one of p or q causes the other.

AREA UNDER A NORMAL CURVE

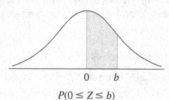

$P(0 \le Z \le b)$

The table below gives the probabilities $P(0 \le Z \le b)$, where Z is a standard normal variable. For example, to find $P(0 \le Z \le 2.43)$, write 2.43 as $2.4 + 0.03$, and read the entry in the row labeled 2.4 and the column labeled 0.03. From the portion of the table shown at left, you will see that $P(0 \le Z \le 2.43) = .4925$.

Z	0.00	0.01	0.02	0.03
2.3	.4893	.4896	.4898	.4901
→ 2.4	.4918	.4920	.4922	.4925
2.5	.4938	.4940	.4941	.4943

Z	0.00	0.01	0.02	0.03	0.04	0.05	0.06	0.07	0.08	0.09
0.0	.0000	.0040	.0080	.0120	.0160	.0199	.0239	.0279	.0319	.0359
0.1	.0398	.0438	.0478	.0517	.0557	.0596	.0636	.0675	.0714	.0753
0.2	.0793	.0832	.0871	.0910	.0948	.0987	.1026	.1064	.1103	.1141
0.3	.1179	.1217	.1255	.1293	.1331	.1368	.1406	.1443	.1480	.1517
0.4	.1554	.1591	.1628	.1664	.1700	.1736	.1772	.1808	.1844	.1879
0.5	.1915	.1950	.1985	.2019	.2054	.2088	.2123	.2157	.2190	.2224
0.6	.2257	.2291	.2324	.2357	.2389	.2422	.2454	.2486	.2517	.2549
0.7	.2580	.2611	.2642	.2673	.2704	.2734	.2764	.2794	.2823	.2852
0.8	.2881	.2910	.2939	.2967	.2995	.3023	.3051	.3078	.3106	.3133
0.9	.3159	.3186	.3212	.3238	.3264	.3289	.3315	.3340	.3365	.3389
1.0	.3413	.3438	.3461	.3485	.3508	.3531	.3554	.3577	.3599	.3621
1.1	.3643	.3665	.3686	.3708	.3729	.3749	.3770	.3790	.3810	.3830
1.2	.3849	.3869	.3888	.3907	.3925	.3944	.3962	.3980	.3997	.4015
1.3	.4032	.4049	.4066	.4082	.4099	.4115	.4131	.4147	.4162	.4177
1.4	.4192	.4207	.4222	.4236	.4251	.4265	.4279	.4292	.4306	.4319
1.5	.4332	.4345	.4357	.4370	.4382	.4394	.4406	.4418	.4429	.4441
1.6	.4452	.4463	.4474	.4484	.4495	.4505	.4515	.4525	.4535	.4545
1.7	.4554	.4564	.4573	.4582	.4591	.4599	.4608	.4616	.4625	.4633
1.8	.4641	.4649	.4656	.4664	.4671	.4678	.4686	.4693	.4699	.4706
1.9	.4713	.4719	.4726	.4732	.4738	.4744	.4750	.4756	.4761	.4767
2.0	.4772	.4778	.4783	.4788	.4793	.4798	.4803	.4808	.4812	.4817
2.1	.4821	.4826	.4830	.4834	.4838	.4842	.4846	.4850	.4854	.4857
2.2	.4861	.4864	.4868	.4871	.4875	.4878	.4881	.4884	.4887	.4890
2.3	.4893	.4896	.4898	.4901	.4904	.4906	.4909	.4911	.4913	.4916
2.4	.4918	.4920	.4922	.4925	.4927	.4929	.4931	.4932	.4934	.4936
2.5	.4938	.4940	.4941	.4943	.4945	.4946	.4948	.4949	.4951	.4952
2.6	.4953	.4955	.4956	.4957	.4959	.4960	.4961	.4962	.4963	.4964
2.7	.4965	.4966	.4967	.4968	.4969	.4970	.4971	.4972	.4973	.4974
2.8	.4974	.4975	.4976	.4977	.4977	.4978	.4979	.4979	.4980	.4981
2.9	.4981	.4982	.4982	.4983	.4984	.4984	.4985	.4985	.4986	.4986
3.0	.4987	.4987	.4987	.4988	.4988	.4989	.4989	.4989	.4990	.4990

Answers to Selected Exercises

Chapter 0

Section 0.1

1. -48 **3.** $2/3$ **5.** -1 **7.** 9 **9.** 1 **11.** 33 **13.** 14
15. $5/18$ **17.** 13.31 **19.** 6 **21.** $43/16$ **23.** 0
25. `3*(2-5)` **27.** `3/(2-5)` **29.** `(3-1)/(8+6)`
31. `3-(4+7)/8` **33.** `2/(3+x)-x*y^2`
35. `3.1x^3-4x^(-2)-60/(x^2-1)`
37. `(2/3)/5` **39.** `3^(4-5)*6`
41. `3*(1+4/100)^(-3)` **43.** `3^(2*x-1)+4^x-1`
45. `2^(2x^2-x+1)`
47. `4*e^(-2*x)/(2-3e^(-2*x))` or
`(4*e^(-2*x))/(2-3e^(-2*x))`
49. `3(1-(-1/2)^2)^2+1`

Section 0.2

1. 27 **3.** -36 **5.** $4/9$ **7.** $-1/8$ **9.** 16 **11.** 2 **13.** 32
15. 2 **17.** x^5 **19.** $-\dfrac{y}{x}$ **21.** $\dfrac{1}{x}$ **23.** x^3y **25.** $\dfrac{z^4}{y^3}$ **27.** $\dfrac{x^6}{y^6}$
29. $\dfrac{x^4y^6}{z^4}$ **31.** $\dfrac{3}{x^4}$ **33.** $\dfrac{3}{4x^{2/3}}$ **35.** $1-0.3x^2-\dfrac{6}{5x}$ **37.** 2
39. $1/2$ **41.** $4/3$ **43.** $2/5$ **45.** 7 **47.** 5 **49.** -2.668
51. $3/2$ **53.** 2 **55.** 2 **57.** ab **59.** $x+9$ **61.** $x\sqrt[3]{a^3+b^3}$
63. $\dfrac{2y}{\sqrt{x}}$ **65.** $3^{1/2}$ **67.** $x^{3/2}$ **69.** $(xy^2)^{1/3}$ **71.** $x^{3/2}$
73. $\dfrac{3}{5}x^{-2}$ **75.** $\dfrac{3}{2}x^{-1.2}-\dfrac{1}{3}x^{-2.1}$ **77.** $\dfrac{2}{3}x-\dfrac{1}{2}x^{0.1}+\dfrac{4}{3}x^{-1.1}$
79. $\dfrac{3}{4}x^{1/2}-\dfrac{5}{3}x^{-1/2}+\dfrac{4}{3}x^{-3/2}$ **81.** $\dfrac{3}{4}x^{2/5}-\dfrac{7}{2}x^{-3/2}$
83. $(x^2+1)^{-3}-\dfrac{3}{4}(x^2+1)^{-1/3}$ **85.** $\sqrt[3]{2^2}$ **87.** $\sqrt[3]{x^4}$
89. $\sqrt[5]{\sqrt{x}\sqrt[3]{y}}$ **91.** $-\dfrac{3}{2\sqrt[4]{x}}$ **93.** $\dfrac{0.2}{\sqrt[3]{x^2}}+\dfrac{3\sqrt{x}}{7}$
95. $\dfrac{3}{4\sqrt{(1-x)^5}}$ **97.** 64 **99.** $\sqrt{3}$ **101.** $1/x$ **103.** xy
105. $\left(\dfrac{y}{x}\right)^{1/3}$ **107.** ±4 **109.** $\pm2/3$ **111.** $-1,-1/3$
113. -2 **115.** 16 **117.** ±1 **119.** $33/8$

Section 0.3

1. $4x^2+6x$ **3.** $2xy-y^2$ **5.** x^2-2x-3
7. $2y^2+13y+15$ **9.** $4x^2-12x+9$
11. x^2+2+1/x^2 **13.** $4x^2-9$ **15.** y^2-1/y^2
17. $2x^3+6x^2+2x-4$ **19.** $x^4-4x^3+6x^2-4x+1$
21. $y^5+4y^4+4y^3-y$ **23.** $(x+1)(2x+5)$
25. $(x^2+1)^5(x+3)^3(x^2+x+4)$
27. $-x^3(x^3+1)\sqrt{x+1}$ **29.** $(x+2)\sqrt{(x+1)^3}$

31. a. $x(2+3x)$ **b.** $x=0,-2/3$
33. a. $2x^2(3x-1)$ **b.** $x=0,1/3$
35. a. $(x-1)(x-7)$ **b.** $x=1,7$
37. a. $(x-3)(x+4)$ **b.** $x=3,-4$
39. a. $(2x+1)(x-2)$ **b.** $x=-1/2,2$
41. a. $(2x+3)(3x+2)$ **b.** $x=-3/2,-2/3$
43. a. $(3x-2)(4x+3)$ **b.** $x=2/3,-3/4$
45. a. $(x+2y)^2$ **b.** $x=-2y$
47. a. $(x^2-1)(x^2-4)$ **b.** $x=\pm1,\pm2$

Section 0.4

1. $\dfrac{2x^2-7x-4}{x^2-1}$ **3.** $\dfrac{3x^2-2x+5}{x^2-1}$ **5.** $\dfrac{x^2-x+1}{x+1}$
7. $\dfrac{x^2-1}{x}$ **9.** $\dfrac{2x-3}{x^2y}$ **11.** $\dfrac{(x+1)^2}{(x+2)^4}$ **13.** $\dfrac{-1}{\sqrt{(x^2+1)^3}}$
15. $\dfrac{-(2x+y)}{x^2(x+y)^2}$

Section 0.5

1. -1 **3.** 5 **5.** $13/4$ **7.** $43/7$ **9.** -1 **11.** $(c-b)/a$
13. $x=-4,1/2$ **15.** No solutions **17.** $\pm\sqrt{\dfrac{5}{2}}$ **19.** -1
21. $-1,3$ **23.** $\dfrac{1\pm\sqrt5}{2}$ **25.** 1 **27.** $\pm1,\pm3$
29. $\pm\sqrt{\dfrac{-1+\sqrt5}{2}}$ **31.** $-1,-2,-3$ **33.** -3 **35.** 1
7. -2 **39.** $1,\pm\sqrt5$ **41.** $\pm1,\pm\dfrac{1}{\sqrt2}$ **43.** $-2,-1,2,3$

Section 0.6

1. $0,3$ **3.** $\pm\sqrt2$ **5.** $-1,-5/2$ **7.** -3 **9.** $0,-1$
11. $x=-1$ ($x=-2$ is not a solution.)
13. $-2,-3/2,-1$ **15.** -1 **17.** $\pm\sqrt[3]{2}$ **19.** ±1
21. ±3 **23.** $2/3$ **25.** $-4,-1/4$

Section 0.7

1. $P(0,2)$, $Q(4,-2)$, $R(-2,3)$, $S(-3.5,-1.5)$, $T(-2.5,0)$, $U(2,2.5)$

3. **5.**

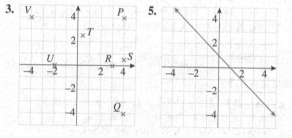

A1

7.

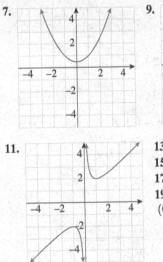

9.

11.

13. $\sqrt{2}$

15. $\sqrt{a^2 + b^2}$

17. $1/2$

19. Circle with center $(0, 0)$ and radius 3

11. a. Not defined **b.** Not defined **c.** Yes, $f(-10) = 0$
13. a. -7 **b.** -3 **c.** 1 **d.** $4y - 3$ **e.** $4(a + b) - 3$
15. a. 3 **b.** 6 **c.** 2 **d.** 6 **e.** $a^2 + 2a + 3$
f. $(x + h)^2 + 2(x + h) + 3$ **17. a.** 2 **b.** 0 **c.** $65/4$
d. $x^2 + 1/x$ **e.** $(s + h)^2 + 1/(s + h)$
f. $(s + h)^2 + 1/(s + h) - (s^2 + 1/s)$

19. **21.**

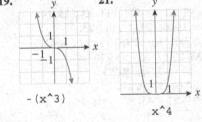

$-(x^3)$

x^4

23.

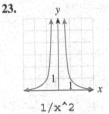

$1/x^2$

25. a. (A) **b.** (D) **c.** (E) **d.** (F) **e.** (C) **f.** (B)
27. $0.1*x^2-4*x+5$

x	0	1	2	3
$f(x)$	5	1.1	-2.6	-6.1
x	4	5	6	7
$f(x)$	-9.4	-12.5	-15.4	-18.1
x	8	9	10	
$f(x)$	-20.6	-22.9	-25	

29. $(x^2-1)/(x^2+1)$

x	0.5	1.5	2.5	3.5
$h(x)$	-0.6000	0.3846	0.7241	0.8491
x	4.5	5.5	6.5	7.5
$h(x)$	0.9059	0.9360	0.9538	0.9651
x	8.5	9.5	10.5	
$h(x)$	0.9727	0.9781	0.9820	

Section 0.8

1.

Exponential Form	$10^2 = 100$	$4^3 = 64$	$4^4 = 256$
Logarithmic Form	$\log_{10} 100 = 2$	$\log_4 64 = 3$	$\log_4 256 = 4$

Exponential Form	$0.45^0 = 1$	$8^{1/2} = 2\sqrt{2}$	$4^{-3} = \dfrac{1}{64}$
Logarithmic Form	$\log_{0.45} 1 = 0$	$\log_8 2\sqrt{2} = \dfrac{1}{2}$	$\log_4\left(\dfrac{1}{64}\right) = -3$

3.

Exponential Form	$0.3^2 = 0.09$	$\left(\dfrac{1}{2}\right)^0 = 1$	$10^{-3} = 0.001$
Logarithmic Form	$\log_{0.3} 0.09 = 2$	$\log_{1/2} 1 = 0$	$\log_{10} 0.001 = -3$

Exponential Form	$9^{-2} = \dfrac{1}{81}$	$2^{10} = 1{,}024$	$64^{-1/3} = \dfrac{1}{4}$
Logarithmic Form	$\log_9 \dfrac{1}{81} = -2$	$\log_2 1{,}024 = 10$	$\log_{64} \dfrac{1}{4} = -\dfrac{1}{3}$

5. 2 **7.** -2 **9.** 5 **11.** 1 **13.** -2 **15.** $1/2$ **17.** 12
19. $1/10$ **21.** $3/8$ **23.** x^4y^5 **25.** $\dfrac{x^2y^3}{z^4}$ **27.** $\dfrac{2^x}{x^2}$
29. $b + c$ **31.** $a + b + c$ **33.** $-c$ **35.** $a - b$
37. $2a - c$ **39.** $4a$ **41.** $b - 2$ **43.** $1 - a$ **45.** $c/2$
47. 2 **49.** 2 **51.** 4 **53.** 0.4210 **55.** 1.3972

Chapter 1

Section 1.1

1. a. 2 **b.** -0.5 **3. a.** -2.5 **b.** 8 **c.** -8 **5. a.** 20 **b.** 30
c. 30 **d.** 20 **e.** 0 **f.** 20 **7. a.** 0 **b.** -3 **c.** 3 **d.** 3
9. a. Yes; $f(4) = 63/16$ **b.** Not defined **c.** Yes; -2

31. a. -1 **b.** 2 **c.** 2 **33. a.** 1 **b.** 0 **c.** 1

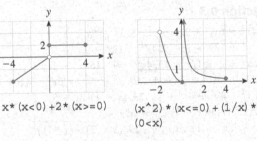

$x* (x<0) +2* (x>=0)$

$(x^2) * (x<=0) + (1/x) *$
$(0<x)$

35. a. 0 **b.** 2 **c.** 3 **d.** 3

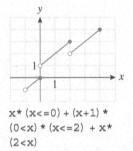

x* (x<=0) + (x+1) *
(0<x) * (x<=2) + x*
(2<x)

37. a. $h(2x + h)$ **b.** $2x + h$ **39. a.** $-h(2x + h)$ **b.** $-(2x + h)$
41. a. $p(2) = 2.95$; Pemex produced 2.95 million barrels of crude oil per day in 2010. $p(3) = 2.94$; Pemex produced 2.94 million barrels of crude oil per day in 2011. $p(6) = 2.79$; Pemex produced 2.79 million barrels of crude oil per day in 2014. **b.** $p(4) - p(2) = 2.91 - 2.95 = -0.04$; Crude oil production by Pemex decreased by 0.04 million barrels/day from 2010 ($t = 2$) to 2012 ($t = 4$).
43. a. Graph of p:

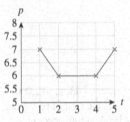

$p(4.5) \approx 6.5$. Interpretation: The popularity of Twitter midway through 2012 was about 6.5%. **b.** (D) **45.** $f(7) \approx 1,000$. Interpretation: Approximately 1,000,000 homes were started in 2007. $f(14) \approx 600$: Approximately 600,000 homes were started in 2014. **b.** $f(9.5) \approx 450$. Interpretation: 450,000 homes were started in the year beginning July 2009.
47. $f(7 - 3) \approx 1,600$, $f(7) - f(3) \approx -500$. Interpretation: 1,600,000 homes were started in 2004; there were 500,000 fewer housing starts in 2007 than in 2003. **49.** $t = 0$. Interpretation: The greatest 5-year increase in the number of housing starts occurred in 2000–2005. **51. a.** $n(2) \approx 400$, $n(4) \approx 400$, $n(4.5) \approx 350$. Interpretation: Abercrombie & Fitch's net income was $400 million in 2006, $400 million in 2008, and $350 million in the year ending June 2009.
b. $t \approx 8$. Interpretation: Between Dec. 2007 and Dec. 2012, Abercrombie & Fitch's net income was increasing most rapidly in Dec. 2012. **c.** $t \approx 5$. Interpretation: Between Dec. 2007 and Dec. 2012, Abercrombie & Fitch's net income was decreasing most rapidly in Dec. 2009. **53. a.** $[0, 8]$. $t \geq 0$ is not an appropriate domain because it would predict federal funding of NASA beyond 1966, whereas the model is based only on data up to 1966. **b.** $p(5) \approx 2.4$. In 1963, 2.4% of the U.S. federal budget was allocated to NASA. **c.** $t = 5$. The percentage of the budget allocated to NASA was increasing most rapidly in 1963. **55. a.** 100* (1-12200/t^4.48)

b. Graph:

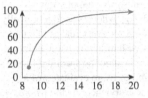

c. Table:

t	9	10	11	12	13	14
$p(t)$	35.2	59.6	73.6	82.2	87.5	91.1
t	15	16	17	18	19	20
$p(t)$	93.4	95.1	96.3	97.1	97.7	98.2

d. 82.2% **e.** 14 months **57. a.** $v(10) \approx 58$, $v(16) = 200$, $v(28) = 3,800$. Processor speeds were about 58 MHz in 1990, 200 MHz in 1996, and 3,800 MHz in 2008.
b. (8* (1.22)^x) * (x<16) + (400*x-6200) *
(x>=16) * (x<25) +3800* (x>=25)
c. Graph:

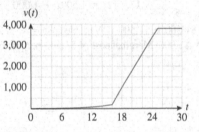

Table:

t	0	2	4	6	8	10
$v(t)$	8.0	12	18	26	39	58
t	12	14	16	18	20	22
$v(t)$	87	130	200	1,000	1,800	2,600
t	24	26	28	30		
$v(t)$	3,400	3,800	3,800	3,800		

d. 2003
59. a.
$$T(x) = \begin{cases} 0.10x & \text{if } 0 < x \leq 9{,}225 \\ 922.50 + 0.15(x - 9{,}225) & \text{if } 9{,}225 < x \leq 37{,}450 \\ 5{,}156.25 + 0.25(x - 37{,}450) & \text{if } 37{,}450 < x \leq 90{,}750 \\ 18{,}481.25 + 0.28(x - 90{,}750) & \text{if } 90{,}750 < x \leq 189{,}300 \\ 46{,}075.25 + 0.33(x - 189{,}300) & \text{if } 189{,}300 < x \leq 411{,}500 \\ 119{,}401.25 + 0.35(x - 411{,}500) & \text{if } 411{,}500 < x \leq 413{,}200 \\ 119{,}996.25 + 0.396(x - 413{,}200) & \text{if } 413{,}200 < x \end{cases}$$
b. $7,043.75 **61.** t; m
63. $y(x) = 4x^2 - 2$ (or $f(x) = 4x^2 - 2$)
65. False. A graph usually gives infinitely many values of the function, while a numerical table will give only a finite number of values.

67. False. In a numerically specified function, only certain values of the function are specified, so we cannot know its value on every real number in $[0, 10]$, whereas an algebraically specified function would give values for every real number in $[0, 10]$. **69.** False: Functions with infinitely many points in their domain (such as $f(x) = x^2$) cannot be specified numerically. **71.** As the text reminds us, to evaluate f of a quantity (such as $x + h$) replace x everywhere by the *whole quantity* $x + h$, getting $f(x + h) = (x + h)^2 - 1$.
73. They are different portions of the graph of the associated equation $y = f(x)$. **75.** The graph of g is the same as the graph of f but shifted 5 units to the right.

Section 1.2

1. a. $s(x) = x^2 + x$ **b.** Domain: $(-\infty, +\infty)$ **c.** 6
3. a. $p(x) = (x - 1)\sqrt{x + 10}$ **b.** Domain: $[-10, 0)$ **c.** -14
5. a. $q(x) = \frac{\sqrt{10 - x}}{x - 1}$ **b.** Domain: $0 \le x \le 10$; $x \ne 1$
c. Undefined **7. a.** $m(x) = 5(x^2 + 1)$ **b.** Domain: $(-\infty, +\infty)$
c. 10 **9.** $N(t) = 200 + 10t$ (N = number of music files, t = time in days) **11.** $A(x) = x^2/2$ **13.** $C(x) = 12x$

15. $h(n) = \begin{cases} 4 & \text{if } 1 \le n \le 5 \\ 0 & \text{if } n > 5 \end{cases}$ **17.** $C(x) = 1{,}500x + 1{,}000$

per day **a.** \$5,500 **b.** \$1,500 **c.** \$1,500 **d.** Variable cost = $1{,}500x$; Fixed cost = \$1,000; Marginal cost = \$1,500 per piano
e. Graph:

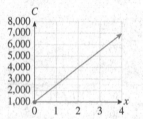

19. a. $C(x) = 0.4x + 70$, $R(x) = 0.5x$, $P(x) = 0.1x - 70$
b. $P(500) = -20$; a loss o \$20 **c.** 700 copies
21. $R(x) = 100x$, $P(x) = -2{,}000 + 90x - 0.2x^2$; at least 24 jerseys **23.** $P(x) = -1.7 - 0.02x + 0.0001x^2$; approximately 264 thousand sq. ft. **25.** $P(x) = 100x - 5{,}132$, with domain $[0, 405]$. For profit, $x \ge 52$ **27.** 5,000 units
29. $FC/(SP - VC)$ **31.** $P(x) = 579.7x - 20{,}000$, with domain $x \ge 0$; $x = 34.50$ g per day for breakeven
33. a. Graph:

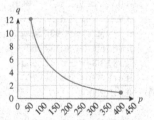

b. Demand decreases by 3.8 million units per year. **c.** (D)
35. a. 1,027 million units **b.** 1,607 million units
c. $R(p) = 0.17p^3 - 63p^2 + 5{,}900p$ million dollars per year; \$113 billion per year **d.** Increases;

Graph:

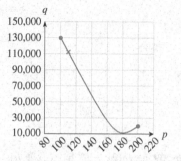

37. \$240 per skateboard **39. a.** \$110 per phone **b.** Shortage of 25 million phones **41. a.** Equilibrium price: \$200; equilibrium demand: 2.8 million units
b. Graph:

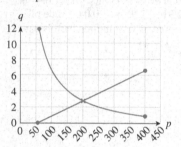

c. A shortage of around 9.2 million e-readers **43. a.** \$12,000
b. $N(q) = 2{,}000 + 100q^2 - 500q$; this is the cost of removing q lb of PCPs per day after the subsidy is taken into account.
c. $N(20) = \$32{,}000$; the net cost of removing 20 lb of PCPs per day is \$32,000. **45. a.** (B) **b.** \$37 billion **47. a.** (C)
b. \$20.80 per shirt if the team buys 70 shirts
Graph:

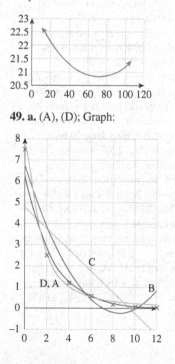

49. a. (A), (D); Graph:

b. Model (A); Approximately $0.0021   **51.** A linear model (A) is the best choice; a plot of the given points gives a straight line.   **53.** Model (D) is the best choice; Model (A) would predict increasing demand with increasing price, Model (B) would correspond to a curve that becomes less steep as p increases, and Model (C) would give a concave-up parabola.   **55.** $A(t) = 5,000(1 + 0.0005/12)^{12t}$; $5,018   **57.** 2033   **59.** 31.0 g, 9.25 g, 2.76 g   **61.** 20,000 years   **63. a.** 1,000 years: 65%, 2,000 years: 42%, 3,000 years: 27%   **b.** 1,600 years   **65.** 30   **67.** Curve fitting. The model is based on fitting a curve to a given set of observed data.   **69.** The cost of downloading a movie was $4 in January and is decreasing by 20¢ per month.   **71.** Variable; marginal.   **73.** Yes, as long as the supply is going up at a faster rate, as illustrated by the following graph:

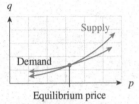

75. Extrapolate both models and choose the one that gives the most reasonable predictions.   **77.** They are ≥ 0.
79. Books per person

Section 1.3

1. 11; $m = 3$ **3.** -4; $m = -1$ **5.** 7; $m = 3/2$
7. $f(x) = -x/2 - 2$ **9.** $f(0) = -5$, $f(x) = -x - 5$
11. f is linear: $f(x) = 4x + 6$ **13.** g is linear: $g(x) = 2x - 1$
15. $-3/2$ **17.** $1/6$ **19.** Undefined   **21.** 0   **23.** $-4/3$
25.   **27.**

29.   **31.**

33.   **35.**

37.

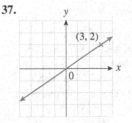

39. 2   **41.** 2   **43.** -2 **45.** Undefined   **47.** 1.5   **49.** -0.09
51. 1/2   **53.** $(d - b)/(c - a)$ **55.** Undefined   **57.** $-b/a$
59. a. 1   **b.** 1/2   **c.** 0   **d.** 3   **e.** $-1/3$ **f.** -1 **g.** Undefined
h. $-1/4$ **i.** -2 **61.** $y = 3x$ **63.** $y = \dfrac{1}{4}x - 1$
65. $y = 10x - 203.5$ **67.** $y = -5x + 6$
69. $y = -3x + 2.25$ **71.** $y = -x + 12$
73. $y = 2x + 4$ **75.** $y = \dfrac{q}{p}x$ **77.** $y = q$ **79.** $y = -\dfrac{q}{p}x$
81. Fixed cost $= $8,000, marginal cost $= $25 per bicycle   **83.** $C = 205x + 20$; $205 per iPhone; $8,220
85. $q = -40p + 2,000$ **87. a.** $q = -5.8p + 2,953$; 1,416 million phones   **b.** $1; 5.8 million
89. a. $q = -4,500p + 41,500$ **b.** Rides per day per $1 increase in the fare; ridership decreases by 4,500 rides per day for every $1 increase in the fare.   **c.** 14,500 rides per day
91. a. $y = 40t + 290$ million pounds of pasta   **b.** 890 million pounds   **93. a.** $N = -0.29t + 0.92$ **b.** Billions of dollars per year; Amazon's net income decreased at a rate of $0.29 billion per year.   **c.** $0.05 billion   **95. a.** 2.5 ft/sec   **b.** 20 ft along the track   **c.** after 6 sec   **97. a.** 130 mph   **b.** $s = 130t - 1,300$
99. a. $L = 42.5n + 500$ **b.** Pages per edition; *Applied Calculus* is growing at a rate of 42.5 pages per edition.   **c.** 24th edition
101. $F = 1.8C + 32$; 86°F; 72°F; 14°F; 7°F
103. a. $J = 0.54S - 86$ **b.** $57 million   **c.** Millions of dollars of JetBlue Airways net income per million dollars of Southwest Airlines net income; JetBlue Airways earned an additional net income of $0.54 per $1 additional net income earned by Southwest Airlines.   **105.** $I(N) = 0.05N + 50,000$; $N = $1,000,000; marginal income is $m = 5$¢ per dollar of net profit
107. Increasing at 400 MHz per year
109. a. $y = 31.1t + 78$ **b.** $y = 112.5t - 1,550$

c. $y = \begin{cases} 31.1t + 78 & \text{if } 0 \leq t < 20 \\ 112.5t - 1,550 & \text{if } 20 \leq t \leq 40 \end{cases}$ or

$\quad y = \begin{cases} 31.1t + 78 & \text{if } 0 \leq t \leq 20 \\ 112.5t - 1,550 & \text{if } 20 < t \leq 40 \end{cases}$

d. $2,275,000, in good agreement with the actual value shown in the graph.

111. $N = \begin{cases} 0.22t + 3 & \text{if } 0 \leq t \leq 5 \\ -0.15t + 4.85 & \text{if } 5 < t \leq 9 \end{cases}$

3.8 million jobs
113. Compute the corresponding successive changes Δx in x and Δy in y, and compute the ratios $\Delta y/\Delta x$. If the answer is always the same number, then the values in the table come from a linear function.

115. $f(x) = -\dfrac{a}{b}x + \dfrac{c}{b}$. If $b = 0$, then $\dfrac{a}{b}$ is undefined, and y cannot be specified as a function of x. (The graph of the resulting equation would be a vertical line.) **117.** slope, 3. **119.** If m is positive, then y will increase as x increases; if m is negative, then y will decrease as x increases; if m is zero, then y will not change as x changes. **121.** The slope increases, because an increase in the y-coordinate of the second point increases Δy while leaving Δx fixed. **123.** Bootlags per zonar; bootlags **125.** It must increase by 10 units each day, including the third. **127.** (B) **129.** It is linear with slope $m + n$. **131.** Answers may vary. For example, $f(x) = x^{1/3}$, $g(x) = x^{2/3}$ **133.** Increasing the number of items from the break-even number results in a profit: Because the slope of the revenue graph is larger than the slope of the cost graph, it is higher than the cost graph to the right of the point of intersection, and hence corresponds to a profit.

Section 1.4

1. 6 **3.** 86 **5. a.** 0.5 (better fit) **b.** 0.75
7. a. 27.42 **b.** 27.16 (better fit)
9. $y = 1.5x - 0.6667$
Graph:

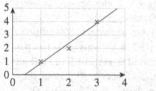

11. $y = 0.7x + 0.85$
Graph:

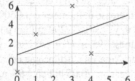

13. a. $r = 0.9959$ (best, not perfect) **b.** $r = 0.9538$
c. $r = 0.3273$ (worst)

15.

x	y	xy	x^2
0	800	0	0
2	1,600	3,200	4
4	2,300	9,200	16
6	4,700	12,400	20

$y = 375x + 816.7$; 3,066.7 million
17. $q = -0.7p + 3.2$; 750 million smartphones
19. $y = 0.135x + 0.15$; 6.9 million jobs
21. a. $I = -0.007S + 0.78$
Graph:

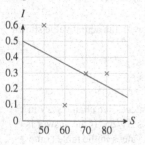

b. Amazon lost $7 million in net income per billion dollars earned in net sales. **c.** $40 billion **d.** The graph shows a poor fit, so the linear model does not seem reasonable.
23. a. $L = 45.8n + 507$
Graph:

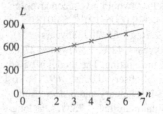

b. *Applied Calculus* is growing at a rate of 45.8 pages per edition. **25. a.** $y = 1.62x - 23.87$
Graph:

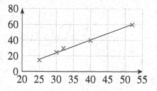

b. Each acre of cultivated land produces about 1.62 tons of soybeans. **27. a.** $y = -11.85x + 797.71$; $r \approx -0.414$
b. Continental's net income is not correlated with the price of oil. **c.** The points are nowhere near the regression line, confirming the conclusion in part (b).
Graph:

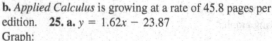

29. a. $y = 1.00x - 102$
Graph:

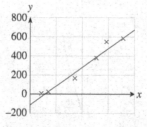

b. There is about one additional doctorate in engineering per additional doctorate in the natural sciences. **c.** $r \approx 0.976$; a strong correlation. **d.** Yes; the graph suggests a linear relationship; the data points are close to the regression line and show no obvious pattern (such as a curve).

31. a. $y = 28.9t + 37.0$
Graph:

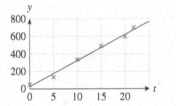

$r \approx 0.992$ **b.** The number of natural science doctorates has been increasing at a rate of about 28.9 per year.
c. More-or-less constant rate; the slopes of successive pairs of points do not show an increasing or decreasing trend as we go from left to right. **d.** Yes; if r had been equal to 1, then the points would lie exactly on the regression line, which would indicate that the number of doctorates is growing at a constant rate. **33. a.** More-or-less constant rate; Exercise 29 suggests a roughly linear relationship between the number of natural science doctorates and the number of engineering doctorates, and Exercise 31 suggests that the number of natural science doctorates has been increasing at a more-or less constant rate. Therefore, the number of engineering doctorates is also increasing at a more-or-less constant rate. **b.** No; $r = 1$ in Exercise 29 would indicate an exactly linear relationship between the number of natural science doctorates and the number of engineering doctorates, so the conclusion would be the same. **c.** No; $r = 1$ in Exercise 31 would indicate that the number of natural science doctorates has been increasing at a constant rate, so the conclusion would be the same.
35. a. $p = 0.13t + 0.22; r \approx 0.97$
Graph:

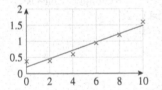

b. Yes; the first and last points lie above the regression line, while the central points lie below it, suggesting a curve.
c.

◇	A	B	C	D
1	t	p (observed)	p (predicted)	Residual
2	0	0.38	0.22	0.16
3	2	0.4	0.48	-0.08
4	4	0.6	0.74	-0.14
5	6	0.95	1	-0.05
6	8	1.2	1.26	-0.06
7	10	1.6	1.52	0.08

Notice that the residuals are positive at first, then become negative, and then become positive, confirming the impression from the graph. **37.** The line that passes through (a, b) and (c, d) gives a sum-of-squares error SSE = 0, which is the smallest value possible. **39.** The regression line is the line passing through the given points. **41.** 0 **43.** No. The

regression line through $(-1, 1)$, $(0, 0)$, and $(1, 1)$ passes through none of these points. **45.** (Answers may vary.) The data in Exercise 35 give $r \approx 0.97$, yet the plotted points suggest a curve, not a straight line.

Chapter 1 Review

1. a. 1 **b.** -2 **c.** 0 **d.** -1 **3. a.** 1 **b.** 0 **c.** 0 **d.** -1
5.

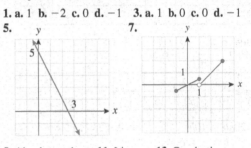

9. Absolute value   **11.** Linear   **13.** Quadratic
15. $y = -3x + 11$ **17.** $y = 1.25x - 4.25$
19. $y = (1/2)x + 3/2$ **21.** $y = 4x - 12$
23. $y = -\dfrac{x}{4} + 1$ **25.** $y = -0.214x + 1.14, r \approx -0.33$

27. a. Exponential
Graph:

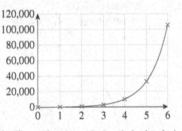

b. The ratios (rounded to 1 decimal place) are:

$V(1)/V(0)$	$V(2)/V(1)$	$V(3)/V(2)$	$V(4)/V(3)$	$V(5)/V(4)$	$V(6)/V(5)$
3	3.3	3.3	3.2	3.2	3.2

They are close to 3.2. **c.** About 343,700 visits per day
29. a. 2.3; 3.5; 6 **b.** For website traffic of up to 50,000 visits per day, the number of crashes is increasing by 0.03 per additional thousand visits. **c.** 140,000   **31. a.** (A)
b. (A) Leveling off (B) Rising (C) Rising; begins to fall after 7 months (D) Rising   **33. a.** The number of visits would increase by 30 per day. **b.** No; it would increase at a slower and slower rate and then begin to decrease. **c.** Probably not. This model predicts that website popularity will start to decrease as advertising increases beyond $8,500 per month and then drop toward zero.   **35. a.** $v = 0.05c + 1,800$
b. 2,150 new visits per day **c.** $14,000 per month
37. $d = 0.95w + 8$; 86 kg   **39. a.** Cost: $C = 5.5x + 500$;
Revenue: $R = 9.5x$; Profit $P = 4x - 500$ **b.** More than 125 albums per week **c.** More than 200 albums per week
41. a. $q = -80p + 1,060$ **b.** 100 albums per week
c. $9.50, for a weekly profit of $700
43. a. $q = -74p + 1,015.5$ **b.** 239 albums per week

Chapter 2

Section 2.1

1. a. $a = 2, b = -1, c = -2$ **b.**

x	-3	-2	-1	0	1	2	3
$f(x)$	19	8	1	-2	-1	4	13

c. $2a^2 + 4ah + 2h^2 - a - h - 2$ **d.** 2x^2-x-2
3. a. $a = 10, b = -5, c = 0$ **b.**

x	-3	-2	-1	0	1	2	3
$f(x)$	105	50	15	0	5	30	75

c. $10a^2 + 20ah + 10h^2 - 5a - 5h$ **d.** 10x^2-5x
5. a. $a = -1, b = -1, c = -1$ **b.**

x	-3	-2	-1	0	1	2	3
$f(x)$	-7	-3	-1	-1	-3	-7	-13

c. $-a^2 - 2ah - h^2 - a - h - 1$ **d.** -(x^2)-x-1
(See the margin note next to Quick Example 2 in the text as to the reason for the parentheses.)
7. Vertex: $(-3/2, -1/4)$,
y-intercept: 2,
x-intercepts: $-2, -1$

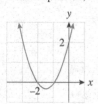

9. Vertex: $(2, 0)$,
y-intercept: -4,
x-intercept: 2

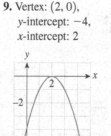

11. Vertex: $(-20, 900)$,
y-intercept: 500,
x-intercepts: $-50, 10$

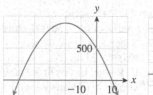

13. Vertex: $(-1/2, -5/4)$,
y-intercept: -1,
x-intercepts: $-1/2 \pm \sqrt{5}/2$

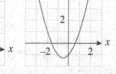

15. Vertex: $(0, 1)$,
y-intercept: 1,
no x-intercepts

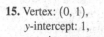
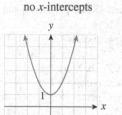

17. $R = -4p^2 + 100p$;
Maximum revenue
when $p = \$12.50$

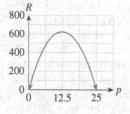

19. $R = -2p^2 + 400p$; Maximum revenue when $p = \$100$

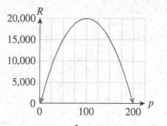

21. $y = -0.7955x^2 + 4.4591x - 1.6000$
23. $y = -1.1667x^2 - 6.1667x - 3.0000$
25. a. Positive because the data suggest a curve that is concave up. **b.** (C) **c.** 1997. Extrapolating in the positive direction leads one to predict more and more steeply rising military expenditure, which may or may not occur; extrapolating in the negative direction predicts more and more steeply increasing military expenditure as we go back in time, contradicting history. (In fact, military expenditures flattened in the years immediately after 2010.) **27.** About one quarter of the way into 2010; About 1,100 thousand barrels per day **29.** 2011; About $13.2 billion; No, as the model predicts net income dropping without bound.
31. Maximum revenue when $p = \$140, R = \$9,800$
33. Maximum revenue with 70 houses, $R = \$9,800,000$
35. a. $q = -4,500p + 41,500$ **b.** $4.61 for a daily revenue of $95,680.55 **c.** No **37. a.** $q = -560x + 1,400$;
$R = -560x^2 + 1,400x$ **b.** $P = -560x^2 + 1,400x - 30$;
$x = \$1.25; P = \$845$ per month **39.** $C = -200x + 620$;
$P = -400x^2 + 1,400x - 620; x = \$1.75$ per log-on;
$P = \$605$ per month **41. a.** $q = -10p + 400$
b. $R = -10p^2 + 400p$ **c.** $C = -30p + 4,200$
d. $P = -10p^2 + 430p - 4,200; p = \$21.50$
43. $f(t) = 6.25t^2 - 100t + 1,450; \$1,675$ billion, which is $75 billion higher than the actual value.
45. a. $S(t) = -0.70t^2 - 6.0t + 50$;

Graph:

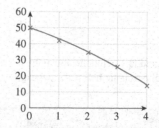

b. 3 million units, -11 million units. Even though we expected 2015 sales to be much lower than the 2014 sales, the 2016 prediction, being negative, shows the danger of exptrapolating curve-fitting models. **47.** The graph is a straight line.
49. (C) **51.** Positive; the x-coordinate of the vertex is negative, so $-b/(2a)$ must be negative. Because a is positive (the parabola is concave up), this means that b must also be positive to make $-b/(2a)$ negative. **53.** The x-coordinate of the vertex represents the unit price that leads to the maximum revenue, the y-coordinate of the vertex gives the maximum possible revenue, the x-intercepts give the unit prices that result in zero revenue, and the y-intercept gives the revenue resulting from zero unit price (which is obviously zero). **55.** Graph the data to see

whether the points suggest a curve rather than a straight line. If the curve suggested by the graph is concave up or concave down, then a quadratic model would be a likely candidate. **57.** No; the graph of a quadratic function is a parabola. In the case of a concave-up parabola, the curve would unrealistically predict sales increasing without bound in the future. In the case of a concave-down parabola, the curve would predict "negative" sales from some point on. **59.** If $q = mp + b$ (with $m < 0$), then the revenue is given by $R = pq = mp^2 + bp$. This is the equation of a parabola with $a = m < 0$ and so is concave down. Thus, the vertex is the highest point on the parabola, showing that there is a single highest value for R, namely, the y-coordinate of the vertex. **61.** Since $R = pq$, the demand must be given by $q = \dfrac{R}{p} = \dfrac{-50p^2 + 60p}{p} = -50p + 60$.

Section 2.2

1. 4^x

x	−3	−2	−1	0	1	2	3
$f(x)$	$\frac{1}{64}$	$\frac{1}{16}$	$\frac{1}{4}$	1	4	16	64

3. 3^(-x)

x	−3	−2	−1	0	1	2	3
$f(x)$	27	9	3	1	$\frac{1}{3}$	$\frac{1}{9}$	$\frac{1}{27}$

5. 2*2^x or 2*(2^x)

x	−3	−2	−1	0	1	2	3
$f(x)$	$\frac{1}{4}$	$\frac{1}{2}$	1	2	4	8	16

7. -3*2^(-x)

x	−3	−2	−1	0	1	2	3
$f(x)$	−24	−12	−6	−3	$-\frac{3}{2}$	$-\frac{3}{4}$	$-\frac{3}{8}$

9. 2^x-1

x	−3	−2	−1	0	1	2	3
$f(x)$	$-\frac{7}{8}$	$-\frac{3}{4}$	$-\frac{1}{2}$	0	1	3	7

11. 2^(x-1)

x	−3	−2	−1	0	1	2	3
$f(x)$	$\frac{1}{16}$	$\frac{1}{8}$	$\frac{1}{4}$	$\frac{1}{2}$	1	2	4

13.

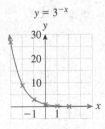

$y = 3^{-x}$

15.

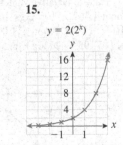

$y = 2(2^x)$

17.

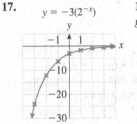

$y = -3(2^{-x})$

19. Both; $f(x) = 4.5(3^x)$, $g(x) = 2(1/2)^x$, or $2(2^{-x})$

21. Neither   **23.** g; $g(x) = 4(0.2)^x$
25. e^(-2*x) or EXP(-2*x)

x	−3	−2	−1	0	1	2	3
$f(x)$	403.4	54.60	7.389	1	0.1353	0.01832	0.002479

27. 1.01*2.02^(-4*x)

x	−3	−2	−1	0	1	2	3
$f(x)$	4,662	280.0	16.82	1.01	0.06066	0.003643	0.0002188

29. 50*(1+1/3.2)^(2*x)

x	−3	−2	−1	0	1	2	3
$f(x)$	9.781	16.85	29.02	50	86.13	148.4	255.6

31. 2^(x-1) *not* 2^x-1 **33.** 2/(1-2^(-4*x)) *not* 2/1-2^-4*x *and not* 2/1-2^(-4*x)
35. (3+x)^(3*x)/(x+1) or ((3+x)^(3*x))/(x+1) *not* (3+x)^(3*x)/x+1 *and not* (3+x^(3*x))/(x+1)
37. 2*e^((1+x)/x) or 2*EXP((1+x)/x) *not* 2*e^1+x/x *and not* 2*e^(1+x)/x *and not* 2*EXP(1+x)/x

39.

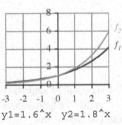

y1=1.6^x y2=1.8^x

41.

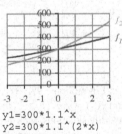

y1=300*1.1^x
y2=300*1.1^(2*x)

43.

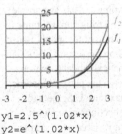

y1=2.5^(1.02*x)
y2=e^(1.02*x)
or exp(1.02*x)

45.

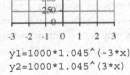

y1=1000*1.045^(-3*x)
y2=1000*1.045^(3*x)

47. $f(x) = 500(0.5)^x$ **49.** $f(x) = 10(3)^x$
51. $f(x) = 500(0.45)^x$ **53.** $f(x) = -100(1.1)^x$

55. $y = 4(3^x)$ **57.** $y = -1(0.2^x)$ **59.** $y = 2.1213(1.4142^x)$
61. $y = 3.6742(0.9036^x)$ **63.** $f(t) = 5,000e^{0.10t}$
65. $f(t) = 1,000e^{-0.063t}$ **67.** $y = 1.0442(1.7564)^x$
69. $y = 15.1735(1.4822)^x$ **71.** $f(t) = 300(0.5)^t$; 9.375 mg
73. a. Linear model: $F = 65t - 60$. Exponential model:
$F = 97.2(1.20)^t$. The exponential model is more appropriate.
b. 418 tons, not too far off the projected figure
75. a. $P = 180(1.01087)^t$ million   **b.** 6 significant digits
c. 344 million   **77. a.** $y = 50,000(1.5^{t/2})$, $t = $ time in years
since 2 years ago **b.** 91,856 tags   **79.** $y = 1,000(2^{t/3})$;
65,536,000 bacteria after 2 days   **81.** $A(t) = 167(1.18)^t$;
1,695 cases   **83.** $C(t) = 100e^{0.72t}$; 1,781 cases
85. $A(t) = 5,000(1 + 0.0005/12)^{12t}$; \$5,018   **87.** 2033
89. \$491.82   **91.** $A(t) = 4.3e^{0.089t}$ million homes;
2012: 4.7 million homes; 2014: 5.6 million homes
93. a.

Year	1950	2000	2050	2100
$C(t)$ (ppm)	361	385	410	437

b. 2030
95. a. $P(t) = 0.339(1.169)^t$.
Graph:

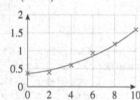

b. \$1.9 million
97. a. $n = 1.127(3.544)^t$

Graph:

b. 3.544 **c.** 178 million   **99.** (B)   **101.** Exponential functions
of the form $f(x) = Ab^x$ ($b > 1$) increase rapidly for large values
of x. In real-life situations, such as population growth, this
model is reliable only for relatively short periods of growth.
Eventually, population growth tapers off because of pressures
such as limited resources and overcrowding.   **103.** The article
was published about a year before the "housing bubble" burst in
2006, whereupon, contrary to the prediction of the graph, house
prices started to fall and continued to drop for several years. This
shows the danger of using any mathematical model to extrapolate. However, the blogger was cautious in the choice of words,
claiming only to be estimating what the future U.S. median
house price "might be."   **105.** Linear functions better: cost
models where there is a fixed cost and a variable cost; simple
interest, where interest is paid on the original amount invested.
Exponential models better: compound interest, population
growth. (In both of these, the rate of growth depends on the present number of items, rather than on some fixed quantity.)

107. Take the ratios y_2/y_1 and y_3/y_2. If they are the same, the
points fit on an exponential curve.   **109.** This reasoning is suspect. The bank need not use its computer resources to update
all the accounts every minute but can instead use the continuous compounding formula to calculate the balance in any
account at any time.

Section 2.3

1. $\log_4 y$ **3.** 8   **5.** x
7.   **9.**

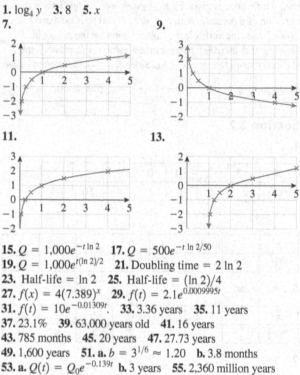

11.   **13.**

15. $Q = 1,000e^{-t \ln 2}$ **17.** $Q = 500e^{-t \ln 2/50}$
19. $Q = 1,000e^{t(\ln 2)/2}$ **21.** Doubling time $= 2 \ln 2$
23. Half-life $= \ln 2$ **25.** Half-life $= (\ln 2)/4$
27. $f(x) = 4(7.389)^x$ **29.** $f(t) = 2.1e^{0.0009995t}$
31. $f(t) = 10e^{-0.01309t}$ **33.** 3.36 years   **35.** 11 years
37. 23.1%   **39.** 63,000 years old   **41.** 16 years
43. 785 months   **45.** 20 years   **47.** 27.73 years
49. 1,600 years   **51. a.** $b = 3^{1/6} \approx 1.20$ **b.** 3.8 months
53. a. $Q(t) = Q_0 e^{-0.139t}$ **b.** 3 years   **55.** 2,360 million years
57. 3.2 hours   **59.** 3.89 days   **61. a.** $P(t) = 6.591 \ln(t) - 17.69$
b. 1 digit   **c.** (A)   **63.** $S(t) = 28.56 \ln t + 164.46$

Graph:

Positive direction; extrapolating in the negative direction
eventually leads to negative values, which do not model reality
65. a. About 4.467×10^{23} ergs   **b.** About 2.24%
c. $E = 10^{1.5R+11.8}$ **d.** Proof   **e.** 1,000   **67. a.** 75 dB, 69 dB,
61 dB   **b.** $D = 95 - 20 \log r$ **c.** 57,000 ft

Graph:

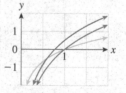

The green curve is $y = \ln x$, the blue curve is $y = 2 \ln x$, and the red curve is $y = 2 \ln x + 0.5$. Multiplying by A stretches the graph in the y-direction by a factor of A. Adding C moves the graph C units vertically up.   **71.** The logarithm of a negative number, were it defined, would be the power to which a base must be raised to give that negative number. But raising a base to a power never results in a negative number, so there can be no such number as the logarithm of a negative number.   **73.** Any logarithmic curve $y = \log_b t + C$ will eventually surpass 100% and hence will not be suitable as a long-term predictor of market share.   **75.** Time is increasing logarithmically with population; solving $P = Ab^t$ for t gives $t = \log_b(P/A) = \log_b P - \log_b A$, which is of the form $t = \log_b P + C$.   **77.** Proof

Section 2.4

1. $N = 7, A = 6, b = 2$;
$7/(1+6*2^\wedge-x)$

3. $N = 10, A = 4, b = 0.3$;
$10/(1+4*0.3^\wedge-x)$

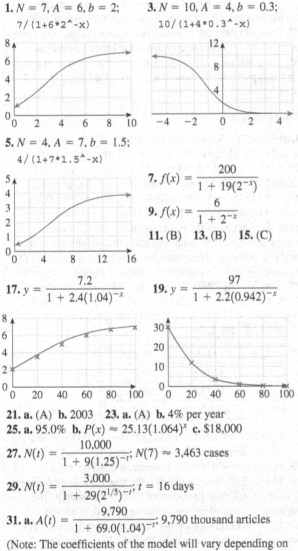

5. $N = 4, A = 7, b = 1.5$;
$4/(1+7*1.5^\wedge-x)$

7. $f(x) = \dfrac{200}{1 + 19(2^{-x})}$

9. $f(x) = \dfrac{6}{1 + 2^{-x}}$

11. (B)   **13.** (B)   **15.** (C)

17. $y = \dfrac{7.2}{1 + 2.4(1.04)^{-x}}$

19. $y = \dfrac{97}{1 + 2.2(0.942)^{-x}}$

21. a. (A) **b.** 2003   **23. a.** (A) **b.** 4% per year

25. a. 95.0% **b.** $P(x) \approx 25.13(1.064)^x$ **c.** \$18,000

27. $N(t) = \dfrac{10,000}{1 + 9(1.25)^{-t}}$; $N(7) \approx 3,463$ cases

29. $N(t) = \dfrac{3,000}{1 + 29(2^{1/5})^{-t}}$; $t = 16$ days

31. a. $A(t) = \dfrac{9,790}{1 + 69.0(1.04)^{-t}}$; 9,790 thousand articles

(Note: The coefficients of the model will vary depending on the initial guesses used.) **b.** 408 thousand articles

33. a. $B(t) = \dfrac{1,090}{1 + 0.410(1.09)^{-t}}$; 1,090 teams

b. $t \approx -10.3$. According to the model, the number of teams was rising fastest about 10.3 years *prior* to 1990, that is, sometime during 1979. **c.** The number of men's basketball teams was growing by about 9% per year in the past, well before 1979.   **35.** $y = \dfrac{4,500}{1 + 1.1466(1.0357)^{-t}}$; 2013   **37.** Just as diseases are communicated via the spread of a pathogen (such as a virus), new technology is communicated via the spread of information (such as advertising and publicity). Further, just as the spread of a disease is ultimately limited by the number of susceptible individuals, so the spread of a new technology is ultimately limited by the size of the potential market.   **39.** It can be used to predict where the sales of a new commodity might level off.   **41.** The curve is still a logistic curve, but decreases when $b > 1$ and increases when $b < 1$.   **43.** Proof

Chapter 2 Review

1.

3. $f : f(x) = 5(1/2)^x$, or $5(2^{-x})$

$(-1, -4)$

5.   **7.**

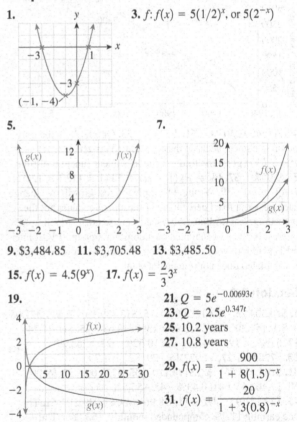

9. \$3,484.85   **11.** \$3,705.48   **13.** \$3,485.50

15. $f(x) = 4.5(9^x)$ **17.** $f(x) = \dfrac{2}{3}3^x$

19.

21. $Q = 5e^{-0.00693t}$
23. $Q = 2.5e^{0.347t}$
25. 10.2 years
27. 10.8 years
29. $f(x) = \dfrac{900}{1 + 8(1.5)^{-x}}$
31. $f(x) = \dfrac{20}{1 + 3(0.8)^{-x}}$

33. a. \$8,500 per month; an average of approximately 2,100 hits per day **b.** \$29,049 per month **c.** The fact that -0.000005, the coefficient of c^2, is negative.   **35. a.** $R = -60p^2 + 950p$; $p = \$7.92$ per novel, Monthly revenue $= \$3,760.42$ **b.** $P = -60p^2 + 1,190p - 4,700$; $p = \$9.92$ per novel, Monthly profit $= \$1,200.42$ **37. a.** 9.1, 19 **b.** About 310,000 pounds   **39.** 2016   **41.** 1.12 million pounds   **43.** $n(t) = 9.6(0.80^t)$ million pounds of lobster   **45.** (C)

Chapter 3

Section 3.1

1. $INT = \$120$, $FV = \$2,120$
3. $INT = \$160$, $FV = \$4,160$
5. $INT = \$505$, $FV = \$20,705$
7. $INT = \$250$, $FV = \$10,250$
9. $INT = \$60$, $FV = \$12,060$ **11.** $PV = \$9,090.91$
13. $PV = \$966.18$ **15.** $PV = \$14,932.80$ **17.** $\$5,200$
19. $\$997.61$ **21.** 5% **23.** $\$170$; $\$3,400$ **25.** $\$8,000$
27. Wells Fargo; $\$1,225.00$ **29.** In 2 years   **31.** Weekly rate
of 1.25%; annual rate of 65% **33.** 10% **35.** 86.957%
37. 4.00% **39.** 4.91% if you had sold in November 2010
41. No. Simple interest increase is linear. The graph is visibly
not linear in that time period. Further, the slopes of the lines
through the successive pairs of marked points are quite different.   **43.** 9.2% **45.** $3,260,000$ **47.** $P = 500 + 46t$ thousand
($t =$ time in years since 1950)

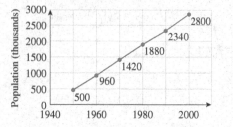

49. About 0.2503% **51.** 3.775% **53.** Graph (A) is the only
possible choice, because the equation $FV = PV(1 + rt) =$
$PV + PVrt$ gives the future value as a linear function of time.
55. 0.05% **57.** $FV = PV(1 + rt) = PV(1 + (12i)(n/12)) =$
$PV(1 + in)$ **59.** Wrong. In simple interest growth the change
each year is a fixed percentage of the *starting* value, not the
preceding year's value. (Also see Exercise 60.)   **61.** Simple
interest is always calculated on a constant amount, PV. If interest is paid into your account, then the amount on which interest
is calculated does not remain constant.

Section 3.2

1. $\$10,304.24$ **3.** $\$12,709.44$ **5.** $\$13,439.16$ **7.** $\$11,327.08$
9. $\$19,154.30$ **11.** $\$613.91$ **13.** $\$810.65$ **15.** $\$1,227.74$
17. 5.09% **19.** 10.47% **21.** 10.52% **23.** $\$268.99$
25. $\$728.91$ **27.** $\$2,927.15$ **29.** $\$21,161.79$
31. $\$163,414.56$ **33.** $\$174,110$ **35.** $\$750.00$ **37.** $\$9,000$
39. $\$7,462.65$ **41.** 0.43% **43.** $\$55,526.45$ per year
45. $\$27,171.92$ **47.** $\$111,678.96$ **49.** $\$1,039.21$ **51.** The
one earning 11.9% compounded monthly   **53.** Yes. The
investment would have grown to about $\$503,096$ million.
55. 160 reals   **57.** 656 bolivianos   **59.** 12 bolivars   **61.** The
Nicaragua investment is better: It is worth about 1.03 units of
currency (in constant units) per unit invested as opposed to
about 1.027 units for Mexico.   **63.** 53.81% **65.** 65.99% if
you had sold in November 2010   **67.** No. Compound interest
increase is exponential, and exponential curves either increase

continually (in the case of appreciation) or decrease continually (in the case of depreciation). The graph of the stock price
has both increases and decreases during the given period,
so the curve cannot model compound interest change.
69. 31 years; about $\$26,100$ **71.** 2.3 years
73. a. $\$1,510.31$ **b.** $\$54,701.29$ **c.** 23.51% **75.** The function
$y = P(1 + r/m)^{mx}$ is not a linear function of x, but an exponential function. Thus, its graph is not a straight line.
77. Wrong. Its growth is exponential and can be modeled by
$0.01(1.10)^t$.   **79.** The graphs are the same because the formulas give the same function of x; a compound interest investment behaves as though it were being compounded once a year
at the effective rate.   **81.** The effective rate exceeds the nominal rate when the interest is compounded more than once a
year because then interest is being paid on interest accumulated during each year, resulting in a larger effective rate.
Conversely, if the interest is compounded less often than
once a year, the effective rate is less than the nominal rate.
83. Compare their future values in constant dollars. The investment with the larger future value is the better investment.
85. The graphs are approaching a particular curve as m gets
larger, approximately the curve given by the largest two values
of m.

Section 3.3

1. $\$15,528.23$ **3.** $\$171,793.82$ **5.** $\$23,763.28$ **7.** $\$147.05$
9. $\$491.12$ **11.** $\$105.38$ **13.** $\$90,155.46$ **15.** $\$69,610.99$
17. $\$95,647.68$ **19.** $\$554.60$ **21.** $\$1,366.41$ **23.** $\$524.14$
25. $\$248.85$ **27.** $\$1,984.65$ **29.** $\$494.87$ **31.** $\$5,615.31$
33. $\$79,573.29$ **35.** $\$923,373.42$ **37.** $\$50,000.46$. This is
more than the original value of the loan. In a 200-year mortgage, the fraction of the initial payments going toward reducing the principal is so small that the rounding upward of the
payment makes it appear that, for many years at the start of the
mortgage, more is owed than the original amount borrowed.
39. $\$999.61$ **41.** $\$998.47$ **43.** $\$917.45$ **45.** $\$584,686.94$
47. $\$348,312.44$ **49.** $\$2,677.02$ **51.** Stock fund: $\$206.33$;
Bond fund: $\$825.32$ **53.** $\$318,794.79$ **55.** $\$7,451.49$
57. $\$973.54$ **59.** $\$278.92$

61.

Age	Male	Female
30	$\$276.62$	$\$235.24$
50	$\$927.11$	$\$756.08$
70	$\$9,469.40$	$\$5,020.06$

63. $\$131.28$ **65.** $\$144,321.81$ **67.** Wait until December, and
pay $\$34.41$ less per month.   **69.** $\$96,454.02$ **71.** $\$153.07$
73. November: $\$34,991.58$; December: $\$34,965.95$
75. $\$74.95$ **77.** You should take the loan from Solid Savings
& Loan: It will have payments of $\$248.85$ per month. The
payments on the other loan would be more than $\$300$ per
month.   **79.** Original monthly payments were $\$824.79$. The
new monthly payments will be $\$613.46$. You will save
$\$36,488.88$ in interest.

81. Answers using correctly rounded intermediate results:

Year	Interest	Payment on Principal
1	$3,934.98	$1,798.98
2	$3,785.69	$1,948.27
3	$3,623.97	$2,109.99
4	$3,448.84	$2,285.12
5	$3,259.19	$2,474.77
6	$3,053.77	$2,680.19
7	$2,831.32	$2,902.64
8	$2,590.39	$3,143.57
9	$2,329.48	$3,404.48
10	$2,046.91	$3,687.05
11	$1,740.88	$3,993.08
12	$1,409.47	$4,324.49
13	$1,050.54	$4,683.42
14	$661.81	$5,072.15
15	$240.84	$5,491.80

83. 10.81%   **85.** 13 years   **87.** 4.5 years   **89.** 24 years
91. He is wrong because his estimate ignores the interest that will be earned by your annuity—both while it is increasing and while it is decreasing. Your payments will be considerably smaller (depending on the interest earned).   **93.** Wrong; the split investment earns more. For instance, after 10 years it earns $31,056.46 + $32,775.87 = $63,832.33, which is more than the $63,803.03 earned by the single investment.   **95.** He is not correct. For instance, the payments on a $100,000 10-year mortgage at 12% are $1,434.71, while for a 20-year mortgage at the same rate, they are $1,101.09, which is a lot more than half the 10-year mortgage payment.   **97.** 3.617%
99. $PV = FV(1 + i)^{-n} = PMT\dfrac{(1 + i)^n - 1}{i}(1 + i)^{-n} =$
$PMT\dfrac{1 - (1 + i)^{-n}}{i}$

Chapter 3 Review

1. $7,425.00   **3.** $7,604.88   **5.** $6,757.41   **7.** $4,848.48
9. $4,733.80   **11.** $5,331.37   **13.** $177.58   **15.** $112.54
17. $187.57   **19.** 14.0 years   **21.** 10.8 years
23. 7.0 years   **25.** $9,584.17   **27.** 5.346%   **29.** 168.85%
31. 85.28% if she sold in February 2010.   **33.** No.
Simple interest increase is linear. We can compare slopes between successive points to see whether the slope remained roughly constant: From December 2002 to August 2004 the slope was $(16.31 - 3.28)/(20/12) = 7.818$,
while from August 2004 to March 2005 the slope was $(33.95 - 16.31)/(7/12) = 30.24$. These slopes are quite different.   **35.** 2013

Year	2010	2011	2012	2013	2014
Revenue	$180,000	$216,000	$259,200	$311,040	$373,248

37. At least 52,515 shares   **39.** $3,234.94   **41.** $231,844
43. 7.75%   **45.** $420,275   **47.** $140,778   **49.** $1,453.06
51. $2,239.90 per month   **53.** $53,055.66   **55.** 5.99%

Chapter 4

Section 4.1

1. Particular solutions (answers may vary): $(-1, -3)$, $(0, -1)$, $(1, 1)$; general solution parameterized by x: $(x, 2x - 1)$; x arbitrary; general solution parameterized by y: $\left(\frac{1}{2}(y + 1), y\right)$; y arbitrary   **3.** Particular solutions (answers may vary): $(-2, 2)$, $(0, 1/2)$, $(2, -1)$; general solution parameterized by x: $\left(x, -\frac{3}{4}x + \frac{1}{2}\right)$; x arbitrary; general solution parameterized by y: $\left(\frac{1}{3}(-4y + 2), y\right)$; y arbitrary   **5.** Particular solutions (answers may vary): $(-5/4, -1)$, $(-5/4, 0)$, $(-5/4, 1)$; general solution parameterized by y: $(-5/4, y)$; y arbitrary
7. $(2, 2)$ **9.** $(3, 1)$ **11.** $(6, 6)$ **13.** $(5/3, -4/3)$ **15.** $(0, -2)$
17. $(x, (1 - 2x)/3)$ or $((1 - 3y)/2, y)$ **19.** No solution
21. $(5, 0)$ **23.** $(0.3, -1.1)$ **25.** $(116.6, -69.7)$
27. $(3.3, 1.8)$ **29.** $(3.4, 1.9)$ **31.** $x - 2y = 0$
33. $x - 1.10y = 0$ **35.** $x - 3y = 0$; $x + y = 12$
37. $x - 4y = 0$; $x - y = 15$ **39.** 200 qt of vanilla, 100 qt of mocha   **41.** 2 servings of Mixed Cereal, 1 serving of Mango Tropical Fruit   **43. a.** 4 servings of beans, 5 slices of bread **b.** No. One of the variables in the solution of the system has a negative value.   **45.** Mix 12 servings of Designer Whey, 2 servings of Muscle Milk for a cost of $9.20.   **47.** 65 g
49. 200 TWTR, 300 MSFT   **51.** 200 TD, 400 CNA   **53.** 242 in favor, 193 against   **55.** 5 soccer games, 7 football games
57. 7   **59.** $1.50 each   **61.** 55 widgets   **63.** Demand: $q = -4p + 47$; supply: $q = 4p - 29$; equilibrium price: $9.50   **65.** 33 pairs of dirty socks, 11 T-shirts   **67.** $1,200
69. The three lines in a plane must intersect in a single point for there to be a unique solution. This can happen in two ways: (1) The three lines intersect in a single point, or (2) two of the lines are the same, and the third line intersects it in a single point.   **71.** Yes. Even if two lines have negative slope, they will still intersect if the slopes differ.   **73.** You cannot round both of them up, since there will not be sufficient eggs and cream. Rounding both answers down will ensure that you will not run out of ingredients. It may be possible to round one answer down and the other up, and this should be tried.
75. (B)   **77.** (B)   **79.** Answers will vary.   **81.** It is very likely. Two randomly chosen straight lines are unlikely to be parallel.

Section 4.2

1. $(3, 1)$ **3.** $(6, 6)$ **5.** $\left(\frac{1}{2}(1 - 3y), y\right)$; y arbitrary
7. No solution   **9.** $(1/4, 3/4)$ **11.** No solution
13. $(10/3, 1/3)$ **15.** $(4, 4, 4)$ **17.** $(-1, -3, 1/2)$
19. (z, z, z); z arbitrary   **21.** No solution   **23.** $(-1, 1, 1)$
25. $(1, z - 2, z)$; z arbitrary   **27.** $(4 + y, y, -1)$; y arbitrary
29. $(4 - y/3 + z/3, y, z)$; y arbitrary, z arbitrary
31. $(-17, 20, -2)$ **33.** $\left(-3/2, 0, 1/2, 0\right)$
35. $(-3z, 1 - 2z, z, 0)$; z arbitrary   **37.** $(7/5 - 17z/5 + 8w/5, 1/5 - 6z/5 - 6w/5, z, w)$; z, w arbitrary
39. $(1, 2, 3, 4, 5)$ **41.** $(-2, -2 + z - u, z, u, 0)$;

z, u arbitrary   **43.** $(16, 12/7, -162/7, -88/7)$
45. $(-8/15, 7/15, 7/15, 7/15, 7/15)$ **47.** $(1.0, 1.4, 0.2)$
49. $(-5.5, -0.9, -7.4, -6.6)$ **51.** A pivot is an entry in a matrix that is selected to "clear a column"; that is, use the row operations of a certain type to obtain zeros everywhere above and below it. "Pivoting" is the procedure of clearing a column using a designated pivot.   **53.** $2R_1 + 5R_4$, or $6R_1 + 15R_4$ (which is less desirable)   **55.** It will include a row of zeros. **57.** The claim is wrong. If there are more equations than unknowns, there can be a unique solution as well as row(s) of zeros in the reduced matrix, as in Example 6.   **59.** Two **61.** The number of pivots must equal the number of variables, since no variable will be used as a parameter.   **63.** A simple example is $x = 1$; $y - z = 1$; $x + y - z = 2$.   **65.** It has to be the zero solution (each unknown is equal to zero): Putting each unknown equal to zero causes each equation to be satisfied because the right-hand sides are zero. Thus, the zero solution is in fact a solution. Because the solution is unique, this solution is the *only* solution.   **67.** No: As was pointed out in Exercise 65, every homogeneous system has at least one solution (namely, the zero solution) and hence cannot be inconsistent.

Section 4.3

1. 100 batches of vanilla, 50 batches of mocha, 100 batches of strawberry   **3.** 3 sections of Finite Math, 2 sections of Applied Calculus, 1 section of Computer Methods   **5.** $32 million for regional music, $18 million for pop/rock music, $8 million for tropical music   **7.** 6 Airbus A330-300s, 4 Boeing 767-300ERs, 8 Boeing Dreamliner 787-9s   **9.** 22 tons from Cheesy Cream, 56 tons from Super Smooth & Sons, 22 tons from Bagel's Best Friend   **11.** 10 evil sorcerers, 50 trolls, 500 orcs   **13.** $600 to each of the MPBF and the SCN and $1,200 to the Jets **15.** United Continental: 120; American: 40; Southwest: 50 **17.** $5,000 in SHPIX, $2,000 in RYURX, $2,000 in RYCWX **19.** 100 shares of WSR, 50 shares of HCC, 50 shares of SNDK **21.** Microsoft: 88 million, Time Warner: 79 million, Yahoo: 75 million, Google: 42 million   **23.** The third equation is $x + y + z + w = 100$. General solution: $x = 50.5 - 0.5w$, $y = 33.5 - 0.3w$, $z = 16 - 0.2w$, w arbitrary. State Farm is most affected by other companies.   **25. a.** Brooklyn to Long Island: 500 books; Brooklyn to Manhattan: 500 books; Queens to Long Island: 1,000 books; Queens to Manhattan: 1,000 books. **b.** Brooklyn to Long Island: none; Brooklyn to Manhattan: 1,000 books; Queens to Long Island: 1,500 books; Queens to Manhattan: 500 books, giving a total cost of $8,000 **27. a.** The associated system of equations has infinitely many solutions. **b.** No; the associated system of equations still has infinitely many solutions. **c.** Yes; North America to Australia: 440,000, North America to South Africa: 190,000, Europe to Australia: 950,000, Europe to South Africa: 950,000. **29. a.** $x + y = 14,000$; $z + w = 95,000$; $x + z = 63,550$; $y + w = 45,450$. The system does not have a unique solution, indicating that the given data are insufficient to obtain the missing data. **b.** $(x, y, z, w) = (5,600, 8,400, 57,950, 37,050)$ **31. a.** No; The general solution is: Eastward Blvd.: $S + 200$;

Northwest La.: $S + 50$; Southwest La.: S, where S is arbitrary. Thus, it would suffice to know the traffic along Southwest La. **b.** Yes, as it leads to the solution Eastward Blvd.: 260; Northwest La.: 110; Southwest La.: 60.   **c.** 50 vehicles per day **33. a.** With $x =$ traffic on middle section of Bree, $y =$ traffic on middle section of Jeppe, $z =$ traffic on middle section of Simmons, $w =$ traffic on middle section of Harrison, the general solution is $x = w - 100$, $y = w$, $z = w$, w arbitrary. **b.** No; there are infinitely many possible values for y. **c.** 500 cars per minute   **d.** 100 cars per minute   **e.** No; a large number of cars can circulate around the middle block without affecting the numbers shown.   **35. a.** No; the corresponding system of equations is underdetermined. The net flow of traffic along any of the three stretches of Broadway would suffice. **b.** West   **37.** $10 billion   **39.** $x =$ water, $y =$ gray matter, $z =$ tumor   **41.** $x =$ water, $y =$ bone, $z =$ tumor, $u =$ air **43.** tumor   **45.** 200 Democrats, 20 Republicans, 13 of other parties   **47.** Yes; $20m in Company X, $5m in Company Y, $10m in Company Z, $30m in Company W   **49.** It is not realistic to expect to use exactly all of the ingredients. Solutions of the associated system may involve negative numbers or not exist. Only solutions with nonnegative values for all the unknowns correspond to being able to use up all of the ingredients. **51.** Yes; $x = 100$ **53.** Yes; $0.3x - 0.7y + 0.3z = 0$ is one form of the equation.   **55.** No; represented by an inequality rather than an equation.   **57.** Answers will vary.

Chapter 4 Review

1. One solution

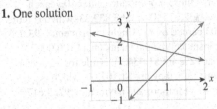

3. Infinitely many solutions

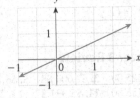

5. One solution

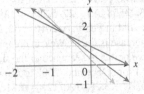

7. $(6/5, 7/5)$ **9.** $(3y/2, y)$; y arbitrary   **11.** $(-0.7, 1.7)$ **13.** $(-1, -1, -1)$ **15.** $(z - 2, 4(z - 1), z)$; z arbitrary **17.** No solution   **19.** $-40°$ **21.** It is impossible; setting $F = 1.8C$ leads to an inconsistent system of equations. **23.** $x + y + z + w = 10$; linear   **25.** $w = 0$; linear

27. $-1.3y + z = 0$ or $1.3y - z = 0$; linear
29. 550 packages from Duffin House, 350 from Higgins Press
31. 1,200 packages from Duffin House, 200 from Higgins Press **33.** \$40 **35.** 7 of each **37.** 5,000 hits per day at OHaganBooks.com, 1,250 at JungleBooks.com, 3,750 at FarmerBooks.com **39.** 100 shares of HAL, 20 shares of POM, 80 shares of WELL **41.** Billy-Sean is forced to take exactly the following combination: Liberal Arts: 52 credits, Sciences: 12 credits, Fine Arts: 12 credits, Mathematics: 48 credits. **43. a.** $x = 100$, $y = 100 + w$, $z = 300 - w$, w arbitrary **b.** 100 book orders per day **c.** 300 book orders per day **d.** $x = 100$, $y = 400$, $z = 0$, $w = 300$ **e.** 100 book orders per day **45.** Yes; New York to OHaganBooks.com: 450 packages, New York to FantasyBooks.com: 50 packages, Illinois to OHaganBooks.com: 150 packages, Illinois to FantasyBooks.com: 150 packages

Chapter 5

Section 5.1

1. 1×4; 0 **3.** 4×1; 5/2 **5.** $p \times q$; e_{22} **7.** 2×2; 3
9. $1 \times n$; d_r **11.** $x = 1$, $y = 2$, $z = 3$, $w = 4$

13. $\begin{bmatrix} 0.25 & -2 \\ 1 & 0.5 \\ -2 & 5 \end{bmatrix}$ **15.** $\begin{bmatrix} -0.75 & -1 \\ 0 & -0.5 \\ -1 & 6 \end{bmatrix}$

17. $\begin{bmatrix} -1 & -1 \\ 1 & -1 \\ -1 & 5 \end{bmatrix}$ **19.** $\begin{bmatrix} 0 & 2 & -2 \\ -2 & 0 & 4 \end{bmatrix}$

21. $\begin{bmatrix} 4 & -1 & -1 \\ 5 & 1 & 0 \end{bmatrix}$ **23.** $\begin{bmatrix} -2 + x & 0 & 1 + w \\ -5 + z & 3 + r & 2 \end{bmatrix}$

25. $\begin{bmatrix} -1 & -2 & 1 \\ -5 & 5 & -3 \end{bmatrix}$ **27.** $\begin{bmatrix} 9 & 15 \\ 0 & -3 \\ -3 & 3 \end{bmatrix}$

29. $\begin{bmatrix} -8.5 & -22.35 & -24.4 \\ 54.2 & 20 & 42.2 \end{bmatrix}$

31. $\begin{bmatrix} 1.54 & 8.58 \\ 5.94 & 0 \\ 6.16 & 7.26 \end{bmatrix}$ **33.** $\begin{bmatrix} 7.38 & 76.96 \\ 20.33 & 0 \\ 29.12 & 39.92 \end{bmatrix}$

35. $\begin{bmatrix} -19.85 & 115.82 \\ -50.935 & 46 \\ -57.24 & 94.62 \end{bmatrix}$

37. 2013: $[17.2 \quad 153.4 \quad 74.2]$; 2014: $[19.6 \quad 192.6 \quad 63.4]$

39. Sales $= \begin{bmatrix} 700 & 1,300 & 2,000 \\ 400 & 300 & 500 \end{bmatrix}$;

Inventory $-$ Sales $= \begin{bmatrix} 300 & 700 & 3,000 \\ 600 & 4,700 & 1,500 \end{bmatrix}$

41. Profit $=$ Revenue $-$ Cost $= \begin{bmatrix} 8,000 & 7,200 & 8,800 \\ 5,600 & 5,760 & 7,040 \\ 2,800 & 3,500 & 4,000 \end{bmatrix}$

43. 2000 distribution $= A = [53.6 \quad 64.4 \quad 100.2 \quad 63.2]$; 2010 distribution $= B = [55.3 \quad 66.9 \quad 114.6 \quad 71.9]$; Net change 2000 to 2010 $= D = B - A = [1.7 \quad 2.5 \quad 14.4 \quad 8.7]$; 2020 Distribution $= B + D = [57.0 \quad 69.4 \quad 129.0 \quad 80.6]$
45. Total foreclosures $=$ Foreclosures in California $+$ Foreclosures in Florida $+$ Foreclosures in Texas $= [55,900 \quad 51,900 \quad 54,100 \quad 56,200 \quad 59,400] + [19,600 \quad 19,200 \quad 23,800 \quad 22,400 \quad 23,600] + [8,800 \quad 9,100 \quad 9,300 \quad 10,600 \quad 10,100] = [84,300 \quad 80,200 \quad 87,200 \quad 89,200 \quad 93,100]$
47. Difference $=$ Foreclosures in California $-$ Foreclosures in Florida $= [55,900 \quad 51,900 \quad 54,100 \quad 56,200 \quad 59,400] - [19,600 \quad 19,200 \quad 23,800 \quad 22,400 \quad 23,600] = [36,300 \quad 32,700 \quad 30,300 \quad 33,800 \quad 35,800]$ The difference was greatest in April.

49. a. Use $= \begin{matrix} & \text{Proc} & \text{Mem} & \text{Tubes} \\ \text{Pom II} & \\ \text{Pom Classic} \end{matrix} \begin{bmatrix} 2 & 16 & 20 \\ 1 & 4 & 40 \end{bmatrix}$;

Inventory $= \begin{bmatrix} 500 & 5,000 & 10,000 \\ 200 & 2,000 & 20,000 \end{bmatrix}$;

Inventory $- 100 \times$ Use $= \begin{bmatrix} 300 & 3,400 & 8,000 \\ 100 & 1,600 & 16,000 \end{bmatrix}$

b. After 4 months

51. a. $A = \begin{bmatrix} 440 & 190 \\ 950 & 950 \\ 1,790 & 200 \end{bmatrix}$, $D = \begin{bmatrix} -20 & 40 \\ 50 & 50 \\ 0 & 100 \end{bmatrix}$

2008 Tourism $= A + D = \begin{bmatrix} 420 & 230 \\ 1,000 & 1,000 \\ 1,790 & 300 \end{bmatrix}$

b. $\frac{1}{2}(A + B)$; $\begin{bmatrix} 430 & 210 \\ 975 & 975 \\ 1,790 & 250 \end{bmatrix}$

53. No; for two matrices to be equal, they must have the same dimensions. **55.** The ijth entry of the sum $A + B$ is obtained by adding the ijth entries of A and B.
57. It would have zeros down the main diagonal:

$A = \begin{bmatrix} 0 & \# & \# & \# & \# \\ \# & 0 & \# & \# & \# \\ \# & \# & 0 & \# & \# \\ \# & \# & \# & 0 & \# \\ \# & \# & \# & \# & 0 \end{bmatrix}$

The symbols # indicate arbitrary numbers.
59. $(A^T)_{ij} = A_{ji}$ **61.** Answers will vary.

a. $\begin{bmatrix} 0 & -4 \\ 4 & 0 \end{bmatrix}$ **b.** $\begin{bmatrix} 0 & -4 & 5 \\ 4 & 0 & 1 \\ -5 & -1 & 0 \end{bmatrix}$

63. The associativity of matrix addition is a consequence of the associativity of addition of numbers, since we add matrices by adding the corresponding entries (which are real numbers).
65. Answers will vary.

Section 5.2

1. $[13]$ **3.** $[5/6]$ **5.** $[-2y + z]$ **7.** Undefined
9. $[3 \quad 0 \quad -6 \quad -2]$ **11.** $[-6 \quad 37 \quad 7]$
13. $\begin{bmatrix} -4 & -7 & -1 \\ 9 & 17 & 0 \end{bmatrix}$ **15.** $\begin{bmatrix} 0 & 1 \\ 0 & 0 \end{bmatrix}$ **17.** $\begin{bmatrix} 1 & -1 \\ 1 & -1 \end{bmatrix}$

19. $\begin{bmatrix} 0 & 0 \\ 0 & 0 \end{bmatrix}$ **21.** Undefined **23.** $\begin{bmatrix} 1 & -5 & 3 \\ 0 & 0 & 9 \\ 0 & 4 & 1 \end{bmatrix}$

25. $\begin{bmatrix} 3 \\ -4 \\ 0 \\ 3 \end{bmatrix}$ **27.** $\begin{bmatrix} 0.23 & 5.36 & -21.65 \\ -13.18 & -5.82 & -16.62 \\ -11.21 & -9.9 & 0.99 \\ -2.1 & 2.34 & 2.46 \end{bmatrix}$

29. $A^2 = \begin{bmatrix} 0 & 0 & 1 & 2 \\ 0 & 0 & 0 & 1 \\ 0 & 0 & 0 & 0 \\ 0 & 0 & 0 & 0 \end{bmatrix}$; $A^3 = \begin{bmatrix} 0 & 0 & 0 & 1 \\ 0 & 0 & 0 & 0 \\ 0 & 0 & 0 & 0 \\ 0 & 0 & 0 & 0 \end{bmatrix}$;

$A^4 = \begin{bmatrix} 0 & 0 & 0 & 0 \\ 0 & 0 & 0 & 0 \\ 0 & 0 & 0 & 0 \\ 0 & 0 & 0 & 0 \end{bmatrix}$; $\ldots$; $A^{100} = \begin{bmatrix} 0 & 0 & 0 & 0 \\ 0 & 0 & 0 & 0 \\ 0 & 0 & 0 & 0 \\ 0 & 0 & 0 & 0 \end{bmatrix}$

31. $\begin{bmatrix} 4 & -1 \\ -1 & -7 \end{bmatrix}$ **33.** $\begin{bmatrix} 4 & -1 \\ -12 & 2 \end{bmatrix}$

35. $\begin{bmatrix} -2 & 1 & -2 \\ 10 & -2 & 2 \\ -10 & 2 & -2 \end{bmatrix}$

37. $\begin{bmatrix} -2 + x - z & 2 - r & -6 + w \\ 10 + 2z & -2 + 2r & 10 \\ -10 - 2z & 2 - 2r & -10 \end{bmatrix}$

39. a.–d. $P^2 = P^4 = P^8 = P^{1,000} = \begin{bmatrix} 0.2 & 0.8 \\ 0.2 & 0.8 \end{bmatrix}$

41. a. $P^2 = \begin{bmatrix} 0.01 & 0.99 \\ 0 & 1 \end{bmatrix}$

b. $P^4 = \begin{bmatrix} 0.0001 & 0.9999 \\ 0 & 1 \end{bmatrix}$

c. and d. $P^8 \approx P^{1,000} \approx \begin{bmatrix} 0 & 1 \\ 0 & 1 \end{bmatrix}$

43. a.–d. $P^2 = P^4 = P^8 = P^{1,000} = \begin{bmatrix} 0.3 & 0.3 & 0.4 \\ 0.3 & 0.3 & 0.4 \\ 0.3 & 0.3 & 0.4 \end{bmatrix}$

The rows of P are the same, and the entries in each row add up to 1. If P is any square matrix with identical rows such that the entries in each row add up to 1, then $P \cdot P = P$.

45. $2x - y + 4z = 3$; $-4x + \dfrac{3}{4}y + \dfrac{1}{3}z = -1$; $-3x = 0$

47. $x - y + w = -1$; $x + y + 2z + 4w = 2$

49. $\begin{bmatrix} 1 & -1 \\ 2 & -1 \end{bmatrix} \begin{bmatrix} x \\ y \end{bmatrix} = \begin{bmatrix} 4 \\ 0 \end{bmatrix}$

51. $\begin{bmatrix} 1 & 1 & -1 \\ 2 & 1 & 1 \\ \frac{3}{4} & 0 & \frac{1}{2} \end{bmatrix} \begin{bmatrix} x \\ y \\ z \end{bmatrix} = \begin{bmatrix} 8 \\ 4 \\ 1 \end{bmatrix}$

53. Revenue = Price × Quantity =

$[15 \quad 10 \quad 12] \begin{bmatrix} 50 \\ 40 \\ 30 \end{bmatrix} = [1{,}510]$

55. \$92.5 million
57. Revenue = Quantity × Price =

$\begin{bmatrix} 700 & 1{,}300 & 2{,}000 \\ 400 & 300 & 500 \end{bmatrix} \begin{bmatrix} 30 \\ 10 \\ 15 \end{bmatrix} = \begin{bmatrix} 64{,}000 \\ 22{,}500 \end{bmatrix}$

59. \$5,100 billion (or \$5.1 trillion)
61. $D = N(F - M)$, where N is the income per person, and F and M are, respectively, the female and male populations in 2020; \$400 billion
63. $[23.1 \quad 5.2]$, which represents the amount, in pounds, by which per capita consumption of ice cream exceeded that of yogurt in 1983 and 2013.
65. Number of foreclosures filings handled by firm = Percentage handled by firm × Total number = $[8{,}460 \quad 8{,}860 \quad 9{,}140]$
67. The number of foreclosures in California and Florida combined in each of the months shown.

69. $[1 \quad -1 \quad 1] \begin{bmatrix} 54{,}100 & 56{,}200 & 59{,}400 \\ 23{,}800 & 22{,}400 & 23{,}600 \\ 9{,}300 & 10{,}600 & 10{,}100 \end{bmatrix} \begin{bmatrix} 1 \\ 1 \\ 1 \end{bmatrix}$

$= [129{,}900]$

71. $\begin{bmatrix} 2 & 16 & 20 \\ 1 & 4 & 40 \end{bmatrix} \begin{bmatrix} 100 & 150 \\ 50 & 40 \\ 10 & 15 \end{bmatrix} = \begin{bmatrix} 1{,}200 & 1{,}240 \\ 700 & 910 \end{bmatrix}$

73. $AB = \begin{bmatrix} 29.6 \\ 85.5 \\ 97.5 \end{bmatrix}$, $AC = \begin{bmatrix} 22 & 7.6 \\ 47.5 & 38 \\ 89.5 & 8 \end{bmatrix}$

The entries of AB give the number of people from each of the three regions who settle in Australia or South Africa, while the entries in AC break those figures down further into settlers in South Africa and settlers in Australia.
75. $[54.6 \quad 66.0 \quad 111.8 \quad 70.6]$
77. Answers will vary. One example:

$A = [1 \quad 2], B = \begin{bmatrix} 1 & 2 & 3 \\ 4 & 5 & 6 \end{bmatrix}$.

Another example: $A = [1], B = [1 \quad 2]$
79. We find that the addition and multiplication of 1×1 matrices is identical to the addition and multiplication of numbers.
81. The claim is correct. Every matrix equation represents the equality of two matrices. When two matrices are equal, each of their corresponding entries must be equal. Equating the corresponding entries gives a system of equations.

83. Here is a possible scenario: Costs of items A, B, and C in 2013 = $\begin{bmatrix} 10 & 20 & 30 \end{bmatrix}$, Percentage increases in these costs in 2014 = $\begin{bmatrix} 0.5 & 0.1 & 0.20 \end{bmatrix}$, Actual increases in costs = $\begin{bmatrix} 10 \times 0.5 & 20 \times 0.1 & 30 \times 0.20 \end{bmatrix}$.
85. It produces a matrix whose ij entry is the product of the ij entries of the two matrices.

Section 5.3

1. Yes **3.** Yes **5.** No

7. $\begin{bmatrix} -1 & 1 \\ 2 & -1 \end{bmatrix}$ **9.** $\begin{bmatrix} 0 & 1 \\ 1 & 0 \end{bmatrix}$ **11.** $\begin{bmatrix} 1 & -1 \\ -1 & 2 \end{bmatrix}$

13. Singular **15.** $\begin{bmatrix} 1 & -1 & 0 \\ 0 & 1 & -1 \\ 0 & 0 & 1 \end{bmatrix}$

17. $\begin{bmatrix} 1 & -1 & 1 \\ \frac{1}{2} & 0 & -\frac{1}{2} \\ -\frac{1}{2} & 1 & -\frac{1}{2} \end{bmatrix}$ **19.** $\begin{bmatrix} 1 & \frac{1}{3} & -\frac{1}{3} \\ 1 & -\frac{2}{3} & -\frac{1}{3} \\ -1 & \frac{1}{3} & \frac{2}{3} \end{bmatrix}$

21. Singular **23.** $\begin{bmatrix} 0 & 1 & -2 & 1 \\ 0 & 1 & -1 & 0 \\ 1 & -1 & 2 & -1 \\ 0 & 1 & -1 & 1 \end{bmatrix}$

25. $\begin{bmatrix} 1 & -2 & 1 & 0 \\ 0 & 1 & -2 & 1 \\ 0 & 0 & 1 & -2 \\ 0 & 0 & 0 & 1 \end{bmatrix}$ **27.** $-2;\ \begin{bmatrix} \frac{1}{2} & \frac{1}{2} \\ \frac{1}{2} & -\frac{1}{2} \end{bmatrix}$

29. $-2;\ \begin{bmatrix} -2 & 1 \\ \frac{3}{2} & -\frac{1}{2} \end{bmatrix}$ **31.** $1/36;\ \begin{bmatrix} 6 & 6 \\ 0 & 6 \end{bmatrix}$

33. 0; Singular

35. $\begin{bmatrix} 0.38 & 0.45 \\ 0.49 & -0.41 \end{bmatrix}$ **37.** $\begin{bmatrix} 0.00 & -0.99 \\ 0.81 & 2.87 \end{bmatrix}$

39. Singular

41. $\begin{bmatrix} 91.35 & -8.65 & 0 & -71.30 \\ -0.07 & -0.07 & 0 & 2.49 \\ 2.60 & 2.60 & -4.35 & 1.37 \\ 2.69 & 2.69 & 0 & -2.10 \end{bmatrix}$

43. $(5/2, 3/2)$ **45.** $(6, -4)$ **47.** $(6, 6, 6)$
49. a. $(10, -5, -3)$ **b.** $(6, 1, 5)$ **c.** $(0, 0, 0)$
51. a. 10/3 servings of beans, 5/6 slices of bread
b. $\begin{bmatrix} -\frac{1}{2} & \frac{1}{6} \\ \frac{7}{8} & -\frac{5}{24} \end{bmatrix}\begin{bmatrix} A \\ B \end{bmatrix} = \begin{bmatrix} -\frac{A}{2} + \frac{B}{6} \\ \frac{7A}{8} - \frac{5B}{24} \end{bmatrix}$; that is,
$-A/2 + B/6$ servings of beans, $7A/8 - 5B/24$ slices of bread **53. a.** 100 batches of vanilla, 50 batches of mocha, 100 batches of strawberry **b.** 100 batches of vanilla, no mocha, 200 batches of strawberry
c. $\begin{bmatrix} 1 & -\frac{1}{3} & -\frac{1}{3} \\ -1 & 0 & 1 \\ 0 & \frac{2}{3} & -\frac{1}{3} \end{bmatrix}\begin{bmatrix} A \\ B \\ C \end{bmatrix}$, or $A - B/3 - C/3$ batches of
vanilla, $-A + C$ batches of mocha, $2B/3 - C/3$ batches of strawberry

55. \$5,000 in MYY, \$2,000 in SH, \$2,000 in REW
57. 100 shares of WSR, 50 shares of HCC, 50 shares of SNDK
59. $\begin{bmatrix} 54.1 & 65.7 & 112.9 & 70.3 \end{bmatrix}$
61. a. $(-0.7071, 3.5355)$ **b.** R^2, R^3 **c.** R^{-1}
63. $\begin{bmatrix} 37 & 81 & 40 & 80 & 15 & 45 & 40 & 96 & 29 & 59 & 4 & 8 \end{bmatrix}$
65. CORRECT ANSWER **67.** (A) **69.** The inverse does not exist; the matrix is singular. (If two rows of a matrix are the same, then row reducing it will lead to a row of zeros, so it cannot be reduced to the identity.)
71. Calculation (See the Student Solutions Manual.)
73. When one or more of the d_i are zero; if that is the case, then the matrix $[D\,|\,I]$ easily reduces to a matrix that has a row of zeros on the left-hand portion, so D is singular. Conversely, if none of the d_i are zero, then $[D\,|\,I]$ easily reduces to a matrix of the form $[I\,|\,E]$, showing that D is invertible.
75. $(AB)(B^{-1}A^{-1}) = A(BB^{-1})A^{-1} = AIA^{-1} = AA^{-1} = I$
77. If A has an inverse, then every system of equations $AX = B$ has a unique solution, namely, $X = A^{-1}B$. But if A reduces to a matrix with a row of zeros, then such a system has either infinitely many solutions or no solution at all.

Section 5.4

1. -1 **3.** -0.25 **5.** $\begin{bmatrix} 0 & 0 & 1 & 0 \end{bmatrix}$; $e = 2.25$
7. $\begin{bmatrix} 1 & 0 & 0 \end{bmatrix}^T$ or $\begin{bmatrix} 0 & 1 & 0 \end{bmatrix}^T$; $e = 1/4$

9. $\begin{matrix} & \overset{p}{} & \overset{r}{} \\ a & 1 & 10 \\ b & 2 & -4 \end{matrix}$ $\begin{bmatrix} \,\,1 & 10 \\ 2 & -4 \end{bmatrix}$ **11.** $3\begin{bmatrix} c \\ -1 \end{bmatrix}$ **13.** $q[0]$

15. Strictly determined. The row player's optimal strategy is a; the column player's optimal strategy is q; Value: 1
17. Not strictly determined. **19.** Not strictly determined.
21. $R = \begin{bmatrix} \frac{1}{4} & \frac{3}{4} \end{bmatrix}, C = \begin{bmatrix} \frac{3}{4} & \frac{1}{4} \end{bmatrix}^T, e = -1/4$
23. $R = \begin{bmatrix} \frac{3}{4} & \frac{1}{4} \end{bmatrix}, C = \begin{bmatrix} \frac{3}{4} & \frac{1}{4} \end{bmatrix}^T, e = -5/4$
25. Row player: you; Column player: your friend;

$$\begin{matrix} & \overset{H}{} & \overset{T}{} \\ H & -1 & 1 \\ T & 1 & -1 \end{matrix}$$

27. $F = $ France; $S = $ Sweden; $N = $ Norway

Your Opponent Defends

$$\begin{matrix} & & F & S & N \\ \text{You Invade} & \begin{matrix} F \\ S \\ N \end{matrix} & \begin{bmatrix} -1 & 1 & 1 \\ 1 & -1 & 1 \\ 1 & 1 & -1 \end{bmatrix} \end{matrix}$$

29. Row player: you; Column player: your opponent; $B = $ Brakpan, $N = $ Nigel, $S = $ Springs;

Your Opponent

$$\begin{matrix} & & B & N & S \\ \text{You} & \begin{matrix} B \\ N \\ S \end{matrix} & \begin{bmatrix} 0 & 0 & 1{,}000 \\ 0 & 0 & 1{,}000 \\ -1{,}000 & -1{,}000 & 0 \end{bmatrix} \end{matrix}$$

31. P = PleasantTap; T = Thunder Rumble; S = Strike the Gold, N = None;

Winner

$$\text{You Bet } \begin{array}{c} \\ P \\ T \\ S \end{array} \begin{array}{cccc} P & T & S & N \\ \left[\begin{array}{cccc} 25 & -10 & -10 & -10 \\ -10 & 35 & -10 & -10 \\ -10 & -10 & 40 & -10 \end{array}\right] \end{array}$$

33. You can expect to lose 39 customers.
35. Option II: Move to the suburbs. **37. a.** About 66%
b. Yes; spend the whole night studying game theory; 75%
c. Game theory; 57.5% **39. a.** Lay off 10 workers; cost: $40,000 **b.** 0 inches of snow, costing $300,000 **c.** Lay off 15 workers. **41. a.** CE should charge $1,000, and GCS should charge $900; 15% gain in market share for CE. **b.** CE should charge $1,200. (The more CE can charge for the same market, the better!) **43.** Pablo vs. Noto; evenly matched **45.** Both commanders should use the northern route; 2 days.
47. Confess

49. a. $\begin{array}{c} \\ F \\ O \end{array} \begin{array}{cc} F & O \\ \left[\begin{array}{cc} 24 & 21 \\ 25 & 24 \end{array}\right] \end{array}$

b. Both candidates should visit Ohio, leaving Romney with a 24% chance of winning the election. **51.** Allocate 1/7 of the budget to WISH and the rest (6/7) to WASH. Softex will lose approximately $2,860. **53.** Like a saddle point in a payoff matrix, the center of a saddle is a low point (minimum height) in one direction and a high point (maximum) in a perpendicular direction. **55.** Although there is a saddle point in the (2, 4) position, you would be wrong to use saddle points (based on the minimax criterion) to reach the conclusion that row strategy 2 is best. One reason is that the entries in the matrix do not represent payoffs, since high numbers of employees in an area do not necessarily represent benefit to the row player. Another reason for this is that there is no opponent deciding what your job will be in such a way as to force you into the least populated job. **57.** If you strictly alternate the two strategies, the column player will know which pure strategy you will play on each move and can choose a pure strategy accordingly. For example, consider the game

$$\begin{array}{c} \\ A \\ B \end{array} \begin{array}{cc} a & b \\ \left[\begin{array}{cc} 1 & 0 \\ 0 & 1 \end{array}\right] \end{array}.$$

By the analysis of Example 3 (or the symmetry of the game), the best strategy for the row player is $[0.5 \quad 0.5]$, and the best strategy for the column player is $[0.5 \quad 0.5]^T$. This gives an expected value of 0.5 for the game. However, suppose that the row player alternates A and B strictly and that the column player catches on to this. Then, whenever the row player plays A the column player will play b, and whenever the row player plays B, the column player will play a. This gives a payoff of 0 each time, worse for the row player than the expected value of 0.5.

Section 5.5

1. a. 0.8 **b.** 0.2 **c.** 0.05 **3.** $\left[\begin{array}{cc} 0.2 & 0.1 \\ 0.5 & 0 \end{array}\right]$
5. $[52,000 \quad 40,000]^T$ **7.** $[50,000 \quad 50,000]^T$
9. $[2,560 \quad 2,800 \quad 4,000]^T$
11. $[27,000 \quad 28,000 \quad 17,000]^T$
13. Increase of 100 units in each sector.
15. Increase of $[1.5 \quad 0.2 \quad 0.1]^T$; the ith column of $(I - A)^{-1}$ gives the change in production necessary to meet an increase in external demand of one unit for the product of Sector i.

17. $A = \left[\begin{array}{ccc} 0.2 & 0.4 & 0.5 \\ 0 & 0.8 & 0 \\ 0 & 0.2 & 0.5 \end{array}\right]$

19. Main DR: $80,000, Bits & Bytes: $38,000 **21.** Equipment Sector production approximately $86,000 million, Components Sector production approximately $140,000 million
23. a. 0.006 **b.** textiles; clothing and footwear

25.

		To		
		Primary	Secondary	Tertiary
	Primary	53.1	330	0
From	Secondary	82.6	2,530	768
	Tertiary	41.3	1,320	1,440
	Total Output	590	11,000	9,600

(Entries are in billions of pesos.)
27. 210 billion pesos of raw materials, 7,600 billion pesos of manufactured goods, 6,800 billion pesos of services.
29. Production in the primary sector would rise by around 2,208 billion pesos, production in the secondary sector would rise by around 303 billion pesos, and production in the tertiary sector would drop by 952 billion pesos.

31. Entries of $\left[\begin{array}{c} 1,177 \\ 1,517 \\ 1,033 \\ 1,421 \end{array}\right]$ (in millions of dollars)

33. a. $0.78 **b.** Other food products **35.** It would mean that all of the sectors require neither their own product nor the product of any other sector. **37.** It would mean that all of the output of that sector was used internally in the economy; none of the output was available for export, and no importing was necessary. **39.** If an entry in the matrix $(I - A)^{-1}$ is zero, then an increase in demand for one sector (the column sector) has no effect on the production of another sector (the row sector). **41.** Usually, to produce one unit of one sector requires less than one unit of input from another. We would expect then that an increase in demand of one unit for one sector would require a smaller increase in production in another sector.

Chapter 5 Review

1. Undefined **3.** $\begin{bmatrix} 1 & 8 \\ 5 & 11 \\ 6 & 13 \end{bmatrix}$ **5.** $\begin{bmatrix} 1 & 3 \\ 2 & 3 \\ 3 & 3 \end{bmatrix}$ **7.** $\begin{bmatrix} 1 & -2 \\ 0 & 1 \end{bmatrix}$

9. $\begin{bmatrix} 2 & 4 \\ 1 & 12 \end{bmatrix}$ **11.** $\begin{bmatrix} 1 & 1 \\ 0 & 1 \end{bmatrix}$ **13.** $\begin{bmatrix} 1 & -\frac{1}{2} & -\frac{5}{2} \\ 0 & \frac{1}{4} & -\frac{1}{4} \\ 0 & 0 & 1 \end{bmatrix}$

15. Singular

17. $\begin{bmatrix} 1 & 2 \\ 3 & 4 \end{bmatrix}\begin{bmatrix} x \\ y \end{bmatrix} = \begin{bmatrix} 0 \\ 2 \end{bmatrix}; \begin{bmatrix} x \\ y \end{bmatrix} = \begin{bmatrix} 2 \\ -1 \end{bmatrix}$

19. $\begin{bmatrix} 1 & 1 & 1 \\ 1 & 2 & 1 \\ 1 & 1 & 2 \end{bmatrix}\begin{bmatrix} x \\ y \\ z \end{bmatrix} = \begin{bmatrix} 2 \\ 3 \\ 1 \end{bmatrix}; \begin{bmatrix} x \\ y \\ z \end{bmatrix} = \begin{bmatrix} 2 \\ 1 \\ -1 \end{bmatrix}$

21. $R = \begin{bmatrix} 1 & 0 & 0 \end{bmatrix}, C = \begin{bmatrix} 0 & 1 & 0 & 0 \end{bmatrix}^T, e = 1$

23. $R = \begin{bmatrix} 0 & 0.8 & 0.2 \end{bmatrix}, C = \begin{bmatrix} 0.2 & 0 & 0.8 \end{bmatrix}^T, e = -0.2$

25. $\begin{bmatrix} 1,100 \\ 700 \end{bmatrix}$ **27.** $\begin{bmatrix} 48,125 \\ 22,500 \\ 10,000 \end{bmatrix}$

29. Inventory − Sales + Purchases =

$\begin{bmatrix} 2,500 & 4,000 & 3,000 \\ 1,500 & 3,000 & 1,000 \end{bmatrix} - \begin{bmatrix} 300 & 500 & 100 \\ 100 & 600 & 200 \end{bmatrix} +$

$\begin{bmatrix} 400 & 400 & 300 \\ 200 & 400 & 300 \end{bmatrix} = \begin{bmatrix} 2,600 & 3,900 & 3,200 \\ 1,600 & 2,800 & 1,100 \end{bmatrix}$

31. $N =$

$\begin{bmatrix} 2,600 & 3,900 & 3,200 \\ 1,600 & 2,800 & 1,100 \end{bmatrix} - x\begin{bmatrix} 280 & 550 & 100 \\ 50 & 500 & 120 \end{bmatrix} +$

$x\begin{bmatrix} 400 & 400 & 300 \\ 200 & 400 & 300 \end{bmatrix} = \begin{bmatrix} 2,600 & 3,900 & 3,200 \\ 1,600 & 2,800 & 1,100 \end{bmatrix} +$

$x\begin{bmatrix} 120 & -150 & 200 \\ 150 & -100 & 180 \end{bmatrix};$ 28 months from now (July 1)

33. Revenue = Quantity × Price =

$\begin{bmatrix} 280 & 550 & 100 \\ 50 & 500 & 120 \end{bmatrix}\begin{bmatrix} 5 \\ 6 \\ 5.5 \end{bmatrix} = \begin{bmatrix} 5,250 \\ 3,910 \end{bmatrix} \begin{matrix} \text{Texas} \\ \text{Nevada} \end{matrix}$

35. July 1: 1,000 shares, August 1: 2,000 shares, September 1: 2,000 shares

37. Loss = Number of shares × (Purchase price − Dividends − Selling price) = $\begin{bmatrix} 1,000 & 2,000 & 2,000 \end{bmatrix}$

$\left(\begin{bmatrix} 20 \\ 10 \\ 5 \end{bmatrix} - \begin{bmatrix} 0.10 \\ 0.10 \\ 0 \end{bmatrix} - \begin{bmatrix} 3 \\ 1 \\ 1 \end{bmatrix} \right) = \begin{bmatrix} 42,700 \end{bmatrix}$

39. $\begin{bmatrix} 2,000 & 4,000 & 4,000 \end{bmatrix}\begin{bmatrix} 0.8 & 0.1 & 0.1 \\ 0.4 & 0.6 & 0 \\ 0.2 & 0 & 0.8 \end{bmatrix} =$

$\begin{bmatrix} 4,000 & 2,600 & 3,400 \end{bmatrix}$ **41.** The matrix shows that no JungleBooks.com customers switched directly to FarmerBooks.com, so the only way to get to FarmerBooks.com is via

OHaganBooks.com.   **43.** Go with the "3 for 1" promotion and gain 20,000 customers from JungleBooks.com.
45. JungleBooks.com will go with "3 for 2," and OHaganBooks.com will go with Finite Math, resulting in a gain of 15,000 customers to OHaganBooks.com.   **47.** Choose between the "3 for 1" and Finite Math promotions with probabilities 60% and 40%, respectively. You would expect to gain 12,000 customers from JungleBooks.com (if you played this game many times).

49. $A = \begin{bmatrix} 0.1 & 0.5 \\ 0.01 & 0.05 \end{bmatrix}$

51. $1,190 worth of paper, $1,802 worth of books

Chapter 6

Section 6.1

1.
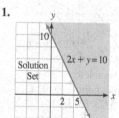
Unbounded

3.
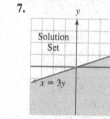
Unbounded

5.
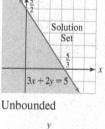
Unbounded

7.

Unbounded

9.
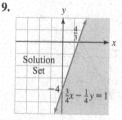
Unbounded

11.
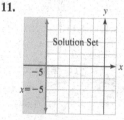
Unbounded

13.
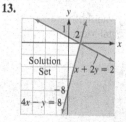
Unbounded;
corner point: (2, 0)

15.
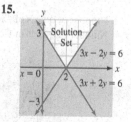
Unbounded;
corner points:
(2, 0), (0, 3)

17.

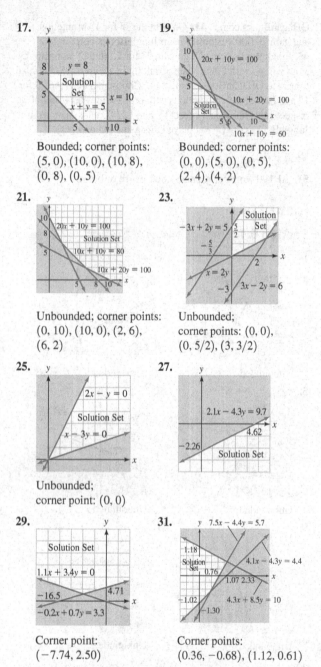

Bounded; corner points:
(5, 0), (10, 0), (10, 8), (0, 8), (0, 5)

19.

Bounded; corner points:
(0, 0), (5, 0), (0, 5), (2, 4), (4, 2)

21.

Unbounded; corner points:
(0, 10), (10, 0), (2, 6), (6, 2)

23.

Unbounded;
corner points: (0, 0), (0, 5/2), (3, 3/2)

25.

Unbounded;
corner point: (0, 0)

27.

29.

Corner point:
$(-7.74, 2.50)$

31.

Corner points:
$(0.36, -0.68), (1.12, 0.61)$

33. x = Number of quarts of Creamy Vanilla,
y = Number of quarts of Continental Mocha

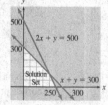

Corner points: (0, 0), (250, 0), (0, 300), (200, 100)

35. x = Number of ounces of chicken,
y = Number of ounces of grain

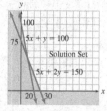

Corner points: (30, 0), (10, 50), (0, 100)

37. x = Number of servings of Mixed Cereal for Baby,
y = Number of servings of Mango Tropical Fruit Dessert

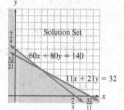

Corner points: (0, 7/4), (1, 1), (32/11, 0)

39. x = Number of dollars in MHI,
y = Number of dollars in BKK

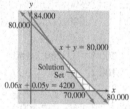

Corner points: (70,000, 0), (80,000, 0), (20,000, 60,000)

41. x = Number of shares of TD,
y = Number of shares of CNA

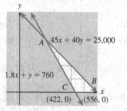

Corner points: (200, 400), (556, 0), (422, 0)

43. x = Number of full-page ads in *Sports Illustrated*,
y = Number of full-page ads in *GQ*

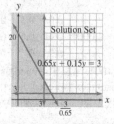

Corner points (rounded): (3, 7), (4, 3)

45. An example is $x \geq 0$, $y \geq 0$, $x + y \geq 1$.   **47.** The given triangle can be described as the solution set of the system $x \geq 0$, $y \geq 0$, $x + 2y \leq 2$.   **49.** Answers may vary. One limitation is that the method is suitable only for situations with two unknown quantities. Accuracy is also limited when graphing. **51.** (C)   **53.** (B)   **55.** There are no feasible solutions; that is, it is impossible to satisfy all the constraints.   **57.** Answers will vary.

Section 6.2

1. $p = 6$, $x = 3$, $y = 3$ **3.** $c = 4$, $x = 2$, $y = 2$
5. $p = 24$, $x = 7$, $y = 3$ **7.** $p = 16$, $x = 4$, $y = 2$
9. $c = 1.8$, $x = 6$, $y = 2$ **11.** Max: $p = 16$, $x = 4$, $y = 6$.
Min: $p = 2$, $x = 2$, $y = 0$ **13.** $p = 16$, $x = 8$, $y = 0$
15. No optimal solution; objective function unbounded
17. No optimal solution; objective function unbounded
19. $c = 28$; $(x, y) = (14, 0)$ and $(6, 4)$ and the line connecting them   **21.** $c = 3$, $x = 3$, $y = 2$ **23.** No solution; feasible region empty   **25.** 200 quarts of Creamy Vanilla and 100 quarts of Continental Mocha   **27.** 100 ounces of grain and no chicken   **29.** 1 serving of cereal and 1 serving of dessert   **31.** Purchase 60 compact fluorescent light bulbs and 960 square feet of insulation for a saving of $312 per year in energy costs.   **33.** Mix 6 servings of Xtend and 7 servings of Gainz for a cost of $13.70.   **35. a.** Yes; use 15 servings of Gainz and 4 servings of Strongevity. **b.** No; the value of the objective function can be made arbitrarily large. (You can use as much Strongevity as you like without violating your trainer's specifications.)   **37.** Make 200 Dracula Salamis and 400 Frankenstein Sausages for a profit of $1,400.
39. 30 spots on *Big Bang Theory* and 30 spots on *American Dad*   **41.** No shares of OCR and 300 shares of RCKY.
43. 422.2 shares of TD and no shares of CNA; minimum risk index $\approx 1,267$ **45.** 10 hours in diplomacy and 40 hours in battle   **47. a.** Use 7 sleep spells and 3 shock spells. **b.** Use 6 sleep spells and 6 shock spells. **c.** No optimal solution; net expenditure of aural energy can be an arbitrarily large negative number.   **49.** 100 hours per week for new customers and 60 hours per week for old customers.   **51.** (A)
53. Every point along the line connecting them is also an optimal solution.   **55. a.** Not necessary; optimal solutions exist. **b.** Necessary **c.** Necessary **d.** Not necessary; no optimal solution exists.   **57.** Answers may vary. Maximize $p = x + y$ subject to $x + y \leq 10$; $x + y \geq 11$, $x \geq 0$, $y \geq 0$.
59. Answers may vary.   **61.** A simple example is the following: Maximize profit $p = 2x + y$ subject to $x \geq 0$, $y \geq 0$. Then p can be made as large as we like by choosing large values of x and/or y. Thus, there is no optimal solution to the problem.   **63.** Mathematically, this means that there are infinitely many possible solutions: one for each point along the line joining the two corner points in question. In practice, select those points with integer solutions (since x and y must be whole numbers in this problem) that are in the feasible region and close to this line, and choose the one that gives the largest profit.   **65.** Proof

Section 6.3

1. $p = 8$; $x = 4$, $y = 0$ **3.** $p = 4$; $x = 4$, $y = 0$ **5.** $p = 80$; $x = 10$, $y = 0$, $z = 10$ **7.** $p = 53$; $x = 5$, $y = 0$, $z = 3$
9. $z = 14{,}500$; $x_1 = 0$, $x_2 = 500/3$, $x_3 = 5{,}000/3$
11. $p = 6$; $x = 2$, $y = 1$, $z = 0$, $w = 3$ **13.** $p = 7$; $x = 1$, $y = 0$, $z = 2$, $w = 0$, $v = 4$ (or: $x = 1$, $y = 0$, $z = 2$, $w = 1$, $v = 3$)   **15.** $p = 21$; $x = 0$, $y = 2.27$, $z = 5.73$
17. $p = 4.52$; $x = 1$, $y = 0$, $z = 0.67$, $w = 1.52$ (or: $x = 1.67$, $y = 0.67$, $z = 0$, $w = 1.52$)   **19.** $p = 7.7$; $x = 1.1$, $y = 0$, $z = 2.2$, $w = 0$, $v = 4.4$ **21.** You should purchase 500 calculus texts, no history texts, and no marketing texts. The maximum profit is $5,000 per semester.   **23.** The company can make a maximum profit of $650 by making 100 gallons of PineOrange, 200 gallons of PineKiwi, and 150 gallons of OrangeKiwi.   **25.** The department should offer no Ancient History, 30 sections of Medieval History, and 15 sections of Modern History, for a profit of $1,050,000. There will be 500 students without classes, but all time slots and professors are used.   **27.** Plant 80 acres of tomatoes, and leave the other 20 acres unplanted. This will give you a profit of $160,000.
29. It can make a profit of $10,000 by selling 1,000 servings of granola, 500 servings of nutty granola, and no nuttiest granola. It is left with 2,000 ounces of almonds.   **31.** Achlúk can inflict a maximum of 70,000 units of damage using an arsenal of 5,000 axes, no maces, and 5,000 spears.   **33.** Allocate 5 million gallons to process A and 45 million gallons to process C. Another solution: Allocate 10 million gallons to process B and 40 million gallons to process C.   **35.** Use 20 servings of Gainz and none of the others for 120 grams of BCAAs.   **37.** She is wrong; you should buy 1,000 shares of OCR and no others.
39. Allocate $2,250,000 to automobile loans, $500,000 to signature loans, and $2,250,000 to any combination of furniture loans and other secured loans.   **41.** Invest $75,000 in Universal, none in the rest. Another optimal solution is: Invest $18,750 in Universal, and $75,000 in EMI.   **43.** Tucson to Honolulu: 290 boards; Tucson to Venice Beach: 330 boards; Toronto to Honolulu: 0 boards; Toronto to Venice Beach: 200 boards, giving 820 boards shipped.   **45.** Fly 10 people from Chicago to Los Angeles, 5 people from Chicago to New York, and 10 people from Denver to New York.   **47.** Yes; the given problem can be stated as: Maximize $p = 3x - 2y$ subject to $-x + y - z \leq 0$, $x - y - z \leq 6$, $x \geq 0$, $y \geq 0$, $z \geq 0$ **49.** The graphical method applies only to LP problems in two unknowns, whereas the simplex method can be used to solve LP problems with any number of unknowns.   **51.** She is correct. There are only two constraints, so there can be only two active variables, giving two or fewer nonzero values for the unknowns at each stage.   **53.** A basic solution to a system of linear equations is a solution in which all the nonpivotal variables are taken to be zero; that is, all variables whose values are arbitrary are assigned the value zero. To obtain a basic solution for a given system of linear equations, one can row-reduce the associated augmented matrix, write down the general solution, and then set all the parameters (variables with "arbitrary" values) equal to zero.   **55.** No. Let us assume for

the sake of simplicity that all the pivots are 1s. (They may certainly be changed to 1s without affecting the value of any of the variables.) Because the entry at the bottom of the pivot column is negative, the bottom row gets replaced by itself plus a positive multiple of the pivot row. The value of the objective function (bottom right entry) is thus replaced by itself plus a positive multiple of the nonnegative rightmost entry of the pivot row. Therefore, it cannot decrease.

Section 6.4

1. $p = 20/3$; $x = 4/3$, $y = 16/3$ **3.** $p = 850/3$; $x = 50/3$, $y = 25/3$ **5.** $p = 750$; $x = 0$, $y = 150$, $z = 0$ **7.** $p = 450$; $x = 10$, $y = 10$, $z = 10$ **9.** $p = 260/3$; $x = 50/3$, $y = 0$, $z = 70/3$, $w = 0$ **11.** $c = 80$; $x = 20/3$, $y = 20/3$ **13.** $c = 100$; $x = 0$, $y = 100$, $z = 0$ **15.** $c = 111$; $x = 1$, $y = 1$, $z = 1$ **17.** $c = 200$; $x = 200$, $y = 0$, $z = 0$, $w = 0$ **19.** $p = 136.75$; $x = 0$, $y = 25.25$, $z = 0$, $w = 15.25$ **21.** $c = 66.67$; $x = 0$, $y = 66.67$, $z = 0$ **23.** $c = -250$; $x = 0$, $y = 500$, $z = 500$, $w = 1,500$ **25.** Plant 100 acres of tomatoes and no other crops. This will give you a profit of $200,000. (You will be using all 100 acres of your farm.) **27.** 10 mailings to the East Coast, none to the Midwest, and 10 to the West Coast. Cost: $900. Another solution resulting in the same cost is no mailings to the East Coast, 15 to the Midwest, and none to the West Coast. **29.** 10,000 quarts of orange juice and 2,000 quarts of orange concentrate **31.** Sell 24,000 regional music albums, 10,000 pop/rock music albums, and 6,000 tropical music albums per day for a maximum revenue of $196,000. **33.** Achlúk can inflict a maximum of 1,000 units of damage using an arsenal of no axes, 100 maces, and 50 spears. **35.** Use 200 axes, no maces, and 100 spears for a minimum cost of 1,800 gold pieces. **37.** One serving of cereal, one serving of juice, and no dessert! **39.** 15 bundles from Nadir, 5 from Sonny, and none from Blunt. Cost: $70,000. Another solution resulting in the same cost is 10 bundles from Nadir, none from Sonny, and 10 from Blunt. **41.** Use no Xtend, 10 servings of Gainz, and 20 servings of Strongevity for a total cost of $37. **43. a.** Build 1 convention-style hotel, 4 vacation-style hotels, and 2 small motels. The total cost will amount to $188 million. **b.** Because 20% of this is $37.6 million, you will still be covered by the subsidy. **45.** Tucson to Honolulu: 500 boards per week; Tucson to Venice Beach: 120 boards per week; Toronto to Honolulu: 0 boards per week; Toronto to Venice Beach: 410 boards per week. Minimum weekly cost is $9,700. **47.** $2,500 from Congressional Integrity Bank, $0 from Citizens' Trust, $7,500 from Checks R Us. **49.** Fly 5 people from Chicago to Los Angeles, 15 from Chicago to New York, 5 from Denver to Los Angeles, and none from Denver to New York at a total cost of $4,000. **51.** Hire no more cardiologists, 12 rehabilitation specialists, and 5 infectious disease specialists. **53.** The solution $x = 0$, $y = 0, \ldots$, represented by the initial tableau may not be feasible. In Phase I we use pivoting to arrive at a basic solution that is feasible. **55.** The basic solution corresponding to the initial tableau has all the unknowns equal to zero, and this is not a fea-

sible solution because it does not satisfy the given inequality. **57.** (C) **59.** Answers may vary. Examples are Exercises 1 and 2. **61.** Answers may vary. A simple example is: Maximize $p = x + y$ subject to $x + y \le 10$, $x + y \ge 20$, $x \ge 0$, $y \ge 0$.

Section 6.5

1. Minimize $c = 6s + 2t$ subject to $s - t \ge 2$, $2s + t \ge 1$, $s \ge 0$, $t \ge 0$. **3.** Maximize $p = 100x + 50y$ subject to $x + 2y \le 2$, $x + y \le 1$, $x \le 3$, $x \ge 0$, $y \ge 0$. **5.** Minimize $c = 3s + 4t + 5u + 6v$ subject to $s + u + v \ge 1$, $s + t + v \ge 1$, $s + t + u \ge 1$, $t + u + v \ge 1$, $s \ge 0$, $t \ge 0$, $u \ge 0$, $v \ge 0$. **7.** Maximize $p = 1,000x + 2,000y + 500z$ subject to $5x + z \le 1$, $-x + z \le 3$, $y \le 1$, $x - y \le 0$, $x \ge 0$, $y \ge 0$, $z \ge 0$. **9.** $c = 4$; $s = 2$, $t = 2$ **11.** $c = 80$; $s = 20/3$, $t = 20/3$ **13.** $c = 1.8$; $s = 6$, $t = 2$ **15.** $c = 25$; $s = 5$, $t = 15$ **17.** $c = 30$; $s = 30$, $t = 0$, $u = 0$ **19.** $c = 100$; $s = 0$, $t = 100$, $u = 0$ **21.** $c = 30$; $s = 10$, $t = 10$, $u = 10$ **23.** $R = [3/5 \quad 2/5]$, $C = [2/5 \quad 3/5 \quad 0]^T$, $e = 1/5$ **25.** $R = [1/4 \quad 0 \quad 3/4]$, $C = [1/2 \quad 0 \quad 1/2]^T$, $e = 1/2$ **27.** $R = [0 \quad 3/11 \quad 3/11 \quad 5/11]$, $C = [8/11 \quad 0 \quad 2/11 \quad 1/11]^T$, $e = 9/11$ **29.** 4 ounces each of fish and cornmeal for a total cost of 40¢ per can; 5/12¢ per gram of protein, 5/12¢ per gram of fat. **31.** 100 ounces of grain and no chicken for a total cost of $1; 1/2¢ per gram of protein, 0¢ per gram of fat. **33.** One serving of cereal, one serving of juice, and no dessert! for a total cost of 37¢; 1/6¢ per calorie and 17/120¢ per % U.S. RDA of vitamin C. **35.** 10 mailings to the East Coast, none to the Midwest, and 10 to the West Coast. Cost: $900; 20¢ per Democrat and 40¢ per Republican. OR 15 mailings to the Midwest and no mailing to the coasts. Cost: $900; 20¢ per Democrat and 40¢ per Republican. **37.** Place 13 ads in *Sports Illustrated* and 8 in *GQ*. Cost: $34,000. **39.** Gillian should use use 12 sleep spells and 12 shock spells, costing 840 therms of energy. **41.** T. N. Spend should spend about 73% of the days in Littleville, 27% in Metropolis, and skip Urbantown. T. L. Down should spend about 91% of the days in Littleville, 9% in Metropolis, and skip Urbantown. The expected outcome is that T. L. Down will lose about 227 votes per day of campaigning. **43.** Each player should show one finger with probability 1/2, two fingers with probability 1/3, and three fingers with probability 1/6. The expected outcome is that player A will win 2/3 point per round, on average. **45.** Write moves as (x, y), where x represents the number of regiments sent to the first location and y represents the number sent to the second location. Colonel Blotto should play $(0, 4)$ with probability 4/9, $(2, 2)$ with probability 1/9, and $(4, 0)$ with probability 4/9. Captain Kije has several optimal strategies, one of which is to play $(0, 3)$ with probability 1/30, $(1, 2)$ with probability 8/15, $(2, 1)$ with probability 16/45, and $(3, 0)$ with probability 7/90. The expected outcome is that Colonel Blotto will win 14/9 points on average. **47.** Two variables and three constraints: In the matrix formulation of an LP problem, the number of rows is one more than the number of constraints, and the number of columns is one more than the number of variables. Thus, the matrix form of the primal problem has three rows and four columns, so its transpose has four rows and three columns, translating to three constraints and two variables. **49.** The dual of a standard minimization problem satisfying the nonnegative objective condition is a standard maximization problem, which can be solved by using the standard simplex algorithm, thus avoiding the need to do Phase I. **51.** Answers will vary. An example is: Minimize $c = x - y$ subject to $x - y \geq 100$, $x + y \geq 200$, $x \geq 0$, $y \geq 0$. This problem can be solved by using the techniques in Section 6.4. **53.** The dual problem is a nonstandard maximization problem, because the right-hand sides of its constraints are the entries in the bottom row of the matrix representation of the primal problem, and at least one of those entries is negative **55.** If the given problem is a standard minimization problem satisfying the nonnegative objective condition, its dual is a standard maximization problem and so can be solved by using a single-phase simplex method. Otherwise, dualizing may not save any labor, since the dual will not be a standard maximization problem.

Chapter 6 Review

1.
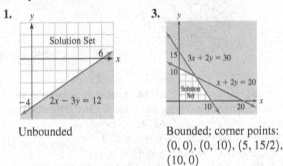
Unbounded

3.
Bounded; corner points:
$(0, 0)$, $(0, 10)$, $(5, 15/2)$, $(10, 0)$

5. $p = 21$; $x = 9$, $y = 3$ **7.** $c = 22$; $x = 8$, $y = 6$
9. $p = 45$; $x = 0$, $y = 15$, $z = 15$ **11.** $p = 220$; $x = 20$, $y = 20$, $z = 60$ **13.** $c = 30$; $x = 30$, $y = 0$, $z = 0$
15. No solution; feasible region unbounded
17. $c = 50$; $x = 20$, $y = 10$, $z = 0$, $w = 20$, OR $x = 30$, $y = 0$, $z = 0$, $w = 20$ **19.** $c = 60$; $x = 24$, $y = 12$ OR $x = 0$, $y = 60$ **21.** $c = 20$; $x = 0$, $y = 20$
23. $R = [1/2 \quad 1/2 \quad 0]$, $C = [0 \quad 1/3 \quad 2/3]^T$, $e = 0$
25. $R = [1/27 \quad 7/9 \quad 5/27]$, $C = [8/27 \quad 5/27 \quad 14/27]^T$, $e = 8/27$ **27.** (A) **29.** 35 **31.** 400 packages from each for a minimum cost of $52,000 **33. a.** (B), (D) **b.** 450 packages from Duffin House and 375 from Higgins Press for a minimum cost of $52,500 **35.** 220 shares of EEE and 20 shares of RRR. The minimum total risk index is 500. **37.** 240 Sprinkles, 120 Storms, and no Hurricanes **39.** Order 600 packages from Higgins and none from the others for a total cost of $90,000. **41. a.** Let x = Number of science credits, y = Number of fine arts credits, z = Number of liberal arts credits, and w = Number of math credits. Minimize $C = 300x + 300y + 200z + 200w$ subject to:
$x + y + z + w \geq 120$; $x - y \geq 0$; $-2x + w \leq 0$;
$-y + 3z - 3w \leq 0$; $x \geq 0$, $y \geq 0$, $z \geq 0$, $w \geq 0$
b. Billy-Sean should take the following combination:

Sciences—24 credits, Fine Arts—no credits, Liberal Arts—48 credits, Mathematics—48 credits for a total cost of $26,400. **43.** Smallest cost is $20,000; New York to OHaganBooks.com: 600 packages, New York to FantasyBooks.com: 0 packages, Illinois to OHaganbooks.com: 0 packages, Illinois to FantasyBooks.com: 200 packages.
45. FantasyBooks.com should choose between "2 for 1" and "3 for 2" with probabilities 20% and 80%, respectively. OHaganBooks.com should choose between "3 for 1" and "Finite Math" with probabilities 60% and 40%, respectively. OHaganBooks.com expects to gain 12,000 customers from FantasyBooks.com.

Chapter 7

Section 7.1

1. $F = \{$spring, summer, fall, winter$\}$
3. $I = \{1, 2, 3, 4, 5, 6\}$ **5.** $A = \{1, 2, 3\}$
7. $B = \{2, 4, 6, 8\}$ **9. a.** $S = \{(H, H), (H, T), (T, H), (T, T)\}$ **b.** $S = \{(H, H), (H, T), (T, T)\}$
11. $S = \{(1, 5), (2, 4), (3, 3), (4, 2), (5, 1)\}$
13. $S = \{(1, 5), (2, 4), (3, 3)\}$ **15.** $S = \varnothing$

17.
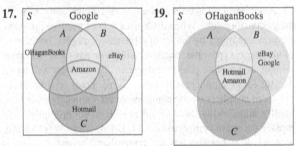
19.

21. A **23.** A **25.** $\{$June, Janet, Jill, Justin, Jeffrey, Jello, Sally, Solly, Molly, Jolly$\}$ **27.** $\{$Jello$\}$ **29.** $\varnothing$
31. $\{$Jello$\}$ **33.** $\{$Janet, Justin, Jello, Sally, Solly, Molly, Jolly$\}$ **35.** $\{$(small, triangle), (small, square), (medium, triangle), (medium, square), (large, triangle), (large, square)$\}$ **37.** $\{$(small, blue), (small, green), (medium, blue), (medium, green), (large, blue), (large, green)$\}$

39.

	A	B	C
1		Triangle	Square
2	Blue	Blue Triangle	Blue Square
3	Green	Green Triangle	Green Square

41.

	A	B	C
1		Blue	Green
2	Small	Small Blue	Small Green
3	Medium	Medium Blue	Medium Green
4	Large	Large Blue	Large Green

43. $B \times A = \{$1H, 1T, 2H, 2T, 3H, 3T, 4H, 4T, 5H, 5T, 6H, 6T$\}$

45. $A \times A \times A = \{$HHH, HHT, HTH, HTT, THH, THT, TTH, TTT$\}$
47. $\{(1, 1), (1, 3), (1, 5), (3, 1), (3, 3), (3, 5), (5, 1), (5, 3), (5, 5)\}$ **49.** $\varnothing$ **51.** $\{(1, 1), (1, 3), (1, 5), (3, 1), (3, 3), (3, 5), (5, 1), (5, 3), (5, 5), (2, 2), (2, 4), (2, 6), (4, 2), (4, 4), (4, 6), (6, 2), (6, 4), (6, 6)\}$ **53–59.** Answers will vary.
61. $A \cap B = \{$Acme, Crafts$\}$ **63.** $B \cup C = \{$Acme, Brothers, Crafts, Dion, Effigy, Global, Hilbert$\}$
65. $A' \cap C = \{$Dion, Hilbert$\}$ **67.** $A \cap B' \cap C' = \varnothing$
69. $\{2003, 2004, 2005, 2006\} \times \{$Sailboats, Motor Boats, Yachts$\}$

	A	B	C	D
1		**Sailboats**	**Motor Boats**	**Yachts**
2	**2003**	(2003 Sailboats)	(2003 Motor Boats)	(2003 Yachts)
3	**2004**	(2004 Sailboats)	(2004 Motor Boats)	(2004 Yachts)
4	**2005**	(2005 Sailboats)	(2005 Motor Boats)	(2005 Yachts)
5	**2006**	(2006 Sailboats)	(2006 Motor Boats)	(2006 Yachts)

71. $I \cup J$ **73.** (B)   **75.** Answers may vary. Let $A = \{1\}$, $B = \{2\}$, and $C = \{1, 2\}$. Then $(A \cap B) \cup C = \{1, 2\}$, but $A \cap (B \cup C) = \{1\}$. In general, $A \cap (B \cup C)$ must be a subset of A, but $(A \cap B) \cup C$ need not be; also, $(A \cap B) \cup C$ must contain C as a subset, but $A \cap (B \cup C)$ need not.
77. A universal set is a set containing all "things" currently under consideration. When discussing sets of positive integers, the universe might be the set of all positive integers, or the set of all integers (positive, negative, and 0), or any other set containing the set of all positive integers.   **79.** Answers will vary. A is the set of suppliers who deliver components on time, B is the set of suppliers whose components are known to be of high quality, and C is the set of suppliers who do not promptly replace defective components.   **81.** Let $A = \{$movies that are violent$\}$, $B = \{$movies that are shorter than 2 hours$\}$, $C = \{$movies that have a tragic ending$\}$, and $D = \{$movies that have an unexpected ending$\}$. The given sentence can be rewritten as "She prefers movies in $A' \cap B \cap (C \cup D)'$." It can also be rewritten as "She prefers movies in $A' \cap B \cap C' \cap D'$."
83. Removing the comma would cause the statement to be ambiguous, as it could then correspond to either WWII $\cup$ (Comix $\cap$ Aliens$'$) or to (WWII $\cup$ Comix) $\cap$ Aliens$'$. (See Exercise 76.)

Section 7.2

1. 9   **3.** 7   **5.** 4   **7.** $n(A \cup B) = 7$,
$n(A) + n(B) - n(A \cap B) = 4 + 5 - 2 = 7$
9. 4   **11.** 18   **13.** 72   **15.** 60   **17.** 20   **19.** 6   **21.** 9
23. 4   **25.** $n((A \cap B)') = 9$
$n(A') + n(B') - n((A \cup B)') = 6 + 7 - 4 = 9$

27.
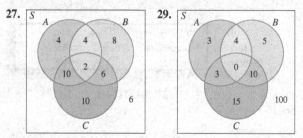
29.

31. 115.4 million   **33.** 2   **35.** 9 million   **37.** $C \cap N$ is the set of authors who are both successful and new. $C \cup N$ is the set of authors who are either successful or new (or both). $n(C) = 30$; $n(N) = 20$; $n(C \cap N) = 5$; $n(C \cup N) = 45$; $45 = 30 + 20 - 5$ **39.** $C \cap N'$ is the set of authors who are successful but not new. $n(C \cap N') = 25$ **41.** 31.25%; 83.33%
43. $M \cap C$; $n(M \cap C) = 110$ thousand units
45. $B \cap T'$; $n(B \cap T') = 290$ thousand units
47. $B \cap (W \cup M)$; $n(B \cap (W \cup M)) = 230$ thousand units
49. $X \cap M'$; $n(X \cap M') = 16$ **51.** 35; the number of industries that either were not in the health-care sector or were unchanged in value (or both)   **53.** 1/10; the fraction of industries that decreased that were from the information technology sector   **55. a.** 931 **b.** 382
57. a.
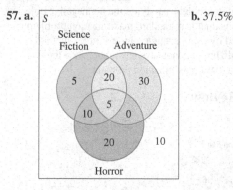
b. 37.5%
59. 17   **61.** $n(A) < n(B)$ **63.** The number of elements in the Cartesian product of two finite sets is the product of the number of elements in the two sets.   **65.** Answers will vary.
67. When $A \cap B \neq \varnothing$ **69.** When $B \subseteq A$
71. $n(A \cup B \cup C) = n(A) + n(B) + n(C) - n(A \cap B) - n(B \cap C) - n(A \cap C) + n(A \cap B \cap C)$

Section 7.3

1. 10   **3.** 30   **5.** 6 outcomes   **7.** 15 outcomes
9. 13 outcomes   **11.** 25 outcomes   **13.** 4   **15.** 93
17. 16   **19.** 30   **21.** 13   **23.** 18   **25.** 25,600   **27.** 3,381
29. a. 288 **b.** 288   **31.** 256   **33.** 10   **35.** 32,760
37. 4   **39. a.** 8,000,000 **b.** 30,000 **c.** 4,251,528
41. a. $2 \times 10^9 = 2$ billion possible card numbers
b. $10^9 \times 9 = 9$ billion possible card numbers
43. a. $4^3 = 64$ **b.** 4^n **c.** $4^{2.1 \times 10^{10}}$
45. a. $16^6 = 16,777,216$ **b.** $16^3 = 4,096$ **c.** $16^2 = 256$ **d.** 766
47. $(10 \times 9 \times 8 \times 7 \times 6 \times 5 \times 4) \times (8 \times 7 \times 6 \times 5) = 1,016,064,000$ possible casts   **49. a.** $26^3 \times 10^3 = 17,576,000$ **b.** $26^2 \times 23 \times 10^3 = 15,548,000$
c. $15,548,000 - 3 \times 10^3 = 15,545,000$ **51. a.** 4   **b.** 4
c. There would be an infinite number of routes.   **53. a.** 72
b. 36   **55.** 96   **57. a.** 36 **b.** 37   **59.** Step 1: Choose a day of the week on which Jan. 1 will fall: seven choices. Step 2: Decide whether or not it is a leap year; two choices. Total: $7 \times 2 = 14$ possible calendars.   **61.** 1,900   **63.** Step 1: Choose a position in the left-right direction; m choices. Step 2: Choose a position in the front-back direction; n choices. Step 3: Choose a position in the up-down direction; r choices. Hence, there are

$m \cdot n \cdot r$ possible outcomes.   **65.** 4   **67.** Cartesian product
69. The decision algorithm produces every pair of shirts twice, first in one order and then in the other.   **71.** Think of placing the five squares in a row of five empty slots. Step 1: Choose a slot for the blue square; five choices. Step 2: Choose a slot for the green square; four choices. Step 3: Choose the remaining three slots for the yellow squares; one choice. Hence, there are 20 possible five-square sequences.

Section 7.4

1. 720   **3.** 56   **5.** 360   **7.** 15   **9.** 3   **11.** 45   **13.** 20
15. 4,950   **17.** 360   **19.** 35   **21.** 120   **23.** 120   **25.** 20
27. 60   **29.** 210   **31.** 7   **33.** 35   **35.** 24   **37.** 126
39. 196   **41.** 105   **43.** $\dfrac{C(30, 5) \times 5^{25}}{6^{30}} \approx 0.192$

45. $\dfrac{C(30, 15) \times 3^{15} \times 3^{15}}{6^{30}} \approx 0.144$

47. $C(11, 1)C(10, 4)C(6, 4)C(2, 2)$
49. $C(11, 2)C(9, 1)C(8, 1)C(7, 3)C(4, 1) \times$
$C(3, 1)C(2, 1)C(1, 1)$
51. $C(10, 2)C(8, 4)C(4, 1)C(3, 1)C(2, 1)C(1, 1)$
53. 24   **55.** $C(13, 2)C(4, 2)C(4, 2) \times 44 = 123{,}552$
57. $13 \times C(4, 2)C(12, 3) \times 4 \times 4 \times 4 = 1{,}098{,}240$
59. $10 \times 4^5 - 10 \times 4 = 10{,}200$ **61. a.** 252   **b.** 20   **c.** 26
63. a. 300   **b.** 3   **c.** 1 in 100 or .01   **65. a.** 16!   **b.** $8! \times 2^8$
67. $C(60, 15) \times 8$ **69. a.** 210   **b.** 91   **c.** No   **71. a.** 23!
b. 18!   **c.** $19 \times 18!$ **73.** (A)   **75.** (D)   **77. a.** 9,880
b. 1,560   **c.** 11,480   **79. a.** $C(20, 2) = 190$ **b.** $C(n, 2)$
81. The multiplication principle; it can be used to solve all problems that use the formulas for permutations.   **83.** (A), (D)
85. A permutation. Changing the order in a list of driving instructions can result in a different outcome; for instance, "1. Turn left. 2. Drive one mile." and "1. Drive one mile. 2. Turn left." will take you to different locations.   **87.** Urge your friend not to focus on formulas but instead to learn to formulate decision algorithms and use the principles of counting.   **89.** It is ambiguous on the following point: Are the three students to play different characters, or are they to play a group of three, such as "three guards"? This should be made clear in the exercise.

Chapter 7 Review

1. $N = \{-3, -2, -1\}$ **3.** $S = \{(1, 2), (1, 3), (1, 4),$
$(1, 5), (1, 6), (2, 1), (2, 3), (2, 4), (2, 5), (2, 6), (3, 1),$
$(3, 2), (3, 4), (3, 5), (3, 6), (4, 1), (4, 2), (4, 3), (4, 5),$
$(4, 6), (5, 1), (5, 2), (5, 3), (5, 4), (5, 6), (6, 1), (6, 2),$
$(6, 3), (6, 4), (6, 5)\}$ **5.** $A \cup B' = \{a, b, d\}$,
$A \times B' = \{(a, a), (a, d), (b, a), (b, d)\}$ **7.** $A \times B$
9. $(E' \cap Q)'$ or $E \cup Q'$ **11.** $n(A \cup B) =$
$n(A) + n(B) - n(A \cap B), n(C') = n(S) - n(C); 100$
13. $n(A \times B) = n(A)n(B), n(A \cup B) = n(A) +$
$n(B) - n(A \cap B), n(A') = n(S) - n(A); 21$
15. $C(12, 1)C(4, 2)C(11, 3)C(4, 1)C(4, 1)C(4, 1)$
17. $C(4, 1)C(10, 1)$ **19.** 6   **21.** $C(4, 4)C(8, 1) = 8$
23. $C(3, 2)C(9, 3) + C(3, 3)C(9, 2) = 288$

25. The set of books that are either sci fi or stored in Texas (or both); $n(S \cup T) = 112{,}000$ **27.** The set of books that are either stored in California or not sci fi; $n(C \cup S') = 175{,}000$
29. The romance books that are also horror books or stored in Texas; $n(R \cap (T \cup H)) = 20{,}000$ **31.** 1,000
33. FarmerBooks.com; 1,800   **35.** FarmerBooks.com;
5,400   **37.** $26 \times 26 \times 26 = 17{,}576$
39. $26 \times 25 \times 9 \times 10 = 58{,}500$ **41.** 60,000   **43.** 19,600

Chapter 8

Section 8.1

1. $S = \{HH, HT, TH, TT\}; E = \{HH, HT, TH\}$
3. $S = \{HHH, HHT, HTH, HTT, THH, THT, TTH, TTT\};$
$E = \{HTT, THT, TTH, TTT\}$

5. $S = \begin{cases} (1, 1), (1, 2), (1, 3), (1, 4), (1, 5), (1, 6), \\ (2, 1), (2, 2), (2, 3), (2, 4), (2, 5), (2, 6), \\ (3, 1), (3, 2), (3, 3), (3, 4), (3, 5), (3, 6), \\ (4, 1), (4, 2), (4, 3), (4, 4), (4, 5), (4, 6), \\ (5, 1), (5, 2), (5, 3), (5, 4), (5, 5), (5, 6), \\ (6, 1), (6, 2), (6, 3), (6, 4), (6, 5), (6, 6) \end{cases};$

$E = \{(1, 4), (2, 3), (3, 2), (4, 1)\}$

7. $S = \begin{cases} (1, 1), (1, 2), (1, 3), (1, 4), (1, 5), (1, 6), \\ (2, 2), (2, 3), (2, 4), (2, 5), (2, 6), \\ (3, 3), (3, 4), (3, 5), (3, 6), \\ (4, 4), (4, 5), (4, 6), \\ (5, 5), (5, 6), \\ (6, 6) \end{cases};$

$E = \{(1, 3), (2, 2)\}$
9. S as in Exercise 7; $E = \{(2, 2), (2, 3), (2, 5), (3, 3),$
$(3, 5), (5, 5)\}$ **11.** $S = \{m, o, z, a, r, t\}$: $E = \{o, a\}$
13. $S = \{(s, o), (s, r), (s, e), (o, s), (o, r), (o, e), (r, s),$
$(r, o), (r, e), (e, s), (e, o), (e, r)\}; E = \{(o, s), (o, r),$
$(o, e), (e, s), (e, o), (e, r)\}$ **15.** $S = \{01, 02, 03, 04, 10, 12,$
$13, 14, 20, 21, 23, 24, 30, 31, 32, 34, 40, 41, 42, 43\};$
$E = \{10, 20, 21, 30, 31, 32, 40, 41, 42, 43\}$
17. $S = \{$domestic car, imported car, van, antique car, antique truck$\}$; $E = \{$van, antique truck$\}$ **19. a.** all sets of four gummy candies chosen from the packet of 12.   **b.** all sets of four gummy candies in which two are strawberry and two are black currant.
21. a. all lists of 15 people chosen from 20.   **b.** all lists of 15 people chosen from 20, in which Hillary Clinton occupies the eleventh position.   **23.** $A \cap B; n(A \cap B) = 1$
25. $B'; n(B') = 33$ **27.** $B' \cap D'; n(B' \cap D') = 2$
29. $C \cup B; n(C \cup B) = 12$ **31.** $W \cap I$ **33.** $E \cup I'$
35. $I \cup (W \cap E')$ **37.** $(I \cup W) \cap E'$ **39.** 56; 4
41. $C(4, 1)C(2, 1)C(2, 1) = 16$
43. $E = \{$Pacific, Mountain, West South Central, South Atlantic$\}$ **45.** $E \cup F$ is the event that you choose a region that saw an increase in housing prices of 6% or more or is on the east coast. $E \cup F = \{$Pacific, Mountain, West South Central, New England, Middle Atlantic, South Atlantic$\}$. $E \cap F$ is the

event that you choose a region that saw an inecrease in housing prices of 6% or more and is on the east coast. $E \cap F =$ {South Atlantic}.   **47. a.** Not mutually exclusive **b.** Mutually exclusive   **49.** $S \cap N$ is the event that an author is successful and new. $S \cup N$ is the event that an author is either successful or new; $n(S \cap N) = 5$; $n(S \cup N) = 45$ **51.** N and E **53.** $S \cap N'$ is the event that an author is successful but not a new author. $n(S \cap N') = 25$ **55.** 31.25%; 83.33%   **57.** $X \cap M'$; $n(X \cap M') = 16$ **59.** The event that an industry either was not in the health care sector or was unchanged in value (or both); 35   **61.** F and M, F and T, M and T, X and Y, Y and Z, X and Z, T and Z **63. a.** $E' \cap H$ **b.** $E \cup H$ **c.** $(E \cup G)' = E' \cap G'$ **65. a.** {9} **b.** {6}   **67. a.** The dog's fight drive is weakest. **b.** The dog's fight and flight drives are either both strongest or both weakest. **c.** Either the dog's fight drive is strongest, or its flight drive is strongest.
69. $C(6, 4) = 15$; $C(1, 1)C(5, 3) = 10$ **71. a.** $n(S) = P(7, 3) = 210$ **b.** $E \cap F$ is the event that Celera wins and Electoral College is in second or third place. In other words, it is the set of all lists of three horses in which Celera is first and Electoral College is second or third. $n(E \cap F) = 10$ **73.** subset of the sample space   **75.** E and F do not both occur   **77.** (B)   **79.** True; consider the following experiment: Select an element of the set S at random.   **81.** Answers may vary. Cast a die, and record the remainder when the number facing up is divided by 2.   **83.** Yes. For instance, $E = \{(2, 5), (5, 1)\}$ and $F = \{(4, 3)\}$ are two such events.

Section 8.2

1. .4   **3.** .8   **5.** .6

7.

Outcome	HH	HT	TH	TT
Rel. Frequency	.275	.2375	.3	.1875

9. .575   **11.** The second coin *seems* slightly biased in favor of heads, as heads comes up approximately 58% of the time. On the other hand, it is conceivable that the coin is fair and that heads came up 58% of the time purely by chance. Deciding which conclusion is more reasonable requires some knowledge of inferential statistics.   **13.** Yes   **15.** No; relative frequencies cannot be negative.   **17.** Yes   **19.** Missing value: .3 **a.** .6 **b.** .4   **21.** Answers will vary.   **23.** Answers will vary.   **25. a.** .54 **b.** .16 **c.** .98
27. a.

Mortgage Status	Current	Past Due	In Foreclosure	Repossessed
Rel. Frequency	.67	.26	.045	.025

b. .33
29. a.

Age	0–14	15–29	30–64	>64
Rel. Frequency	.30	.27	.37	.06

b. .36

31. a.

Test Rating	3	2	1	0
Rel. Frequency	.1	.4	.4	.1

b. .5   **33.** Dialup: 1,256, cable modem: 412, DSL: 302, Other: 30

35.

Outcome	Surge	Plunge	Steady
Rel. Frequency	.2	.3	.5

37. .25   **39.** .2   **41.** .7   **43.** 5/6   **45.** 5/16

47.

Outcome	U	C	R
Rel. Frequency	.2	.64	.16

49.

Conventional	No pesticide	Single pesticide	Multiple pesticide
Probability	.27	.13	.60
Organic	No pesticide	Single pesticide	Multiple pesticide
Probability	.77	.13	.10

51. P(false negative) $= 10/400 = .025$, P(false positive) $= 10/200 = .05$ **53.** Answers will vary.   **55.** The fraction of times E occurs   **57.** 101; $fr(E)$ can be any number between 0 and 100 inclusive, so the possible answers are $0/100 = 0$, $1/100 = .01$, $2/100 = .02, \ldots, 99/100 = .99$, $100/100 = 1$.
59. Wrong. For a pair of fair dice, the probability of a pair of matching numbers is 1/6, as Ruth says. However, it is quite possible, although not very likely, that if you cast a pair of fair dice 20 times, you will never obtain a matching pair. (In fact, there is approximately a 2.6% chance that this will happen.) In general, a nontrivial claim about probability can never be absolutely validated or refuted experimentally. All we can say is that the evidence suggests that the dice are not fair.   **61.** For a (large) number of days, record the temperature prediction for the next day, and then check the actual high temperature the next day. Record whether the prediction was accurate (within, say, 2°F of the actual temperature). The fraction of times the prediction was accurate is the relative frequency.

Section 8.3

1. $P(e) = .2$ **a.** .9 **b.** .95 **c.** .1 **d.** .8   **3.** $P(E) = 1/4$
5. $P(E) = 1$ **7.** $P(E) = 3/4$ **9.** $P(E) = 3/4$
11. $P(E) = 1/2$ **13.** $P(E) = 1/9$ **15.** $P(E) = 0$
17. $P(E) = 1/4$ **19.** 1/12; {(4, 4), (2, 3), (3, 2)}

21.

Outcome	1	2	3	4	5	6
Probability	$\frac{1}{9}$	$\frac{2}{9}$	$\frac{1}{9}$	$\frac{2}{9}$	$\frac{1}{9}$	$\frac{2}{9}$

$P(\{1, 2, 3\}) = 4/9$

23.

Outcome	1	2	3	4
Probability	$\frac{8}{15}$	$\frac{4}{15}$	$\frac{2}{15}$	$\frac{1}{15}$

25. .65 **27.** .1 **29.** .7 **31.** .4 **33.** .25 **35.** 1.0 **37.** .3
39. 1.0 **41.** No; $P(A \cup B)$ should be $\leq P(A) + P(B)$.
43. Yes **45.** No; $P(A \cup B)$ should be $\geq P(A)$. **47. a.** .93
b. .33
49.

Outcome	Hispanic or Latino	White (not Hispanic)	African American	Asian	Other
Probability	0.48	0.29	0.08	0.08	0.07

P(neither White nor Asian) = .63
51. a. $S = \{$stock market success, sold to other concern, fail$\}$

b.

Outcome	Stock Market Success	Sold to Other Concern	Fail
Probability	.2	.3	.5

c. .5

53.

Outcome	SUV	Pickup	Passenger Car	Minivan
Probability	.25	.15	.50	.10

55. $P(1) = 0$, $P(6) = 0$; $P(2) = P(3) = P(4) =$
$P(5) = 1/4 = .25$; $P(\text{odd}) = .5$ **57.** $P(1) = P(6) = 1/10$;
$P(2) = P(3) = P(4) = P(5) = 1/5$, $P(\text{odd}) = 1/2$
59. $P(1, 1) = P(2, 2) = \ldots = P(6, 6) = 1/66$;
$P(1, 2) = \ldots = P(6, 5) = 1/33$, $P(\text{odd sum}) = 6/11$
61. $P(2) = 15/38$; $P(4) = 3/38$, $P(1) = P(3) =$
$P(5) = P(6) = 5/38$, $P(\text{odd}) = 15/38$ **63.** 5/6
65. .39 **67.** .35 **69.** .20 **71.** .00 **73.** .80 **75.** .38
77. .62 **79.** .01 **81.** .61 **83.** .38 **85.** 22%; 43% **87.** All
of them **89.** 88.4% **91.** Here is one possible experiment:
Roll a die, and observe which of the following outcomes
occurs. Outcome A: 1 or 2 facing up; $P(A) = 1/3$, Outcome B:
3 or 4 facing up; $P(B) = 1/3$, Outcome C: 5 or 6 facing up;
$P(C) = 1/3$. **93.** He is wrong. It is possible to have a run of
losses of any length. Tony may have grounds to *suspect* that
the game is rigged, but he has no proof. **95.** they are mutually
exclusive. **97.** Wrong. For example, the modeled probability of
winning a state lottery is small but nonzero. However, the vast
majority of people who play the lottery every day of their lives
never win no matter how frequently they play, so the relative
frequency is zero for these people. **99.** When $A \cap B = \varnothing$
we have $P(A \cap B) = P(\varnothing) = 0$, so $P(A \cup B) =$
$P(A) + P(B) - P(A \cap B) = P(A) + P(B) - 0 =$
$P(A) + P(B)$. **101.** Zero. According to the assumption,
no matter how many thunderstorms occur, lightning cannot
strike a given spot more than once, so, after n trials the relative
frequency will never exceed $1/n$ and so will approach zero as
the number of trials gets large. Since the modeled probability
models the limit of relative frequencies as the number of trials
gets large, it must therefore be zero. **103.** $P(A \cup B \cup C) =$
$P(A) + P(B) + P(C) - P(A \cap B) - P(A \cap C) -$
$P(B \cap C) + P(A \cap B \cap C)$

Section 8.4

1. 1/42 **3.** 7/9 **5.** 1/7 **7.** 1/2 **9.** 41/42 **11.** 1/15
13. 4/15 **15.** 1/5 **17.** $1/(2^8 \times 5^5 \times 5!)$ **19.** .4226
21. .0475 **23.** .0020 **25.** $1/27^{39}$ **27.** 1/7
29. Probability of being a Big Winner = $1/2,118,760 \approx$
.000000472. Probability of being a Small-Fry Winner =
$225/2,118,760 \approx$ .000106194. Probability of being either a
Big Winner or a Small-Fry Winner = $226/2,118,760 \approx$
.000106666. **31. a.** $C(600, 300)/C(700, 400)$
b. $C(699, 399)/C(700, 400)$ or $400/700$ **33.** $P(10, 3)/10^3 =$
$18/25 = .72$ **35.** 1/8 **37.** $(8! \times 2^8)/16!$ **39. a.** $1/2^{63}$
b. $[C(60, 15) \times 8]/2^{63}$ **41.** $8!/8^8$ **43.** 1/8 **45.** 37/10,000
47. a. 90,720 **b.** 25,200 **c.** $25,200/90,720 \approx .28$
49. The four outcomes listed are not equally likely; for
example, (red, blue) can occur in four ways. The methods
of this section yield a probability for (red, red) of
$C(2, 2)/C(4, 2) = 1/6$. **51.** No. If we do not pay attention to
order, the probability is $C(5, 2)/C(9, 2) = 10/36 = 5/18$.
If we do pay attention to order, the probability is
$P(5, 2)/P(9, 2) = 20/72 = 5/18$ again. The difference
between permutations and combinations cancels when we
compute the probability. **53.** Answers will vary.

Section 8.5

1. .4 **3.** .08 **5.** .75 **7.** .2 **9.** .5 **11.** $P(D) = .10$;
$P(D|M) = .30$ **13.** $P(A|L) = .30$; $P(L|A) = .10$
15. $P(E|M) = .55$; $P(E|M') = .05$ **17.** 1/10 **19.** 1/5
21. 2/9 **23.** 1/84 **25.** 5/21 **27.** 24/175
29.

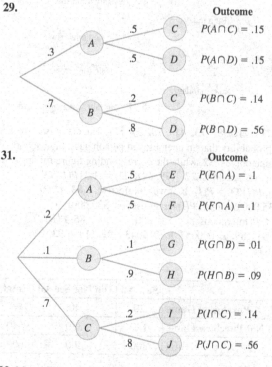

31.

33. Mutually exclusive **35.** Neither

37. $\frac{1}{2} \cdot \frac{1}{2} = \frac{1}{4}$ Independent   **39.** $\frac{5}{18} \cdot \frac{1}{2} \ne \frac{1}{9}$ Dependent

41. $\frac{25}{36} \cdot \frac{5}{18} \ne \frac{2}{9}$ Dependent   **43.** $(1/2)^{11} = 1/2{,}048$

45. .8   **47. a.** .24 **b.** .092   **49.** .34   **51.** Not independent; $P(\text{giving up}\,|\,\text{used Brand X}) = .1$ is larger than $P(\text{giving up}) = .05$.   **53.** .00015   **55.** 5/6   **57.** 3/4   **59.** 11/16   **61.** 11/14

63.

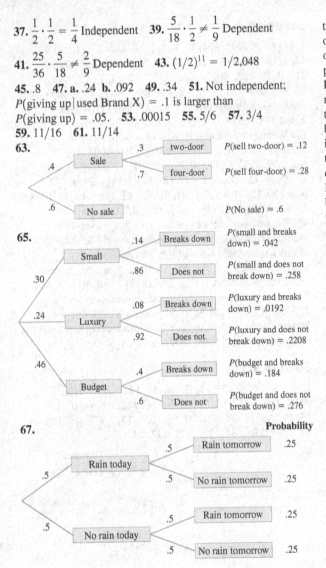

65.

67.
				Probability

69. .73   **71.** .38   **73.** .41   **75.** .97   **77.** The claim is correct. The probability that an unemployed person has a high school diploma only is .32, while the corresponding figure for an employed person is .27.   **79.** $P(K\,|\,D) = 1.31 P(K\,|\,D')$ **81. a.** $P(I\,|\,T) > P(I)$ **b.** It was ineffective.   **83. a.** .59 **b.** $35{,}000 or more: $P(\text{Internet user}\,|\,< \$35{,}000) \approx .27 < P(\text{Internet user}\,|\,\ge \$35{,}000) \approx .59$.   **85.** $P(R\,|\,J)$ **87.** (D)   **89. a.** .000057 **b.** .015043   **91.** 11%   **93.** 106   **95.** .631   **97.**

	Saw Ad	Did Not See Ad	Total
Purchased Game	20	40	60
Did Not Purchase Game	180	360	540
Total	200	400	600

99. $100p^2\%$ **101.** Answers will vary. Here is a simple one: E: The first toss is a head; F: The second toss is a head; G: The

third toss is a head.   **103.** The probability you seek is $P(E\,|\,F)$, or should be. If, for example, you were going to place a wager on whether E occurs or not, it is crucial to know that the sample space has been reduced to F. (You know that F did occur.) If you base your wager on $P(E)$ rather than $P(E\,|\,F)$ you will misjudge your likelihood of winning.   **105.** You might explain that the conditional probability of E is not the *a priori* probability of E, but it is the probability of E in a hypothetical world in which the outcomes are restricted to be what is given. In the example she is citing, yes, the probability of throwing a double-six is 1/36 in the absence of any other knowledge. However, by the "conditional probability" of throwing a double-six given that the sum is larger than 7, we might mean the probability of a double-six in a situation in which the dice have already been thrown, but all we know is that the sum is greater than 7. Because there are only 15 ways in which that can happen, the conditional probability is 1/15. For a more extreme case, consider the conditional probability of throwing a double-six given that the sum is 12.   **107.** If $A \subseteq B$ then $A \cap B = A$, so $P(A \cap B) = P(A)$ and $P(A\,|\,B) = P(A \cap B)/P(B) = P(A)/P(B)$.   **109.** Your friend is correct. If A and B are mutually exclusive, then $P(A \cap B) = 0$. On the other hand, if A and B are independent, then $P(A \cap B) = P(A)P(B)$. Thus, $P(A)P(B) = 0$. If a product is 0, then one of the factors must be 0, so either $P(A) = 0$ or $P(B) = 0$. Thus, it cannot be true that A and B are mutually exclusive, have non-zero probabilities, and are independent all at the same time.   **111.** $P(A' \cap B') = 1 - P(A \cup B) = 1 - [P(A) + P(B) - P(A \cap B)] = 1 - [P(A) + P(B) - P(A)P(B)] = (1 - P(A))(1 - P(B)) = P(A')P(B')$

Section 8.6

1. .4   **3.** .7887   **5.** .7442   **7.** .1163   **9.** 26.8%   **11.** .1724   **13.** 61%   **15.** .73   **17.** .71   **19.** .165   **21.** 82%   **23.** 12%   **25. a.** 14.43%; **b.** 19.81% of single homeowners have pools. Thus, they should go after the single homeowners.   **27.** 9   **29.** .9310   **31.** 1.76%   **33.** .20   **35.** .30   **37.** Show him an example such as Example 1 of this section, where $P(T\,|\,A) = .95$ but $P(A\,|\,T) \approx .64$.   **39.** Suppose that the steroid test gives 10% false negatives and that only 0.1% of the tested population uses steroids. Then the probability that an athlete uses steroids, given that he or she has tested positive, is

$$\frac{(.9)(.001)}{(.9)(.001) + (.01)(.999)} \approx .083.$$ **41.** Draw a tree in which the first branching shows which of R_1, R_2, or R_3 occurred and the second branching shows which of T or T' then occurred. There are three final outcomes in which T occurs: $P(R_1 \cap T) = P(T\,|\,R_1)P(R_1)$, $P(R_2 \cap T) = P(T\,|\,R_2)P(R_2)$, and $P(R_3 \cap T) = P(T\,|\,R_3)P(R_3)$. In only one of these, the first, does R_1 occur. Thus, $P(R_1\,|\,T) = \dfrac{P(R_1 \cap T)}{P(T)} =$

$$\frac{P(T\,|\,R_1)P(R_1)}{P(T\,|\,R_1)P(R_1) + P(T\,|\,R_2)P(R_2) + P(T\,|\,R_3)P(R_3)}$$

43. The reasoning is flawed. Let A be the event that a Democrat agrees with Safire's column, and let F and M be the events that a Democrat reader is female and male, respectively. Then A. D. makes the following argument: $P(M|A) = .9$, $P(F|A') = .9$. Therefore, $P(A|M) = .9$. According to Bayes' theorem, we cannot conclude anything about $P(A|M)$ unless we know $P(A)$, the percentage of all Democrats who agreed with Safire's column. This was not given.

Section 8.7

1. $\begin{bmatrix} \frac{1}{4} & \frac{3}{4} \\ \frac{1}{2} & \frac{1}{2} \end{bmatrix}$ **3.** $\begin{bmatrix} 0 & 1 \\ \frac{1}{6} & \frac{5}{6} \end{bmatrix}$

5. $\begin{bmatrix} 0 & .8 & .2 \\ .9 & 0 & .1 \\ 0 & 0 & 1 \end{bmatrix}$ **7.** $\begin{bmatrix} 1 & 0 & 0 \\ 0 & 1 & 0 \\ 0 & 0 & 1 \end{bmatrix}$

9. $\begin{bmatrix} 1 & 0 & 0 & 0 & 0 & 0 \\ \frac{2}{3} & 0 & \frac{1}{3} & 0 & 0 & 0 \\ 0 & \frac{2}{3} & 0 & \frac{1}{3} & 0 & 0 \\ 0 & 0 & \frac{2}{3} & 0 & \frac{1}{3} & 0 \\ 0 & 0 & 0 & \frac{2}{3} & 0 & \frac{1}{3} \\ 0 & 0 & 0 & 0 & 1 & 0 \end{bmatrix}$

11. a. $\begin{bmatrix} .25 & .75 \\ 0 & 1 \end{bmatrix}$ **b.** distribution after one step: $[.5 \quad .5]$; after two steps: $[.25 \quad .75]$; after three steps: $[.125 \quad .875]$

13. a. $\begin{bmatrix} .36 & .64 \\ .32 & .68 \end{bmatrix}$ **b.** distribution after one step: $[.3 \quad .7]$; after two steps: $[.34 \quad .66]$; after three steps: $[.332 \quad .668]$

15. a. $\begin{bmatrix} \frac{3}{4} & \frac{1}{4} \\ \frac{1}{2} & \frac{1}{2} \end{bmatrix}$ **b.** distribution after one step: $[\frac{2}{3} \quad \frac{1}{3}]$; after two steps: $[\frac{2}{3} \quad \frac{1}{3}]$; after three steps: $[\frac{2}{3} \quad \frac{1}{3}]$

17. a. $\begin{bmatrix} \frac{3}{4} & \frac{1}{4} \\ \frac{3}{4} & \frac{1}{4} \end{bmatrix}$ **b.** distribution after one step: $[\frac{3}{4} \quad \frac{1}{4}]$; after two steps: $[\frac{3}{4} \quad \frac{1}{4}]$; after three steps: $[\frac{3}{4} \quad \frac{1}{4}]$

19. a. $\begin{bmatrix} .25 & .75 & 0 \\ 0 & 1 & 0 \\ 0 & .75 & .25 \end{bmatrix}$ **b.** distribution after one step: $[.5 \quad .5 \quad 0]$; after two steps: $[.25 \quad .75 \quad 0]$; after three steps: $[.125 \quad .875 \quad 0]$

21. a. $\begin{bmatrix} \frac{1}{3} & \frac{1}{3} & \frac{1}{3} \\ \frac{4}{9} & \frac{4}{9} & \frac{1}{9} \\ 0 & 1 & 0 \end{bmatrix}$ **b.** distribution after one step: $[\frac{1}{2} \quad \frac{1}{2} \quad 0]$; after two steps: $[\frac{1}{6} \quad \frac{2}{3} \quad \frac{1}{6}]$; after three steps: $[\frac{7}{18} \quad \frac{7}{18} \quad \frac{2}{9}]$

23. a. $\begin{bmatrix} .01 & .99 & 0 \\ 0 & 1 & 0 \\ 0 & .36 & .64 \end{bmatrix}$ **b.** distribution after one step: $[.05 \quad .55 \quad .4]$; after two steps: $[.005 \quad .675 \quad .32]$; after three steps: $[.0005 \quad .7435 \quad .256]$ **25.** $[\frac{2}{3} \quad \frac{1}{3}]$

27. $[\frac{3}{7} \quad \frac{4}{7}]$ **29.** $[\frac{2}{5} \quad \frac{3}{5}]$ **31.** $[\frac{2}{5} \quad \frac{1}{5} \quad \frac{2}{5}]$

33. $[\frac{1}{3} \quad \frac{1}{2} \quad \frac{1}{6}]$ **35.** $[0 \quad 1 \quad 0]$

37. 1 = Sorey State, 2 = C&T;
$P = \begin{bmatrix} \frac{1}{2} & \frac{1}{2} \\ \frac{1}{4} & \frac{3}{4} \end{bmatrix}$; $\frac{3}{8} = .375$ **39. a.** 1 = not checked in;
2 = checked in;
$P = \begin{bmatrix} .4 & .6 \\ 0 & 1 \end{bmatrix}$, $P^2 = \begin{bmatrix} .16 & .84 \\ 0 & 1 \end{bmatrix}$,
$P^3 = \begin{bmatrix} .064 & .936 \\ 0 & 1 \end{bmatrix}$ **b.** 1 hour: .6; 2 hours: .84; 3 hours: .936

c. Eventually, all the roaches will have checked in.
41. 16.67% fall into the high-risk category, and 83.33% into the low-risk category. **43. a.** $47/300 \approx .156667$ **b.** 3/13
45. 41.67% of the customers will be in the Paid Up category, 41.67% in the 0–90 days category, and 16.67% in the bad debt category.

47. a. $P = \begin{bmatrix} .729 & .271 & 0 \\ .075 & .84 & .085 \\ 0 & .304 & .696 \end{bmatrix}$ **b.** 2.3% **c.** Affluent:
17.8%; middle class: 64.3%; poor: 18.0%
49. Long-term income distribution (top to bottom): $[8.43\%, 41.57\%, 41.57\%, 8.43\%]$. The reason they are not the "expected" 10%, 40%, 40%, and 10% is that the movement between the income groups changes their relative sizes.

51. a. $P = \begin{bmatrix} .981 & .005 & .005 & .009 \\ .01 & .972 & .006 & .012 \\ .01 & .006 & .973 & .011 \\ .008 & .006 & .005 & .981 \end{bmatrix}$

b. Verizon: 29.6%, Cingular: 19.4%, AT&T: 18.2%, Other: 32.8% **c.** Verizon: 30.3%, Cingular: 18.6%, AT&T: 17.6%, Other: 33.5%. The biggest gainers are Verizon and Other, each gaining 0.6%. **53.** $[\frac{1}{5} \quad \frac{1}{5} \quad \frac{1}{5} \quad \frac{1}{5} \quad \frac{1}{5}]$ **55.** Answers will vary. **57.** There are two assumptions made by Markov systems that may not be true about the stock market: the assumption that the transition probabilities do not change over time and the assumption that the transition probability depends only on the current state. **59.** If q is a row of Q, then by assumption, $qP = q$. Thus, when we multiply the rows of Q by P, nothing changes, and $QP = Q$. **61.** At each step, only 0.4 of the population in state 1 remains there, and nothing enters from any other state. Thus, when the first entry in the steady-state distribution vector is multiplied by 0.4 it must remain unchanged. The only number for which this is true is 0.
63. An example is

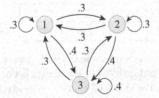

65. If $vP = v$ and $wP = w$, then $\frac{1}{2}(v + w)P = \frac{1}{2}vP + \frac{1}{2}wP = \frac{1}{2}v + \frac{1}{2}w = \frac{1}{2}(v + w)$. Further, if the entries of v and w add up to 1, then so do the entries of $(v + w)/2$.

Chapter 8 Review

1. $n(S) = 8$, $E = \{$HHT, HTH, HTT, THH, THT, TTH, TTT$\}$, $P(E) = 7/8$ **3.** $n(S) = 36$; $E = \{(1, 6), (2, 5), (3, 4),$ $(4, 3), (5, 2), (6, 1)\}$; $P(E) = 1/6$ **5.** $n(S) = 6$; $E = \{2\}$; $P(E) = 1/8$ **7.** .76   **9.** .25   **11.** .5   **13.** 7/15   **15.** 8/792
17. 48/792   **19.** 288/792   **21.** $C(8, 5)/C(52, 5)$
23. $C(4, 3)C(1, 1)C(3, 1)/C(52, 5)$
25. $C(9, 1)C(8, 1)C(4, 3)C(4, 2)/C(52, 5)$ **27.** 1/5;
dependent   **29.** 1/6; independent   **31.** 1; dependent

33. $P = \begin{bmatrix} \frac{1}{2} & \frac{1}{2} \\ \frac{1}{4} & \frac{3}{4} \end{bmatrix}$ **35.** Brand A: $65/192 \approx .339$,

Brand B: $127/192 \approx .661$ **37.** 14/25   **39.** 15/94
41. 79/167   **43.** 98%   **45.** 6.9%   **47.** .931   **49.** $P(H \cap C)$,
since $P(H \mid C) > P(H)$ gives $P(H \cap C) > P(H)P(C)$
51. .246   **53.** 91%   **55.** 40% for OHaganBooks.com, 26%
for JungleBooks.com, and 34% for FarmerBooks.com
57. Here are three: (1) It is possible for someone to be a customer at two different enterprises; (2) some customers may
stop using all three of the companies; and (3) new customers
can enter the field.

Chapter 9

Section 9.1

1. Finite; $\{2, 3, \ldots, 12\}$ **3.** Discrete infinite;
$\{0, 1, -1, 2, -2, \ldots\}$ (Negative profits indicate loss.)
5. Continuous; X can assume any value between 0 and 60
(including 0).   **7.** Finite; $\{0, 1, 2, \ldots, 10\}$ **9.** Discrete infinite; $\{k/1, k/4, k/9, k/16, \ldots\}$ **11. a.** $S = \{$HH, HT, TH, TT$\}$
b. X is the rule that assigns to each outcome the number of tails.

c.

Outcome	HH	HT	TH	TT
Value of X	0	1	1	2

13. a. $S = \{(1, 1), (1, 2), \ldots, (1, 6), (2, 1), (2, 2), \ldots,$
$(6, 6)\}$ **b.** X is the rule that assigns to each outcome the sum of
the two numbers.

c.

Outcome	(1, 1)	(1, 2)	(1, 3)	...	(6, 6)
Value of X	2	3	4	...	12

15. a. $S = \{(4, 0), (3, 1), (2, 2)\}$ (listed in order (red, green))
b. X is the rule that assigns to each outcome the number of red
marbles.

c.

Outcome	(4, 0)	(3, 1)	(2, 2)
Value of X	4	3	2

17. a. $S = $ the set of students in the study group.
b. X is the rule that assigns to each student his or her final
exam score.   **c.** The values of X, in the order given, are 89%,
85%, 95%, 63%, 92%, 80%.
19. a. $P(X = 8) = P(X = 6) = .3$ **b.** .7; .5

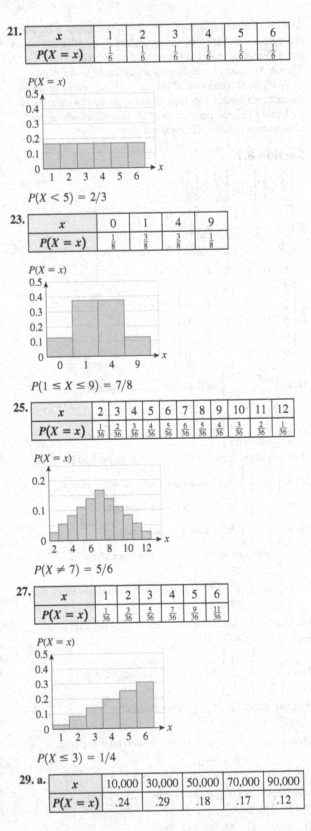

21.

x	1	2	3	4	5	6
$P(X = x)$	$\frac{1}{6}$	$\frac{1}{6}$	$\frac{1}{6}$	$\frac{1}{6}$	$\frac{1}{6}$	$\frac{1}{6}$

$P(X < 5) = 2/3$

23.

x	0	1	4	9
$P(X = x)$	$\frac{1}{8}$	$\frac{3}{8}$	$\frac{3}{8}$	$\frac{1}{8}$

$P(1 \leq X \leq 9) = 7/8$

25.

x	2	3	4	5	6	7	8	9	10	11	12
$P(X = x)$	$\frac{1}{36}$	$\frac{2}{36}$	$\frac{3}{36}$	$\frac{4}{36}$	$\frac{5}{36}$	$\frac{6}{36}$	$\frac{5}{36}$	$\frac{4}{36}$	$\frac{3}{36}$	$\frac{2}{36}$	$\frac{1}{36}$

$P(X \neq 7) = 5/6$

27.

x	1	2	3	4	5	6
$P(X = x)$	$\frac{1}{36}$	$\frac{3}{36}$	$\frac{5}{36}$	$\frac{7}{36}$	$\frac{9}{36}$	$\frac{11}{36}$

$P(X \leq 3) = 1/4$

29. a.

x	10,000	30,000	50,000	70,000	90,000
$P(X = x)$	.24	.29	.18	.17	.12

b. .29; histogram:

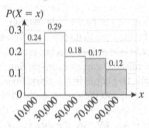

31. The random variable is X = age of a resident in Mexico.

x	7	22	47	70
$P(X = x)$	.300	.272	.368	.060

33. a. 2,000, 3,000, 4,000, 5,000, 6,000, 7,000, 8,000 (7,000 is optional)
b.

x	2,000	3,000	4,000	5,000	6,000	7,000	8,000
Freq.	2	1	1	1	2	0	3
$P(X = x)$	.2	.1	.1	.1	.2	0	.3

c. $P(X \leq 5,000) = .5$ **35. a.** $-700, -600, -500, -400,$
$-300, -200, -100, 0, 100, 200, 300, 400, 500, 600, 700,$
$800, 900$ ($-600, 0, 100, 300, 500, 600, 700,$ and 800 are optional.)
b.

x	-700	-600	-500	-400	-300	-200	-100	0
Freq.	2	0	2	1	1	4	4	0
$P(X = x)$	.1	0	.1	.05	.05	.2	.2	0
x	100	200	300	400	500	600	700	800	900
Freq.	0	2	0	2	0	0	0	0	2
$P(X = x)$	0	.1	0	.1	0	0	0	0	.1

c. .3

37.

Class	1.1–2.0	2.1–3.0	3.1–4.0
Freq.	4	7	9

x	1.5	2.5	3.5
$P(X = x)$	.20	.35	.45

39. 95.5%

41.

x	3	2	1	0
$P(X = x)$	.0625	.6875	.125	.125

43. .75; the relative frequency that a randomly selected small car is rated Good or Acceptable is .75.   **45.** $P(Y \geq 2) = .50$, $P(Z \geq 2) \approx .53$, suggesting that medium SUVs are safer than small SUVs in frontal crashes   **47.** Small cars   **49.** .375

51.

x	1	2	3	4
$P(X = x)$	$\frac{4}{35}$	$\frac{18}{35}$	$\frac{12}{35}$	$\frac{1}{35}$

$P(X \geq 2) = 31/35 \approx .886$
53. Answers will vary.   **55.** No; for instance, if X is the number of times you must toss a coin until heads comes up, then X is infinite but not continuous.   **57.** By measuring the values of X for a large number of outcomes and then using the estimated probability (relative frequency)   **59.** Answers will vary. Here is an example: Let X be the number of days a diligent student waits before beginning to study for an exam scheduled in 10 days' time.   **61.** The bars should be 1 unit wide so that their height is numerically equal to their area.   **63.** Answers may vary. If we are interested in exact page counts, then the number of possible values is very large, and the values are (relatively speaking) close together, so using a continuous random variable might be advantageous. In general, the finer and more numerous the measurement classes, the more likely it becomes that a continuous random variable could be advantageous.

Section 9.2

1. .0729   **3.** .59049   **5.** .00001   **7.** .99144   **9.** .00856
11. .27648   **13.** .54432   **15.** .04096   **17.** .77414

19.

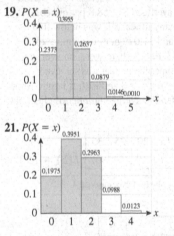

$P(X \leq 2) \approx .8889$
23. .2637   **25.** .8926   **27.** .875   **29. a.** .0081   **b.** .08146
31. .41   **33. a.** .0509   **b.** Probability distribution (entries rounded to four decimal places):

x	0	1	2	3	4
$P(X = x)$	.0643	.2030	.2885	.2429	.1343
5	6	7	8	9	10
.0509	.0134	.0024	.0003	.0000	.0000

c. 2   **35.** .000298   **37.** .8321   **39. a.** 21   **b.** 20   **c.** The graph for $n = 50$ trials is more widely distributed than the graph for $n = 20$.   **41.** 69 trials   **43.** $.562 \times 10^{-5}$ **45.** .0266; because there is only a 2.66% chance of detecting the disease in a given year, the government's claim seems dubious.   **47.** No; in a sequence of Bernoulli trials, the occurrence of one success does not affect the probability of success on the next attempt. **49.** No; if life is a sequence of Bernoulli trials, then the occurrence of one misfortune ("success") does not affect the probability of a misfortune on the next trial. Hence, misfortunes may very well not "occur in threes."   **51.** Think of performing the experiment as a Bernoulli trial with "success" being the occurrence of E. Performing the experiment n times independently in succession would then be a sequence of n Bernoulli trials. **53.** The probability of selecting a red marble changes after each selection, as the number of marbles left in the bag decreases. This violates the requirement that, in a sequence of Bernoulli trials, the probability of "success" does not change.

Section 9.3

1. $\bar{x} = 6$, median $= 5$, mode $= 5$ **3.** $\bar{x} = 3$, median $= 3.5$, mode $= -1$ **5.** $\bar{x} = -0.1875$, median $= 0.875$, every value is a mode   **7.** $\bar{x} = 0.2$, median $= -0.1$, mode $= -0.1$ **9.** Answers may vary. Two examples are: 0, 0, 0, 0, 0, 6 and 0, 0, 0, 1, 2, 3   **11.** 0.9   **13.** 21   **15.** -0.1 **17.** 3.5   **19.** 1 **21.** 4.472   **23.** 2.667   **25.** 2   **27.** 0.385   **29.** $\bar{x} = -150$, $m = -150$; -150 **31.** $\bar{x} = 1{,}068.8$, median $= 1{,}071.5$; modes $= 1{,}062$ and $1{,}072$; Over the 10-business-day period sampled, the price of gold averaged \$1,068.8 per ounce. It was above \$1,071.5 as many times as it was below that price, and stood at \$1,062 and \$1,072 per ounce more often than at any other price.   **33. a.** 6.5; there were, on average, 6.5 checkout lanes in each supermarket that was surveyed. **b.** $P(X < \mu) = .42$; $P(X > \mu) = .58$ and is thus larger. Most supermarkets have more than the average number of checkout lanes.

35.

x	5	10	15	20	25	35
$P(X = x)$	.17	.33	.21	.19	.03	.07

$E(X) = 14.3$; the average age of a school goer in 1998 was 14.3. **37.** 29.6   **39.** \$43,000

41.

x	3	2	1	0
$P(X = x)$	.0625	.6875	.125	.125

$E(X) = 1.6875$

y	3	2	1	0
$P(Y = y)$	.1	.4	.4	.1

$E(Y) = 1.5$; small cars   **43.** Large cars   **45.** Expect to lose 5.3¢.   **47.** 25.2 students   **49. a.** Two defective air bags   **b.** 120 air bags

51.

x	1	2	3	4
$P(X = x)$	$\frac{4}{35}$	$\frac{18}{35}$	$\frac{12}{35}$	$\frac{1}{35}$

$E(X) = 16/7 \approx 2.2857$ tents

53. A loss of about 51¢   **55.** About half a cent   **57.** FastForward: 3.97%; SolidState: 5.51%; SolidState gives the higher expected return.   **59.** A loss of \$29,390   **61.** (A)   **63.** He is wrong; for example, the collection 0, 0, 300 has mean 100 and

median 0.   **65.** No; the expected number is the average number of times you will hit the bull's-eye per 50 shots; the average of a set of whole numbers need not be a whole number. **67.** Not necessarily; it might be the case that only a small fraction of people in the class scored better than you but received exceptionally high scores that raised the class average. Suppose, for instance, that there are 10 people in the class. Four received 100%, you received 80%, and the rest received 70%. Then the class average is 83%, 5 people have lower scores than you, but only 4 have higher scores.   **69.** No; the mean of a very large sample is only an *estimate* of the population mean. The means of larger and larger samples *approach* the population mean as the sample size increases.   **71.** Wrong; the statement attributed to President Bush asserts that the mean tax saving would be \$1,000, whereas the statements referred to as "The Truth" suggest that the *median* tax saving would be close to \$100 (and that the 31st percentile would be zero). **73.** Select a U.S. household at random, and let X be the income of that household. The expected value of X is then the population mean of all U.S. household incomes.

Section 9.4

1. $s^2 = 29$; $s = 5.39$ **3.** $s^2 = 12.4$; $s = 3.52$ **5.** $s^2 = 6.64$; $s = 2.58$ **7.** $s^2 = 13.01$; $s = 3.61$ **9.** 1.04   **11.** 9.43 **13.** 3.27   **15.** Expected value $= 3.5$, variance ≈ 2.92, standard deviation ≈ 1.71 **17.** Expected value $= 1$, variance $= 0.5$, standard deviation ≈ 0.71 **19.** Expected value ≈ 4.47, variance ≈ 1.97, standard deviation ≈ 1.40 **21.** Expected value ≈ 2.67, variance ≈ 0.36, standard deviation ≈ 0.60 **23.** Expected value $= 2$, variance $= 1.8$, standard deviation ≈ 1.34 **25. a.** $\bar{x} = 3$, $s \approx 3.54$ **b.** $[0, 6.54]$ We must assume that the population distribution is bell shaped and symmetric. **27. a.** $\bar{x} = 5.0$, $s \approx 0.6$ **b.** 3.8, 6.2   **29. a.** $\bar{x} = -150$, $s \approx 495$ **b.** 645, 20%   **31. a.** 2.18   **b.** $[11.22, 24.28]$ **c.** 100%; empirical rule   **33.** $\mu = 1.5$, $\sigma = 1.43$; 100%   **35.** $\mu = 43$, $\sigma \approx 26.6$; \$53,000   **37. a.** $\mu \approx 30.2$ years old, $\sigma \approx 11.78$ years **b.** 18–42   **39.** At most 6.25%   **41.** At most; 12.5 **43. a.** $\mu = 25.2$, $\sigma = 3.05$ **b.** 31   **45. a.** $\mu = 780$, $\sigma \approx 13.1$ **b.** 754, 806   **47. a.** $\mu = 6.5$, $\sigma^2 = 4.0$, $\sigma = 2.0$ **b.** $[2.5, 10.5]$; three checkout lanes   **49.** \$10,700 or less   **51.** \$65,300 or more **53.** U.S.   **55.** U.S.   **57.** 16%   **59.** 0–\$76,000   **61.** 2000 data: $\mu = 12.56$, $\sigma \approx 1.8885$; 2010 data: $\mu = 13.30$, $\sigma \approx 1.6643$ **63.** (B)   **65.** 72%; the empirical rule predicts 68%. The associated probability distribution is roughly bell shaped but not symmetric.   **67.** 94%; Chebyshev's rule is valid, since it predicts that *at least* 75% of the scores are in this range.   **69.** (B), (D) **71.** (B), (E)   **73.** The sample standard deviation is bigger; the formula for sample standard deviation involves division by the smaller term $n - 1$ instead of n, which makes the resulting number larger.   **75.** The grades in the first class were clustered fairly close to 75. By Chebyshev's inequality, at least 88% of the class had grades in the range 60–90. On the other hand, the grades in the second class were widely dispersed. The second class had a much wider spread of ability than did the first class.   **77.** The variable must take on only the value 10, with probability 1.   **79.** $(y - x)/2$

Section 9.5

1. .1915   **3.** .5222   **5.** .6710   **7.** .2417   **9.** .8664   **11.** .8621
13. .2286   **15.** .3830   **17.** .5028   **19.** 108.4   **21.** 117.5
23. .35   **25.** .05   **27.** .3830   **29.** .8185   **31.** 26%
33. 34,100,000   **35.** 665   **37.** 0   **39.** About 6,680   **41.** 28%
43. 5%   **45.** U.S.   **47.** Wechsler; as this test has a smaller
standard deviation, a greater percentage of scores fall within
20 points of the mean.   **49.** This is surprising, because the
time between failures was more than five standard deviations
away from the mean, which happens with an extremely small
probability.   **51.** .6103   **53.** .6103 × .5832 ≈ .3559
55. .6255   **57.** .7881   **59.** .9049   **61.** .2912   **63.** Probability
that a person will say Goode = .54. Probability that Goode
polls more than 52% ≈ .8925.   **65.** 23.4   **67.** When the
distribution is normal   **69.** Neither. They are equal.
71. $1/(b - a)$ **73.** A normal distribution with standard deviation 0.5, because it is narrower near the mean but must enclose
the same amount of area as the standard curve, so it must be
higher.

Chapter 9 Review

1.

x	0	1	2
$P(X = x)$	$\frac{1}{4}$	$\frac{1}{2}$	$\frac{1}{4}$

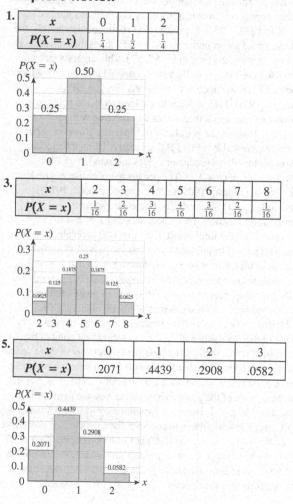

3.

x	2	3	4	5	6	7	8
$P(X = x)$	$\frac{1}{16}$	$\frac{2}{16}$	$\frac{3}{16}$	$\frac{4}{16}$	$\frac{3}{16}$	$\frac{2}{16}$	$\frac{1}{16}$

5.

x	0	1	2	3
$P(X = x)$	.2071	.4439	.2908	.0582

7. $\bar{x} = 2$, $m = 2$, $s ≈ 2.7386$ **9.** Two examples are: 0, 0, 0, 4
and −1, −1, 1, 5   **11.** An example is −1, −1, −1, 1, 1, 1
13. .4165   **15.** .9267   **17.** .0067   **19.** .7330   **21.** $\mu = 1.5$,
$\sigma = 0.8660$; 2
23.

x	−3	−2	−1	0	1	2	3
$P(X = x)$	$\frac{1}{16}$	$\frac{2}{16}$	$\frac{3}{16}$	$\frac{4}{16}$	$\frac{3}{16}$	$\frac{2}{16}$	$\frac{1}{16}$

$\mu = 0$, $\sigma = 1.5811$; within 1.3 standard deviations of the
mean   **25.** [49.4, 150.6]   **27.** 260   **29.** .4332   **31.** .0358
33. .3085   **35.** $12.15   **37.** $27,210   **39.** False; let X = price
and Y = weekly sales. Then weekly revenue = XY. However,
$27,210 ≠ 12.15 × 2,620$. In other words, $E(XY) ≠ E(X)E(Y)$.
41. a.

x	2	4	6	8	10
$P(X = x)$	.25	.35	.15	.15	.10

$\mu = 5$, $\sigma = 2.5690$ **b.** Between 2.431 and 7.569 orders per
million residents; the empirical rule does not apply because the
distribution is not symmetric.   **c.** (A)   **43.** .190   **45.** .060
47. 0.5   **49.** .284   **51.** .108   **53.** Using normal distribution
table: 420,000 people; more accurate answer, using technol-
ogy: 436,000 people   **55.** 148

Chapter 10

Section 10.1

1. a. −6   **b.** +∞   **c.** Does not exist   **d.** −4   **3. a.** −∞   **b.** −∞
c. −∞   **d.** Undefined   **5.** 0   **7.** 4   **9.** Does not exist   **11.** 0
13. 3   **15.** 6   **17.** Diverges to +∞   **19.** 0   **21.** 1.5   **23.** 0.5
25. Diverges to +∞   **27.** 0   **29.** 1   **31.** 0   **33.** 0   **35. a.** −2
b. −1   **37. a.** 2   **b.** 1   **c.** 0   **d.** +∞   **39. a.** 0   **b.** 2   **c.** −1
d. Does not exist   **e.** 2   **f.** +∞   **41. a.** 1   **b.** 1   **c.** 2   **d.** Does not
exist   **e.** 1   **f.** 2   **43. a.** 1   **b.** Does not exist   **c.** 1   **d.** 1   **45. a.** 1
b. +∞   **c.** +∞   **d.** +∞   **e.** Undefined   **f.** −1   **47. a.** −1
b. +∞   **c.** −∞   **d.** Does not exist   **e.** 2   **f.** 1   **49.** 890 PhD graduates per year. In the long term, the model predicts that there will
be 890 PhD graduates each year in the natural sciences in
Mexico.   **51. a.** 4.7. The model predicts that, had spending on
NASA continued to follow the pattern leading up to 1966, annual
spending on NASA in the long term would have amounted to
4.7% of the U.S. federal budget.   **b.** Not even close; current
spending (as of 2014) is less than 0.5% of the U.S. federal budget.   **53.** 7.0. In the long term, the number of research articles in
Physical Review written by researchers in Europe approaches
7,000 per year.   **55.** 573. This suggests that students with an
exceptionally large household income earn an average of 573
on the math SAT test.   **57. a.** $\lim_{t \to 14.75^-} r(t) = 21$,
$\lim_{t \to 14.75^+} r(t) = 21$, $\lim_{t \to 14.75} r(t) = 21$, $r(14.75) = 0.01$
b. Just before 2:45 pm, the stock was approaching $21, but it
then fell suddenly to a penny ($0.01) at 2:45 exactly, after which
time it jumped back to values close to $21.   **59.** 155; In the long
term, the home price index will level off at 155 points.

61. $\lim_{t \to 1^-} C(t) = 0.06$, $\lim_{t \to 1^+} C(t) = 0.08$, so $\lim_{t \to 1} C(t)$ does not exist. **63.** $\lim_{t \to +\infty} I(t) = +\infty$, $\lim_{t \to +\infty}(I(t)/E(t)) \approx 2.5$. In the long term, U.S. imports from China will rise without bound and be 2.5 times U.S. exports to China. In the real world, imports and exports cannot rise without bound. Thus, the given models should not be extrapolated far into the future. **65.** To approximate $\lim_{x \to a} f(x)$ numerically, choose values of x closer and closer to, and on either side of $x = a$, and evaluate $f(x)$ for each of them. The limit (if it exists) is then the number that these values of $f(x)$ approach. A disadvantage of this method is that it may never give the exact value of the limit, but only an approximation. (However, we can make this as accurate as we like.) **67.** Any situation in which there is a sudden change can be modeled by a function in which $\lim_{t \to a^+} f(t)$ is not the same as $\lim_{t \to a^-} f(t)$. One example is the value of a stock market index before and after a crash: $\lim_{t \to a^-} f(t)$ is the value immediately before the crash at time $t = a$, while $\lim_{t \to a^+} f(t)$ is the value immediately after the crash. Another example might be the price of a commodity that is suddenly increased from one level to another. **69.** It is possible for $\lim_{x \to a} f(x)$ to exist even though $f(a)$ is not defined. An example is $\lim_{x \to 1} \dfrac{x^2 - 3x + 2}{x - 1}$.

71. An example is $f(x) = (x - 1)(x - 2)$. **73.** These limits are all 0.

Section 10.2

1. Continuous on its domain **3.** Continuous on its domain **5.** Discontinuous at $x = 0$ **7.** Discontinuous at $x = -1$ **9.** Continuous on its domain **11.** Continuous on its domain **13.** Discontinuous at $x = -1$ and 0 **15.** (A), (B), (D), (E) **17.** Continuous **19.** Discontinuous **21.** Singular **23.** Continuous **25.** 0 **27.** -1 **29.** No value possible **31.** -1 **33.** Continuous on its domain **35.** Continuous on its domain **37.** Discontinuity at $x = 0$ **39.** Discontinuity at $x = 0$ **41.** Continuous on its domain **43.** (B) **45.** (C) **47.** Not unless the domain of the function consists of all real numbers. (It is impossible for a function to be continuous at points not in its domain.) For example, $f(x) = 1/x$ is continuous on its domain—the set of nonzero real numbers—but not at $x = 0$. **49.** True. If the graph of a function has a break in its graph at any point a, then it cannot be continuous at the point a. **51.** Answers may vary. $f(x) = 1/[(x - 1)(x - 2)(x - 3)]$ is such a function; it is undefined at $x = 1, 2, 3$, so its graph consists of three distinct curves. **53.** Answers may vary.

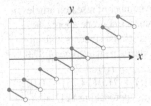

55. Answers may vary. The price of OHaganBooks.com stocks suddenly drops by $10 as news spreads of a government investigation. Let $f(x) = $ Price of OHaganBooks.com stocks.

Section 10.3

1. $x = 1$ **3.** 2 **5.** Determinate; diverges to $+\infty$ **7.** Determinate; does not exist **9.** Determinate; diverges to $-\infty$ **11.** Determinate; 0 **13.** Indeterminate; $-1/3$ **15.** Indeterminate; 0 **17.** Determinate; 0 **19.** Determinate; -60 **21.** 1 **23.** 2 **25.** 0 **27.** 6 **29.** 4 **31.** 2 **33.** 0 **35.** 0 **37.** 12 **39.** $+\infty$ **41.** Does not exist; left and right (infinite) limits differ. **43.** $-\infty$ **45.** Does not exist: left and right (infinite) limits differ. **47.** $+\infty$ **49.** 0 **51.** 1/6 **53.** 3/2 **55.** 1/2 **57.** $+\infty$ **59.** 3/2 **61.** 1/2 **63.** $-\infty$ **65.** 0 **67.** 12 **69.** 0 **71.** $+\infty$ **73.** 0 **75.** Singular point at $x = 3$ **77.** Discontinuity at $x = 5$ **79.** Discontinuity at $x = 0$ **81.** Singularity at $x = 0$ **83.** Continuous everywhere **85.** Discontinuity at $x = 0$ **87.** Discontinuity at $x = 0$ **89. a.** $\lim_{t \to 15^-} v(t) = 3{,}800$, $\lim_{t \to 15^+} v(t) = 3{,}800$; Shortly before 2005, the speed of Intel processors was approaching 3,800 MHz. Shortly after 2005, the speed of Intel processors was close to 3,800 MHz. **b.** Continuous at $t = 15$; No abrupt change. **91. a.** 0.49, 1.16. Shortly before 1999, annual advertising expenditures were close to $0.49 billion. Shortly after 1999, annual advertising expenditures were close to $1.16 billion. **b.** Not continuous; movie advertising expenditures jumped suddenly in 1999. **93.** 1.59; if the trend continued indefinitely, the annual spending on police would be 1.59 times the annual spending on courts in the long run. **95.** 573. This suggests that students with an exceptionally large household income earn an average of 573 on the math SAT test. **97.** $\lim_{t \to +\infty} W(t) = +\infty$, $\lim_{t \to +\infty} W(t)/L(t) = 8.25$. In the long term, the popularity of Twitter among social media sites will increase without bound and be 8.25 times the popularity of LinkedIn. However, a percentage cannot rise beyond 100, so extrapolating the models to obtain long-term predictions gives meaningless results. **99.** $\lim_{t \to +\infty} p(t) = 100$. The percentage of children who learn to speak approaches 100% as their age increases. **101.** To evaluate $\lim_{x \to a} f(x)$ algebraically, first check whether $f(x)$ is a closed-form function. Then check whether $x = a$ is in its domain. If so, the limit is just $f(a)$; that is, it is obtained by substituting $x = a$. If not, then try to first simplify $f(x)$ in such a way as to transform it into a new function such that $x = a$ is in its domain, and then substitute. A disadvantage of this method is that it is sometimes extremely difficult to evaluate limits algebraically, and rather sophisticated methods are often needed. **103.** Rita's side; closed-form functions are continuous at every point of their domain; a discontinuity would be a point in the domain at which the function was *not* continuous, so there cannot be any such points. Richard's example is of a function with a singular point at $x = 0$ and not a discontinuity. **105.** $x = 3$ is not in the domain of the given function f, so, yes, the *function* is undefined at $x = 3$. However, the *limit* may well be defined. In this case, it leads to the indeterminate form 0/0, telling us that we need to try to simplify, and that leads us to the correct limit of 27. **107.** She is wrong. Closed-form functions are continuous only at points in their domains, and $x = 2$ is not in the domain of the closed-form function $f(x) = 1/(x - 2)^2$. (It is a singular point.)

109. Answers may vary. (1) See Example 1(b): $\lim\limits_{x \to 2} \dfrac{x^3 - 8}{x - 2}$, which leads to the indeterminate form 0/0, but the limit is 12.
(2) $\lim\limits_{x \to +\infty} \dfrac{60x}{2x}$, which leads to the indeterminate form ∞/∞ but where the limit exists and equals 30.   **111.** $\pm\infty/\infty$; The limits are zero. This suggests that limits resulting in $\dfrac{p(-\infty)}{e^{\infty}}$ are zero.

113. The statement may not be true if f is not a closed-form function (for instance, a piecewise-defined function). The statement can be corrected by requiring that f be a closed-form function: "If f is a closed-form function, and $f(a)$ is defined, then $\lim_{x \to a} f(x)$ exists and equals $f(a)$."

115. Answers may vary, for example
$$f(x) = \begin{cases} 0 & \text{if } x \text{ is any number other than 1 or 2} \\ 1 & \text{if } x = 1 \text{ or } 2 \end{cases}$$

117. Answers may vary.
(1) $\lim\limits_{x \to +\infty} [(x + 5) - x] = \lim\limits_{x \to +\infty} 5 = 5$
(2) $\lim\limits_{x \to +\infty} [x^2 - x] = \lim\limits_{x \to +\infty} x(x - 1) = +\infty$
(3) $\lim\limits_{x \to +\infty} [(x - 5) - x] = \lim\limits_{x \to +\infty} -5 = -5$

Section 10.4

1. -3 **3.** 0.3   **5.** $-\$25,000$ per month   **7.** -200 items per dollar   **9.** $\$1.33$ per month   **11.** 0.75 percentage point increase in unemployment per 1 percentage point increase in the deficit   **13.** 4   **15.** 2   **17.** 7/3

19.

h	Avg. Rate of Change
1	2
0.1	0.2
0.01	0.02
0.001	0.002
0.0001	0.0002

21.

h	Avg. Rate of Change
1	-0.1667
0.1	-0.2381
0.01	-0.2488
0.001	-0.2499
0.0001	-0.24999

23.

h	Avg. Rate of Change
1	9
0.1	8.1
0.01	8.01
0.001	8.001
0.0001	8.0001

25. a. $\$50$ billion per year; World military expenditure increased at an average rate of about $\$50$ billion per year during 2006–2012. **b.** Approximately $\$54.17$ billion per year; World military expenditure increased at an average rate of about $\$54.17$ billion per year during 2000–2012.   **27. a.** $-10,000$ barrels per year; During 2010–2013, daily oil production by Pemex was decreasing at an average rate of 10,000 barrels of oil per year. **b.** (A)   **29. a.** 1.7; The percentage of mortgages classified as subprime was increasing at an average rate of around 1.7 percentage points per year between 2000 and 2006. **b.** 2004–2006   **31. a.** 2010–2012; During 2010–2012, immigration to Ireland was increasing at an average rate of 5,500 people per year. **b.** 2011–2013; During 2011–2013, immigration to Ireland was increasing at an average rate of 1,500 people per year.   **33. a.** $[25, 30]$; 10 thousand articles per year. During the period 2005–2010 the number of articles authored by U.S. researchers increased at an average rate of 10,000 per year. **b.** Percentage rate 100%; Average rate $\approx$ 5.667 thousand articles per year. Over the period 1980–2010 the number of articles authored by U.S. researchers increased at an average rate of about 5,667 per year, representing a 100% increase over that period.   **35. a.** 12 teams per year **b.** Decreased   **37. a.** (A) **b.** (C) **c.** (B) **d.** Approximately $-\$0.088$ per year (if we round to two significant digits). This is less than the slope of the regression line, about $-\$0.063$ per year.   **39.** Answers may vary.

Graph:

41. The index was increasing at an average rate of 300 points per day.   **43. a.** $\$0.15$ per year **b.** No; according to the model, during that 25-year period the price of oil went down from around $\$93$ to a low of around $\$25$ in 1993 before climbing back up.   **45. a.** 0.057, 0.131, 0.205, 0.279 **b.** 0.74; 0.74 AU per million years per million years.   **47. a.** 47.3 new cases per day; the number of SARS cases was growing at an average rate of 47.3 new cases per day over the period March 17 to March 23. **b.** (A)   **49.** Successive 2-month rates of change: 154.43, 317.27, 651.81, 1,339.10, and 2,751.10 cases per month **b.** exponential; The 2-month average rate of increase in the number of Ebola cases increased by a factor of about 2.05 each month.   **51. a.** 8.85 manatee deaths per 100,000 boats; 23.05 manatee deaths per 100,000 boats **b.** More boats result in more manatee deaths per additional boat.   **53. a.** The average rates of change are shown in the following table:

Interval	$[0, 40]$	$[40, 80]$	$[80, 120]$	$[120, 160]$	$[160, 200]$
Avg. Rate of Change of S	1.35	0.80	0.48	0.28	0.17

b. For household incomes between $40,000 and $80,000 a student's math SAT increases at an average rate of 0.80 points per $1,000 of additional income. **c.** (A) **d.** (B)   **55.** The average rate of change of f over an interval $[a, b]$ can be determined numerically, using a table of values; graphically, by measuring the slope of the corresponding line segment through two points on the graph; or algebraically, using an algebraic formula for the function. Of these, the least precise is the graphical method, because it relies on reading coordinates of points on a graph.
57. No, the formula for the average rate of a function f over $[a, b]$ depends only on $f(a)$ and $f(b)$, and not on any values of f between a and b.   **59.** Answers will vary.

Graph:

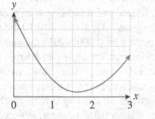

61. 6 units of quantity A per unit of quantity C   **63.** (A)
65. Yes. Here is an example:

Year	2000	2001	2002	2003
Revenue ($ billion)	10	20	30	5

67. (A)

Section 10.5

1. 6   **3.** −5.5

5.

h	1	0.1	0.01
Avg. Rate	39	39.9	39.99

Instantaneous rate = $40 per day

7.

h	1	0.1	0.01
Avg. Rate	140	66.2	60.602

Instantaneous rate = $60 per day

9.

h	10	1
C_{avg}	4.799	4.7999

$C'(1,000) = \$4.80$ per item

11.

h	10	1
C_{avg}	99.91	99.90

$C'(100) = \$99.90$ per item

13. 1/2   **15.** 0   **17. a.** R **b.** P **19. a.** P **b.** R
21. a. Q **b.** P **23. a.** Q **b.** R **c.** P
25. a. R **b.** Q **c.** P **27. a.** $(1, 0)$ **b.** None **c.** $(-2, 1)$
29. a. $(-2, 0.3), (0, 0), (2, -0.3)$ **b.** None **c.** None

31. $(a, f(a)); f'(a)$ **33.** (B)   **35. a.** (A) **b.** (C) **c.** (B)
d. (B) **e.** (C)   **37.** −2   **39.** −1.5   **41.** −5   **43.** 16
45. 0   **47.** −0.0025
49. a. 3 **b.** $y = 3x + 2$

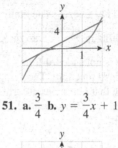

51. a. $\dfrac{3}{4}$ **b.** $y = \dfrac{3}{4}x + 1$

53. a. $\dfrac{1}{4}$ **b.** $y = \dfrac{1}{4}x + 1$

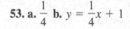

55. 1.000   **57.** 1.000   **59.** (C)   **61.** (A)   **63.** (F)
65. Increasing for $x < 0$; decreasing for $x > 0$.
67. Increasing for $x < -1$ and $x > 1$; decreasing for $-1 < x < 1$.   **69.** Increasing for $x > 1$; decreasing for $x < 1$.   **71.** Increasing for $x < 0$; decreasing for $x > 0$.
73. $x = -1.5, x = 0$

Graph:

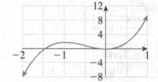

75. Note: Answers depend on the form of technology used.
Excel ($h = 0.1$):

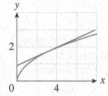

Graphs:

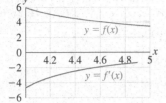

77. −35°F; 40°F per hour   **79.** $q(100) = 50,000$, $q'(100) = -500$. A total of 50,000 pairs of sneakers can be sold at a price of $100, but the demand is decreasing at a rate of 500 pairs per $1 increase in the price.   **81. a.** −60; Daily imports from Mexico in 2011 were 1.08 million barrels and declining at a rate of 0.06 million barrels (or 60,000 barrels) per year.   **b.** Decreasing; the slope is decreasing.   **83. a.** (B)   **b.** (B)   **c.** (A)   **d.** 2004   **e.** 0.033; in 2004 the U.S. prison population was increasing at a rate of 0.033 million prisoners (33,000 prisoners) per year.   **85. a.** −96 ft/sec   **b.** −128 ft/sec   **87. a.** $0.60 per year; the price per barrel of crude oil in constant 2008 dollars was growing at an average rate of about 60¢ per year over the 28-year period beginning at the start of 1980.   **b.** −$12 per year; the price per barrel of crude oil in constant 2008 dollars was dropping at an instantaneous rate of about $12 per year at the start of 1980.   **c.** The price of oil was decreasing in January 1980 but eventually began to increase (making the average rate of change in part (a) positive).   **89. a.** 144.7 new cases per day; the number of SARS cases was growing at a rate of about 144.7 new cases per day on March 27.   **b.** (A)

91. $C(5) \approx 3,510$, $\left.\dfrac{dC}{dt}\right|_{t=5} \approx 2,527$. Five months after the outbreak, the number of cases was around 3,510 and increasing at a rate of about 2,527 per month.   **93.** $A(0) = 4.5$ million; $A'(0) = 60,000$ subscribers per week   **95. a.** 60% of children can speak at the age of 10 months. At the age of 10 months this percentage is increasing by 18.2 percentage points per month.   **b.** As t increases, p approaches 100 percentage points (all children eventually learn to speak), and dp/dt approaches zero because the percentage stops increasing.   **97. a.** $A(6) \approx 12$; $A'(6) \approx 1.4$; At the start of 2006, about 12% of U.S. mortgages were subprime, and this percentage was increasing at a rate of about 1.4 percentage points per year.   **b.** Graphs:

Graph of A: Graph of A':

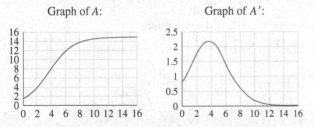

From the graphs, $A(t)$ approaches 15 as t becomes large (in terms of limits, $\lim_{x \to +\infty} A(t) = 15$) and $A'(t)$ approaches 0 as t becomes large (in terms of limits, $\lim_{x \to +\infty} A'(t) = 0$). Interpretation: If the trend modeled by the function A had continued indefinitely, in the long term 15% of U.S. mortgages would have been subprime, and this percentage would not be

changing.   **99. a.** (D)   **b.** 33 days after the egg was laid   **c.** 50 days after the egg was laid.

Graph:

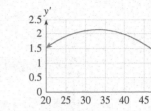

101. $L(.95) \approx 31.2$ meters and $L'(.95) \approx -304.2$ meters per warp. Thus, at a speed of warp 0.95, the spaceship has an observed length of 31.2 meters, and its length is decreasing at a rate of 304.2 meters per unit warp, or 3.042 meters per increase in speed of 0.01 warp.   **103.** None   **105.** The difference quotient is not defined when $h = 0$ because there is no such number as $0/0$.   **107.** (D)   **109.** The derivative is positive and decreasing toward zero.   **111.** Company B. Although the company is currently losing money, the derivative is positive, showing that the profit is increasing. Company A, on the other hand, has profits that are declining.   **113.** (C) is the only graph in which the instantaneous rate of change on January 1 is greater than the 1-month average rate of change.   **115.** The tangent to the graph is horizontal at that point, so the graph is almost horizontal near that point. **117.** Answers may vary.

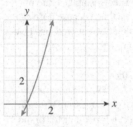

119. If $f(x) = mx + b$, then its average rate of change over any interval $[x, x + h]$ is $\dfrac{m(x + h) + b - (mx + b)}{h} = m$.

Because this does not depend on h, the instantaneous rate is also equal to m.   **121.** Increasing because the average rate of change appears to be rising as we get closer to 5 from the left. (See the bottom row.)
123. Answers may vary.

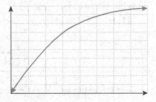

125. Answers may vary.

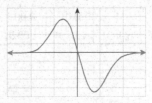

127. (B)   **129.** Answers will vary.

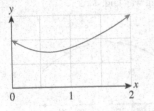

Section 10.6

1. 4   **3.** 3   **5.** 7   **7.** 4   **9.** 14   **11.** 1   **13.** m **15.** $2x$ **17.** 3
19. $6x + 1$ **21.** $2 - 2x$ **23.** $3x^2 + 2$ **25.** $1/x^2$ **27.** m
29. -1.2 **31.** 30.6   **33.** -7.1 **35.** 4.25   **37.** -0.6
39. $y = 4x - 7$ **41.** $y = -2x - 4$ **43.** $y = -3x - 1$
45. $s'(t) = -32t$; $s'(4) = -128$ ft/sec   **47.** $dI/dt =$
$-78t + 800$; Daily oil imports were decreasing at a rate of
136,000 barrels per year.   **49.** $R'(t) = 0.16t - 0.26$; Increasing at a rate of 540 million gallons per year   **51.** $f'(8) = 26.6$
manatee deaths per 100,000 boats. At a level of 800,000 boats,
the number of manatee deaths is increasing at a rate of
26.6 manatees per 100,000 additional boats.   **53.** Yes;
$\lim_{t \to 20^-} C(t) = \lim_{t \to 20^+} C(t) = 700 = C(20)$. **b.** No;
$\lim_{t \to 20^-} C'(t) = 31.1$ while $\lim_{t \to 20^+} C'(t) = 90$. Until 1990
the cost of a Super Bowl ad was increasing at a rate of $31,100
per year. Immediately thereafter, it was increasing at a rate of
$90,000 per year.   **55.** The algebraic method because it gives
the exact value of the derivative. The other two approaches give
only approximate values (except in some special cases).
57. The error is in the second line: $f(x + h)$ is *not* equal to
$f(x) + h$. For instance, if $f(x) = x^2$, then $f(x + h) =$
$(x + h)^2$, whereas $f(x) + h = x^2 + h$.   **59.** The error is in
the second line: One could cancel the h only if it were a *factor*
of both the numerator and denominator; it is not a factor of the
numerator.   **61.** Because the algebraic computation of $f'(a)$ is
exact and not an approximation, it makes no difference whether
one uses the balanced difference quotient or the ordinary difference quotient in the algebraic computation.   **63.** The computation results in a limit that cannot be evaluated.

Chapter 10 Review

1. 5   **3.** Does not exist   **5. a.** -1 **b.** 3 **c.** Does not exist
7. $-4/5$ **9.** -1 **11.** -1 **13.** Does not exist   **15.** 10/7
17. Does not exist   **19.** $+\infty$ **21.** 0   **23.** Diverges to $-\infty$
25. 0   **27.** 2/5   **29.** 1

31.

h	1	0.01	0.001
Avg. Rate of Change	-0.5	-0.9901	-0.9990

Slope ≈ -1

33.

h	1	0.01	0.001
Avg. Rate of Change	6.3891	2.0201	2.0020

Slope ≈ 2

35. a. P **b.** Q **c.** R **d.** S **37. a.** Q **b.** None **c.** None **d.** None
39. a. (B) **b.** (B) **c.** (B) **d.** (A) **e.** (C)   **41.** $2x + 1$ **43.** $2/x^2$

45.

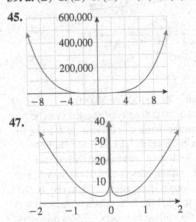

47.

49. a. $P(3) = 25$: O'Hagan purchased the stock at $25.
$\lim_{t \to 3^-} P(t) = 25$: The value of the stock had been approaching
$25 up to the time he bought it. $\lim_{t \to 3^+} P(t) = 10$: The value
of the stock dropped to $10 immediately after he bought it.
b. Continuous but not differentiable. Interpretation: the stock
price changed continuously but suddenly reversed direction
(and started to go up) the instant O'Hagan sold it.
51. a. $\lim_{t \to 3} p(t) \approx 40$; $\lim_{t \to +\infty} p(t) = +\infty$. Close to 2007
($t = 3$), the home price index was about 40. In the long term, the
home price index will rise without bound. **b.** 10 (The slope of the
linear portion of the curve is 10.) In the long term, the home price
index will rise about 10 points per year.   **53. a.** 500 books per
week **b.** $[3, 4]$, $[4, 5]$ **c.** $[3, 5]$; 650 books per week
55. a. 3 percentage points per year **b.** 0 percentage points per
year **c.** (D)   **57. a.** $72t + 250$ **b.** 322 books per week
c. 754 books per week.

Chapter 11

Section 11.1

1. $5x^4$ **3.** $-4x^{-3}$ **5.** $-0.25x^{-0.75}$ **7.** $8x^3 + 9x^2$

9. $-1 - 1/x^2$ **11.** $\dfrac{dy}{dx} = 10(0) = 0$ (constant multiple

and power rule)   **13.** $\dfrac{dy}{dx} = \dfrac{d}{dx}(x^2) + \dfrac{d}{dx}(x)$

(sum rule) $= 2x + 1$ (power rule)

15. $\dfrac{dy}{dx} = \dfrac{d}{dx}(4x^3) + \dfrac{d}{dx}(2x) - \dfrac{d}{dx}(1)$ (sum and

difference) $= 4\dfrac{d}{dx}(x^3) + 2\dfrac{d}{dx}(x) - \dfrac{d}{dx}(1)$

(constant multiples) $= 12x^2 + 2$ (power rule)
17. $f'(x) = 2x - 3$ **19.** $f'(x) = 1 + 0.5x^{-0.5}$

21. $g'(x) = -2x^{-3} + 3x^{-2}$ **23.** $g'(x) = -\dfrac{1}{x^2} + \dfrac{2}{x^3}$

25. $h'(x) = -\dfrac{0.8}{x^{1.4}}$ **27.** $h'(x) = -\dfrac{2}{x^3} - \dfrac{6}{x^4}$

29. $r'(x) = -\dfrac{2}{3x^2} + \dfrac{0.1}{2x^{1.1}}$ **31.** $r'(x) = \dfrac{2}{3} - \dfrac{0.1}{2x^{0.9}} - \dfrac{4.4}{3x^{2.1}}$

33. $t'(x) = |x|/x - 1/x^2$ **35.** $s'(x) = \dfrac{1}{2\sqrt{x}} - \dfrac{1}{2x\sqrt{x}}$

37. $s'(x) = 3x^2 \ (x \neq 0)$ **39.** $t'(x) = 1 - 4x \ (x \neq 0)$
41. $2.6x^{0.3} + 1.2x^{-2.2}$ **43.** $1.2(1 - |x|/x)$
45. $3at^2 - 4a$ **47.** $5.15x^{9.3} - 99x^{-2}$

49. $-\dfrac{2.31}{t^{2.1}} - \dfrac{0.3}{t^{0.4}}$ **51.** $4\pi r^2$ **53.** 3   **55.** -2 **57.** -5

59. $y = 3x + 2$ **61.** $y = \dfrac{3}{4}x + 1$

63. $y = \dfrac{1}{4}x + 1$ **65.** $x = -3/4$
67. No such values
69. $x = 1, -1$
71. See Solutions Manual.
73. a. 2/3   **b.** Not differentiable
at 0
75. a. 5/2   **b.** Not differentiable
at 0

77. Yes; 0   **79.** Yes; 12   **81.** No; 3   **83.** Yes; 3/2
85. Yes; diverges to $-\infty$ **87.** Yes; diverges to $-\infty$
89. $P'(t) = 0.54t - 8.6$; $P'(30) = 7.6$; the price of a barrel of
crude oil was increasing at a rate of $7.60 per year in 2010.
91. 4.8   **93. a.** $s'(t) = -32t$; 0, -32, -64, -96, -128 ft/sec
b. 5 seconds; downward at 160 ft/sec   **95. a.** 20 sec; at the
highest point, h stops increasing and begins to decrease, so its
rate of change, h', changes from positive to negative, meaning
it must be zero.   **b.** 760 m   **97. a.** $P'(t) = -0.78t + 5.2$;
increasing at a rate of $0.52 billion per year   **b.** (B)
99. a. $f'(x) = 7.1x - 30.2$; $f'(8) = 26.6$ manatees per
100,000 boats; at a level of 800,000 boats, manatee deaths are
increasing at a rate of 26.6 deaths each year per 100,000 additional boats.   **b.** Increasing; the number of manatees killed per
additional 100,000 boats increases as the number of boats
increases.   **101. a.** $A - I$ measures the amount by which the
Android market share exceeds the iOS market share. $(A - I)'$
measures the rate at which this difference is changing.   **b.** (A)
c. $9t^2 - 58t + 102.3$ percentage points per year; (A); The vertical distance between the graphs increases; Android increases
its advantage over iOS through this range of dates.   **d.** 9.3 percentage points per year; in the second quarter of 2013 $(t = 3)$,
Android's advantage over iOS was increasing at a rate of
9.3 percentage points per year.   **103.** After graphing the curve
$y = 3x^2$, draw the line passing through $(-1, 3)$ with slope -6.
105. The slope of the tangent line of g is twice the slope of the
tangent line of f.   **107.** $g'(x) = -f'(x)$ **109.** The left-hand
side is not equal to the right-hand side. The *derivative* of the

left-hand side is equal to the right-hand side, so your friend
should have written $\dfrac{d}{dx}(3x^4 + 11x^5) = 12x^3 + 55x^4$.

111. $\dfrac{1}{2x}$ is not equal to $2x^{-1}$. Your friend should have

written $y = \dfrac{1}{2x} = \dfrac{1}{2}x^{-1}$, so $\dfrac{dy}{dx} = -\dfrac{1}{2}x^{-2}$.   **113.** The

derivative of a constant times a function is the constant times
the derivative of the function, so that $f'(x) = (2)(2x) = 4x$.
Your enemy mistakenly computed the *derivative* of the constant times the derivative of the function. (The derivative of
a product of two functions is not the product of the derivative
of the two functions. The rule for taking the derivative of a
product is discussed later in the chapter.).
115. For a general function f, the derivative of f is defined to

be $f'(x) = \lim\limits_{h \to 0} \dfrac{f(x + h) - f(x)}{h}$. One then finds by calculation

that the derivative of the specific function x^n is nx^{n-1}. In short,
nx^{n-1} is the derivative of a specific function: $f(x) = x^n$, it is
not the *definition* of the derivative of a general function or even
the definition of the derivative of the function $f(x) = x^n$.

117. Answers may vary.

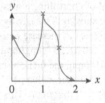

Section 11.2

1. $C'(1,000) = \$4.80$ per item   **3.** $C'(100) = \$99.90$ per item
5. $C'(x) = 4$; $R'(x) = 8 - 0.002x$; $P'(x) = 4 - 0.002x$;
$P'(x) = 0$ when $x = 2,000$. Thus, at a production level of
2,000, the profit is stationary (neither increasing nor decreasing)
with respect to the production level. This may indicate a maximum profit at a production level of 2,000.   **7. a.** (B)   **b.** (C)
c. (C)   **9. a.** $C'(x) = 4,000 + 0.1x$; the cost is increasing at
a rate of $4,000,400 per television commercial. The exact cost
of airing the fifth television commercial is $4,000,450.
b. $\overline{C}(x) = 20/x + 4,000 + 0.05x$; $\overline{C}(4) = 4,005.2$ thousand
dollars. The average cost of airing the first four television
commercials is $4,005,200.   **11. a.** $C'(x) = 160 + 0.002x$; the
cost is increasing at a rate of $180 per iPhone. Actual cost of the
10,001st iPhone is $180.001.   **b.** $\overline{C}(x) = 400,000/x + 160 +$
$0.001x$; the average cost to produce the first 10,000 iPhones is
$210 per iPhone.   **c.** The average cost is falling at a production
level of 10,000 iPhones.   **13. a.** $R'(x) = 0.90$, $P'(x) =$
$0.80 - 0.002x$ **b.** Revenue: $450, profit: $80, marginal revenue: $0.90, marginal profit: $-\$0.20$. The total revenue from
the sale of 500 copies is $450. The profit from the production
and sale of 500 copies is $80. Approximate revenue from the
sale of the 501st copy is 90¢. Approximate loss from the sale
of the 501st copy is 20¢.   **c.** $x = 400$. The profit is a maximum
when you produce and sell 400 copies.   **15.** The profit on
the sale of 1,000 Blu-ray discs is $3,000, and is decreasing
at a rate of $3 per additional Blu-ray disc sold.

17. Profit $\approx$ \$257.07; marginal profit $\approx$ \$5.07 per magazine. Your current profit is \$257.07 per month, and this would increase at a rate of \$5.07 per additional magazine sold. **19. a.** \$2.50 per pound **b.** $R(q) = 20{,}000/q^{0.5}$ **c.** $R(400) = \$1{,}000$. This is the monthly revenue that will result from setting the price at \$2.50 per pound. $R'(400) = -\$1.25$ per pound of tuna. Thus, at a demand level of 400 pounds per month, the revenue is decreasing at a rate of \$1.25 per pound. **d.** The fishery should raise the price (to reduce the demand). **21.** $P'(50) = 35$ cars per worker. This means that, at an employment level of 50 workers, the firm's daily production will increase at a rate of 35 cars washed per additional worker it hires. **23. a.** (B) **b.** (B) **c.** (C) **25. a.** $C(x) = 500{,}000 + 1{,}900{,}000x - 100{,}000\sqrt{x}$; $C'(x) = 1{,}900{,}000 - 50{,}000/\sqrt{x}$; $\overline{C}(x) = 500{,}000/x + 1{,}900{,}000 - 100{,}000/\sqrt{x}$ **b.** $C'(3) \approx \$1{,}870{,}000$ per spot; $\overline{C}(3) \approx \$2{,}010{,}000$ per spot. The average cost will decrease as x increases. **27. a.** \$2,000 per 1-pound reduction in emissions. **b.** 2.5 pounds per day reduction. **c.** $N(q) = 100q^2 - 500q + 4{,}000$; 2.5 pounds per day reduction. The value of q is the same as that for part (b). The net cost to the firm is minimized at the reduction level for which the cost of controlling emissions begins to increase faster than the subsidy. This is why we get the answer by setting these two rates of increase equal to each other. **29.** $M'(10) \approx 0.0002557$ mpg/mph. This means that, at a speed of 10 mph, the fuel economy is increasing at a rate of 0.0002557 miles per gallon per 1 mile per hour increase in speed. $M'(60) = 0$ mpg/mph. This means that, at a speed of

60 mph, the fuel economy is neither increasing nor decreasing with increasing speed. $M'(70) \approx -0.00001799$. This means that, at 70 mph, the fuel economy is decreasing at a rate of 0.00001799 miles per gallon per 1 mile per hour increase in speed. Thus, 60 mph is the most fuel-efficient speed for the car. **31.** (C) **33.** (D) **35.** (B) **37.** Cost is often measured as a function of the number of items x. Thus, $C(x)$ is the cost of producing (or purchasing, as the case may be) x items. **a.** The average cost function $\overline{C}(x)$ is given by $\overline{C}(x) = C(x)/x$. The marginal cost function is the derivative, $C'(x)$, of the cost function. **b.** The average cost $\overline{C}(r)$ is the slope of the line through the origin and the point on the graph where $x = r$. The marginal cost of the rth unit is the slope of the tangent to the graph of the cost function at the point where $x = r$. **c.** The average cost function $\overline{C}(x)$ gives the average cost of producing the first x items. The marginal cost function $C'(x)$ is the rate at which cost is changing with respect to the number of items x, or the incremental cost per item, and approximates the cost of producing the $(x + 1)$st item. **39.** Answers may vary. An example is $C(x) = 300x$. **41.** The marginal cost **43.** Not necessarily. For example, it may be the case that the marginal cost of the 101st item is larger than the average cost of the first 100 items (even though the marginal cost is decreasing). Thus, adding this additional item will *raise* the average cost. **45.** The circumstances described suggest that the average cost function is at a relatively low point at the current production level, so it would be appropriate to advise the company to maintain current production levels; raising or lowering the production level will result in increasing average costs.

Section 11.3

1. 3 **3.** $3x^2$ **5.** $2x + 3$ **7.** $210x^{1.1}$ **9.** $-2/x^2$ **11.** $2x/3$ **13.** $36x^2 - 3$ **15.** $3x^2 - 5x^4$
17. $8x + 12$ **19.** $-8/(5x - 2)^2$ **21.** $-14/(3x - 1)^2$ **23.** 0 **25.** $-|x|/x^3$ **27.** $3\sqrt{x}/2$
29. $(x^2 - 1) + 2x(x + 1) = (x + 1)(3x - 1)$ **31.** $(x^{-0.5} + 4)(x - x^{-1}) + (2x^{0.5} + 4x - 5)(1 + x^{-2})$
33. $8(2x^2 - 4x + 1)(x - 1)$ **35.** $(1/3.2 - 3.2/x^2)(x^2 + 1) + 2x(x/3.2 + 3.2/x)$
37. $2x(2x + 3)(7x + 2) + 2x^2(7x + 2) + 7x^2(2x + 3)$
39. $5.3(1 - x^{2.1})(x^{-2.3} - 3.4) - 2.1x^{1.1}(5.3x - 1)(x^{-2.3} - 3.4) - 2.3x^{-3.3}(5.3x - 1)(1 - x^{2.1})$

41. $\dfrac{1}{2\sqrt{x}}\left(\sqrt{x} + \dfrac{1}{x^2}\right) + (\sqrt{x} + 1)\left(\dfrac{1}{2\sqrt{x}} - \dfrac{2}{x^3}\right)$

43. $\dfrac{(4x + 4)(3x - 1) - 3(2x^2 + 4x + 1)}{(3x - 1)^2} = (6x^2 - 4x - 7)/(3x - 1)^2$

45. $\dfrac{(2x - 4)(x^2 + x + 1) - (x^2 - 4x + 1)(2x + 1)}{(x^2 + x + 1)^2} = (5x^2 - 5)/(x^2 + x + 1)^2$

47. $\dfrac{(0.23x^{-0.77} - 5.7)(1 - x^{-2.9}) - 2.9x^{-3.9}(x^{0.23} - 5.7x)}{(1 - x^{-2.9})^2}$ **49.** $\dfrac{\frac{1}{2}x^{-1/2}(x^{1/2} - 1) - \frac{1}{2}x^{-1/2}(x^{1/2} + 1)}{(x^{1/2} - 1)^2} = \dfrac{-1}{\sqrt{x}(\sqrt{x} - 1)^2}$

51. $-3/x^4$ **53.** $\dfrac{[(x + 1) + (x + 3)](3x - 1) - 3(x + 3)(x + 1)}{(3x - 1)^2} = (3x^2 - 2x - 13)/(3x - 1)^2$

55. $\dfrac{[(x + 1)(x + 2) + (x + 3)(x + 2) + (x + 3)(x + 1)](3x - 1) - 3(x + 3)(x + 1)(x + 2)}{(3x - 1)^2}$

57. $4x^3 - 2x$ **59.** 64 **61.** 3 **63.** Difference; $4x^3 - 12x^2 + 2x - 480$ **65.** Sum; $1 + 2/(x + 1)^2$

67. Product; $\left[\dfrac{x}{x+1}\right] + (x+2)\dfrac{1}{(x+1)^2}$ **69.** Difference;

$2x - 1 - 2/(x+1)^2$ **71.** $y = 12x - 8$ **73.** $y = x/4 + 1/2$
75. $y = -2$ **77.** $q'(5) = 1{,}000$ units per month (sales are
increasing at a rate of 1,000 units per month); $p'(5) = -\$10$
per month (the price of a sound system is dropping at a rate of
\$10 per month); $R'(5) = 900{,}000$ (revenue is increasing at a
rate of \$900,000 per month). **79.** \$703 million; increasing at
a rate of \$67 million per year **81.** Decreasing at a rate of
\$1 per day **83.** Decreasing at a rate of approximately

\$0.10 per month **85.** $M'(x) = \dfrac{3{,}000(3{,}600x^{-2} - 1)}{(x + 3{,}600x^{-1})^2}$;

$M'(10) \approx 0.7670$ mpg/mph. This means that, at a speed of
10 mph, the fuel economy is increasing at a rate of 0.7670 miles
per gallon per 1 mile per hour increase in speed. $M'(60) = 0$
mpg/mph. This means that, at a speed of 60 mph, the fuel economy is neither increasing nor decreasing with increasing speed.
$M'(70) \approx -0.0540$. This means that, at 70 mph, the fuel economy is decreasing at a rate of 0.0540 miles per gallon per 1 mile
per hour increase in speed. 60 mph is the most fuel-efficient
speed for the car. (In the next chapter we shall discuss how to
locate largest values in general.) **87. a.** $P(t) - I(t)$ represents
the daily production of oil in Mexico that was not exported to
the United States. $I(t)/P(t)$ represents U.S. imports of oil from
Mexico as a fraction of the total produced there. **b.** -0.020 per
year; at the start of 2011 the fraction of oil produced in Mexico
that was imported by the United States was decreasing at a rate
of 0.020 (or 2.0 percentage points) per year.
89. Increasing at a rate of about \$50 million per year

91. $R'(p) = -\dfrac{5.625}{(1 + 0.125p)^2}$; $R'(4) = -2.5$ thousand

organisms per hour per 1,000 organisms. This means that the
reproduction rate of organisms in a culture containing 4,000
organisms is declining at a rate of 2,500 organisms per hour
per 1,000 additional organisms. **93.** Oxygen consumption is
decreasing at a rate of 1,600 milliliters per day. This must be
due to the fact that the number of eggs is decreasing, as $C'(25)$
is positive. **95.** 20; 33 **97.** 5/4; $-17/16$ **99.** The analysis
is suspect, as it seems to be asserting that the annual increase
in revenue, which we can think of as dR/dt, is the product of
the annual increases, dp/dt in price, and dq/dt in sales.
However, because $R = pq$, the product rule implies that
dR/dt is not the product of dp/dt and dq/dt but is instead
$\dfrac{dR}{dt} = \dfrac{dp}{dt} \cdot q + p \cdot \dfrac{dq}{dt}$. **101.** Answers will vary. $q =$
$-p + 1{,}000$ is one example. **103.** Mine; it is increasing
twice as fast as yours. The rate of change of revenue is given
by $R'(t) = p'(t)q(t)$ because $q'(t) = 0$. Thus, $R'(t)$ does not
depend on the selling price $p(t)$. **105.** (A)

Section 11.4

1. $4(2x + 1)$ **3.** $-(x - 1)^{-2}$ **5.** $2(2 - x)^{-3}$
7. $(2x + 1)^{-0.5}$ **9.** $-3/(3x - 1)^2$
11. $4(x^2 + 2x)^3(2x + 2)$ **13.** $-4x(2x^2 - 2)^{-2}$
15. $-5(2x - 3)(x^2 - 3x - 1)^{-6}$ **17.** $-6x/(x^2 + 1)^4$

19. $1.5(0.2x - 4.2)(0.1x^2 - 4.2x + 9.5)^{0.5}$
21. $4(2s - 0.5s^{-0.5})(s^2 - s^{0.5})^3$ **23.** $-x/\sqrt{1 - x^2}$
25. $\dfrac{3|3x - 6|}{3x - 6}$ **27.** $\dfrac{(-3x^2 + 5)|-x^3 + 5x|}{-x^3 + 5x}$
29. $-[(x + 1)(x^2 - 1)]^{-3/2}(3x - 1)(x + 1)$
31. $6.2(3.1x - 2) + 6.2/(3.1x - 2)^3$
33. $2[(6.4x - 1)^2 + (5.4x - 2)^3] \times$
$[12.8(6.4x - 1) + 16.2(5.4x - 2)^2]$
35. $-2(x^2 - 3x)^{-3}(2x - 3)(1 - x^2)^{0.5}$
$-x(x^2 - 3x)^{-2}(1 - x^2)^{-0.5}$
37. $-56(x + 2)/(3x - 1)^3$ **39.** $3z^2(1 - z^2)/(1 + z^2)^4$
41. $3[(1 + 2x)^4 - (1 - x)^2]^2[8(1 + 2x)^3 + 2(1 - x)]$
43. $6|3x - 1|$ **45.** $\dfrac{|x - (2x - 3)^{1/2}|}{x - (2x - 3)^{1/2}}[1 - (2x - 3)^{-1/2}]$

47. $-\dfrac{\left(\dfrac{1}{\sqrt{2x + 1}} - 2x\right)}{(\sqrt{2x + 1} - x^2)^2}$

49. $54(1 + 2x)^2(1 + (1 + 2x)^3)^2(1 + (1 + (1 + 2x)^3)^3)^2$
51. $2(x + 2)$ **53.** $4(2t - 1) + 2$ **55.** $1/3$
57. $1/(2\sqrt{y})$ **59.** $-5/3$ **61.** $3/\sqrt{x}$ **63.** $1/4$
65. $3/4$ **67.** $(100x^{99} - 99x^{-2})\, dx/dt$
69. $(-3r^{-4} + 0.5r^{-0.5})\, dr/dt$ **71.** $4\pi r^2\, dr/dt$ **73.** $-47/4$
75. $P'(t) = 0.54(t - 1980) - 8.6$; $P'(2010) = 7.6$; the price
of a barrel of crude oil was increasing at a rate of \$7.60 per
year in 2010. **77.** Profit $\approx \$260.49$; marginal profit $\approx \$5.10/$
magazine. Your current profit is \$260.49 per month, and this
would increase at a rate of \$5.10 per additional magazine sold.
79. $M'(x) = -\dfrac{3{,}000(1 - 3{,}600x^{-2})}{(x + 3{,}600x^{-1})^2}$; $M'(10) \approx$

0.7670 mpg/mph. This means that, at a speed of 10 mph, the
fuel economy is increasing at a rate of 0.7670 miles per gallon
per 1 mile per hour increase in speed. $M'(60) = 0$ mpg/mph.
This means that, at a speed of 60 mph, the fuel economy is
neither increasing nor decreasing with increasing speed.
$M'(70) \approx -0.0540$. This means that, at 70 mph, the fuel
economy is decreasing at a rate of 0.0540 miles per gallon
per 1 mile per hour increase in speed. 60 mph is the most
fuel-efficient speed for the car. (In the next chapter we shall
discuss how to locate largest values in general.)
81. $\left.\dfrac{dP}{dn}\right|_{n=10} = 146{,}454.9$. At an employment level of
10 engineers, Paramount will increase its annual profit at a
rate of \$146,454.90 per additional engineer hired.
83. $y = 35(7 + 0.2t)^{-0.25}$; -0.11 percentage point per
month. **85.** $-\$30$ per additional ruby sold. The revenue is
decreasing at a rate of \$30 per additional ruby sold.
87. $\dfrac{dy}{dt} = \dfrac{dy}{dx}\dfrac{dx}{dt} = (1.5)(-2) = -3$ murders per
100,000 residents per year each year. **89.** $5/6 \approx 0.833$;
relative to the 2003 levels, home sales were changing
at a rate of about 0.833 percentage points per percentage
point change in price. (Equivalently, home sales in 2008

were dropping at a rate of about 0.833 percentage points per percentage point drop in price.)   **91.** 12π square miles per hour   **93.** $200,000\pi$ per week $\approx$ $628,000 per week   **95. a.** $q'(4) \approx 333$ units per month **b.** $dR/dq = \$800$ per unit **c.** $dR/dt \approx \$267,000$ per month   **97.** 3% per year   **99.** 8% per year   **101.** The glob squared, times the derivative of the glob.   **103.** The derivative of a quantity cubed is three times the *original quantity* squared times the derivative of the quantity, not three times the derivative of the quantity squared. Thus, the correct answer is $3(3x^3 - x)^2(9x^2 - 1)$.   **105.** First, the derivative of a quantity cubed is three times the *original quantity* squared times the derivative of the quantity, not three times the derivative of the quantity squared. Second, the derivative of a quotient is not the quotient of the derivatives; the quotient rule needs to be used in calculating the derivative of $\dfrac{3x^2 - 1}{2x - 2}$. Thus, the correct result (before simplifying) is

$$3\left(\frac{3x^2 - 1}{2x - 2}\right)^2\left(\frac{6x(2x - 2) - (3x^2 - 1)(2)}{(2x - 2)^2}\right).$$

107. Following the calculation thought experiment, pretend that you were evaluating the function at a specific value of x. If the last operation you would perform is addition or subtraction, look at each summand separately. If the last operation is multiplication, use the product rule first; if it is division, use the quotient rule first; if it is any other operation (such as raising a quantity to a power or taking a radical of a quantity) then use the chain rule first.   **109.** An example is

$$f(x) = \sqrt{x + \sqrt{x + \sqrt{x + \sqrt{x + \sqrt{x + 1}}}}}.$$

Section 11.5

1. $1/(x - 1)$ **3.** $2x/(x^2 + 3)$ **5.** $1/(x \ln 2)$
7. $\dfrac{1}{(x + 1)\ln 2}$ **9.** $\dfrac{1 - 1/t^2}{(t + 1/t)\ln 3}$ **11.** e^{x+3}
13. $(2x - 1)e^{x^2 - x + 1}$ **15.** $4(e^{2x-1})^2$ **17.** $4^x \ln 4$
19. $2^{x^2 - 1}2x \ln 2$ **21.** $2x \ln x + (x^2 + 1)/x$
23. $10x(x^2 + 1)^4 \ln x + (x^2 + 1)^5/x$
25. $4x/(2x^2 + 1)$ **27.** $(2x - 0.63x^{-0.7})/(x^2 - 2.1x^{0.3})$
29. $-2/(-2x + 1) + 1/(x + 1)$
31. $3/(3x + 1) - 4/(4x - 2)$
33. $1/(x + 1) + 1/(x - 3) - 2/(2x + 9)$ **35.** $5.2/(4x - 2)$
37. $2/(x + 1) - 9/(3x - 4) - 1/(x - 9)$
39. $\dfrac{2\ln|x|}{x}$ **41.** $\dfrac{2}{x} - \dfrac{2\ln(x - 1)}{x - 1}$ **43.** $e^x(1 + x)$
45. $1/(x + 1) + 3e^x(x^3 + 3x^2)$ **47.** $e^x(\ln|x| + 1/x)$
49. $2xe^{2x-1}(1 + x)$ **51.** $2 \cdot 3^{2x+1}\ln 3 + 3e^{3x+1}$
53. $\dfrac{2x3^{x^2}[(x^2 + 1)\ln 3 - 1]}{(x^2 + 1)^2}$ **55.** $-4/(e^x - e^{-x})^2$
57. $5e^{5x-3}$ **59.** $-\dfrac{\ln x + 1}{(x \ln x)^2}$ **61.** $2(x - 1)$ **63.** $\dfrac{1}{x \ln x}$
65. $\dfrac{1}{2x \ln x}$ **67.** $y = (e/\ln 2)(x - 1) \approx 3.92(x - 1)$

69. $y = x$ **71.** $y = -[1/(2e)](x - 1) + e$ **73.** 0
75. 0   **77.** 1   **79.** $231 billion and increasing at a rate of $2.9 billion per year   **81.** $231 billion and increasing at a rate of $2.9 billion per year   **83.** $-1,653$ years per gram; the age of the specimen is decreasing at a rate of about 1,653 years per additional 1 gram of carbon 14 present in the sample. (Equivalently, the age of the specimen is increasing at a rate of about 1,653 years per additional 1 gram less of carbon 14 in the sample.)   **85.** Average price: $1.4 million; increasing at a rate of about $220,000 per year.   **87. a.** $N(15) \approx 1,894 \approx 1,900$ (rounded to two significant digits) wiretap orders; $N'(15) \approx 113.6 \approx 110$ wiretap orders per year (rounded to two significant digits). The constants in the model are specified to two significant digits, so we cannot expect the answer to be accurate to more than two digits. **b.** In 2005 the number of people whose communications were intercepted was about 190,000 and increasing at a rate of about 11,000 people per year. **c.** (C)   **89.** $451.00 per year   **91.** $446.02 per year
93. $A(t) = 167(1.18)^t$; 280 new cases per day
95. $C(t) = 100e^{0.72t}$; 1,280 new cases per month
97. a. (A) **b.** The math SAT increases by approximately 0.97 points. **c.** $S'(x)$ decreases with increasing x, so as parental income increases, the effect on math SAT scores decreases.
99. a. -6.25 years per child; when the fertility rate is 2 children per woman, the average age of a population is dropping at a rate of 6.25 years per 1-child increase in the fertility rate. **b.** 0.160   **101.** 3,300,000 cases per week; 11,000,000 cases per week; 640,000 cases per week   **103.** 2.1 percentage points per year; the rate of change is the slope of the tangent at $t = 3$. This is also approximately the average rate of change over $[2, 4]$, which is about $4/2 = 2$, in approximate agreement with the answer.   **105. a.** 2.1 percentage points per year **b.** $\lim_{t \to +\infty} A(t) = 15$; had the trend continued indefinitely, the percentage of mortgages that were subprime would have approached 15% in the long term. $\lim_{t \to +\infty} A'(t) = 0$; had the trend continued indefinitely, the rate of change of the percentage of mortgages that were subprime would have approached 0 percentage points per year in the long term.
107. 277,000 people per year   **109.** 0.000283 grams per year
111. $R(t) = 350e^{-0.1t}(39t + 68)$ million dollars; $R(2) \approx \$42$ billion; $R'(2) \approx \$7$ billion per year   **113.** e raised to the glob, times the derivative of the glob.   **115.** 2 raised to the glob, times the derivative of the glob, times the natural logarithm of 2.
117. The derivative of $\ln|u|$ is not $\dfrac{1}{|u|}\dfrac{du}{dx}$; it is $\dfrac{1}{u}\dfrac{du}{dx}$.

Thus, the correct derivative is $\dfrac{3}{3x + 1}$.   **119.** The power rule does not apply when the exponent is not constant. The derivative of 3 raised to a quantity is 3 raised to the quantity, times the derivative of the quantity, times ln 3. Thus, the correct answer is $3^{2x} 2 \ln 3$.   **121.** No. If $N(t)$ is exponential, so is its derivative.   **123.** If $f(x) = e^{kx}$, then the fractional rate of change is $\dfrac{f'(x)}{f(x)} = \dfrac{ke^{kx}}{e^{kx}} = k$.   **125.** If $A(t)$ is growing exponentially, then $A(t) = A_0e^{kt}$ for constants A_0 and k. Its percentage rate of change is then $\dfrac{A'(t)}{A(t)} = \dfrac{kA_0e^{kt}}{A_0e^{kt}} = k$, a constant.

Section 11.6

1. $-2/3$ **3.** x **5.** $(y-2)/(3-x)$ **7.** $-y$

9. $-\dfrac{y}{x(1+\ln x)}$ **11.** $-x/y$ **13.** $-2xy/(x^2-2y)$

15. $-(6+9x^2y)/(9x^3-x^2)$ **17.** $3y/x$

19. $(p+10p^2q)/(2p-q-10pq^2)$

21. $(ye^x - e^y)/(xe^y - e^x)$ **23.** $se^{st}/(2s - te^{st})$

25. $ye^x/(2e^x + y^3e^y)$ **27.** $(y-y^2)/(-1+3y-y^2)$

29. $-y/(x+2y-xye^y - y^2e^y)$ **31. a.** 1

b. $y = x - 3$ **33. a.** -2 **b.** $y = -2x$

35. a. -1 **b.** $y = -x + 1$ **37. a.** $-2{,}000$

b. $y = -2{,}000x + 6{,}000$ **39. a.** 0 **b.** $y = 1$

41. a. -0.1898 **b.** $y = -0.1898x + 1.4720$

43. $\dfrac{2x+1}{4x-2}\left[\dfrac{2}{2x+1} - \dfrac{4}{4x-2}\right]$

45. $\dfrac{(3x+1)^2}{4x(2x-1)^3}\left[\dfrac{6}{3x+1} - \dfrac{1}{x} - \dfrac{6}{2x-1}\right]$

47. $(8x-1)^{1/3}(x-1)\left[\dfrac{8}{3(8x-1)} + \dfrac{1}{x-1}\right]$

49. $(x^3+x)\sqrt{x^3+2}\left[\dfrac{3x^2+1}{x^3+x} + \dfrac{1}{2}\dfrac{3x^2}{x^3+2}\right]$

51. $x^x(1+\ln x)$ **53.** $-\$3{,}000$ per worker. The monthly budget to maintain production at the fixed level P is decreasing by approximately \$3,000 per additional worker at an employment level of 100 workers and a monthly operating budget of \$200,000. **55.** -125 T-shirts per dollar; when the price is set at \$5, the demand is dropping by 125 T-shirts per \$1 increase in price. **57.** $\dfrac{dk}{de}\bigg|_{e=15} = -0.307$ carpenters per electrician.
This means that, for a \$200,000 house whose construction employs 15 electricians, adding one more electrician would cost as much as approximately 0.307 additional carpenters. In other words, one electrician is worth approximately 0.307 carpenters. **59. a.** 22.93 hours. (The other root is rejected because it is larger than 30.) **b.** $\dfrac{dt}{dx} = \dfrac{4t-20x}{0.4t-4x}; \dfrac{dt}{dx}\bigg|_{x=3.0} \approx$
-11.2 hours per grade point. This means that, for a 3.0 student who scores 80 on the examination, 1 grade point is worth approximately 11.2 hours. **61.** $\dfrac{dr}{dy} = 2\dfrac{r}{y}$, so $\dfrac{dr}{dt} = 2\dfrac{r}{y}\dfrac{dy}{dt}$ by the chain rule. **63.** x, y, y, x **65.** Let $y = f(x)g(x)$. Then
$\ln y = \ln f(x) + \ln g(x)$, and $\dfrac{1}{y}\dfrac{dy}{dx} = \dfrac{f'(x)}{f(x)} + \dfrac{g'(x)}{g(x)}$, so
$\dfrac{dy}{dx} = y\left(\dfrac{f'(x)}{f(x)} + \dfrac{g'(x)}{g(x)}\right) =$
$f(x)g(x)\left(\dfrac{f'(x)}{f(x)} + \dfrac{g'(x)}{g(x)}\right) = f'(x)g(x) + f(x)g'(x).$

67. Writing $y = f(x)$ specifies y as an explicit function of x. This can be regarded as an equation giving y as an *implicit* function of x. The procedure of finding dy/dx by implicit differentiation is then the same as finding the derivative of y as an explicit function of x: We take d/dx of both sides. **69.** Differentiate both sides of the equation $y = f(x)$ with respect to y to get $1 = f'(x) \cdot \dfrac{dx}{dy}$, giving $\dfrac{dx}{dy} = \dfrac{1}{f'(x)} = \dfrac{1}{dy/dx}$.

Chapter 11 Review

1. $50x^4 + 2x^3 - 1$ **3.** $9x^2 + x^{-2/3}$ **5.** $1 - 2/x^3$

7. $-\dfrac{4}{3x^2} + \dfrac{0.2}{x^{1.1}} + \dfrac{1.1x^{0.1}}{3.2}$ **9.** $e^x(x^2 + 2x - 1)$

11. $(-3x|x| + |x|/x - 6x)/(3x^2 + 1)^2$

13. $-4(4x-1)^{-2}$ **15.** $20x(x^2-1)^9$

17. $-0.43(x+1)^{-1.1}[2 + (x+1)^{-0.1}]^{3.3}$

19. $2e^{2x+1}$ **21.** $2 \cdot 3^{2x-4} \ln 3$

23. $e^x(x^2+1)^9(x^2+20x+1)$

25. $3^x[(x-1)\ln 3 - 1]/(x-1)^2$ **27.** $2xe^{x^2-1}$

29. $3/(3x-1)$ **31.** $2x/(x^2-1)$ **33.** $x = 7/6$

35. $x = \pm 2$ **37.** $x = (1 - \ln 2)/2$ **39.** None

41. $\dfrac{2x-1}{2y}$ **43.** $-y/x$ **45.** $\dfrac{(2x-1)^4(3x+4)}{(x+1)(3x-1)^3} \times$

$\left[\dfrac{8}{2x-1} + \dfrac{3}{3x+4} - \dfrac{1}{x+1} - \dfrac{9}{3x-1}\right]$

47. $y = -x/4 + 1/2$ **49.** $y = -3ex - 2e$

51. $y = x + 2$ **53.** 0 **55.** 1 **57. a.** 274 books per week
b. 636 books per week **c.** The function w begins to decrease more and more rapidly after $t = 14$. Graph:

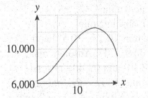

Not realistic.
d. Because the data suggest an upward curving parabola, the long-term prediction of sales for a quadratic model would be that sales will increase without bound, in sharp contrast to (c).
59. a. \$2.88 per book **b.** \$3.715 per book **c.** Approximately $-\$0.000104$ per book per additional book sold. **d.** At a sales level of 8,000 books per week, the cost is increasing at a rate of \$2.88 per book (so that the 8,001st book costs approximately \$2.88 to sell), and it costs an average of \$3.715 per book to sell the first 8,000 books. Moreover, the average cost is decreasing at a rate of \$0.000104 per book per additional book sold. **61. a.** \$3,000 per week (rising) **b.** 300 books per week **63.** $R = pq$ gives $R' = p'q + pq'$. Thus, $R'/R = R'/(pq) = (p'q + pq')/pq = p'/p + q'/q$

65. \$110 per year   **67. a.** $s'(t) = \dfrac{2,475e^{-0.55(t-4.8)}}{(1 + e^{-0.55(t-4.8)})^2};$

556 books per week   **b.** 0; In the long term, the rate of increase of weekly sales slows to zero.   **69.** 616.8 hits per day per week.   **71. a.** -17.24 copies per \$1. The demand for the gift edition of *The Complete Larry Potter* is dropping at a rate of about 17.24 copies per \$1 increase in the price.   **b.** \$138 per dollar is positive, so the price should be raised.

Chapter 12

Section 12.1

1. Absolute min: $(-3, -1)$, relative max: $(-1, 1)$, relative min: $(1, 0)$, absolute max: $(3, 2)$ **3.** Absolute min: $(3, -1)$ and $(-3, -1)$, absolute max: $(1, 2)$ **5.** Absolute min: $(-3, 0)$ and $(1, 0)$, absolute max: $(-1, 2)$ and $(3, 2)$ **7.** Relative min: $(-1, 1)$ **9.** Absolute min: $(-3, -1)$, relative max: $(-2, 2)$, relative min: $(1, 0)$, absolute max: $(3, 3)$ **11.** Relative max: $(-3, 0)$, absolute min: $(-2, -1)$, stationary nonextreme point: $(1, 1)$ **13.** Absolute max: $(0, 1)$, absolute min: $(2, -3)$, relative max: $(3, -2)$ **15.** Absolute min: $(-4, -16)$, absolute max: $(-2, 16)$, absolute min: $(2, -16)$, absolute max: $(4, 16)$ **17.** Absolute min: $(-2, -10)$, absolute max: $(2, 10)$ **19.** Absolute min: $(-2, -4)$, relative max: $(-1, 1)$, relative min: $(0, 0)$ **21.** Relative max: $(-1, 5)$, absolute min: $(3, -27)$ **23.** Absolute min: $(0, 0)$ **25.** Absolute max: $(0, 1)$ and $(2, 1)$, absolute min: $(1, 0)$ **27.** Relative max: $(-2, -1/3)$, relative min: $(-1, -2/3)$, absolute max: $(0, 1)$ **29.** Relative min: $(-2, 5/3)$, relative max: $(0, -1)$, relative min: $(2, 5/3)$ **31.** Relative max: $(0, 0)$; absolute min: $(1/3, -2\sqrt{3}/9)$ **33.** Relative max: $(0, 0)$, absolute min: $(1, -3)$ **35.** No relative extrema   **37.** Absolute min: $(1, 1)$ **39.** Relative max: $(-1, 1 + 1/e)$, absolute min: $(0, 1)$, absolute max: $(1, e - 1)$ **41.** Relative max: $(-6, -24)$, relative min: $(-2, -8)$ **43.** Absolute max: $(1/\sqrt{2}, \sqrt{e}/2)$, absolute min: $(-1/\sqrt{2}, -\sqrt{e}/2)$ **45.** Relative min: $(0.15, -0.52)$ and $(2.45, 8.22)$, relative max: $(1.40, 0.29)$ **47.** Absolute max: $(-5, 700)$, relative max: $(3.10, 28.19)$ and $(6, 40)$, absolute min: $(-2.10, -392.69)$, relative min: $(5, 0)$.   **49.** Stationary minimum at $x = -1$ **51.** Stationary minima at $x = -2$ and $x = 2$, stationary maximum at $x = 0$ **53.** Singular minimum at $x = 0$, stationary nonextreme point at $x = 1$ **55.** Stationary minimum at $x = -2$, singular nonextreme points at $x = -1$ and $x = 1$, stationary maximum at $x = 2$ **57.** Answers will vary.   **59.** Answers will vary.

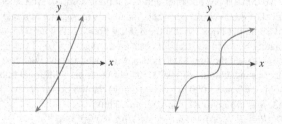

61. Not necessarily; it could be neither a relative maximum nor a relative minimum, as in the graph of $y = x^3$ at the origin.   **63.** Answers will vary.

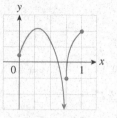

65. The graph oscillates faster and faster above and below zero as it approaches the endpoint at 0, so 0 cannot be either a relative minimum or maximum.

Section 12.2

1. $x = y = 5$; $P = 25$ **3.** $x = y = 3$; $S = 6$ **5.** $x = 2$, $y = 4$; $F = 20$ **7.** $x = 20$, $y = 10$, $z = 20$; $P = 4,000$ **9.** 5×5 **11.** 20 ads for an average cost of \$4,002,000 per ad   **13.** 20,000 per hour for an average cost of \$200 per iPhone. The marginal cost is the same as the average cost at the optimal production level.   **15.** $\sqrt{40} \approx 6.32$ pounds of pollutant per day, for an average cost of about \$1,265 per pound   **17.** 2.5 lb   **19.** 5 ft $\times$ 10 ft   **21.** 50 ft $\times$ 10 ft for an area of 250 sq. ft.   **23.** 11 ft $\times$ 22 ft   **25.** \$10   **27.** \$252.50 for a quarterly revenue of \$382,540 million, or \$382.54 billion   **29.** \$4.61 for a daily revenue of \$95,680.55   **31. a.** \$1.41 per pound   **b.** 5,000 pounds   **c.** \$7,071.07 per month   **33.** 34.5¢ per pound, for an annual (per capita) revenue of \$5.95   **35.** \$292.50 for an annual profit of \$270,940 million, or \$270.94 billion   **37. a.** 656 headsets, for a profit of \$28,120   **b.** \$143 per headset   **39.** Height = Radius of base $\approx$ 20.48 cm.   **41.** Height $\approx$ 10.84 cm; Radius $\approx$ 2.71 cm; Height/Radius = 4   **43.** $13\frac{1}{3}$ in $\times$ $3\frac{1}{3}$ in $\times$ $1\frac{1}{3}$ in for a volume of $1,600/27 \approx 59$ in^3 **45.** 5 $\times$ 5 $\times$ 5 cm   **47.** $l = w = h \approx 20.67$ in, volume $\approx 8,827$ in^3 **49.** $l = 30$ in, $w = 15$ in, $h = 30$ in   **51.** $l = 36$ in, $w = h = 18$ in, $V = 11,664$ in^3 **53. a.** 1.6 years, or year 2001.6;   **b.** $R_{max} = \$28,241$ million   **55.** $t = 2.5$ or midway through 1972; $D(2.5)/S(2.5) \approx 4.09$. The number of new (approved) drugs per \$1 billion of spending on research and development reached a high of around four approved drugs per \$1 billion midway through 1972.   **57.** 30 years from now   **59.** 55 days   **61.** 1,600 copies. At this value of x, average profit equals marginal profit; beyond this the marginal profit is smaller than the average.   **63.** 40 laborers and 250 robots   **65.** 71 employees   **67.** Increasing most rapidly in 1990; increasing least rapidly in 2007   **69.** Maximum when $t = 17$ days. This means that the embryo's oxygen consumption is increasing most rapidly 17 days after the egg is laid.

71. Graph of derivative:

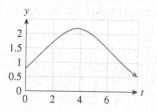

The absolute maximum occurs at approximately (3.7, 2.2) during the year 2003. The percentage of mortgages that were subprime was increasing most rapidly during 2003, when it increased at a rate of around 2.2 percentage points per year. **73.** You should sell them in 17 years' time, when they will be worth approximately \$3,960.   **75.** 25 additional trees   **77.** (D) **79.** (A); (B)   **81.** The problem is uninteresting because the company can accomplish the objective by cutting away the entire sheet of cardboard, resulting in a box with surface area zero. **83.** Not all absolute extrema occur at stationary points; some may occur at an endpoint or singular point of the domain, as in Exercises 31 and 32.   **85.** The minimum of dq/dp is the fastest that the demand is dropping in response to increasing price.

Section 12.3

1. 6   **3.** $4/x^3$ **5.** $-0.96x^{-1.6}$ **7.** $e^{-(x-1)}$ **9.** $2/x^3 + 1/x^2$ **11. a.** $a = -32$ ft/sec^2 **b.** $a = -32$ ft/sec^2 **13. a.** $a = 2/t^3 + 6/t^4$ ft/sec^2 **b.** $a = 8$ ft/sec^2 **15. a.** $a = -1/(4t^{3/2}) + 2$ ft/sec^2 **b.** $a = 63/32$ ft/sec^2 **17.** $(1, 0)$ **19.** $(1, 0)$ **21.** None   **23.** $(-1, 0), (1, 1)$ **25.** Points of inflection at $x = -1$ and $x = 1$ **27.** One point of inflection, at $x = -2$ **29.** Points of inflection at $x = -2$, $x = 0, x = 2$ **31.** Points of inflection at $x = -2$ and $x = 2$ **33.** $x = 2$; minimum   **35.** Maximum at $x = -2$, minimum at $x = 2$ **37.** Maximum at $t = -1/\sqrt{3}$, minimum at $t = 1/\sqrt{3}$ **39.** Nonextreme stationary point at $x = 0$, minimum at $x = 3$ **41.** Maximum at $x = 0$ **43.** Minimum at $x = -1/\sqrt{2}$; maximum at $x = 1/\sqrt{2}$ **45.** $f'(x) = 8x - 1$; $f''(x) = 8$; $f'''(x) = f^{(4)}(x) = \cdots = f^{(n)}(x) = 0$ **47.** $f'(x) = -4x^3 + 6x$; $f''(x) = -12x^2 + 6$; $f'''(x) = -24x$; $f^{(4)}(x) = -24$; $f^{(5)}(x) = f^{(6)}(x) = \cdots = f^{(n)}(x) = 0$ **49.** $f'(x) = 8(2x + 1)^3$; $f''(x) = 48(2x + 1)^2$; $f'''(x) = 192(2x + 1)$; $f^{(4)}(x) = 384$; $f^{(5)}(x) = f^{(6)}(x) = \cdots = f^{(n)}(x) = 0$ **51.** $f'(x) = -e^{-x}$; $f''(x) = e^{-x}$; $f'''(x) = -e^{-x}$; $f^{(4)}(x) = e^{-x}$; $f^{(n)}(x) = (-1)^n e^{-x}$ **53.** $f'(x) = 3e^{3x-1}$; $f''(x) = 9e^{3x-1}$; $f'''(x) = 27e^{3x-1}$; $f^{(4)}(x) = 81e^{3x-1}$; $f^{(n)}(x) = 3^n e^{3x-1}$ **55.** -3.8 m/s^2 **57.** $6t - 2$ ft/sec^2; increasing   **59.** Accelerating by 0.16 billion gal/year^2 **61. a.** 400 ml   **b.** 36 ml/day   **c.** -1 ml/day^2 **63. a.** 0.6% **b.** Speeding up   **c.** Speeding up for $t < 3.33$ (before 1/3 of the way through March) and slowing for $t > 3.33$ (after that time)   **65. a.** December 2005: -0.202% (deflation rate of 0.202%) February 2006: 0.363%   **b.** Speeding up   **c.** Speeding up for $t > 4.44$ (after mid-November) and decreasing for $t < 4.44$ (before that time).   **67.** Concave up for $8 < t < 20$, concave down for $0 < t < 8$, point of inflection around $t = 8$.

The percentage of articles written by researchers in the United States was decreasing most rapidly at around $t = 8$ (1991). **69. a.** (B)   **b.** (B)   **c.** (A) **71.** Graphs:

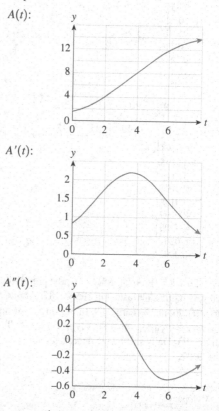

$A(t)$:

$A'(t)$:

$A''(t)$:

Concave up when $t < 4$; concave down when $t > 4$; point of inflection when $t \approx 4$. The percentage of U.S. mortgages that were subprime was increasing fastest at the beginning of 2004. **73. a.** 2 years into the epidemic   **b.** 2 years into the epidemic **75. a.** 2024   **b.** 2026   **c.** 2022; (A)   **77. a.** There are no points of inflection in the graph of S.   **b.** Because the graph is concave up, the derivative of S is increasing, and so the rate of *decrease* of SAT scores with increasing numbers of prisoners was diminishing. In other words, the apparent effect of more prisoners on SAT scores was diminishing.

79. a. $\left.\dfrac{d^2n}{ds^2}\right|_{s=3} = -21.494$. Thus, for a firm with annual sales of \$3 million the rate at which new patents are produced decreases with increasing firm size. This means that the returns (as measured in the number of new patents per increase of \$1 million in sales) are diminishing as the firm size increases.

b. $\left.\dfrac{d^2n}{ds^2}\right|_{s=7} = 13.474$. Thus, for a firm with annual sales of \$7 million the rate at which new patents are produced increases with increasing firm size by 13.474 new patents per \$1 million increase in annual sales.   **c.** There is a point of inflection when $s \approx 5.4587$, so in a firm with sales of \$5,458,700 per year the number of new patents produced per additional \$1 million in sales is a minimum.

81. Graphs:

$I(t)/P(t)$:

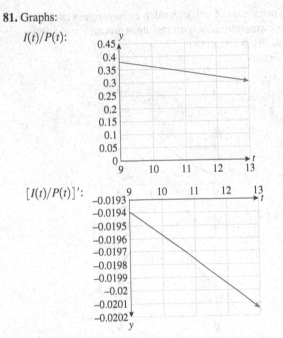

$[I(t)/P(t)]'$:

Concave down; (D) **83.** (Proof) **85.** $t \approx 4$; the population of Puerto Rico was increasing fastest in 1954. **87.** About $570 per year, after about 12 years **89.** Increasing most rapidly in 17.64 years, decreasing most rapidly now (at $t = 0$) **91.** Nonnegative **93.** Daily sales were decreasing most rapidly in June 2002.

95.

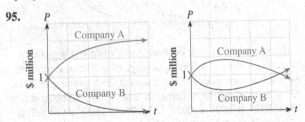

97. At a point of inflection the graph of a function changes either from concave up to concave down or vice versa. If it changes from concave up to concave down, then the derivative changes from increasing to decreasing and hence has a relative maximum. Similarly, if it changes from concave down to concave up, the derivative has a relative minimum.

Section 12.4

1. a. x-intercept: -1; y-intercept: 1 **b.** Absolute min: $(-1, 0)$ **c.** None **d.** None **e.** $y \to +\infty$ as $x \to \pm\infty$

Graph:

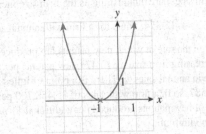

3. a. x-intercepts: $-\sqrt{12}, 0, \sqrt{12}$; y-intercept: 0 **b.** Absolute min: $(-4, -16)$ and $(2, -16)$, absolute max: $(-2, 16)$ and $(4, 16)$ **c.** $(0, 0)$ **d.** None **e.** None

Graph:

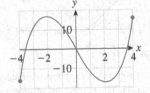

5. a. x-intercepts: $-3.6, 0, 5.1$; y-intercept: 0 **b.** Relative max: $(-2, 44)$, relative min: $(3, -81)$ **c.** $(0.5, -18.5)$ **d.** None **e.** $y \to -\infty$ as $x \to -\infty$; $y \to +\infty$ as $x \to +\infty$

Graph:

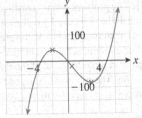

7. a. x-intercepts: $-3.3, 0.1, 1.8$; y-intercept: 1 **b.** Relative max: $(-2, 21)$, relative min: $(1, -6)$ **c.** $(-1/2, 15/2)$ **d.** None **e.** $y \to -\infty$ as $x \to -\infty$; $y \to +\infty$ as $x \to +\infty$

Graph:

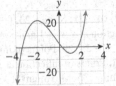

9. a. x-intercepts: $-2.9, 4.2$; y-intercept: 10 **b.** Relative max: $(-2, 74)$, relative min: $(0, 10)$, absolute max: $(3, 199)$ **c.** $(-1.12, 44.8)$, $(1.79, 117.1)$ **d.** None **e.** $y \to -\infty$ as $x \to -\infty$; $y \to -\infty$ as $x \to +\infty$

Graph:

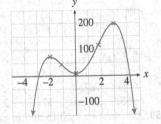

11. a. t-intercept: $t = 0$; y-intercept: 0 **b.** Absolute min: $(0, 0)$ **c.** $(1/3, 11/324)$ and $(1, 1/12)$ **d.** None **e.** $y \to +\infty$ as $t \to -\infty$; $y \to +\infty$ as $t \to +\infty$

Graph:

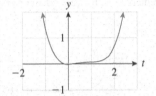

13. a. x-intercepts: None; y-intercept: None **b.** Relative min: $(1, 2)$, relative max: $(-1, -2)$ **c.** None **d.** $y \to -\infty$ as $x \to 0^-$; $y \to +\infty$ as $x \to 0^+$, so there is a vertical asymptote at $x = 0$. **e.** $y \to -\infty$ as $x \to -\infty$; $y \to +\infty$ as $x \to +\infty$

Graph:

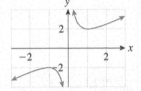

15. a. x-intercept: 0; y-intercept: 0 **b.** None **c.** $(0, 0)$, $(-3, -9/4)$, and $(3, 9/4)$ **d.** None **e.** $y \to -\infty$ as $x \to -\infty$; $y \to +\infty$ as $x \to +\infty$

Graph:

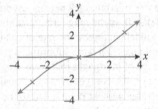

17. a. t-intercepts: None; y-intercept: -1 **b.** Relative min: $(-2, 5/3)$ and $(2, 5/3)$, relative max: $(0, -1)$ **c.** None **d.** $y \to +\infty$ as $t \to -1^-$; $y \to -\infty$ as $t \to -1^+$; $y \to -\infty$ as $t \to 1^-$; $y \to +\infty$ as $t \to 1^+$; so there are vertical asymptotes at $t = \pm 1$. **e.** None

Graph:

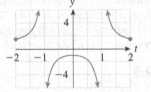

19. a. x-intercept: -0.7; y-intercept: 1 **b.** Relative max: $(-2, -1/3)$, relative min: $(-1, -2/3)$ **c.** None **d.** None. **e.** $y \to -\infty$ as $x \to -\infty$; $y \to +\infty$ as $x \to +\infty$

Graph:

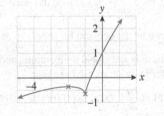

21. a. x-intercepts: None; y-intercept: None **b.** Absolute min: $(1, 1)$ **c.** None **d.** Vertical asymptote at $x = 0$ **e.** $y \to +\infty$ as $x \to +\infty$

Graph:

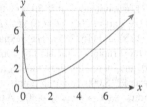

23. a. x-intercepts: ± 0.8; y-intercept: None **b.** None **c.** $(1, 1)$ and $(-1, 1)$ **d.** $y \to -\infty$ as $x \to 0$; vertical asymptote at $x = 0$ **e.** $y \to +\infty$ as $x \to \pm\infty$

Graph:

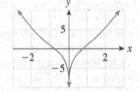

25. a. t-intercepts: None; y-intercept: 1 **b.** Absolute min: $(0, 1)$. Absolute max: $(1, e - 1)$, relative max: $(-1, e^{-1} + 1)$. **c.** None **d.** None **e.** None

Graph:

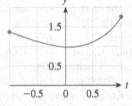

27. Absolute min: $(1.40, -1.49)$; points of inflection: $(0.21, 0.61)$, $(0.79, -0.55)$

Graph:

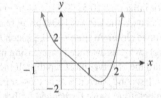

29. Relative min: $(-0.46, 0.73)$, relative max: $(0.91, 1.73)$, absolute min: $(3.73, -10.22)$; points of inflection at $(0.20, 1.22)$ and $(2.83, -5.74)$

Graph:

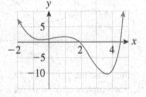

31. *y*-intercept: 150; *t*-intercepts: none. The median home price was about $150,000 at the start of 2000($t = 0$). Extrema: absolute min: (0, 150) and (12, 150); relative max: (6, 225). The median home price was lowest in 2000 ($t = 0$) and again in 2012 ($t = 12$), when it stood at $150,000; the median home price peaked at the start of 2006 ($t = 6$) at $225,000. Points of inflection at (9, 175) and (15, 225). The median home price was decreasing most rapidly at the start of 2009 ($t = 9$), when it was $175,000, and increasing most rapidly at the start of 2015, when it was $225,000. Singular points of f: none. Behavior at infinity: As $t \to +\infty$, $y \to 300$. Assuming that the trend shown in the graph continued indefinitely, the median home price would approach a value of $300,000 in the long term.   **33. a.** *r*-intercept: slightly more than 1; *t*-intercept: 5.5. At the start of the period shown, the radius of the Earth's orbit will be slightly more than one AU, and five and a half million years later, it will be zero after it has spiraled into the core of the Sun. Extrema: absolute min: (5.5, 0); absolute max: (5, 1.07). The Earth's orbital radius will reach a maximum of 1.07 AU at $t = 5$, after which point it will spiral into the core of the Sun ($r = 0$ AU) at $t = 5.5$. The radius will be increasing most rapidly at $t = 4$, when it will be 1.05 AU. Singular points of f: none. Behavior at infinity: As $t \to -\infty$, $r \to 1$. At times much earlier than the period shown, the radius of the Earth was close to 1 AU.   **b.** increase; decrease   **35. a.** Intercepts: No *t*-intercept; *y*-intercept at $I(0) = 195$. The CPI was never zero during the given period; in July 2005 the CPI was 195. Absolute min: (0, 195), absolute max: (8, 199.3), relative max: (2.9, 198.7), relative min: (6.0, 197.8). The CPI was at a low of 195 in July 2005, rose to 198.7 around October 2005, dipped to 197.8 around January 2006, and then rose to a high of 199.3 in March 2006. There is a point of inflection at (4.4, 198.2). The rate of change of the CPI (inflation) reached a minimum around mid-November 2005 when the CPI was 198.2. **b.** The inflation rate was zero at around October 2005 and January 2006.   **37.** Extrema: Relative max: (0, 100), absolute min: (1, 99); point of inflection: (0.5, 99.5); $s \to +\infty$ as $t \to +\infty$. At time $t = 0$ seconds the UFO is 100 ft away from the observer, and begins to move closer. At time $t = 0.5$ seconds, when the UFO is 99.5 feet away, its distance is decreasing most rapidly (it is moving toward the observer most rapidly). It then slows down to a stop at $t = 1$ second when it is at its closest point (99 ft away) and then begins to move farther and farther away.

Graph:

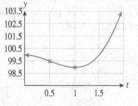

39. Intercepts: none; absolute min: (20,000, 200); no points of inflection; vertical asymptote at $x = 0$. As $x \to +\infty$, $y \to +\infty$. The average cost is never zero, nor is it defined for zero iPhone 6's. The average cost is a minimum ($200) when 20,000 iPhone 6's are manufactured per hour. The average cost

becomes extremely large for very small or very large numbers of iPhone 6's.

Graph:

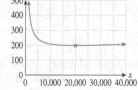

41. Graph of derivative:

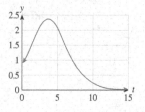

The absolute maximum occurs at approximately (3.7, 2.2); during the year 2003. The percentage of mortgages that were subprime was increasing most rapidly during 2003, when it increased at a rate of around 2.2 percentage points per year. As $t \to +\infty$, $A'(t) \to 0$; in the long term, assuming the trend shown in the model continues, the rate of change of the percentage of mortgages that were subprime approaches zero; that is, the percentage of mortgages that were subprime approaches a constant value.   **43.** No; yes. Near a vertical asymptote the value of y increases without bound, and so the graph could not be included between two horizontal lines; hence, no vertical asymptotes are possible. Horizontal asymptotes are possible as, for instance, in the graph in Exercise 31.   **45.** It too has a vertical asymptote at $x = a$; the magnitude of the derivative increases without bound as $x \to a$.   **47.** No. If the leftmost critical point is a relative maximum, the function will decrease from there until it reaches the rightmost critical point, so it can't have a relative maximum there.   **49.** Between every pair of zeros of $f(x)$ there must be a local extremum, which must be a stationary point of $f(x)$, hence a zero of $f'(x)$.

Section 12.5

1. $P = 10,000$; $\dfrac{dP}{dt} = 1,000$ **3.** Let R be the annual revenue of my company, and let q be annual sales. $R = 7,000$, and $\dfrac{dR}{dt} = -700$. Find $\dfrac{dq}{dt}$.   **5.** Let p be the price of a pair of shoes, and let q be the demand for shoes. $\dfrac{dp}{dt} = 5$. Find $\dfrac{dq}{dt}$.   **7.** Let T be the average global temperature, and let q be the number of Bermuda shorts sold per year. $T = 60$, and $\dfrac{dT}{dt} = 0.01$. Find $\dfrac{dq}{dt}$.   **9. a.** $6/(100\pi) \approx 0.019$ km/sec   **b.** $3/(4\sqrt{\pi}) \approx 0.4231$ km/sec   **11.** $3/(4\pi) \approx 0.24$ ft/min   **13.** 326×10^{12} cubic miles per hour   **15.** 7.5 ft/sec

17. 80 m/sec   **19.** Decreasing at a rate of $1.66 per player per week   **21.** Monthly sales will drop at a rate of 26 T-shirts per month.   **23.** Raise the price by 3¢ per week.   **25.** Decreasing at a rate of $75.48 million per year   **27.** 1 laborer per month   **29.** Dropping at a rate of $2.40 per year.   **31.** The price is decreasing at a rate of approximately 31¢ per pound per month.   **33.** $2,300/\sqrt{4,100} \approx 36$ miles per hour.   **35.** About 10.7 ft/sec   **37.** The y-coordinate is decreasing at a rate of 16 units per second.   **39.** $534 per year   **41.** Their prior experience must increase at a rate of approximately 0.97 years every year.   **43.** $\dfrac{2,500}{9\pi}\left(\dfrac{3}{5,000}\right)^{2/3} \approx 0.63$ m/sec

45. $\dfrac{\sqrt{1 + 128\pi}}{4\pi} \approx 1.6$ cm/sec   **47.** 0.5137 computers per household and increasing at a rate of 0.0230 computers per household per year.   **49.** The average SAT score was 904.71 and decreasing at a rate of 0.11 per year.   **51.** Decreasing by 2 percentage points per year   **53.** The section is called "Related Rates" because the goal is to compute the rate of change of a quantity based on a knowledge of the rate of change of a related quantity.   **55.** Answers may vary: A rectangular solid has dimensions 2 cm × 5 cm × 10 cm, and each side is expanding at a rate of 3 cm/sec. How fast is the volume increasing?   **57.** Proof   **59.** Linear   **61.** Let $x = $ my grades and $y = $ your grades. If $dx/dt = 2\,dy/dt$, then $dy/dt = (1/2)\,dx/dt$.

Section 12.6

1. $E = 1.5$; the demand is going down 1.5% per 1% increase in price at that price level; revenue is maximized when $p = \$25$; weekly revenue at that price is $12,500.

3. a. $E = \dfrac{6p}{-6p + 3,030}$ **b.** 1.97; The demand was going down 1.97% per 1% increase in price at that price level.   **c.** Price for maximum revenue: $252.50 per phone for an annual revenue of $382,540 million, or $382.54 billion   **5. a.** The elasticity would have dropped from 1.81 to 0.96, suggesting that the tuition for maximum annual revenue would have been between these two values.   **b.** They should have charged an average of $2,250 per student, and this would have resulted in an enrollment of about 4,950 students, giving an annual revenue of about $11,137,500.   **7. a.** $E = 6/7$; the demand is going down 6% per 7% increase in price at that price level; thus, a price increase is in order.   **b.** Revenue is maximized when $p = 100/3 \approx \$33.33$ **c.** 4,444 cases per week   **9. a.** $E = (4p - 33)/(-2p + 33)$ **b.** 0.54; the demand for T-shirts is going down by about 0.54% per 1% increase in the price.   **c.** $11 per shirt for a daily revenue of $1,331   **11.** $E = 0.01p$; 0.5, 4; yes; $E(50) < 1$ and $E(400) > 1$, so the price that would result in $E = 1$ lies between 50 and 400.   **13.** $q = 175,502/p^{10/13}$; $E = 10/13$, showing an inelastic demand. Thus, increasing the price will result in increasing revenue   **15. a.** $E = 51$; the demand is going down 51% per 1% increase in price at that price level; thus, a large price decrease is advised.   **b.** ¥50   **c.** About

78 paint-by-number sets per month   **17. a.** $E = -\dfrac{mp}{mp + b}$

b. $p = -\dfrac{b}{2m}$ **19. a.** $E = r$ **b.** E is independent of p.   **c.** If $r = 1$, then the revenue is not affected by the price. If $r > 1$, then the revenue is always elastic, while if $r < 1$, the revenue is always inelastic. This is an unrealistic model because there should always be a price at which the revenue is a maximum.   **21. a.** $q = -1,500p + 6,000$ **b.** $2 per hamburger, giving a total weekly revenue of $6,000   **23. a.** $q = 1,000e^{-0.30p}$ **b.** At $p = \$3$, $E = 0.9$; at $p = \$4$, $E = 1.2$; at $p = \$5$, $E = 1.5$ **c.** $p = \$3.33$ **d.** $p = \$5.36$. Selling at a lower price would increase demand, but you cannot sell more than 200 lb anyway. You should charge as much as you can and still be able to sell all 200 lb.   **25.** $E \approx 0.77$. At a family income level of $20,000 the fraction of children attending a live theatrical performance is increasing by 0.77% per 1% increase in household income.   **27. a.** $E = \dfrac{1.554xe^{-0.021x}}{-74e^{-0.021x} + 92}$;

$E(100) \approx 0.23$: At a household income level of $100,000 the percentage of people using broadband in 2010 was increasing by 0.23% per 1% increase in household income.   **b.** The model predicts elasticity approaching zero for households with large incomes.   **29. a.** $E \approx 0.46$. The demand for computers was increasing by 0.46% per 1% increase in household income.   **b.** E decreases as income increases.   **c.** Unreliable; it predicts a likelihood greater than 1 at incomes of $123,000 and above. In a more appropriate model we would expect the curve to level off at or below 1.   **d.** $E \approx 0$ **31.** 0.24; When the price of oil is $60 per barrel, Saudi production increases at a rate of 0.24% per 1% increase in the price.   **33.** The income elasticity of

demand is $\dfrac{dQ}{dY}\cdot\dfrac{Y}{Q} = a\beta P^{\alpha}Y^{\beta-1}\dfrac{Y}{aP^{\alpha}Y^{\beta}} = \beta$.   **35.** The price is lowered.   **37.** Start with $R = pq$, and differentiate with respect to p to obtain $\dfrac{dR}{dp} = q + p\dfrac{dq}{dp}$. For a stationary point,

$dR/dp = 0$, so $q + p\dfrac{dq}{dp} = 0$. Rearranging this result gives

$p\dfrac{dq}{dp} = -q$ and hence $-\dfrac{dq}{dp}\cdot\dfrac{p}{q} = 1$, or $E = 1$, showing that stationary points of R correspond to points of unit elasticity.   **39.** The distinction is best illustrated by an example. Suppose that q is measured in weekly sales and p is the unit price in dollars. Then the quantity $-dq/dp$ measures the drop in weekly sales per $1 increase in price. The elasticity of demand E, on the other hand, measures the *percentage* drop in sales per 1% increase in price. Thus, $-dq/dp$ measures absolute change, while E measures fractional, or percentage, change.

Chapter 12 Review

1. Relative max: $(-1, 5)$, absolute min: $(-2, -3)$ and $(1, -3)$ **3.** Absolute max: $(-1, 5)$, absolute min: $(1, -3)$ **5.** Absolute min: $(1, 0)$ **7.** Absolute min: $(-2, -1/4)$ **9.** Relative max: $x = 1$, point of inflection: $x = -1$

11. Relative max: $x = -2$, relative min: $x = 1$, point of inflection: $x = -1$ **13.** One point of inflection, at $x = 0$
15. a. $a = 4/t^4 - 2/t^3$ m/sec² **b.** 2 m/sec² **17.** Relative max: $(-2, 16)$; absolute min: $(2, -16)$; point of inflection: $(0, 0)$; no horizontal or vertical asymptotes

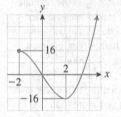

19. Relative min: $(-3, -2/9)$; relative max: $(3, 2/9)$; points of inflection: $(-3\sqrt{2}, -5\sqrt{2}/36)$, $(3\sqrt{2}, 5\sqrt{2}/36)$; vertical asymptote: $x = 0$; horizontal asymptote: $y = 0$

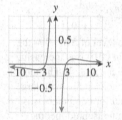

21. Relative max: $(0, 0)$, absolute min: $(1, -2)$, no asymptotes

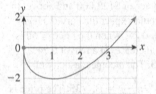

23. $22.14 per book **25. a.** Profit $= -p^3 + 42p^2 - 288p - 181$ **b.** $24 per copy; $3,275 **c.** For maximum revenue the company should charge $22.14 per copy. At this price, the cost per book is decreasing with increasing price, while the revenue is not decreasing (its derivative is zero). Thus, the profit is increasing with increasing price, suggesting that the maximum profit will occur at a higher price. **27.** 30 ft × 10 ft, for an area of 300 sq. ft. **29.** 12 in × 12 in × 6 in, for a volume of 864 in³ **31. a.** Week 5 **b.** Point of inflection on the graph of s; maximum on the graph of s', t-intercept in the graph of s''.
c. 10,500; if weekly sales continue as predicted by the model, they will level off at around 10,500 books per week in the long term. **d.** 0; if weekly sales continue as predicted by the model, the rate of change of sales approaches zero in the long term.
33. a.–d. $10/\sqrt{2}$ ft/sec **35. a.** $E = \dfrac{2p^2 - 33p}{-p^2 + 33p + 9}$ **b.** 0.52,
2.03; when the price is $20, demand is dropping at a rate of 0.52% per 1% increase in the price; when the price is $25, demand is dropping at a rate of 2.03% per 1% increase in the price. **c.** $22.14 per book **37. a.** $E = 2p^2 - p$ **b.** 6; the demand is dropping at a rate of 6% per 1% increase in the price. **c.** $1.00, for a monthly revenue of $1,000

Chapter 13

Section 13.1

1. $x^6/6 + C$ **3.** $6x + C$ **5.** $x^2/2 + C$
7. $x^3/3 - x^2/2 + C$ **9.** $x + x^2/2 + C$ **11.** $-x^{-4}/4 + C$
13. $x^{3.3}/3.3 - x^{-0.3}/0.3 + C$ **15.** $u^3/3 - \ln|u| + C$
17. $4x^{5/4}/5 + C$ **19.** $3x^5/5 + 2x^{-1} - x^{-4}/4 + 4x + C$

21. $2\ln|u| + u^2/8 + C$ **23.** $\ln|x| - \dfrac{2}{x} + \dfrac{1}{2x^2} + C$

25. $3x^{1.1}/1.1 - x^{5.3}/5.3 - 4.1x + C$ **27.** $\dfrac{x^{0.9}}{0.3} + \dfrac{40}{x^{0.1}} + C$

29. $2.55t^2 - 1.2\ln|t| - \dfrac{15}{t^{0.2}} + C$ **31.** $2e^x + 5x|x|/2 +$

$x/4 + C$ **33.** $12.2x^{0.5} + x^{1.5}/9 - e^x + C$

35. $\dfrac{2^x}{\ln 2} - \dfrac{3^x}{\ln 3} + C$ **37.** $\dfrac{100(1.1^x)}{\ln(1.1)} - \dfrac{x|x|}{3} + C$

39. $x^3/3 + 3x^{-5}/10 + C$ **41.** $-1/x - 1/x^2 + C$
43. $f(x) = x^2/2 + 1$ **45.** $f(x) = e^x - x - 1$
47. $C(x) = 5x - x^2/20{,}000 + 20{,}000$
49. $C(x) = 5x + x^2 + \ln x + 994$
51. a. $M(t) = -2.2t^3 + 9t^2 + 220t + 360$ **b.** 1,332 million members **53.** $I(t) = 42{,}000 + 1{,}200t$; $48,000
55. $S(t) = 0.08t^3/3 - 0.13t^2 + 8.8t$; 64 billion gal
57. a. $H'(t) = 3.5t + 65$ billion dollars per year
b. $H(t) = 1.75t^2 + 65t + 700$ billion dollars
59. a. $-0.4t + 1$ percentage points per year
b. $-0.2t^2 + t + 13$; 13.8 **61. a.** $s = t^3/3 + t + C$
b. $C = 1$; $s = t^3/3 + t + 1$ **63.** 320 ft/sec downward
65. a. $v(t) = -32t + 16$ **b.** $s(t) = -16t^2 + 16t + 185$; zenith at $t = 0.5$ sec, $s = 189$ ft, 4 ft above the top of the tower. **67. a.** $s = 525t + 25t^2$ **b.** 3 hours **c.** The negative solution indicates that, at time $t = -24$, the tailwind would have been large and negative, causing the plane to be moving backward through that position 24 hours before departure and arrive at the starting point of the flight at time 0! **69.** Proof
71. $(1,280)^{1/2} \approx 35.78$ ft/sec **73. a.** 80 ft/sec **b.** 60 ft/sec
c. 1.25 sec **75.** $\sqrt{2} \approx 1.414$ times as fast **77.** The term *indefinite* refers to the arbitrary constant term in the indefinite integral; we do not obtain a definite value for C, and hence the integral is "not definite." **79.** Constant; because the derivative of a linear function is constant, linear functions are antiderivatives of constant functions. **81.** No; there are infinitely many antiderivatives of a given function, each pair of them differing by a constant. Knowing the value of the function at a specific point suffices. **83.** They differ by a constant, $G(x) - F(x) =$ Constant **85.** Antiderivative, marginal **87.** Up to a constant, $\int f(x)\,dx$ represents the total cost of manufacturing x items. The units of $\int f(x)\,dx$ are the product of the units of $f(x)$ and the units of x. **89.** The indefinite integral of the constant 1 is not zero; it is x (+ constant). Correct answer: $3x^2/2 + x + C$ **91.** There should be no integral sign $\left(\int\right)$ in the answer. Correct answer: $2x^6 - 2x^2 + C$ **93.** The integral of a constant times a function is the constant times the integral of the function, not the *integral* of the constant times the integral of the function.

(In general, the integral of a product is *not* the product of the integrals.) Correct answer: $4(e^x - x^2) + C$ **95.** It is the *integral* of $1/x$ that equals $\ln|x| + C$, not $1/x$ itself. Correct answer: $\int \frac{1}{x}\,dx = \ln|x| + C$ **97.** $\int (f(x) + g(x))\,dx$ is, by definition, an antiderivative of $f(x) + g(x)$. Let $F(x)$ be an antiderivative of $f(x)$, and let $G(x)$ be an antiderivative of $g(x)$. Then, because the derivative of $F(x) + G(x)$ is $f(x) + g(x)$ (by the rule for sums of derivatives), this means that $F(x) + G(x)$ is an antiderivative of $f(x) + g(x)$. In symbols, $\int (f(x) + g(x))\,dx = F(x) + G(x) + C = \int f(x)\,dx + \int g(x)\,dx$, the sum of the indefinite integrals.   **99.** Answers will vary. $\int x \cdot 1\,dx = \int x\,dx = x^2/2 + C$, whereas $\int x\,dx \cdot \int 1\,dx = (x^2/2 + D) \cdot (x + E)$, which is not the same as $x^2/2 + C$, no matter what values we choose for the constants C, D, and E.   **101.** Derivative; indefinite integral; indefinite integral; derivative

Section 13.2

1. $(3x - 5)^4/12 + C$ **3.** $(3x - 5)^4/12 + C$ **5.** $-e^{-x} + C$
7. $-e^{-x} + C$ **9.** $\frac{1}{2}e^{(x+1)^2} + C$ **11.** $(3x + 1)^6/18 + C$

13. $1.6(3x - 4)^{3/2} + C$ **15.** $2e^{(0.6x+2)} + C$
17. $(3x^2 + 3)^4/24 + C$ **19.** $2(3x^2 - 1)^{3/2}/9 + C$
21. $-(x^2 + 1)^{-0.3}/0.6 + C$ **23.** $(4x^2 - 1)|4x^2 - 1|/16 + C$ **25.** $x + 3e^{3.1x-2} + C$ **27.** $-(1/2)e^{-x^2+1} + C$
29. $-(1/2)e^{-(x^2+2x)} + C$ **31.** $(x^2 + x + 1)^{-2}/2 + C$
33. $(2x^3 + x^6 - 5)^{1/2}/3 + C$ **35.** $(x - 2)^7/7 + (x - 2)^6/3 + C$ **37.** $4[(x + 1)^{5/2}/5 - (x + 1)^{3/2}/3] + C$
39. $20\ln|1 - e^{-0.05x}| + C$ **41.** $3e^{-1/x} + C$
43. $-\dfrac{(4 + 1/x^2)^4}{8} + C$ **45.** $(e^x - e^{-x})/2 + C$
47. $\ln(e^x + e^{-x}) + C$ **49.** $-(1 - e^{3x-1})|1 - e^{3x-1}|/6 + C$
51. $(e^{2x^2-2x} + e^x)/2 + C$ **53.** Derivation   **55.** Derivation
57. $-e^{-x} + C$ **59.** $(1/2)e^{2x-1} + C$ **61.** $(2x + 4)^3/6 + C$
63. $(1/5)\ln|5x - 1| + C$ **65.** $(1.5x)^4/6 + C$
67. $\dfrac{1.5^{3x}}{3\ln(1.5)} + C$ **69.** $\dfrac{1}{4}(2x + 4)|2x + 4| + C$
71. $\dfrac{2^{3x+4} - 2^{-3x+4}}{3\ln 2} + C$ **73.** $f(x) = (x^2 + 1)^4/8 - 1/8$
75. $f(x) = (1/2)e^{x^2-1}$ **77.** $(5x^2 - 3)^7/70 + C$
79. $2(3e^x - 1)^{1/2}/3 + C$ **81.** $e^{(x^4-8)}/4 + C$
83. $\dfrac{1}{6}\ln|1 + 2e^{3x}| + C$ **85.** $C(x) = 5x - 1/(x + 1) + 995.5$
87. $G(t) = 2{,}000t + 8{,}000e^{-0.06t} - 8{,}000$; 7,107 billion pesos
89. $P(t) = -\dfrac{(-0.075t + 0.97)^6}{0.45} + 0.75t + 1.9$; \$7.1 billion
91. a. $N(t) = 35\ln(5 + e^{0.2t}) - 63$ **b.** 80,000 articles
93. $S(t) = 3{,}600[\ln(3 + e^{0.25t}) - \ln 4]$; 6,310 sets
95. a. $s = (t^2 + 1)^5/10 + t^2/2 + C$ **b.** $C = 9/10$; $s = (t^2 + 1)^5/10 + t^2/2 + 9/10$
97. a. $S(t) = 0.08(t - 2{,}007)^3/3 - 0.13(t - 2{,}007)^2 + 8.8(t - 2{,}007) - 25.95$ million gal **b.** Approximately

38.43 million gal   **99.** None; the substitution $u = x$ simply replaces the letter x throughout by the letter u and thus does not change the integral at all. For instance, the integral $\int x(3x^2 + 1)\,dx$ becomes $\int u(3u^2 + 1)\,du$ if we substitute $u = x$.   **101.** It may mean that, but it may not; see Example 4.   **103.** (D); to compute the integral, first break it up into a sum of two integrals, $\displaystyle\int \frac{x}{x^2 - 1}\,dx + \int \frac{3x}{x^2 + 1}\,dx$, and then compute the first using $u = x^2 - 1$ and the second using $u = x^2 + 1$.   **105.** There are several errors: First, the term "dx" is missing in the integral, and this affects all the subsequent steps (since we must substitute for dx when changing to the variable u). Second, when there is a noncanceling x in the integrand, we cannot treat it as a constant. Correct answer: $3(x^2 - 1)^2/4 + C$ **107.** In the fourth step, u was substituted back for x before the integral was taken, and du was just changed to dx; they're not equal. Correct answer: $(x^3 - 1)^2/6 + C$ **109.** Proof

Section 13.3

1. 4   **3.** 6   **5.** 0   **7.** 0.7456   **9.** 2.3129   **11.** 30   **13.** 22
15. −2   **17.** 0   **19.** 1   **21.** 1/2   **23.** 1/4   **25.** 2   **27.** 0
29. 6   **31.** 0   **33.** 0.5   **35.** 3.3045, 3.1604, 3.1436
37. 0.0275, 0.0258, 0.0256   **39.** 15.76 liters   **41.** \$99.95
43. \$4,480,000   **45.** 54 billion gal   **47.** \$300 billion
49. a. Left sum: about 5,200; right sum: 5,680 **b.** 5,440; A total of about 5.44 million articles were published by researchers in the United States in the 20-year period beginning 1990.
51. 118,750 degrees   **53.** 54,000 students   **55.** Left sum: 76; right sum: 71; Left sum, as it is the sum of the annual net incomes for the given years.   **57. a.** Left sum = 5.44; right sum = 5.34 **b.** Pemex produced a total of 5.34 billion barrels of crude oil in the period 2009 through 2013.   **59.** −84.8; after 4 sec, the stone is about 84.8 ft below where it started.
61. 91.2 ft   **63.** 2,527; A total of about 2,527 million members joined Facebook from the start of 2008 to the start of 2013.
65. 34,150; A total of about 34,150 wiretaps were authorized by U.S. state and federal courts during the 15-year period starting January 2000.   **67.** Yes. The Riemann sum gives an estimated area of 420 sq. ft.
69. a. Graph:

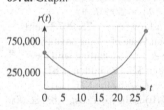

Total expenditure on oil in the United States from 1990 to 2000. **b.** 2,010,000; a total of \$2,010,000 million, or \$2.01 trillion, was spent on oil in the United States from 1990 to 2000.
71. a. 99.4% **b.** 0 (to at least 15 decimal places)   **73.** Stays the same   **75.** Increases   **77.** The area under the curve and above the x-axis equals the area above the curve and below the x-axis.   **79.** Answers will vary. One example: Let $r(t)$ be the

rate of change of net income at time t. If $r(t)$ is negative, then the net income is decreasing, so the change in net income, represented by the definite integral of $r(t)$, is negative.
81. Answers may vary.

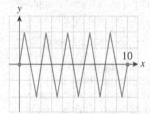

83. The total cost is $c(1) + c(2) + \cdots + c(60)$, which is represented by the Riemann sum approximation of $\int_1^{61} c(t)\, dt$ with $n = 60$.

85. $[f(x_1) + f(x_2) + \cdots + f(x_n)]\,\Delta x = \sum_{k=1}^{n} f(x_k)\,\Delta x$

87. Answers may vary.

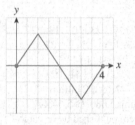

Section 13.4

1. 14/3 **3.** 5 **5.** 0 **7.** 40/3 **9.** $1.05 - 4.3/2.2 \approx -0.9045$
11. $2(e - 1)$ **13.** 2/3 **15.** $1/\ln 2$ **17.** 4,095
19. $(e^1 - e^{-3})/2$ **21.** $3/(2\ln 2)$ **23.** 40/3 **25.** 5/4
27. 0 **29.** $(5/2)(e^3 - e^2)$ **31.** $(1/3)(\ln 26 - \ln 7)$
33. $\dfrac{0.1}{2.2\ln(1.1)}$ **35.** $e - e^{1/2}$ **37.** 0.2221 **39.** $2 - \ln 3$
41. $-4/21$ **43.** $3^{5/2}/10 - 3^{3/2}/6 + 1/15$ **45.** 1/2
47. 16/3 **49.** 9/2 **51.** 56/3 **53.** 1/2 **55.** 18 liters
57. \$783 **59.** \$4,500,000 **61.** 296 miles **63.** 260 ft
65. 9 gal **67.** 56 billion gal **69.** 1,595 million members
71. 34,310; A total of about 34,310 wiretaps were authorized by U.S. state and federal courts during the 15-year period starting January 2000. **73.** $G(T) = 2,000T + 8,000e^{-0.06T} - 8,000$; 7,107 billion pesos **75.** 907 T-shirts
77. 68 milliliters **79.** The total value of online payments through PayPal during the 1-year period starting with the fourth quarter of 2013 was about \$222.85 billion. **81.** Change in cost $= \int_0^x m(t)\, dt = C(x) - C(0)$ by the FTC, so $C(x) = C(0) + \int_0^x m(t)\, dt$. $C(0)$ is the *fixed cost*. **83.** 80,000 articles **85. a., b.** Proofs **c.** 2,401 thousand students
87. Proof **89.** They are related by the Fundamental Theorem of Calculus, which (briefly) states that the definite integral of a suitable function can be calculated by evaluating the indefinite integral at the two endpoints and subtracting. **91.** Computing its definite integral from a to b **93.** Calculate definite integrals by using antiderivatives. **95.** An example is $v(t) = t - 5$.

97. An example is $f(x) = e^{-x}$. **99.** By the FTC, $\int_a^x f(t)\, dt = G(x) - G(a)$, where G is an antiderivative of f. Hence, $F(x) = G(x) - G(a)$. Taking derivatives of both sides, $F'(x) = G'(x) + 0 = f(x)$, as required. The result gives us a formula, in terms of area, for an antiderivative of any continuous function.

Chapter 13 Review

1. $x^3/3 - 5x^2 + 2x + C$ **3.** $4x^3/15 + 4/(5x) + C$
5. $(1/2)\ln|2x| + C$ or $(1/2)\ln|x| + C$
7. $-e^{-2x+11}/2 + C$ **9.** $(x^2 + 1)^{2.3}/4.6 + C$
11. $2\ln|x^2 - 7| + C$ **13.** $\dfrac{1}{6}(x^4 - 4x + 1)^{3/2} + C$
15. $-e^{x^2/2} + C$ **17.** $(x + 2) - \ln|x + 2| + C$ or $x - \ln|x + 2| + C$ **19.** 1 **21.** 2.75 **23.** -0.24
25. 2.5048 **27.** 0.7778, 0.7500, 0.7471 **29.** 0 **31.** 1
33. 2/7 **35.** $50(e^{-1} - e^{-2})$ **37.** 52/9
39. $(\ln 5 - \ln 2)/8 = \ln(2.5)/8$ **41.** 32/3 **43.** $(1 - e^{-25})/2$
45. a. $N(t) = 196t + t^3/3 - 0.16t^6/6$ **b.** 4 books
47. a. At a height of $-16t^2 + 100t$ ft **b.** 156.25 ft **c.** After 6.25 sec **49. a.** $24.8e^{0.25t+3} + C$ **b.** $24.8[e^{0.25t+3} - e^3]$ thousand books **51.** 25,000 copies **53.** 0 books
55. 39,200 hits **57.** \$8,200 **59.** About 86,000 books
61. About 35,800 books

Chapter 14

Section 14.1

1. $2e^x(x - 1) + C$ **3.** $-e^{-x}(2 + 3x) + C$
5. $e^{2x}(2x^2 - 2x - 1)/4 + C$
7. $-e^{-2x+4}(2x^2 + 2x + 3)/4 + C$
9. $2^x[(2 - x)/\ln 2 + 1/(\ln 2)^2] + C$
11. $-3^{-x}[(x^2 - 1)/\ln 3 + 2x/(\ln 3)^2 + 2/(\ln 3)^3] + C$
13. $-e^{-x}(x^2 + x + 1) + C$
15. $\dfrac{1}{7}x(x + 2)^7 - \dfrac{1}{56}(x + 2)^8 + C$
17. $-\dfrac{x}{2(x - 2)^2} - \dfrac{1}{2(x - 2)} + C$ **19.** $(x^4 \ln x)/4 - x^4/16 + C$
21. $(t^3/3 + t)\ln(2t) - t^3/9 - t + C$
23. $(3/4)t^{4/3}(\ln t - 3/4) + C$ **25.** $x\log_3 x - x/\ln 3 + C$
27. $e^{2x}(x/2 - 1/4) - 4e^{3x}/3 + C$
29. $e^x(x^2 - 2x + 2) - e^{x^2}/2 + C$
31. $\dfrac{1}{3}(3x - 4)(2x - 1)^{3/2} - \dfrac{1}{5}(2x - 1)^{5/2} + C$
33. e **35.** 38,229/286 **37.** $(7/2)\ln 2 - 3/4$ **39.** 1/4
41. $1 - 11e^{-10}$ **43.** $4\ln 2 - 7/4$
45. $\dfrac{1}{2}x(x - 3)|x - 3| - \dfrac{1}{6}(x - 3)^2|x - 3| + C$
47. $2x|x - 3| - (x - 3)|x - 3| + C$
49. $-x^2(-x + 4)|-x + 4| - \dfrac{2}{3}x(-x + 4)^2|-x + 4| - \dfrac{1}{6}(-x + 4)^3|-x + 4| + C$

51. $\frac{1}{2}(x^2 - 2x + 3)(x - 4)|x - 4| -$

$\frac{1}{3}(x - 1)(x - 4)^2|x - 4| + \frac{1}{12}(x - 4)^3|x - 4| + C$

53. $28,800,000(1 - 2e^{-1})$ ft

55. $5,001 + 10x - 1/(x + 1) - [\ln(x + 1)]/(x + 1)$

57. $1,760 billion   **59.** 19 billion square feet

61. 20,800 million gallons   **63.** $e^{0.046x}[1,040(6.2x^2 - 146x + 1,910) - 22,600(12.4x - 146) + 491,000(12.4)] - 12,000,000$ **65.** 33,598

67. a. $r(t) = -0.075t + 2.75 + [0.025t - 0.25]\dfrac{|t - 10|}{t - 10}$

b. 42.5 million people   **69.** Answers will vary. Examples are xe^{x^2} and $e^{x^2} = 1 \cdot e^{x^2}$.   **71.** Answers will vary. Examples are Exercises 31 and 32, or, more simply, integrals like $\int x(x + 1)^5\,dx$.   **73.** Substitution   **75.** Parts   **77.** Substitution   **79.** Parts   **81.** $n + 1$ times   **83.** Proof.

Section 14.2

1. 16/3   **3.** 9.75   **5.** 2   **7.** 31/3   **9.** 8/3   **11.** 4   **13.** 1/3
15. 1   **17.** 2   **19.** 39   **21.** $e - 3/2$ **23.** 2/3   **25.** 3/10
27. 1/20   **29.** 4/15   **31.** 1/3   **33.** 32   **35.** $2\ln 2 - 1$
37. $8\ln 4 + 2e - 16$ **39.** 0.9138   **41.** 0.3222   **43.** 112.5. This represents your total profit for the week, $112.50.
45. 608; there were approximately 608,000 housing starts from the start of 2002 to the start of 2006 not for sale purposes.
47. a. Graph: (The upper curve is MySpace.)

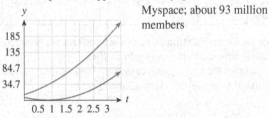

Myspace; about 93 million members

b. The area between the curves $y = f(t)$ and $y = m(t)$ over $[0.5, 2]$ **49.** $12,833(e^{0.060t} - 1) - 5,774.6(e^{0.071t} - 1)$; the total number of wiretaps authorized by federal courts from the start of 1990 up to time t was about $12,833(e^{0.060t} - 1) - 5,774.6(e^{0.071t} - 1)$.   **51.** Wrong: It could mean that the graphs of f and g cross, as shown in the caution at the start of this topic in the textbook.   **53.** The area between the export and import curves represents the accumulated U.S. trade deficit (that is, the total excess of imports over exports) from 1960 to 2007.
55. (A)   **57.** The claim is wrong because the area under a curve can represent income only if the curve is a graph of income *per unit time.* The value of a stock price is not income per unit time—the income can be realized only when the stock is sold, and it amounts to the current market price. The total net income (per share) from the given investment would be the stock price on the date of sale minus the purchase price of $50.

Section 14.3

1. Average = 2

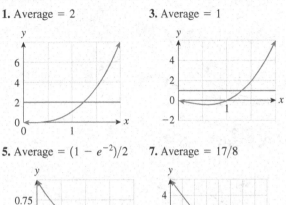

3. Average = 1

5. Average = $(1 - e^{-2})/2$ **7.** Average = 17/8

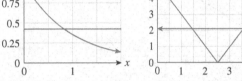

9.

x	0	1	2	3	4	5	6	7
$r(x)$	3	5	10	3	2	5	6	7
$\bar{r}(x)$			6	6	5	$\frac{10}{3}$	$\frac{13}{3}$	6

11.

x	0	1	2	3	4	5	6	7
$r(x)$	1	2	6	7	11	15	10	2
$\bar{r}(x)$			3	5	8	11	12	9

13. Moving average:

$\bar{f}(x) = x^3 - (15/2)x^2 + 25x - 125/4$

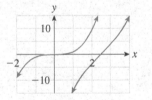

15. Moving average:

$\bar{f}(x) = \dfrac{3}{25}[x^{5/3} - (x - 5)^{5/3}]$

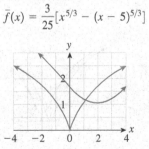

17. $\bar{f}(x) = \dfrac{2}{5}(e^{0.5x} - e^{0.5(x-5)})$

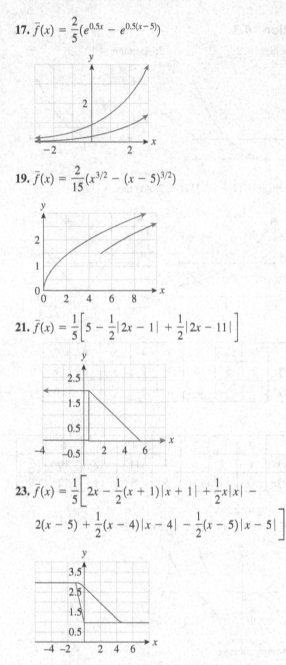

19. $\bar{f}(x) = \dfrac{2}{15}(x^{3/2} - (x - 5)^{3/2})$

21. $\bar{f}(x) = \dfrac{1}{5}\left[5 - \dfrac{1}{2}|2x - 1| + \dfrac{1}{2}|2x - 11|\right]$

23. $\bar{f}(x) = \dfrac{1}{5}\left[2x - \dfrac{1}{2}(x + 1)|x + 1| + \dfrac{1}{2}x|x| -\right.$

$\left. 2(x - 5) + \dfrac{1}{2}(x - 4)|x - 4| - \dfrac{1}{2}(x - 5)|x - 5|\right]$

25.

27.

29.

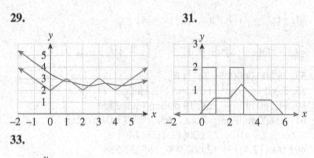

31.

33.

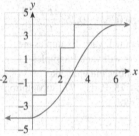

35. \$1.8 million   **37.** 16 million members per year
39. 277 million tons   **41.** \$10,410.88   **43.** \$1,500
45. \$51 billion per quarter
47.

Year t	2005	2006	2007	2008	2009	2010	2011	2012	2013	2014
Stock Price	56	77	94	80	68	73	85	87	101	92
Moving Avg. (rounded)	46	56	70	77	80	79	77	78	87	91

The moving average continued to rise at a lower rate, began to fall in 2010, then started to rise again in 2012.
49. a. To obtain the moving averages from January to June, use the fact that the data repeat every 12 months.

Graph:

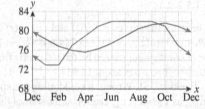

b. The 12-month moving average is constant and equal to the year-long average of approximately 79°.
51. a. Graph:

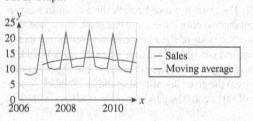

b. Approximately −0.2 million iPods per quarter

53. a. 9.2 billion gallons per year

b. $\frac{1}{2}[0.0267(t^3 - (t - 2)^3) - 0.13(t^2 - (t - 2)^2) + 17.6]$

c. The function is quadratic because the t^3 terms cancel.
55. a. $s = 41t + 526$ **b.** $\bar{s}(t) = 41t + 444$ **c.** The slope of the moving average is the same as the slope of the original

function. **57.** $\bar{f}(x) = mx + b - \dfrac{ma}{2}$ **59.** The moving aver-

age "blurs" the effects of short-term oscillations in the price and shows the longer-term trend of the stock price. **61.** They repeat every 6 months. **63.** The area above the x-axis equals the area below the x-axis. Example: $y = x$ on $[-1, 1]$
65. This need not be the case; for instance, the function $f(x) = x^2$ on $[0, 1]$ has average value $1/3$, whereas the value midway between the maximum and minimum is $1/2$.
67. (C) A shorter-term moving average most closely approximates the original function because it averages the function over a shorter period, and continuous functions change by only a small amount over a small period.

Section 14.4

1. $6.25 **3.** $512 **5.** $119.53 **7.** $900 **9.** $416.67
11. $326.27 **13.** $25 **15.** $0.50 **17.** $386.29 **19.** $225
21. $25.50 **23.** $12,684.63 **25.** $TV = \$300,000$,
$FV = \$434,465.45$ **27.** $TV = \$350,000$, $FV = \$498,496.61$
29. $TV = \$389,232.76$, $FV = \$547,547.16$
31. $TV = \$100,000$, $PV = \$82,419.99$ **33.** $TV = \$112,500$,
$PV = \$92,037.48$ **35.** $TV = \$107,889.50$, $PV = \$88,479.69$
37. $\bar{p} = \$5,000$, $\bar{q} = 10,000$, $CS = \$25$ million,
$PS = \$100$ million. The total social gain is $125 million.
39. €200 billion **41.** $3,680 billion **43.** €220 billion
45. $2,990 billion **47.** $1,943,162.44 **49.** $3,086,245.73
51. $54,594.20 **53.** $1,792,723.35 **55.** total

57. $CS = \dfrac{1}{2m}(b - m\bar{p})^2$ **59.** She is correct, provided that

there is a positive rate of return, in which case the future value (which includes interest) is greater than the total value (which does not). **61.** $PV < TV < FV$

Section 14.5

1. Diverges **3.** Converges to $2e$ **5.** Converges to e^2
7. Converges to $1/2$ **9.** Converges to $1/108$ **11.** Converges
to $3 \times 5^{2/3}$ **13.** Diverges **15.** Diverges **17.** Converges to
$\frac{5}{4}(3^{4/5} - 1)$ **19.** Diverges **21.** Converges to 0

23. Diverges **25.** Diverges **27.** 0.9, 0.99, 0.999, . . . ;
converges to 1. **29.** 7.602, 95.38, 993.1, . . . ; diverges.
31. 1.368, 1.800, 1.937, 1.980, 1.994, 1.998, 1.999, 2.000, . . . ;
converges to 2.000. **33.** 9.000, 99.00, 999.0, . . . ; diverges to
$+\infty$. **35.** 4.45 million homes **37.** 10,200 billion cigarettes
39. No; you will not sell more than 2,000 of them. **41.** The

number of graduates each year will rise without bound.
43. a. $R(t) = 350e^{-0.1t}(39t + 68)$ million dollars/year
b. $1,603,000 million **45.** $17,900 billion **47.** $\int_0^{+\infty} N(t)\, dt$
diverges, indicating that there is no bound to the expected
future total online sales of mousse. $\int_{-\infty}^0 N(t)\, dt$ converges to
approximately 2.006, indicating that total online sales of
mousse prior to the current year amounted to approximately
2 million gallons. **49.** 1 **51.** 0.1587 **53.** $70,833
55. a. 2.468 meteors on average **b.** The integral diverges. We
can interpret this as saying that the number of impacts by
meteors smaller than 1 megaton is very large. (This makes
sense because, for example, this number includes meteors no
larger than a grain of dust.) **57. a.** $\Gamma(1) = 1$; $\Gamma(2) = 1$
b. and **c.** Proofs **59.** The integrand is neither continuous nor
piecewise-continuous on the interval $[-1, 1]$, so the FTC does
not apply (the integral is improper). **61.** Yes; the integrals
converge to 0, and the FTC also gives 0. **63. a.** Not improper.
$|x|/x$ is not defined at zero, but $\lim_{x\to 0^-} |x|/x = -1$ and
$\lim_{x\to 0^+} |x|/x = 1$. Because these limits are finite, the integrand is piecewise-continuous on $[-1, 1]$ and so the integral is
not improper. **b.** Improper, because $x^{-1/3}$ has infinite left and
right limits at 0. **c.** Improper, since $(x - 2)/(x^2 - 4x + 4) =$
$1/(x - 2)$, which has an infinite left limit at 2. **65.** In all
cases you need to rewrite the improper integral as a limit and
use technology to evaluate the integral of which you are taking
the limit. Evaluate for several values of the endpoint approaching the limit. In the case of an integral in which one of the limits of integration is infinite, you may have to instruct the calculator or computer to use more subdivisions as you approach
$+\infty$. **67.** Answers will vary.

Section 14.6

1. $y = \dfrac{x^3}{3} + \dfrac{2x^{3/2}}{3} + C$ **3.** $\dfrac{y^2}{2} = \dfrac{x^2}{2} + C$ **5.** $y = Ae^{x^2/2}$

7. $y = -\dfrac{2}{(x + 1)^2 + C}$ **9.** $y^2 = (\ln x)^2 + C$

11. $y = \dfrac{x^4}{4} - x^2 + 1$ **13.** $y = (x^3 + 8)^{1/3}$ **15.** $y = 2x$

17. $y = e^{x^2/2} - 1$ **19.** $y = -\dfrac{2}{\ln(x^2 + 1) + 2}$ **21.** With

$s(t) = $ monthly sales after t months, $\dfrac{dS}{dt} = -0.05s$; $s = 1,000$

when $t = 0$. Solution: $s = 1,000e^{-0.05t}$ quarts per month
23. a. $75 + 125e^{-0.05t}$ **b.** 64.4 minutes **25.** $k \approx 0.04274$;
$H(t) = 75 + 115e^{-0.04274t}$ degrees Fahrenheit after t minutes

27. With $S(t) = $ total sales after t months, $\dfrac{dS}{dt} =$

$0.1(100,000 - S)$; $S(0) = 0$. Solution: $S = 100,000(1 - e^{-0.1t})$
monitors after t months. **29.** $q = 0.6078e^{-0.05p}p^{1.5}$
31. $y = e^{-t}(t + 1)$ **33.** $y = e^{t/2}[-2te^{-t/2} - 4e^{-t/2} + 5]$

35. $i = 5e^{-t}(e^t - e)\left[1 + \dfrac{|t-1|}{t-1}\right]$

Graph:

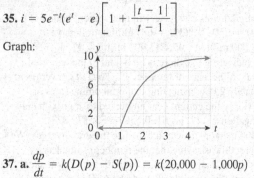

37. a. $\dfrac{dp}{dt} = k(D(p) - S(p)) = k(20{,}000 - 1{,}000p)$

b. $p = 20 - Ae^{-1{,}000kt}$ **c.** $p = 20 - 10e^{-0.2231t}$ dollars after

t months **39.** Verification **41.** $S = \dfrac{2/1{,}999}{e^{-0.5t} + 1/1{,}999}$

Graph:

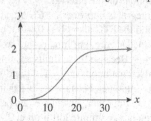

It will take about 30 months to saturate the market.
43. a. $y = be^{Ae^{-at}}$, $A =$ constant **b.** $y = 10e^{-0.69315e^{-t}}$

Graph:

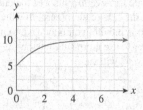

45. A general solution gives all possible solutions to the equation, using at least one arbitrary constant. A particular solution is one specific function that satisfies the equation. We obtain a particular solution by substituting specific values for any arbitrary constants in the general solution. **47.** Example: $y'' = x$ has general solution $y = \frac{1}{6}x^3 + Cx + D$ (integrate twice).
49. $y' = -4e^{-x} + 3$

Chapter 14 Review

1. $(x^2 - 2x + 4)e^x + C$ **3.** $(1/3)x^3 \ln 2x - x^3/9 + C$

5. $\dfrac{1}{2}x(2x + 1)|2x + 1| - \dfrac{1}{12}(2x + 1)^2|2x + 1| + C$

7. $-5x|-x + 3| - \dfrac{5}{2}(-x + 3)|-x + 3| + C$

9. $-e^2 - 39/e^2$ **11.** $\dfrac{3}{2 \cdot 2^{1/3}} - \dfrac{1}{2}$ **13.** $\dfrac{2\sqrt{2}}{3}$ **15.** -1

17. $e - 2$ **19.** $3x - 2$ **21.** $\dfrac{3}{14}[x^{7/3} - (x - 2)^{7/3}]$

23. $\$1{,}600$ **25.** $\$2{,}500$ **27.** $1/4$ **29.** Diverges **31.** 1

33. $y = -\dfrac{3}{x^3 + C}$ **35.** $y = \sqrt{2 \ln|x| + 1}$ **37.** $\$18{,}200$

39. a. $\$2{,}260$ **b.** $50{,}000e^{0.01t}(1 - e^{-0.04}) \approx 1{,}960.53e^{0.01t}$
41. a. $\bar{p} = 20$, $\bar{q} = 40{,}000$ **b.** $CS = \$240{,}000$, $PS = \$30{,}000$
43. Approximately $\$910{,}000$ **45. a.** $\$5{,}549{,}000$ **b.** Principal:
$\$5{,}280{,}000$, interest: $\$269{,}000$ **47.** $\$51$ million **49.** The amount in the account would be given by $y = 10{,}000/(1 - t)$, where t is time in years, so would approach infinity 1 year after the deposit.

Chapter 15

Section 15.1

1. a. 1 **b.** 1 **c.** 2 **d.** $a^2 - a + 5$ **e.** $y^2 + x^2 - y + 1$
f. $(x + h)^2 + (y + k)^2 - (x + h) + 1$ **3. a.** 0 **b.** 0.2
c. -0.1 **d.** $0.18a + 0.2$ **e.** $0.1x + 0.2y - 0.01xy$
f. $0.2(x + h) + 0.1(y + k) - 0.01(x + h)(y + k)$
5. a. 1 **b.** e **c.** e **d.** e^{x+y+z} **e.** $e^{x+h+y+k+z+l}$
7. a. Does not exist **b.** 0 **c.** 0 **d.** $xyz/(x^2 + y^2 + z^2)$
e. $(x + h)(y + k)(z + l)/[(x + h)^2 + (y + k)^2 + (x + l)^2]$
9. a. Increases; 2.3 **b.** Decreases; 1.4 **c.** f decreases; 1 unit increase in z **11.** Neither **13.** Linear **15.** Linear
17. Interaction **19. a.** 107 **b.** -14 **c.** -113

21.

	$x \rightarrow$			
		10	**20**	**30**	**40**
y	**10**	52	107	162	217
$\downarrow$	**20**	94	194	294	394
	30	136	281	426	571
	40	178	368	558	748

23. Spreadsheet **25.** 18, 4, 0.0965, 47,040
27. 6.9078, 1.5193, 5.4366, 0
29. Let $z =$ annual sales of Z (in millions of dollars), $x =$ annual sales of X, and $y =$ annual sales of Y. The model is $z = -2.1x + 0.4y + 16.2$.
31. **33.** **35.** **37.**

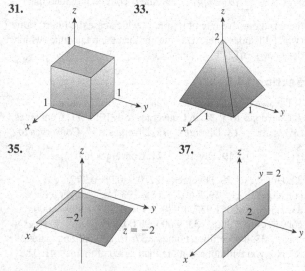

39.

41. (H) **43.** (B)
45. (F) **47.** (C)

49.

51.

53.

55. a. 4 **b.** 5 **c.** -1
57. $(2, 2)$ and $(-2, -2)$

59.

61.

63.

65.

67.

69.

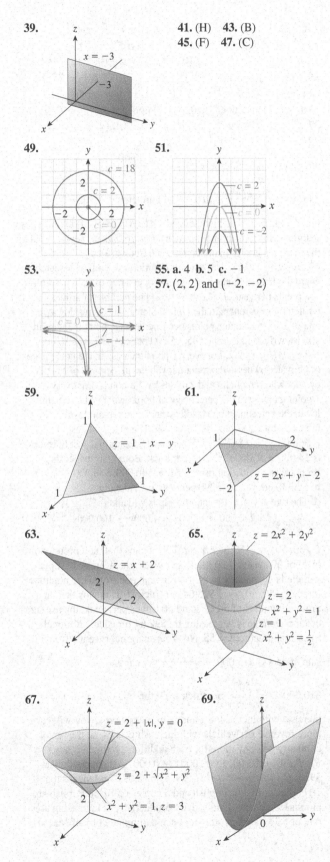

71.

73.

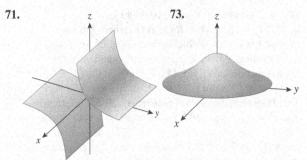

75. a. The marginal cost of cars is $6,000 per car. The marginal cost of trucks is $4,000 per truck. **b.** The graph is a plane with x-intercept -40, y-intercept -60, and z-intercept 240,000. **c.** The slice $x = 10$ is the straight line with equation $z = 300,000 + 4,000y$. It describes the cost function for the manufacture of trucks if car production is held fixed at 10 cars per week. **d.** The level curve $z = 480,000$ is the straight line $6,000x + 4,000y = 240,000$. It describes the number of cars and trucks you can manufacture to maintain weekly costs at $480,000. **77.** $C(x, y) = 10 + 0.03x + 0.04y$, where C is the cost in dollars, $x = $ # video clips sold per month, $y = $ # audio clips sold per month **79. a.** 28% **b.** 21% **c.** Percentage points per year **81.** The graph is a plane with x_1-intercept 0.3, x_2-intercept 33, and x_3-intercept 0.66. The slices by $x_1 = $ constant are straight lines that are parallel to each other. Thus, the rate of change of General Motors' share as a function of Ford's share does not depend on Chrysler's share. Specifically, GM's share decreases by 0.02 percentage points per 1 percentage point increase in Ford's market share, regardless of Chrysler's share. **83. a.** 181 thousand prisoners **b.** $y = 300$: $N = 0.01x + 56$; $y = 500$: $N = 0.09x + 4$. When there are 300,000 prisoners in local jails, the number in federal prisons increases by 10 per 1,000 additional prisoners in state prisons. When there are 500,000 prisoners in local jails, the number in federal prisons increases by 90 per 1,000 additional prisoners in state prisons. **85. a.** The slices $x = $ constant and $y = $ constant are straight lines. **b.** No. Even though the slices $x = $ constant and $y = $ constant are straight lines, the level curves are not, so the surface is not a plane. **c.** The slice $x = 10$ has a slope of 3,800. The slice $x = 20$ has a slope of 3,600. Manufacturing more cars lowers the marginal cost of manufacturing trucks. **87. a.** $9,980 **b.** $R(z) = 9,850 + 0.04z$ **89.** $f(x, t) = 7.14x + 3.57t - 72.86$; $456 billion **91.** $U(11, 10) - U(10, 10) \approx 5.75$. This means that, if your company now has 10 copies of Macro Publish and 10 copies of Turbo Publish, then the purchase of one additional copy of Macro Publish will result in a productivity increase of approximately 5.75 pages per day. **93. a.** Answers will vary. $(a, b, c) = (3, 1/4, 1/\pi)$; $(a, b, c) = (1/\pi, 3, 1/4)$. **b.** $a = \left(\frac{3}{4\pi}\right)^{1/3}$. The resulting ellipsoid is a sphere with radius a. **95.** 7,000,000 **97. a.** $100 = K(1,000)^a(1,000,000)^{1-a}$; $10 = K(1,000)^a(10,000)^{1-a}$ **b.** $\log K - 3a = -4$; $\log K - a = -3$ **c.** $a = 0.5$, $K \approx 0.003162$ **d.** $P = 71$ pianos (to the nearest piano) **99. a.** 4×10^{-3} g/m^2 **b.** The total weight of sulfates in the Earth's atmosphere

101. a. The value of N would be doubled.
b. $N(R, f_p, n_e, f_l, f_i, L) = R f_p n_e f_l f_i f_c L$, where L is the average lifetime of an intelligent civilization. **c.** Take the logarithm of both sides, since this would yield the linear function $\ln(N) = \ln(R) + \ln(f_p) + \ln(n_e) + \ln(f_l) + \ln(f_i) + \ln(f_c) + \ln(L)$. **d.** Answers will vary.
103. They are reciprocals of each other. **105.** For example, $f(x, y) = x^2 + y^2$. **107.** For example, $f(x, y, z) = xyz$.
109. For example, take $f(x, y) = x + y$. Then setting $y = 3$ gives $f(x, 3) = x + 3$. This can be viewed as a function of the single variable x. Choosing other values for y gives other functions of x. **111.** The slope is independent of the choice of $y = k$. **113.** That CDs cost more than cassettes
115. plane **117.** (B) Traveling in the direction B results in the shortest trip to nearby isotherms and hence the fastest rate of increase in temperature. **119.** Agree: Any slice through a plane is a straight line. **121.** The graph of a function of three or more variables lives in four-dimensional (or higher) space, which makes it difficult to draw and visualize. **123.** We need one dimension for each of the variables plus one dimension for the value of the function.

Section 15.2

1. $f_x(x, y) = -40$; $f_y(x, y) = 20$; $f_x(1, -1) = -40$; $f_y(1, -1) = 20$ **3.** $f_x(x, y) = 6x + 1$; $f_y(x, y) = -3y^2$; $f_x(1, -1) = 7$; $f_y(1, -1) = -3$ **5.** $f_x(x, y) = -40 + 10y$; $f_y(x, y) = 20 + 10x$; $f_x(1, -1) = -50$; $f_y(1, -1) = 30$
7. $f_x(x, y) = 6xy$; $f_y(x, y) = 3x^2$; $f_x(1, -1) = -6$; $f_y(1, -1) = 3$ **9.** $f_x(x, y) = 2xy^3 - 3x^2y^2 - y$; $f_y(x, y) = 3x^2y^2 - 2x^3y - x$; $f_x(1, -1) = -4$; $f_y(1, -1) = 4$
11. $f_x(x, y) = 6y(2xy + 1)^2$; $f_y(x, y) = 6x(2xy + 1)^2$; $f_x(1, -1) = -6$; $f_y(1, -1) = 6$ **13.** $f_x(x, y) = e^{x+y}$; $f_y(x, y) = e^{x+y}$; $f_x(1, -1) = 1$; $f_y(1, -1) = 1$
15. $f_x(x, y) = 3x^{-0.4}y^{0.4}$; $f_y(x, y) = 2x^{0.6}y^{-0.6}$; $f_x(1, -1)$ undefined; $f_y(1, -1)$ undefined **17.** $f_x(x, y) = 0.2ye^{0.2xy}$; $f_y(x, y) = 0.2xe^{0.2xy}$; $f_x(1, -1) = -0.2e^{-0.2}$; $f_y(1, -1) = 0.2e^{-0.2}$ **19.** $f_{xx}(x, y) = 0$; $f_{yy}(x, y) = 0$; $f_{xy}(x, y) = f_{yx}(x, y) = 0$; $f_{xx}(1, -1) = 0$; $f_{yy}(1, -1) = 0$; $f_{xy}(1, -1) = f_{yx}(1, -1) = 0$ **21.** $f_{xx}(x, y) = 0$; $f_{yy}(x, y) = 0$; $f_{xy}(x, y) = f_{yx}(x, y) = 10$; $f_{xx}(1, -1) = 0$; $f_{yy}(1, -1) = 0$; $f_{xy}(1, -1) = f_{yx}(1, -1) = 10$ **23.** $f_{xx}(x, y) = 6y$; $f_{yy}(x, y) = 0$; $f_{xy}(x, y) = f_{yx}(x, y) = 6x$; $f_{xx}(1, -1) = -6$; $f_{yy}(1, -1) = 0$; $f_{xy}(1, -1) = f_{yx}(1, -1) = 6$
25. $f_{xx}(x, y) = e^{x+y}$; $f_{yy}(x, y) = e^{x+y}$; $f_{xy}(x, y) = f_{yx}(x, y) = e^{x+y}$; $f_{xx}(1, -1) = 1$; $f_{yy}(1, -1) = 1$; $f_{xy}(1, -1) = f_{yx}(1, -1) = 1$ **27.** $f_{xx}(x, y) = -1.2x^{-1.4}y^{0.4}$; $f_{yy}(x, y) = -1.2x^{0.6}y^{-1.6}$; $f_{xy}(x, y) = f_{yx}(x, y) = 1.2x^{-0.4}y^{-0.6}$; $f_{xx}(1, -1)$ undefined; $f_{yy}(1, -1)$ undefined; $f_{xy}(1, -1)$ and $f_{yx}(1, -1)$ undefined **29.** $f_x(x, y, z) = yz$; $f_y(x, y, z) = xz$; $f_z(x, y, z) = xy$; $f_x(0, -1, 1) = -1$; $f_y(0, -1, 1) = 0$; $f_z(0, -1, 1) = 0$ **31.** $f_x(x, y, z) = 4/(x + y + z^2)^2$; $f_y(x, y, z) = 4/(x + y + z^2)^2$; $f_z(x, y, z) = 8z/(x + y + z^2)^2$; $f_x(0, -1, 1)$ undefined; $f_y(0, -1, 1)$ undefined;

$f_z(0, -1, 1)$ undefined **33.** $f_x(x, y, z) = e^{yz} + yze^{xz}$; $f_y(x, y, z) = xze^{yz} + e^{xz}$; $f_z(x, y, z) = xy(e^{yz} + e^{xz})$; $f_x(0, -1, 1) = e^{-1} - 1$; $f_y(0, -1, 1) = 1$; $f_z(0, -1, 1) = 0$
35. $f_x(x, y, z) = 0.1x^{-0.9}y^{0.4}z^{0.5}$; $f_y(x, y, z) = 0.4x^{0.1}y^{-0.6}z^{0.5}$; $f_z(x, y, z) = 0.5x^{0.1}y^{0.4}z^{-0.5}$; $f_x(0, -1, 1)$ undefined; $f_y(0, -1, 1)$ undefined, $f_z(0, -1, 1)$ undefined
37. $f_x(x, y, z) = yze^{xyz}$, $f_y(x, y, z) = xze^{xyz}$, $f_z(x, y, z) = xye^{xyz}$; $f_x(0, -1, 1) = -1$; $f_y(0, -1, 1) = f_z(0, -1, 1) = 0$
39. $f_x(x, y, z) = 0$; $f_y(x, y, z) = -\dfrac{600z}{y^{0.7}(1 + y^{0.3})^2}$;

$f_z(x, y, z) = \dfrac{2,000}{1 + y^{0.3}}$; $f_x(0, -1, 1)$ undefined; $f_y(0, -1, 1)$ undefined; $f_z(0, -1, 1)$ undefined **41.** $\partial C/\partial x = 6{,}000$; the marginal cost to manufacture each car is \$6,000. $\partial C/\partial y = 4{,}000$; the marginal cost to manufacture each truck is \$4,000.
43. $\partial y/\partial t = -0.78$. The number of articles written by researchers in the United States was decreasing at a rate of 0.78 percentage points per year. $\partial y/\partial x = -1.02$. The number of articles written by researchers in the United States was decreasing at a rate of 1.02 percentage points per 1 percentage point increase in articles written in Europe. **45.** \$5,600 per car **47. a.** $\partial M/\partial c = -3.8$, $\partial M/\partial f = 2.2$. For every 1 point increase in the percentage of Chrysler owners who remain loyal, the percentage of Mazda owners who remain loyal decreases by 3.8 points. For every 1 point increase in the percentage of Ford owners who remain loyal, the percentage of Mazda owners who remain loyal increases by 2.2 points. **b.** 16% **49.** The marginal cost of cars is $6{,}000 + 1{,}000e^{-0.01(x+y)}$ per car. The marginal cost of trucks is $4{,}000 + 1{,}000e^{-0.01(x+y)}$ per truck. Both marginal costs decrease as production rises. **51. a.** \$40,900; \$58,800
b. $-\$330$ per year; $-\$290$ per year **c.** Widening
d. The rate at which the income gap is widening
53. $\overline{C}(x, y) = \dfrac{200{,}000 + 6{,}000x + 4{,}000y - 100{,}000e^{-0.01(x+y)}}{x + y}$;

$\overline{C}_x(50, 50) = -\$2.64$ per car. This means that, at a production level of 50 cars and 50 trucks per week, the average cost per vehicle is decreasing by \$2.64 for each additional car manufactured. $\overline{C}_y(50, 50) = -\$22.64$ per truck. This means that, at a production level of 50 cars and 50 trucks per week, the average cost per vehicle is decreasing by \$22.64 for each additional truck manufactured. **55.** No. Your marginal revenue from the sale of cars is $\$15{,}000 - \dfrac{2{,}500}{\sqrt{x + y}}$ per car and

$\$10{,}000 - \dfrac{2{,}500}{\sqrt{x + y}}$ per truck from the sale of trucks. These increase with increasing x and y. In other words, you will earn more revenue per vehicle with increasing sales, so the rental company will pay more for each additional vehicle it buys.
57. $P_z(10, 100{,}000, 1{,}000{,}000) \approx 0.0001010$ papers/dollars
59. a. $U_x(10, 5) = 5.18$, $U_y(10, 5) = 2.09$. This means that if 10 copies of Macro Publish and 5 copies of Turbo Publish are purchased, the company's daily productivity is increasing at a rate of 5.18 pages per day for each additional copy of Macro

purchased and by 2.09 pages per day for each additional copy of Turbo purchased. **b.** $\dfrac{U_x(10, 5)}{U_y(10, 5)} \approx 2.48$ is the ratio of the usefulness of one additional copy of Macro to one of Turbo. Thus, with 10 copies of Macro and 5 copies of Turbo, the company can expect approximately 2.48 times the productivity per additional copy of Macro compared to Turbo.
61. 6×10^9 N/sec   **63. a.** $A_P(100, 0.1, 10) = 2.59$; $A_r(100, 0.1, 10) = 2{,}357.95$; $A_t(100, 0.1, 10) = 24.72$. Thus, for a $100 investment at 10% interest, after 10 years the accumulated amount is increasing at a rate of $2.59 per $1 of principal, at a rate of $2,357.95 per increase of 1 in r (note that this would correspond to an increase in the interest rate of 100%), and at a rate of $24.72 per year. **b.** $A_P(100, 0.1, t)$ tells you the rate at which the accumulated amount in an account bearing 10% interest with a principal of $100 is growing per $1 increase in the principal, t years after the investment.
65. a. $P_x = Ka\left(\dfrac{y}{x}\right)^b$ and $P_y = Kb\left(\dfrac{x}{y}\right)^a$. They are equal precisely when $\dfrac{a}{b} = \left(\dfrac{x}{y}\right)^b\left(\dfrac{x}{y}\right)^a$. Substituting $b = 1 - a$ now gives $\dfrac{a}{b} = \dfrac{x}{y}$. **b.** The given information implies that $P_x(100, 200) = P_y(100, 200)$. By part (a) this occurs precisely when $a/b = x/y = 100/200 = 1/2$. But $b = 1 - a$, so $a/(1 - a) = 1/2$, giving $a = 1/3$ and $b = 2/3$. **67.** Decreasing at 0.0075 parts of nutrient per part of water per second
69. f is increasing at a rate of s units per unit of x, f is increasing at a rate of t units per unit of y, and the value of f is r when $x = a$ and $y = b$ **71.** the marginal cost of building an additional orbicus; zonars per unit **73.** Answers will vary. One example is $f(x, y) = -2x + 3y$. Others are $f(x, y) = -2x + 3y + 9$ and $f(x, y) = xy - 3x + 2y + 10$.
75. a. b is the z-intercept of the plane. m is the slope of the intersection of the plane with the xz-plane. n is the slope of the intersection of the plane with the yz-plane. **b.** Write $z = b + rx + sy$. We are told that $\partial z/\partial x = m$, so $r = m$. Similarly, $s = n$. Thus, $z = b + mx + ny$. We are also told that the plane passes through (h, k, l). Substituting gives $l = b + mh + nk$. This gives b as $l - mh - nk$. Substituting in the equation for z therefore gives $z = l - mh - nk + mx + ny = l + m(x - h) + n(y - k)$, as required.

Section 15.3

1. P: relative minimum; Q: none of the above; R: relative maximum **3.** P: saddle point; Q: relative maximum; R: none of the above **5.** Relative minimum **7.** Neither **9.** Saddle point **11.** Relative minimum at $(0, 0, 1)$ **13.** Relative maximum at $(-1/2, 1/2, 3/2)$ **15.** Saddle point at $(0, 0, 0)$ **17.** Minimum at $(4, -3, -10)$ **19.** Maximum at $(-7/4, 1/4, 19/8)$ **21.** Relative maximum at $(0, 0, 0)$, saddle points at $(\pm 4, 2, -16)$ **23.** Relative minimum at $(0, 0, 0)$, saddle points at $(-1, \pm 1, 1)$ **25.** Relative minimum at $(0, 0, 1)$ **27.** Relative minimum at $(-2, \pm 2, -16)$, $(0, 0)$ a

critical point that is not a relative extremum   **29.** Saddle point at $(0, 0, -1)$ **31.** Relative maximum at $(-1, 0, e)$ **33.** Relative minimum at $(2^{1/3}, 2^{1/3}, 3(2^{2/3}))$ **35.** Relative minimum at $(1, 1, 4)$ and $(-1, -1, 4)$ **37.** Absolute minimum at $(0, 0, 1)$ **39.** None; the relative maximum at $(0, 0, 0)$ is not absolute.   **41.** Minimum of $1/3$ at $(c, f) = (2/3, 2/3)$. Thus, at least $1/3$ of all Mazda owners would choose another new Mazda, and this lowest loyalty occurs when $2/3$ of Chrysler and Ford owners remain loyal to their brands.   **43.** It should remove 2.5 lb of sulfur and 1 lb of lead per day.   **45.** You should charge $580.81 for the Ultra Mini and $808.08 for the Big Stack.
47. $l = w = h \approx 20.67$ in, volume $\approx 8{,}827$ in^3
49. 18 in $\times$ 18 in $\times$ 36 in, volume $= 11{,}664$ in^3
51.   **53.** Continues up indefinitely

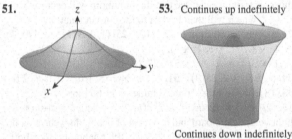

Continues down indefinitely
Function not defined on circle

55. H must be positive.   **57.** No. For there to be a relative maximum at (a, b), *all* vertical planes through (a, b) should yield a curve with a relative maximum at (a, b). It could happen that a slice by another vertical plane through (a, b) (such as $x - a = y - b$) does not yield a curve with a relative maximum at (a, b). [An example is $f(x, y) = \sqrt{xy} - x^2 - y^2$, at the point $(0, 0)$. Look at the slices through $x = 0$, $y = 0$, and $y = x$.]   **59.** $\overline{C}_x = \dfrac{\partial}{\partial x}\left(\dfrac{C}{x + y}\right) = \dfrac{(x + y)C_x - C}{(x + y)^2}$. If this is zero, then $(x + y)C_x = C$, or $C_x = \dfrac{C}{x + y} = \overline{C}$. Similarly, if $\overline{C}_y = 0$, then $C_y = \overline{C}$. This is reasonable because if the average cost is decreasing with increasing x, then the average cost is greater than the marginal cost C_x. Similarly, if the average cost is increasing with increasing x, then the average cost is less than the marginal cost C_x. Thus, if the average cost is stationary with increasing x, then the average cost equals the marginal cost C_x. (The situation is similar for the case of increasing y.)   **61.** The equation of the tangent plane at the point (a, b) is $z = f(a, b) + f_x(a, b)(x - a) + f_y(a, b)(y - b)$. If f has a relative extremum at (a, b), then $f_x(a, b) = 0 = f_y(a, b)$. Substituting these into the equation of the tangent plane gives $z = f(a, b)$, a constant. But the graph of $z = constant$ is a plane parallel to the xy-plane.

Section 15.4

1. 1; $(0, 0, 0)$ **3.** 1.35; $(1/10, 3/10, 1/2)$ **5.** Minimum value $= 6$ at $(1, 2, 1/2)$ **7.** 200; $(20, 10)$ **9.** 16; $(2, 2)$ and $(-2, -2)$ **11.** 20; $(2, 4)$ **13.** 1; $(0, 0, 0)$ **15.** 1.35; $(1/10, 3/10, 1/2)$ **17.** Minimum value $= 6$ at $(1, 2, 1/2)$ **19. a.** $f(x, y, z)$ is the

square of the distance from the point (x, y, z) to $(3, 0, 0)$, and the constraint tells us that (x, y, z) must lie on the paraboloid $z = x^2 + y^2$. Because there must be such a point (or points) on the paraboloid closest to $(3, 0, 0)$, the given problem must have at least one solution. Solution: $(x, y, z) = (1, 0, 1)$ for a minimum value of 5. **b.** Same solution as part (a) **c.** There are no critical points using this method. **d.** The constraint equation $y^2 = z - x^2$ tells us that $z - x^2$ cannot be negative and thus restricts the domain of f to the set of points (x, y, z) with $z - x^2 \geq 0$. However, this information is lost when $z - x^2$ is substituted in the expression for f, so the substitution in part (c) results in a different optimization problem, one in which there is no requirement that $z - x^2$ be ≥ 0. If we pay attention to this constraint we can see that the minimum will occur when $z = x^2$, which will then lead us to the correct solution.
21. $5 \times 10 = 50$ sq. ft. **23.** \$10 **25.** $(1/\sqrt{3}, 1/\sqrt{3}, 1/\sqrt{3})$, $(-1/\sqrt{3}, -1/\sqrt{3}, 1/\sqrt{3})$, $(1/\sqrt{3}, -1/\sqrt{3}, -1/\sqrt{3})$, $(-1/\sqrt{3}, 1/\sqrt{3}, -1/\sqrt{3})$ **27.** $(0, 1/2, -1/2)$
29. $(-5/9, 5/9, 25/9)$ **31.** $l \times w \times h = 1$ ft $\times$ 1 ft $\times$ 2 ft
33. 18 in $\times$ 18 in $\times$ 36 in, volume $= 11{,}664$ in^3
35. $(2l/h)^{1/3} \times (2l/h)^{1/3} \times 2^{1/3}(h/l)^{2/3}$, where $l =$ cost of lightweight cardboard and $h =$ cost of heavy-duty cardboard per square foot **37.** $1 \times 1 \times 1/2$ **39.** 6 laborers, 10 robots for a productivity of 368 pairs of socks per day **41.** Method 1: Solve $g(x, y, z) = 0$ for one of the variables, and substitute in $f(x, y, z)$. Then find the maximum value of the resulting function of two variables. Advantage (answers may vary): We can use the second derivative test to check whether the resulting critical points are maxima, minima, saddle points, or none of these. Disadvantage (answers may vary): We may not be able to solve $g(x, y, z) = 0$ for one of the variables. Method 2: Use the method of Lagrange multipliers. Advantage (answers may vary): We do not need to solve the constraint equation for one of the variables. Disadvantage (answers may vary): The method does not tell us whether the critical points obtained are maxima, minima, saddle points, or none of these. **43.** If the only constraint is an equality constraint and if it is impossible to eliminate one of the variables in the objective function by substitution (solving the constraint equation for a variable or some other method). **45.** Answers may vary: Maximize $f(x, y) = 1 - x^2 - y^2$ subject to $x = y$. **47.** Yes. There may be relative extrema at points on the boundary of the domain. The partial derivatives of the function need not be 0 at such points. **49.** In a linear programming problem the objective function is linear, so the partial derivatives can never all be zero. (We are ignoring the simple case in which the objective function is constant.) It follows that the extrema cannot occur in the interior of the domain (since the partial derivatives must be zero at such points).

Section 15.5

1. $-1/2$ **3.** $e^2/2 - 7/2$ **5.** $(e^3 - 1)(e^2 - 1)$ **7.** $7/6$
9. $[e^3 - e - e^{-1} + e^{-3}]/2$ **11.** $1/2$ **13.** $(e - 1)/2$
15. $45/2$ **17.** $8/3$ **19.** $4/3$ **21.** 0 **23.** $2/3$ **25.** $2/3$
27. $2(e - 2)$ **29.** $1/3$

31. $\displaystyle \int_0^1 \int_0^{1-x} f(x, y)\, dy\, dx$ **33.** $\displaystyle \int_0^{\sqrt{2}} \int_{x^2-1}^1 f(x, y)\, dy\, dx$

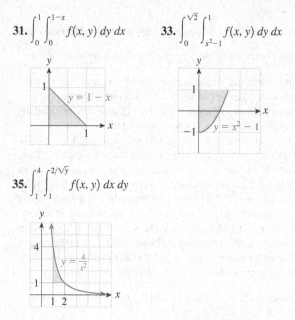

35. $\displaystyle \int_1^4 \int_1^{2/\sqrt{y}} f(x, y)\, dx\, dy$

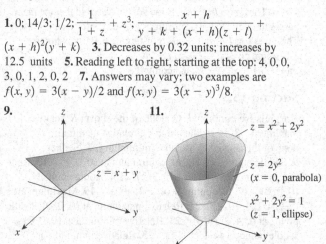

37. $4/3$ **39.** $1/6$ **41.** 162,000 gadgets **43.** \$312,750
45. \$17,500 **47.** 8,216 **49.** 1 degree Celsius **51.** The area between the curves $y = r(x)$ and $y = s(x)$ and the vertical lines $x = a$ and $x = b$ is given by $\int_a^b \int_{r(x)}^{s(x)} dy\, dx$, assuming that $r(x) \leq s(x)$ for $a \leq x \leq b$. **53.** The first step in calculating an integral of the form $\int_a^b \int_{r(x)}^{s(x)} f(x, y)\, dy\, dx$ is to evaluate the integral $\int_{r(x)}^{s(x)} f(x, y)\, dy$, obtained by holding x constant and integrating with respect to y. **55.** Paintings per picasso per dali **57.** The left-hand side is $\int_a^b \int_c^d f(x)g(y)\, dx\, dy = \int_a^b \left(g(y) \int_c^d f(x)\, dx \right) dy$ [because $g(y)$ is treated as a constant in the inner integral] $= \left(\int_c^d f(x)\, dx \right)\left(\int_a^b g(y)\, dy \right)$ [because $\int_c^d f(x)\, dx$ is a constant and can therefore be taken outside the integral with respect to y]. For example, $\int_0^1 \int_1^2 ye^x\, dx\, dy = \frac{1}{2}(e^2 - e)$, no matter how we compute it.

Chapter 15 Review

1. 0; $14/3$; $1/2$; $\dfrac{1}{1+z} + z^3$; $\dfrac{x+h}{y+k+(x+h)(z+l)} + (x+h)^2(y+k)$ **3.** Decreases by 0.32 units; increases by 12.5 units **5.** Reading left to right, starting at the top: 4, 0, 0, 3, 0, 1, 2, 0, 2 **7.** Answers may vary; two examples are $f(x, y) = 3(x - y)/2$ and $f(x, y) = 3(x - y)^3/8$.

9.   **11.**

13.

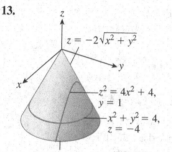

$z = -2\sqrt{x^2 + y^2}$

$z^2 = 4x^2 + 4,$
$y = 1$

$x^2 + y^2 = 4,$
$z = -4$

15. $f_x = 2x + y, f_y = x, f_{yy} = 0$ **17.** 0

19. $\dfrac{\partial f}{\partial x} = \dfrac{-x^2 + y^2 + z^2}{(x^2 + y^2 + z^2)^2}, \dfrac{\partial f}{\partial y} = -\dfrac{2xy}{(x^2 + y^2 + z^2)^2},$

$\dfrac{\partial f}{\partial z} = -\dfrac{2xz}{(x^2 + y^2 + z^2)^2}, \dfrac{\partial f}{\partial x}\Big|_{(0,1,0)} = 1$ **21.** Absolute

minimum at $(1, 3/2)$ **23.** Maximum at $(0, 0)$, saddle
points at $(\pm\sqrt{2}, 1)$ **25.** Saddle point at $(0, 0)$
27. $1/27$ at $(1/3, 1/3, 1/3)$ **29.** $(0, 2, \sqrt{2})$ **31.** 4; $(\sqrt{2}, \sqrt{2})$
and $(-\sqrt{2}, -\sqrt{2})$ **33.** $(0, 2, \sqrt{2})$ **35.** 2   **37.** ln 5
39. 1   **41. a.** $h(x, y) = 5{,}000 - 0.8x - 0.6y$ hits per day
(x = number of new customers at JungleBooks.com,
y = number of new customers at FarmerBooks.com)
b. 250   **c.** $h(x, y, z) = 5{,}000 - 0.8x - 0.6y + 0.0001z$
(z = number of new Internet shoppers)   **d.** 1.4 million
43. a. 2,320 hits per day   **b.** $0.08 + 0.00003x$ hits (daily)
per dollar spent on television advertising per month;
increases with increasing x **c.** \$4,000 per month   **45.** (A)
47. a. About 15,800 additional orders per day   **b.** 11
49. \$23,050

Chapter 16

Section 16.1

1.

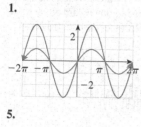

3.

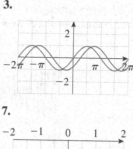

5.

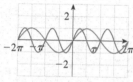

7.

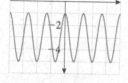

9.

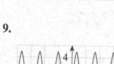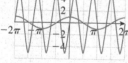

11.

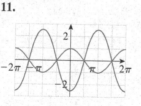

13. $f(x) = \sin(2\pi x) + 1$ **15.** $f(x) = 1.5 \sin[4\pi(x - 0.25)]$
17. $f(x) = 50 \sin[\pi(x - 5)/10] - 50$ **19.** $f(x) = \cos(2\pi x)$
21. $f(x) = 1.5 \cos[4\pi(x - 0.375)]$
23. $f(x) = 40 \cos[\pi(x - 10)/10] + 40$
25. $f(t) = 4.2 \sin(\pi/2 - 2\pi t) + 3$
27. $g(x) = 4 - 1.3 \sin[\pi/2 - 2.3(x - 4)]$ **29.** Proof
31. $\sqrt{3}/2$ **33.** Proof   **35.** Proof   **37.** $\tan(x + \pi) = \tan(x)$
39. a. $2\pi/0.602 \approx 10.4$ years.   **b.** Maximum: $58.8 + 57.7 = 116.5 \approx 117$; minimum: $58.8 - 57.7 = 1.1 \approx 1$
c. $1.43 + P/4 + 2P = 1.43 + 23.48 \approx 25$ years, or about the
beginning of 2022   **41. a.** Sales were highest when $t \approx 0, 4,$
8, and 12, which correspond to the end of the last quarter or
beginning of the first quarter of each year. Sales were lowest
when $t \approx 2, 6,$ and 10, which correspond to the beginning of
the third quarter of each year.   **b.** The maximum quarterly sales
were approximately 21 million iPods per quarter; minimum
quarterly sales were approximately 9 million iPods per quarter.
c. Maximum: $15 + 6 = 21$; minimum: $15 - 6 = 9$
43. Amplitude $= 6.00$, vertical offset $= 15$, phase shift $= -1.85/1.51 \approx -1.23$, angular frequency $= 1.51$,
period ≈ 4.16. From 2008 through 2010, Apple's sales of
iPods fluctuated in cycles of 4.16 quarters about a baseline of
15 million iPods per quarter. Every cycle, sales peaked at
$15 + 6 = 21$ million iPods per quarter and dipped to a low of
$15 - 6 = 9$ million iPods per quarter. Sales first peaked at
$t = -1.23 + (5/4) \times 4.16 = 3.97$, the end of 2008.
45. $P(t) = 7.5 \sin[\pi(t - 13)/26] + 12.5$
47. $T(t) = 3.5 \cos[\pi(t - 7)/6] + 78.5$
49. $n(t) = 1.25 \sin[\pi(t - 1)/2] + 5.75$
51. $n(t) = 1.25 \cos[\pi(t - 2)/2] + 5.75$
53. $d(t) = 5 \sin[2\pi(t - 1.625)/13.5] + 10$
55. a. $u(t) = 2.5 \sin(2\pi(t - 0.75)) + 7.5$
b. $c(t) = 1.04^t[2.5 \sin(2\pi(t - 0.75)) + 7.5]$
57. a. $C \approx 50, A \approx 8, P \approx 12, \beta \approx 6$

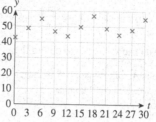

b. $f(t) = 5.882 \cos[2\pi(t - 5.696)/12.263] + 49.238$

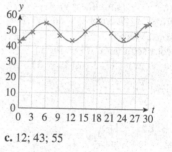

c. 12; 43; 55

59. a.

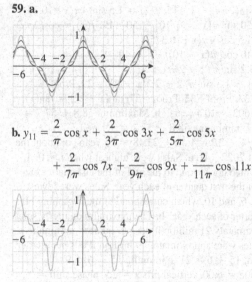

b. $y_{11} = \dfrac{2}{\pi}\cos x + \dfrac{2}{3\pi}\cos 3x + \dfrac{2}{5\pi}\cos 5x$

$\qquad + \dfrac{2}{7\pi}\cos 7x + \dfrac{2}{9\pi}\cos 9x + \dfrac{2}{11\pi}\cos 11x$

c. Multiply the amplitudes by 3 and change ω to 1/2:

$y_{11} = \dfrac{6}{\pi}\cos\dfrac{x}{2} + \dfrac{6}{3\pi}\cos\dfrac{3x}{2} + \dfrac{6}{5\pi}\cos\dfrac{5x}{2}$

$\qquad + \dfrac{6}{7\pi}\cos\dfrac{7x}{2} + \dfrac{6}{9\pi}\cos\dfrac{9x}{2} + \dfrac{6}{11\pi}\cos\dfrac{11x}{2}.$

61. The period is approximately 12.6 units.

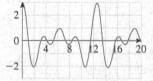

63. Lows: $B - A$; highs: $B + A$.   **65.** He is correct. The other trigonometric functions can be obtained from the sine function by first using the formula $\cos x = \sin(x + \pi/2)$ to obtain cosine and then using the formulas $\tan x = \dfrac{\sin x}{\cos x}$, $\cot x = \dfrac{\cos x}{\sin x}$, $\sec x = \dfrac{1}{\cos x}$, and $\csc x = \dfrac{1}{\sin x}$ to obtain the rest.   **67.** The largest B can be is A. Otherwise, if B is larger than A, the low figure for sales would have the negative value of $A - B$.

Section 16.2

1. $\cos x + \sin x$ **3.** $(\cos x)(\tan x) + (\sin x)(\sec^2 x)$
5. $-2\csc x \cot x - \sec x \tan x + 3$ **7.** $\cos x - x \sin x + 2x$
9. $(2x - 1)\tan x + (x^2 - x + 1)\sec^2 x$
11. $-[\csc^2 x(1 + \sec x) + \cot x \sec x \tan x]/(1 + \sec x)^2$
13. $-2\cos x \sin x$ **15.** $2\sec^2 x \tan x$ **17.** $3\cos(3x - 5)$
19. $2\sin(-2x + 5)$ **21.** $\pi \cos\left[\dfrac{\pi}{5}(x - 4)\right]$
23. $-(2x - 1)\sin(x^2 - x)$
25. $(2.2x^{1.2} + 1.2)\sec(x^{2.2} + 1.2x - 1) \times$
$\tan(x^{2.2} + 1.2x - 1)$ **27.** $\sec x \tan x \tan(x^2 - 1) +$
$2x \sec x \sec^2(x^2 - 1)$ **29.** $e^x[-\sin(e^x) + \cos x - \sin x]$

31. $\sec x$ **33.** Proof   **35.** Proof
37. $e^{-2x}[-2\sin(3\pi x) + 3\pi \cos(3\pi x)]$
39. $1.5[\sin(3x)]^{-0.5}\cos(3x)$
41. $\dfrac{x^4 - 3x^2}{(x^2 - 1)^2}\sec\left(\dfrac{x^3}{x^2 - 1}\right)\tan\left(\dfrac{x^3}{x^2 - 1}\right)$
43. $\dfrac{\cot(2x - 1)}{x} - 2\ln|x|\ \csc^2(2x - 1)$
45. a. Not differentiable at 0   **b.** $f'(1) \approx 0.5403$
47. 0   **49.** 2   **51.** Does not exist   **53.** $1/\sec^2 y$
55. $-[1 + y\cos(xy)]/[1 + x\cos(xy)]$
57. $c'(t) = 7\pi \cos[2\pi(t - 0.75)]$; $c'(0.75) \approx \$21.99$ per year $\approx \$0.42$ per week   **59.** $N'(6) \approx -32.12$. On January 1, 2003, the number of sunspots was decreasing at a rate of 32.12 sunspots per year.   **61.** $c'(t) = 1.035^t \times$
$[\ln(1.035)(0.8\sin(2\pi t) + 10.2) + 1.6\pi \cos(2\pi t)]$;
$c'(1) = 1.035[10.2\ln(1.035) + 1.6\pi] \approx \$5.57$ per year, or
$\$0.11$ per week.   **63. a.** $d(t) = 5\cos(2\pi t/13.5) + 10$
b. $d'(t) = -(10\pi/13.5)\sin(2\pi t/13.5)$; $d'(7) \approx 0.270$. At noon the tide was rising at a rate of 0.270 feet per hour.

65. $\dfrac{dV}{dt} = 11{,}000\pi\dfrac{|\sin(100\pi t)|}{\sin(100\pi t)}\cos(100\pi t)$

Graph:

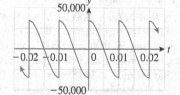

The sudden jumps in the graph are due to the nondifferentiability of V at the times $0, \pm 0.01, \pm 0.02, \ldots$. The derivative is negative immediately to the left and positive immediately to the right of these points.   **67. a.** 1.2 cm above the rest position
b. 0 cm/sec; not moving; moving downward at 18.85 cm/sec
c. 2.5 cycles per second   **69. a.** Moving downward at 0.12 cm/sec; moving downward at 18.66 cm/sec   **b.** 0.1 sec

Graphs: of p: $p(t)$

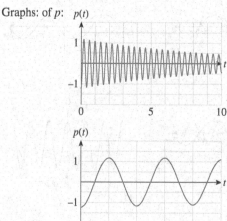

Graphs of p': $p'(t)$

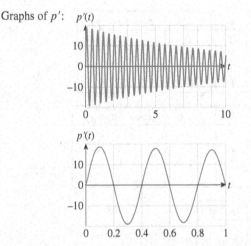

71. a. (III) **b.** Increasing at a rate of 0.157 degrees per thousand years **73.** -6; 6 **75.** Answers will vary. Examples: $f(x) = \sin x$; $f(x) = \cos x$ **77.** Answers will vary. Examples: $f(x) = e^{-x}$; $f(x) = -2e^{-x}$ **79.** The graph of $\cos x$ slopes down over the interval $(0, \pi)$, so its derivative is negative over that interval. The function $-\sin x$, and not $\sin x$, has this property. **81.** The velocity is $p'(t) = A\omega \cos(\omega t + d)$, which is a maximum when its derivative, $p''(t) = -A\omega^2 \sin(\omega t + d)$, is zero. But this occurs when $\sin(\omega t + d) = 0$, so $p(t)$ is zero as well, meaning that the stock is at yesterday's close. **83.** The derivative of $\sin x$ is $\cos x$. When $x = 0$, this is $\cos(0) = 1$. Thus, the tangent to the graph of $\sin x$ at the point $(0, 0)$ has slope 1, which means that it slopes upward at $45°$.

Section 16.3

1. $-\cos x - 2 \sin x + C$ **3.** $2 \sin x + 4.3 \cos x - 9.33x + C$
5. $3.4 \tan x + (\sin x)/1.3 - 3.2e^x + C$
7. $(7.6/3) \sin(3x - 4) + C$ **9.** $-(1/6) \cos(3x^2 - 4) + C$
11. $-2 \cos(x^2 + x) + C$ **13.** $(1/6) \tan(3x^2 + 2x^3) + C$
15. $-(1/6) \ln|\cos(2x^3)| + C$
17. $3 \ln|\sec(2x - 4) + \tan(2x - 4)| + C$
19. $(1/2) \sin(e^{2x} + 1) + C$ **21.** -2 **23.** $\ln(2)$

25. 0 **27.** 1 **29.** Proof **31.** Proof **33.** $-\dfrac{1}{4}\cos(4x) + C$

35. $-\sin(-x + 1) + C$ **37.** $[\cos(-1.1x - 1)]/1.1 + C$

39. $-\dfrac{1}{4}\ln|\sin(-4x)| + C$ **41.** 0 **43.** 2π

45. $-x \cos x + \sin x + C$

47. $\left[\dfrac{x^2}{2} - \dfrac{1}{4}\right]\sin(2x) + \dfrac{x}{2}\cos(2x) + C$

49. $-\dfrac{1}{2}e^{-x}\cos x - \dfrac{1}{2}e^{-x}\sin x + C$ **51.** $\pi^2 - 4$

53. Average $= 2/\pi$

55. Diverges **57.** Converges to $1/2$

59. $C(t) = 0.04t + \dfrac{2.6}{\pi}\cos\left[\dfrac{\pi}{26}(t - 25)\right] + 1.02$

61. 12 feet **63.** 79 sunspots
65. $P(t) = 7.5 \sin[(\pi/26(t - 13)] + 12.5$; 7.7%
67. a. Average voltage over $[0, 1/6]$ is zero; 60 cycles per second.
b.

c. 116.673 volts **69.** $50,000 **71.** It is always zero. **73.** 1

75. $s = -\dfrac{K}{\omega^2}\sin(\omega t - \alpha) + Lt + M$ for constants L and M

Chapter 16 Review

1. $f(x) = 1 + 2 \sin x$
3. $f(x) = 2 + 2 \sin[\pi(x - 1)] = 2 + 2 \sin[\pi(x + 1)]$
5. $f(x) = 1 + 2 \cos(x - \pi/2)$
7. $f(x) = 2 + 2 \cos[\pi(x + 1/2)] = 2 + 2 \cos[\pi(x - 3/2)]$
9. $-2x \sin(x^2 - 1)$ **11.** $2e^x \sec^2(2e^x - 1)$
13. $4x \sin(x^2) \cos(x^2)$ **15.** $2 \sin(2x - 1) + C$

17. $\tan(2x^2 - 1) + C$ **19.** $-\dfrac{1}{2}\ln|(\cos(x^2 + 1)| + C$

21. 1 **23.** $-x^2 \cos x + 2x \sin x + 2 \cos x + C$
25. $s(t) = 10,500 + 1,500 \sin[(2\pi/52)t - \pi] =$
$10,500 + 1,500 \sin(0.12083t - 3.14159)$ **27.** Decreasing at a rate of $3,852 per month **29.** $2,029,700

31. $150t - \dfrac{100}{\pi}\cos\left[\dfrac{\pi}{2}(t - 1)\right]$ grams

Appendix A

1. False statement **3.** Not a statement, because it is not a declarative sentence **5.** True statement **7.** True (we hope!) statement **9.** Not a statement, because it is self-referential **11.** $(\sim p) \wedge q$ **13.** $(p \wedge r) \wedge q$ or just $p \wedge q \wedge r$ **15.** $p \vee (\sim p)$ **17.** Willis is a good teacher and his students do not hate math. **19.** Either Carla is a good teacher or she is not. **21.** Willis' students both hate and do not hate math. **23.** It is not true that either Carla is a good teacher or her students hate math. **25.** F **27.** F **29.** T **31.** T **33.** T **35.** F **37.** T **39.** F **41.** T **43.** T **45.** T **47.** T

49.

p	q	$\sim q$	$p \wedge \sim q$
T	T	F	F
T	F	T	T
F	T	F	F
F	F	T	F

51.

p	$\sim p$	$\sim(\sim p)$	$\sim(\sim p) \vee p$
T	F	T	T
F	T	F	F

53.

p	q	$\sim p$	$\sim q$	$(\sim p) \wedge (\sim q)$
T	T	F	F	F
T	F	F	T	F
F	T	T	F	F
F	F	T	T	T

55.

p	q	r	$p \wedge q$	$(p \wedge q) \wedge r$
T	T	T	T	T
T	T	F	T	F
T	F	T	F	F
T	F	F	F	F
F	T	T	F	F
F	T	F	F	F
F	F	T	F	F
F	F	F	F	F

57.

p	q	r	$q \vee r$	$p \wedge (q \vee r)$
T	T	T	T	T
T	T	F	T	T
T	F	T	T	T
T	F	F	F	F
F	T	T	T	F
F	T	F	T	F
F	F	T	T	F
F	F	F	F	F

59.

p	q	$q \vee p$	$p \to (q \vee p)$
T	T	T	T
T	F	T	T
F	T	T	T
F	F	F	T

61.

p	q	$p \vee q$	$p \leftrightarrow (p \vee q)$
T	T	T	T
T	F	T	T
F	T	T	F
F	F	F	T

63.

p	$p \wedge p$
T	T
F	F

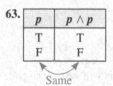
Same

65.

p	q	$p \vee q$	$q \vee p$
T	T	T	T
T	F	T	T
F	T	T	T
F	F	F	F

Same

67.

p	q	$p \vee q$	$\sim(p \vee q)$	$\sim p$	$\sim q$	$(\sim p) \wedge (\sim q)$
T	T	T	F	F	F	F
T	F	T	F	F	T	F
F	T	T	F	T	F	F
F	F	F	T	T	T	T

Same

69.

p	q	r	$p \wedge q$	$(p \wedge q) \wedge r$	$q \wedge r$	$p \wedge (q \wedge r)$
T	T	T	T	T	T	T
T	T	F	T	F	F	F
T	F	T	F	F	F	F
T	F	F	F	F	F	F
F	T	T	F	F	T	F
F	T	F	F	F	F	F
F	F	T	F	F	F	F
F	F	F	F	F	F	F

Same

71.

p	q	$p \to q$	$\sim p$	$\sim q$	$(\sim q) \to (\sim p)$
T	T	T	F	F	T
T	F	F	F	T	F
F	T	T	T	F	T
F	F	T	T	T	T

Same

73. Contradiction   **75.** Contradiction   **77.** Tautology
79. $(\sim p) \vee p$ **81.** $(\sim p) \vee \sim(\sim q)$
83. $(p \vee (\sim p)) \wedge (p \vee q)$ **85.** Either I am not Julius Caesar
or you are no fool.   **87.** It is raining and I have forgotten either
my umbrella or my hat.   **89.** Contrapositive: "If I do not exist,
then I do not think." Converse: "If I am, then I think."
91. (A); it is the contrapositive of the given statement.

93. $h \rightarrow t$
$$\frac{h}{\therefore\ t}$$
Valid; Modus
Ponens

95. $r \rightarrow u$
$$\frac{\sim r}{\therefore\ \sim u}$$
Invalid

97. $g \rightarrow m$
$$\frac{\sim m}{\therefore\ \sim g}$$
Valid: Modus
Tollens

99. $m \vee b$
$$\frac{\sim b}{\therefore\ m}$$
Valid; Disjunc-
tive Syllogism

101. $s \vee a$
$$\frac{a}{\therefore\ \sim s}$$
Invalid

103. John is green.   **105.** John is not a swan.   **107.** Peter is a
gentleman.   **109.** Their truth tables have the same truth values
for corresponding values of the variables.   **111.** A and B are
both contradictions.   **113.** Answers will vary. Example: Let p:
"You have smoker's cough," and let q: "You smoke."
115. Answers will vary. Example: Let p: "It is summer in New
York," and let q: "It is summer in Seattle."

Index

3.6 Determinants

We said in Section 3.3 that a 2×2 matrix $\begin{bmatrix} a & b \\ c & d \end{bmatrix}$ is invertible if and only if its *determinant, ad − bc*, is nonzero, and we saw the determinant used in the formula for the inverse of a 2×2 matrix. In this section we see how to compute the determinant of $n \times n$ matrices for arbitrary n and also, in the case of 2×2 and 3×3 matrices, how to interpret it geometrically. In the next section we will see one of its important applications: we can use it to write down explicit formulas for solutions of systems of linear equations.

Determinant of an $n \times n$ Matrix

Although it is possible to write down a formula for the determinant of an $n \times n$ matrix in terms of its entries, this formula is rarely actually used to *calculate* determinants. From the point of view of calculation, it is better to specify the determinant of an $n \times n$ matrix *recursively*—we state how to find the determinant of a larger matrix in terms of the determinants of smaller matrices.

If A is a square matrix, we will write its determinant as $\det(A)$. We already know from Section 3.3 how to calculate the determinant of a 2×2 matrix: If

$$A = \begin{bmatrix} a & b \\ c & d \end{bmatrix}$$

then

$$\det(A) = ad - bc.$$

The determinant of a 1×1 matrix is even simpler: If $A = [a]$, then

$$\det(A) = a.$$

Before generalizing to $n \times n$ matrices, we introduce a new term:

The Minor Matrix and Minor of an Entry

If A is an $n \times n$ matrix with $n \geq 2$ and a_{ij} is one of its entries, the associated **minor matrix** m_{ij} is the $(n-1) \times (n-1)$ matrix obtained by deleting both the row and the column passing through a_{ij}. The *determinant* of the minor matrix m_{ij} is called the minor M_{ij}. Thus,

$m_{ij} =$ Minor matrix (delete row and column through a_{ij})
$M_{ij} =$ Minor $= \det(m_{ij})$

Quick Examples

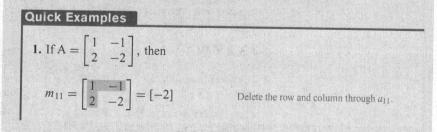

1. If $A = \begin{bmatrix} 1 & -1 \\ 2 & -2 \end{bmatrix}$, then

$m_{11} = \begin{bmatrix} 1 & -1 \\ 2 & -2 \end{bmatrix} = [-2]$ Delete the row and column through a_{11}.

$M_{11} = \det(m_{11}) = \det([-2]) = -2$ The determinant of a 1×1 matrix is its only entry.

$m_{12} = \begin{bmatrix} 1 & -1 \\ 2 & -2 \end{bmatrix} = [2]$ Delete the row and column through a_{12}.

$M_{12} = \det(m_{12}) = \det([2]) = 2$

$m_{21} = \begin{bmatrix} 1 & -1 \\ 2 & -2 \end{bmatrix} = [-1]$ Delete the row and column through a_{21}.

$M_{21} = \det(m_{21}) = \det([-1]) = -1$

$m_{22} = \begin{bmatrix} 1 & -1 \\ 2 & -2 \end{bmatrix} = [1]$ Delete the row and column through a_{22}.

$M_{22} = \det(m_{22}) = \det([1]) = 1$

2. If $A = \begin{bmatrix} 3 & 1 & -1 \\ 2 & -2 & 0 \\ 7 & 5 & 1 \end{bmatrix}$, then

$m_{12} = \begin{bmatrix} 3 & 1 & -1 \\ 2 & -2 & 0 \\ 7 & 5 & 1 \end{bmatrix} = \begin{bmatrix} 2 & 0 \\ 7 & 1 \end{bmatrix}$ Delete the row and column through a_{12}.

$M_{12} = \det(m_{12}) = \det \begin{bmatrix} 2 & 0 \\ 7 & 1 \end{bmatrix} = (2)(1) - (0)(7) = 2$

$m_{31} = \begin{bmatrix} 3 & 1 & -1 \\ 2 & -2 & 0 \\ 7 & 5 & 1 \end{bmatrix} = \begin{bmatrix} 1 & -1 \\ -2 & 0 \end{bmatrix}$ Delete the row and column through a_{31}.

$M_{31} = \det(m_{31}) = \det \begin{bmatrix} 1 & -1 \\ -2 & 0 \end{bmatrix} = (1)(0) - (-1)(-2) = -2$

We now give the promised recursive definition of the determinant of a matrix. Since we know how to compute the determinants of 1×1 and 2×2 matrices, we start with the determinants of 3×3 matrices.

Computing the Determinant of a Square Matrix

The **determinant** of the $n \times n$ matrix A, written $\det(A)$ or sometimes $|A|$, is an associated real number computed for 1×1 and 2×2 matrices as above, and for larger matrices as follows:

3×3 Matrix

The determinant of the 3×3 matrix $A = \begin{bmatrix} a_{11} & a_{12} & a_{13} \\ a_{21} & a_{22} & a_{23} \\ a_{31} & a_{32} & a_{33} \end{bmatrix}$ is given by

$$\det(A) = a_{11} \times M_{11} - a_{12} \times M_{12} + a_{13} \times M_{13}.$$

(The formula involves computing 2×2 minors.)

Quick Example

Let $A = \begin{bmatrix} 3 & 1 & -1 \\ 2 & -2 & 0 \\ 7 & 5 & 1 \end{bmatrix}$. Then

$$\det(A) = a_{11} \times M_{11} - a_{12} \times M_{12} + a_{13} \times M_{13}$$

$$= 3 \times \det \begin{bmatrix} -2 & 0 \\ 5 & 1 \end{bmatrix} - 1 \times \det \begin{bmatrix} 2 & 0 \\ 7 & 1 \end{bmatrix} + (-1) \times \det \begin{bmatrix} 2 & -2 \\ 7 & 5 \end{bmatrix}$$

$$= 3 \times (-2) - 1 \times 2 + (-1) \times 24 = -32.$$

4 × 4 Matrix

The determinant of the 4 × 4 matrix $A = \begin{bmatrix} a_{11} & a_{12} & a_{13} & a_{14} \\ a_{21} & a_{22} & a_{23} & a_{24} \\ a_{31} & a_{32} & a_{33} & a_{34} \\ a_{41} & a_{42} & a_{43} & a_{44} \end{bmatrix}$ is given by

$$\det(A) = a_{11} \times M_{11} - a_{12} \times M_{12} + a_{13} \times M_{13} - a_{14} \times M_{14}.$$

Notice the alternating pattern in the signs.

(The formula involves computing 3 × 3 minors.)

Quick Example

Let $A = \begin{bmatrix} 1 & 0 & 0 & 0 \\ 2 & 4 & 0 & 0 \\ -1 & 2 & 2 & 0 \\ 1 & 2 & 3 & 4 \end{bmatrix}$. Then

$$\det(A) = a_{11} \times M_{11} - a_{12} \times M_{12} + a_{13} \times M_{13} - a_{14} \times M_{14}$$

$$= 1 \times \det \begin{bmatrix} 4 & 0 & 0 \\ 2 & 2 & 0 \\ 2 & 3 & 4 \end{bmatrix} - 0 \times \det \begin{bmatrix} 2 & 0 & 0 \\ -1 & 2 & 0 \\ 1 & 3 & 4 \end{bmatrix}$$

$$+ 0 \times \det \begin{bmatrix} 2 & 4 & 0 \\ -1 & 2 & 0 \\ 1 & 2 & 4 \end{bmatrix} - 0 \times \det \begin{bmatrix} 2 & 4 & 0 \\ -1 & 2 & 2 \\ 1 & 2 & 3 \end{bmatrix}$$

$$= 1 \times 4 \times 2 \times 4 = 32.$$

Notice that the determinant of a lower triangular matrix like this (no entries above the main diagonal) is just the product of the entries on the main diagonal.

n × n Matrix

In general, the determinant of an $n \times n$ matrix is given by the following formula with alternating signs:

$$\det(A) = a_{11} \times M_{11} - a_{12} \times M_{12} + a_{13} \times M_{13} - \cdots \pm a_{1n} \times M_{1n}$$

The formula involves computing $(n - 1) \times (n - 1)$ minors.

Technology: Computing Determinants with the TI-83/84 Plus

On a TI-83/84, you can find the inverse of the square matrix [A] by entering

$$\det([A])\ \boxed{\text{ENTER}}$$

det is found in the $\boxed{\text{MATRX}}$ MATH menu

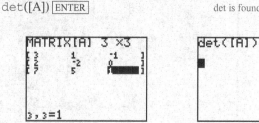

Computing Determinants with Excel

The formula MDETERM can be used to compute the determinant of any square matrix.

In the following worksheet, the determinant of $\begin{bmatrix} 3 & 1 & -1 \\ 2 & -2 & 0 \\ 7 & 5 & 1 \end{bmatrix}$ is computed in cell E3 by entering the formula shown:

	A	B	C	D	E	F	G
1	3	1	-1				
2	2	-2	0				
3	7	5	1		=MDETERM(A1:C3)		
4							

Computing Determinants with the Online Matrix Algebra Tool

On the Web site, follow On-Line Utilities → Matrix Algebra Tool. There, enter your matrix A and the formula det(A) as shown, and press "Compute." The figure shows how one would compute the determinant of $A = \begin{bmatrix} 3 & 1 & -1 \\ 2 & -2 & 0 \\ 7 & 5 & 1 \end{bmatrix}$:

```
                                    Enter your matrices
A = [3,1,-1
2,-2,0
7,5,1]



        Formulas: det(A)
                            Formula(s) or names of matri
                    Compute     Example     E
```

: *Now we know how to compute the determinant, but what is it good for?*

A: Determinants give us a method to compute volumes, to determine whether a square matrix is singular, and to compute the inverse of a nonsingular matrix. In the next section we will see how they give us explicit solutions for systems of linear equations. There are also numerous theoretical applications that go beyond the scope of this book.

Computing Areas and Volumes

Consider the parallelogram shown on the left in Figure 1. Notice that its shape and size are completely determined by the coordinates of the two points (a, b) and (c, d)— once we know these points, we can draw in the rest of the parallelogram, as shown on the right.

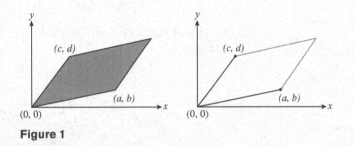

Figure 1

It follows that the *area* of this parallelogram is also determined by the four numbers a, b, c, and d, and, in fact, the area is the absolute value of the following determinant:

$$\text{Area of parallelogram} = \left| \det \begin{bmatrix} a & b \\ c & d \end{bmatrix} \right| = |ad - bc|$$

Q: *Why?*

A: Figure 2 shows the parallelogram inside a rectangle. The area of the rectangle is

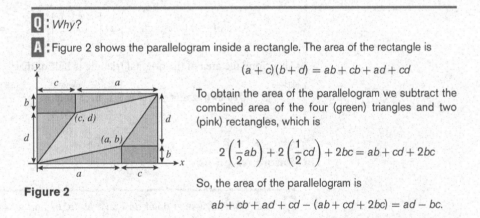

Figure 2

$$(a + c)(b + d) = ab + cb + ad + cd$$

To obtain the area of the parallelogram we subtract the combined area of the four (green) triangles and two (pink) rectangles, which is

$$2\left(\frac{1}{2}ab\right) + 2\left(\frac{1}{2}cd\right) + 2bc = ab + cd + 2bc$$

So, the area of the parallelogram is

$$ab + cb + ad + cd - (ab + cd + 2bc) = ad - bc.$$

EXAMPLE 1 Computing Areas

Use determinants to compute the areas of the following regions:

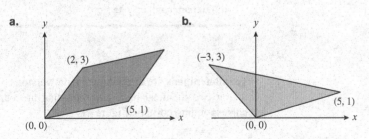

Solution

a. We are given a parallelogram with $(a, b) = (5, 1)$ and $(c, d) = (2, 3)$. (You could also reverse the choice by taking $(a, b) = (2, 3)$ and $(c, d) = (5, 1)$—see *Before we go on* below). Therefore,

$$\text{Area} = \left| \det \begin{bmatrix} 5 & 1 \\ 2 & 3 \end{bmatrix} \right| = |(5)(3) - (1)(2)| = |13| = 13 \text{ square units}$$

b. Although the figure is not a parallelogram, it can be thought of as *half* a parallelogram (Figure 3).

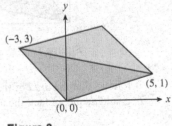

Figure 3

The area of the complete parallelogram is

$$\text{Area of parallelogram} = \left| \det \begin{bmatrix} 5 & 1 \\ -3 & 3 \end{bmatrix} \right| = |18| = 18 \text{ square units.}$$

Therefore, the area of the original triangle is half of that:

$$\textit{Area of triangle} = \frac{1}{2} 18 = 9 \text{ square units.}$$

➡ **Before we go on . . .**

Q : *In Example 1, which point do I take as (a, b) and which point do I take as (c, d)?*

A : It makes no difference. If we reverse our choice, we get

$$\text{Area} = \left| \det \begin{bmatrix} 2 & 3 \\ 5 & 1 \end{bmatrix} \right| = |(2)(1) - (3)(5)| = |-13| = 13 \text{ square units.}$$

This is always true: Changing the order of the rows does not affect the absolute value of the determinant, only its sign.

∎

Parallelepipeds are three-dimensional versions of parallelograms: You can form one by taking two identical parallelograms that are parallel to each other, and then joining corresponding corners (Figure 4).

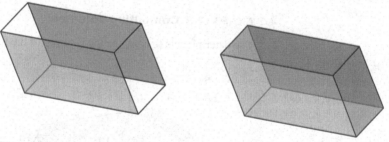

Figure 4

To specify a parallelepiped, one of whose corners is at the origin, we use three points as shown in Figure 5.

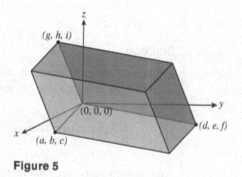

Figure 5

Notice that the three labeled points are on the ends of the three edges that contain the origin $(0, 0, 0)$.

Q: *Why are we labeling points with 3 coordinates now?*

A: Answer We need 3 coordinates to specify a point in 3-dimensional space. Look at the point (a, b, c). We get to this point from the origin $(0, 0, 0)$ as follows: Move a units in the x-direction (towards you if a is positive, away from you if a is negative), then move b units in the y-direction (to the right if a is positive, to the left if a is negative), and finally move c units in the z-direction (straight up if a is positive, down if a is negative).

Just as the area of a parallelogram is given by the determinant of a 2×2 matrix, so the volume of a parallelepiped is given by the determinant of a 3×3 matrix:

$$\text{Volume of parallelepiped} = \left| \det \begin{bmatrix} a & b & c \\ d & e & f \\ g & h & i \end{bmatrix} \right|$$

Q: *Does it matter in what order we write the rows?*

A: No. Changing the order of the rows in a matrix effects only the *sign* of its determinant, not the absolute value.

EXAMPLE 2 **Computing Volumes**

Use determinants to compute the volumes of the following solids:

a.   **b.**

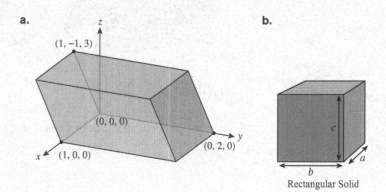

Rectangular Solid

Solution

a. Since we are given the coordinates of the three points on the ends of the three edge containing the origin, we can use the formula directly:

$$\text{Volume of parallelepiped} = \left| \det \begin{bmatrix} 1 & 0 & 0 \\ 0 & 2 & 0 \\ 1 & -1 & 3 \end{bmatrix} \right| = (1)(2)(3) = 6.$$

Notice that we arranged the three points in such a way as to obtain an upper triangular matrix, so that the determinant is just the product of the diagonal entries. As w said above, the determinant of a matrix does not change in absolute value if w rearrange the rows.

b. Since the figure is a rectangular solid, we know that its volume is

$$\text{depth} \times \text{width} \times \text{height} = abc$$

However, we were asked to compute it using determinants. To do this we first place on corner at the origin and find the coordinates of the three adjacent points. Figure 6 show a way of doing that.

We have placed the far corner at the origin so that the point a has coordinates $(a, 0, 0$ the point b has coordinates $(0, b, 0)$, and the point c has coordinates $(0, 0, c)$.

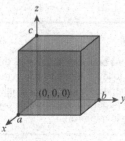

Figure 6

Q: *Why?*

A: To get to the point labeled a, just move a units in the x-direction, and no units in any of the other directions. Therefore, its coordinates are $(a, 0, 0)$. The coordinates of the other points are computed in a similar way.

We now have

$$\text{Volume of parallelepiped} = \left| \det \begin{bmatrix} a & 0 & 0 \\ 0 & b & 0 \\ 0 & 0 & c \end{bmatrix} \right| = abc,$$

as expected.

Some Shortcuts

There are quicker ways of calculating the determinants of matrices of certain types. The justifications of the following shortcuts are beyond the scope of this book, but can be found in standard linear algebra texts.

Shortcuts and Special Cases

- The determinant of a triangular matrix (one in which either all the entries above the main diagonal are zero or all the entries below it are) is the product of the entries on the diagonal.

Quick Example

$$\det \begin{bmatrix} 5 & 198 & 44 \\ 0 & 2 & -101 \\ 0 & 0 & 1 \end{bmatrix} = (5)(2)(1) = 10 \qquad \text{Check this by calculating minors.}$$

- The determinant of a matrix is the same as the determinant of its transpose: $\det(A) = \det(A^T)$

Quick Example

$$\det \begin{bmatrix} 0 & 30 & -1 \\ 1 & 200 & 4 \\ 0 & 0 & 1 \end{bmatrix} = \det \begin{bmatrix} 0 & 1 & 0 \\ 30 & 200 & 0 \\ -1 & 4 & 1 \end{bmatrix} = -30$$

- Switching two rows changes the sign of the determinant, but leaves its magnitude unchanged. (The same is true if we switch two columns.)

Quick Example

$$\det \begin{bmatrix} -99 & 13 & 4 \\ 6 & 1 & 0 \\ 3 & 0 & 0 \end{bmatrix} = -\det \begin{bmatrix} 3 & 0 & 0 \\ 6 & 1 & 0 \\ -99 & 13 & 4 \end{bmatrix} = -12 \qquad R_1 \leftrightarrow R_3$$

- If a matrix has a row or column of zeros, or if one row or column is a multiple of another, then its determinant is zero.

Quick Examples

$$\det \begin{bmatrix} -99 & 0 & 4 \\ 0 & 0 & 1 \\ 3 & 0 & 1 \end{bmatrix} = 0 \qquad \text{Second column is zero}$$

$$\det \begin{bmatrix} 3 & 0 & 0 \\ 6 & 1 & 0 \\ 12 & 2 & 0 \end{bmatrix} = 0 \qquad R_3 \text{ is twice } R_2$$

EXAMPLE 3 **Shortcuts & Special Cases**

Compute the determinant of each of the following matrices.

a. $A = \begin{bmatrix} 3 & 0 & 0 \\ 6 & -1 & 0 \\ -99 & 0 & 4 \end{bmatrix}$ **b.** $B = \begin{bmatrix} 1 & 2 & -3 \\ -2 & -4 & 6 \\ 99 & 40 & 1 \end{bmatrix}$ **c.** $C = \begin{bmatrix} 1 & 2 & 3 & 4 \\ 0 & 0 & -1 & 0 \\ 1 & 0 & 1 & 3 \\ 0 & 0 & 3 & 4 \end{bmatrix}$

Solution

a. The matrix $A = \begin{bmatrix} 3 & 0 & 0 \\ 6 & -1 & 0 \\ -99 & 0 & 4 \end{bmatrix}$ is lower triangular (it has only zeros above the main diagonal). Therefore, its determinant is the product of the diagonal entries:

$$\det(A) = (3)(-1)(4) = -12.$$

b. Notice that in the matrix $B = \begin{bmatrix} 1 & 2 & -3 \\ -2 & -4 & 6 \\ 99 & 40 & 1 \end{bmatrix}$, Row 2 is (-2) times Row 1. Therefore its determinant is zero:

$$\det(B) = 0.$$

c. We notice that the second row of $C = \begin{bmatrix} 1 & 2 & 3 & 4 \\ 0 & 0 & -1 & 0 \\ 1 & 0 & 1 & 3 \\ 0 & 0 & 3 & 4 \end{bmatrix}$, is almost all zero. It would therefore be easier to compute the determinant if we first switched Rows 1 and 2.

$$\det(C) = \det \begin{bmatrix} 1 & 2 & 3 & 4 \\ 0 & 0 & -1 & 0 \\ 1 & 0 & 1 & 3 \\ 0 & 0 & 3 & 4 \end{bmatrix} = -\det \begin{bmatrix} 0 & 0 & -1 & 0 \\ 1 & 2 & 3 & 4 \\ 1 & 0 & 1 & 3 \\ 0 & 0 & 3 & 4 \end{bmatrix} \quad \text{Rows 1 and 2 switched}$$

$$= -[a_{11} \times M_{11} - a_{12} \times M_{12} + a_{13} \times M_{13} - a_{14} \times M_{14}]$$

$$= -[(-1) \times M_{13}] \qquad \text{All the other terms are zero.}$$

$$= \det \begin{bmatrix} 1 & 2 & 4 \\ 1 & 0 & 3 \\ 0 & 0 & 4 \end{bmatrix}$$

$$= -\det \begin{bmatrix} 0 & 0 & 4 \\ 1 & 0 & 3 \\ 1 & 2 & 4 \end{bmatrix} \qquad \text{Rows 1 and 3 switched}$$

$$= -4 \times \det \begin{bmatrix} 1 & 0 \\ 1 & 2 \end{bmatrix} = -4 \times 2 = -8$$

3.6 EXERCISES

▼ more advanced

Let $A = \begin{bmatrix} -1 & 0 & 5 \\ 3 & -1 & 5 \\ 2 & 0 & 1 \end{bmatrix}$. In Exercises 1–6, write the associated

minor matrix and then compute the indicated minor.

1. M_{23} **2.** M_{32} **3.** M_{22}

4. M_{11} **5.** M_{12} **6.** M_{21}

In Exercises 7–16 compute the determinant of the given matrix directly (no shortcuts).

7. $\begin{bmatrix} 1 & 0 & -1 \\ -1 & 1 & -1 \\ 5 & 0 & 2 \end{bmatrix}$ **8.** $\begin{bmatrix} 2 & 1 & 0 \\ -2 & 1 & 0 \\ 0 & 1 & 2 \end{bmatrix}$

9. $\begin{bmatrix} 1 & -2 & 3 \\ 0 & 1 & 3 \\ 2 & 0 & 0 \end{bmatrix}$ **10.** $\begin{bmatrix} 1 & 0 & 2 \\ -2 & 1 & 0 \\ 3 & 3 & 0 \end{bmatrix}$

11. $\begin{bmatrix} 1 & 2 & 3 \\ -1 & 3 & 1 \\ 3 & 4 & 5 \end{bmatrix}$ **12.** $\begin{bmatrix} 1 & 2 & 3 \\ 2 & -3 & 4 \\ 3 & -4 & 5 \end{bmatrix}$

13. $\begin{bmatrix} 1 & 0 & 1 & 0 \\ 2 & 0 & 1 & 0 \\ 1 & 1 & 1 & 1 \\ 0 & 2 & 0 & 1 \end{bmatrix}$ **14.** $\begin{bmatrix} 0 & 2 & 0 & 1 \\ 2 & 0 & 1 & 0 \\ 1 & 1 & 1 & 1 \\ 1 & 0 & 0 & 1 \end{bmatrix}$

15. $\begin{bmatrix} 1 & 3 & -2 & 1 \\ 0 & 1 & 3 & 1 \\ 0 & 0 & 6 & -3 \\ 0 & 0 & 0 & -4 \end{bmatrix}$ **16.** $\begin{bmatrix} 1 & 0 & 0 & 0 \\ 3 & 4 & 0 & 0 \\ -2 & 3 & 1 & 0 \\ 1 & 1 & -3 & -1 \end{bmatrix}$

In Exercises 17–22, use a determinant to compute the area of the given region.

17.
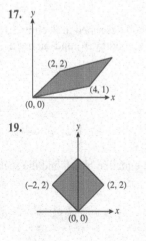

18.
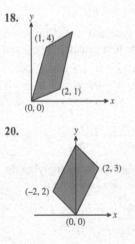

19.

20.

In Exercises 23–28, use a determinant to compute the volume of the given solid.

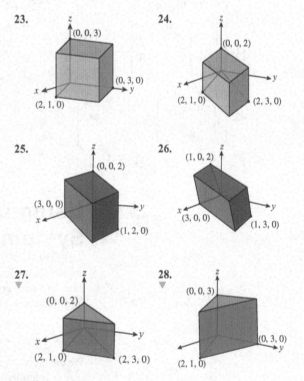

21.

22.
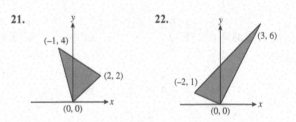

23.

24.

25.

26.

27. ▼

28. ▼

In Exercises 29–44, use shortcuts to find the determinant of the given matrix.

29. $\begin{bmatrix} 1 & -2 & 0 \\ 0 & 1 & 0 \\ 2 & 0 & 0 \end{bmatrix}$ **30.** $\begin{bmatrix} 1 & 0 & 0 \\ 0 & -3 & 0 \\ 0 & 0 & 4 \end{bmatrix}$

31. $\begin{bmatrix} -1 & 0 & 0 \\ 2 & 3 & 0 \\ 1 & 0 & 4 \end{bmatrix}$ **32.** $\begin{bmatrix} 1 & 2 & 3 \\ 0 & 0 & 0 \\ 0 & 0 & -4 \end{bmatrix}$

33. $\begin{bmatrix} 1 & -2 & 3 \\ 0 & 1 & 3 \\ -2 & 4 & -6 \end{bmatrix}$ **34.** $\begin{bmatrix} 4 & -2 & 3 \\ 0 & 1 & 3 \\ 0 & 0 & -1 \end{bmatrix}$

35. $\begin{bmatrix} 1 & -2 & 0 \\ 0 & 1 & 0 \\ 2 & 0 & 0 \end{bmatrix}$ **36.** $\begin{bmatrix} -2 & 0 & 0 \\ 0 & 0 & 5 \\ 0 & -2 & 0 \end{bmatrix}$

37. $\begin{bmatrix} 0 & -3 & 0 \\ 4 & 0 & 0 \\ 0 & 0 & -5 \end{bmatrix}$ **38.** $\begin{bmatrix} -3 & 3 & 2 \\ 1 & -1 & -2 \\ 2 & -2 & 0 \end{bmatrix}$

39. $\begin{bmatrix} 2 & 0 & 0 & 0 \\ 0 & 0 & 3 & 1 \\ 0 & 0 & 6 & -3 \\ 0 & 0 & 0 & -4 \end{bmatrix}$ **40.** $\begin{bmatrix} 4 & -1 & 2 & 3 \\ 3 & 4 & 0 & 0 \\ -2 & 3 & 1 & 0 \\ -8 & 2 & -4 & -6 \end{bmatrix}$

41. $\begin{bmatrix} 1 & 3 & -2 & 2 \\ 1 & -1 & 2 & -2 \\ 1 & -1 & 4 & -4 \\ 1 & -1 & 1 & -1 \end{bmatrix}$ **42.** $\begin{bmatrix} 1 & 0 & 0 & 0 \\ 0 & 4 & 0 & 0 \\ 0 & 0 & 0 & 1 \\ 0 & 0 & -3 & 0 \end{bmatrix}$

43. $\begin{bmatrix} 1 & 3 & 1 & 1 \\ 0 & 0 & 1 & 2 \\ 0 & 1 & 4 & 1 \\ 0 & 0 & 0 & 4 \end{bmatrix}$ **44.** $\begin{bmatrix} 3 & 0 & 0 & 0 \\ 3 & 4 & 0 & 0 \\ -1 & 1 & 1 & 0 \\ 1 & 5 & -3 & -1 \end{bmatrix}$

COMMUNICATION AND REASONING EXERCISES

45. Multiple Choice: If the $n \times n$ matrix B is obtained from A b▮ switching two rows, then:

    (A) $\det(B) = -\det(A)$
    (B) $\det(B) = \det(A)$
    (C) $\det(B) = 1/\det(A)$
    (D) $\det(B) = 2\det(A)$

46. Multiple Choice: If A is an $n \times n$ matrix all of whose entrie▮ are 1s, then:

    (A) $\det(A) = 1$
    (B) $\det(A) = 0$
    (C) $\det(A) = n^2$
    (D) $\det(A) = n$

47. ▼ Thinking of 3×3 matrices as volumes, explain why the de▮ terminant of a matrix is zero if two rows are identical.

48. ▼ Thinking of 3×3 matrices as volumes, decide what effec▮ doubling all the entries in one row has on the magnitude of th▮ determinant.

3.7 Using Determinants to Solve Systems: Cramer's Rule

As we claimed, determinants can be used to write down formulas for solutions of sys▮ tems of linear equations. To see how, let us first take a look at a general system of tw▮ linear equations in two unknowns:

$$a_{11}x + a_{12}y = b_1$$
$$a_{21}x + a_{22}y = b_2$$

Matrix form $\overset{A}{\begin{bmatrix} a_{11} & a_{12} \\ a_{21} & a_{22} \end{bmatrix}} \overset{X}{\begin{bmatrix} x \\ y \end{bmatrix}} = \overset{B}{\begin{bmatrix} b_1 \\ b_2 \end{bmatrix}}$

We can solve the system by the elimination method described in Section 2.1: To elim▮ nate y, multiply the first equation by a_{22} and the second by a_{12} and subtract:

$$a_{22}a_{11}x + a_{22}a_{12}y = a_{22}b_1$$
$$\underline{a_{12}a_{21}x + a_{12}a_{22}y = a_{12}b_2}$$
$$(a_{22}a_{11} - a_{12}a_{21})x = a_{22}b_1 - a_{12}b_2$$

so $\quad x = \dfrac{a_{22}b_1 - a_{12}b_2}{a_{11}a_{22} - a_{12}a_{21}}$ Assuming that $a_{11}a_{22} - a_{12}a_{21} \neq 0$

If we instead eliminate x by multiplying the first equation by a_{21} and the second by a_{1}▮ and subtracting, we similarly obtain

$$y = \dfrac{a_{11}b_2 - a_{21}b_1}{a_{11}a_{22} - a_{12}a_{21}}$$ Again assuming that $a_{11}a_{22} - a_{12}a_{21} \neq 0$

The denominator in both cases, $a_{11}a_{22} - a_{12}a_{21}$, you might recognize as the determinant of the coefficient matrix $A = \begin{bmatrix} a_{11} & a_{12} \\ a_{21} & a_{22} \end{bmatrix}$. The numerators are also determinants:

$$a_{22}b_1 - a_{12}b_2 = \det \begin{bmatrix} b_1 & a_{12} \\ b_2 & a_{22} \end{bmatrix} \qquad a_{11}b_2 - a_{21}b_1 = \det \begin{bmatrix} a_{11} & b_1 \\ a_{21} & b_2 \end{bmatrix}$$

Numerator of solution for x Numerator of solution for y

In the first, we have replaced the first column of the coefficient matrix A by the column B of right-hand sides, and in the second, we have replaced the second column of A by B. We can now write the solutions as follows:

Cramer's Rule for Solution of a System of 2 Linear Equations in 2 Unknowns

The system of two linear equations in two unknowns

$$\begin{aligned} a_{11}x + a_{12}y &= b_1 \\ a_{21}x + a_{22}y &= b_2 \end{aligned}$$

Matrix form $\quad \overset{A}{\begin{bmatrix} a_{11} & a_{12} \\ a_{21} & a_{22} \end{bmatrix}} \; \overset{X}{\begin{bmatrix} x \\ y \end{bmatrix}} = \overset{B}{\begin{bmatrix} b_1 \\ b_2 \end{bmatrix}}$

has a unique solution if and only if $\det(A) = \det \begin{bmatrix} a_{11} & a_{12} \\ a_{21} & a_{22} \end{bmatrix} = a_{11}a_{22} - a_{12}a_{21} \neq 0$, in which case the solution is given by

$$x = \frac{\det \begin{bmatrix} b_1 & a_{12} \\ b_2 & a_{22} \end{bmatrix}}{\det(A)} \qquad y = \frac{\det \begin{bmatrix} a_{11} & b_1 \\ a_{21} & b_2 \end{bmatrix}}{\det(A)}$$

Quick Examples

1. The system

$$\begin{aligned} x + 2y &= 3 \\ 3x + 4y &= 5 \end{aligned}$$

has $\det(A) = \det \begin{bmatrix} 1 & 2 \\ 3 & 4 \end{bmatrix} = (1)(4) - (2)(3) = -2 \neq 0$. Therefore the system has the unique solution

$$x = \frac{\det \begin{bmatrix} b_1 & a_{12} \\ b_2 & a_{22} \end{bmatrix}}{\det(A)} = \frac{\det \begin{bmatrix} 3 & 2 \\ 5 & 4 \end{bmatrix}}{-2} = \frac{(3)(4) - (2)(5)}{-2} = \frac{2}{-2} = -1$$

$$x = \frac{\det \begin{bmatrix} a_{11} & b_1 \\ b_{21} & a_2 \end{bmatrix}}{\det(A)} = \frac{\det \begin{bmatrix} 1 & 3 \\ 3 & 5 \end{bmatrix}}{-2} = \frac{(1)(5) - (3)(3)}{-2} = \frac{-4}{-2} = 2$$

2. The system

$$\begin{aligned} x - y &= 3 \\ 2x - 2y &= 5 \end{aligned}$$

has $\det \begin{bmatrix} a_{11} & a_{12} \\ a_{21} & a_{22} \end{bmatrix} = \det \begin{bmatrix} 1 & -1 \\ 2 & -2 \end{bmatrix} = (1)(-2) - (-1)(2) = 0$

As the coefficient matrix is singular, Cramer's rule does not apply (in fact the given system is inconsistent), and so we would need to analyze the system using the methods of Chapter 2.

Q: *What happens when the determinant of the coefficient matrix is zero?*

A: Notice first that in this case the Cramer's rule formulas have zero in their denominators and hence make no sense. In general, the coefficient matrix of a system of n linear equations in n unknowns has determinant zero if and only if the system is inconsistent (there is no solution) or underdetermined (there are infinitely many solutions). In either case, we would need to analyze the system using a method like row-reduction discussed in Section 2.2.

One advantage of Cramer's rule over row reduction is that the explicit formulas it gives allow us to write down the solution of a linear system even when the coefficients are parameters (algebraic variables) instead of numbers. (In such cases, attempting to solve the system by row-reduction might be extremely messy.) The next example illustrates the use of Cramer's rule for solving such a system.

EXAMPLE 1   Using Cramer's Rule with Parameters: Regression

We shall see in Chapter 15 that the equations for the slope m and intercept b of the regression line associated with a set of data points are given by solving the system

$$m \sum (x^2) + b \sum x = \sum xy$$
$$m \sum x + nb = \sum y$$

for m and b. Here, n is the number of data points, $\sum x$ is the sum of their x-coordinates, $\sum xy$ is the sum of the products xy, and $\sum (x^2)$ is the sum of the squares of the x-coordinates. What are m and b, and what condition is necessary to ensure a unique solution?

Solution

The determinant of the coefficient matrix is

$$\det(A) = \det \begin{bmatrix} \sum(x^2) & \sum x \\ \sum x & n \end{bmatrix} = n \sum (x^2) - \left(\sum x \right)^2$$

For a unique solution, we require that $n \sum (x^2) - \left(\sum x \right)^2 \neq 0$. (It can be shown that this condition holds whenever there is more than a single x-coordinate.) When this condition is satisfied, the unique solution is given by

$$m = \frac{\det \begin{bmatrix} b_1 & a_{12} \\ b_2 & a_{22} \end{bmatrix}}{\det(A)} = \frac{\det \begin{bmatrix} \sum xy & \sum x \\ \sum y & n \end{bmatrix}}{\det(A)} = \frac{n \sum xy - \left(\sum x \right)\left(\sum y \right)}{n \sum (x^2) - \left(\sum x \right)^2}$$

$$b = \frac{\det\begin{bmatrix} a_{11} & b_1 \\ a_{21} & b_2 \end{bmatrix}}{\det(A)} = \frac{\det\begin{bmatrix} \sum(x^2) & \sum xy \\ \sum x & \sum y \end{bmatrix}}{\det(A)} = \frac{\sum(x^2)\sum y - (\sum xy)(\sum x)}{n\sum(x^2) - (\sum x)^2}$$

The method described above can be extended to systems of n linear equations in n unknowns. To see how to extend it, is useful to look first a general system of three equations in three unknowns:

$$a_{11}x + a_{12}y + a_{13}z = b_1$$
$$a_{21}x + a_{22}y + a_{23}z = b_2$$
$$a_{31}x + a_{32}y + a_{33}z = b_3$$

As in the case of two equations in two unknowns, it is possible to solve this system by elimination: First eliminate z from the first two equations by multiplying the first by a_{23} and the second by a_{13} and subtracting. Then eliminate z from the second and third equations in a similar way (multiply the second by a_{33} and the third by a_{23} and subtract). This will leave us with two equations in x and y:

$$(a_{11}a_{23} - a_{21}a_{13})x + (a_{12}a_{23} - a_{13}a_{22})y = a_{23}b_1 - a_{13}b_2$$
$$(a_{21}a_{33} - a_{31}a_{23})x + (a_{22}a_{33} - a_{23}a_{32})y = a_{33}b_2 - a_{23}b_3$$

At this point we can calculate x and y as we did earlier: Eliminate y by multiplying each equation by the coefficient of y in the other and subtracting to obtain x, and similarly we can obtain y by eliminating x. To obtain z with this method, we would start all over again by first eliminating x and then y. If we actually went through these remaining steps we would find that the results can again be expressed in terms of determinants:

Cramer's Rule for Solution of System of 3 Linear Equations in 3 Unknowns

The system of 3 linear equations in 3 unknowns

$$a_{11}x + a_{12}y + a_{13}z = b_1$$
$$a_{21}x + a_{22}y + a_{23}z = b_2$$
$$a_{31}x + a_{32}y + a_{33}z = b_3$$

Matrix form
$$\underset{A}{\begin{bmatrix} a_{11} & a_{12} & a_{13} \\ a_{21} & a_{22} & a_{23} \\ a_{31} & a_{32} & a_{33} \end{bmatrix}} \underset{X}{\begin{bmatrix} x \\ y \\ z \end{bmatrix}} = \underset{B}{\begin{bmatrix} b_1 \\ b_2 \\ b_3 \end{bmatrix}}$$

has a unique solution if and only if $\det(A) = \det\begin{bmatrix} a_{11} & a_{12} & a_{13} \\ a_{21} & a_{22} & a_{23} \\ a_{31} & a_{32} & a_{33} \end{bmatrix} \neq 0$, in which

case the solution is given by

$$x = \frac{\det\begin{bmatrix} b_1 & a_{12} & a_{13} \\ b_2 & a_{22} & a_{23} \\ b_3 & a_{32} & a_{33} \end{bmatrix}}{\det(A)}, \quad y = \frac{\det\begin{bmatrix} a_{11} & b_1 & a_{13} \\ a_{21} & b_2 & a_{23} \\ a_{31} & b_3 & a_{33} \end{bmatrix}}{\det(A)}, \quad z = \frac{\det\begin{bmatrix} a_{11} & a_{12} & b_1 \\ a_{21} & a_{22} & b_2 \\ a_{31} & a_{32} & b_3 \end{bmatrix}}{\det(A)}$$

Notice again that the matrices in the numerators are obtained from the coefficient matrix A by replacing each column in turn by the column B of right-hand sides.

Cramer's Rule for Solution of a System of n Linear Equations in n Unknowns

If A is an $n \times n$ matrix, then the system of linear equations $AX = B$ has a unique solution if and only if $\det(A) \neq 0$, in which case the unique solution is given by

$$x_1 = \frac{\det \begin{bmatrix} b_1 & a_{12} & \cdots & a_{1n} \\ b_2 & a_{22} & \cdots & a_{2n} \\ \cdots & \cdots & & \cdots \\ b_n & a_{n2} & \cdots & a_{nn} \end{bmatrix}}{\det(A)}$$

$$x_2 = \frac{\det \begin{bmatrix} a_{11} & b_1 & a_{13} & \cdots & a_{1n} \\ a_{21} & b_2 & a_{23} & \cdots & a_{2n} \\ \cdots & \cdots & \cdots & & \cdots \\ a_{n1} & b_n & a_{n3} & \cdots & a_{nn} \end{bmatrix}}{\det(A)}$$

$$\cdots$$

$$x_n = \frac{\det \begin{bmatrix} a_{11} & \cdots & a_{1(n-1)} & b_1 \\ a_{21} & \cdots & a_{2(n-1)} & b_2 \\ \cdots & & \cdots & \cdots \\ a_{n1} & \cdots & a_{n(n-1)} & b_n \end{bmatrix}}{\det(A)}$$

EXAMPLE 2   Using Cramer's Rule: 3 Equations in 3 Unknowns

Use Cramer's rule to solve the system

$$\begin{aligned} 2x \quad\;\; + z &= 1 \\ 2x + y - z &= 1 \\ 3x + y - z &= 1 \end{aligned}$$

Solution

We first compute the determinant of the coefficient matrix:

$$\det(A) = \det \begin{bmatrix} 2 & 0 & 1 \\ 2 & 1 & -1 \\ 3 & 1 & -1 \end{bmatrix}$$

$$= (2) \det \begin{bmatrix} 1 & -1 \\ 1 & -1 \end{bmatrix} - (0) \det \begin{bmatrix} 2 & -1 \\ 3 & -1 \end{bmatrix} + (1) \det \begin{bmatrix} 2 & 1 \\ 3 & 1 \end{bmatrix}$$

$$= (2)(0) - (0)(1) + (1)(-1) = -1$$

Since the determinant is nonzero, the system has a unique solution. The unknowns are

$$x = \frac{\det \begin{bmatrix} 1 & 0 & 1 \\ 1 & 1 & 1 \\ 1 & 1 & 1 \end{bmatrix}}{\det(A)}$$

$$= \frac{(1) \det \begin{bmatrix} 1 & -1 \\ 1 & -1 \end{bmatrix} - (0) \det \begin{bmatrix} 1 & -1 \\ 1 & -1 \end{bmatrix} + (1) \det \begin{bmatrix} 1 & 1 \\ 1 & 1 \end{bmatrix}}{-1}$$

$$= \frac{(1)(0) - (0)(0) + (1)(0)}{-1} = \frac{0}{-1} = 0$$

$$y = \frac{\det \begin{bmatrix} 2 & 1 & 1 \\ 2 & 1 & -1 \\ 3 & 1 & -1 \end{bmatrix}}{\det(A)}$$

$$= \frac{(2) \det \begin{bmatrix} 1 & -1 \\ 1 & -1 \end{bmatrix} - (1) \det \begin{bmatrix} 2 & -1 \\ 3 & -1 \end{bmatrix} + (1) \det \begin{bmatrix} 2 & 1 \\ 3 & 1 \end{bmatrix}}{-1}$$

$$= \frac{(2)(0) - (1)(1) + (1)(-1)}{-1} = \frac{-2}{-1} = 2$$

$$z = \frac{\det \begin{bmatrix} 2 & 0 & 1 \\ 2 & 1 & 1 \\ 3 & 1 & 1 \end{bmatrix}}{\det(A)}$$

$$= \frac{(2) \det \begin{bmatrix} 1 & 1 \\ 1 & 1 \end{bmatrix} - (0) \det \begin{bmatrix} 2 & 1 \\ 3 & 1 \end{bmatrix} + (1) \det \begin{bmatrix} 2 & 1 \\ 3 & 1 \end{bmatrix}}{1}$$

$$= \frac{(2)(0) - (0)(-1) + (1)(-1)}{-1} = \frac{-1}{-1} = 1$$

Thus, the unique solution is $(x, y, z) = (0, 2, 1)$.

In the next example we solve a system of four linear equations in four unknowns with the aid of a spreadsheet. From the general case for $n \times n$ systems, we can write down the solution of the 4×4 system

$$a_{11}x + a_{12}y + a_{13}z + a_{14}t = b_1$$
$$a_{21}x + a_{22}y + a_{23}z + a_{24}t = b_2$$
$$a_{31}x + a_{32}y + a_{33}z + a_{34}t = b_3$$
$$a_{41}x + a_{42}y + a_{43}z + a_{44}t = b_4$$

as

$$x = \frac{\det \begin{bmatrix} b_1 & a_{12} & a_{13} & a_{14} \\ b_2 & a_{22} & a_{23} & a_{24} \\ b_3 & a_{32} & a_{33} & a_{34} \\ b_4 & a_{42} & a_{43} & a_{44} \end{bmatrix}}{\det(A)}, \quad y = \frac{\det \begin{bmatrix} a_{11} & b_1 & a_{13} & a_{14} \\ a_{21} & b_2 & a_{23} & a_{24} \\ a_{31} & b_3 & a_{33} & a_{34} \\ a_{41} & b_4 & a_{43} & a_{44} \end{bmatrix}}{\det(A)}$$

$$z = \frac{\det \begin{bmatrix} a_{11} & a_{12} & b_1 & a_{14} \\ a_{21} & a_{22} & b_2 & a_{24} \\ a_{31} & a_{32} & b_3 & a_{34} \\ a_{41} & a_{42} & b_4 & a_{44} \end{bmatrix}}{\det(A)} \quad z = \frac{\det \begin{bmatrix} a_{11} & a_{12} & a_{13} & b_1 \\ a_{21} & a_{22} & a_{23} & b_2 \\ a_{31} & a_{32} & a_{33} & b_3 \\ a_{41} & a_{42} & a_{43} & b_4 \end{bmatrix}}{\det(A)}$$

$$\text{provided } \det(A) = \det \begin{bmatrix} a_{11} & a_{12} & a_{13} & a_{14} \\ a_{21} & a_{22} & a_{23} & a_{24} \\ a_{31} & a_{32} & a_{33} & a_{34} \\ a_{41} & a_{42} & a_{43} & a_{44} \end{bmatrix} \neq 0,$$

EXAMPLE 3 Four Equations in Four Unknowns with Excel

Use Cramer's rule to solve the system

$$\begin{aligned} x \quad + z - t &= 1 \\ 2x - y - z \quad &= 1 \\ x + y + z - t &= 2 \\ x + y + z + t &= 1 \end{aligned}$$

Solution

Doing this calculation by hand would be tedious. We show how to use Excel to help. First enter the coefficients and the right-hand sides in your spreadsheet:

◇	A	B	C	D	E
1	1	0	1	-1	1
2	2	-1	-1	0	1
3	1	1	1	-1	2
4	1	1	1	1	1

The formulas for the solution shown above require the determinants of four more matrices, each obtained from the original coefficient matrix (A1:D4) by changing a single column. We therefore make four copies of (A1:D4) (this takes seconds using copy-and-paste) and then paste the column (E1:E4) in the appropriate place of each (again using copy-and-paste):

◇	A	B	C	D	E
1	1	0	1	-1	1
2	2	-1	-1	0	1
3	1	1	1	-1	2
4	1	1	1	1	1
5					
6	1	0	1	-1	
7	1	-1	-1	0	
8	2	1	1	-1	
9	1	1	1	1	
10					
11	1	1	1	-1	
12	2	1	-1	0	
13	1	2	1	-1	
14	1	1	1	1	
15					
16	1	0	1	-1	
17	2	-1	1	0	
18	1	1	2	-1	
19	1	1	1	1	
20					
21	1	0	1	1	
22	2	-1	-1	1	
23	1	1	1	2	
24	1	1	1	1	

Next, we compute the determinant of the coefficient matrix in cell A5 using the MDETERM function we saw on p. 4:

◇	A	B	C	D	E
1	1	0	1	-1	1
2	2	-1	-1	0	1
3	1	1	1	-1	2
4	1	1	1	1	1
5	=MDETERM(A1:D4)				
6					

↓ Control+Shift+Enter

◇	A	B	C	D	E
1	1	0	1	-1	1
2	2	-1	-1	0	1
3	1	1	1	-1	2
4	1	1	1	1	1
5	6				

Since the determinant is nonzero, the system has a unique solution. We next obtain the numerators of the solutions for x, y, z, and t by copying and pasting the formula of cell A5 into cells A10, A15, A20, and A25:

◇	A	B	C	D	E
1	1	0	1	-1	1
2	2	-1	-1	0	1
3	1	1	1	-1	2
4	1	1	1	1	1
5	6				
6	1	0	1	-1	
7	1	-1	-1	0	
8	2	1	1	-1	
9	1	1	1	1	
10	5				
11	1	1	1	-1	
12	2	1	-1	0	
13	1	2	1	-1	
14	1	1	1	1	
15	6				
16	1	0	1	-1	
17	2	-1	1	0	
18	1	1	2	-1	
19	1	1	1	1	
20	-2				
21	1	0	1	1	
22	2	-1	-1	1	
23	1	1	1	2	
24	1	1	1	1	
25	-3				

Finally, the solution for x is computed in cell B10 and then pasted into B15, B20, and B25. Note the use of the absolute reference to cell $A$5:

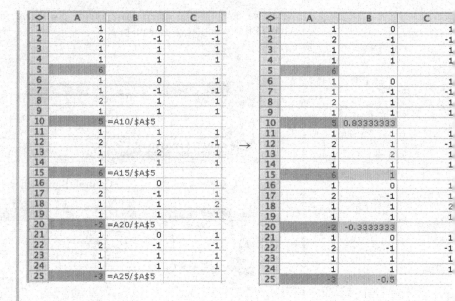

so we conclude that $(x, y, z, t) = \left(\frac{5}{6}, \frac{6}{6}, \frac{2}{6}, \frac{3}{6}\right) \approx (0.8333, 1, -0.3333, -0.5)$

3.7 EXERCISES

▼ more advanced

■ indicates exercises that should be solved using technology

In Exercises 1–12 solve the given system of linear equations using Cramer's Rule.

1. $x + y = 4$
    $x - y = 1$

2. $2x + y = 2$
    $2x - 3y = 2$

3. $0.1x - 0.2y = 0$
    $0.4x + 0.2y = 1.2$

4. $0.5x - 0.1y = 0.3$
    $2.5x + 0.3y = 2.2$

5. $\dfrac{x}{3} + \dfrac{y}{2} = 0$
    $\dfrac{x}{2} + y = 1$

6. $\dfrac{2x}{3} - \dfrac{y}{2} = \dfrac{1}{6}$
    $\dfrac{x}{2} - \dfrac{y}{2} = -1$

7. $-x + 2y + z = 0$
    $-x - y + 2z = 0$
    $2x \quad\;\; - z = 7$

8. $x + 2y \quad\;\; = 4$
    $\quad\;\; y - z = 0$
    $x + 3y - 2z = 5$

9. $-x - 4y + 2z = 4$
    $x + 2y - z = 3$
    $x + y - z = 8$

10. $-x - 4y + 2z = 8$
    $x \qquad\quad - z = 3$
    $x + y - z = 2$

11. $-0.1x + \qquad 0.2z = 4$
    $\qquad 0.2y - 1.1z = 2$
    $x + \qquad\quad z = 2$

12. $0.1x \qquad - 0.2z = 6$
    $\qquad y \quad\; - z = 6$
    $0.1x - 1.1y \qquad = 3$

■ *In Exercises 13–18 use Cramer's Rule with technology to solve the given system of linear equations in the event that is has*

a unique solution. If there is no unique solution, indicate why.
HINT [See Example 3.]

13. ■ $x + y + 5z \qquad = 1$
    $\quad\; y + 2z + w = 1$
    $x + 3y + 7z + 2w = 2$
    $x + y + 5z + w = 1$

14. ■ $x + y \qquad + 4w = 1$
    $2x - 2y - 3z + 2w = -$
    $\qquad 4y + 6z + w = 4$
    $2x + 4y + 9z \qquad = 6$

15. ■ $x + y + 5z \qquad = 1$
    $\quad\; y + 2z + w = 1$
    $x + \;\; y + 5z + w = 1$
    $x + 2y + 7z + 2w = 2$

16. ■ $x + y \qquad + 4w = 1$
    $2x - 2y - 3z + 2w = -1$
    $\qquad 4y + 6z + w = 4$
    $3x + 3y + 3z + 6w = 4$

17. ■ $x + y + 5z \qquad = 1$
    $\quad\; y + 2z + w = 1$
    $x + \;\; y + 5z + w = 1$
    $x + 2y + 7z + 2w = 2$

18. ■ $x + y \qquad + 4w = 1$
    $2x - 2y - 3z + 2w = -$
    $\qquad 4y + 6z + w = 4$
    $3x + 3y + 3z + 6w = 4$

In Exercises 19–22, write down an equation the parameters must satisfy for there to be a unique solution, and then solve for the indicated variables assuming that condition is met.
HINT [See Example 1.]

19. $(a + b)p + cq = a - b$
$cp - (a - b)q = b - a$
Solve for p and q.

20. $a^2 p - (r + s)q = a^3$
$(r + s)q - \dfrac{q}{a^2} = r$
Solve for p and q.

21. $ax_1 \qquad + qx_3 = q$
$rx_1 + x_2 \qquad = 0$
$r^2 x_1 - x_2 + ax_3 = a$
Solve for x_1, x_2, and x_3.

22. $bx_1 + \quad ax_2 + \quad qx_3 = 2a$
$\qquad a^2 x_2 + \quad qx_3 = 2a^2$
$bx_1 + \qquad\qquad qx_3 = 0$
Solve for x_1, x_2, and x_3.

APPLICATIONS

Some of the following exercises are similar or identical to exercises and examples in Section 3.3. All should be solved using Cramer's Rule.

23. *Resource Allocation* You manage an ice cream factory that makes three flavors: Creamy Vanilla, Continental Mocha, and Succulent Strawberry. Into each batch of Creamy Vanilla go two eggs, one cup of milk, and two cups of cream. Into each batch of Continental Mocha go one egg, one cup of milk, and two cups of cream. Into each batch of Succulent Strawberry go one egg, two cups of milk, and one cup of cream. Your stocks of eggs, milk, and cream vary from day to day. How many batches of each flavor should you make in order to use up all of your ingredients if you have the following amounts in stock?

(a) 350 eggs, 350 cups of milk, and 400 cups of cream

(b) 400 eggs, 500 cups of milk, and 400 cups of cream

24. *Resource Allocation* The Arctic Juice Company makes three juice blends: PineOrange, using 2 quarts of pineapple juice and 2 quarts of orange juice per gallon; PineKiwi, using 3 quarts of pineapple juice and 1 quart of kiwi juice per gallon; and OrangeKiwi, using 3 quarts of orange juice and 1 quart of kiwi juice per gallon. The amount of each kind of juice the company has on hand varies from day to day. How many gallons of each blend can it make on a day with the following stocks?

(a) 800 quarts of pineapple juice, 650 quarts of orange juice, 350 quarts of kiwi juice.

(b) 650 quarts of pineapple juice, 800 quarts of orange juice, 350 quarts of kiwi juice.

Investing In Mutual Funds Exercises 25 and 26 are based on the following data on three mutual funds.[1]

	2007 Yield
FHIFX (Fidelity Focused High Income Fund)	6%
FFRHX (Fidelity Floating Rate High Income Fund)	5%
FASIX (Fidelity Asset Manager 20%)	7%

25. You invested a total of $9,000 in the three funds at the beginning of 2007, including an equal amount in FFRHX and FASIX. Your 2007 yield for the year from the first two funds amounted to $400. How much did you invest in each of the three funds?

26. You invested a total of $6,000 in the three funds at the beginning of 2007, including an equal amount in FHIFX and FFRHX. Your total yields for 2007 amounted to $360. How much did you invest in each of the three funds?

Investing in Stocks Exercises 27 and 28 are based on the following data on three computer-related stocks.[2]

	Price per Share	Dividend Yield
MSFT (Microsoft)	$30	1.5%
INTC (Intel)	25	1.8
YHOO (Yahoo)	25	0

27. ▼ You invested a total of $5,400 in Microsoft, Intel, and Yahoo shares at the above prices, and expected to earn $45 in annual dividends. If you purchased a total of 200 shares, how many shares of each stock did you purchase?

28. ▼ You invested a total of $5,800 in Microsoft, Intel, and Yahoo shares at the above prices, and expected to earn $54 in annual dividends. If you purchased a total of 220 shares, how many shares of each stock did you purchase?

COMMUNICATION AND REASONING EXERCISES

29. Name one advantage and one disadvantage of Cramer's rule versus row-reduction for solving a system of linear equations.

30. What does it mean about a system of n linear equations in n unknowns when the determinant of the coefficient matrix is zero?

31. Multiple Choice: If the determinant of the coefficient matrix is zero for a system of linear equations, then:

(A) Cramer's Rule yields the exact solution.

(B) Cramer's Rule fails, but we can obtain the solution by row-reducing the augmented matrix.

(C) Cramer's Rule fails, but we can obtain the solution by using the inverse of the coefficient matrix.

(D) There is only the zero solution.

32. Multiple Choice: If the determinant of the coefficient matrix is nonzero for a system of linear equations, but the right-hand sides are zero, then:

(A) There are infinitely many solutions.

(B) Cramer's Rule fails, but we can obtain the solution by row-reducing the augmented matrix.

(C) Cramer's Rule fails, but we can obtain the solution by using the inverse of the coefficient matrix.

(D) There is only the zero solution.

---

[1]Yields are for the year ending September, 2007 and rounded. Source: http://money.excite.com, October 2007

[2]Stocks were trading at or near the given prices in September, 2007. Dividends are rounded. Source: http://money.excite.com, October 2007.

Answers to Odd-Numbered Exercises

3.6

1. $m_{23} = \begin{bmatrix} -1 & 0 \\ 2 & 0 \end{bmatrix}$; $M_{23} = 0$ **3.** $m_{22} = \begin{bmatrix} -1 & 5 \\ 2 & 1 \end{bmatrix}$; $M_{22} = -11$

5. $m_{12} = \begin{bmatrix} 3 & 5 \\ 2 & 1 \end{bmatrix}$; $M_{12} = -7$ **7.** 7 **9.** -18 **11.** -12

13. -1 **15.** -24 **17.** 6 **19.** 8 **21.** 5 **23.** 18 **25.** 12 **27.** 4 **29.** 0 **31.** -12 **33.** 0 **35.** 0 **37.** -60 **39.** 0 **41.** 0 **43.** -4 **45.** (A) **47.** The determinant a 3×3 matrix gives the volume of the solid parallelepiped obtained with corner points the three rows of the matrix. If two are the same, then two of the three edges are on top of each other, and the solid has zero volume.

3.7

1. $(2.5, 1.5)$ **3.** $(2.4, 1.2)$ **5.** $(6, -4)$ **7.** $(5, 1, 3)$
9. $(10, -5, -3)$ **11.** $(-12, 87, 14)$ **13.** $(-1.5, 0, 0.5, 0)$
15. No unique solution as $\det(A) = 0$ **17.** $(0, 1, 0, 0)$

19. $-a^2 + b^2 - c^2 \neq 0$; $p = \dfrac{(a-b)(-a+b+c)}{-a^2+b^2-c^2}$,

$q = \dfrac{(b-a)(a+b+c)}{-a^2+b^2-c^2}$

21. $a^2 - rq(1+r) \neq 0$; $(x_1, x_2, x_3) = (0, 0, 1)$ **23. (a)** 100 batches of vanilla, 50 batches of mocha, 100 batches of strawberry **(b)** 100 batches of vanilla, no mocha, 200 batches of strawberry. **25.** \$5,000 in FHIFX, \$2,000 in FFRHX, \$2,000 in FASIX **27.** 80 MSFT, 20 INTC, 100 YHOO **29.** Advantage: Cramer's Rule allows us to write own the solution explicity, and this is useful when, for instance, the coefficients are parameters. Disadvantage: Cramer's Rule applies only to systems in which the number of equations equals the number of unknowns and then only when there is a unique solution. Row reduction can be used to analyze any system of linear equations. **31.** (B)

Extreme Values: Boundaries and the Extreme Value Theorem

In our discussion of maxima and minima of functions of a single variable in Section 12.1, we saw that extrema frequently occurred at endpoints of the domain. To generalize this idea to functions of more than one variable, we should think of the endpoints of the domain of a function of a single variable as *boundary points* of the domain; for instance, the boundary of the closed interval [1, 3] consists of the two endpoints 1 and 3, whereas the open interval (1, 3) has no boundary points. (The boundary points 1 and 3 are outside the interval.)

As we have seen, the domains of functions of two variables are subsets of the plane; for instance, the natural domain of the function $f(x, y) = \sqrt{x^2 + y^2 - 1}$ consists of all points (x, y) in the plane with $x^2 + y^2 - 1 \geq 0$, or $x^2 + y^2 \geq 1$, and its boundary is the unit circle (Figure 1).

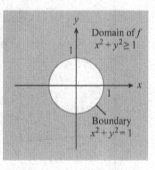

Figure 1

Even if the function is mathematically defined for all x and y, we may need to restrict the domain in real life applications: For example, if $C(x, y) = 10,000 + 20x + 40y$ is the monthly cost of producing x Ultra Mini speakers and y Big Stack speakers (see Example 1 of Section 15.1), then the function makes sense only if $x \geq 0$ and $y \geq 0$, and would be restricted further by the maximum number of Ultra Minis and Big Stacks the company can produce in a month—for instance, $x \leq 100$ and $y \leq 75$. The domain of the cost function would then be the region of the plane described by $0 \leq x \leq 100$ and $0 \leq y \leq 75$ (Figure 2), and its boundary is a rectangle.

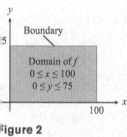

Figure 2

We can now state the counterpart of the method we used in Chapter 12 to locate maxima and minima:

Locating Candidates for Extrema for a Function f of Two Variables

Step 1: *Locate critical points in the interior of the domain.*
To locate interior points, we use the method discussed in Section 15.3: Set $f_x = 0$ and $f_y = 0$ simultaneously, and solve for x and y.

Step 2: *Locate extrema on the boundary of the domain.*
To locate critical extrema on the boundary of the domain, we examine the behavior of the function along each segment of the boundary.

Quick Example

Consider the function f with domain $0 \leq x \leq 4$, $0 \leq y \leq 4$, whose graph is shown here:

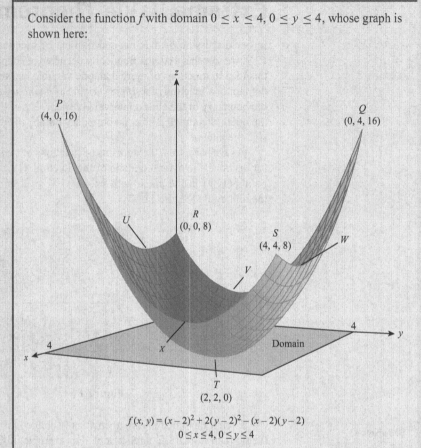

$$f(x, y) = (x - 2)^2 + 2(y - 2)^2 - (x - 2)(y - 2)$$
$$0 \leq x \leq 4, 0 \leq y \leq 4$$

We observe the following:

- There is an absolute minimum at the critical point $T(2, 2, 0)$. Note that $(2, 2)$ is an interior point of the domain.

- There are absolute maxima at $P(4, 0, 16)$ and $Q(0, 4, 16)$. These are not critical points but correspond to points on the boundary of the domain (endpoints of its edges).

- There are relative maxima at $R(0, 0, 8)$ and $S(4, 4, 8)$, again corresponding to points on the boundary of the domain.

- The points U, V, W, X are critical points on boundary segments, but neither maxima nor minima. (Can you see why?)

The domains illustrated in the above examples are all **closed** sets: sets that include all their boundary points. The rectangular domain in the quick example above is al[so] **bounded**—that is, the entire domain can be enclosed in a (large enough) disc. Th[e] domain shown in Figure 1 is **unbounded**, as it cannot be enclosed in any disc, no matt[er] how large. The following result states that, when the domain of a continuous function both closed and bounded, we can always expect to find an absolute maximum and an absolute minimum, as in the quick example above.

Extreme Value Theorem for Functions of Two Variables

If f is a continuous function of two variables whose domain D is both closed and bounded, then there are points (x_1, y_1) and (x_2, y_2) in D such that f has an absolute minimum at (x_1, y_1) and an absolute maximum at (x_2, y_2).

Quick Examples

1. In the quick example above, we saw from its graph that the function
$$f(x, y) = (x - 2)^2 + 2(y - 2)^2 - (x - 2)(y - 2),$$
with closed and bounded domain $0 \le x \le 4$ and $0 \le y \le 4$, has an absolute minimum at $(2, 2)$ and absolute maxima at both $(4, 0)$ and $(0, 4)$.

2. If the domain is not closed and bounded, the function need not have an absolute maximum or minimum: The function
$$f(x, y) = x^2 + y^2$$
with domain all of the xy-plane has an absolute minimum at $(0, 0)$ but no absolute maximum. (Its graph is the paraboloid shown in Example 5 of Section 15.1.)

EXAMPLE 1 Absolute Maximum: Rectangular Domain

You own a company that makes two models of stereo speakers, the Ultra Mini and the Big Stack. Your monthly profit is estimated to be
$$f(x, y) = 10x + 20y - 0.5xy.$$

Here, x is the number of Ultra Minis, y is the number of Big Stacks, and f is your profit in dollars. You can produce up to 100 Ultra Minis and 75 Big Stacks in a month. Find the number of each model you should make each week in order to maximize your profit.

Solution We are asked to find the absolute maximum value of the function f. The domain of f is specified by the production limits: $0 \le x \le 100$ and $0 \le y \le 75$, and is the one shown in Figures 2 and 3. Because the domain is closed and bounded, we know from the Extreme Value Theorem that there is a point somewhere in the domain at which f is a maximum. To identify that point, we locate all candidates for extrema in the interior of the domain and on its boundary by using the procedure outlined earlier:

Step 1: Locate critical points in the interior of the domain.
The partial derivatives are

$$f_x = 10 - 0.5y \qquad\qquad f_y = 20 - 0.5x$$

Setting these equal to zero and solving for x and y gives the only critical point as $(40, 20)$. This point is in the interior of the domain, so it is one of our candidates for extrema.

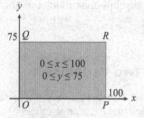

Figure 3

Step 2: Locate extrema on the boundary of the domain.

The boundary of the domain consists of four line segments OP, OQ, QR, and PR (Figure 3 which we consider one at a time.

Segment OP: $y = 0, 0 \leq x \leq 100$:
The behavior of the function f along this segment is seen by substituting $y = 0$ into th expression for f:

$$f(x, 0) = 10x + 20(0) - 0.5x(0) = 10x, \ 0 \leq x \leq 100$$

This means that, *along the line segment OP*, the value of f is determined by the functic $f(x, 0) = 10x$ of a single variable, with domain $0 \leq x \leq 100$. We now find the relativ extrema of this function of one variable by the methods we used in the chapter on application of the derivative. The endpoints are 0 and 100, while there are no critical points because

$$f'(x, 0) = 10 \qquad\qquad \text{We are taking the derivative of this function of } x.$$

and so is never zero. The endpoints $x = 0$ and $x = 100$ give, with $y = 0$ for this segmen the points $O(0, 0)$ and $P(100, 0)$ as two candidates for extrema.

Segment OQ: $x = 0, 0 \leq y \leq 75$:
Substitute $x = 0$ into the function f to obtain

$$f(0, y) = 10(0) + 20y - 0.5(0)y = 20y, \ 0 \leq y \leq 75,$$

a function of the single variable y that determines the value of f along the segment OQ Again, there are no critical points, only the endpoints $y = 0$ and $y = 75$. These give $O(0, 0)$ again and $Q(0, 75)$ as candidates for extrema.

Segment QR: $y = 75, 0 \leq x \leq 100$:
Substitute $y = 75$ into the function f to obtain

$$f(x, 75) = 10x + 20(75) - 0.5x(75) = -27.5x + 1,500, \ 0 \leq x \leq 100.$$

Since the derivative of this function is $-27.5 \neq 0$, we find again that there are no critica points; only the endpoints $x = 0$ and 100. Since here $y = 75$, these give us $Q(0, 75)$ agai and one new point $R(100, 75)$ as candidates for extrema.

Segment PR: $x = 100, 0 \leq y \leq 75$:
Substitute $x = 100$ into the function f to obtain

$$f(100, y) = 10(100) + 20y - 0.5(100)y = 1,000 - 30y, \ 0 \leq y \leq 75.$$

Again, there are no critical points, only the endpoints $y = 0$ and $y = 75$. These give $P(100, 0)$ and $R(100, 75)$ again as candidates for extrema.

Our analysis has yielded the following five candidate points, shown here along wit the values of f:

Point	Value of f	
(40, 20)	400	
(0, 0)	0	
(100, 0)	1,000	
(0, 75)	1,500	Absolute maximum
(100, 75)	−1,250	Absolute minimum

Since the absolute maximum *has* to be at one of these points, it must be at the poin $(0, 75)$, which yields a maximum monthly profit of $1,500.

➡ **Before we go on...** In Example 1 we did not classify the three points (40, 20), (0, 0), and (100, 0) as relative maxima, minima, or neither. While we could analyze the function further to obtain this information, it is easier to simply graph the function. Figure 4 shows the graph of $f(x, y) = 10x + 20y - 0.5xy$ as plotted on the Surface Grapher at the Website.

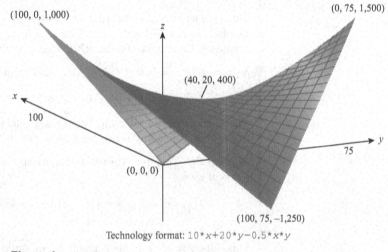

(100, 0, 1,000)

(0, 75, 1,500)

(40, 20, 400)

100

75

(0, 0, 0)

(100, 75, −1,250)

Technology format: `10*x+20*y-0.5*x*y`

Figure 4

From the figure, we see that f has a saddle point at the interior critical point (40, 20), a relative minimum at (0, 0), and a relative maximum at (100, 0).

We can restate the problem in Example 1 as a *constrained optimization problem* as follows:

Maximize $f = 10x + 20y - 0.5xy$	Objective function
subject to $0 \le x \le 100$	Inequality constraint
and $0 \le y \le 75$	Inequality constraint

If you have studied linear programming, this example should remind you of the problems you solved by that technique. However, the techniques of linear programming cannot, in general, be used to solve problems with nonlinear objective functions. ■

EXAMPLE 2 Absolute Extrema: Triangular Domain

Find the maximum and minimum value of $f(x, y) = 8 + xy - x - 2y$ on the triangular region R with vertices (0, 0), (2, 0), and (0, 4).

Solution The domain of f is the region R shown in Figure 5.

Step 1: Locate critical points in the interior of the domain.
We take the partial derivatives as usual.

$$f_x = y - 1 \qquad\qquad f_y = x - 2$$

Setting these partial derivatives equal to zero, we find that the only critical point is (2, 1). Since this lies outside the domain (the region R), we ignore it. Thus, there are no critical points in the interior of the domain of f.

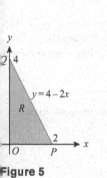

Figure 5

Step 2: Locate extrema on the boundary of the domain.

The boundary of the domain consists of three line segments, *OP, OQ,* and *PQ.*

Segment OP: $y = 0, 0 \leq x \leq 2$. The behavior of the function f along this segment seen by substituting $y = 0$ into the expression for f:

$$f(x, 0) = 8 + x(0) - x - 2(0) = 8 - x$$

There are no critical points (the derivative of this function is never zero) and there a two endpoints, $x = 0$ and $x = 2$. Since $y = 0$, these endpoints give us the following tw candidates for relative extrema: $O(0, 0)$ and $P(2, 0)$.

Segment OQ: $x = 0, 0 \leq y \leq 4$. Along this segment we see

$$f(0, y) = 8 + (0)y - 0 - 2y = 8 - 2y.$$

Once again, there are no critical points, and only the endpoints $y = 0$ and $y = 4$. Sin $x = 0$, this again gives us two candidates, $O(0, 0)$ and $Q(0, 4)$.

Segment PQ: This line segment has equation $y = 4 - 2x$ with $0 \leq x \leq 2$. Along th segment we see

$$f(x, 4 - 2x) = 8 + x(4 - 2x) - x - 2(4 - 2x) \qquad \text{Substitute } y = 4 - 2x.$$
$$= -2x^2 + 7x.$$

This function of x (whose graph is an upside-down parabola) has a maximu when its derivative, $-4x + 7$, is 0, which occurs when $x = 7/4$. When $x = 7/$ $y = 4 - 2(7/4) = 1/2$. Thus, we have a critical point at $(7/4, 1/2) = (1.75, 0.5)$. T endpoints are $x = 0$ and $x = 2$, giving us $P(2, 0)$ and $Q(0, 4)$ once again.

If we compute the value of f at each candidate point, we obtain:

Point	Value of f	
$(0, 0)$	8	Absolute maximum
$(2, 0)$	6	
$(0, 4)$	0	Absolute minimum
$(1.75, 0.5)$	6.125	

We see that f has an absolute maximum of 8 at the point $(0, 0)$ and an absolute minimu of 0 at the point $(0, 4)$.

➡ **Before we go on...** Figure 6 shows the graph[1] of $f(x, y) = 8 + xy - x - 2y$ fro Example 2, and tells us that f has a relative minimum at $P(2, 0)$. It also shows that has neither a relative maximum nor a minimum at $(1.75, 0.5)$—it has a maximum

---

[1] We sketched it on the Surface Grapher at the Website. To show the restriction to the triangular domain, we used the parametric surface feature with
$$x = u, \quad y = (4 - 2*u)*(1 - v), \quad z = 8 + u*(4 - 2*u)*(1 - v)$$
$$- u - 2*(4 - 2*u)*(1 - v) \ (0 \leq u \leq 2, \ 0 \leq v \leq 1)$$

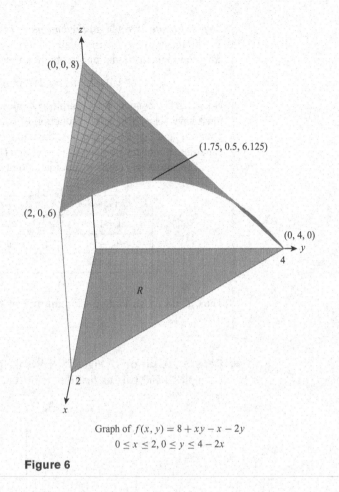

Graph of $f(x, y) = 8 + xy - x - 2y$
$0 \leq x \leq 2, 0 \leq y \leq 4 - 2x$

Figure 6

$(1.75, 0.5)$ *along the edge PQ*, but the value $f(1.75, 0.75) = 6.125$ is smaller than the values of f at interior points immediately behind it. ∎

EXAMPLE 3 **Absolute Extrema: Circular Domain**

Find the maximum and minimum value of $f(x, y) = x^2 + y^2 + y + 1$ subject to $x^2 + y^2 \leq 1$.

Solution The domain D of the function f is the unit disc $\{(x, y)|x^2 + y^2 \leq 1\}$ shown in Figure 7.

Step 1: Locate critical points in the interior of the domain.
We take the partial derivatives:

$$f_x = 2x \qquad\qquad f_y = 2y + 1$$

Setting these partial derivatives equal to zero, we find that the only critical point is $(0, -1/2)$, which is in the interior of D.

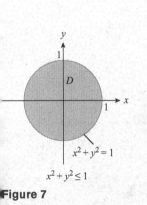

Figure 7

Step 2: Locate extrema on the boundary of the domain.

The boundary of D consists of all points (x, y) with $x^2 + y^2 = 1$. We can substitute th[is] equation in the formula for f to obtain a function of a single variable:

$$f = (x^2 + y^2) + y + 1 = 2 + y$$

Notice that y cannot take an arbitrary value—since (x, y) is a point on the circle, w[e] must have $-1 \le y \le 1$. This function of y has no critical points but does have two en[d] points: 1 and -1. When $y = \pm 1$, the equation $x^2 + y^2 = 1$ tells us that $x = 0$. So, ou[r] candidate boundary points are $(0, -1)$ and $(0, 1)$.

The values of f at these candidate points are shown in the following table:

Point	Value of f	
$(0, -1/2)$	3/4	Absolute minimum
$(0, -1)$	1	
$(0, 1)$	3	Absolute maximum

Thus, f has an absolute maximum of 3 at $(0, 1)$ and an absolute minimum of 3/4 a[t] $(0, -1/2)$.

⟹ **Before we go on...** Figure 8 shows the graph of $f(x, y) = x^2 + y^2 + y + 1$ fro[m] Example 3, and tells us that the point $(0, -1, 1)$ is not a relative extremum. (It is

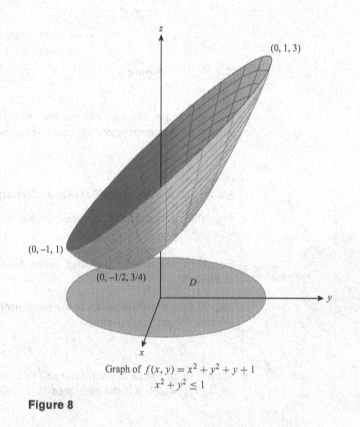

Graph of $f(x, y) = x^2 + y^2 + y + 1$
$x^2 + y^2 \le 1$

Figure 8

minimum along the boundary, but the value of f there is higher than its value at interior points immediately to its right.)

Notice also, that in locating extreme points on the boundary, we were actually solving the following constrained optimization problem:

Find the optimum values of $f(x, y) = x^2 + y^2 + y + 1$ subject to $x^2 + y^2 = 1$.

Here, the constraint takes the form of an equation rather than an inequality. Similarly, in the preceding examples, restricting to each of the various line segments amounted to solving an optimization problem with an equation constraint; for instance, in Example 2, on the segment PQ, we were finding the optimum values of $f(x, y) = 8 + xy - x - 2y$ subject to $y = 4 - 2x$. Solving optimization problems with equality constraints is discussed further in Section 15.4. ∎

Some software packages, such as Excel, have built-in algorithms that seek absolute extrema with or without constraints. In the next example, we use the "Solver" add-in[2] in Excel to solve an optimization problem whose objective function has a more complicated domain.

EXAMPLE 4 ⓘ Solving an Optimization Problem Using Excel's Solver

Use Excel's Solver to solve the following problem:

Maximize $P = 10x + 60y + 0.5xy$		Objective function
subject to	$x + 5y \le 100$	Constraint 1
	$3x + 9y \le 270$	Constraint 2
	$x \ge 0$ and $y \ge 0$	Constraints 3 and 4

Solution First, we set up the problem in spreadsheet form as follows:

◇	A	B	C	D	E	F
1	x	y	Objective	Constraints		
2	0	0	=10*A2+60*B2+0.5*A2*B2	=A2+5*B2	100	Constraint 1
3	Initial value of x	Initial value of y		=3*A2+9*B2	270	Constraint 2
4				=A2	0	Constraint 3
5				=B2	0	Constraint 4

A2 will be the cell that contains the value of x and B2 the cell that contains the value of y. Solver requires us to give them initial values, so we've set them both equal to 0; Solver will adjust them to find the optimal solution. Next, we select "Solver" in the "Tools" menu to bring up the Solver dialog box. Here is the dialog box with all the necessary fields completed to solve the problem:

---

[2] If "Solver" does not appear in the "Tools" menu, you should first install it using your Excel installation software. (Solver is one of the "Excel Add-Ins.")

Solver Parameters dialog box with:

Set Target Cell: $C$2

Equal To: ● Max ○ Min ○ Value of: 0

By Changing Cells: $A$2:$B$2

Subject to the Constraints:
$D$2 <= $E$2
$D$3 <= $E$3
$D$4 >= $E$4
$D$5 >= $E$5

Buttons: Solve, Close, Options..., Guess, Reset All, Add, Help, Change, Delete

Notes

- The Target Cell refers to the cell that contains the objective function.
- "Max" is selected because we are maximizing the objective function.
- "Changing Cells" are obtained by selecting the cells that contain the current values of x and y.
- Constraints are added one at a time by pressing the "Add" button and selecting the cells that contain the left- and right-hand sides of each inequality, as well as the type of inequality. (Equality constraints are also permitted.)

Once we've entered the parameters, we click on "Solve" and the (approximate) optimal solution appears in A2 and B2, with the maximum value of P appearing in cell C2. The optimal solution is therefore $x = 40$, $y = 12$, $P = 1,360$.

◇	A	B	C	D	E
1	x	y	Objective	Constraints	
2	40	12	1360	100	100
3	Final value of x	Final value of y		228	270
4				40	0
5				12	0

➡ **Before we go on...**

Q: *Can a software package such as Excel Solver be used interchangeably with the analytic method?*

A: Some optimization problems lead to equations that cannot be solved analytically, and so some form of numerical approach (such as that used in Solver) is essential in those cases. However, with all numerical approaches there is always a chance of running into one or more of these problems:

- The solution given will be a relative extremum rather than an absolute extremum.
- The solution is not exact.
- Roundoff errors lead to an incorrect solution or prevent finding a solution.
- Only one solution is given even if there is more than one absolute extremum.

So, use Solver with caution.

▪

EXERCISES

▼ more advanced

ℹ In all of the exercises for this section, a software package such as Excel Solver can be used as a check on your analytic work. (Bear in mind, however, the cautions at the end of Example 4.)

In Exercises 1–16, find the maximum and minimum values of the given function and the points at which they occur.

1. $f(x, y) = x^2 + y^2$; $0 \leq x \leq 2, 0 \leq y \leq 2$

2. $g(x, y) = \sqrt{x^2 + y^2}$; $1 \leq x \leq 2, 1 \leq y \leq 2$

3. $h(x, y) = (x - 1)^2 + y^2$; $x^2 + y^2 \leq 4$

4. $k(x, y) = x^2 + (y - 1)^2$; $x^2 + y^2 \leq 9$

5. $f(x, y) = e^{x^2 + y^2}$; $4x^2 + y^2 \leq 4$

6. $g(x, y) = e^{-(x^2 + y^2)}$; $x^2 + 4y^2 \leq 4$

7. $h(x, y) = e^{4x^2 + y^2}$; $x^2 + y^2 \leq 1$

8. $k(x, y) = e^{-(x^2 + 4y^2)}$; $x^2 + y^2 \leq 4$

9. $f(x, y) = x + y + 1/(xy)$; $x \geq 1/2, y \geq 1/2, x + y \leq 3$

10. $g(x, y) = x + y + 8/(xy)$; $x \geq 1, y \geq 1, x + y \leq 6$

11. $h(x, y) = xy + 8/x + 8/y$; $x \geq 1, y \geq 1, xy \leq 9$

12. $k(x, y) = xy + 1/x + 4/y$; $x \geq 1, y \geq 1, xy \leq 10$

13. ▼ $f(x, y) = x^2 + 2x + y^2$; on the region in the figure

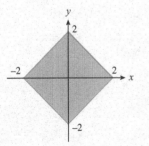

14. ▼ $g(x, y) = x^2 + y^2$; on the region in the figure

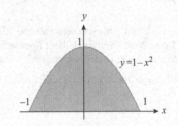

15. ▼ $h(x, y) = x^3 + y^3$; on the region in the figure

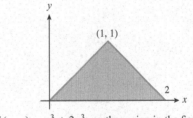

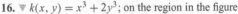

16. ▼ $k(x, y) = x^3 + 2y^3$; on the region in the figure

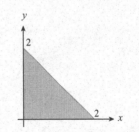

APPLICATIONS

17. *Cost* Your bicycle factory makes two models, five-speeds and ten-speeds. Each week, your total cost (in dollars) to make x five-speeds and y ten-speeds is

$$C(x, y) = 10{,}000 + 50x + 70y - 0.5xy$$

You want to make between 100 and 150 five-speeds and between 80 and 120 ten-speeds. What combination will cost you the least? What combination will cost you the most?

18. **Cost** Your bicycle factory makes two models, five-speeds and ten-speeds. Each week, your total cost (in dollars) to make x five-speeds and y ten-speeds is

$$C(x, y) = 10{,}000 + 50x + 70y - 0.46xy$$

You want to make between 100 and 150 five-speeds, and between 80 and 120 ten-speeds. What combination will cost you the least? What combination will cost you the most?

19. ▼ **Profit** Your software company sells two operating systems, Walls and Doors. Your profit (in dollars) from selling x copies of Walls and y copies of Doors is given by

$$P(x, y) = 20x + 40y - 0.1(x^2 + y^2).$$

If you can sell a maximum of 200 copies of the two operating systems together, what combination will bring you the greatest profit?

20. ▼ **Profit** Your software company sells two operating systems, Walls and Doors. Your profit (in dollars) from selling x copies of Walls and y copies of Doors is given by

$$P(x, y) = 20x + 40y - 0.1(x^2 + y^2).$$

If you can sell a maximum of 400 copies of the two operating systems together, what combination will bring you the largest profit?

21. **Temperature** The temperature at the point (x, y) on the square with vertices $(0, 0)$, $(0, 1)$, $(1, 0)$, and $(1, 1)$ is given by $T(x, y) = x^2 + 2y^2$. Find the hottest and coldest points of the square.

22. **Temperature** The temperature at the point (x, y) on the square with vertices $(0, 0)$, $(0, 1)$, $(1, 0)$, and $(1, 1)$ is given by $T(x, y) = x^2 + 2y^2 - x$. Find the hottest and coldest points on the square.

23. ▼ **Temperature** The temperature at the point (x, y) on the disc $\{(x, y)|x^2 + y^2 \le 1\}$ is given by $T(x, y) = x^2 + 2y^2 - $. Find the hottest and coldest points on the disc.

24. ▼ **Temperature** The temperature at the point (x, y) on the disc $\{(x, y)|x^2 + y^2 \le 1\}$ is given by $T(x, y) = 2x^2 + y$. Find the hottest and coldest points on the disc.

Extreme Values: Answers to Odd-Numbered Exercises

1. Maximum value of 8 at $(2, 2)$, minimum value of 0 at $(0, 0)$
3. Maximum value of 9 at $(-2, 0)$, minimum value of 0 at $(1, 0)$
5. Maximum value of e^4 at $(0, \pm 2)$, minimum value of 1 at $(0, 0)$
7. Maximum value of e^4 at $(\pm 1, 0)$, minimum value of 1 at $(0, 0)$
9. Maximum value of 5 at $(1/2, 1/2)$, minimum value of 3 at $(1, 1)$
11. Maximum value of $161/9$ at $(1, 9)$ and $(9, 1)$, minimum value of 12 at $(2, 2)$

13. Maximum value of 8 at $(2, 0)$, minimum value of -1 at $(-1, 0)$
15. Maximum value of 8 at $(2, 0)$, minimum value of 0 at $(0, 0)$
17. For minimum cost of $16,600$, make 100 5-speeds and 80 10-speeds. For maximum cost of $17,400$, make 100 5-speeds and 120 10-speeds.
19. For a maximum profit of $4,500$, sell 50 copies of Walls and 150 copies of Doors.
21. Hottest point: $(1, 1)$, coldest point: $(0, 0)$
23. Hottest points: $(-1/2, \pm\sqrt{3}/2)$, coldest point: $(1/2, 0)$

P

Calculus Applied to Probability and Statistics

Case Study: Creating a Family Trust

You are a financial planning consultant at a neighborhood bank. A 22-year-old client asks you the following question: "I would like to set up my own insurance policy by opening a trust account into which I can make monthly payments starting now, so that upon my death or my ninety-fifth birthday—whichever comes sooner—the trust can be expected to be worth $500,000. How much should I invest each month?" Assuming a 5% rate of return on investments, how should you respond?

Introduction

To answer the question on the previous page, we must know something about the probability of the client's dying at various ages. There are so many possible ages to consider (particularly because we should consider the possibilities month by month) that it would be easier to treat his age at death as a *continuous* variable, one that can take on any real value (between 22 and 95 in this case). The mathematics needed to do probability and statistics with continuous variables is calculus.

The material on statistics in this chapter is accessible to any reader with "common-sense" knowledge of probability, but it also supplements any previous study you may have made of probability and statistics without using calculus.

P.1 Continuous Random Variables and Histograms

Suppose that you have purchased stock in Colossal Conglomerate, Inc., and each day you note the closing price of the stock. The result each day is a real number X (the closing price of the stock) in the unbounded interval $[0, +\infty)$. Or, suppose that you time several people running a 50-meter dash. The result for each runner is a real number X, the race time in seconds. In both cases, the value of X is somewhat random. Moreover, X can take on essentially any real value in some interval, rather than, say, just integer values. For this reason, we refer to X as a **continuous random variable**. Here is the formal definition.

Continuous Random Variable

A **random variable** is a function X that assigns to each possible outcome in an experiment a real number. If X may assume any value in some given interval I (the interval may be bounded or unbounded), it is called a **continuous** random variable. If it can assume only a number of separated values, it is called a **discrete** random variable.

Quick Examples

1. Roll a die and take X to be the number on the uppermost face. Then X is a discrete random variable with possible values 1, 2, 3, 4, 5, and 6.

2. Locate a star in the cosmos and take X to be its distance from the solar system in light years. Then X is a continuous random variable whose values are real numbers in the interval $(0, +\infty)$.

3. Open the business section of your newspaper and take X to be the closing price of Colossal Conglomerate stock. Then X can take on essentially any positive real value, so we can think of X as a continuous random variable.

If X is a random variable, we are usually interested in the **probability** that X takes on a value in a certain range. For instance, if X is the closing price of Colossal

Conglomerate stock and we find that 60% of the time the price is between $10 and $20, we would say

The probability that X is between $10 and $20 is .6.

We can write this statement mathematically as follows:

$$P(10 \leq X \leq 20) = .6$$

The probability that $10 \leq X \leq 20$ is .6.

We can use a bar chart, called a **probability distribution histogram**, to display the probabilities that X lies in selected ranges. This is shown in the following example:

EXAMPLE 1 College Population by Age

The following table shows the distribution according to age of U.S. residents (16 years old and over) attending college in 1980.[1]

Age (years)	15–19	20–24	25–29	30–34	35–?
Number in 1980 (millions)	2.7	4.8	1.9	1.2	1.8

Draw the probability distribution histogram for $X =$ the age of a randomly chosen college student.

Solution The Summing the entries in the bottom row, we see that the total number of students in 1980 was 12.4 million. We can therefore convert all the data in the table to probabilities by dividing by this total.

$X =$ Age (years)	15–19	20–24	25–29	30–34	35–?
Probability	.22	.39	.15	.10	.15

The probabilities in the above table have been rounded, with the consequence that they add to 1.01 instead of the expected 1. In the category 15–19, we have actually included anyone at least 15 years old and less than 20 years old. For example, someone $19\frac{1}{2}$ years old would be in this range. We would like to write 15–20 instead, but this would be ambiguous, because we would not know where to count someone who was exactly 20 years old. However, the probability that a college student is *exactly* 20 years old (and not, say, 20 years and 1 second) is essentially 0, so it doesn't matter.[2] We can therefore rewrite the table with the following ranges.

$X =$ Age (years)	15–20	20–25	25–30	30–35	≥ 35
Probability	.22	.39	.15	.10	.15

---

[1] Source: 1980 Census of Population, U.S. Department of Commerce/Bureau of the Census.
[2] Also see the discussion after Example 2 below.

The table tells us that, for instance,

$$P(15 \leq X \leq 20) = .22$$

and

$$P(X \geq 35) = .15.$$

The probability distribution histogram is the bar graph we get from these data (Figure

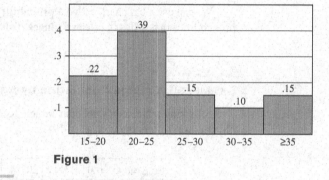

Figure 1

➡ **Before we go on...** Had the grouping into ranges been finer—for instance into divsions of 1 year instead of 5, then the histogram would appear smoother, and with low bars, as in Figure 2. (Why?)

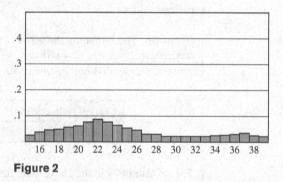

Figure 2

This smoother-looking distribution suggests a smooth curve. It is this kind of curve th we shall be studying in the next section. ■

EXAMPLE 2 Age of a Rented Car

A survey finds the following probability distribution for the age of a rented car.[3]

Age (years)	0–1	1–2	2–3	3–4	4–5	5–6	6–7
Probability	.20	.28	.20	.15	.10	.05	.02

---

[3]As in the preceeding example, we allow the brackets to intersect. However, because the probability that a car is *exactly* 1 or 2 or 3 or ... years old (to a fraction of a second) is essentially zero, we can ignore the apparent overlap. The discussion at the end of this example further clarifies this point.

Plot the associated probability distribution histogram, and use it to evaluate (or estimate) the following:

(a) $P(0 \leq X \leq 4)$ (b) $P(X \geq 4)$

(c) $P(2 \leq X \leq 3.5)$ (d) $P(X = 4)$

Solution The histogram is shown in Figure 3.

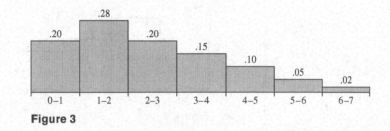

Figure 3

(a) We can calculate $P(0 \leq X \leq 4)$ from the table by adding the corresponding probabilities:

$$P(0 \leq X \leq 4) = .20 + .28 + .20 + .15 = .83$$

This corresponds to the shaded region of the histogram shown in Figure 4.

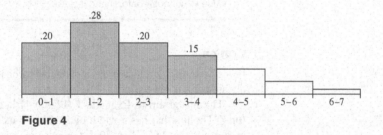

Figure 4

Notice that because each rectangle has width equal to 1 unit and height equal to the associated probability, its *area* is equal to the probability that X is in the associated range. Thus, $P(0 \leq X \leq 4)$ is also equal to the area of the shaded region.

(b) Similarly, $P(X \geq 4)$ is given by the area of the *unshaded* portion of Figure 4, so

$$P(X \geq 4) = .10 + .05 + .02 = .17.$$

(Notice that $P(0 \leq X \leq 4) + P(X \geq 4) = 1$. Why?)

(c) To calculate $P(2 \leq X \leq 3.5)$, we need to make an educated guess, because neither the table nor the histogram has subdivisions of width .5. Referring to the graph, we can approximate the probability by the shaded area shown in Figure 5.

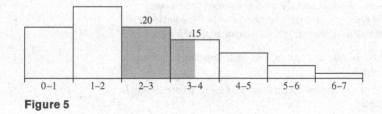

Figure 5

Thus,

$$P(2 \leq X \leq 3.5) \approx .20 + \frac{1}{2}(.15) = .275.$$

(d) To calculate $P(X = 4)$, we would need to calculate $P(4 \leq X \leq 4)$. But this woul[d] correspond to a region of the histogram with zero area (Figure 6), so we conclud[e] that $P(X = 4) = 0$.

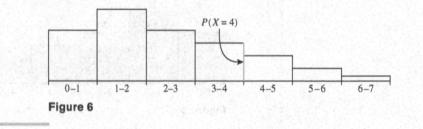

Figure 6

Q : *In Example 2, $P(X = 4)$ was zero. Is it true that $P(X = a)$ is zero for every number in the interval associated with X?*

A : As a general rule, yes. If X is a *continuous* random variable, then X can assume infinite[ly] many values, and so it is reasonable that the probability of its assuming any specifi[c] value we choose beforehand is zero.

Caution

If you wish to use a histogram to calculate probability as *area*, make sure that the sub[-] divisions for X have width 1—for instance, $1 \leq X \leq 2, 2 \leq X \leq 3$, and so on.

The histogram in Example 1 (Figure 1) had bars corresponding to larger range[s] for X. The first bar has a width of 5 units, so its area is 5×0.22, which is 5 times th[e] probability that $15 \leq X \leq 20$. If you wish to use a histogram to give probability as are[a,] divide the area by the width of the intervals.

There is another way around this problem that we shall not use, but which i[s] used by working statisticians: Draw your histograms so that the heights are n[ot] necessarily the probabilities but are chosen so that the *area* of each bar gives the co[r-] responding probability. This is necessary if, for example, the bars do not all have th[e] same width.

P.1 EXERCISES

▼ more advanced

In Exercises 1–10, identify the random variable (for example, "X is the price of rutabagas") and say whether it is continuous or discrete, and if continuous, give its interval of possible values.

1. A die is cast and the number that appears facing up is recorded.

2. A die is cast and the time it takes for the die to become still is recorded.

3. A dial is spun, and the angle the pointer makes with the vert[i-] cal is noted. (See the figure.)

4. A dial is spun, and the quadrant in which the pointer comes to rest is noted.

5. The temperature is recorded at midday.

6. The U.S. Balance of Payments is recorded (fractions of a dollar permitted).

7. The U.S. Balance of Payments is recorded, rounded to the nearest billion dollars.

8. The time it takes a new company to become profitable is recorded.

9. In each batch of 100 computer chips manufactured, the number that fail to work is recorded.

10. The time it takes a TV set to break down after sale is recorded.

In Exercises 11–14, sketch the probability distribution histogram of the given continuous random variable.

11.

X = Height of a jet fighter (ft.)	0–20,000	20,000–30,000	30,000–40,000	40,000–50,000	50,000–60,000
Probability	.1	.2	.3	.3	.1

12.

X = Time to next eruption of a volcano (yrs.)	0–2,000	2,000–3,000	3,000–4,000	4,000–5,000	5,000–6,000
Probability	.1	.3	.3	.2	.1

13.

X = Average temperature (°F)	0–50	50–60	60–70	70–80	80–90
Number of cities	4	7	2	5	2

14.

X = Cost of a used car ($)	0–2,000	2,000–4,000	4,000–6,000	6,000–8,000	8,000–10,000
Number of cars	200	500	800	500	500

APPLICATIONS

15. ▼ *U.S. Population, Female* The following table shows the number of females in the United States in 2000, broken down by age.[4] Numbers are in millions.

Age	0–18	18–25	25–35	35–45	45–55	55–65	65–75	75 and over
Number	35.2	13.3	19.8	22.7	19.2	12.6	10.1	10.5

Construct the associated probability distribution (with probabilities rounded to four decimal places) and use the distribution to compute the following.

(a) $P(18 \leq X \leq 55)$ **(b)** $P(X \leq 45)$ **(c)** $P(X \leq 45)$

16. ▼ *U.S. Population, Male* The following table shows the number of males in the United States in 2000, broken down by age.[5] Numbers are in millions.

Age	0–18	18–25	25–35	35–45	45–55	55–65	65–75	75 and over
Number	37.1	13.9	20.1	22.4	18.5	11.6	8.3	6.1

Construct the associated probability distribution (with probabilities rounded to four decimal places) and use the distribution to compute the following.

(a) $P(25 \leq X \leq 65)$ **(b)** $P(X \leq 18)$ **(c)** $P(X \geq 15)$

17. ▼ *Meteors* The following histogram shows part of the probability distribution of the size (in megatons of released energy) of large meteors that hit the Earth's atmosphere. (A large meteor is one that releases at least one megaton of energy, equivalent to the energy released by a small nuclear bomb.)[6]

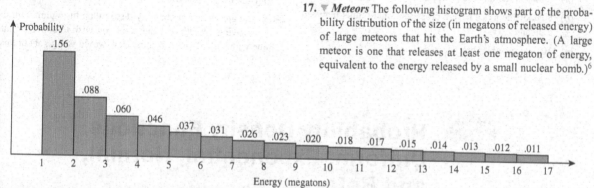

Source: U.S. Census Bureau, Census 2000 Summary File 1, obtained from http://factfinder.census.gov/.
Ibid.
The authors' model, based on data released by NASA International Near-Earth-Object Direction Workshop/*The New York Times*, January 25, 1994, p. C1.

Calculate or estimate the following probabilities.

(a) That a large meteor hitting the Earth's atmosphere will release between 1 and 4 megatons of energy.

(b) That a large meteor hitting the Earth's atmosphere will release between 3 and 4.5 megatons of energy.

(c) That a large meteor will release at least 5 megatons of energy.

18. ▼ *Meteors* Repeat the preceding exercise using the following histogram for meteor impacts on the planet Zor in the Cygnus III system in Andromeda.

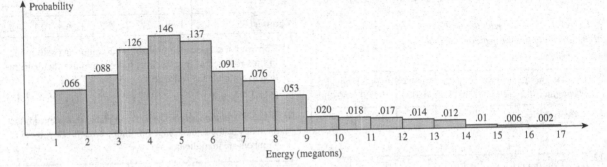

19. ▼ *Quality Control* An automobile parts manufacturer makes heavy-duty axles with a cross-section radius of 2.3 cm. In order for one of its axles to meet the accuracy standard demanded by the customer, the radius of the cross section cannot be off by more than 0.02 cm. Construct a histogram with $X =$ the measured radius of an axle, using categories of width 0.01 cm, so that all of the following conditions are met.

(a) X lies in the interval [2.26, 2.34].

(b) 80% of the axles have a cross-sectional radius between 2.29 and 2.31.

(c) 10% of the axles are rejected.

20. ▼ *Damage Control* As a campaign manager for a presidential candidate who always seems to be getting himself into embarrassing situations, you have decided to conduct a statistical analysis of the number of times per week he makes a blunder. Construct a histogram with $X =$ the number of times he blunders in a week, using categories of width 1 unit, so that all of the following conditions are met.

(a) X lies in the interval [0, 10].

(b) During a given week, there is an 80% chance that he will make 3 to 5 blunders.

(c) Never a week goes by that he doesn't make at least one blunder.

(d) On occasion, he has made 10 blunders in one week.

COMMUNICATION AND REASONING EXERCISES

21. ▼ How is a random variable related to the outcomes in an experiment?

22. ▼ Give an example of an experiment and two associated continuous random variables.

23. ▼ You are given a probability distribution histogram with the bars having a width of 2 units. How is the probability $P(a \leq X \leq b)$ related to the area of the corresponding portion of the histogram?

24. ▼ You are given a probability distribution histogram with the bars having a width of 1 unit, and you wish to convert it into one with bars of width 2 units. How would you go about this?

P.2 Probability Density Functions: Uniform, Exponential, Normal, and Beta

We have seen that a histogram is a convenient way to picture the probability distribution associated with a continuous random variable X and that if we use subdivisions of 1 unit the probability $P(c \leq X \leq d)$ is given by the area under the histogram between $X =$ and $X = d$. But we have also seen that it is difficult to calculate probabilities for range of X that are not a whole number of units. The following example—based on an example in the previous section—introduces the solution to this problem.

EXAMPLE 1 Car Rentals

A survey finds the following probability distribution for the age of a rented car.

X = Age (Years)	0-1	1–2	2–3	3-4	4–5	5-6	6-7
Probability	.20	.28	.20	.15	.10	.05	.02

The histogram of this distribution is shown in Figure 7a, and it suggests a curve something like the one given in Figure 7b.[7]

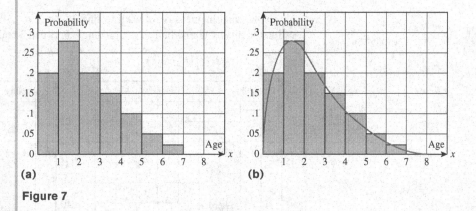

(a)

(b)

Figure 7

This curve is the graph of some function f, which we call a **probability density function**. We take the domain of f to be $[0, +\infty)$, because this is the possible range of values X can take (in principle). Also, we use x to refer to specific values of X, so it is no coincidence that these values are shown on the x-axis. In general, a probability distribution function will have some (possibly unbounded) interval as its domain.

Suppose now that as in Section P.1, we wanted to calculate the probability that a rented car is between 0 and 4 years old. Referring to the table, we find

$$P(0 \leq X \leq 4) = .20 + .28 + .20 + .15 = .83.$$

Referring to Figure 8, we can obtain the same result by adding the areas of the corresponding bars, because each bar has a width of 1 unit. Ideally, our probability density curve should have the property that the area under it for $0 \leq X \leq 4$ is the same, that is,

$$P(0 \leq X \leq 4) = \int_0^4 f(x)\,dx = .83.$$

(This area is shown in Figure 8 as well.)

---

[7]There are many similarly shaped curves suggested by the bar graph. The question of finding the most appropriate curve is one we shall be considering below.

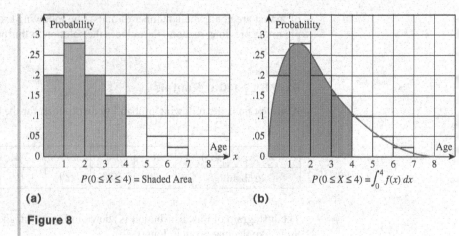

$P(0 \leq X \leq 4) =$ Shaded Area

(a)

$P(0 \leq X \leq 4) = \int_0^4 f(x)\, dx$

(b)

Figure 8

Now, what happens if we want to find $P(2 \leq X \leq 3.5)$? In the previous section we estimated this by taking half of the rectangle between 3 and 4 (see Figure 9).

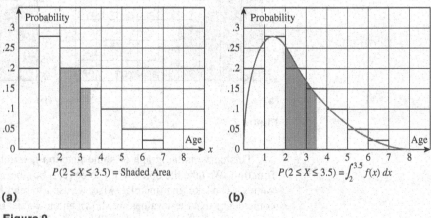

$P(2 \leq X \leq 3.5) =$ Shaded Area

(a)

$P(2 \leq X \leq 3.5) = \int_2^{3.5} f(x)\, dx$

(b)

Figure 9

Instead, we could use the definite integral

$$P(2 \leq X \leq 3.5) = \int_2^{3.5} f(x)\, dx.$$

➡ **Before we go on...** Although we haven't given you a formula for $f(x)$, we would *like* $f(x)$ to behave as described above. Here is something else we would like: Because a car has probability 1 of having an age between 0 and $+\infty$, we want

$$P(0 \leq X < +\infty) = \int_0^{+\infty} f(x)\, dx = 1. \blacksquare$$

The discussion in Example 1 motivates the following.

Probability Density Function

A **probability density function** is a function f defined on an interval (a, b) and having the following properties.

(a) $f(x) \geq 0$ for every x

(b) $\int_a^b f(x)\,dx = 1$

We allow a, b, or both to be infinite, as in the above example; this would make the integral in (b) an improper one.

Using a Probability Density Function to Compute Probability

A continuous random variable X **admits a probability density function** f if, for every c and d,

$$P(c \leq X \leq d) = \int_c^d f(x)\,dx.$$

Quick Example

Let $f(x) = \dfrac{2}{x^2}$ on the interval $[a, b] = [1, 2]$. Then property (a) holds, because $\dfrac{2}{x^2}$ is positive on the interval $[1, 2]$. For property (b),

$$\int_a^b f(x)\,dx = \int_1^2 \frac{2}{x^2}\,dx = \left[-\frac{2}{x}\right]_1^2 = -1 + 2 = 1.$$

If X admits this probability density function, then

$$P(1.5 \leq x \leq 2) = \int_{1.5}^2 \frac{2}{x^2}\,dx = \frac{1}{3}.$$

Note If X is specified by a probability density function f, then

$$P(X = c) = P(c \leq X \leq c) = \int_c^c f(x)\,dx = 0,$$

showing once again that there is a zero probability that X will assume any specified value. ■

Uniform Density Function

A **uniform density function** f is a density function that is constant, making it the simplest kind of density function. Because we require $f(x) = k$ for some constant k, requirement (b) in the definition of a probability density function tells us that

$$1 = \int_a^b f(x)\,dx = \int_a^b k\,dx = k(b - a).$$

Thus, we must have

$$k = \frac{1}{b - a}.$$

In other words, a uniform density function must have the following form.

Uniform Density Function

The **uniform density function on the interval [a, b]** is given by

$$f(x) = \frac{1}{b - a}.$$

Its graph is a horizontal line.

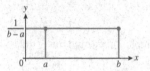

Calculating Probability with a Uniform Density Function

Because probability is given by area, it is not hard to compute probabilities based on a uniform distribution.

$$P(c \leq X \leq d) = \text{Area of shaded rectangle} = \frac{d - c}{b - a}.$$

Quick Example

Let X be a random real number between 0 and 5. Then X has a uniform distribution given by

$$f(x) = \frac{1}{5 - 0} = \frac{1}{5},$$

and $P(2 \leq X \leq 4.5) = \dfrac{4.5 - 2}{5 - 0} = .5.$

Figure 10

EXAMPLE 2 Spinning a Dial

Suppose that you spin the dial shown in Figure 10 so that it comes to rest at a rando[m] position. Model this with a suitable probability density function, and use it to find t[he] probability that the dial will land somewhere between 5° and 300°.

Solution We take X to be the angle at which the pointer comes to rest, so we use the inte[r]val [0, 360]. Because all angles are equally likely, the probability density function shou[ld] not depend on x and therefore should be constant. That is, we take f to be uniform.

$$f(x) = \frac{1}{b - a}$$

$$= \frac{1}{360 - 0} = \frac{1}{360}.$$

Thus,

$$P(5 \leq X \leq 300) = \frac{300 - 5}{360 - 0} = \frac{295}{360} \approx .8194.$$

➡ **Before we go on...** Notice that, in Example 2, we could have used the integral fo[r]mula and obtained the same answer:

$$\int_5^{300} \frac{1}{360}dx = \frac{1}{360}(300 - 5) = \frac{295}{360}.$$

You can also check the following probabilities. Why are these the answers you expect?

$P(0 \leq X \leq 90) = 1/4.$

$P(90 \leq X \leq 180) = 1/4.$

$P(0 \leq X \leq 180) = 1/2.$

$P(0 \leq X \leq 270) = 3/4.$

$P(0 \leq X \leq 120) = 1/3.$ ∎

Exponential Density Functions

Suppose that troubled saving and loan (S&L) institutions are failing continuously at a fractional rate of 5% per year. What is the probability that a troubled S&L will fail sometime within the next T years?

To answer the question, suppose that you started with 100 troubled S&Ls. Because they are failing continuously at a fractional rate of 5% per year, the number left after T years is given by the decay equation

$$\text{Number left} = 100e^{-0.05T},$$

so

$$\text{Number that fail} = \text{Total number} - \text{Number left}$$
$$= 100 - 100e^{-0.05T}$$
$$= 100(1 - e^{-0.05T}).$$

Thus, the percentage that will have failed by that time—and hence the probability that we are asking for—is given by

$$P = \frac{100(1 - e^{-0.05T})}{100} = 1 - e^{-0.05T}.$$

Now let X be the number of years a randomly chosen troubled S&L will take to fail. We have just calculated the probability that X is between 0 and T. In other words,

$$P(0 \leq X \leq T) = 1 - e^{-0.05T}.$$

Notice that this result can also be obtained by calculating a certain integral:

$$\int_0^T 0.05e^{-0.05x}dx = [e^{-0.05x}]_0^T = 1 - e^{-0.05T}.$$

Thus,

$$P(0 \leq X \leq T) = \int_0^T 0.05e^{-0.05x}dx,$$

and so we use $f(x) = 0.05e^{-0.05x}$ as a probability density function to model this situation.

Q: *Does this function satisfy the mathematical conditions necessary for it to be a probability density function?*

A: First, the domain of f is $[0, +\infty)$, since x refers to the number of years from now. Checking requirements (a) and (b) for a probability density function,

(a) $0.05e^{-0.05x} \geq 0$,

(b) $\displaystyle\int_0^{+\infty} 0.05e^{-0.05x}\,dx = \lim_{M \to +\infty} \int_0^M 0.05e^{-0.05x}\,dx$

$$= \lim_{M \to +\infty} [-e^{-0.05x}]_0^M$$

$$= \lim_{M \to +\infty} (e^0 - e^{-0.05M}) = 1 - 0 = 1.$$

There is nothing special about the number 0.05. Any function of the form

$$f(x) = ae^{-ax} \qquad\qquad a > 0 \quad \text{constant}$$

is a probability density function. A density function of this form is referred to as a**n** **exponential density function**.

Exponential Density Function

An **exponential density function** is a function of the form

$$f(x) = ae^{-ax} \ (a \text{ a positive constant})$$

with domain $[0 + \infty)$. Its graph is shown in Figure 11.

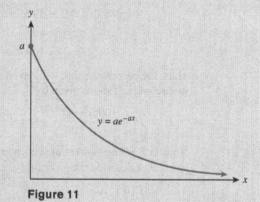

Figure 11

Quick Example

Continuing the example in the text, we find that the probability that a given troubled S&L will fail between 2 and 4 years from now is

$$P(2 \leq X \leq 4) = \int_2^4 0.05e^{-0.05x}\,dx = \left[-e^{-0.05x}\right]_2^4$$

$$= -e^{-0.2} + e^{-0.1} \approx .086.$$

The probability that it will last 5 or more years is

$$P(X \geq 5) = \int_0^{+\infty} 0.05e^{-0.05x}\,dx$$

$$= \lim_{M \to +\infty} \int_5^M 0.05e^{-0.05x}\,dx$$

$$= \lim_{M \to +\infty} \left[-e^{-0.05x} \right]_5^M = \lim_{M \to +\infty} (e^{-0.25} - e^{-0.05M})$$

$$= e^{-0.25} \approx .779.$$

So there is an 8.6% chance that a given S&L will fail between 2 and 4 years from now, and a 77.9% chance that it will last 5 or more years.

EXAMPLE 3   Radioactive Decay

Plutonium 239 decays continuously at a rate of 0.00284% per year. If X is the time a randomly chosen plutonium atom will decay, write down the associated probability density function, and use it to compute the probability that a plutonium atom will decay between 100 and 500 years from now.

Solution Using the discussion on failing S&Ls as our guide, we see that $a = 0.0000284$, so the probability density function is

$$f(x) = 0.0000284e^{-0.0000284x}.$$

For the second part of the question,

$$P(100 \leq X \leq 500) = \int_{100}^{500} (0.0000284e^{-0.0000284x})\,dx$$

$$\approx .011.$$

Thus, there is a 1.1% chance that a plutonium atom will decay sometime during the given 400- year period.

Normal Density Functions

Perhaps the most interesting class of probability density functions are the **normal density functions**, defined as follows.[8]

Normal Density Function

A **normal density function** is a function of the form

$$f(x) = \frac{1}{\sigma\sqrt{2\pi}}\, e^{-\frac{(x-\mu)^2}{2\sigma^2}},$$

with domain $(-\infty, +\infty)$. The quantity μ is called the **mean** and can be any real number, while σ is called the **standard deviation** and can be any positive real number. The graph of a normal density function is shown in Figure 12.

---

[8]You may recall encountering exercises using the normal density function in the chapter on integration.

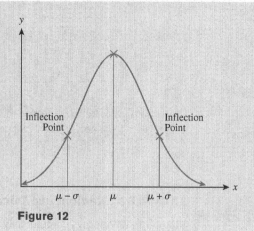

Figure 12

The following properties can be checked using calculus and a little algebra.

Properties of a Normal Density Curve

(a) It is "bell-shaped" with the peak occurring at $x = \mu$.

(b) It is symmetric about the vertical line $x = \mu$.

(c) It is concave down in the range $\mu - \sigma \leq x \leq \mu + \sigma$.

(d) It is concave up outside that range, with inflection points at $x = \mu - \sigma$ and $x = \mu + \sigma$.

The normal density function applies in many situations that involve measureme and testing. For instance, repeated imprecise measurements of the length of a single o ject, a measurement made on many items from an assembly line, and collections of SA scores tend to be distributed normally. It is partly for this reason that the normal densi curve is so important in quality control and in assessing the results of standardized test

In order to use the normal density function to compute probabilities, we need calculate integrals of the form $\int_a^b f(x)\,dx$. However, the antiderivative of the norm density function cannot be expressed in terms of any commonly used functions. Trad tionally, statisticians and others have used tables coupled with transformatic techniques to evaluate such integrals. This approach is rapidly becoming obsolete as t technology of spreadsheets, handheld computers, and programmable calculators pu the ability to do numerical integration quickly and accurately in everybody's hands (li erally). In keeping with this trend, in the Technology Guides at the end of this chapter v show how to use technology to do the calculations in the following example.

⊞ Using Technology

See the Technology Guides at the end of the chapter to find out how to compute the definite integral of a normal distribution using a TI-83/84 Plus or Excel.

⊞ EXAMPLE 4 Quality Control

Pressure gauges manufactured by Precision Corp. must be checked for accuracy befo being placed on the market. To test a pressure gauge, a worker uses it to measure the pressu of a sample of compressed air known to be at a pressure of exactly 50 pounds per square inc If the gauge reading is off by more than 1% (0.5 pounds/square inch), the gauge is rejecte Assuming that the reading of a pressure gauge under these circumstances is a normal rando variable with mean 50 and standard deviation 0.5, find the percentage of gauges rejecte

Solution For a gauge to be accepted, its reading X must be 50 to within 1%, in other words, $49.5 \leq X \leq 50.5$. Thus, the probability that a gauge will be accepted is $P(49.5 \leq X \leq 50.5)$. X is a normal random variable with $\mu = 50$ and $\sigma = 0.5$. The formula tells us that

$$P(49.5 \leq X \leq 50.5) = \int_{49.5}^{50.5} f(x)\,dx,$$

where f is the normal distribution with mean $\mu = 50$ and standard deviation $\sigma = 0.5$;

$$f(x) = \frac{1}{\sigma\sqrt{2\pi}}\, e^{-\frac{(x-\mu)^2}{2\sigma^2}}$$

$$= \frac{1}{0.5\sqrt{2\pi}}\, e^{-\frac{(x-50)^2}{0.5}}.$$

Using technology, we can calculate that

$$P(49.5 \leq X \leq 50.5) = \int_{49.5}^{50.5} f(x)\,dx \approx .6827.$$

In other words, 68.27% of the gauges will be accepted. Thus, the remaining 31.73% of the gauges will be rejected.

➡ **Before we go on...** As we mentioned above, the traditional and still common way of calculating normal probabilities is to use tables. The tables most commonly published are for the **standard normal distribution**, the one with mean 0 and standard deviation 1. If X is a normal variable with mean μ and standard deviation σ, the variable $Z = (X - \mu)/\sigma$ is a standard normal variable (see the exercises). Thus, to use a table we first write

$$P(a \leq X \leq b) = P\left(\frac{a-\mu}{\sigma} \leq Z \leq \frac{b-\mu}{\sigma}\right)$$

and then use the table to calculate the latter probability. ∎

Q : *Why can we assume in Example 4 that the reading of a pressure gauge is given by a normal distribution? Why is the normal distribution so common in this kind of situation?*

A : The reason for this is rather deep. There is a theorem in probability theory called the Central Limit Theorem, which says that a large class of probability density functions, given, for example, by repeated measurement of the same random variable, may be approximated by normal density functions.

Beta Density Functions

There are many random variables whose values are percentages or fractions. These variables have density functions defined on [0,1]. A large class of random variables, such as the percentage of new businesses that turn a profit in their first year, the percentage of banks that default in a given year, and the percentage of time a plant's machinery is inactive, can be modeled by a **beta density function**.

Beta Density Function

A **beta density function** is a function of the form

$$f(x) = (\beta + 1)(\beta + 2)x^\beta(1 - x),$$

with domain [0, 1]. The number β can be any constant ≥ 0. Figure 13 shows the graph of $f(x)$ for several values of β.

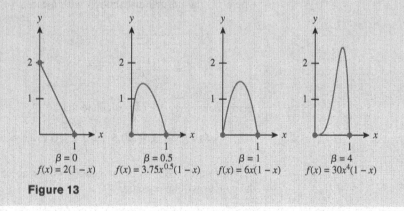

$\beta = 0$ $\beta = 0.5$ $\beta = 1$ $\beta = 4$

$f(x) = 2(1 - x)$ $f(x) = 3.75x^{0.5}(1 - x)$ $f(x) = 6x(1 - x)$ $f(x) = 30x^4(1 - x)$

Figure 13

EXAMPLE 5 Downsizing in the Utilities Industry

A utilities industry consultant predicts a cutback in the Canadian utilities industry during 2000–2005 by a percentage specified by a beta distribution with $\beta = 0.25$. Calculate the probability that Ontario Hydro will downsize by between 10% and 30% during the given five-year period.[9]

Solution The beta density function with $\beta = 0.25$ is

$$\begin{aligned}
f(x) &= (\beta + 1)(\beta + 2)x^\beta(1 - x) \\
&= 2.8125x^{0.25}(1 - x) \\
&= 2.8125(x^{0.25} - x^{1.25}).
\end{aligned}$$

Thus,

$$\begin{aligned}
P(0.10 \leq X \leq 0.30) &= \int_{0.10}^{0.30} 2.8125(x^{0.25} - x^{1.25})dx \\
&= 2.8125 \int_{0.10}^{0.30} (x^{0.25} - x^{1.25})dx \\
&= 2.8125 \left[\frac{x^{1.25}}{1.25} - \frac{x^{2.25}}{2.25} \right]_{0.10}^{0.30} \\
&\approx .2968.
\end{aligned}$$

So there is approximately a 30% chance that Ontario Hydro will downsize by between 10% and 30%.

➡ **Before we go on...** Figure 14 shows the density function. Notice that its shape is "in between" those for $\beta = 0$ and $\beta = 0.5$ in Figure 13. ■

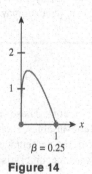

$\beta = 0.25$

Figure 14

---

[9]This model is fictitious. Ontario Hydro did announce plans to downsize by 8.4% in 1995, however [*Report on Business* (Canada), Feb. 15, 1994, p. B1].

P.2 EXERCISES

 more advanced   ◆ challenging

 indicates exercises that should be solved using technology

n Exercises 1–12, check whether the given function is a robability density function. If a function fails to be a robability density function, say why.

1. $f(x) = 1$ on $[0, 1]$

2. $f(x) = x$ on $[0, 2]$

3. $f(x) = \dfrac{x}{2}$ on $[0, 1]$

4. $f(x) = 2$ on $[0, \dfrac{1}{2}]$

5. ▼ $f(x) = \dfrac{3}{2}(x^2 - 1)$ on $[0, 2]$

6. ▼ $f(x) = \dfrac{1}{3}(1 - x^2)$ on $[0, 1]$

7. ▼ $f(x) = \dfrac{1}{x}$ on $[1, e]$

8. ▼ $f(x) = e^x$ on $[0, \ln 2]$

9. ▼ $f(x) = 2xe^{-x^2}$ on $[0, +\infty)$

0. ▼ $f(x) = -2xe^{-x^2}$ on $(-\infty, 0]$

1. ▼ $f(x) = xe^{-x^2}$ on $(-\infty, +\infty)$

2. ▼ $f(x) = |x|e^{-x^2}$ on $(-\infty, +\infty)$

n Exercises 13–16, find the values of k for which the given unctions are probability density functions.

3. ▼ $f(x) = 2k$ on $[-1, 1]$

4. ▼ $f(x) = k$ on $[-2, 0]$

5. ▼ $f(x) = ke^{kx}$ on $[0, 1]$

6. ▼ $f(x) = kxe^{x^2}$ on $[0, 1]$

n Exercises 17–26, say which kind of probability density unction is most appropriate for the given random variable: niform, exponential, normal, beta, or none of these.

7. ▼ The time it takes a Carbon-14 atom to decay.

8. ▼ The time it takes you to drive home.

9. ▼ The SAT score of a randomly selected student.

0. ▼ The value of a random number between 0 and 1.

1. ▼ The time of day at a randomly chosen moment.

2. ▼ The time it takes a careless driver to be involved in an accident.

3. ▼ The fraction of fast-food restaurants that are profitable in their first year.

4. ▼ The time it will take for the sun to die.

5. ▼ The time it takes before a gambler loses on a bet.

6. ▼ The length of a 2000 Ford Mustang®

APPLICATIONS

Unless otherwise stated, round answers to all applications to four decimal places.

27. *Salaries* Assuming that workers' salaries in your company are uniformly distributed between \$10,000 and \$40,000 per year, find the probability that a randomly chosen worker earns an annual salary between \$14,000 and \$20,000.

28. *Grades* The grade point averages of members of the Gourmet Society are uniformly distributed between 2.5 and 3.5. Find the probability that a randomly chosen member of the society has a grade point average between 3 and 3.2.

29. ▼ *Boring Television Series* Your company's new series "Avocado Comedy Hour" has been a complete flop, with viewership continuously declining at a rate of 30% per month. Use a suitable density function to calculate the probability that a randomly chosen viewer will be lost sometime in the next three months.

30. ▼ *Bad Investments* Investments in junk bonds are declining continuously at a rate of 5% per year. Use a suitable density function to calculate the probability that a dollar invested in junk bonds will be pulled out of the junk bond market within the next two years.

31. ▼ *Radioactive Decay* The half-life of Carbon-14 is 5,730 years. What is the probability that a randomly selected Carbon-14 atom will not yet have decayed in 4,000 years' time?

32. ▼ *Radioactive Decay* The half-life of Plutonium-239 is 24,400 years. What is the probability that a randomly selected Plutonium-239 atom will not yet have decayed in 40,000 years' time?

33. ▼ *The Doomsday Meteor* The probability that a "doomsday meteor" will hit the Earth in any given year and release a billion megatons or more of energy is on the order of 0.000 000 01.[10]

   (a) What is the probability that the Earth will be hit by a doomsday meteor at least once during the next 100 years? (Use an exponential distribution with $a = 0.000\ 000\ 01$. Give the answer correct to 2 significant digits.)

   (b) What is the probability that the Earth has been hit by a doomsday meteor at least once since the appearance of life (about 4 billion years ago)?

34. ▼ *Galactic Cataclysm* The probability that the galaxy MX-47 will explode within the next million years is estimated to be 0.0003.

   (a) What is the probability that MX-47 will explode within the next 5 million years? (Use an exponential distribution with $a = 0.0003$.)

   (b) What is the probability that MX-47 will still be around 10 million years hence?

---

[10]Source: NASA International Near-Earth-Object Detection Workshop/*The New York Times*, January 25, 1994, p. C1.

Exercises 35–42 use the normal probability density function and require the use of either technology or a table of values of the standard normal distribution.

35. ⬛ ▼ *Physical Measurements* Repeated measurements of a metal rod yield a mean of 5.3 inches, with a standard deviation of 0.1. What is the probability that the rod is between 5.25 and 5.35 inches long?

36. ⬛ ▼ *IQ Testing* Repeated measurements of a student's IQ yield a mean of 135, with a standard deviation of 5. What is the probability that the student has an IQ between 132 and 138?

37. ⬛ ▼ *Psychology Tests* It is known that subjects score an average of 100 points on a new personality test. If the standard deviation is 10 points, what percentage of all subjects will score between 75 and 80?

38. ⬛ ▼ *Examination Scores* Professor Easy's students earned an average grade of 3.5, with a standard deviation of 0.2. What percentage of his students earned between 3.5 and 3.9?

39. ⬛ ▼ *Operating Expenses* The cash operating expenses of the regional *Bell* companies during the first half of 1994 were distributed about a mean of $29.87 per access line per month, with a standard deviation of $2.65. *Ameritech Corporation*'s operating expenses were $28.00 per access line per month.[11] Assuming a normal distribution of operating expenses, estimate the percentage of regional Bell companies whose operating expenses were closer to the mean than those of Ameritech.

40. ⬛ ▼ *Operating Expenses Nynex Corporation*'s operating expenses were $35.80 per access line per month in the first half of 1994.[12] Referring to the distribution in the previous exercise, estimate the percentage of regional Bell companies whose operating expenses were higher than those of Nynex.

41. ⬛ ▼ *Operating Expenses SBC Corporation* (formerly Southwestern Bell) had operating expenses of $27.70 per access line per month in the first half of 1994.[13] Could SBC justifiably claim that its operating expenses were among the lowest 25% of all the regional Bell companies? Explain. (Use the normal distribution of the above exercises.)

42. ⬛ ▼ *Operating Expense U.S. West Corporation* had operating expenses of $29.10 per access line per month in the first half of 1994.[14] Were U.S. West's operating expenses closer to the mean than those of most other regional Bells? Explain. (Use the normal distribution of the above exercises.)

Cumulative Distribution *If f is a probability density function defined on the interval (a, b), then the* **cumulative distribution function** *F is given by*

$$F(x) = \int_a^x f(t)\,dt.$$

Exercises 43–52 deal with the cumulative distribution function

43. ◆ Why is $F'(x) = f(x)$?

44. ◆ Use the result of the previous exercise to show that

$$P(c \le X \le d) = F(d) - F(c)$$

for $a \le c \le d \le b$.

45. ◆ Show that $F(a) = 0$ and $F(b) = 1$.

46. ◆ Can $F(x)$ can have any local extrema? (Give a reason your answer.)

47. ▼ Find the cumulative distribution functions for the situati described in Exercise 27.

48. ▼ Find the cumulative distribution functions for the situati described in Exercise 28.

49. ▼ Find the cumulative distribution functions for the situati described in Exercise 29.

50. ▼ Find the cumulative distribution functions for the situati described in Exercise 30.

51. ▼ Find the cumulative distribution functions for the situati described in Exercise 31.

52. ▼ Find the cumulative distribution functions for the situati described in Exercise 32.

COMMUNICATION AND REASONING EXERCISES

53. ▼ Why is a probability density function often more conv nient than a histogram?

54. ▼ Give an example of a probability density function that is i creasing everywhere on its domain.

55. ▼ Give an example of a probability density function that concave up everywhere on its domain.

56. ▼ Suppose that X is a normal random variable with mean μ a standard deviation σ, and that Z is a standard normal variab Using the substitution $z = (x - \mu)/\sigma$ in the integral, show th

$$P(a \le X \le b) = P\left(\frac{a - \mu}{\sigma} \le Z \le \frac{b - \mu}{\sigma}\right).$$

57. ▼ Your friend thinks that if f is a probability density function the continuous random variable X, then $f(a)$ is the probabil that $X = a$. Explain to your friend why this is wrong.

58. ◆ Not satisfied with your explanation in the previous exerci your friend then challenges you by asking, "If $f(a)$ is not t probability that $X = a$, then just what does $f(a)$ signify How would you respond?

59. ◆ Your friend now thinks that if F is a *cumulative* probabili density function for the continuous random variable X, th $F(a)$ is the probability that $X = a$. Explain why your friend still wrong.

60. ◆ Once again not satisfied with your explanation in the pre ous exercise, your friend challenges you by asking, "If $F(a)$ not the probability that $X = a$, then just what does $F(a)$ si nify?" How would you respond?

---

[11] Source: NatWest Securities/Company Reports/*The New York Times*, November 22, 1994, p. D1.
[12]*Ibid.*
[13]*Ibid.*
[14]*Ibid.*

P.3 Mean, Median, Variance, and Standard Deviation

Mean

In the last section we saw that if savings and loan institutions are continuously failing at a rate of 5% per year, then the associated probability density function is

$$f(x) = 0.05e^{-0.05x}$$

with domain $[0, +\infty)$. An interesting and important question to ask is: What is the average length of time such an institution will last before failing? To answer this question, we use the following:

Mean or Expected Value

If X is a continuous random variable with probability density function f defined on an interval with (possibly infinite) endpoints a and b, then the **mean** or **expected value** of X is

$$E(X) = \int_a^b x f(x)\, dx.$$

$E(X)$ is also called the **average value** of X. It is what we expect to get if we take the average of many values of X obtained in experiments.

Quick Example

Let X have probability density function given by $f(x) = 3x^2$, with domain $[0, 1]$. Then

$$E(X) = \int_a^b x f(x)\, dx = \int_0^1 (x \cdot 3x^2)\, dx = \int_0^1 3x^3\, dx = \left[\frac{3x^4}{4}\right]_0^1 = \frac{3}{4}.$$

We shall explain shortly why $E(X)$ is given by the integral formula.

EXAMPLE 1 Failing S&Ls

Given that troubled S&Ls are failing continuously at a rate of 5% per year, how long will the average troubled S&L last?

Solution If X is the number of years that a given S&L will last, we know that its probability density function is $f(x) = 0.05e^{-0.05x}$. To answer the question we compute $E(X)$.

$$E(X) = \int_a^b x f(x)\,dx$$

$$= \int_0^{+\infty} (0.05x e^{-0.05x})\,dx$$

$$= \lim_{M \to +\infty} \int_0^M (0.05x e^{-0.05x})\,dx$$

Using integration by parts, we get

$$E(x) = \lim_{M \to +\infty} -0.05\left[e^{-0.05x}(20x + 400)\right]_0^M = (0.05)(400) = 20.$$

Thus, the expected lifespan of a troubled S&L is 20 years.

➡ **Before we go on...** Notice that in Example 1, the answer, 20, is the reciprocal of th failure rate 0.05. This is true in general: if $f(x) = ae^{-ax}$, then $E(X) = 1/a$. ∎

Q: *Why is E(X) given by that integral formula?*

A: Suppose for simplicity that the domain of f is a finite interval $[a, b]$. Break up the interv into n subintervals $[x_{k-1}, x_k]$, each of length Δx, as we did for Riemann sums. Now, th probability of seeing a value of X in $[x_{k-1}, x_k]$ is approximately $f(x_k)\Delta x$ (the approxima area under the graph of f over $[x_{k-1}, x_k]$). Think of this as the fraction of times we expe to see values of X in this range. These values, all close to x_k, then contribute approx mately $x_k f(x_k)\Delta x$ to the average, if we average together many observations of . Adding together all of these contributions, we get

$$E(X) \approx \sum_{k=1}^n x_k f(x_k)\Delta x.$$

Now, these approximations get better as $n \longrightarrow \infty$, and the sum above is a Riemann su converging to

$$E(X) = \int_a^b x f(x)\,dx,$$

which is the formula we have been using.

We can compute, one by one, the expected values of the distributions we discusse in the preceding section.

Mean of a Uniform Distribution

If X is uniformly distributed on $[a, b]$, then

$$E(X) = \frac{a + b}{2}.$$

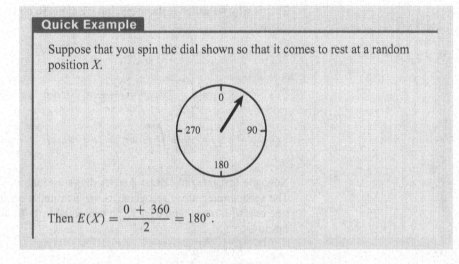

Quick Example

Suppose that you spin the dial shown so that it comes to rest at a random position X.

Then $E(X) = \dfrac{0 + 360}{2} = 180°$.

Mean of an Exponential Distribution

If X has the exponential distribution function $f(x) = ae^{-ax}$, then

$$E(X) = \frac{1}{a}.$$

Quick Example

If Internet startup companies are failing at a rate of 10% per year, then the expected lifetime of an Internet startup company is

$$E(X) = \frac{1}{0.1} = 10 \text{ years}.$$

We saw why this formula works in Example 1.

Mean of a Normal Distribution

If X is normally distributed with parameters μ and σ, then

$$E(X) = \mu.$$

Quick Example

If the final exam scores in your class are normally distributed with mean 72.6 and standard deviation 8.3, then the expected value for a test score is

$$E(X) = \mu = 72.6.$$

That is why we called μ the mean, but we ought to do the calculation. Here we go.

$$E(X) = \int_{-\infty}^{+\infty} x \cdot \frac{1}{\sigma\sqrt{2\pi}}\, e^{-(x-\mu)^2/2\sigma^2}dx$$

$$= \int_{-\infty}^{+\infty} (\sigma w + \mu)\frac{1}{\sqrt{2\pi}}e^{-w^2/2}dw \qquad \text{after substituting } w = (x-\mu)/\sigma$$

$$= \frac{\sigma}{\sqrt{2\pi}} \int_{-\infty}^{+\infty} we^{-w^2/2}dw + \mu \int_{-\infty}^{+\infty} \frac{1}{\sqrt{2\pi}}\, e^{-w^2/2}\, dw.$$

Now, the first integral can be done easily (substitute $v = -w^2/2$) and converges to
The second integral we recognize as the area under another normal distribution curv
(the one with $\mu = 0$ and $\sigma = 1$), so it is equal to 1. Therefore, the whole thing simpl
fies to

$$E(X) = \mu$$

as claimed.

Mean of a Beta Distribution

If X has the beta distribution function $f(x) = (\beta + 1)(\beta + 2)x^\beta(1 - x)$, then

$$E(X) = \frac{\beta + 1}{\beta + 3}.$$

Again, we shall leave this as an exercise.

EXAMPLE 2 Downsizing in the Utilities Industry

A utilities industry consultant predicts a cutback in the Canadian Utilities industry du
ing 2000–2005 by a percentage specified by a beta distribution with $\beta = 0.25$. What
the expected size of the cutback by Ontario Hydro?[15]

Solution Because $\beta = 0.25$,

$$E(X) = \frac{\beta + 1}{\beta + 3} = \frac{1.25}{3.25} \approx 0.38.$$

Therefore, we can expect about a 38% cutback by Ontario Hydro.

➡ **Before we go on...** What $E(X)$ really tells us is that the *average* downsizing
many utilities will be 38%. Some will cut back more, and some will cut back less.

---

[15]This model is fictitious. Ontario Hydro did announce plans to downsize by 8.4% in 1995, however (*Repor
on Business* (Canada), Feb. 15, 1994, p. B1).

There is a generalization of the mean that we shall use below. If X is a random variable on the interval (a, b) with probability density function f, and if g is any function defined on that interval, then we can define the **expected value of g** to be

$$E(g(X)) = \int_a^b g(x)f(x)\,dx.$$

Thus, in particular, the mean is just the expected value of the function $g(x) = x$. We can interpret this as the average we expect if we compute $g(X)$ for many experimental values of X.

Variance and Standard Deviation

Statisticians use the variance and standard deviation of a continuous random variable X as a way of measuring its dispersion, or the degree to which is it "scattered." The definitions are as follows:

Variance and Standard Deviation

Let X be a continuous random variable with density function f defined on the interval (a, b), and let $\mu = E(X)$ be the mean of X. Then the **variance** of X is given by

$$Var(X) = E((X - \mu)^2) = \int_a^b (x - \mu)^2 f(x)\,dx.$$

The **standard deviation** of X is the square root of the variance,

$$\sigma(X) = \sqrt{Var(X)}.$$

Notes

1. In order to calculate the variance and standard deviation, we first need to calculate the mean.
2. $Var(X)$ is the expected value of the function $(x - \mu)^2$, which measures the square of the distance of X from its mean. It is for this reason that $Var(X)$ is sometimes called the *mean square deviation*, and $\sigma(X)$ is called the *root mean square deviation*. $Var(X)$ will be larger if X tends to wander far away from its mean, and smaller if the values of X tend to cluster near its mean.
3. The reason we take the square root in the definition of $\sigma(X)$ is that $Var(X)$ is the expected value of the *square* of the deviation from the mean, and thus is measured in square units. Its square root $\sigma(X)$, therefore, gives us a measure in ordinary units. ■

We now state the variances and standard deviations of the distributions we discussed in the previous section. We'll leave the actual computations (or special cases) for the exercises.

Variance and Standard Deviation of Some Distributions

Uniform Distribution
If X is uniformly distributed on $[a, b]$, then

$$Var(X) = \frac{(b - a)^2}{12}$$

and

$$\sigma(X) = \frac{b-a}{\sqrt{12}}.$$

Exponential Distribution

If X has the exponential distribution function $f(x) = ae^{-ax}$, then

$$Var(X) = \frac{1}{a^2}$$

and

$$\sigma(X) = \frac{1}{a}.$$

Normal Distribution

If X is normally distributed with parameters μ and σ, then

$$Var(X) = \sigma^2$$

and

$$\sigma(X) = \sigma. \qquad \text{This is what you might have expected.}$$

Beta Distribution

If X has the beta distribution function $f(x) = (\beta+1)(\beta+2)x^\beta(1-x)$, then

$$Var(X) = \frac{2(\beta+1)}{(\beta+4)(\beta+3)^2}$$

and

$$\sigma(X) = \sqrt{\frac{2(\beta+1)}{(\beta+4)(\beta+3)^2}}.$$

You can see the significance of the standard deviation quite clearly in the normal distribution. As we mentioned in the previous section, σ is the distance from the maximum at μ to the points of inflection at $\mu - \sigma$ and $\mu + \sigma$. The larger σ is, the wider the bell. Figure 15 shows three normal distributions with three different standard deviations (all with $\mu = 0.5$).

Again, a small standard deviation means that the values of X will be close to the mean with high probability, while a large standard deviation means that the values may wander far away with high probability.

Median

The *median income* in the United States is the income M such that half the population earns incomes $\leq M$ (so the other half earns incomes $\geq M$). In terms of probability, we can think of income as a random variable X. Then the probability that $X \leq M$ is $1/2$ and the probability that $X \geq M$ is also $1/2$.

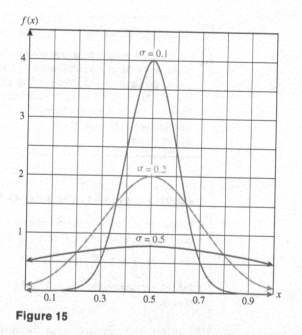

Figure 15

Median

Let X be a continuous random variable. The **median** of X is the number M such that

$$P(X \le M) = \frac{1}{2}.$$

Then, $P(M \le X) = \frac{1}{2}$ also.

If f is the probability density function for X and f is defined on (a, b), then we can calculate M by solving the equation

$$P(a \le X \le M) = \int_a^M f(x)\,dx = \frac{1}{2}$$

for M. Graphically, the vertical line $x = M$ divides the total area under the graph of f into two equal parts (Figure 16).

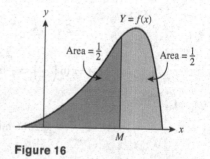

Figure 16

Q: *What is the difference between the median and the mean?*

A: Roughly speaking, the median divides the area under the distribution curve into two equal parts, while the mean is the value of X at which the graph would *balance*. If a probability curve has as much area to the left of the mean as to the right, then the mean is equal to the median. This is true of uniform and normal distributions, which are *symmetric* about their means. On the other hand, the medians and means are different for the exponential distributions and most of the beta distributions, because their areas are not distributed symmetrically.

EXAMPLE 3 Lines at the Post Office

The time in minutes between individuals joining the line at an Ottawa Post Office is a random variable with the exponential distribution

$$f(x) = 2e^{-2x}, (x \geq 0).$$

Find the mean and median time between individuals joining the line and interpret the answers.

Solution The expected value for an exponential distribution $f(x) = ae^{-ax}$ is $1/a$. Here, $a = 2$, so $E(X) = 1/2$. We interpret this to mean that, on average, a new person will join the line every half a minute, or 30 seconds. For the median, we must solve

$$\int_a^M f(x)\,dx = \frac{1}{2}.$$

That is,

$$\int_0^M (2e^{-2x})\,dx = \frac{1}{2}.$$

Evaluating the integral gives

$$-\left[e^{-2x}\right]_0^M = \frac{1}{2},$$

or

$$1 - e^{-2M} = \frac{1}{2}$$

so

$$e^{-2M} = \frac{1}{2},$$

or

$$-2M = \ln\left(\frac{1}{2}\right) = -\ln 2.$$

Thus,

$$M = \frac{\ln 2}{2} \approx 0.3466 \text{ minutes.}$$

This means that half the people get in line less than 0.3466 minutes (about 21 seconds) after the previous person, while half arrive more than 0.3466 minutes later. The mean time for a new person to arrive in line is larger than this because there are some occasional long waits between people, and these pull the average up.

Sometimes we cannot solve the equation $\int_a^M f(x)\,dx = 1/2$ for M analytically, as the next example shows.

EXAMPLE 4 Median

Find the median of the random variable with beta density function for $\beta = 4$.

Solution Here,

$$
\begin{aligned}
f(x) &= (\beta + 1)(\beta + 2)x^{\beta}(1 - x) \\
&= 30x^4(1 - x).
\end{aligned}
$$

Thus we must solve

$$
\int_0^M (30x^4(1 - x))\,dx = \frac{1}{2}.
$$

That is,

$$
30\int_0^M (x^4 - x^5)\,dx = \frac{1}{2}.
$$

So

$$
30\left[\frac{M^5}{5} - \frac{M^6}{6}\right] = \frac{1}{2},
$$

or, multiplying through and clearing denominators,

$$
12M^5 - 10M^6 - 1 = 0.
$$

This is a degree six polynomial equation that has no easy factorization. Because there is no general analytical method for obtaining the solution, the only method we can use is numerical. Figure 17 shows three successive views of a TI-83/84 Plus plot of $Y = 12X^5 - 10X^6 - 1$, obtained by zooming in toward one of the zeros.

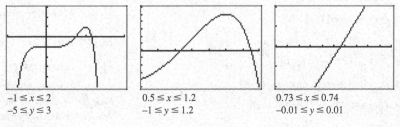

$-1 \le x \le 2$ $0.5 \le x \le 1.2$ $0.73 \le x \le 0.74$
$-5 \le y \le 3$ $-1 \le y \le 1.2$ $-0.01 \le y \le 0.01$

Figure 17

In the first two plots we can see two zeros, one between 0.7 and 0.8 and the other between 1.1 and 1.2. We are interested only in the zero that occurs between 0 and 1 (Why?) In the third plot, each tick on the horizontal axis represents 0.001, and we see that $M \approx 0.736$ to three decimal places.

➡ **Before we go on...** This method required us first to calculate $\int_a^M f(x)\,dx$ analytically. What if even this is impossible to do? We could solve the equation $\int_a^M f(x)\,dx = 1/2$ graphically by having the calculator compute and graph this function of M by numerical integration. For example, to redo the above example on the TI-83/84 Plus, enter

$$Y_1 \; = \; \texttt{fnInt(30T\textasciicircum 4(1-T),T,0,X)-0.5}$$

which corresponds to

$$y = \int_0^x 30t^4(1 - t)\, dt - \frac{1}{2},$$

a function of x. Because the median of M is the solution obtained by setting $y = 0$, we can obtain the answer by plotting Y_1 and finding its x-intercept. The plot should be identical to the one we obtained above, except half as high. (Why?) ■

P.3 EXERCISES

▼ more advanced   ◆ challenging

🅣 indicates exercises that should be solved using technology

Find the expected value $E(X)$, the variance $Var(X)$ and the standard deviation $\sigma(X)$ for each of the density functions in Exercises 1–20.

1. $f(x) = \dfrac{1}{3}$ on $[0, 3]$

2. $f(x) = 3$ on $[0, \dfrac{1}{3}]$

3. ▼ $f(x) = \dfrac{x}{50}$ on $[0, 10]$

4. ▼ $f(x) = 5x$ on $[0, \sqrt{2/5}]$

5. ▼ $f(x) = \dfrac{3}{2}(1 - x^2)$ on $[0, 1]$

6. ▼ $f(x) = \dfrac{3}{4}(1 - x^2)$ on $[-1, 1]$

7. ▼ $f(x) = e^x$ on $[0, \ln 2]$

8. ▼ $f(x) = \dfrac{1}{x}$ on $[1, e]$

9. ▼ $f(x) = 0.1e^{-0.1x}$ on $[0, +\infty)$

10. ▼ $f(x) = 4e^{4x}$ on $(-\infty, 0]$

11. ▼ $f(x) = 0.03e^{0.03x}$ on $(-\infty, 0]$

12. ▼ $f(x) = 0.02e^{-0.02x}$ on $[0, +\infty)$

13. ▼ $f(x) = \dfrac{2}{x^3}$ on $[1, +\infty)$

14. ▼ $f(x) = \dfrac{1}{2\sqrt{x}}$ on $(0, 1]$

15. Normal density function with $\mu = 1$ and $\sigma = 1$ on $(-\infty, +\infty)$

16. Normal density function with $\mu = -1$ and $\sigma = 1$ on $(-\infty, +\infty)$

17. Beta density function with $\beta = 0.5$

18. Beta density function with $\beta = 1.5$

19. Beta density function with $\beta = 3.2$

20. Beta density function with $\beta = 4.6$

🅣 *Use technology to find $E(X)$, $Var(X)$ and $\sigma(X)$ for each of the density functions in Exercises 21–24. (Round all answers to four significant digits.)*

21. 🅣 ▼ $f(x) = \dfrac{4}{\pi(1 + x^2)}$ on $[0, 1]$

22. 🅣 ▼ $f(x) = \dfrac{3}{\pi\sqrt{1 - x^2}}$ on $[\dfrac{1}{2}, 1]$

23. 🅣 ▼ $f(x) = 2xe^{-x^2}$ on $[0, +\infty)$

24. 🅣 ▼ $f(x) = -2xe^{-x^2}$ on $(-\infty, 0]$

Find the medians of the random variables with the probability density functions given in Exercises 25–34.

25. $f(x) = 0.25$ on $[0, 4]$

26. $f(x) = 4$ on $[0, 0.25]$

27. ▼ $f(x) = 3e^{-3x}$ on $[0, +\infty)$

28. ▼ $f(x) = 0.5e^{-0.5x}$ on $[0, +\infty)$

29. ▼ $f(x) = 0.03e^{0.03x}$ on $(-\infty, 0]$

30. ▼ $f(x) = 0.02e^{-0.02x}$ on $[0, +\infty)$

31. ▼ $f(x) = 2(1 - x)$ on $[0, 1]$

32. ▼ $f(x) = \dfrac{1}{x^2}$ on $[1, +\infty)$

33. ▼ $f(x) = \dfrac{1}{2\sqrt{x}}$ on $(0, 1]$

34. ▼ $f(x) = \dfrac{1}{x}$ on $[1, e]$

35. ▼ **Mean of a Uniform Distribution** Verify the formula for the mean of a uniform distribution by computing the integral.

36. ▼ **Mean of a Beta Distribution** Verify the formula for the mean of a beta distribution by computing the integral.

37. ▼ **Variance of a Uniform Distribution** Verify the formula for the variance of a uniform distribution by computing the integral.

38. ▼ **Variance of an Exponential Distribution** Verify the formula for the variance of an exponential distribution by computing the integral.

39. ▼ **Median of an Exponential Random Variable** Show that if X is a random variable with density function $f(x) = ae^{-ax}$ on $[0, +\infty)$, then X has median $\ln 2/a$.

40. ▼ **Median of a Uniform Random Variable** Show that if X is a uniform random variable taking values in the interval $[a, b]$, then X has median $(a + b)/2$.

Use technology to find the medians of the random variables with the probability density functions given in Exercises 41–50. (Round all answers to two decimal places.)

41. ⬛▼ $f(x) = \dfrac{3}{2}(1 - x^2)$ on $[0, 1]$

42. ⬛▼ $f(x) = \dfrac{3}{4}(1 - x^2)$ on $[-1, 1]$

43. ⬛▼ beta density function with $\beta = 2$

44. ⬛▼ beta density function with $\beta = 3$

45. ⬛▼ beta density function with $\beta = 2.5$

46. ⬛▼ beta density function with $\beta = 0.5$

47. ⬛▼ $f(x) = \dfrac{4}{\pi(1 + x^2)}$ on $[0, 1]$

48. ⬛▼ $f(x) = \dfrac{3}{\pi\sqrt{1 - x^2}}$ on $\left[\dfrac{1}{2}, 1\right]$

49. ⬛▼ $f(x) = 2xe^{-x^2}$ on $[0, +\infty)$

50. ⬛▼ $f(x) = -2xe^{-x^2}$ on $(-\infty, 0]$

*The **mean square** of a random variable X with density function f is given by the formula*

$$E(X^2) = \int_a^b x^2 f(x)\,dx.$$

51–60. ▼ In Exercises 1–10, compute $E(X^2)$. In each case, compute also $E(X^2) - E(X)^2$.

61. ▼ Compare the answers in 51–60 to those in 1–10, and hence suggest a formula expressing $E(X^2)$ in terms of $E(X)$ and $Var(X)$.

62. ◆ Calculate $E(e^{tX}) = \displaystyle\int_a^b e^{tx}f(x)\,dx$ with $f(x) = 0.1e^{-0.1x}$ on $[0, +\infty)$. Then evaluate $\dfrac{d}{dt}E(e^{tX})\Big|_{t=0}$ and $\dfrac{d^2}{dt^2}E(e^{tX})\Big|_{t=0}$, comparing these answers with the answer to Exercise 59. What do you notice?

APPLICATIONS

63. **Salaries** Assuming that workers' salaries in your company are uniformly distributed between $10,000 and $40,000 per year, calculate the average salary in your company.

64. **Grades** The grade point averages (GPAs) of members of the Gourmet Society are uniformly distributed between 2.5 and 3.5. Find the average GPA in the Gourmet Society.

65. ▼ **Boring Television Series** Your company's new series "Avocado Comedy Hour" has been a complete flop, with viewership continuously declining at a rate of 30% per month. How long will the average viewer continue to watch the show?

66. ▼ **Bad Investments** Investments in junk bonds are declining continuously at a rate of 5% per year. How long will an average dollar remain invested in junk bonds?

67. ▼ **Radioactive Decay** The half-life of Carbon-14 is 5,730 years. How long, to the nearest year, do you expect it to take for a randomly selected Carbon-14 atom to decay?

68. ▼ **Radioactive Decay** The half-life of plutonium-239 is 24,400 years. How long, to the nearest year, do you expect it to take for a randomly selected plutonium-239 atom to decay?

69. ▼ **The Doomsday Meteor** The probability that a "doomsday meteor" will hit the Earth in any given year and release a billion megatons or more of energy is on the order of 0.00000001.[16] When do you expect the Earth to be hit by a doomsday meteor? (Use an exponential distribution with $a = 0.00000001$.)

70. ▼ **Galactic Cataclysm** The probability that the galaxy MX-47 will explode within the next million years is estimated to be 0.0003. When do you expect MX-47 to explode? (Use an exponential distribution with $a = 0.0003$.)

[16]Source: NASA International Near-Earth-Object Detection Workshop (*New York Times*, January 25, 1994, p. C1.)

Exercises 71–74 use the normal probability density function and require the use of technology for numerical integration. (Alternatively, see Exercise 61.) Find the root mean square value for X (i.e., $\sqrt{E(X^2)}$) in each exercise.

71. ▼ *Physical Measurements* Repeated measurements of a metal rod yield a mean of 5.3 inches, with a standard deviation of 0.1.

72. ▼ *IQ Testing* Repeated measurements of a student's IQ yield a mean of 135, with a standard deviation of 5.

73. ▼ *Psychology Tests* It is known that subjects score an average of 100 points on a new personality test, with a standard deviation of 10 points.

74. ▼ *Examination Scores* Professor May's students earned an average grade of 3.5 with a standard deviation of 0.2.

75. ◆ *Learning* A graduate psychology student finds that 64% of all first-semester calculus students in Prof. Mean's class have a working knowledge of the derivative by the end of the semester.

   (a) Take X = percentage of students who have a working knowledge of calculus after 1 semester, and find a beta density function that models X, assuming that the performance of students in Prof. Mean's is average.

   (b) Find the median of X (rounded to two decimal places) and comment on any difference between the median and the mean.

76. ◆ *Plant Shutdowns* An automobile plant is open an average of 78% of the year.

   (a) Take X = fraction of the year for which the plant is open, and find a beta density function that models X.

   (b) Find the median of X (rounded to two decimal places) and comment on any difference between the median and the mean.

COMMUNICATION AND REASONING EXERCISES

77. ▼ Sketch the graph of a probability distribution function with the property that its median is larger than its mean.

78. ▼ Sketch the graph of a probability distribution function with a large standard deviation and a small mean.

79. Complete the following sentence. The ___ measures the degree to which the values of X are distributed, while the ___ is the value of X such that half the measurements of X are below and half are above (for a large number of measurements).

80. Complete the following sentence. (See Exercise 61.) Given two of the quantities ___, ___ and ___, we can calculate the third using the formula ___.

81. ▼ A value of X for which the probability distribution function f has a local maximum is called a **mode** of the distribution. (If there is more than one mode, the distribution is called bimodal (2 modes), trimodal (3 modes), etc. as the case may be.) If a distribution has a single mode, what does it tell you?

82. ▼ Referring to Exercise 81, sketch a bimodal distribution whose mean coincides with neither of the modes.

KEY CONCEPTS

P.1 Continuous Random Variables and Histograms

Random variables, continuous and discrete *p. 2*

Probability *p. 2*

Probability distribution histogram *p. 3*

P.2 Probability Density Functions: Uniform, Exponential, Normal, and Beta

Probability density function *p. 11*

Calculation of probability from a probability density function *p. 11*

Uniform density function on $[a, b]$: $f(x) = 1/(b - a)$ *p. 12*

Exponential density function on $[0, +\infty)$: $f(x) = ae^{-ax}$ *p. 14*

Normal density function on $(-\infty, +\infty)$:
$f(x) = \frac{1}{\sigma\sqrt{2\pi}} e^{-\frac{(x-\mu)^2}{2\sigma^2}}$ *p. 15*

Beta density function on $[0, 1]$: $f(x) = (\beta + 1)(\beta + 2)x^\beta(1 - x)$ *p. 18*

P.3 Mean, Median, Variance, and Standard Deviation

Mean, expected, or average value of a random variable *p. 21*

Mean of a uniform distribution: $(a + b)/2$ *p. 22*

Mean of an exponential distribution: $1/a$ *p. 23*

Mean of a normal distribution: μ *p. 23*

Mean of a beta distribution: $(\beta + 1)/(\beta + 3)$ *p. 24*

Expected value of a function of a random variable *p. 25*

Variance and standard deviation of a random variable *p. 25*

Variance and standard deviation of a uniform distribution: $Var(X) = (b - a)^2/12$, $\sigma(X) = (b - a)/\sqrt{12}$ *p. 25*

Variance and standard deviation of an exponential distribution: $Var(X) = 1/a^2$, $\sigma(X) = 1/a$ *p. 26*

Variance and standard deviation of a normal distribution: $Var(X) = \sigma^2$, $\sigma(X) = \sigma$ *p. 26*

Variance and standard deviation of a beta distribution: $Var(X) = 2(\beta + 1)/[(\beta + 4)(\beta + 3)^2]$, $\sigma(X) = \sqrt{2(\beta + 1)/[(\beta + 4)(\beta + 3)^2]}$ *p. 26*

Median of a random variable *p. 27*

REVIEW EXERCISES

In each of Exercises 1–10, (a) determine the value of k *that makes the function a probability density function, (b) find the expected value of the corresponding random variable, and (c) find the variance and standard deviation of the random variable.*

1. $f(x) = k$ on $[-2, 2]$

2. $f(x) = k$ on $[1, 10]$

3. $f(x) = kx$ on $[0, 4]$

4. $f(x) = kx$ on $[0, 10]$

5. $f(x) = kx^2$ on $[-1, 1]$

6. $f(x) = kx^2$ on $[0, 1]$

7. $f(x) = k(1 - x^2)$ on $[-1, 1]$

8. $f(x) = k(1 - x^2)$ on $[0, 1]$

9. $f(x) = ke^x$ on $(-\infty, 0]$

10. $f(x) = ke^{-x}$ on $[0, +\infty)$

11. If X is the random variable with the distribution from Exercise 1, find $P(-1 \leq X \leq 1)$.

12. If X is the random variable with the distribution from Exercise 2, find $P(1 \leq X \leq 4)$.

13. If X is the random variable with the distribution from Exercise 3, find $P(0 \leq X \leq 2)$.

14. If X is the random variable with the distribution from Exercise 4, find $P(4 \leq X \leq 6)$.

15. If X is the random variable with the distribution from Exercise 5, find $P(1/2 \leq X \leq 1)$.

16. If X is the random variable with the distribution from Exercise 6, find $P(1/2 \leq X \leq 1)$.

17. If X is the random variable with the distribution from Exercise 7, find $P(0 \leq X \leq 1/2)$.

18. If X is the random variable with the distribution from Exercise 8, find $P(0 \leq X \leq 1/2)$.

19. If X is the random variable with the distribution from Exercise 9, find $P(X \leq -1)$.

20. If X is the random variable with the distribution from Exercise 10, find $P(2 \leq X)$.

21–30. Find the medians of the distributions given in Exercises 1–10.

APPLICATIONS

31. *Farm Population, Female* OHagansBooks.com is considering a new advertising campaign aimed at women living on farms. The following table shows the number of females residing on U.S. farms in 1990, broken down by age.[17] Numbers are in thousands.

Age	0–15	15–25	25–35	35–45	45–55	55–65	65–75	75–95
Number	459	265	247	319	291	291	212	126

OHaganBooks.com is interested in the probability of reaching various age groups with random mailings to farms. Construct the associated probability distribution for the ages of women

[17]Source: Economic Research Service, U.S. Department of Agriculture and Bureau of the Census, U.S. Department of Commerce, 1990.

living on farms (with probabilities rounded to four decimal places) and use the distribution to compute the following:

(a) $P(15 \leq X \leq 55)$ (b) $P(X \leq 45)$ (c) $P(X \geq 45)$

32. Farm Population, Male OHagansBooks.com is considering a new advertising campaign aimed at men living on farms. The following table shows the number of males residing on U.S. farms in 1990, broken down by age.[18] Numbers are in thousands.

Age	0–15	15–25	25–35	35–45	45–55	55–65	65–75	75–95
Number	480	324	285	314	302	314	247	118

OHaganBooks.com is interested in the probability of reaching various age groups with random mailings to farms. Construct the associated probability distribution for the ages of men living on farms (with probabilities rounded to four decimal places) and use the distribution to compute the following:

(a) $P(25 \leq X \leq 65)$ (b) $P(X \leq 15)$ (c) $P(X \geq 15)$

33. Quality Control OHaganBooks.com is worried about quality control of the boxes they use to ship their books. The widths of the boxes are normally distributed with a mean of 6 inches and a standard deviation of 0.1 inches. Any box with a width smaller than 5.8 inches must be rejected. Find the probability that a randomly chosen box will be rejected. (Give your answer to three significant digits.)

34. Book Weight OHaganBooks.com stocks books of many sizes. The weights of the books are normally distributed with a mean of 10 ounces and a standard deviation of 2 ounces. If a customer chooses a book at random, what is the probability that it will weigh at least 11 ounces? (Give your answer to three significant digits.)

35. Book Sales Few books sell well. For each new book published OHaganBooks.com orders a certain number of copies and tracks how many they can sell in the first year. It has found that the fraction, X, of copies they sell of the number they ordered, is a random variable with a beta distribution with parameter $\beta = 0.6$. Find the probability that a given book will sell, in its first year, between 0.5 and 0.7 of the number of copies ordered. (Give your answer to three significant digits.)

36. Book Sales Given the information in Exercise 35, what is the expected fraction of new books sold in the first year, and what is the standard deviation?

Case Study   Creating a Family Trust

Your position as financial consultant to the clients of Family Bank, Inc., often entails you having to give financial advice to clients with complex questions about savings. One of your newer clients, 22-year old Malcolm Adams, recently graduated from college, presents you with a perplexing question. "I would like to set up my own insurance policy by opening a trust account into which I can make monthly payments starting now, so that upon my death or my ninety-fifth birthday—whichever comes sooner—the trust can be expected to be worth $500,000. How much should I invest each month?"

This is not one of those questions that you can answer by consulting a table, so you promise Malcolm an answer by the next day and begin to work on the problem. After a little thought, you realize that the question is one about *expected value*—the expected future value of an annuity into which monthly payments are made. Because the annuity would terminate upon his death (or his ninety-fifth birthday), you decide that you need a model for the probability distribution of the life span of a male in the United States. To obtain this information, you consult mortality tables and come up with the histogram in Figure 18. (You work with the actual numbers, but they are not important for the discussion to follow).[19]

From the data, you calculate that the mean is $\mu = 70.778$ and the standard deviation is $\sigma = 16.5119$.

[19]Probabilities are normalized (scaled) so that the total area of the histogram is one square unit. Thus the area (not the height) of each bar is the probability of mortality in a two-year period. The data on which the histogram is based were obtained from the 1980 Standard Ordinary Mortality Table, Male Lives (Source: Black/Skipper, *Life Insurance*, Eleventh Edition, Englewood Cliffs, NJ: Prentice-Hall, Inc., 1987, p. 314).

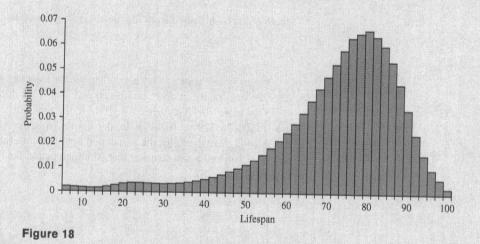

Figure 18

Next, you decide to model these data with a suitable probability density function. You rule out the uniform and exponential density functions, because they have the wrong shape, and you first try the normal distribution. The normal distribution is

$$f(x) = \frac{1}{\sigma\sqrt{2\pi}} \, e^{-\frac{(x-\mu)^2}{2\sigma^2}}$$

$$= \frac{1}{16.5119\sqrt{2\pi}} \, e^{-\frac{(x-70.778)^2}{2(16.5119)^2}}.$$

Figure 19 shows the graph of the normal density function superimposed on the actual data.

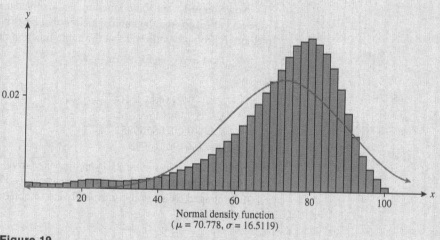

Normal density function
($\mu = 70.778$, $\sigma = 16.5119$)

Figure 19

This does not seem like a very good fit at all! Because the actual histogram looks as though it is "pushed over" to the right, you think of the beta distribution, which has that general shape. The beta distribution is given by

$$f(x) = (\beta + 1)(\beta + 2)x^\beta(1 - x),$$

where β can be obtained from the mean μ using the equation

$$\mu = \frac{\beta + 1}{\beta + 3}.$$

There is one catch: The beta distribution assumes that X is between 0 and 1, whereas your distribution is between 0 and 100. This doesn't deter you: all you need to do is scale the X-values to $1/100$ of their original value. Thus you substitute $\mu = 1/100(70.778) = 0.70778$ in the above equation and solve for β, you obtain $\beta = 3.8442$. You then plot the associated beta function (after scaling it to fit the range $0 \leq X \leq 100$ and again discover that, although better, the fit still leaves something to be desired (Figure 20).

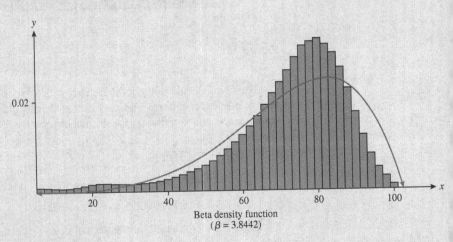

Beta density function
($\beta = 3.8442$)

Figure 20

Now you just want some function that fits the data. You turn to your statistical software and ask it to find the cubic equation that best fits the data using the least squares method. It promptly tells you that the cubic function that best fits the data is

$$f(x) = ax^3 + bx^2 + cx + d,$$

where

$$a = -3.815484 \times 10^{-7}$$
$$b = 5.7399145 \times 10^{-5}$$
$$c = -0.0020856085$$
$$d = 0.0190315095.$$

Its graph is shown in Figure 21. Note that the curve, although erratic for small values of X, fits the large peak on the right more closely than the others.

Encouraged, you use the same software to obtain a quartic (degree 4) approximation and you find:

$$f(x) = ax^4 + bx^3 + cx^2 + dx + e,$$

where

$$a = -9.583507 \times 10^{-9}$$
$$b = 1.650155 \times 10^{-6}$$
$$c = -8.523081 \times 10^{-5}$$
$$d = 0.0016190575$$
$$e = -0.007865381.$$

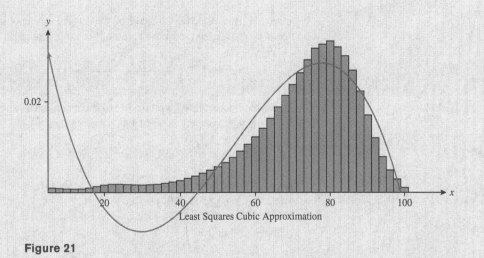

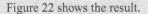
Least Squares Cubic Approximation

Figure 21

Figure 22 shows the result.

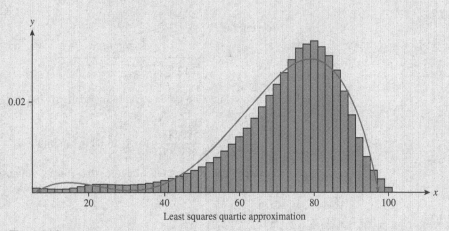

Least squares quartic approximation

Figure 22

This seems like the best fit of them all—especially for the range of X you are interested in: $22 \leq X \leq 95$. (Malcolm is 22 years old and the trust will mature at 95.)

Now that you have the density function you wish to use, you use it to find the expected future value of an annuity into which monthly payments are made. The simplest formula for the future value V of an annuity is

$$V = 12P \left(\frac{\left(1 + \frac{i}{12}\right)^{12n} - 1}{i} \right).$$

(This is a standard formula from finance. This formula assumes that interest is paid at the end of each month.) Here, P is the monthly payment—the quantity that Malcolm wants to know—i is the interest rate, and n is the number of years for which payments are made. Because Malcolm will be making investments starting at age 22, this means that $n = x - 22$, so the future value of his annuity at age x is

$$V(x) = 12P\left(\frac{\left(1 + \frac{i}{12}\right)^{12(x-22)} - 1}{i}\right).$$

As for the interest rate i, you decide to use a conservative estimate of 5%.

Now the expected value of $V(X)$ is given by

$$E(V) = \int_{22}^{95} V(x)f(x)\,dx,$$

where $f(x)$ is the quartic approximation to the distribution function. Because Malcolm wants this to be $500,000, you set

$$500,000 = \int_{22}^{95} V(x)f(x)\,dx$$

$$= \int_{22}^{95} 12P\left(\frac{\left(1 + \frac{i}{12}\right)^{12(x-22)} - 1}{i}\right)f(x)\,dx$$

$$= P\int_{22}^{95} 12\left(\frac{\left(1 + \frac{0.05}{12}\right)^{12(x-22)} - 1}{0.05}\right)f(x)\,dx$$

Solving for P,

$$P = \frac{500,000}{\int_{22}^{95} 12\left(\frac{(1 + \frac{0.005}{12})^{12(x-22)} - 1}{0.05}\right)f(x)\,dx}$$

You now calculate the integral numerically (using the quartic approximation to $f(x)$), obtaining

$$P \approx \frac{500,000}{3,409.8019} \approx \$146.64 \text{ per month}$$

The next day, you can tell Malcolm that at a 5% interest rate, his family can expect the trust to be worth $500,000 upon maturity if he deposits $146.64 each month.

EXERCISES

1. How much smaller will the payments be if the interest rate is 6%?

2. How much larger would the payments be if Malcolm began payments at the age of 30?

3. Repeat the original calculation using the normal distribution described above. Give reasons for the discrepancy between the answers, explaining why your answer is smaller or larger than the one calculated above.

4. Repeat Exercise 3 using the cubic distribution.

5. If Malcolm wanted to terminate the trust at age 65, which model would you use for the probability density? Give reasons for your choice.

6. Suppose you were told by your superior that, because the expected male life span is 71, you could have saved yourself a lot of trouble by using the formula for the future value of an annuity maturing at age 71. Based on that, the payment comes out to about $198 per month. Why is it higher? Why is it the wrong amount?

7. Explain how an insurance company might use the above calculations to compute life insurance premiums.

TI-83/84 Plus Technology Guide

Section P.2

Example 4 Pressure gauges manufactured by Precision Corp. must be checked for accuracy before being placed on the market. To test a pressure gauge, a worker uses it to measure the pressure of a sample of compressed air known to be at a pressure of exactly 50 pounds per square inch. If the gauge reading is off by more than 1% (0.5 pounds), the gauge is rejected. Assuming that the reading of a pressure gauge under these circumstances is a normal random variable with mean 50 and standard deviation 0.5, find the percentage of gauges rejected.

Solution with Technology

As in the text, the solution of this example comes down to the calculation

$$P(49.5 \le X \le 50.5) = \int_{49.5}^{50.5} f(x)\, dx,$$

where f is the normal distribution with mean $\mu = 50$ and standard deviation $\sigma = 0.5$:

$$f(x) = \frac{1}{\sigma\sqrt{2\pi}} e^{-\frac{(x-\mu)^2}{2\sigma^2}}$$

$$= \frac{1}{0.5\sqrt{2\pi}} e^{-\frac{(x-50)^2}{0.5}}.$$

There are two methods to calculate this integral on a TI-83/84 Plus.

Method 1: *Calculate the integral directly.*

1. Enter

$$Y_1 = (1/(0.5(2\pi)^{\wedge}0.5))e^{\wedge}(-(X - 50)^{\wedge}2/0.5)$$

in the Y = screen.

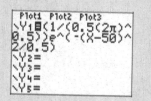

2. Enter

$$\text{fnInt}(Y_1, X, 49.5, 50.5)$$

in the home screen.

Method 2: *Use the built-in normal distribution function.*

The TI-83/84 Plus has a built-in normal distribution function.

1. Press [2nd] [VARS] to obtain the selection of distribution functions. The second function, normalcdf, gives $P(a \le X \le b)$ directly.

2. To compute $P(49.5 \le X \le 50.5)$, enter

$$\text{normalcdf}(49.5, 50.5, 50, .5)$$

Format: normalcdf (Lower bound, Upper bound, μ, σ)

in the home screen.

Both methods yield an answer of approximately 0.6827. In other words, 68.27% of the gauges will be accepted. Thus, the remaining 31.73% of the gauges will be rejected.

EXCEL Technology Guide

Section P.2

Example 4 Pressure gauges manufactured by Precision Corp. must be checked for accuracy before being placed on the market. To test a pressure gauge, a worker uses it to measure the pressure of a sample of compressed air known to be at a pressure of exactly 50 pounds per square inch. If the gauge reading is off by more than 1% (0.5 pounds), the gauge is rejected. Assuming that the reading of a pressure gauge under these circumstances is a normal random variable with mean 50 and standard deviation 0.5, find the percentage of gauges rejected.

Solution with Technology

As in the text, the solution of this example comes down to the calculation

$$P(49.5 \leq X \leq 50.5) = \int_{49.5}^{50.5} f(x)\,dx,$$

where f is the normal distribution with mean $\mu = 50$ and standard deviation $\sigma = 0.5$;

$$f(x) = \frac{1}{\sigma\sqrt{2\pi}}\, e^{-\frac{(x-\mu)^2}{2\sigma^2}}$$

$$= \frac{1}{0.5\sqrt{2\pi}}\, e^{-\frac{(x-50)^2}{0.5}}.$$

Excel has built-in statistical software that allows you to compute $P(a \leq X \leq b)$. The function NORMDIST $(a, \mu, \sigma, 1)$ computes $P(X \leq a)$ for the normal distribution with mean μ and standard deviation σ. (The last argument, 1, tells Excel that we want the cumulative distribution, i.e., the integral, rather than the value of the density function at a.) To compute $P(49.5 \leq X \leq 50.5)$ in Excel, enter

```
= NORMDIST(50.5,50,0.5,1)
  -NORMDIST(49.5,50,0.5,1)
```

in any vacant cell.

Excel yields an answer of approximately 0.6827. In other words, 68.27% of the gauges will be accepted. Thus, the remaining 31.73% of the gauges will be rejected.

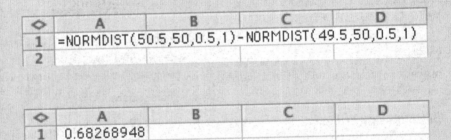

Index of Companies and Agencies